KNOW YOUR CODE

A GUIDE TO THE OBC

2015 Edition

Issued in August 2015

By

Thomas S. Marcey

THOMSON REUTERS™

For Customer Assistance Call 1-800-328-4880

Mat #41611524

Introduction to the 2015 Edition

Know Your Code: A Guide to the OBC is a compendium of building requirements derived from the Ohio Building Code, Ohio Mechanical Code, Ohio Plumbing Code, Ohio Fire Code, National Electrical Code, the Residential Code of Ohio, and EPA standards, as well as relevant provisions of the Ohio Revised Code.

Know Your Code has value for architects, engineers, and other design professionals; contractors and construction managers; building officials, inspectors, and plans examiners; consultants, teachers, and administrators of education programs; and others who need a quick reference to the rules, standards, and requirements of the Building Code and related Codes in Ohio. Suitable for use either in the office or on the job, it is an alphabetical series of entries, from **Accessibility Guidelines** to **Yards**, each consisting of a concise restatement of the various applicable Code requirements.

This edition of *Know Your Code* presents updated and revised coverage of the following subjects:

- Accessibility guidelines
- Boilers
- Egress and exits
- Fire Code
- Nursing homes and hospitals
- Plumbing

The Publisher
Rochester, NY
August 2015

Dedication

I dedicate this book to my wife Barbara, who despite undergoing the isolation and the annoyances of being an author's spouse, kept her humor and offered valuable insights.

Thomas S. Marcey
April 2015

About the Author

Thomas S. Marcey is a retired contracts attorney for the U.S. Air Force, experienced in both the formation and the administration sides of federal government contracts practice. His practice in the U.S. Air Force encompassed construction and environmental concerns as well as those pertaining to government contracting. He has a B.A. degree from the University of Dayton (1971) and a J.D. degree from Case Western Reserve University (1974). He is currently an inactive member of the Ohio Bar, engaged in various legal writing pursuits.

How to Use This Publication

Scope of Coverage

Municipal and other local building regulations are not included in *Know Your Code*. And, although the OBOA Ohio Residential Code is referenced, coverage is limited to overlapping technical requirements and does not include administrative requirements unique to each adopting jurisdiction.

Organization and Format

Entries are arranged alphabetically, and the information is presented in outline form. The entries are followed by a collection of useful Reference Materials, including a Glossary and Tables of Use Group Classifications, and Sources for Referenced Documents.

For clarity and convenience, some entries are accompanied by tables, charts, or illustrations. For example, OBC Table 601, Fire Resistance Rating Requirements for Building Elements, is reprinted under **Construction Type—Classification of Buildings**; OBC Table 503, Allowable Height and Building Areas, is reprinted under **Building Areas**; and illustrations of guardrails and handrails are included in the entry on **Egress and Exits**.

Sample Entry

Below is the entry for **VENEERS (1400)**, illustrating several features of the publication:

VENEERS

   A. Glass veneers: See GLASS.
   B. Metal veneers (1405.11)
   1. Veneer must be corrosion-resistant on both sides.
   2. Caulk all joints and ventilate all panels. (1405.11.2)
   3. Fasteners maximum 24" o.c.
   4. Minimum veneer thickness of 0.0149".
   5. Bonding and grounding must comply with Chapter 27. (1405.11.4)
   6. Metal attachments cross-sectional area $\leq$ that provided by W 1.7 wire, and able with their supports to resist horizontal force per WIND LOADS, but in no case less than 20 psf (0.958 kg/m2).

Items B.2 and B.5 are followed by parenthetical references to the OBC where the full text of the primary source requirement can be found. Item D.6 cross references with the entry for WIND LOADS.

Brief Background on OBC

Prior to July 1, 1979, the rules of the Ohio Board of Building Standards were compiled in a document known as the *Ohio Building Code*, which was published first by the Board and later (beginning in 1975) by Banks-Baldwin (now West, a division of Thomson Reuters). On October 20, 1978, the Board adopted a rule, effective July 1, 1979, repealing most of the existing *Ohio Building Code* and adopting by reference, with special Ohio modifications, the "Basic Building Code/1978, Seventh Edition" and the "Basic Mechanical Code/1978, Third Edition," as published and copyrighted by Building Officials and Code Administrators International, Inc. (BOCA).

The resulting collection of model code sections and superseding Ohio provisions—together with the CABO Model Energy Code and the Ohio Plumbing Code became the "Ohio Basic Building Code" (OBBC). In the years since its original adoption, the Board amended the OBBC, primarily to incorporate subsequent changes to the model codes.

Following its August 14, 2001 public hearing, the Board adopted "The ICC International Building Code/2000, First Edition," along with the March 2001 "Supplement to the International Codes" and applicable errata, as published and copyrighted by International

Code Council, Inc. (ICC): the "International Mechanical Code—2000, Second Edition:" and the "International Plumbing Code—2000, Second Edition," as published and copyrighted by ICC, again with modifications to conform with Ohio law. With this first-time adoption of these ICC International model codes, the resulting collection is once again known as the "Ohio Building Code" (OBC).

Subsequently, following its August 27, 2004, public hearing, the Board adopted the 2003 Edition of the "International Building Code," the 2003 Edition of the "International Mechanical Code," and the 2003 Edition of the "International Plumbing Code" as published and copyrighted by ICC and all applicable errata, with modifications to conform them to Ohio law. The 'Residential Code of Ohio' was issued in 2006.

The OBC is published by West in two formats—a two-volume set of *OBC and Related Codes*, and single-volume compilations of specific Codes to meet the needs of individual users (see Related Publications, below).

Cross References

Cross references to OBC and other sources are provided throughout *Know Your Code*. A parenthetical reference without a prefix refers to the Building Code, and the form of the reference indicates whether the rule was modified by the Board or adopted from the ICC model code without modification. The former are citations to the Ohio Administrative Code (OAC)— e.g., 4101:2-1-11; the latter cite the ICC provision—e.g., 917.1. A citation preceded by "M" refers to a section of the Mechanical Code. A citation preceded by "P" refers to a section of the Plumbing Code. OAC 4101:4 refers to the Ohio Boiler Code; OAC 1301:7 refers to the Ohio Fire Code, which is promulgated by the Division of State Fire Marshal in the Department of Commerce.

Other references in *Know Your Code* are to sources for related requirements. These are listed in the Table of Sources for Referenced Standards in the Reference Materials section. Addresses and phone numbers are included for the benefit of users who wish to obtain the full text of referenced documents.

Cross references to other main entries are provided where applicable. These references are printed in CAPITAL LETTERS.

Related Publications

Following is a list of other West publications that subscribers to the *Know Your Code* may find valuable for research and reference. To order any West publication, or to obtain further information, contact your local West Sales Representative or call our Customer Service Department toll-free at (800) 328-4880.

- *Ohio Building Code and Related Codes*, 2 volumes. West's edition is the only comprehensive collection of Code documents available in a single convenient source. In terms of comprehensiveness, reliability, and ease of use, it is unsurpassed. Individual units (for example, the Building Code only) are also available on a subscription basis, either separately or in combination.

- *Ohio Construction Law Manual*. (Baldwin's Practice Series). Written and updated by Ohio attorneys who are experts in the field, this one-volume treatise provides a thorough and practical analysis of Ohio's construction law. It is designed for practicing lawyers, contractors, owners, design professionals, and subcontractors subject to Ohio law, and it offers information to guide subscribers through a myriad of construction issues and situations. It is an invaluable resource, whether you are involved in construction claims or are being proactive in trying to avoid litigation.

Table of Abbreviations

ACI	American Concrete Institute
ADAAG	Americans with Disabilities Act Accessibility Guidelines
AFF	above finished floor
AFPA	American Forest and Paper Association
AHA	American Hardboard Association
AISC	American Institute of Steel Construction
AISI	American Iron and Steel Institute
amp	ampere
ANSI	American National Standards Institute
ASCE	American Society of Civil Engineers
ASME	American Society of Mechanical Engineers
ASTM	American Society of Testing Materials
AWPA	American Wood Preservers Association
BOCA	Building Officials and Code Administrators International, Inc.
Btu	British Thermal Unit
CABO	Council of American Building Officials
cfm	cubic feet per minute
cu. ft.	cubic foot
cu. in.	cubic inch
cu. yd.	cubic yard
F	Fahrenheit
FDN	foundation
FHAG	Fair Housing Accessibility Guidelines
FRTW	fire retardant treated wood
gal.	gallon
gpm	gallons per minute
HPM	hazardous production materials
HPVA	Hardwood Plywood Veneer Association
hr.	hour
HVAC	heating, ventilating, and air conditioning
kVA	Kilo Volt-amps
lb.	pound
LP	liquified petroleum
NEC	National Electrical Code
NFPA	National Fire Protection Association
no.	number
NP	not permitted
OAC	Ohio Administrative Code
OBC	Ohio Building Code
OBC	Ohio Building Code and Related Codes (West)
OBBS	Ohio Board of Building Standards
o.c.	on center
OFC	Ohio Fire Code

plf	pounds per lineal foot
psi	pounds per square inch
psig	pounds per square inch, gravity
PVC	polyvinyl chloride
R.C.	Ohio Revised Code
SJI	Steel Joist Institute
sq. ft.	square foot
sq. in.	square inch
TMS	The Masonry Society
U	unlimited
UL	Underwriters Laboratories
<	less than
≤	less than or equal to
>	greater than
≥	greater than or equal to

WestlawNext™

THE NEXT GENERATION OF ONLINE RESEARCH

WestlawNext is the world's most advanced legal research system. By leveraging more than a century of information and legal analysis from Westlaw, this easy-to-use system not only helps you find the information you need quickly, but offers time-saving tools to organize and annotate your research online. As with Westlaw.com, WestlawNext includes the editorial enhancements (e.g., case headnotes, topics, key numbers) that make it a perfect complement to West print resources.

- FIND ANYTHING by entering citations, descriptive terms, or Boolean terms and connectors into the WestSearch™ box at the top of every page.

- USE KEYCITE® to determine whether a case, statute, regulation, or administrative decision is good law.

- BROWSE DATABASES right from the home page.

- SAVE DOCUMENTS to folders and add notes and highlighting online.

SIGN ON: next.westlaw.com
LEARN MORE: store.westlaw.com/westlawnext
FOR HELP: 1–800–WESTLAW (1–800–937–8529)

RELATED PRODUCTS

STATUTES, CONSTITUTIONS, AND COURT RULES

Baldwin's Ohio Revised Code Annotated

Baldwin's Ohio Legislative Service Annotated

Ohio Constitution Handbook

Ohio Rules of Court, State and Federal

United States Code Annotated

CASE LAW, REPORTERS, DIGESTS, ATTORNEY GENERAL OPINIONS

Ohio Official Reports

West's Ohio Digest

Ohio Attorney General Opinions

SERB Official Reporter

Federal Reporter

Federal Supplement

West's Supreme Court Reporter

ADMINISTRATIVE LAW

Baldwin's Ohio Administrative Code

Ohio Administrative Law Handbook and Agency Directory
Lepp and McNeil

Baldwin's Ohio Monthly Record

Administrative Law and Practice 2d

Administrative Law: Practice and Procedure

GENERAL LEGAL REFERENCES

Ohio Jurisprudence 3d

American Jurisprudence 2d

American Law Reports

Corpus Juris Secundum

OHIO DATABASES ON WESTLAW

Cases, General & Topical

Statutes & Court Rules

Legislative Service, Bills & Bill Tracking

Administrative & Executive Materials

Public Information, Records & Filings

Baldwin's Ohio Practice Series

Ohio Jurisprudence 3d

Ohio Forms, Legal & Business

Law Reviews, Bar Journals & Legal Periodicals

Newspapers & Periodicals

Miscellany

CD-ROM

Baldwin's Ohio Revised Code Annotated with Ohio Administrative Code, and SERB Official Reporter

Ohio Reports

Ohio Unreported Appellate Decisions

Baldwin's Ohio Practice Library

West's Ohio Digest

Ohio Jurisprudence 3d

United States Code Annotated

West's Sixth Circuit Reporter

West's Federal District Court Reporter—Sixth Circuit

West's Supreme Court Reporter

Federal Reporter, 1st, 2d, and 3d Series

Federal Supplement

Federal Rules Decisions

Wright & Miller, Federal Practice and Procedure

Topical CD-ROM Libraries

Ohio Jurisprudence Pleading and Practice Forms

Ohio Criminal Defense Motions
Hennenberg and Reinhart

CIVIL PRACTICE AND PROCEDURE

Baldwin's Ohio Practice, Civil Practice 2d
Klein, Darling, and Terez

Baldwin's Ohio Practice, Civil Practice Laws & Rules Annotated

Ohio Personal Injury Practice
O'Reilly and Ruck

Baldwin's Ohio Practice, Tort Law
Ernst

Ohio Trial Practice
Markus and Dickinson

CRIMINAL LAW AND PRACTICE

Baldwin's Ohio Practice, Criminal Law 3d
Katz, Lipton, Crocker, and Martin

Baldwin's Ohio Practice, Statutory Charges
Terez

Ohio Arrest, Search and Seizure
Katz

Baldwin's Ohio Practice, Ohio Criminal Laws and Rules
Katz and Giannelli (Eds.)

Ohio Domestic Violence Law
Adrine and Ruden

Ohio Driving Under the Influence Law
Weiler and Weiler

Ohio Felony Sentencing Law
Griffin and Katz

Ohio Trial Practice
Markus and Dickinson

TRIAL AND APPELLATE PRACTICE

Baldwin's Ohio Practice, Evidence 3d
Giannelli

Baldwin's Ohio Practice, Rules of Evidence Handbook
Giannelli

Ohio Appellate Practice
Painter and Pollis

Ohio Trial Objections
Giannelli and Snyder

Ohio Trial Practice
Markus and Dickinson

DOMESTIC RELATIONS AND FAMILY LAW

Baldwin's Ohio Practice, Domestic Relations Law 4th
Sowald and Morganstern

**Baldwin's Ohio Practice, Domestic Relations Laws
and Rules Annotated**

Ohio Domestic Violence Law
Adrine and Ruden

Ohio Elder Law
Kreiner and Durbin

Domestic Relations Journal of Ohio
Morganstern

PROBATE AND JUVENILE LAW

Baldwin's Ohio Practice, Merrick-Rippner Probate Law 7th
Carlin

Ohio Probate Code Annotated

Probate Law Journal of Ohio
Brucken

Ohio Juvenile Law
Giannelli and Yeomans Salvador

REAL ESTATE

Ohio Landlord Tenant Law
White

Baldwin's Ohio Practice, Ohio Real Estate Law 3d

Kuehnle and Levey

Ohio Condominium Law
Kuehnle and Williams

BUSINESS AND LEGAL

Baldwin's Ohio Practice, Business Organizations 2d
Blackford

Baldwin's Ohio Practice, Business Organizations Laws & Rules
Ekonomon and Heinle (Eds.)

Ohio Consumer Law
Legal Aid Society of Cleveland

LEGAL FORMS

Ohio Forms Legal and Business

Ohio Forms and Transactions

Ohio Jurisprudence Pleading and Practice Forms

West's Legal Forms, 2d

TAX LAW

Baldwin's Ohio Tax Law and Rules
Engel

LABOR LAW

Ohio Civil Service & Collective Bargaining Laws & Rules Annotated

Ohio Employment Practices Law
Siegel and Stephen

Ohio Workers' Compensation Law
Wasil and Mastrangelo

Workers' Compensation Journal of Ohio
Harris

GOVERNMENT

Baldwin's Ohio Practice, Local Government Law—Township
Princehorn

Baldwin's Ohio Practice, Local Government Law—Municipal
Gotherman, Babbit and Lang

Baldwin's Ohio Practice, Local Government Law—County
Conard II

Rutter's Ohio Municipal Service
Rutter

Ohio Election Laws Annotated

Ohio Planning and Zoning Law
Meck and Pearlman

SCHOOL LAW

Baldwin's Ohio School Law
Hastings, Manoloff, Sharb, Sheeran and Jaffe

Ohio School Law Handbook

Hastings, Manoloff, Sharb, Sheeran and Jaffe

Baldwin's Ohio School Law Journal

Lentz

Lentz School Security

Lentz

United States School Laws and Rules

BUILDING CONSTRUCTION AND CODE ENFORCEMENT

Ohio Building Code and Related Codes

Know Your Code: A Guide to the OBC

Ohio Construction Law Manual

Code News

Thomson Reuters® thanks you for subscribing to this product. Should you have any questions regarding this product please contact Customer Service at 1-800-328-4880 or by fax at 1-800-340-9378. If you would like to inquire about related publications or place an order, please contact us at 1-800-344-5009.

 THOMSON REUTERS™

Thomson Reuters
610 Opperman Drive
Eagan, MN 55123

legalsolutions.thomsonreuters.com

Table of Contents

PART 1 OHIO BUILDING AND RELATED CODES

PART 2 RESIDENTIAL CODE OF OHIO (4101:8)

APPENDICES

Glossary

Part 1

OHIO BUILDING AND RELATED CODES

ACCESSIBILITY GUIDELINES (CH. 11, ADAAG, AND ICC)

A.   Scope of Application—Buildings and Facilities
1.   All sites, buildings, structures, facilities, elements and spaces, temporary or permanent must be handicap accessible. (1103.1)
2.   There are no general exceptions, but the following specific requirements apply. (1103.2; ADAAG section 4.1)
   a.   Existing buildings that undergo a change of group or occupancy must, to the maximum extent technically feasible, have at least one accessible building entrance, at least one accessible route from that entrance to primary function areas, and signage:
      i.   If parking is provided it must be accessible.
      ii.   At least one accessible route connecting accessible parking and passenger loading zones to an accessible entrance is required. (ICC 3411)
   b.   Detached one, two- and three family dwellings and accessory structures and associated sites and facilities do not have to be handicap accessible.
   c.   Residential Group R-1 buildings with not more than five rental sleeping units that are owner-occupied do not have to be handicap accessible.
   d.   Temporary structures and construction such as reviewing stands, temporary classrooms, bleacher areas, exhibit areas, temporary banking facilities, temporary health screening services, and temporary safe pedestrian passageways around a construction site must be handicap accessible. (ADAAG 4.4.1(4))
   e.   Employee work areas must allow individuals with disabilities to approach, enter, and exit.
      i.   Work areas, or portions of work areas, that are less than 150 square feet in area and elevated 7 inches or more above the ground or finish floor, where the elevation is essential to the function of the space, do not have to be handicap accessible.
      ii.   Common use circulation paths within work areas must be handicap accessible. Exceptions:
         (a)   Common use circulation paths in work areas less than 300 square feet with permanent partitions, counters, casework or furnishings.
         (b)   Circulation paths that are an integral component of equipment.
         (c)   Circulation paths that are fully exposed to the weather. (ICC 1104.3.1)
      iii.   If employee work areas have audible alarm coverage, the system must allow integration of visible alarm notification appliances. (ICC 907.9.1.2)
   f.   Construction sites, structures and construction equipment such as scaffolding, bridging, materials hoists and materials storage or construction trailers, do not have to be handicap accessible. (ADAAG 4.1.1(4)) Portable toilet units exclusively for use by construction personnel need not be accessible or on an accessible route.

1

g. Raised areas used primarily for purposes of security, life safety or fire safety such as observation galleries, prison guard towers, fire towers or lifeguard stands do not have to be handicap accessible. (ADAAG 4.1.1.1(5)(b)(i))

h. Non-occupied spaces reachable only by ladders, catwalks, crawl spaces, freight elevators or very narrow passageways do not have to be handicap accessible if they are used only by service personnel for maintenance, repair, or occasional monitoring of equipment.

   i. Examples are:
      (a) elevator pits
      (b) elevator penthouses
      (c) piping or equipment catwalks
      (d) water or sewage treatment pump rooms and stations
      (e) electric substations and transformer vaults
      (f) highway and tunnel utility facilities (ADAAG 4.1.1.1(5)(b))

i. Spaces used only for maintenance, repair or monitoring of equipment by service personnel for occasional maintenance. Group U occupancies need not be accessible UNLESS agricultural buildings not used for agricultural purposes, where access required to paved work areas and areas are open to the public, and agricultural buildings used for agricultural purposes, per federal 2010 "ADA Standards for Accessible Design."

j. Operable parts of fuel dispensers must be 54 maximum unobstructed side and high reach, measured from the surface of the vehicular way if installed on existing curbs. (ADAAG 308.3)

   i. Should be able to operate gas pump nozzle with one hand without tightly grasping, pinching, or twisting the wrist, requiring an activating force of $\leq$ 5 lbs.

k. Raised or lowered areas in places of religious worship < 300 sq.ft. (30 m^2) and 7" or more (178 mm) above or below the finished floor, and used primarily for religious ceremonies need not be accessible.

l. Highway Toll Booths accessed only by bridges located above vehicular traffic or by underground tunnels need not be handicap accessible.

m. Only that portion of a day care facilities incorporated into dwelling units that is specifically used for day care needs to be handicap accessibility.

n. Common use areas used only by inmates or detainees and security personnel in detention and correctional facilities, and do not serve holding cells or housing cells that are required to accessible do not need to be handicap accessible.

o. Walk-in coolers and freezers intended for employee use only need not be handicap accessible.

B. Scope of Application—Accessibility Routes
   1. Site Arrival Points (1104.2)
      a. Accessible routes within the site are required from public transportation stops, including parking, passenger loading zones and public streets or sidewalks to the accessible building entrance served. Exception:
         i. Other than in buildings or facilities containing or serving Type B units, no accessible route is required between such points and the building or facility entrance if the only means of access between them is a vehicular way without pedestrian access.
      b. At least one accessible route must connect accessible buildings, facilities, elements and spaces that are on the same site.

2. Connected Spaces (1104.3)
   a. If a building or portion of a building must be accessible, an accessible route must be provided to each portion of the building, to accessible building entrances connecting accessible pedestrian walkways, and the public way. Exception:
      i. Assembly areas with fixed accessible seating do not require a handicap accessible route if wheelchair spaces or designated aisle seats required to be on an accessible route are not provided.
      ii. The judge's bench, clerk's station, bailiff's station, deputy clerk's station and court reporter's station must be on an accessible route. However, vertical access to elevated employee work stations in a courtroom need not be provided during initial construction, if a ramp, lift or elevator can be installed without reconfiguration or extension of either the courtroom or the electrical system.
3. Employee Work Area Circulation Paths (1104.3.1)
   a. Common use circulation paths in employee work areas must be accessible routes, unless they are an integral component of equipment.
      i. Areas dedicated solely as work areas must allow disabled individuals to approach, enter, and exit.
      ii. Such areas need not be built to allow maneuvering within the work area, or be built or equipped with racks or shelves to be accessible.
      iii. Press boxes in assembly areas must be on an accessible route. (1104.3.1; ADAAG 4.1.1.1(3))
4. Multilevel Buildings and Facilities (1104.4)
   a. At least one accessible route must connect each level, including mezzanines, in multilevel buildings and facilities.
   b. Exceptions:
      i. An accessible route is not required to stories and mezzanines above and below accessible levels with an aggregate area of not more than 3,000 square feet.
         (a) This exception does not apply to:
            (1) shopping centers and malls
            (2) levels containing offices of health care providers
            (3) passenger transportation facilities and airports
            (4) building or portions of buildings owned or leased by public entities such as school districts, cities, villages, townships, counties and the state of Ohio.
            (5) Public university, college and school system structures, facilities.
            (6) Stories or mezzanines lacking accessible elements.
      ii. Group A, I and S Occupancies with levels without entry doors to patient rooms, dwelling or sleeping units, public or common use elements or other spaces required by paragraphs 5 and 6 do not need an accessible route from an accessible level.
      iii. R-2 Occupancies that are three stories or less in height do not need levels connected by an accessible route to other dwelling units above and below unless garages and other accessory structures intended for use by occupants of accessible, Type A or Type B units.
      iv. R-3 Occupancy levels must be accessible, but do not need to be connected by an accessible route to other dwelling units above and below,

3

except for garages and other accessory structures for use by occupants of Type B units.

    v. Two-story buildings or facilities with one story having an occupant load of five or fewer persons, and without public use space do not need to connect that story by an accessible route to the story above or below.

5. Location (1104.5)
    a. Accessible routes must coincide with or be located in the same area as general circulation paths.
        i. If circulation paths are interior, the accessible route must be interior as well.
        ii. If only one accessible route is present, it must not pass through kitchens, storage rooms, restrooms, closets or similar spaces.
    b. Exceptions:
        i. Accessible routes from parking garages built in and serving Type B dwelling units.
        ii. A single accessible route may pass through a kitchen or storage room in an Accessible, Type A or Type B dwelling unit.

6. Security Barriers (1104.6)
    a. Security barriers such as security bollards and security check points must not obstruct a required accessible route or accessible means of egress.
    b. Exception: If metal detectors, fluoroscopes, etc. are used, the accessible route may be adjacent to security screening devices, as long as disabled persons passing around security barriers can have visual contact with their personal items as others passing through the security barrier.

C. Scope of Application—Accessible Entrances (1105)
1. At least 60% of all public entrances must be handicap accessible. Areas not required to be accessible, and loading and service entrances that are not the only entrance to a tenant space.
2. Also accessible:
    a. Direct access for pedestrians from parking structures to buildings or facility entrances if provided.
    b. At least one entrance to a building or facility from each tunnel or walkway if direct access from a pedestrian tunnel or elevated walkway is provided.
    c. At least one entrance to a building or facility with has restricted entrances.
    d. At least one entrance used strictly by inmates or detainees and security personnel at judicial facilities, detention facilities or correctional facilities.
    e. Service entrances where the only access to a building or a tenant space in a facility.
    f. At least one accessible entrance to each tenant, because self-storage units in a facility unless they do not need to be accessible, or Type A or Type B units.

D. Scope of Application—Parking and Passenger Loading Facilities (1106)
1. Accessible parking spaces must be provided in accordance with Table 1106.1 if parking is provided.
    a. The number of accessible parking spaces must be calculated separately for each parking facility. Exception:
    b. Parking spaces used exclusively for buses, trucks, other delivery vehicles, law enforcement vehicles or vehicular impound and motor pools where lots accessed by the public are provided with an accessible passenger loading zone.
    c. Other exceptions:
        i. In multilevel parking structures, van-accessible parking spaces are permitted on one level.

      ii. Accessible parking spaces may be located in different parking facilities if providing substantially equivalent or greater accessibility in distance from an accessible entrance or entrances, parking fee and user convenience.

2. Accessible parking for Groups I-1, R-1, R-2, R-3 and R-4 as follows:

      a. Groups R-2, R-3, and R-4 with accessible, Type A or Type B dwelling or sleeping units must have $\geq$ 2%, but not less than one, of each type of parking space provided as accessible.

      b. Groups I-1 and R-1require accessible parking per Table 1106.1. 3. If a parking space is provided for each dwelling unit or sleeping unit, $\geq$ one accessible parking space must be provided for each Accessible and Type A unit.

      c. If underground parking, provide accessible parking spaces within or beneath the building.

3. Ten percent of patient and visitor parking spaces provided to serve hospital outpatient facilities must be accessible.

4. 20%, but $\geq$ 1, of the patient and visitor parking spaces serving rehabilitation facilities and outpatient physical therapy facilities must be accessible.

5. For every six or fraction of six accessible parking spaces, at least one must be a van-accessible parking space.

6. Accessible parking spaces must be located on the shortest accessible route of travel from adjacent parking to an accessible building entrance.

      a. Parking facilities that do not serve a particular building require accessible parking spaces on the shortest route to an accessible pedestrian entrance to the parking facility.

      b. Buildings having multiple accessible entrances with adjacent parking require accessible parking spaces dispersed and located near the accessible entrances.

7. Passenger loading zones for existing buildings, or portions thereof, that undergo a change of group or occupancy require at least one accessible route connecting accessible parking and accessible passenger loading zones to an accessible entrance, to the maximum technical extent feasible. (ADAAG 3409.3)

8. If passenger loading zones are provided, one such zone in every continuous 100 linear feet (30.4 m) maximum of loading zone space must be accessible.

9. A passenger loading zone must have an accessible entrance to licensed medical and long-term care facilities where the period of stay exceeds 24 hours.

j. A passenger loading zone must be provided at valet parking services.

k. A passenger loading zone is required at vehicle drop-off and pickup areas in mechanical access parking garages.

TABLE 1106.1
ACCESSIBLE PARKING SPACES

TOTAL PARKING SPACES PROVIDED	REQUIRED MINIMUM NUMBER OF ACCESSIBLE SPACES
1 to 25	1
26 to 50	2
51 to 75	3
76 to 100	4
101 to 150	5
151 to 200	6
201 to 300	7
301 to 400	8

TOTAL PARKING SPACES PROVIDED	REQUIRED MINIMUM NUMBER OF ACCESSIBLE SPACES
401 to 500	9
501 to 1,000	2% of total
1,001 and over	20, plus one for each 100, or fraction thereof, over 1,000

E. Scope of Application—Dwelling Units and Sleeping Units (1107)
   1. Accessible dwelling and sleeping units must have at least one accessible entrance to each unit. (1107.2)
      a. Type A units and Type B units must comply with Chapter 10 of ICC 117.1.
         i. Type A units may be accessible units.
         ii. Type B units may be accessible or Type A units.
   2. Accessible spaces (1107.3)
      a. Rooms and spaces available to the general public or by residents of accessible, Type A or Type B units must be accessible. Including:
         i. Toilet and bathing rooms, kitchen, living and dining areas.
   3. Accessible Routes
      a. At least one accessible route must connect accessible building or facility entrances with the primary entrance of each accessible, Type A and Type B unit within the building or facility and with exterior and interior spaces and facilities serving them. (1107.4)
      b. Exceptions:
         i. If without the owner's fault, either the slope of the finished ground level between accessible facilities and buildings exceeds one unit vertical in 12 units horizontal (1:12), or physical barriers or legal restrictions prevent the installation of an accessible route, a vehicular route with accessible parking at each public or common use facility or building substitutes for the accessible route.
         ii. For Group I-3, an accessible route need not connect stories or mezzanines if accessible route connects accessible units, common areas serving them, and public use areas.
         iii. For Group R-2 with type A units, no need for accessible route connecting stories or mezzanines if such units, servicing common use areas and public use areas are on an accessible route.
         iv. For other Group R-2 facilities, no need for accessible route to connect stories or mezzanines if units, servicing common use areas and public use areas are on an accessible route.
         v. For Group R-1, no need for accessible route connecting stories or mezzanines if sleeping accommodations for ≥ 2 persons and a toilet are on that level.
         vi. For Group R-3 and R-4 congregate residences, accessible route need not connect floors or mezzanines if accessible or Type B units, servicing common use areas and public use areas area on an accessible route.
         vii. Exterior decks, patios or balconies with impervious surfaces in Type B units not more than 4 inches below the finished floor level of the adjacent interior space of the unit.
   4. Group I-1 (1107.5.1)
      a. Group I-1 buildings providing custodial care where residents are capable of responding to an emergency situation without assistance require $\geq 4\%$, but not less than one, of the dwelling and sleeping units to be accessible. Group

I-1 assisted living facilities buildings providing custodial care where residents require limited verbal or physical assistance to respond to an emergency situation, $\geq$ 10%, but not less than one, of the dwelling and sleeping units must be accessible.

 b. Every dwelling and sleeping unit provided in structures with four or more such units must be Type B, subject to allowable reduction.

5. Group I-2 Nursing Homes (1107.5.2)
 a. Accessible and Type B units must be provided in Group I-2 nursing homes.
  i. At least 50% but not less than one of each type of the dwelling and sleeping units must be accessible.
  ii. Structures with four or more dwelling or sleeping units must have all such as Type B units, subject to allowable reduction.

6. Group I-2 Hospitals (1107.5.3)
 a. Accessible and Type B units are required in Group I-2 general-purpose hospitals, psychiatric facilities, detoxification facilities and residential care/assisted living facilities.
  i. At least 10%, but not less than one, of the dwelling and sleeping units must be accessible.
  ii. Structures with four or more dwelling or sleeping units must have all such as Type B units, subject to allowable reduction.

7. Group I-2 Rehabilitation Facilities (1107.5.4)
 a. Rehabilitation facilities treating mobility or of such must have 100% of the dwelling and sleeping units accessible.

8. Group I-3 (1107.5.5)
 a. Group I-3 occupancies require at least 2%, but not less than one of the dwelling and sleeping units to be accessible.
  i. If special holding cells or special housing cells or rooms are provided, at least one serving each purpose must be accessible. Examples:
  ii. Cells or rooms used for orientation, protective custody, administrative or disciplinary detention or segregation, detoxification and medical isolation. Cells or rooms specially designed without protrusions and used solely for suicide prevention do not need grab bars.
 b. At least 3% of accessible patient sleeping units or cells are required in medical care facilities in addition to medical isolation cells.

9. Group R-1 (1107.6.1)
 a. Accessible units, Type A and Type B units must be provided in Group R-1 occupancies in accordance with Table 1107.6.1.1.
  i. Consider all facilities on a site to determine the total number of accessible units. If building has >50 dwelling or sleeping units, the number of required accessible units is per Table 1107.6.1.1. If building has <50 units, use table for all dwelling and sleeping units on site.
  ii. Roll-in showers in accessible units must have a permanently mounted folding shower seat.
  iii. Structures with four or more dwelling or sleeping units must have all units as Type B units, subject to allowable reduction.

10. Group R-2 (1107.6.2)
 a. Group R-2 apartment houses, monasteries and convents must have accessible, Type A or Type B units.
  i. If more than 20 dwelling or sleeping units, there must be at least 2% but not less than I of the units as a Type A unit.
   (a) Consider all units on a site to determine the total number of units and the required number of Type A units.

(b) Type A units must be dispersed among the various classes of units.

(c) If there are four or more dwelling or sleeping units in a single structure, every unit must be a Type B unit.

(d) Exceptions: The number of Type A or Type B units is subject to allowable reduction. Existing structures on a site do not count towards the total number of units on a site for purposes of Type A units.

(e) Count bedrooms in monasteries and convents as sleeping units for determining the number of units. If sleeping units are grouped in suites, count only one sleeping unit in each suite towards the number of required accessible Type A units.

(f) Count bedrooms within congregate living facilities other than live/work units apartment complexes, monasteries and convents as sleeping units to determine the number of units. If sleeping units are grouped in suites, count only one sleeping unit in each suite towards the number of required accessible units.

  ii. Group R-2 units other than apartment houses, monasteries and convents must have accessible or Type B units.

(a) Provide accessible and sleeping units in accordance with Table 1107.6.1.1.

(b) If there are four or more dwelling or sleeping units in a single structure, every unit must be a Type B unit. (1107.6.2)

(c) Two percent, but not less than one, of each type of parking space provided for Group R-2 occupancies which have accessible, Type A or Type B dwelling or sleeping units must be accessible.

(d) If parking is provided in or beneath a building, accessible parking spaces must be provided in or beneath the building.

  b. Nonresidential portions of live-work units must be accessible. If $\geq$ 4 live-work units in a structure intended to be used as a residence, residential portion is evaluated separately as a Type B unit.

11. Group R-3 (1107.6.3)

  a. Group R-3 occupancies with four or more dwelling or sleeping units in a single structure must have every such unit as a Type B unit, subject to allowable reduction.

12. Group R-4 (1107.6.4)

  a. Group R-4 buildings, other assisted living facilities, providing custodial care to persons capable of responding to an emergency situation without assistance, must have at least one accessible dwelling or sleeping unit. Group 4 assisted living facilities where residents require limited verbal or physical assistance to respond to an emergency situation must have at least two accessible dwelling or sleeping units. Bedrooms in Group R-4 facilities are considered sleeping units for purposes of calculating the number of units.

  b. In Group R-4 structures with four or more dwelling or sleeping units, all such units must be Type B unit, UNLESS an exception under 13.a.-e. applies.

13. Allowable Reductions in Type A and Type B Units

  a. Structures Without Elevator Service (1107.7.1)

    i. Type A units are determined as per Group R-2 occupancies.

    ii. Type B units

(a) If one story requires Type B units, they must have an accessible entrance from the exterior of the structure, and all units on that story must be Type B units.

    (b) All other stories with a building entrance adjacent to arrival points for units on that story must have all dwelling and sleeping units served by that entrance as Type B units, if the slopes of both the undisturbed site and the planned finish grade, between the entrance and all vehicular or pedestrian arrival points within 50 feet of the planned entrance are 10% or less.

        (1) If there are no such arrival points within 50 feet of the entrance, use the closest arrival point unless that point serves the story containing dwelling or sleeping units.

b. A multistory dwelling or sleeping unit which has no elevator service need not be a Type B unit. If a multistory unit has external elevator service to only one floor, that floor must be the primary entry to the unit, and must be a Type B unit, with a toilet facility on that floor. (1107.7.2)

c. If elevator service goes only to the lowest story with units intended as residences, only the units on that story must be Type B units. (1107.7.3)

d. If the site has multiple buildings without elevator service, the number of required Type B units may be reduced to the percentage of the entire site having grades, prior to development of less than 10%, if all of the following apply (1107.7.4):

    i. At least 20% of the units are Type B units;

    ii. The slope between the building entrance serving the units on that story and a pedestrian or vehicular arrival point is no greater than 8.33%;

    iii. An elevated walkway is planned between a building entrance for the units on that story and a pedestrian or vehicular arrival point, and the slope between them is 10% or less; and

    iv. The Type B units are served by an elevator that goes only to the lowest story with dwelling or sleeping units.

e. Required numbers of Type A and Type B units do not apply if the elevation of the lowest floor or the lowest horizontal structural building members of buildings without elevator service are at or above the design floor elevation, in which case:

    i. a difference in elevation between the minimum floor elevation at the primary entrances and vehicular and pedestrian arrival points within 50′ exceeding 30"; and

    ii. a slope exceeding 10% between the minimum floor elevation at the primary entrances and vehicular and pedestrian arrival points is within 50′.

F.   Scope of Application—Special Occupancies (i.e., Wheelchair Spaces)

    1. Assembly Area With Fixed Seating (1108.2)

        a. Services and facilities in areas where accessibility is not required must be accessible (1108.2.1)

        b. Wheelchair Spaces (1108.2.2)

            i.   Provide accessible wheelchair spaces in accordance with Table 1108.2.2.1, in:

                (a) theaters

                (b) bleachers

                (c) grand-stands

                (d) stadiums

    (e) arenas

    (f) other fixed seating assembly areas

ii.   Spectators in wheelchair spots at events where spectators expect to remain seated must have a line of sight to the performance area or playing field comparable to that of spectators in closest proximity to the wheelchair space spots. (ADAAG 4.3.3., section 802.9.1 of ICC A117.1)

iii.   Spectators in wheelchair spots with lines of sight over heads must see over the heads of seated individuals in the first row in front of the wheelchair spots. (ADAAG 4.3.3., section 802.9.1.1 of ICC A117.1)

iv.   Spectators in wheelchair spots with lines of sight between heads and over shoulders must see over the shoulders of seated individuals in the first row in front of the wheelchair spots. (ADAAG 4.3.3, section 802.9.12 of ICC A117.1)

v.   If spectators in front of wheelchair spots expect to stand at their seats, the front of the wheelchair spots must be 12" maximum from the back of the chair or bench in front. The tread elevation of wheelchair spots must comply with Table 802.9.2.2. of ICC A117.1. For other riser heights, interpolations are allowed. (ADAAG 4.33.3, sections 802.9.2.1 and 809.9.2.2. of ICC A117.1)

vi.   Provide row companion seating with shoulder alignment with the wheelchair spot occupant (36" from the front of the wheelchair spot), comparable in size and quality to adjacent seats. The companion seat floor surface must be at the same elevation as the wheelchair spot and may be moveable. (section 802.7 of ICC A117.1)

vii.   Provide general seating in accordance with Table 1108.2.2.1.

viii.   Luxury and club boxes, and suites within arenas, stadiums and grandstands, wheelchair spaces must comply with Table 1108.2.2.1.

ix.   Other boxes must have wheelchair spaces in accordance with Table 1108.2.2.1, in not less than 20% of all boxes provided.

x.   Wheelchair spaces in multilevel assembly seating areas must be dispersed on the main floor level and on one of each two additional floor or mezzanine levels, including in:

    (a) luxury boxes

    (b) club boxes

    (c) suites

    (d) Exceptions:

        (1) In multilevel spaces used for worship if the second floor or mezzanine level contains 25% or less of the total seating capacity, wheelchair spaces may be on the main level.

        (2) In multilevel assembly seating where the second floor or mezzanine level provides 25% or less of the total seating capacity and 300 or fewer seats, all wheelchair spaces may be on the main level.

        (3) Wheelchair spaces in sport team or player seating areas need not be dispersed. (1108.2.3)

xi.   Designated aisle seats are required for at least 5%, but not less than one, of the total of aisle seats, except in sport team or player seating serving areas. If armrests are provided on seating adjacent to designated aisle seats, provide folding or retractable armrests on the aisle side of the designated aisle seat. Identify designated aisle seats by a sign or marker. (1108.2.4, section 802.8 of ICC A117.1) Wheelchair spaces must be in each balcony or mezzanine that is located on an accessible route.

xii. Lawn and exterior overflow seating areas without fixed seats must connect to an accessible route. (1108.2.5)

xiii. Assistive listening systems are necessary for each assembly area where audible communications are integral to the use. Exception: other than in courtrooms, none is needed where there is no audio amplification system. (1108.2.7)

  (a) Receivers are required for assistive listening systems in accordance with Table 1108.2.7.1. Exceptions:

    (1) If a building contains more than one assembly area, the total number of required receivers is calculated by the total number of seats in all of the assembly areas, if all receivers are usable with all systems, and if assembly areas required to provide assistive listening are under one management.

    (2) If all seats in an building, room, or assembly area are served by an induction loop assistive listening system, the minimum number of receivers required by Table 1108.2.7.1 to be hearing-aid does not apply.

    (3) If stadiums, arenas and grandstands provide audible public announcements, they must also provide equivalent text information regarding events and facilities.

      (i) If electronic signs are provided and can display prerecorded text messages with the same, or substantially equivalent, information audibly provided, they must so display, except for announcements that cannot be prerecorded in advance of the event.

      (ii) If electronic signs are provided and can display real-time messages containing the same, or substantially equivalent, information audibly provided, they must so display.

    (4) $\geq$ 1 ticket window in stadiums or arenas must have an assistive listening system.

    (5) For stadiums, arenas, and grandstands with $\geq$ 15,000 seats, pre-recorded or real-time captions of audible public announcements are required.

xiv. Performance areas must have an accessible route directly connecting those areas to the assembly seating area, where a circulation path directly connects a performance area to an assembly seating area. (1108.2.8)

  (a) An accessible route must connect performance areas with ancillary areas or facilities used by performers.

xv. Dining Areas (1108.2.9)

  (a) In dining areas, the total floor area allotted for seating and tables must be accessible. Exceptions:

    (1) In buildings or facilities where it is not necessary to provide an accessible route between levels, an accessible route to a mezzanine seating area is also not required, if the mezzanine contains less than 25% of the total area and the same services are provided in the accessible area.

(2) In sports facilities, tiered dining areas providing seating required to be accessible must have accessible routes serving at least 25% of the dining area, if accessible routes serve accessible seating and where each tier is provided with the same services.

(b) If dining surfaces for the consumption of food or drink are provided, at least 5%, but not less than one, of the seating and standing spaces must be accessible and be distributed throughout the facility (1108.2.9).

xvi. Provide self-storage spaces in service storage facilities in accordance with Table 1108.3.

(a) Accessible individual self-service storage spaces must be dispersed throughout the various classes of spaces provided.

(b) If more classes of spaces are provided than the number of required accessible spaces, the number of accessible spaces need not exceed that required by Table 1108.2.7.1

(c) Accessible spaces may be dispersed in a single building of a multi-building facility.

TABLE 1108.2.2.1
ACCESSIBLE WHEELCHAIR SPACES

CAPACITY OF SEATING IN ASSEMBLY AREAS	MINIMUM REQUIRED NUMBER OF WHEELCHAIR SPACES
4 to 25	1
26 to 50	2
51 to 100	4
101 to 300	5
301 to 500	6
501 to 5,000	6, plus 1 for each 150, or fraction thereof, between 501 through 5,000
5,001 and over	36, plus 1 for each 200, or fraction thereof, over 5,000

TABLE 1108.3
ACCESSIBLE SELF-SERVICE STORAGE FACILITIES

TOTAL SPACES IN FACILITY	MINIMUM NUMBER OF REQUIRED ACCESSIBLE SPACES
1 to 200	5%, but not less than 1
Over 200	10, plus 2% of total number of units over 200

xvii. Judicial Facilities (1108.4)

(a) All courtrooms must be accessible. (1108.4.1)

(b) Separate central holding cells for adult males, juvenile males, adult females or juvenile females must have one of each type accessible. (1108.4.2)

(i.) Central holding cells not separated by age or sex must have at least one accessible cell.

(c) Separate court-floor holding cells for adult males, juvenile males, adult females or juvenile females must serve each courtroom by one accessible cell of each type. (1108.4.2)

(1) Court-floor holding cells not separated by age or sex require that each courtroom be served by at least one accessible cell.

(2) Accessible cells may serve more than one courtroom.

G. Scope of Application—Accessibility of Other Features and Facilities

1. Toilet rooms and bathing facilities, other than Type A and Type B units, which must comply with ICC A117.1, must be accessible: (1109.1)

   a. Exceptions: (1109.2)

      i. They are only accessed through a private office, for use by one occupant.

      ii. They serve dwelling or sleeping units not otherwise required to be accessible under paragraph E.

      iii. If multiple single-user toilet rooms or bathing facilities are clustered at a single location, at least 50% but not less than one room for each use at each cluster shall be accessible.

      iv. Toilet rooms that are part of critical care or intensive care patient sleeping rooms need not be accessible.

      v. Toilet facilities that are primarily for children's use require accessible water closets, toilet compartments and lavatories complying with children's provision of ICC A117.1.

      vi. Toilet rooms for bariatric patients must comply with ICC A.117.1, and do not count towards required number of sleeping units.

   b. If a floor level shall not be connected by an accessible route, the only toilet rooms or bathing facilities in the facility shall not be on the inaccessible floor. (1109.2)

   c. At least one of each type of fixture, element, control or dispenser in each accessible toilet room and bathing facility must be accessible.

  d. Provide an accessible family or assisted use toilet room if an aggregate of six or more male and female water closets is required in assembly and mercantile occupancies. (1109.2.1)

      i. In buildings of mixed occupancy, only water closets used for the assembly or mercantile occupancy are counted.

      ii. In recreational facilities, if separate-sex bathing rooms are provided, there must be an accessible family or assisted use bathing room.

  e. Fixtures in family or assisted use toilet and bathing rooms are counted towards the number of fixtures in an occupancy, except that if each separate-sex bathing room has only one shower or bathtub fixture, a family or assisted use bathing room is not required. (1109.2.1.2)

      i. Family or assisted use toilet rooms need include only one water closet and only one lavatory.

      ii. There may be a urinal in addition to the water closet in a family or assisted use toilet room.

  f. ≥ 5% of lavatories, but > 1, must be accessible. If an accessible lavatory is located in an accessible water closet compartment, ≥ 1 additional accessible lavatory must be located in the multicompartment toilet room outside the water closet compartment. If ≥ 6 total lavatories in a toilet room or bathing facility, there must be ≥ 1 lavatory with enhanced reach ranges.

  g. Family or assisted use toilet and bathing rooms must be on accessible routes. (1109 2.4)

      i. Family or assisted use toilet rooms must be not more than one story above or below separate-sex toilet rooms.

      ii. The accessible route from any separate-sex toilet room to a family or assisted use toilet room cannot exceed 500′.

        iii. In passenger transportation facilities and airports, the accessible route from separate-sex toilet rooms to a family or assisted use toilet room cannot pass through security checkpoints. (1109.2.5)

  h. If doors swing into a family or assisted use toilet or bathing room, a clear floor space not less than 30" minimum by 48" minimum is required beyond the swing. (1109.2.6)

        i. Doors to family or assisted use toilet and bathing rooms must be secured from inside the room. (1109.2.7)

  i. Family or assisted use bathing rooms need only one shower or bathtub fixture, and one water closet and one lavatory. (1109.2.2)

        i. If water closet compartments are provided in a toilet room or bathing facility, there must be at least one wheelchair-accessible compartment.

        ii. If the combined total water closet compartments and urinals in a toilet room or bathing facility is six or more, provide at least one ambulatory-accessible water closet compartment in addition to the wheelchair-accessible compartment.

        iii. ADAAG requirements apply to water closets.

  j. At least 5% but not less than one sink in accessible spaces must comply with ADAAG, except that mop or service sinks need not be accessible. (1109.3)

2. Where accessible spaces or rooms contain kitchens, kitchenettes, and/or bars, those must be accessible as well per ADAAG.

  a. If there are kitchens, kitchenettes and or bars in accessible spaces or rooms, counters, appliances or cabinets must be on two opposing sides. If counters, appliances or cabinets are opposite a parallel wall, clearance between all opposing base cabinets, counter tops, appliances, or walls within kitchen work areas must be 40 inches minimum.

        i. Pass through kitchens must have two entries, except for spaces that do not provide a cook top or conventional range.

  b. If there are U-shaped kitchens, kitchenettes and wet bars in accessible spaces or rooms enclosed on three contiguous sides, clearance between all opposing base cabinets, counter tops, appliances, or walls within kitchen work must be 60" minimum, except for spaces that do not provide a cook top or conventional range. (ADAAG 804.2)

  c. Residential dwelling units require at least one 30 inches wide minimum section of counter with a kitchen work surface. (ADAAG 804.2)

  d. Kitchens, kitchenettes and wet bars in accessible spaces and rooms require a clear floor space allowing for a forward approach, centered on the kitchen work surface, with knee and toe clearance. (ADAAG 804.2)

        i. Exceptions:

            (a) Cabinetry may be under the work surface if it can be removed without removal or replacement of the work surface.

            (b) The finish floor extends under the cabinetry.

            (c) The walls behind and surrounding the cabinetry are finished.

        ii. The kitchen work surface must be 34" maximum above the finish floor or ground, except that an adjustable counter giving a work surface at variable heights, 29" minimum and 36" maximum is allowed.

            (a) No sharp or abrasive surfaces under the work surface counters are allowed.

3. Drinking Fountains (1109.5)

  a. No fewer than two drinking fountains on an exterior site or within a secured area are for people using wheel-chairs and one for standing persons. Exception:

        i. A single fountain suitable for both may be substituted for separate fountains.

    b. If more than two fountains are present, 50% must be usable by persons in wheelchairs and 50% suitable for standing persons. Exception:

        i. If 50% yields a fraction, round up or down.

    c. If drinking fountains are primarily for children's use, drinking fountains for people in wheelchairs comply with the children's provisions in ICC A117.1. Drinking fountains for standing children can provide spout at 30" (762 mm) minimum above the floor.

4.   Saunas and steam rooms must be accessible UNLESS in a cluster, where 5% but $\geq$ 1 must be accessible.

5.   Passenger elevators on an accessible route must be accessible (1109.7)

6.   Platform (Wheelchair) Lifts (1109.8)

    a. Platform (wheelchair) lifts may be a part of a required accessible route in new construction, including performing area and speaker platforms in Group A occupancies:

        i. as part of an accessible route to wheelchair spaces that must meet wheelchair space dispersion rules;

        ii. as part of an accessible route to spaces that are not open to the general public with an occupant load of not more than five; and

        iii. as part of an accessible route where existing exterior site constraints make use of a ramp or elevator infeasible.

        iv. As part an accessible route to jury boxes, witness stands, judicial benches, clerk/deputy clerk/bailiff/court reporter stations, and the well of the court.

7.   Storage Cabinets, Shelves, Medicine Cabinets, Closets and Drawers (1109.9)

    a. If there are fixed or built-in storage elements such as cabinets, shelves, medicine cabinets, closets and drawers in required accessible spaces, at least one of each type must contain accessible storage space per ADAAG.

    b. $\geq$ 5% and $\geq$ 1, of each type of locker provided must be accessible including centralized parcel lockers and individualized home and curb-mounted mail receptacles, must be accessible if provided.

    c. Self-service shelves and display units must be located on an accessible route, but need not comply with reach-range provisions.

    d. If coat hooks and shelves are provided in toilet rooms or toilet compartments or in dressing, fitting or locker rooms, at least one of each type must be accessible and in accessible toilet rooms without toilet compartments, accessible toilet compartments and accessible dressing, fitting and locker rooms.

8.   Seating or Standing Space at Fixed or Built-in Tables, Counters or Work Surfaces (1109.11)

    a. If fixed or built-in seating is provided at tables, counters or work surfaces, accessible seating must be distributed throughout the area, and the level must be on an accessible route:

        i. In judicial facilities and Group I-3, $\geq$ 5% but > 1 of the cubicles, must be accessible on both visitor and detainee sides. > 1 counters must be accessible on both visitor and detainee sides, if counters are provided, UNLESS detainee side of cubicles, or counters at noncontact visiting areas not serving accessible unit holding cells.

        ii. If visitor are separated from detainees by solid partitions or security glazing, $\geq$ 1 of each cubicle or counter partition must be accessible.

9.   Service Facilities (1109.12)

    a. Dressing rooms, fitting rooms or locker rooms require $\geq$ 5% and $\geq$ 1 of each type of use in each cluster provided to be accessible.

b. Check-out aisles, if provided, require accessibility in accordance with Table 1109.11.2.

    i. If public use areas are ≤ 5,000 square feet, no more than one accessible check-out aisle is needed.

    ii. If check-out aisles are dispersed throughout the building or facility, accessible check-out aisles must also be dispersed.

    iii. Traffic control devices, security devices and turnstiles located in accessible check-out aisles or lanes must be accessible.

TABLE 1109.11.2
ACCESSIBLE CHECK-OUT AISLES

TOTAL CHECK-OUT AISLES OF EACH FUNCTION	MINIMUM NUMBER OF ACCESSIBLE CHECK-OUT AISLES OF EACH FUNCTION
1 to 4	1
5 to 8	2
9 to 15	3
Over 15	3, plus 20% of additional aisles

c. Point of sale and service counters for sales or distribution of goods or services require that at least one of each type provided be accessible.

    i. If such counters are dispersed throughout the building or facility, accessible counters must also be dispersed (1109.11.3).

d. Food service lines require that if self-service shelves are provided, ≥ 5% and ≥ 1 of each type of shelf be accessible (1109.11.4).

e. Queue and waiting lines servicing accessible counters or check-out aisles must be accessible (1109.11.5).

10. Controls, Operating Mechanisms and Hardware Intended for the Occupant's Use (1109.13)

    a. Controls, operating mechanisms, and hardware, including switches that control lighting and ventilation and electrical convenience outlets, if located in accessible spaces, along accessible routes or as parts of accessible elements, must be accessible. Exceptions:

        i. Operable parts intended for use only by service or maintenance personnel.

        ii. Electrical or communication receptacles serving a dedicated use.

        iii. If two or more outlets are provided in a kitchen above a length of counter top that is uninterrupted by a sink or appliance, one outlet.

        iv. Floor electrical receptacles.

        v. HVAC diffusers.

        vi. Except for light switches, if redundant controls are provided for a single element, one control in each space.

11. 2% of gaming machines, but ≥ one of each type, must be accessible with a front approach, distributed through the different types of gaming machines. (1109.15)

12. Recreational Facilities (1110)

    a. Recreational facilities serving Group R-2, R-3 and R-4 occupancies of a single building with Type A or Type B units require 25%, but not less than one, of each type of facility to be accessible. Every facility of each type on a site is considered to determine the required number accessible.

    b. Group R-2, R-3 and R-4 occupancies on a single site with multiple buildings having Type A or Type B units served by recreational facilities require 25%, but not less than one, of each type of facility serving each building to accessible. The total number of each type of facility required to be accessible is determined based on every facility of each type serving each building on the site.

    c. At least one wheelchair space required in team or player seating areas serving areas of sport activity. Exception: bowling lanes not required to be accessible.

    d. Accessible routes required to at least 5%, but no less than one, of each type of bowling lane.

    e. At least one accessible route must directly connect both sides in court sports.

    f. Raised boxing or wrestling rings need not be accessible or on an accessible route.

    g. Raised structures used solely for refereeing, judging or scoring need not be accessible or on an accessible route.

    h. Animal containment areas not for public use need not be accessible or be on an accessible route.

    i. Load and unload areas for nonmobile, permanent amusement rides must be accessible and on an accessible route. If more than one loading or unloading position, at least one must be on an accessible route.

    j. Amusement ride load and unload areas (unless mobile or portable amusement rides) must be accessible and on accessible routes. If load/unload areas have > 1 loading/unloading position, ≥ 1 loading/unloading position must be on an accessible route:

        i. When amusement ride transfer devices are positioned for loading/unloading, and the loading and unloading positions serving on amusement rides having a wheelchair space or serving amusement ride seats designed for transfer, must be on an accessible route.

        ii. Coordinate with Ohio Department of Agriculture as to whether amusement rides provide wheelchair spaces, ride seats are designed for transfer, or transfer devices are present. EXCEPTIONS:

        (a) Amusement rides controlled or operated by the rider.

        (b) Amusement rides meant primarily for children (where assisted on and off by an adult).

        (c) Amusement rides that do not provide seats that are built-in or mechanically fastened shall not be required to comply with this section.

    k. Buildings and amenities serving golf courses must be accessible and on an accessible route. Exceptions:

        1. Golf course elements directly associated with practicing and playing, i.e., tee grounds, tee boxes, putting greens, golf cart paths, practice putting greens, practice teeing grounds, and teeing stations at driving ranges. See Federal law, as a part of the 2010 ADA Standards for Accessible Design, sections 238 and 1006.

    l. At least 50% of holes on miniature golf facilities need be accessible. Configure course so that accessible holes are consecutive. Provide an accessible route from the last accessible hole to the course entrance or exit without requiring travel through any other holes on the course. Exception:

        1. One break in the sequence of consecutive holes allowed if the last hole on the course is the last hole in the sequence.

    m. Recreational boating facilities, boat slips and boating piers must be on an accessible route. Boat slips are per Table 1110.4.9.1.

    n. Play areas must be accessible and on an accessible route.

    o. Swimming pools, wading pools, hot tubs and spas must be accessible and on an accessible route. Exception:

        1. Catch Pools or designated pool sections used as a terminus for a water slide flume, if the catch pool edge is on an accessible route.

If spas or hot tubs are clustered, $\leq 5\%$, but no fewer than one in each cluster must be accessible and on an accessible route. Raised diving boards, diving platforms, and water slides need not be accessible or on an accessible route.

p. Shooting facilities with firing positions require at least 5%, but no fewer than one, of each type of position to accessible and on an accessible route.

13. Signage (1111)

a. Signage must identify required accessible elements in accordance with the "International Symbol of Accessibility" at the following locations:

   i. Accessible parking and van-accessible spaces.

     (a) Provide with a vertical sign clearly visible to drivers parked in such locations, stating the fine under O.R.C. § 4511.99 ($\geq$ \$250 and $\leq$ \$500) for parking a vehicle in such space if not legally authorized.

   ii. Accessible passenger loading zones.

   iii. Accessible areas of refuge.

   iv. Exterior areas designated for assisted rescue.

   v. Accessible rooms where multiple single-user toilet or bathing rooms are clustered at a single location.

   vi. Accessible entrances if not all entrances are accessible.

   vii. Accessible check-out aisles if not all aisles are accessible. The sign must be above the check-out aisle in the same location as the check-out aisle number or type of check-out identification.

   viii. Unisex toilet and bathing rooms.

   ix. Accessible dressing, fitting and locker rooms if not all such rooms are accessible.

   x. At any other locations as required in ADAAG.

   xi. Signage is not required in Groups I-1, R-2, and R-3 if parking spaces are assigned to specific dwelling or sleeping units.

b. Directional signage identified by the "International Symbol of Accessibility" indicating the route to the nearest like accessible element must be provided at the following locations:

   i. Inaccessible building entrances.

   ii. Inaccessible public toilets and bathing facilities.

   iii. Elevators not serving an accessible route.

   iv. At each separate sex toilet and bathing room indicating the location of the nearest accessible unisex toilet or bathing room.

   v. At exits and elevators serving a required accessible space, but without an approved accessible means of egress.

   vi. At other locations as required in ADAAG.

   vii. At nonadjacent drinking fountains for wheelchair and standing persons, signs must indicate the location of the other fountains.

c. Signage Indicating Special Accessibility

   i. Each assembly area required must have a sign notifying patrons of the availability of assistive listening systems

     (a) Exception: if ticket offices or windows are provided, signs are not required at each assembly area if signs are displayed at each ticket office or window informing patrons of the availability of assistive listening systems.

   ii. Signage required at each door to area of refuge, exterior area for assisted refuge, egress stairway, exit passageway, exit discharge.

   iii. Signage required at areas of refuge.

   iv. Signage required at exterior areas for assisted refuge.

   v. Signage required at two-way communication systems.

   vi. Signage required within exit enclosures.

   vii. Signage required as otherwise mandated in locations per ADAAG.

TABLE 1107.6.1.1
ACCESSIBLE DWELLING AND SLEEPING UNITS

Total Number of Units Provided	Minimum Required Number of Accessible Units Associated With Roll-In Showers	Total Number of Required Accessible Units
1 to 25	0	1
26 to 50	0	2
51 to 75	1	4
76 to 100	1	5
101 to 150	2	7
151 to 200	2	8
201 to 300	3	10
301 to 400	4	12
401 to 500	4	13
501 to 1,000	1% of total	3% of total
Over 1,000	10, plus 1 for each 100, or fraction thereof, over 1,000	30, plus 2 for each 100, or fraction thereof, over 1,000

TABLE 1108.2.7.1
RECEIVERS FOR ASSISTIVE LISTENING SYSTEMS

Capacity of Seating in Assembly Areas	Minimum Required Number of Receivers	Minimum Number of Receivers to be Hearing-Aid Compatible
50 or less	2	2
51 to 200	2, plus 1 per 25 seats over 50 seats*	2
201 to 500	2, plus 1 per 25 seats over 50 seats*	1 per 4 receivers*
501 to 1,000	20, plus 1 per 33 seats over 500 seats*	1 per 4 receivers*
1,001 to 2,000	35, plus 1 per 50 seats over 1,000 seats*	1 per 4 receivers*
Over 2,000	55, plus 1 per 100 seats over 2,000 seats*	1 per 4 receivers*

NOTE: * = or fraction thereof

    viii. At amusement rides, signs are required at entrances to queues, waiting lines, and load/unload areas.

    ix. Variable message signs are required at transportation facilities and emergency shelters.

    x. Signage per ORC 2902.4 and 2902.4.1 at toilet rooms and at entrances.

ACCESS PANELS

A. Attics: An opening of 20" × 30" minimum must be provided for attic areas of over 30 clear height. A 30" minimum clear headroom must be provided in the attic space at or above the access opening.

B. Clearances around appliances to permanent construction and other installed equipment and appliances must be sufficient to allow inspection, service, repair or replacement without removing that permanent construction or disabling the function of a required fire-resistance-rated assembly. (M-506.3.10)

    1. Grease ducts must allow visual inspection on all sides

        a. Any portion of a grease duct system without access from the duct entry or discharge must have cleanout openings. Provide cleanout at both inlet and outlet side of an in-line fan if duct connects to fan, and within 3' (914 mm) of fan duct connections. Cleanouts on horizontal duct sections must be ≤ 20' (6096 mm) apart, located on the side of the duct with the opening ≥ 1½" (38 mm) above bottom of the duct, and ≥ 1" (25 mm) below top of the duct. Opening minimum dimensions are 12" (305 mm) on each side, unless duct dimensions do not allow; then openings are on top or bottom of the duct. If on the top, the opening edges are minimum 1" (25 mm) from edges of the duct. If on the bottom, cleanout openings must provide internal damming around the opening, have gasketing to preclude grease leakage, provide for drainage of grease down the duct around the dam, and be approved for the application. If dimensions of sides, top, or bottom preclude this installation, locate cleanout on duct face affording largest opening dimension and use prescribed distances for opening edges.

b. Grease duct fire-resistant access openings at each cleanout point are required if cleanout openings are located in ducts within a fire-resistance-rated enclosure.

c. If ductwork is large enough to allow personnel entry, not less than one approved or listed opening having dimensions not less than 22" by 20" (508 mm by 508 mm) must be provided in the horizontal sections, and in the top of vertical risers. If such entry is provided, the duct and its supports must be capable of supporting the additional load.

d. Access openings must have tight-fitting sliding or hinged doors that are equal in fire-resistive protection to that of the shaft or enclosure, and door assemblies must not have fasteners penetrating the duct.

e. An approved sign must be placed on access opening panels with wording as follows: "ACCESS PANEL. DO NOT OBSTRUCT." M-506.3.8, M-506.3.11

f. All grease duct joints, seams, and penetrations must be of continuous liquid-tight weld or braze on external surface of duct. Exceptions:
   (1) Penetrations sealed by application-listed devices.
   (2) Internal welding or brazing allowed if joint formed or ground smooth and readily accessible for inspection.
   (3) Factory-built commercial kitchen grease ducts per UL 1978.

g. Duct joints can be either:
   (1) butt joints
   (2) welded flange joints with maximum ½" (12.7 mm) flange depth
   (3) overlapping telescoping or bell type duct joints. Use overlapping joints to prevent ledges and obstructions from collecting grease or interfering with planned gravity drainage. Difference of inside cross-sectional dimensions ≤ ¼", and overlap length ≤ 2" (51 mm).

h. Perform leakage test prior to use on grease duct system. Perform light test by passing lamp rated ≥ 100 watts through ductwork, lighting equally in all directions perpendicular to walls, covering entire duct including hood-to-duct connection. Limit to field-assembled duct joints and exclude factory welds for listed factory-built grease ducts.

i. Grease duct bracing and supports must be noncombustible, securely attached to structure, and designed for gravity and seismic loads within building code's stress limitations. Bolts, screws, rivets, and other mechanical fasteners cannot penetrate duct walls.

2. Fire and smoke dampers must have an approved means of access large enough to permit inspection and maintenance of the damper and its operating parts (M-607.4)

   a. Access shall not affect the integrity of fire-resistance-rated assemblies.

        b. Access openings shall not reduce the fire-resistance rating of the assembly.

        c. Access points shall be permanently identified on the exterior by a label having letters not less than 0.5" (12.7 mm) in height reading: FIRE/SMOKE DAMPER, SMOKE DAMPER or FIRE DAMPER.

        d. Access doors in ducts shall be tight fitting and suit-able for the required duct construction.

    3. Masonry chimney flues must have a cleanout opening having a minimum height of 6" (152 mm) (M-801.13)

        a. The upper edge of the opening shall be located not less than 6" (152 mm) below the lowest chimney inlet opening.

        b. The cleanout shall be provided with a tight-fitting, noncombustible cover.

        c. Cleanouts are not required for chimney flues serving masonry fireplaces, if such flues can be accessed through the fireplace opening.

    4. Panels, grilles and access doors for sauna heaters that must be removed for normal servicing operations cannot be attached to the building (M-914.2, M-914.3)

    5. Access is necessary to solar energy equipment and appliances for maintenance (M-1402.1)

        a. Solar systems and appurtenances cannot obstruct or interfere with the operation of any doors, windows or other building components requiring operation or access.

  C. Courts require access to the bottom for cleaning purposes. (1206.3.1)

  D. Crawl spaces must have an 18" x 24" minimum opening. (1209.1)

ADJOINING ROOMS (1203.4.1.1)

  A. If rooms and spaces without openings to the outdoors are ventilated through an adjoining room, the opening to the adjoining room must be unobstructed and have an area of not less than 8% of the floor area of the interior room or space, but not less than 25' square. (1203.4.1.1)

    1. The minimum area to the outdoors that can be open must be based on the total floor area being ventilated.

  B. Exception: Exterior openings required for ventilation may open into a thermally isolated sunroom addition or patio cover, provided that the openable area between the sunroom addition or patio cover and the interior room must have an area of not less than 8% of the floor area of the interior room or space, but not less than 20' square.

    1. The minimum area to the outdoors that can be open must be based on the total floor area being ventilated.

ADMIXTURES (1903.6)

  A. Admixtures may be used in mortars if they do not have an adverse effect on the mortar properties nor any imbedded reinforcement. (ACI 318, Section 3.6)

    1. Accelerators reduce curing time, improve high early strength, and speed handling and form removal. They do not act as an anti-freeze. Calcium chloride is the most common type of accelerator, but cannot be used in prestressed concrete, concrete containing aluminum, or in concrete cast against stay-in-place galvanized metal forms.

    2. Retarders are used in hot weather to aid required handling time, and allow dead load deflection before set begins. Retarders may be an asset when pumping concrete, and are used to control set time.

    3. Superplasticizers:

        a. Are used as water reducers; raise the slump without additional water.

        b. Increase both compressive and flexural strength.

    c. Improve workability, require less vibration, reduce honey-combing, and provide better wall textures.

    d. Reduce slab deviation due to self-leveling properties.

    e. Save finishing time, placement labor, and improve pumping.

4. Air-entraining (1904.4)

    a. Resist freezing and thawing action, de-icers, sulfates, and bleeding.

    b. Improve workability, plasticity, and water tightness.

    c. Reduce density and water content, but may reduce concrete strength slightly.

    d. Air entrainment of concrete exposed to freezing and thawing while moist per ACI 318, Section 4.4.1.

    e. If concrete exposed to freezing and thawing in the presence of moisture and deicing chemicals, maximum weight of fly ash, other pozzolans, silica fume, or slag in concrete must be ≤ percentages of total weight of cementitious materials allowed per ACI 318, Section 4.4.2.

5. Pozzolans (ASTM C618) have a wide variety of individual uses such as helping to reduce shrinkage, improving workability and durability, aiding in water tightness, and improving finished appearance.

6. Miscellaneous: Special admixtures have been developed for bonding to bars and cables, as surface hardeners, and coloring pigments.

7. The proper admixture should only be determined by a specialist.

AISLES AND AISLE ACCESSWAYS (1028)

A. Buildings of Use Group A and assembly occupancies accessory to Group E that contain seats, tables, displays, or equipment that would require the occupants to pass by them must have aisles leading to exits.

B. Outdoor/stadium type seating. (Chapters 1 to 4 of ICC 300)

C. Aisle width: (1028.9.2)

1. Must serve area ("catchment") naturally egressing to the aisle. Assume as to catchment areas that there is a balanced use of all means of egress, i.e., the number of persons in proportion to egress capacity.

2. Converging aisles must have sufficient capacity for combined load. (1028.9.3)

3. Must be uniform in both directions when egressing two ways. (1028.9.4)

4. Design clear width (except handrail projections) must be provided as follows: (1028.10)

    a. 12"

       – back of row ahead to front of seat

       – measure with seat in raised position when automatic

       – measure seats with folding tablet arms with tablet arms in the used position. Exception: row spacing may be calculated with the tablet arm in the stored position if arm when raised manually to vertical position in one motion automatically returns to the stored position through gravity alone.

    b. If rows of seating served by aisles or doorways at both ends, ≤ 100 seats per row. Increase minimum 12" (305 mm) clear width between rows by 0.3" (7.6 mm) for every additional seat beyond 14, but minimum clear width need not exceed 22" (559 mm). Exception: If smoke-protected assembly seating, row length limits for 12"-wide (305 mm) aisle accessway, beyond which increase aisle accessway minimum clear width per Table 1028.10.1.

TABLE 1028.10.1
SMOKE-PROTECTED
ASSEMBLY AISLE ACCESSWAYS

TOTAL NUMBER OF SEATS IN THE SMOKE-PROTECTED ASSEMBLY OCCUPANCY	MAXIMUM NUMBER OF SEATS PER ROW PERMITTED TO HAVE A MINIMUM 12-INCH CLEAR WIDTH AISLE ACCESSWAY	
	Aisle or doorway at both ends of row	Aisle or doorway at one end of row only
Less than 4,000	14	7
4,000	15	7
7,000	16	8
10,000	17	8
13,000	18	9
16,000	19	9
19,000	20	10
22,000 and greater	21	11

For SI: 1 inch = 25.4 mm.

5. Minimum clear width of aisles must be provided as follows: (1028.9.1)
   a. 48" (1219 mm) if aisle stairs have seating on each side, UNLESS aisle serves < 50 seats; then 36" (914 mm) allowed.
   b. 36" (914 mm) if aisle stairs have seating on only one side.
   c. 23" (584 mm) between aisle stair handrail or guard and seating if aisle is subdivided by handrail.
   d. 42" (1067 mm) for level or ramped aisles with seating on both sides. Exceptions:
      1. 36" (914 mm) if aisle serves < 50 seats.
      2. 36" (762 mm) where the aisle serves ≤ 14 seats.
      3. 36" (914 mm) if level or ramped aisles have seating on only one side. Exceptions:
         a. 30" (762 mm) if aisle serves ≤ 14 seats.
         b. 23" (584 mm) between aisle stair handrail and seating if aisle serves ≤ 5 rows on one side.
6. All aisles must terminate at cross aisle, foyer, doorway, vomitory or concourse accessing an exit. Exceptions:
   a. Dead-end aisles ≤ 20′ (6096 mm) in length.
   b. Dead-end aisles longer than 20′ (6096 mm) allowed if seats beyond 20′ are ≤ 24 seats from another aisle, measured along row of seats with minimum clear width of 12" (305 mm), plus 0.6" (15.2 mm) for each additional seat above 7 in the row.
   c. For smoke-protected assembly seating, the dead-end aisle length of vertical aisles ≤ 21 rows.
   d. For smoke-protected assembly seating, longer dead-end aisle allowed if seats beyond 21 are ≤ 40 seats from another aisle, measured along row of seats

with a 12" (305 mm) minimum clear width aisle accessway, plus 0.3" (7.6 mm) for each additional seat above 7 in the row.

D. Aisle slopes must meet the following conditions: (1028.11)
    1. Gradient must not exceed 1:8, unless risers and treads extend across full width of aisle.
    2. Steps in aisle must meet the following conditions:
        a. Tread depth must be at least 11" and be uniform in each aisle with maximum variation of 3/16".
        b. Riser height must be at least 4", but no more than 8". Heights not exceeding 9" are allowed if necessitated by the slope of the adjacent seating areas to maintain sightlines. Variations in height over 3/16" due to seating rise must be marked with a stripe which is a minimum of 1", but no more than 2", wide.

E. Handrails in aisles must meet the following conditions (1028.13)
    1. Handrails are required where aisle slope exceeds 1:15.
    2. Handrails not necessary on ramped aisles with ≤ 1:8 gradient and seating on both sides.
    3. Handrails not necessary if guard at side of the aisle meeting graspability requirements.
    4. Handrail extensions not necessary at top and bottom of aisle stairs and aisle ramp runs allowing crossovers within the aisles.
    5. If seating on both sides of the aisle, handrails must be discontinuous with gaps or breaks at intervals ≤ 5 rows for access to seating and permitting crossing from one side of aisle to the other. Gaps or breaks must have 22" (559 mm) clear width and ≤ 36" (914 mm) measured horizontally. Handrail needs rounded terminations or bends.
    6. For rails in middle of aisles, add an intermediate rail 12" below top rail. (1028.13.2)

F. Guardrails on boxes, balconies, and galleries (1028.14)
    1. Fascia or railing system with 26" (660 mm) minimum height needed if floor or footboard elevation ≥ 30" above floor or grade below AND fascia or railing would otherwise obstruct immediate sightlines immediately adjacent.
    2. Fascia or railing system needed for full width of aisle if foot of aisle ≥ 30" (762 mm) above floor or grade below. Fascia or railing must be 36" (914 mm) minimum height, with 42" (1067 mm) measured diagonally from top of rail and nosing of nearest tread.
    3. Guards needed at cross aisles ≥ 30" (762 mm) above floor or grade below, otherwise 26" Exception:
        a. No guard needed if backs of seats on front of cross aisle ≥ 24" (610 mm) above adjacent floor of aisle.
        b. Guard needed at bleachers per ICC 300.

G. Row width (1028.10)
    1. Minimum clear row width must be 12", in rows with not more than 14 seats, with seats in raised position for automatic seats. If not automatic seat, measure with seat in down position. If seat with folding tablet arms, measure with tablet arm in used position. Exception:
        a. Per folding tablet arms, allow row spacing measured with arm in stored position if gravity sufficient to return arm to stored position.
    2. When rows have aisles on both sides, a maximum of 100 seats per row is permitted. Add 3" for each seat beyond 14 maximum 22" required. (1025.10.1)
    3. For rows with aisles at one end, increase row width per Table 1028.1.1
    4. Maximum common path of travel is 30′ (9144 mm) from seat to point where occupant can choose two paths of travel to two exits, Exceptions:

  a. Area serving < 50 occupants, 75′ maximum common path of travel.

  b. For smoke-protected assembly seating, 50′ maximum common path of travel.

 5. Maximum 24 seats between two aisles if one of two paths of travel is across aisle through a row of seats to another aisle. Minimum clear width of 12′ (305 mm) between rows for the row between the two aisles, plus 0.6" (15.2 mm) for each additional seat above 7 in the row between aisles. Exception:

  a. For smoke-protected assembly seating, ≤ 40 seats between the two aisles, with 12" minimum clear width plus 0.3" (7.6 mm) for each additional seat.

TABLE 1028.6.2
WIDTH OF AISLES FOR SMOKE-PROTECTED ASSEMBLY

TOTAL NUMBER OF SEATS IN THE SMOKE-PROTECTED ASSEMBLY OCCUPANCY	INCHES OF CLEAR WIDTH PER SEAT SERVED			
	Stairs and aisle steps with handrails within 30 inches	Stairs and aisle steps without handrails within 30 inches	Passageways, doorways and ramps not steeper than 1 in 10 in slope	Ramps steeper than 1 in 10 in slope
Equal to or less than 5,000	0.200	0.250	0.150	0.165
10,000	0.130	0.163	0.100	0.110
15,000	0.096	0.120	0.070	0.077
20,000	0.076	0.095	0.056	0.062
Equal to or greater than 25,000	0.060	0.075	0.044	0.048

For SI: 1 inch = 25.4 mm.

 H. At tables (1017.4)

  1. Except for access to 4 persons within 6′ of an aisle, the minimum width of 12" and ¹/₂" per foot of aisle beyond 12′ along the access from any seat to an aisle.

  2. Measure 19" away from front of table with loose chairs.

  3. Measure from the back of fixed chairs.

 I. Fixed seating (1028.12)

  1. Required in assembly if > 200 seats, unless tables present and without ramped or tiered floors. If without ramped or tiered floors, seats fastened together as groups of 3 and securely fastened to floor.

  2. If seating flexibility is design function, and tiered seating, maximum of 200 seats need not be fastened to floor, but plan approval required.

  3. If seat groupings of ≤ 14 on level floors separated from other seating by railings, guards, etc., need not be fastened to floor.

  4. Seats for musicians and other performers separated by railings, guards, partial height walls or similar barriers, no need to fasten to floor.

APPLICATION (OAC CHAPTER 4101:1-1)

 A. The OBC applies to:

  1. Construction, alteration, movement, enlargement, replacement, repair, equipment, use and occupancy, location, maintenance, removal and demolition of every building and every appurtenance connected or attached to it.

  2. All new construction—Exceptions:

   a. Detached one-, two-, and three-family dwellings and structures accessory to those dwellings;

   b. All federal government buildings;

   c. Buildings or structures that are incident to agricultural use on that land, provided they are not also used in retail trade (i.e., 50% or more of the gross income for that building or structure derives from sales of products produced or raised in a normal crop year on seller's owned or operated farms);

    d. Agricultural labor camps;

    e. Type A or Type B family day-care homes with the exception of Ohio Department of jobs and Family Services (ODJFS) inspections, conducted by certified building department with jurisdiction OR Division of Industrial Compliance and Labor per OBBS website inspection checklist;

    f. Buildings or structures that are designed, constructed, and maintained in accordance with federal standards and regulations and are used primarily for federal and state military purposes where the Department of Defense, pursuant to 10 U.S.C.A. §§ 18233(A)(1) and 18237, acquires by purchase, lease, or transfer, and constructs, expands, rehabilitates, or corrects and equips, such as considered necessary to carry out the purposes of Chapter 1803 of the U.S.C.A.;

    g. Manufactured homes constructed under 24 C.F.R. Part 3280, Manufactured Home Construction and Safety Standards and governed by rules adopted by the Ohio Manufactured Home Commission;

    h. Sewerage systems, treatment works, and disposal systems (including associated tanks, piping, and process equipment) regulated by a municipal corporation or county or special district owning or operating a publicly owned treatment works or sewerage system per O.R.C. section 6111.032, division A;

    i. Building sewer piping;

    j. Portable electric generators and wiring for carnival and amusement park rides regulated by the Ohio Department of Agriculture;

    k. Structures directly related to the operation of a generating plant or major utility facilities regulated by the power siting board. Board may request building department to review and inspect for OBBS compliance, but building department lacks enforcement authority.

B. The OBC focuses on energy conservation, safety and building sanitation, while considering performance objectives, costs of construction, and standardization. (101.2)

C. Building Department approval is not required for the following (102):

1. Constructing single-story detached accessory structures for use as tool and storage sheds, playhouses and similar uses, IF floor area ≤ 120' square (11.15 m²), and playground structures.

2. Fences ≤ 6' (1829 mm) in height.

3. Oil derricks.

4. Retaining walls ≤ 4' (1219 mm) in height, from bottom of footing to top of wall, unless supporting a surcharge or impounding Class I, II or III-A liquids.

5. Water tanks supported directly upon grade if capacity ≤ 5,000 gallons (18 927 L) and ratio of height to diameter or width ≤ two to one.

6. Sidewalks and driveways ≤ 30" (762 mm) above grade and not over any basement or story below, and are not part of an accessible route.

7. Finishes not regulated by OBC, decorating, or other work defined as maintenance or minor repair.

8. Temporary motion picture, television and theater stage sets and scenery.

9. Window awnings supported by a Group R-3 exterior wall.

10. Exempted tents and membrane structures per MARQUEES.

11. Minor electrical repair work, i.e., lamp replacement, connection of approved portable electrical equipment to approved permanent receptacles.

12. Electrical equipment used for radio and television transmission EXCEPT equipment and wiring used for power supply, and tower and antenna installation.

13. Installation of temporary systems for testing or servicing of electrical equipment or apparatus.
14. Electrical wiring, devices, appliances, apparatus or equipment operating at < 25 volts and not capable of supplying more than 50 watts of energy, UNLESS OBC otherwise directs.
15. Electrical process equipment and associated wiring on load side of power disconnect to equipment.
16. Portable gas heating appliances.
17. Replacement of any gas part that does not alter equipment approval or render it unsafe.
18. Gas distribution piping owned and maintained by public or municipal utilities and located upstream of point of delivery.
19. Portable mechanical heating appliances.
20. Portable ventilation equipment.
21. Portable cooling units.
22. Replacement of any parts which do not alter approval or render unsafe.
23. Portable evaporative cooler.
24. Process equipment and associated piping. For combination building services/process or power piping systems, the power or process piping located downstream of control valve separating process from building services piping is exempt from approval.
25. Heating and cooling distribution piping installed and maintained by municipal or public utilities.
26. Repair of leaks in drains, water, soil, waste or vent pipe. UNLESS any concealed trap, drain-pipe, water, soil, waste or vent pipe becomes defective, necessitating removal/replacement.
27. Clearance of pipe, valve, or fixture stoppages or leak repairs, and water closet removal and reinstallation, IF valve, pipe, or fixture replacement or rearrangement is not involved.
28. For process equipment and associated piping for combination building services/process or power piping systems, the power or process piping downstream of control valve separating process from building services piping is exempt from approval.
29. If emergency situation requiring equipment replacements and repairs, application for approval is required within the next working business day to the building official.
30. Minor repairs to structures which cannot include cutting away of any wall, partition or portion thereof, the removal or cutting of any structural beam or load bearing support, or the removal or change of a required means of egress, or rearrangement of parts of a structure affecting egress requirements. Ordinary repairs also cannot include addition to, alteration of, replacement or relocation of a standpipe, water supply, sewer, drainage, drain leader, gas, soil, waste, vent or similar piping, electric wiring or mechanical or other work affecting public health or general safety.

D. Municipalities may establish Code provisions not in conflict with the Ohio Revised Code and OBC. The OBC governs over the rules of the State Fire Marshall, the Department of Health, and county and township rules in the event of a conflict.

E. Building plans (105)
1. Construction must begin within 12 months of issuance of a permit.
2. Invalid plans must be re-approved.
3. A 12-month extension may be granted if requested at least 10 days prior to the expiration date.

4. Partial plan approval may be granted and owner may proceed on the approved part only, with no assurance as to approval of remainder.

5. Plans certified by an Ohio registered architect and/or engineer do not require a detailed technical analysis by the building official.

    a. Technical design analysis is defined as integrated solutions which involve analytical methods using scientific and engineering principles.

6. One set of approved plans shall be kept on the site, or be available at all times, for the building official.

7. Electronic media documents may be used if approved by the building official.

F. Municipal, township, or county building departments enforce the OBC, EXCEPTION:

1. Fire prevention rules are enforced by the State Fire Marshal or by local fire departments.

2. Sewage, sanitary, and drainage rules are enforced by the city engineer, the boards of health of health districts, or the sewer purveyor.

3. Power plant or major utility facility rules are enforced by power plant siting boards.

G. Delayed work (105.1)

1. If work is delayed more than 6 months, plans become invalid and must be re-approved.

2. Two extension periods of 6 months each may be granted if requested at least 10 days prior to the expiration date along with a fee of not more than $100 for each extension.

3. Conditional approval if no other OBC provision applies and an objection to any portion of the construction documents results from minor conflicting code interpretations, or minor modifications needed to the design or construction. Work may proceed to the point of objection. Conditional approval conditions form appealable adjudication order under O.R.C. 3781.19.

4. Phased approval for portion(s) of project prior to submission of construction documents for entire project, if portion complies with OBC. Phased approval holder proceeds at own risk. Work may proceed only to the approved point. Phased plan approval fees per Table 115.2. The processing fee for plan examination of each subsequent of each phase is $250.00.

5. Annual approval available in lieu of individual approvals individual alterations to electrical, gas, mechanical, plumbing, or piping installation.

H. All buildings require a certificate of occupancy to occupy (with use group, type of construction, sprinkler data, and any special conditions of permit). (111.1 and 111.3) This requirement also applies to building alterations or additions, and changes in occupancy. Temporary certificates of occupancy can be issued at the owner's request before the work is completed, if the building official determines that the space can be safely occupied prior to full completion, structure, or portion without endangering life or public welfare, and stating the extent of the certificate as to space and time limits. A building changed in part from one occupancy to another for a limited time may receive a certificate of occupancy if there are no violations of law or building official orders pending, inspection indicates the proposed use will not endanger public safety and welfare safely, and the certificate delineates special conditions. If a building will be built and used for ≤ 180 days, the building official may issue a "Certificate of Occupancy for Temporary Structures," extendable for demonstrated cause.

1. Certificates must include the following:

    a. The plan approval application number.

    b. The address.

    c. A description of that portion of the structure for which the certificate is issued.

    d. The signature of all building officials having jurisdiction. If more than one building official has jurisdiction for a building (when the building department certification is limited for, i.e., plumbing or piping systems) each shall sign the certificate of occupancy, indicating the scope of their individual approvals.

  e. The OBC edition under which the plan approval was issued.
  f. The use and occupancy.
  g. The type of construction.
  h. The design occupant load.
  i. If an automatic sprinkler system is provided, whether the sprinkler system is required.
  j. The hazard classification or storage configuration, including aisle widths, for which the automatic sprinkler system is designed.
  k. The automatic sprinkler and standpipe system demand at the base of the riser.
  l. Any special stipulations and conditions of plan approval, including variances granted to OBC requirements.

I. Plan contents (106.1)

  1. Plans must be clear and comprehensive and submitted with multiple copies. The number of copies required varies locally due to review by additional departments. If approval is granted by the building official, plans may be submitted in electronic format.
  2. An index of the drawings is required on the first sheet. The index must designate type of construction and all ratings of structural elements including structural design loads, maximum design occupancy, and seismic design category and site class.
  3. The plot plan must show street location, location of the building and all other existing buildings on the site, property lines, utility easements, and general features, setbacks, side yard distances, and distances between all buildings, as well as locate and size all utility lines. Include location of any fences, the elevations of all proposed finished grades, and draw in accordance with an accurate boundary line survey. If demolition is involved, the site plan must show what construction is to be demolished and the location and size of existing structures and construction that are to remain at the site. If in a flood hazard area, construction documents submitted must include current FEMA "Flood Hazard Boundary Map" (FHBM), "Flood Insurance Rate Map" (FIRM) or "Flood Boundary Floodway Map" (FBFM) for the location. Elevations on the site plan must correlate with the datum on the related flood hazard map.
  4. Floor plans, sections, and details must show:
      a. Full or partial basements and floor layouts, attics, or penthouses and grade elevations.
      b. All door swings; stairs, ramps, windows, shafts, egress, plumbing fixtures, built-in fixtures, special equipment, and vertical transportation.
      c. All wall materials; and roof plan.
      d. Elevations must show floor-to-floor heights and overall building height exterior and interior.
      e. Structural drawings must indicate all live loads.
      f. All floor layouts, roof plan, electrical, plumbing, mechanicals, and structural designs must be provided.
      g. Include plumbing, mechanical, and electrical systems, including all R-values.

J. Enforcement by Building Departments (104.1)

  1. Enforcement of the OBC is the responsibility of the certified chief building official in all building departments.

a. A certified plans examiner must approve the plans and the certified building inspector must inspect the construction.

b. If the building department employs or has them under contract, electrical and plumbing plans examiners are responsible for examining construction documents as to electrical and plumbing compliance with the OBC, respectively; otherwise that is the responsibility of the master certified plans examiner.

c. An inspector is responsible for inspections to ensure that work performed complies with the approved construction documents.

d. Inspectors may be either Building Inspectors, Plumbing Inspectors, Electrical Inspectors, Mechanical Inspectors (e.g. HVAC and associated refrigeration, fuel gas, and heating piping systems), Fire Inspectors, Fire Inspectors, or Medical Gas Piping Inspectors.

e. (If a Medical Gas Piping Inspector is not employed or under contract, such inspection is deferred to either the local health district or the superintendent of the Division of Industrial Compliance of the Department of Commerce. Exception: If the building department does not have a full-time certified master plan examiner, the building official must approve the plans.

2. The adjudication of orders of local building officials is the responsibility of certified municipal and county boards of building appeals, with the power to reverse or modify orders if found contrary to the OBC or the Code, if contrary to a fair interpretation thereof, or if a variance from the OBC or the Code in the specific case will result in unnecessary hardship and the variance will not be contrary to the public interest. The Ohio Board of Building Appeals adjudicates orders for political subdivisions lacking certified boards or contracts with certified boards. Appeals of building department orders are by written complaint.

K. General plan processing fees: each department establishes its own fee structure through the jurisdiction it serves.

L. Testing and Certification (114)

a. All building materials, products, assemblies, and methods of production are to be approved by the local building official. Testing may be performed for the building official by various entities, per:

Figure 114.2 ORGANIZATION OF BOARD RECOGNIZED BODIES AND
CERTIFICATION PROGRAMS

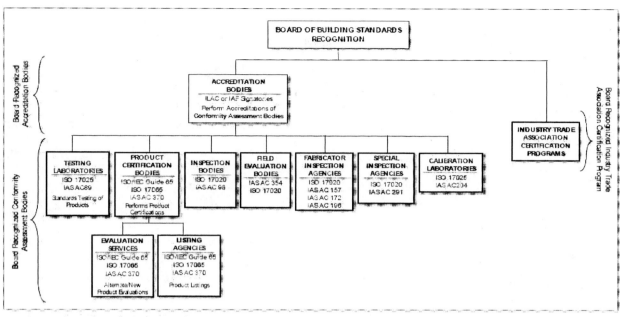

BOARD OF BUILDING STANDARDS RECOGNITION

Board Recognized Accreditation Bodies

Board Recognized Conformity Assessment Bodies

Board Recognized Industry Trade Association Certification Program

ACCREDITATION BODIES
ILAC or IAF Signatories
Perform Accreditations of Conformity Assessment Bodies

INDUSTRY TRADE ASSOCIATION CERTIFICATION PROGRAMS

TESTING LABORATORIES
ISO 17025
IAS AC89
Standards Testing of Products

PRODUCT CERTIFICATION BODIES
ISO/IEC Guide 65
ISO 17065
IAS AC 370
Performs Product Certifications

INSPECTION BODIES
ISO 17020
IAS AC 98

FIELD EVALUATION BODIES
IAS AC 354
ISO 17020

FABRICATOR INSPECTION AGENCIES
ISO 17020
IAS AC 157
IAS AC 172
IAS AC 196

SPECIAL INSPECTION AGENCIES
ISO 17020
IAS AC 291

CALIBRATION LABORATORIES
ISO 17025
IAS AC204

EVALUATION SERVICES
ISO/IEC Guide 65
ISO 17065
IAS AC 370
Alternate/New Product Evaluations

LISTING AGENCIES
ISO/IEC Guide 65
ISO 17065
IAS AC 370
Product Listings

ILAC – International Laboratory Accreditation Cooperation
IAF – International Accreditation Forum
ISO – International Organization for Standardization
IAS – International Accreditation Service
IEC – International Electrotechnical Commission

31

   b. No testing entity may be used unless it is approved by the Board and its identity is posted at: http://www.com.ohio.gov/dico/bbs. as a "Recognized Conformity Assessment Body."

   c. Building officials may approve listed and labeled materials, products, assemblies or methods of construction once they have verified that the product is listed on the certification agency's current website directory, the listing is current, the product will be installed per the listing, assemblies are installed per the Code, and the listing is not in any way in conflict with the Code.

   d. Building service equipment is tested by the local building official at the owner's expense.

   e. Alternative materials, products, assemblies, or methods of construction may be used if in accordance with the test report or listing on the testing agency's website.

   f. Used products and materials may be used only if approved by the building official.

ATRIUMS (404.0)

An atrium is one form of shaft enclosure which is acceptable in all buildings except Group H.

A. Enclosure
1. All walls adjacent to atrium must have a 1-hour minimum fire barrier, the same as for corridors. The adjacent spaces of any 3 floors of the atrium are not required to be separated from the atrium.
2. The use of glass partitions facing an atrium is permitted if the following conditions are met:
   a. Sprinklers required on both sides when there are walkways on both sides of the glass.
   b. Sprinklers not required when no walkway exists.
   c. Sprinklers located maximum 6' on center and 4"–12" from glass.
   d. Openings shall be self-closing, shall resist the passage of smoke, and shall be positive latching.

B. Smoke detectors designed to activate a smoke control and alarm are required in all atriums that connect more than 2 stories. (Manual pull systems are required.) (907.2.14)
1. Smoke detectors in a 2 story atrium only activate an alarm at a constantly attended location.

C. Voice alarm
1. Voice alarms are required in buildings of use groups A, E, and M which have atriums. (907.2.14)
2. Alarms shall be initiated by sprinklers, smoke detectors, and manual alarms.

D. A smoke control system is required. (See SMOKE CONTROL.) Except for atriums that only connect two stories.

E. The maximum travel distance to an exit is 200 at all levels above the lowest level, when the exit is through the atrium. (404.9)

F. All atriums must be sprinkled to the limits of the shaft fire separation. The sprinkler system cannot be a limited area system. The area of a building adjacent to or above the atrium need not be sprinkled IF separated from atrium portion by not less than two-hour fire barriers OR horizontal assemblies, or both. If atrium ceiling is > 55' (16,764 mm) above the floor, sprinkler protection at atrium ceiling of the atrium is not required.

G. Does not apply to Group R-3 exits, in dwelling units, two-level floor openings, or open parking structure stairs or other exceptions to 707.2.

H. Only low hazard uses of open well floors are permitted, except when individual space can be sprinkled.

    I. Standby power is required for smoke control systems. (2702.2.2)

    J. Interior finish of atrium walls and ceilings cannot be less than Class B; no reduction in class for sprinkler protection.

ATTICS

    A. Attic is defined as the space between ceiling beams and roof rafters. (202)

    B. Natural ventilation (1203.2)

Attics and rafter spaces must have screened cross-ventilation which meets the following requirements:

1. When using ridge and gable vents, a minimum of 50% of the ventilation area must be by soffit and eave vents. 50% must be provided by ventilators in the upper portion of the space to be ventilated, at least 3′ (914 mm) above eave or cornice vents.

2. Minimum of 1″ (25 mm) of airspace needed between insulation and roof sheathing.

3. Net free ventilating area $\geq$ 1/300 of space ventilated.

4. Protect exterior openings into attic space, if building meant for human occupancy, against birds, squirrels, rodents, snakes, etc., entry. Allow openings for ventilation with 1/16″ (1.6 mm) minimum and 1/4″ (6.4 mm) maximum; if greater than 1/4″ (6.4 mm), cover with corrosion-resistant wire cloth screening, hardware cloth, perforated vinyl or similar material, with openings having least dimension of 1/16″ (1.6 mm) minimum and 1/4″ (6.4 mm) maximum. If combustion air is obtained from an attic area, per Mechanical Code.

5. Space from bottom of floor joists to the earth under a building (unless occupied by basements or cellars) needs ventilation openings through foundation walls or exterior, placed to give cross ventilation. Openings $\geq$ 1 square ′ per 150 square ′ (0.67 m^2 for each 100 m^2) of crawl-space area, and fully covered with any of following, assuming least dimension of covering $\leq$ 1/4″ (6 mm):

    a. Perforated sheet metal plates $\geq$ 0.070″ (1.8 mm) thick.

    b. Expanded sheet metal plates $\geq$ 0.047″ (1.2 mm) thick.

    c. Cast-iron grilles or gratings.

    d. Extruded load-bearing vents.

    e. Hardware cloth 0.035″ (0.89 mm) wire or heavier.

    f. Corrosion-resistant wire mesh with least dimension $\leq$ 1/8″ (3.2 mm).

6. If climate allows, do not need outdoor ventilation openings IF interior ventilation openings, OR continuously operated mechanical ventilation at 1.0 cubic ′ per minute (CFM) for each 50 square ′ (1.02 L/s for each 10 m^2) of crawl space AND Class I vapor retarder on ground OR Class I vapor retarder, perimeter walls insulated, and space conditioned per applicable energy code. May reduce total area of ventilation openings to 1/1,500 of under-floor area if Class I vapor retarder AND openings give cross ventilation. Operable louvers allowed.

7. Flood hazard area, under-floor and ventilation openings must meet ASCE 24.

8. Natural ventilation through windows, doors, louvers, or other openings, if minimum 4% floor area ventilated. Ready access operating mechanism required. Adjoining spaces ventilated if opening to adjoining room unobstructed and area $\geq$ 8% of floor area of the interior room or space, but $\geq$ 25 square feet (2.3 m^2). Minimum openable area to outdoors based on total floor area being ventilated. Exception:

    a. Exterior ventilation openings may open into thermally isolated sunroom addition or patio cover IF openable area between addition/patio cover and interior room has area $\geq$ 8% of floor of total floor area, but $\geq$ 20 square feet (1.86 m^2).

9. If openings below grade, outside horizontal clear space perpendicular to opening is one and one-half x depth of opening. Depth of opening is measured from average adjoining ground level to bottom of opening.

C. Access: A minimum opening of 20" × 30" must be provided and a minimum clear height over the opening of 30". (1209.2)

D. Install draftstopping in combustible construction to subdivide attic and concealed roof spaces per 717.4.

E. Insulation must have a maximum flame spread of 25 and a smoke-developed index of ≤ 450. Exposed insulation materials installed on attic floors needs critical radiant flux ≥ 0.12 watt per square centimeter when tested per ASTM E 970.

AWNINGS AND CANOPIES (3105)

A. All awnings must comply with Chapter 6.
   1. Structural members protected to prevent deterioration.
   2. Frames non-combustible, fire-retardant treated, Type IV, or 1-hour.

B. Materials flame resistant per NPPA 701 or maximum 25 flame spread.

BALCONIES, PORCHES, AND DECKS (1406.3)

A. When attached to buildings of Type I and II construction, balconies must be constructed of noncombustible materials, except that FRT Wood allowed when 3 stories or less, when not exits.

B. When attached to buildings of Type III, IV, and V construction, balconies may be combustible or unprotected noncombustible:
1. Combustible, and must be Type IV or match floor rating.
2. Noncombustible or FRT Wood, no rating required.
3. Combustible or noncombustible, no rating when they have exterior sprinkler coverage.

C. The sum of the lengths of combustible construction (except fire retardant treated wood) shall not exceed 50% of the building perimeter, except for sprinkled balconies on sprinkled buildings.

D. Balcony railings must meet the following requirements: (1013)
1. Minimum height is 42".
2. Maximum opening is 4" for Use Groups A, B, E, I-1, I-2, M, R, and public garages; 21" for Use Groups I-3, F, H, S, and mechanical access walkways; 6" 2 for triangular openings at stairway open sides formed by riser, tread and bottom rail.
3. Design criteria (1607.7.1)
   a. Railings shall be designed and constructed to resist a concentrated load of 200 lbs. applied at any point in any direction along the top rail.
   b. In addition to the above, the top rail shall resist a uniform load of 50 lbs./ft except 20 plf for I-3, F, H, S and non-public areas with less than 50 occupants. The concentrated and uniform conditions shall not be applied simultaneously.
4. The infill area (guard) of all railings shall resist a concentrated load of 200 lbs. applied at any point along the top rail. Except in dwelling units, grounds shall simultaneously resist 50 lbs./ft. horizontal and 100 lbs./ft. downward on the top.
5. At assembly balconies: (1028.14)
   a. Fascia must be a minimum of 26" in height, but only permitted when < 30" above floor below or fascia and railing otherwise interfere with sightlines of immediately adjacent seating.
   b. When at the end of an aisle, fascia must have a maximum opening of 4" up to 26", then maximum 8" up to 42".
   c. At cross-aisles, railings should be at least 26" high. Where seat-backs are 24" or more above the floor of the aisle, railings are not required.
   d. Base number of persons for bench seating on one per each 18" (457 mm) of length of bench. (1028.15)

BASEMENTS (1612, 1805)

A. Definition: Any story below grade. (1612.2, 502.1)

B. Basement dampproofing: If story above grade plane and finished ground level adjacent to basement wall below basement floor elevation for ≥ 25% of perimeter, drain must be installed for that portion of perimeter below ground level.
1. Finished ground level of under-floor (i.e., crawl space) area cannot be below bottom of footings.
2. If ground-water table can reach within 6" (152 mm) of ground level at outside perimeter, OR surface water does not readily drain from site, make ground level of under-floor space at same level as outside ground level.

3. If building in flood hazard area, crawl space or other under-floor ground level must be higher than outside finished ground level on $\geq$ 1 side. Exception:
    a. If under-floor of Group R-3 building meeting FEMA/FIA-TB-11.
4. If lowering and maintaining ground water table $\geq$ 6" (152 mm) below lowest floor level, drainage design must consider soil permeability, rate of water entering drainage system, rated capacity of pumps, head against which pumps are to operate, and rated capacity of disposal area.

C. Wall thickness: Walls must be at least 7½" thick for reinforced concrete and masonry; depending on soil conditions thicker walls may be required. Minimum concrete floor thickness is 3½", and a vapor barrier is required, except in accessory detached buildings, storage rooms less than 70 sq. ft., or where migration of moisture would not be a problem. (1909.6.1, 1910.1)

D. Dampproofing. If no hydrostatic pressure present, wood foundations dampproofed per AF&PA PWF.

E. Install dampproofing materials for non-wood floors between floor and base course, UNLESS separate floor above a concrete slab. If installed beneath a slab, 6-mil (0.006"; 0.152 mm) polyethylene dampproofing with joints $\geq$ 6" (152 mm), or other approved method. May use bitumen $\geq$ 4-mil (0.004"; 0.102 mm) polyethylene on top of slab. Follow manufacturer's instructions for lapping, sealing.

F. Wall dampproofing materials go on exterior surface from top of footing to above ground level. Use 3 lb/ per square yard (16 N/m^2) of acrylic modified cement ⅛" (3.2 mm) coat of surface bonding mortar per ASTM C 887, or other approved materials. Seal holes and recesses from form tie removal before applying dampproofing, using either bituminous material or approved method. Parg masonry walls on exterior below ground level with $\geq$ ⅜" (9.5 mm) of Portland cement mortar, coved at the footing, UNLESS material is approved for direct application to masonry.

G. Basements in garages, see FIRE RESISTANCE RATING.

H. Occupied levels below basement level, see UNDERGROUND STRUCTURES.

BAY WINDOWS (1406.4)

A. All bay and oriel windows must be framed with materials and ratings according to the construction type of the building, except that fire-retardant-treated wood is permitted on buildings 3 stories or less of Types I, II, III and IV.

BEAMS (See WOOD.)

BEDROOMS

A. Every sleeping room in Groups R and I-1 below the 4th floor shall have at least one operable escape window with a sill not over 44" above the floor. No escape windows are required for sleeping rooms when the door opens to a corridor with remote exits, or when the building is sprinkled. (1029)

B. Escape windows shall open to 5.7 sq. ft. (5.0 sq. ft. on the first floor) with a minimum 20" width and 24" height. (1026.2, 1029.2)

C. All habitable rooms must be no smaller than 70 sq. ft., with a minimum dimension of 7' in any direction. (1208.1, 1208.3)

D. Natural light equal to 8% and natural venting 4% of floor area is required. (1203.4 and 1205.2)

BOILERS (O.R.C. § 4104 AND OBC 4104)

A. General (4104.01)
1. Boilers are closed vessels wherein water (or other liquids where the units are sep-

arate from processing systems) is superheated to steam under pressure or vacuum. (C)

    a. Power Boilers generate steam or other vapors at >15 psig. (D)

    b. High pressure Boilers are water heating boilers operating at > 160 psig or > 250°. (E)

    c. Low Pressure Boilers are steam boilers operating at pressures < 160 psig or < 250°. (F)

2. Pressure Vessels are containers for the confinement of pressure, derived either from an external source or by the application of heat from a direct or indirect source or from any combination thereof. (G)

B. Board of Building Standards (4104.02)

1. The Board issues rules for construction, operation and repair of boilers and pressure vessels, including tests of the quality of materials used in their construction. (A), (B)

2. It regulates construction of safety valves, fusible plugs, steam pressure indicators and water level indicators, and other safety appliances. (C)

3. The Board qualifies inspectors of boilers and pressure vessels. (A)

4. It also establishes fees for the review, survey, or audit of boiler and pressure vessel manufacturers by the Division of Labor for certification by ASME and by the National Board of Boiler and Pressure Vessel Inspectors. (D)

C. Inspectors (4104.06-09)

1. Inspectors, who are under the direction of the Superintendent of Labor, may perform inspections of any building or premise at any reasonable hour. (4104.06(A),(D))

2. The Division of Labor establishes rules for the issuance, renewal, suspension, and revocation of certificates of competency and certificates of operation, for inspecting boilers and pressure vessels, and for conducting hearings related to such actions. (4104.06(B))

3. General inspectors are certified for competency by written examination. (4104.07)

4. Special inspectors are designated and paid by companies authorized by the Board to insure boilers and pressure vessels from (4104.08):

    a. Special inspectors certified in Ohio. (B)

    b. Holders of certificates of competency issued by other states with exams approved by the Board. (B)

    c. Holders of certificates of competency issued by other nations with exams approved by the Board. (B)

5. Neither general nor special inspectors may have either a direct or an indirect interest in the manufacture or sale of boilers or pressure vessels. (4104.08(E))

6. Inspectors' certifications may be revoked for incompetence, untrustworthiness, or willful falsification of material in application for certificate or in report issued by inspector. (4104.09)

D. Inspections and Permit Issuance (4104.10-13, 15, 17, 18)

1. Major repairs or modifications to boilers require permit ($100) from the Superintendent of Labor. (4104.101(B))

2. All contractors involved in boiler installation or modification must register annually for inspection with the Superintendent of Labor.

3. All power boilers are inspected annually, internally and externally. (4104.13)

4. All boilers are inspected upon installation. (4104.12)

    a. Inspections subject to $50 fee, payable by owner/operator. (4104.101, 18(A))

5. All low pressure boilers are subject to internal inspection every year ($50 fee), and to external inspection every 3 years, with a $150 fee. (4104.11(A), 18)

6. All process boilers are subject to internal and external inspection every 3 years, with a $150 fee. (4104.13, 18(A))

7. Power boilers and high pressure, high temperature water boilers with internal continuous water treatment under the general supervision of a registered professional engineer require internal and external inspection every 2 years with $100 fee. (4104.13, 18(A))

8. Process boilers with internal continuous water treatment under the general supervision of a registered professional engineer where water treatment is to control and limit corrosion are subject to internal and external inspection every 5 years with a $250 fee. (4104.13, 18(A))

9. All unfired pressure vessels are inspected during fabrication and upon completion.
   a. Manufacturer's data report must be filed with Division of Labor. (4104.10)

10. Inspection of boilers and pressure vessels during construction (boilers) or manufacturing (pressure vessels) is done for a fee of $35. (4104.18(B))

11. Additional fee to those in 3-9 above assessed by Board of Building Standards of $3.25 per each certificate of operation or renewal thereof. (4104.18(F))

12. Permits may be suspended, revoked or denied by Superintendent of Labor if inspector finds fittings are lacking or are improperly arranged. Boiler operation is not permitted until the permit has been restored. (4104.15(C))

13. Operator application license fee for steam engineer, high pressure boiler operator, or low pressure boiler operator, is $75; renewal fee is $50. (4104.18(C))

14. Failure to pay required license fee within 45 days subjects owner/operator to 25% late payment fee. (4104.18(E))

15. Inspector must require immediate stop to boiler or pressure vessel operation if he finds an explosion hazard that could reasonably pose an imminent danger of death or serious harm. (4104.15(C))
    a. Immediate stop is effective for 72 hours, or until problem is corrected, whichever occurs first. (4104.15(D))
    b. Superintendent may request injunction during 72 hours restraining owner/ operator from restarting until correction occurs. (4104.15(D))
       (1) Restraining order available from either local or Franklin County prosecutor. (4104.15(D))
    c. Owner/operator may appeal inspector order to Superintendent. (4104.15(F))
    d. If owner becomes aware of danger on his own, he must notify Superintendent. (4104.16)

E. Permits (4104.15)
   1. Inspectors issue certificates of operation stating:
      a. Maximum operating pressure
      b. Name and location of owner
      c. Location, size, and number of each boiler
      d. Date of certificate issuance (B)
   2. Permits kept in boiler room; those for portable boilers kept on premises. (B)

F. Operator's License (Steam Engineer, High/Low Pressure) (4104.19)
   1. Requires written application submitted not more than 60 nor less than 30 days before examination. (A)
   2. Operator must be:
      a. 18 or older.
      b. 1 year of experience in operation of boilers, or combination of experience/ education. (B)
      c. Cannot violate 4104 or obtain license by fraud, misrepresentation, or deception. (C)

3. License is good for 1 year. Renewal within that year does not require Examination. (F)

4. a. The operator of a low pressure steam boiler with > 360 square feet of heating surface, a power steam boiler with > 360 square feet of heating surface, or a stationary steam engine with > 30 horsepower, must:

(1) be licensed per 4104.05, or

(2) work under the direct supervision of a person so licensed.

b. The operator must maintain continuous, manned attendance during steam boiler operation except that:

(1) attendance may be at a central control room on the premises from where the apparatus can be monitored, controlled, and shut down, if it has manual operational resets

(2) continuous, manned attendance may not be required for a maximum time equal to that required for the boiler to go into a low water condition when subjected to an annual evaporation test conducted per "ASME Boiler and Pressure Vessel Code, Section VI, 7.05 (H)" referenced in OBC 4101:4-3-01

(3) a non-solid-fuel-fired steam boiler or stationary steam engine may not need continuous, manned attendance when the superintendent of the division of industrial compliance approves a site-specific, detailed written plan for automated electronic monitoring controlling all operational functions, with properly labeled manual operational resets, if:

(a) The control equipment is in the same facility;

(b) An operator licensed per 4104.19 is always present to respond to emergencies if summoned by the automated electronic monitoring system;

(c) There is a secondary means of alerting a licensed person if the primary electronic monitoring system fails;

(d) A qualified individual per OBC 4101:4-1-01 does annual operational tests on the automated electronic monitoring system per the original manufacturer's specification;

(e) A copy of the dated and signed service report or checklist, listing each control and safety device tested with the manufacturer's name, model number, set point, and actual operational test point is available for the superintendent upon request, with failure to do so resulting in the issuance of an adjudication order under Chapter 119 of the O.R.C.

(4) a non-solid-fuel-fired steam boiler with fuel input rating of < 12,500,000 BTU/hr may not need continuous, manned attendance when an automated electronic control system per "ASME CSD-1" under OBC 4101:4-3-01 is used, if:

(a) The boiler manufacturer and the installing contractor complete and sign a certification report (per Appendix C of ASME CSD-1) for each boiler, meeting the requirements of Section CG-510 of the ASME CSD-1 and identifying the manufacturer, model number, and operational test date for each boiler control and safety device and certifying they were installed and tested per the manufacturer's installation instructions and the ASME CSD-1.

(b) The installing contractor, registered per OBC 4101:4-7-01, provides the owner or user the operating, testing, servicing, and cleaning instructions for the controls and safety devices, along with complete wiring and piping diagrams and a written warning written that their use is only by a qualified individual. The contractor must get a receipt from the owner or user for the delivery of the instructions.

(c) The certification report and receipt must be submitted to the superintendent prior to the required inspection and issuance of the certificate of operation, with failure to do so resulting in the issuance of an adjudication order under Chapter 119 of the O.R.C.

(d) The owner or user must have a preventive maintenance program and ensure that the employee responsible for maintaining the boiler is trained, knowledgeable, and competent to operate and maintain the boiler, controls, and safety devices. The program must be consistent with the manufacturer's recommendations and include regular inspections and operational testing. Annual inspection and operational testing is per OBC 4101:4-1-01, and daily, weekly, monthly, and semi-annual inspections and operational testing are per Appendix D of the ASME CSD-1, with inspections performed and documented by trained, knowledgeable and competent employees. The maintenance records must identify the manufacturer, model number, set point, the operational tests performed, the operational test date, the inspection results, who performed the tests or inspection for each specific boiler control and safety device, and must available to the certificate inspector for review, with failure resulting in the issuance of an adjudication order under Chapter 119 of the O.R.C.

(5) a non-solid-fuel-fired steam boiler with a fuel input rating $\geq$ 12,500,000 BTU/hr per "NFPA 85" under OBC 4101:4-3-01 may not need continuous, manned attention when an automated electronic control system is used per ASME CSD-1 under OBC 4101:4-3-01, if:

(a) The certification report, wiring diagrams, instructions, maintenance, and testing requirements for the control system outlined above apply.

(b) Prior to boiler installation, the owner submits a detailed, written, process hazard analysis (PHA) to the superintendent identifying and evaluating the hazards associated with the unattended operation of the boiler, identifying 4101:4-10-01 3 possible incident scenarios, the proposed protection/solution for each scenario, justifying proposed method(s) for addressing hazards, and any additional information required by the superintendent. The PHA must be updated at least every five years, and submitted to the superintendent for review and filing, with failure resulting in the issuance of an adjudication order under Chapter 119 of the O.R.C.

G. Historical Boilers Licensing Board (4104.33)
   1. Historical boilers are preserved, restored, or maintained for hobby or demonstration purposes, and are of riveted construction. If open to the public, the operator must be licensed, and the owner must have a valid certificate of operation. (4104.31, 32)
   2. Board consists of 7 members, 3 appointed by the governor with advice and consent of the Senate:
      a. 1 employee of Division of Boiler Inspection, 1 independent mechanical engineer not involved with historical boilers, 1 active members of an association representing managers of fairs or festivals
   3. 2 members appointed by Senate President, 2 by Speaker of the House of Representatives:
      a. Each must own historical boiler.
      b. Each must have at least 10 years experience operating historical boilers.
      c. Each member resides in different area of the state.
H. Building Services Piping (4104.43)
   1. The Board is to establish rules for design, installation, inspection of and design review procedure for:
      a. Nonflammable medical gas
      b. Medical oxygen
      c. Medical vacuum piping systems (A)
   2. A certified municipal, township, or county building department may enforce rules. (B)

  3. A health district employee in a health district lacking a certified municipal, township, or county department may enforce rules if:
    a. Employee obtains special certification from Board.
    b. Health district notifies Superintendent of Labor that employee is to enforce rules. (C)
  4. If 2 or 3 do not apply, Superintendent of Labor enforces rules. (D)

I. Welding and Brazing (4104.44)
  1. All welding and brazing of metallic piping systems must be in accordance with Section IX of the Boiler and Pressure Code of the ASME.
  2. Owner must maintain at the job site the certified performance qualification records for all welders and brazers employed at the site.
  3. Owner must provide copies to the Superintendent of Labor of:
    a. All certified welding and brazing procedure specifications.
    b. Procedure qualification records.
    c. Performance qualification records for building services piping.

J. Pressure Piping Standards (4104.42)
  1. The owner of any power piping or process piping system must comply with the applicable sections of the B31 standards of the Code for pressure Piping of the ASME, as to:
    a. Design, fabrication, assembly, installation, testing, examination, and inspection of power and process piping systems
    b. Qualification of personnel
    c. Qualification of welding and brazing procedures
    d. Implementation of an inspection program (A)
  2. Owner must also:
    a. Maintain for 5 years records of design, examination, and testing of piping system including;
      (1) code edition for pressure piping used in design
      (2) design assumptions
      (3) calculations, piping material specifications, and construction documents for piping
      (4) records of piping alterations
      (5) piping examination and inspection records (B)(1)
    b. Disclose the types and quantities of flammable, combustible, or hazardous materials used in facility to the building and fire code enforcement authorities in accordance with O.R.C. 3781.10 and State Fire Marshall Rules. (B)(2)

TABLE 4.3-01 OHIO BUILDING CODE BOILER STANDARDS

Table 4-3-01

Authority	Edition Date	Designation	Title
ASME	2010	BPVC -Section I (see footnote a)	Power Boilers.
ASME	2010	BPVC -Section II	Material Specifications. Part A-Ferrous. Part B-Non-Ferrous. Part C-Welding Rods, Electrodes and Filler Metals. Part D-Properties.

Authority	Edition Date	Designation	Title
ASME	2010	BPVC -Section III	Nuclear Facility Components.
ASME	2010	BPVC -Section IV	Heating Boilers.
ASME	2010	BPVC -Section V	Nondestructive Examination.
ASME	2010	BPVC -Section VI	Recommended Rules for Care and Operation of Heating Boilers.
ASME	2010	BPVC -Section VII	Recommended Guidelines for Care of Power Boilers.
ASME	2010	BPVC -Section VIII	Pressure Vessels- Division 1.
ASME	2010	BPVC -Section VIII	Pressure Vessels- Division 2.
ASME	2010	BPVC -Section VIII	Pressure Vessels- Division 3.
ASME	2010	BPVC -Section IX	Welding and Brazing Qualifications.
ASME	2010	BPVC -Section X	Fiber-Reinforced Plastic Pressure Vessels.
ASME	2010	BPVC -Section XI	Rules for Inservice Inspection of Nuclear Power Plant Components.
ASME	2010	BPVC	Code Cases.
ASME	2010	B 31.1	Power Piping.
ASME	2012	CSD-1	"Controls and Safety Devices for Automatically Fired Boilers."
NFPA	2011	NFPA 85	"Boiler and Combustion Systems Hazards Code"
National Board	2011	NBIC	National Board Inspection Code.
National Board	Jul. 2012, Rev.0	NB-27	A Guide for Blowoff Vessels.
National Board	May 2012, Rev. 5	NB-263	Rules for National Board Inservice and New Construction Commissioned Inspectors.
National Board	Feb. 2011, Rev. 4	NB-371	Accreditation of Owner-User Inspection Organizations (OUIO).

Footnote a: For riveted construction, see "ASME, BPVC-Section I, Power Boilers, Part PR (1971 edition)."

BRICK MASONRY VENEER (INSTALLATION) (1405)
A. No. 15 felt or paper is required over all sheathing. (1404.2)
B. Anchored veneer (1405.10)
   1. Minimum $2^5/_8$" thick
   2. Deflection maximum $1/_{600}$ when supported on wood
   3. Installation must also comply with ACI 530/ASCE 5/TMS 402.
C. Adhered Veneer (Table 1405.2)
   1. $1/_4$" min. thickness
   2. Approved backing.
   3. Maximum deflection of $1/_{600}$ when wood-supported.
D. Flashing at all openings and sills required. (1405.4)
E. Weep holes required at 33" o.c.

BUILDING AREAS (500)
(See also SPRINKLERS; MIXED USES; USE GROUP CLASSIFICATION.)
A. Allowable height and area is defined as maximum horizontal projection of building. (502.1)

TABLE 503
ALLOWABLE HEIGHT AND BUILDING AREAS
Height limitations shown as stories and feet above grade plane.
Area limitations as determined by the definition of "Area, building," per floor.

GROUP	HGT- (feet) HGT(S)	TYPE I A	TYPE I B	TYPE II A	TYPE II B	TYPE III A	TYPE III B	TYPE IV HT	TYPE V A	TYPE V B
		UL	160	65	55	65	55	65	50	40
A-1	S A	UL UL	5 UL	3 15,500	2 8,500	3 14,000	2 8,500	3 15,000	2 11,500	1 5,500
A-2	S A	UL UL	11 UL	3 15,500	2 9,500	3 14,000	2 9,500	3 15,000	2 11,500	1 6,000
A-3	S A	UL UL	11 UL	3 15,500	2 9,500	3 14,000	2 9,500	3 15,000	2 11,500	1 6,000
A-4	S A	UL UL	11 UL	3 15,500	2 9,500	3 14,000	2 9,500	3 15,000	2 11,500	1 6,000
A-5	S A	UL UL	UL UL	UL UL	UL UL	UL UL	UL UL	UL UL	UL UL	UL UL
B	S A	UL UL	11 UL	5 37,500	4 23,000	5 28,500	4 19,000	5 36,000	3 18,000	2 9,000
E	S A	UL UL	5 UL	3 26,500	2 14,500	3 23,500	2 14,500	3 25,500	1 18,500	1 9,500
F-1	S A	UL UL	11 UL	4 25,000	2 15,500	3 19,000	2 12,000	4 33,500	2 14,000	1 8,500
F-2	S A	UL UL	11 UL	5 37,500	3 23,000	4 28,500	3 18,000	5 50,500	3 21,000	2 13,000
H-1	S A	1 21,000	1 16,500	1 11,000	1 7,000	1 9,500	1 7,000	1 10,500	1 7,500	NP NP
H-2d	S A	UL 21,000	3 16,500	2 11,000	1 7,000	2 9,500	1 7,000	2 10,500	1 7,500	1 3,000
H-3d	S A	UL UL	6 60,000	4 26,500	2 14,000	4 17,500	2 13,000	4 25,500	2 10,000	1 5,000
H-4	S A	UL UL	7 UL	5 37,500	3 17,500	5 28,500	3 17,500	5 36,000	3 18,000	2 6,500
H-5	S A	4 UL	4 UL	3 37,500	3 23,000	3 28,500	3 19,000	3 36,000	3 18,000	2 9,000
I-1	S A	UL UL	9 55,000	4 19,000	3 10,000	4 16,500	3 10,000	4 18,000	3 10,500	2 4,500
I-2	S A	UL UL	4 UL	2 15,000	1 11,000	1 12,000	NP NP	1 12,000	1 9,500	NP NP

GROUP	HGT-(feet) HGT(S)	TYPE OF CONSTRUCTION								
		TYPE I		TYPE II		TYPE III		TYPE IV	TYPE V	
		A	B	A	B	A	B	HT	A	B
		UL	160	65	55	65	55	65	50	40
I-3	S A	UL UL	4 UL	2 15,000	1 10,000	2 10,500	1 7,500	2 12,000	2 7,500	1 5,000
I-4	S A	UL UL	5 60,500	3 26,500	2 13,000	3 23,500	2 13,000	3 25,500	1 18,500	1 9,000
M	S A	UL UL	11 UL	4 21,500	4 12,500	4 18,500	4 12,500	4 20,500	3 14,000	1 9,000
R-1	S A	UL UL	11 UL	4 24,000	4 16,000	4 24,000	4 16,000	4 20,500	3 12,000	2 7,000
R-2	S A	UL UL	11 UL	4 24,000	4 16,000	4 24,000	4 16,000	4 20,500	3 12,000	2 7,000
R-3	S A	UL UL	11 UL	4 UL	4 UL	4 UL	4 UL	4 UL	3 UL	3 UL
R-4	S A	UL UL	11 UL	4 24,000	4 16,000	4 24,000	4 16,000	4 20,500	3 12,000	2 7,000
S-1	S A	UL UL	11 48,000	4 26,000	3 17,500	3 26,000	3 17,500	4 25,500	3 14,000	1 9,000
S-2[b, c]	S A	UL UL	11 79,000	5 39,000	4 26,000	4 39,000	4 26,000	5 38,500	4 21,000	2 13,500
U[c]	S A	UL UL	5 35,500	4 19,000	2 8,500	3 14,000	2 8,500	4 18,000	2 9,000	1 5,500

For SI: 1 foot = 304.8 mm, 1 square foot = 0.0929 m^2.

UL = Unlimited, NP = Not permitted.

a. See the following sections for general exceptions to Table 503:
1. Section 504.2, Allowable height increase due to automatic sprinkler system installation.
2. Section 506.2, Allowable area increase due to street frontage.
3. Section 506.3, Allowable area increase due to automatic sprinkler system installation.
4. Section 507, Unlimited area buildings.
b. For open parking structures, see Section 406.3.
c. For private garages, see Section 406.1.
d. See Section 415.5 for limitations.

$$AA = \frac{SP + OP + 100}{100} \times \text{Area in table 503.}$$

1.a. Where

AA = adjusted total allowable area per floor (See 1.b.).

SP = sprinkler increase (in percent) for totally suppressed buildings. (No increase for 13R or 13D systems.)

    i. No increase for Group H-1, H-2, or H-3 uses.

    ii. 300% for 1-story, 200% for others.

OP = open perimeter increase (in percent). Length of perimeter where it is open 20′ or more and accessible (by 20 fire lane), expressed as percentage of total perimeter. Take open perimeter, subtract 25%, and multiply remainder by factor of width, using the minimum width counted. This factor cannot exceed 1, so the maximum increase permitted for OP is 0.75. The open space can be measured to the lot line or non-buildable easement (or other permanently dedicated space).

$$OP = \left(\frac{\text{Open Perim.}}{\text{Total Perim.}} - .25\right) \times \frac{\text{Min. Width of} \geq 20'}{30}$$

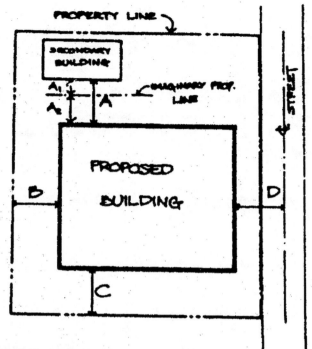

PROPERTY LINE

SECONDARY BUILDING

A₁

A

IMAGINARY PROP. LINE

A₂

PROPOSED BUILDING

B

D

C

STREET

FOR STREET FRONTAGE INCREASE:
ONLY WHEN COUNTING SIDES A-D OF AT LEAST 20 FT.
CAN COUNT SIDE B ONLY WHEN A OR C IS AT LEAST 20 FT.

FOR FIRE SEPARATION DISTANCE:
USE B-D AND A₂ FOR TABLES 504.2, 906.2 & 906 3
SEE DEFINITION OF "FIRE SEPARATION DISTANCE" FOR
IMAGINARY PROPERTY LINE (TO A₂). POSITION OF
LINE AT DISCRETION OF DESIGNER

      b. The maximum total allowable area cannot exceed 3 times the maximum allowable area per floor (except Unlimited Area buildings). One story of basement (if less than allowable first floor) does not count. Maximum area not limited by this for buildings sprinkled under NFPA 13 R.

      c. Multiple buildings on the same lot can be treated as one total building if they comply when added together. This exempts the individual buildings from fire separation distance requirements.

  2. Height (504.0)

      a. Height may be increased one story and 20' when building is totally sprinkled.

      b. No sprinkler increase may be made for Use Groups H-1, H-2, H-3, or H-5, or in Group I-2 of Construction types IIB, III, IV or V.

B. Unlimited area buildings (507.0)

  1. One-story buildings:

      a. Type I not affected by these requirements.

      b. F-2 and S-2 allowed without sprinklers if surrounded by a public way at least 60' wide.

      c. B, M, F, S (or A-4 which is not Type V) when fully sprinkled if surrounded by a public way at least 60' wide.

      d. E of Type II, IIIA, or IV when fully sprinkled and all classrooms have direct exit to exterior.

      e. H-2 aircraft paint hangar of Type I or II when fully sprinkled and limited in paint quantity by Section 412.4. Open space of $1\frac{1}{2}$ times the height required on all sides.

      f. Motion picture theatres when Type II and fully sprinkled.

      g. A-3 used as church, hall, gym, pool, or tennis court when Type II and fully sprinkled, and floor level is within 21" of grade and has no steps (only flat or ramps) *and* if surrounded by a public way at least 60' wide.

      h. F-2 and S-2 rack storage is also not limited in height when of Type I or II.

      i. A-4 with indoor participant sports when all sport areas have exits direct to exterior, a manual fire alarm system is provided, and all other areas are sprinkled.

  2. Two-story buildings if surrounded by a public way at least 60' wide:

      a. Groups B, F, M, or S when fully sprinkled (507.4).

  3. All unlimited area buildings (except special industrial and aircraft painting) must have at least 60 feet of open space on all sides.

      a. This can be reduced to 40' for up to 75% of the perimeter if the walls less than 60' are 3 hour rated with 3 hour openings.

  4. Special industrial buildings of low hazard use such as power plants, foundries, rolling mills, and metal fabricating may be of unlimited areas. Sprinklers may be omitted when detrimental to the use or occupancy. (503.1.1)

  5. H-2, H-3, and H-4 fire areas in unlimited buildings in F and S Use Groups (507.8)

      a. Must be located at perimeter of building.

      b. 10% of the building and less than or equal to Table 503 limits using open perimeter of the H fire area.

      c. Other H fire areas cannot exceed 25% of tabular area for that H Group.

C

CEILING HEIGHT (1208.2)

A. Minimum height is 7′6″ for exit access and occupiable rooms. Bathrooms, kitchens, storage and laundry rooms minimum 7′0″.

B. Exceptions
   1. In Group R-3, ceiling can have projections of 6″ if there are beams and girders spaced at least 4′0″ o.c.
   2. If sloped ceiling, minimum applies to one-half of area. Do not include room portion less than 5′ from floor to ceiling.

C. Furred ceilings must have ⅔ of room at 7′6″, but none less than 7′0″.

CERTIFICATE OF OCCUPANCY (111.0)

A. When required: Before occupancy is allowed, a certificate of occupancy must be issued by building department upon completion of permit work.

B. Where required: A certificate of occupancy is required for all new buildings, additions, alterations, and changes of occupancy.

C. Conditions: A certificate of occupancy may be issued, at the request of the owner, for existing buildings where the existing occupancy is confirmed and no serious hazards exist. Inspection is required.

D. Temporary: A certificate of occupancy may be issued when a portion of the work completed allows safe occupancy. The Certificate must indicate the time period and all conditions of occupancy. ("TIME-LIMITED" OCCUPANCY)

E. Partial: A certificate of occupany can be issued for partial completion if safe to occupy, for limited time.

F. Contents—A Certificate of Occupancy must include:
   1. Certify compliance with 3781 and 3791 ORC.
   2. The occupancy type(s) permitted.
   3. Plan number.
   4. Address.
   5. Portion(s) of building covered.
   6. Signature of CBO.
   7. Code edition in effect for review.
   8. Type of construction.
   9. Design occupant load.
   10. For sprinkler systems:
       a. if required
       b. hazard class of system
       c. hydraulic demand at base of riser
   11. Any and all conditions and appeal variances.

CHIMNEYS AND VENTS (2113.0, M-CHAPTER 8)

A. General
   1. Chimney or vent must be capable of producing the required natural draft at 2′0″ above any portion of the roof within 10′0″, and 3′0″ above the adjacent roof (2113.9).
   2. Minimum area of the masonry chimney or vent should be calculated per Table 2113.16, depending on fireplace opening size and chimney height.
   3. Factory-built chimneys must comply with M-805.
   4. Sizes may be by engineered systems.
   5. In low-heat, appliance-type chimneys or vents, combustion gases at the point of

entrance to the flue must not reach more than 1000°F. (M-202—definition of "Appliance type")

6. Medium-heat appliances must be kept at less than 2000°F at the entrance to the flue.

7. High-heat appliances are more than 2000°F at entrance to the flue.

B. Masonry chimney (general requirements) (2113)

1. Chimney may act as a supporting member if enough thickness exists.

2. Masonry chimneys must be anchored laterally at each floor which is more than 6' above grade and ceiling in Seismic Category D. (2113.4)

3. Corbeling (2113.5)

    a. Maximum corbeling of ½ wall thickness in steps ⅓ the thickness of the brick or ½ the brick height (whichever is less).

    b. When wall thickness under 12", wall corbel equally on each side.

4. Cleanout is required within 6" of the base of each flue. (2113.18)

5. Fireblocking of noncombustible materials to 1" (2113.20)

6. A change of size is not permitted within 6" of floor or roof. (2113.6)

7. Minimum 4" thick solid or solid-grouted masonry. (2113.10)

8. When there are 2 flues or more, they must be separated with a 4" solid wythe bonded to the chimney walls. (2113.14)

9. Allow 2" clearance from any framing. There are exceptions for UL 1777, 12" of solid masonry when chimney is part of wall, and 12" of solid masonry to exterior siding. (2113.19)

C. Metal chimneys (Chapter M-8)

1. Metal chimneys must be installed per NFPA 211.

2. Cleanouts are not required if flue opening is accessible. (M-801.13)

D. Masonry chimneys and appliances

1. Low-heat appliances (2113.10 and 2113.11.1)

    a. Walls shall be 4" solid masonry with full head and bed of mortar, or reinforced concrete.

    b. Lining is required for the full height.

    c. Lining may consist of:

        1. Clay flue lining complying with ASTM C 315.

        2. Lining systems complying with UL 1777.

        3. Factory-built chimneys or chimney units listed for use with masonry chimneys.

        4. Equivalent approved materials that will resist corrosion, erosion, softening or cracking up to 1800°F.

2. Medium-heat appliances (2113.11.2)

    a. 8" of solid masonry or reinforced concrete is required, 12" minimum is required if constructed of stone.

    b. 4½" lining of medium density refractory brick or equivalent is required.

    c. Lining shall start 2' below the lowest connector and extend 25' above the highest connection or the chimney height.

    d. Chimney shall terminate not less than 10' above the nearest building component within 25' of the chimney.

    e. Provide 4" minimum clearance from any combustibles.

3. High-heat appliances (2113.11.3)

    a. Double 8" solid masonry or concrete walls with 2" air space between the walls is required.

    b. Chimneys must be lined with 4½" high-duty refractory brick and mortar.

      c. Chimney height shall be a minimum of 20' above any portion of any building within 50'.

      d. All clearances shall be approved by the building official.

E. Vent connectors (M-803)

  1. Joints must be securely fastened with rivets or screws.

  2. Maximum horizontal connector length is 75% of vent height.

  3. Pitch 1/4" per foot toward the chimney.

  4. Connector shall not go through rated walls or any floor or ceiling. No single-wall permitted in unheated space.

  5. Do not extend the connector beyond the flue liner.

  6. A flue thimble may be used.

  7. Minimum thickness for low heat:

      a. 0-5" diameter: 26 gauge galvanized

      b. 6-9" diameter: 24 gauge galvanized

      c. 10-16" diameter: 22 gauge galvanized

      d. Over 16" diameter: 16 gauge galvanized, and

  8. Minimum thickness for medium and high heat:

      a. 0-14" diameter: 16 gauge

      b. 15-16" diameter: 14 gauge

      c. 17-18" diameter: 12 gauge

      d. More than 18" diameter: 10 gauge

  9. Four systems are acceptable for clearances to combustibles for domestic appliances. (See illustrations in Table M-803.10.4.)

      a. System A—12" clearance with brick and clay liner

      b. System B—9" clearance with insulated factory liner

      c. System C—6" clearance with insulation and double-wall thimble, and

      d. System D—2" clearance with factory chimney section.

 10. Minimum clearance to combustibles. (Table M-803.10.6)

      a. Appliances with labeled clearances are acceptable.

      b. For low-heat appliances, the following minimum clearance standards apply.

        i. Chimney connectors

          (a) Electric and oil incinerators: 18".

          (b) Oil and solid fuel appliances: 18".

          (c) Oil appliances with Type L vents: 9".

      c. Commercial appliances (chimney connectors for medium-heat appliances) Gas, oil and solid fuel boilers, water heaters, and furnaces: 36".

      d. Commercial appliances (masonry or metal connectors for high-heat appliances) Gas, oil and solid fuel boilers, water heaters, and furnaces: determined by building official.

F. Vent gas-fired appliances in accordance with the "International Fuel Gas Code."

  1. System must be UL tested and labeled by an approved agency.

  2. System must be installed per manufacturer's instructions.

  3. Approved special vent systems are acceptable.

  4. Vent system must be firestopped at all floors and ceilings.

G. Direct vent appliances (M-804): Labeled appliances with sealed combustion chambers and where combustion and exhaust air is derived from the exterior of the building are acceptable as a complete unit.

  1. Outlet is more than 9" from openings, when appliance designed for natural venting with integral venting.

2. Outlet is more than 12" from opening, when appliance has forced draft venting.

H. Terminations (M-804)

1. The vent must terminate 12" min. above grade.
2. Locate exhaust vents 10' from the lot line.
3. Horizontal vent termination
   a. 7' above adjacent walk.
   b. 3' above forced air outlet within 10'.
   c. 4' below, 4' horizontally or 1' above a door, window, or gravity air vent.
   d. 3' from an internal corner, or gas meter.
   e. 12" above grade.
4. Vertical vent termination.
   a. 7' above adjacent walk.
   b. 3' above forced air inlet within 10'.
   c. 3' from adjacent roofs.
   d. 4' below, 4' horizontal, or 1' above door or window or gravity vent.
   e. Vent cap required.

I. Unvented appliances

1. Unvented appliances which are not required to be vented by manufacturer's instructions are not required to be vented.
   a. Domestic ranges and wall ovens.
   b. Type I clothes dryers.
   c. Single booster-type automatic instantaneous water heater used solely for sanitizing rinse on a dishwashing machine:
      (1) Installed in a commercial kitchen having a mechanical exhaust system.
      (2) Draft hood not less than 36" vertical and 6" horizontal from any surface other than the heater.
   d. Refrigerators.
   e. Counter appliances.
   f. Room heaters listed for unvented use.
   g. Direct-fired make-up air heaters.
   h. Other equipment listed for unvented use and not provided with flue collars.
   i. Specialized equipment of limited input such as laboratory burners and gas lights.
2. If the aggregate input rating of c. through i. exceeds 20 Btu per hour per cubic feet of volume of the room or space where installed, one or more must be provided with approved venting systems to the outdoors. If the room is directly connected to another room by a doorway of comparable size that cannot be closed, that volume is included in the calculations. (International Fuel Gas Code 501.8)

CONCRETE (CHAPTER 19 AND ACI 318)

A. Acceptable conditions for Ohio

1. Ohio is considered a severe weathering area (Figure 1904.2.2)
2. Materials
   a. Cements must comply with ACI 318.
   b. Aggregate must comply with ACI 318.
   c. Water must be clean.
   d. See Section 1908 for modifications to ACI 318.
3. Air entrainment

   Air entrainment is required for normal and lightweight concrete exposed to freezing and thawing. (ACI Section 4.4.2)

4. Admixtures (See ACI 318.) (See also ADMIXTURES.)
Calcium chloride is not acceptable when exposed to sulfate solutions.
5. Strength (at 28 days)
   a. Concrete quality in footings must be at least 2500 psi (overall minimum) at 28 days.
   b. Basements (Table 1904.2.2)
      i. Basement: 2500
      ii. Foundation, exposed: 3000 (air entrained)
      iii. Exposed flatwork: 3500 (air entrained)
6. Minimum thickness for slab-on-grade is 3½". A vapor barrier is required for occupiable areas. (1910.1)
7. Frequency of testing is regulated by ACI 318, Section 5.6.2.

B. Plain concrete: (per ACI 318)
1. Plain concrete is defined as having either no reinforcement or less, required by ACI 318.
2. Minimum strength for plain concrete is 2500 psi.

C. Reinforced concrete
1. Reinforced concrete should be designed and used according to ACI 318.
2. Minimum strength for reinforced concrete is 2500 psi.

D. Water used must be clean.

E. Aggregate size (per ASTM C33 or C330)
1. Aggregate must be no larger than ⅓ of the slab depth.
2. Aggregate must be no more than ¾ of the clear distance between reinforcement components.
3. Aggregate must be no more than ⅕ of the narrowest dimension between forms.

F. The concrete must be thoroughly consolidated.

G. Hot and cold weather precautions are required. Aggregate cannot be frozen. (1905.12 and 1905.13) (ACI sections 5.12 and 5.13)

H. Construction joints must comply with ACI 318, section 6.4.

I. Rebars
1. Bars must be free of flaky rust, oil, mud, or anything that might reduce the bond.
2. Bars must be properly supported and spaced within the tolerances permitted, per ACI 318.
3. Concrete cover for reinforcement is governed by ACI 318, section 7.

J. Conduits and pipe in concrete of a material not harmful to concrete and within the limitations of ACI 318, Section 6.3, may be embedded in concrete if approved by the design professional. (1906.3)

K. Concrete-filled pipe columns (1915)
1. Standard, extra strong, or double extra strong pipe must be used.
2. Pipes must be filled with no voids.
3. Connections (base, cap, and others) shall be anchored to the concrete mechanically, and require welding to the pipe shell.
4. Keep interior reinforcement 1" from the shell.
5. Column must meet the fire-rating requirements.
6. Any outer shell steel pipe covering the fireproofing system cannot be considered as part of the column strength.
7. Minimum diameter is 4", except in Type V buildings not more than 3 stories; diameter may be 3" for basement and secondary members.

L. Shotcrete (1913)
1. Maximum size for aggregate is ¾".

2. Maximum size rebars to be used: no. 5.
3. Minimum clearance between rebars must be 2½".
4. Curing must be maintained above 40°F.
5. Shotcrete must be kept moist for 24 hours or seal.
6. Non-contact lap splices must allow 2" between bars.
7. "Rebound" may not be re-used as aggregate.
8. Unfinished work cannot stand for more than 30 minutes without being designed as a "cold joint."

CONSTRUCTION PRECAUTIONS (CHAPTER 33)

A. Demolition (Partial)
   1. Pedestrian protection required.
   2. A schedule and construction documents required.
   3. Utilities must be cut off.
   4. Required exits must have substitutes.
B. Excavations
   1. Permanent fill and cut slopes no steeper than 1:2.
   2. No surcharge to adjacent structure without design.
C. Storage of materials shall not endanger the public or overload the structure under construction.
D. Adjoining property must be completely protected at all times during construction.
E. Protection of pedestrians
   1. Railings or walkways with barriers. (See Table 3306.1.)
   2. Minimum walkway width of 4', minimum live load of 150 psf.
   3. Construction railings minimum 42".
   4. Construction barriers minimum 8', minimum ¼ thick wood panels.
   5. When adjacent to excavation, minimum 6' barrier when less than 5' horizontal.
F. Structures more than 50' or 4 stories in height require lighted stairs (permanent or temporary).
G. Fire hazard protection
   1. Fire extinguishers are required at each stair where floor has combustibles, storage sheds, flammable liquid storage, and as directed by building official.
   2. Permanent standpipes shall be made available when the building rises above 40'. Two-way fire department connections at street level are required. (3311.1)

CONSTRUCTION TYPE—CLASSIFICATION OF BUILDINGS (CHAPTER 6)

TABLE 601
FIRE-RESISTANCE RATING REQUIREMENTS FOR BUILDING ELEMENTS
(hours)

BUILDING ELE-MENT	TYPE I		TYPE II		TYPE III		TYPE IV	TYPE V	
	A	B	A[e]	B	A[e]	B	HT	A[e]	B
Structural frame[a]	3[b]	2[b]	1	0	1	0	HT	1	0
Bearing walls									
Exterior[g]	3	2	1	0	2	2	2	1	0
Interior	3[b]	2[b]	1	0	1	0	1/HT	1	0
Nonbearing walls and partitions Exterior	See Table 602								
Nonbearing walls and partitions Interior[f]	0	0	0	0	0	0	See Section 602.4.6	0	0

BUILDING ELE-MENT	TYPE I		TYPE II		TYPE III		TYPE IV	TYPE V	
	A	B	A[e]	B	A[e]	B	HT	A[e]	B
Floor construction, including supporting beams and joists	2	2	1	0	1	0	HT	1	0
Roof construction, including supporting beams and joists	1½[c]	1[c, d]	1[c, d]	0[d]	1[c,d]	0[d]	HT	1[c,d]	0

For SI: 1 foot = 304.8 mm.

a. The structural frame shall be considered to be the columns and the girders, beams, trusses and spandrels having direct connections to the columns and bracing members designed to carry gravity loads. The members of floor or roof panels which have no connection to the columns shall be considered secondary members and not a part of the structural frame.

b. Roof supports: Fire-resistance ratings of structural frame and bearing walls are permitted to be reduced by 1 hour where supporting a roof only.

c. Except in Group F-1, H, M and S-1 occupancies, fire protection of structural members shall not be required, including protection of roof framing and decking where every part of the roof construction is 20 feet or more above any floor immediately below. Fire-retardant-treated wood members shall be allowed to be used for such unprotected members.

d. In all occupancies, heavy timber shall be allowed where a 1-hour or less fire-resistance rating is required.

e. An approved automatic sprinkler system in accordance with Section 903.3.1.1shall be allowed to be substituted for 1-hour fire-resistance-rated construction, provided such system is not otherwise required by other provisions of the code or used for an allowable area increase in accordance with Section 506.3 or an allowable height increase in accordance with Section 504.2. The 1-hour substitution for the fire resistance of exterior walls shall not be permitted.

f. Not less than the fire-resistance rating required by other sections of this code.

g. Not less than the fire-resistance rating based on fire separation distance (see Table 602).

A. General
   1. All buildings shall be classified in one type according to the least fire resistance rating classification (See 602.1 and 602.1.1.) of structural and other building elements.
   2. Construction must conform to or exceed designated type.
   3. Fire-retardant wood is acceptable. Noncombustible types may use it where specifically allowed. (603.1.1)
   4. Combustible elements are acceptable where specifically allowed. (603)
B. Type I (protected, noncombustible)
   I-A: All bearing walls, structural elements, floors, ceilings, roofs, and exits are of protected noncombustible materials with specific fire ratings. Fire retardant treated wood is permitted in non-structural walls and roof. Type IV roof is permitted where a 1-hour or less roof is required. Exception: In buildings exceeding two stories, fire-retardant-treated wood is not permitted in roof construction when the vertical distance from the upper floor to the roof is less than 20'.
   I-B: Same as I-A, except with lower fire ratings.
C. Type II (protected or not protected, noncombustible)
   II-A: All walls, partitions, structural elements, floors, ceilings, roofs, and exits are of protected noncombustibles. Fire retardant treated wood is permitted in non-structural walls and roof. Type IV roof is permitted.
   II-B: Same as II-A but with unprotected noncombustibles.
D. Type III (typically exterior masonry walls with interior of wood)
   III-A: Exterior bearing walls are protected noncombustible, usually masonry. All other bearing elements are 1-hour rated.
   III-B: Exterior same as III-A, with interior elements of unprotected nominal 2"-thick wood or other combustibles, or noncombustibles.
E. Type IV (heavy timber construction)
   1. Exterior walls are noncombustible of the required rating with interior structural members of large solid or laminated wood timbers without concealed spaces.
   2. Minimum dimensions set forth in Table 602.4.

F. Type V (wood-frame construction)

V-A: Wood or other materials with rated structural elements of 1-hour (except party walls and fire walls).

V-B: Same as V-A, but with no ratings (except party walls and fire walls).

G. Fire walls and party walls must always be noncombustible, except between Type V buildings, and of 2-hour rating or more, depending on occupancy fire grading.

COVERED MALLS (402.0)

A. This section applies to malls not more than 3 floor levels at any one point (as defined for "Mall").

B. The location of each occupancy and its exits must be kept current by mall owner as a condition of the certificate of occupancy.

C. Complete compliance with 402.0 is not required if the mall complies with all other code restrictions.

D. Structural elements shall be Type I, II, III, or IV construction for the mall (and anchor buildings up to 3 stories), except in foyers and lobbies of Groups R-1, R-2, and B. Height and area for the mall and anchors up to 3 stories are not limited by Table 503, provided total building has min. 60' open perimeter.

E. Tenant separation (Fire Partition per Section 709)

1. 1-hour wall must be continued to the ceiling.

2. Attic separation is not required.

3. No separation is required between the tenant and mall.

4. No protected openings are required for anchor stores of Type I or II construction, where they meet the mall (Group R's still require separation).

F. Anchor separation: (402.7.3)

1. Fire wall required unless 3 stories or less and same occupancy as mall—then 2-hours.

2. Openings from anchor to mall need no protectives (except for R-1 sleeping units).

G. Design occupant load (Leasable areas are based on gross leasable area of mall—except in Groups A and E uses.)

1. Requirements do not apply to anchor stores, and anchor store load not added to mall.

2. OLF = (0.000007) (GLA)+25

   a. OLF = Occupant load factor (sq. ft./person)

   b. GLA = Gross leasable area (sq. ft.)

   c. OLF minimum = 30/maximum = 50

3. Food courts computed using Section 1004 (15 sq. ft./person), and then added to mall design load.

H. Mall aisle widths: (402.5)

1. 20' minimum, and

2. 10' minimum × 8' high between tenant and kiosk, vending machines, displays, or other obstructions.

I. Kiosks (temporary or permanent booths, etc.) (402.11)

1. Kiosks must be noncombustible, constructed of fire-retardant treated wood, limited foam plastics or aluminium composites.

2. Covered kiosk requires a fire suppression system.

3. Maximum area is 300 sq. ft.

4. Minimum distance between kiosk and stores is 20'.

J. Plastic panels and plastic signs (402.16)

1. Panels and signs must not be more than 20% of the store area facing the mall.

    2. Maximum size is 36" × 96" for vertical signs, 36" height × unlimited for horizontal.

    3. 18" minimum distance from adjacent tenants is required.

    4. Encase edges and back of panels and signs in metal.

    5. Sign faces are test-limited for flame spread.

    6. Foam plastic signs limited to $1/2$" thickness and maximum 20 pounds/cubic foot density.

K. Security grilles and doors (402.13)

    1. When part of the required egress, they must be open to public when the stores are occupied, and openable after hours.

    2. When 2 or more exits are required, not more than $1/2$ may be equipped with security type grilles or doors.

L. Parking structures:

    1. Closed or open garages may be considered a separate building when separated from the mall with a 2-hour fire separation wall. (402.7.1)

    2. Parking garages at least 10 ft. from malls, use Table 602 for ratings.

M. Egress (402.4)

    1. Group A occupancies shall have $1/2$ of their required exits next to main mall exit or to exterior when occupant load > 500.

    2. A 200′ maximum travel distance to an exit from any point in the mall is required. Travel distance for tenant is measured to entrance to the mall.

    3. Anchor store exits shall be direct to the exterior and not to the mall; anchor store load is not added to the mall. Malls cannot egress through anchors.

    4. The minimum width of exit passageways and corridors from the mall is 66".

    5. Rear exit passageways and corridors from the tenant spaces must have 1-hour doors.

    6. Storage in exit corridors used for tenant service is prohibited.

    7. When travel from within tenant to mall is over 75′. or capacity over 50, need 2 egress routes.

    8. Mall maximum dead end is twice mall width.

N. Sprinklers (402.9)

    1. Sprinklers are required throughout in all malls.

    2. All systems serving tenant spaces and anchors shall be independent of the mall system.

O. Standpipes (402.9.1) (905.3.3)

    1. Each outlet shall be capable of 250 gpm.

    2. Standpipes must be located in the mall at each passageway, exterior mall entrance, enclosed stairs, and exterior exits.

P. A fire emergency ventilation system is required in the mall and tenant spaces, as for atriums in Section 404.

Q. Emergency systems

    1. Standby power is required. (402.13)

    2. Voice and alarm system required in malls over 50,000 sq. ft. (402.14)

    3. Rooms for Fire Department access must be identified.

CRAWL SPACES

A. Uninsulated crawl spaces must be ventilated (1203.3)

    1. Natural ventilation

        a. Not required when crawl space has vapor barrier and is conditioned space.

        b. Screened vents are required $1/150$ of vent-to-horizontal floor area, maximum $1/4$" least dimension for vent.

  c. With vapor barrier, $^1/_{1500}$ ratio is allowed, and must be used with manual louvers.

 2. Mechanical ventilation must be a minimum 0.02 cfm/sq. ft., humidity must not exceed 60%, and vapor retarder must be installed. (M-406)

B. Insulated

 1. Supply or return air plenum—See PLENUMS.

 2. Foam plastic is allowed, if covered and space is used only for a utility entrance. (2603.4.1.6)

C. Crawl space configuration

 1. Crawl space cannot be below footing level. (1807.1.2)

 2. Crawl space must be as high as exterior grade or have drainage.

 3. Minimum clearances (2304.11)

  a. Non-durable wood and untreated wood must allow 18" clearance;

  b. Girders must allow 12" clearance;

  c. Columns must allow 8" clearance;

  d. Treated and naturally durable has no minimum clearance requirement.

D. Access

 1. A minimum 18" × 24" opening is required. (1209.1)

DAY CARE CENTERS

A. Group identifications
1. Group I-4 is used for a day care center for more than five adults or children under 2½ years of age. (308.5.1, 308.5.2)
2. Group E is used for a day care center for six or more children with no more than five children under 2½ years of age, or when there are more than five but no more than 100 children 2½ years of age or less and all day-care rooms have direct exit doors to grade. (305.2)
3. Group I-2 is used for day care when there is 24-hour care for more than 5 children under 2½ years old. (308.3.1)
4. Type A is a day care center with seven to twelve children (four to twelve children, if four or more of the children are less than 2 years of age). The center must be the residence of the owner. (202—not regulated by OBC)

B. General (Ohio Board of Health): Specific rules adopted by the Ohio Board of Health and local boards of health regulate special provisions for day care in their licensure procedures.

C. Exits (See also EGRESS AND EXITS.)
1. Buildings of Use Group E with more than 50 occupants and I-4 rooms with more than 10 occupants require 2 exits. (Table 1015.1) For Group I-2, see 1014.2.2 for rooms and suites.
2. Maximum exit travel distance is 150′, and 200′ if sprinkled for Use Group I-2 and I-4. Maximum exit travel distance is 200′ and 250′ if sprinkled for Use Group E. (Table 1015.1)

D. Fire protection systems
1. Use Group I-2 and I-4
   a. Sprinklers required throughout. (903.2.5)
   b. Alarm system and smoke detectors are required for I-2. (907.2.6)
2. Use Group E:
   a. No suppression is required when fire area is less than 20,000 sq. ft. (903.2.2), unless below grade.
   b. An alarm system is required. (907.2.3)
      1. Not required when < 50 occupants.
      2. Pull stations not required when has special detection and alarm system.

DECAY PROTECTION (2302, 2304)

A. Decay protection is required when: (2304.11.2)
1. Joists are less than 18", or girders are less than 12" from the ground in crawl and similar spaces.
2. Sills, plates, and sleepers are on concrete slabs that bear on soil.
3. Sills are on concrete walls within 8" of the grade.
4. When girder ends in masonry wall with no clearance, protection is not required with a ½" air space between the wood and wall.
5. Exterior wood siding is within 6" of the ground. Siding must be 2" vertical from concrete steps, porch slabs, patio slabs and other externally exposed horizontal surfaces UNLESS naturally durable or preservative-treated wood.
6. All exposed structural members that support loads. (2304.11.5)
7. All wood is in contact with the ground.
8. Interior basement columns that are less than 1" above floors and on pedestals less than 6" above exposed earth.

9. A wood retaining wall requires treated or natural resistant wood. (2304.11.7)
10. Wood is in contact with the ground or fresh water (unless continuously submerged).
11. Wood members that support porous floors (like concrete) exposed to weather. (2304.11.4.2)
12. Fasteners for preservative-treated wood must be galvanized, silicon bronze, or copper. (2304.9.5)
13. Glued-laminated timber portions that are not fully weather protected by roof or eave and serve as structural supports of a building or structure must be pressure treated with preservative or be from naturally durable or preservative-treated wood.

B. Naturally durable wood (2302)
 1. Natural resistant woods are redwood, cedar, black walnut, and black locust.
 2. Termite-resistant woods are redwood and eastern red cedar.
C. Preservative-treated wood (2302, 2304.11.6)
 1. All preservative-treated wood shall be labeled and treated per AWPA standards.
 2. Maximum moisture content is 19% when installed.

DOORS See EGRESS AND EXITS.

DUCTS (CHAPTER M-6)
A. General
 1. The minimum thickness of steel and aluminum ducts is regulated by size and shape. See Table M-603.4 for dwelling units, see SMACNA Manual for all other occupancies.
 2. Gypsum board construction may be used for low temperature (125°F or less) return air ducts except for evaporative cooling systems and other condensating conditions. (M-603.5.1)
 3. Ducts and plenums may be self-contained or formed by parts of the building, but must have acceptable rigidity, permeability, combustibility, friction, and flexibility as sheet metal.
 4. Metal ducts without an approved protective coating underground must be encased in 2" of concrete, and sloped to drain at access point. (M-603.8)
 5. Ducts connected to heat exchanger must provide approved manufacturer's clearance to combustibles.
 6. Rigid ducts must be supported, except per manufacturer for flexible ducts, at least 10′ o.c.
 7. All duct joints shall be fastened and sealed. (M-603.9)
 8. Firestop around all ducts through floors and ceilings. (603.7, 607)
 9. Do not conceal duct access panels. (M-604.10)
B. Flexible ducts and connectors (M-603.6)
 1. Maximum connector length is 14′.
 2. Ducts must be rated Class 0 or 1, per UL 181.
 3. Ducts shall not penetrate fire-rated assemblies without fire dampers. (M-607.5)
 4. Maximum use temperature is 250°F.
 5. Ducts must resist pressure system rating for low, medium, or high. (M-604.3)
C. Insulation (M-604)
 1. Insulation must be labeled as to R value, flame spread, and smoke. (M-604.7)
 2. Duct covering shall not penetrate fire assemblies. (M-604.6)
 3. Duct lining shall not interfere with the operation of fire dampers. (M-604.8)
 4. Service openings shall not be concealed by duct coverings or linings. (M-604.10)

5. Maximum flame spread is 25; maximum smoke rating is 50.
6. Limit surface temperature to a maximum of 120°F. (M-604.2)
7. All ducts shall use vapor retarders. (M-604.11)

D. Minimum duct gauge and/or thickness for sheet metal ducts

TABLE 603.4
DUCT CONSTRUCTION MINIMUM SHEET METAL THICKNESS FOR SINGLE DWELLING UNITS

DUCT SIZE	GALVANIZED		APPROXIMATE ALUMINUM B&S GAGE
Minimum thickness (inches)	Equivalent galvanized gage no.		
Round ducts and enclosed rectangular ducts			
14" or less	0.013	30	26
Over 14"	0.016	28	24
Exposed rectangular ducts			
14" or less	0.016	28	24
Over 14"	0.019	26	22

For SI: 1 inch = 25.44 mm.

DWELLING

A "dwelling unit" provides complete, independent living facilities for one or more individuals, including living, sleeping, eating, cooking, and sanitation. It may also include accessory space for the occupants, e.g., private garage, greenhouse. A "dwelling" is a building exclusively containing one, two, or three dwelling units, each occupied by a family and five lodgers or boarders at most, and intended or designed for occupancy purposes alone, A dwelling is physically separate from any adjacent structures, and has an independent exit for each dwelling unit.

A "building," by way of contrast, is a structure or building containing two or three dwelling units that share an exit.

A "home" is an institution, residence, or facility that must be licensed by the Ohio Department of Health, that provides for a fee or otherwise, for a minimum of 24 hours, accommodations for three or more unrelated individuals who are dependent upon the services of others. The definition includes nursing homes, residential care facilities, home for the aging, veterans' homes operated under Code Chapter 5907, and county homes or district homes that are or have been licensed as residential care facilities. Residences, institutions, hotels, congregate housing projects, or similar facilities meeting the definition of a home are such, regardless of how they hold themselves out to the public.

The RCO applies to structures that are exclusively one-, two-, or three-family dwellings, with independent exits, as well as the accessory structures, in jurisdictions having a Board-certified residential department. In jurisdictions lacking a certified residential department, the construction documents for such structures need not be submitted for approval. Buildings solely for residential use that are three or fewer stories, with each dwelling unit having an independent egress/exit, may come under the RCO as opposed to R-3 of the Code if only one dwelling unit is located above another. Fire separation between two dwelling units, including a unit partially or totally above another, is per RCO section R317.1 302.2. Fire separation between groupings of two dwelling units and adjacent units is per RCO sections R317.2 302.2 through R317.3.2 302.6.

"SRO facilities" (SRO) are meant to hold more than five sleeping rooms and are kept, used, maintained, advertised or held out to the public as places affording an individual with separate sleeping accommodations, and which is intended as the permanent residence of a single occupant. SRO facilities must be licensed by the Ohio Fire Marshal and do not include agricultural labor camps, apartment houses, lodging houses, rooming houses or college dormitories.

E

EARTHQUAKES

(See also EXISTING STRUCTURES; FLOOD RESISTANCE PROTECTION; STRUCTURAL LOADS)

A. All structures and parts of structures (including permanent-attached nonstructural components) must resist all Design Earthquake Ground Motion per this entry and ASCE 7 (except Ch. 14 and Appendix 11A). Exceptions:
  1. Wood frame structures with seismic-force-resisting systems.
  2. Agricultural storage structures with incidental human occupancy.
  3. Structures with special characteristics—vehicular bridges, electrical transmission towers, hydraulic structures, buried utility lines plus appurtenances, nuclear reactors.
  4. Existing structures—see entry for EXISTING STRUCTURES

B. Definitions:
  1. Design Earthquake Ground Motion—What structures designed per this entry must meet.
  2. Maximum Considered Earthquake Ground Motion (MCEGM)—most severe earthquake per OBC.
  3. Mechanical Systems—For seismic load purposes in ASCE 7, Include pluming systems as specified.
  4. Orthagonal—two horizontal directions at 90° (1.57 rad) angle.
  5. Seismic Design Category—For structure, base on occupancy category and Design Earthquake Ground Motion severity.
  6. Seismic Force-Resisting System—Part of structural system meant to resist prescribed seismic forces.
  7. Site Class—Based on soil type and engineering propensities per this entry.
  8. Site Coefficients—Tables 1613.5.3(1) and 1613.5.3(2) values for Fa and Fv.

C. Determine S_s and S_1 parameters from 0.2 and 1-second spectral response accelerations per Figures 1613.5 OR using longitude/latitude OR by zip code with downloadable Java application. Determine seismic design values for structures from U.S. Geological Survey at (http://earthquake.usgs.gov/research/hazmaps/design/). If S_1 is ≤ 0.04 and S_s is ≤ 0.15, structure may be Seismic Design Category A.

D. Site Classes—per soil properties, either A, B, C, D, E, or F, per Table 1613.5.2. If soil properties indeterminate, use Site Class D UNLESS geotechnical data shows likelihood of E or F soil at site.

E. Maximum considered earthquake spectral response acceleration parameters for short periods, SMS, and at 1-second period, SM1, when adjusted for site class effects, per Equations 16-36 and 16-37, respectively:

$$S_{MS} = F_a S_s \hspace{4cm} \textbf{(Equation 16-36)}$$

$$S_{M1} = F_v S_1 \hspace{4cm} \textbf{(Equation 16-37)}$$

where:

F_a = Site coefficient defined in Table 1613.5.3(1).

F_v = Site coefficient defined in Table 1613.5.3(2).

S_S = The mapped spectral accelerations for short periods as determined in Section 1613.5.1.

S_1 = The mapped spectral accelerations for a 1-second period as determined in Section 1613.5.1.

$$S_{DS} = \frac{2}{3} S_{MS} \hspace{4cm} \textbf{(Equation 16-38)}$$

$$S_{D1} = \frac{2}{3} S_{M1} \hspace{4cm} \textbf{(Equation 16-39)}$$

where:

S_{MS} = The maximum considered earthquake spectral response accelerations for short period as determined in Section 1613.5.3.

S_{M1} = The maximum considered earthquake spectral response accelerations for 1-second period as determined in Section 1613.5.3.

TABLE 1613.5.2
SITE CLASS DEFINITIONS

SITE CLASS	SOIL PROFILE NAME	AVERAGE PROPERTIES IN TOP 100 feet, SEE SECTION 1613.5.5		
		Soil shear wave velocity, $\bar{v}_s$, (ft/s)	Standard penetration resistance, $\bar{N}$	Soil undrained shear strength, $\bar{s}_u$,(psf)
A	Hard rock	$\bar{v}_s > 5,000$	N/A	N/A
B	Rock	$2,500 < \bar{v}_s \le 5,000$	N/A	N/A
C	Very dense soil and soft rock	$1,200 < \bar{v}_s \le 2,500$	$\bar{N} > 50$	$\bar{s}_u \ge 2,000$
D	Stiff soil profile	$600 \le \bar{v}_s \le 1,200$	$15 \le \bar{N} \le 50$	$1,000 \le \bar{s}_u \le 2,000$
E	Soft soil profile	$\bar{v}_s < 600$	$\bar{N} < 15$	$\bar{s}_u < 1,000$
E	—	Any profile with more than 10 feet of soil having the following characteristics: 1. Plasticity index $PI > 20$, 2. Moisture content $w \ge 40\%$, and 3. Undrained shear strength $\bar{s}_u < 500$ psf		
F	—	Any profile containing soils having one or more of the following characteristics: 1. Soils vulnerable to potential failure or collapse under seismic loading such as liquefiable soils, quick and highly sensitive clays, collapsible weakly cemented soils. 2. Peats and/or highly organic clays ($H > 10$ feet of peat and/or highly organic clay where H = thickness of soil) 3. Very high plasticity clays ($H > 25$ feet with plasticity index $PI > 75$) 4. Very thick soft/medium stiff clays ($H > 120$ feet)		

For SI: 1 foot = 304.8 mm, 1 square foot = 0.0929 m^2, 1 pound per square foot = 0.0479 kPa. N/A = Not applicable

TABLE 1613.5.3(1)
VALUES OF SITE COEFFICIENT F$_a$ [a]

SITE CLASS	MAPPED SPECTRAL RESPONSE ACCELERATION AT SHORT PERIOD				
	$S_s \le 0.25$	$S_s = 0.50$	$S_s = 0.75$	$S_s = 1.00$	$S_s \ge 1.25$
A	0.8	0.8	0.8	0.8	0.8
B	1.0	1.0	1.0	1.0	1.0
C	1.2	1.2	1.1	1.0	1.0
D	1.6	1.4	1.2	1.1	1.0
E	2.5	1.7	1.2	0.9	0.9
F	Note b	Note b	Note b	Note b	Note b

a. Use straight-line interpolation for intermediate values of mapped spectral response acceleration at short period, S_s.
b. Values shall be determined in accordance with Section 11.4.7 of ASCE 7.

TABLE 1613.5.3(2)
VALUES OF SITE COEFFICIENT F_V [a]

SITE CLASS	MAPPED SPECTRAL RESPONSE ACCELERATION AT 1-SECOND PERIOD				
	$S_1 \leq 0.1$	$S_1 = 0.2$	$S_1 = 0.3$	$S_1 = 0.4$	$S_1 \geq 0.5$
A	0.8	0.8	0.8	0.8	0.8
B	1.0	1.0	1.0	1.0	1.0
C	1.7	1.6	1.5	1.4	1.3
D	2.4	2.0	1.8	1.6	1.5
E	3.5	3.2	2.8	2.4	2.4
F	Note b	Note b	Note b	Note b	Note b

a. Use straight-line interpolation for intermediate values of mapped spectral response acceleration at 1-second period, S1.
b. Values shall be determined in accordance with Section 11.4.7 of ASCE 7.

F. Site Classification—per Table 1613.5.5. Use notations per Equation 16-40 for upper 100′ (30,480 mm) of site profile; if different soil and/or rock layers, subdivide into layers designated from 1 to n at bottom. Symbol i refers to layers between 1 and n. To classify site"

1. See if site corresponds to any of four categories requiring site specific evaluation if so, classify as Site F and conduct the evaluation.
2. If soft clay layer > 10′ (3,048 mm), Site Class E. Soft clay layer is us < 500 psf (24 kPa), w $\geq$ 40% and PI > 20.
3. Categorize site using one of these methods:
    a. $_s$ v method—$_s$ v for the top 100 feet (30 480 mm)
    b. N method—N for the top 100 feet (30 480 mm)
    c. $_u$ s method—$_{ch}$ N for cohesionless soil layers (PI < 20) in the top 100 feet(30 and average, $_u$ s for cohesive soil layers (PI >20) in the top 100 feet (30, 480 mm)

where:

v_{si} = The shear wave velocity in feet per second (m/s).
d_i = The thickness of any layer between 0 and 100 feet (30 480 mm).

where:

$$\bar{v}_x = \frac{\sum_{i=1}^{n} d_i}{\sum_{i=1}^{n} \frac{d_i}{v_{si}}} \qquad \textbf{(Equation 16-40)}$$

$\sum_{i=1}^{n} d_i = 100$ feet (30 480 mm)

N_i is the Standard Penetration Resistance (ASTM D 1586) not to exceed 100 blows/foot (328 blows/m) as directly measured in the field without corrections. When refusal is met for a rock layer, N_i shall be taken as 100 blows/foot (328 blows/m).

$$\bar{N} = \frac{\sum_{i=1}^{n} d_i}{\sum_{i=1}^{n} \frac{d_i}{N_i}} \qquad \textbf{(Equation 16-41)}$$

where N_i and d_i in Equation 16-41 are for cohesionless soil, cohesive soil and rock layers.

$$\bar{N}_{ch} = \frac{d_s}{\sum_{i=1}^{m} \frac{d_i}{N_i}}$$

where:

$$\sum_{i=1}^{m} d_i = d_s$$

Use d_i and N_i for cohesionless soil layers only in Equation 16-42.

$d_s =$ The total thickness of cohesionless soil layers in the top 100 feet (30 480 mm).

$m =$ The number of cohesionless soil layers in the top 100 feet (30 480 mm).

$s_{ui} =$ The undrained shear strength in psf (kPa), not to exceed 5,000 psf (240 kPa), ASTM D 2166 or D 2850.

$$\overline{s_u} = \frac{d_c}{\sum\limits_{i=1}^{k} s_{ui}}$$ **(Equation 16-43)**

where:

$$\sum_{i=1}^{k} d_i = d_c$$

$d_c =$ The total thickness of cohesive soil layers in the top 100 feet (30 480 mm).

$k =$ The number of cohesive soil layers in the top 100 feet (30 480 mm).

$PI =$ The plasticity index, ASTM D 4318.

TABLE 1613.5.5
SITE CLASSIFICATION[a]

SITE CLASS	$\overline{v_s}$	$\overline{N}$ or $\overline{N_{ch}}$	$\overline{s_u}$
E	< 600 ft/s	≤ 15	< 1,000 psf
D	600 to 1,200 ft/s	15 to 50	1,000 to 2,000 psf
C	1,200 to 2,500 ft/s	> 50	> 2,000

For SI: 1 foot per second = 304.8 mm per second, 1 pound per square foot = 0.0479 kN/m[2].

a. If the $\overline{s_u}$ method is used and the $\overline{N_{ch}}$ and $\overline{s_u}$ criteria differ, select the category with the softer soils (for example, use Site Class E instead of D).

TABLE 1613.5.6(1)
SEISMIC DESIGN CATEGORY BASED ON SHORT-PERIOD RESPONSE ACCELERATIONS

VALUE OF S_{DS}	OCCUPANCY CATEGORY		
	I or II	III	IV
S_{DS} < 0.167g	A	A	A
0.167g ≤ S_{DS} < 0.33g	B	B	C
0.33g ≤ S_{DS} < 0.50g	C	C	D
0.50g ≤ S_{DS}	D	D	D

TABLE 1613.5.6(2)
SEISMIC DESIGN CATEGORY BASED ON 1-SECOND PERIOD
RESPONSE ACCELERATION

VALUE OF S_{D1}	OCCUPANCY CATEGORY		
	I or II	III	IV
$S_{D1} < 0.067g$	A	A	A
$0.067g \leq S_{D1} < 0.133g$	B	B	C
$0.133g \leq S_{D1} < 0.20g$	C	C	D
$0.20g \leq S_{D1}$	D	D	D

G. Seismic Design Category (1613.5)—
   1. Category E if Occupancy Category I, II, or III structure sited where mapped spectral response acceleration parameter at 1-second interval, S_1, is ≥ 0.75.
   2. Category F if Occupancy IV structure and mapped spectral response acceleration parameter S_1 is ≥ 0.75.
   3. Other structures assigned category by occupancy category coefficients S_{DS} and S_{D1}, per Table 1613.5.6 or site-specific method under ASCE 7. Assign more severe seismic design category per Table 1613.5.6(1) or 1613.5.6(2) regardless of fundamental period of vibration of structure, T.
      a. Use table 1613.5.6(1) if S_1 is < 0.75, AND for both orthagonal directions, app. fundamental period of structure T_a per ASCE 7, Section 12.8.2.1 is < 0.8 T_s per ASCE 7, Section 11.4.5 AND for both orthagonal directions, structure's fundamental period for calculating story drift is < T_s. AND use ASCE 7, Equation 12.8.2 for calculating seismic response coefficient C_s. AND diaphragms per ASCE 7, Section 12.3.1 are rigid OR flexible and vertical distances between elements of seismic-resisting-force system $\leq$ 40′ (12,192 mm).
      b. If using ASCE 7 alternate simplified design method, use ASCE 7 for seismic design category.
H. ASCE 7 provisions can be waived in favor of the following (1613.6):
   1. At end of Section 12.3.1.1 of ASCE 7, add:
      "Diaphragms constructed of wood structural panels or untopped steel decking shall also be permitted to be idealized as flexible, provided all of the following conditions are met:
         1. Toppings of concrete or similar materials are not placed over wood structural panel diaphragms except for nonstructural toppings no greater than 1½ inches (38 mm) thick.
         2. Each line of vertical elements of the seismic-force-resisting system complies with the allowable story drift of Table 12.12-1.
         3. Vertical elements of the seismic-force-resisting system are light-frame walls sheathed with wood structural panels rated for shear resistance or steel sheets.
         4. Portions of wood structural panel diaphragms that cantilever beyond the vertical elements of the lateral-force-resisting system are designed in accordance with Section 4.2.5.2 of AF&PA SDPWS."
   2. At end of Section 17.5.4.2, add:
      "**Exception:** For isolated structures designed in accordance with this standard, the Structural System Limitations and the Structure Height Limitations in Table 12.2-1

for ordinary steel concentrically braced frames (OCBFs) as defined in Chapter 11 and ordinary moment frames (OMFs) as defined in Chapter 11 are permitted to be taken as 160 feet (48 768 mm) for structures assigned to Seismic Design Category D, E or F, provided that the following conditions are satisfied:

1. The value of RI as defined in Chapter 17 is taken as
2. For OMFs and OCBFs, design is in accordance with AISC 341."

3. A 13-compliant automatic sprinkler systems (design and installation) meet Section 13.6.8 requirements.

4. At end of Section 12.2.1, add (reference autoclaved aerated (AAC) masonry shear wall design coefficients and system limitations):

"For ordinary reinforced AAC masonry shear walls used in the seismic-force-resisting system of structures, the response modification factor, R, shall be permitted to be taken as 2, the deflection amplification factor, Cd, shall be permitted to be taken as 2 and the system overstrength factor, $_o\Omega$, shall be permitted to be taken as 2^1/$_2$. Ordinary reinforced AAC masonry shear walls shall not be limited in height for structures assigned to Seismic Design Category B, shall be limited in height to 35 feet (10 668 mm) for structures assigned to Seismic Design Category C and are not permitted for structures assigned to Seismic Design Categories D, E and F. For ordinary plain (unreinforced) AAC masonry shear walls used in the seismic-force-resisting system of structures, the response modification factor, R, shall be permitted to be taken as 1^1/$_2$, the deflection amplification factor, Cd, shall be permitted to be taken as 1^1/$_2$ and the system overstrength factor, $_o\Omega$, shall be permitted to be taken as 2^1/$_2$. Ordinary plain unreinforced) AAC masonry shear walls shall not be limited in height for structures assigned to Seismic Design Category B and are not permitted for structures assigned to Seismic Design Categories C, D, E and F."

5. ASME A17.1, Section 8.4.10-compliant seismic switches meet ASCE 7, Section 13.6.10.3.

6. Modify ASCE 7, Section 12.2.5.4 as follows:

"**12.2.5.4 Increased structure height limit for steel-braced frames, special steel plate shear walls and special reinforced concrete shear walls.** The height limits in Table 12.2-1 are permitted to be increased from 160 feet (48 768 mm) to 240 feet (75 152 mm) for structures assigned to Seismic Design Category D or E and from 100 feet (30 480 mm) to 160 feet (48 768 mm) for structures assigned to Seismic Design Category F that have steel-braced frames, special steel plate shear walls or special reinforced concrete cast-in-place shear walls and that meet both of the following requirements:

1. The structure shall not have an extreme torsional irregularity as defined in Table 12.2-1 (horizontal structural irregularity Type 1b).
2. The braced frames or shear walls in any one plane shall resist no more than 60% of the total seismic forces in each direction, neglecting accidental torsional effects."

7. Separate all structures from adjoining structures to allow maximum inelastic response displacement ($_M\delta$)—determine at critical spots, consider structure's translational and torsional displacements, using Equation 16-44. Set back structure from property line by $\leq$ ($_M\delta$) of structure, if it adjoins property line separate from public way. Exceptions:

a. Allow smaller setbacks or separations if rational.
b. Category A, B, or C structures.

8. Seismic supports for HVAC ductwork with I_p = 1.5 unnecessary if, on full length of each duct run:

a. HVAC ducts suspended from $\leq$ 12" (305 mm) long, configured to avoid hanger/attachment bending OR
b. Cross-section of ducts < 6' (0.557 square m^2) square.

9. Modify ASCE 7, Section 11.7.5 as follows:

"**11.7.5 Anchorage of walls**. Walls shall be anchored to the roof and all floors and members that provide lateral support for the wall or that are supported by the wall.

The anchorage shall provide a direct connection between the walls and the roof or floor construction. The connections shall be capable of resisting the forces specified in Section 11.7.3 applied horizontally, substituted for E in load combinations of Section 2.3 or 2.4."

$$\delta_M = \frac{C_d \delta_{max}}{I} \hspace{2cm} \text{(Equation 16-44)}$$

where:

$C_d =$ Deflection amplification factor in Table 12.2-1 of ASCE 7.

$\delta_{max} =$ Maximum displacement defined in Section 12.8.4.3 of ASCE 7.

$I =$ Importance factor in accordance with Section 11.5.1 of ASCE 7.

Adjacent buildings on the same property shall be separated by a distance not less than δ_{MT}, determined by Equation 16-45.

$$\delta_{MT} = \sqrt{(\delta_{M1})^2 + (\delta_{M2})^2} \hspace{2cm} \text{(Equation 16-45)}$$

where:

$\delta_{M1}, \delta_{M2} =$ The maximum inelastic response displacements of the adjacent buildings in accordance with Equation 16-44.

EGRESS AND EXITS

(Chapter 10 Means of Egress and Exits)

A. Fire safety and evacuation plans are required per the Ohio Fire Code.

B. Capacity of exits (1005)

  1. The minimum width is figured by the number of inches required, using the number of occupants and the tables below, but not less than the minimum prescribed for each egress component. The table also shows the number of occupants allowed for the minimum required widths.

TABLE OF REQUIREMENTS

Width

Use Group:	STAIRS	STAIRS/SPRK
H-1 thru H-4	0.7 in.	0.3 in.
I-2	0.4	0.3
all others	0.3	0.2

Use Group:	ALL OTHER	ALL OTHER/SPRK
H-1 thru H-4	0.4 in.	0.2 in.
I-2	0.2	0.2
all others	0.2	0.15

TABLE OF CAPACITY

Clear Width/Capacity

Use Group:	STAIRS	STAIRS/SPRK	DOORS	DOORS/SPRK
		44"		32" clear
all others	146	220	160	213
H-1 thru H-4	63	146	80	160

| I-2 | 110 | 146 | 160 | 160 |

Note:
1. /SPRK means sprinklers throughout the building.
2. Minimum clear width for I-2 beds is 41½ inches clear.

2. Assembly uses with an occupant load over 300 (1027, 1028)
   a. All assembly buildings must have at least one main entrance and exit discharge, supporting half the total exit load for the assembly occupancy.
   b. Main exit must be equal to one-half of the total occupant load capacity, but not less than the sum of the widths of exits leading to it. Exception: Where there is no well-defined main exit, or if there are multiple main exits, distribution of exits can be along the building perimeter if the total width of egress $\geq$ 100% of the required width.
   c. Main exit must front on a street or open space at least 10' wide that leads to a public way.
   d. Besides main exit, each floor's other exits must provide at least half the required exit width.
3. If the exists from a floor above and below converge at an intermediate floor, the exit capacity (door passage, stair, ramp, etc.) must be equal to at least the sum of both exits.
4. An exit serving more than one floor shall be sized using only the floor with the highest occupancy.
5. Exit stair width must not be decreased in direction of travel.
6. Minimum width for stairs, ramps, and corridors should meet the following requirements:
   a. 50 occupants or fewer: 36".
   b. More than 50 occupants requiring movement: 44".
   c. Use Group I-2 with beds: 96".
   d. Use Group E with more than 100 occupants: 72".
   e. Stairs must be at least 44" wide. Exceptions:
      i. In single-exit buildings, stairs must be at least 36" wide, and
      ii. In areas of rescue assistance, stairs must be at least 48" wide. (1007.3)
      iii. Within dwelling units that have stair lifts, the minimum clear width is 20'.
   f. Inside dwelling units: 36".
7. Doors swinging into the egress width cannot reduce required width by more than 7", and not by more than half for the entire swing.
8. Nonstructural projections (i.e., trim) are allowed $\leq$ 1 ½" per side.
9. Longest distance to exit door $\leq$ 200' in nonsprinkled buildings, and $\leq$ 250' in sprinkled buildings. Measure the distance along the aisles and aisle accessway, without traveling over or on the seats. Exceptions:
   a. If smoke protected assembly seating, travel distance from each seat to nearest vomitory or concourse entrance $\leq$ 200'; from entrance to vomitory or concourse to an exterior stair, ramp or walk $\leq$ 200'.
   b. Travel distance from open air seats to exterior $\leq$ 400', but Unlimited in Type I or II.
10. The common egress path must be $\leq$ 30' from any seat to choice point for two paths to two exits. Exceptions:
    a. $\leq$ 75' for areas serving < 50 occupants.
    b. $\leq$ 50' for smoke protected assembly seating.

69

11. If one of the two paths of travel is across the aisle through a row of seats to another aisle, allow $\leq$ 24 seats between the two aisles, with a minimum clear width between rows for the row between the two aisles of 12" (305 mm) plus 0.6" (15.2 mm) for each additional seat above seven in that row. Exception:

    a. Smoke-protected assembly seating requires $\leq$ 40 seats between the aisles, and a minimum clear width of 12" (305 mm) plus 0.3" (7.6 mm) for each additional seat.

TABLE 1028.6.2
WIDTH OF AISLES FOR SMOKE-PROTECTED ASSEMBLY

TOTAL NUMBER OF SEATS IN THE SMOKE-PROTECTED ASSEMBLY OCCUPANCY	INCHES OF CLEAR WIDTH PER SEAT SERVED			
	Stairs and aisle steps with handrails within 30 inches	Stairs and aisle steps without handrails within 30 inches	Passageways, doorways and ramps not steeper than 1 in 10 in slope	Ramps steeper than 1 in 10 in slope
Equal to or less than 5,000	0.200	0.250	0.150	0.165
10,000	0.130	0.163	0.100	0.110
15,000	0.096	0.120	0.070	0.077
20,000	0.076	0.095	0.056	0.062
Equal to or greater than 25,000	0.060	0.075	0.044	0.048

For SI: 1 inch = 25.4 mm.

C. Doors (components of an exit system) (1015)
(See also WINDOWS, DOORS, AND OTHER OPENINGS.)
  1. Doors must swing in the direction of travel when serving more than 50 occupants, or in a high hazard area. (1015)
  2. A room, area, or tenant space must have more than one exit door depending on occupant load and travel distance, except:
      a. Use Group R-3.
      b. In Group I-2 with sleeping compartments (suites) of more than 1000 sq. ft.
      c. In boiler and furnace rooms when equipment is more than 400,000 Btu/hr. or floor is more than 500 sq. ft. (second access may be approved ladder). (1015)
  3. Minimum door size (1008)
      a. Single door must allow 32" clear width.
      b. Group I-2 occupancy for bed use must allow 41½" clear width.
      c. Double doors must individually allow a minimum of 32" clear width.
      d. Door leaf must be a maximum of 48" wide.
      e. Minimum height is 6'8"; in dwellings, minimum height is 6'6".
      f. Unoccupied storage rooms of up to 800 sq. ft. may use a 10' door.
      g. Requirements do not apply to revolving doors.
      h. A minimum of 28" clear width is required for I-3 sleeping rooms.
      i. Interior egress doors which are not required to be accessible must have a minimum clear width of 29¾".
      j. Type B dwelling units—minimum 31¾" (for 2'10" nominal door) for openings required to be an accessible route.
  4. Egress door hardware
      a. Side hinges are required. Exceptions:
          i. Private garages, factory, and storage areas with an occupant load less than or equal to 10
          ii. Sliding doors in Group I-3
          iii. Devices on doors in or serving a single dwelling
          iv. Revolving doors
          v. Horizontal sliding doors complying with 1017.4.4
          vi. In sleeping areas for I-2 with non-combustible partition and under constant observation and in a single dwelling unit.

b. Surface bolts are unacceptable.

c. Panic hardware is required on latched doors serving more than 50 occupants in Groups A and E and Group H occupancies.

d. Power-operated doors must open with 50 lb. of force when there is loss of power.

e. Latch release at 15 lb. is required along with 30 lb. door force to move door, 15 lb. to open door (except when ADAAG applies). Hardware must be 34" to 38" above floor.

f. Special locking: In Groups B, F, I, M, S, and R buildings with automatic sprinkler and/or fire alarm, an approved egress control device which will unlock egress doors may be used.

    i. If Group I-2,

        (a) Doors unlock when sprinkler or fire detection system actuates.

        (b) Doors unlock when power controlling lock is lost.

        (c) Door locks can be unlocked by a signal from the fire command center, a nursing station or other approved location.

        (d) Building occupants are not required to pass through more than one special egress lock-equipped door before entering an exit.

        (e) The emergency planning and preparedness required by Chapter 4 of the Fire Code shall describe and include the procedures for operating the unlocking system.

        (f) Emergency lighting must be provided at the door. All members of the clinical staff must have the keys, codes or other means necessary for operation of the locking devices.

        (g) Exception: (a)–(d) do not apply to doors to areas housing individuals requiring restraint or containment as part of the function of a psychiatric treatment area.

g. Delayed egress locks can be unlocked from nurses' station, all clinical staff have keys and codes for doors, and doors have emergency lighting.

h. All fire-rated doors require latches and closers. (715.4)

i. Doors in a series shall be spaced 7' apart when closed, except power-operated doors and doors of Groups I-1 and R-3.

j. Revolving doors (1008.1.4)

    i. See Table 1008.1.4.1 for speed. Speed varies with diameter.

TABLE 1008.1.4.1
REVOLVING DOOR SPEEDS

INSIDE DIAMETER (feet-inches)	POWER-DRIVEN-TYPE SPEED CONTROL (rpm)	MANUAL-TYPE SPEED CONTROL (rpm)
6-6	11	12
7-0	10	11
7-6	9	11
8-0	9	10
8-6	8	9
9-0	8	9
9-6	7	8
10-0	7	8

For SI: 1 inch = 25.4 mm, 1 foot = 304.8 mm.

ii. Doors must be able to collapse by a 130 lb. force at the outer 3" edge (with exceptions).

iii. Revolving doors must be 10′ from stairs and escalators.

iv. Adjacent swinging doors within 10′ of revolving doors must be provided, in same wall unless revolving door is in a non-egress lobby.

v. Revolving doors can be used as egress doors when door also has a 130 lb. collapse force, a maximum 50-person capacity, and when it is not used for more than 50% of the building capacity.

k. Access-controlled doors (1008.1.4.4)

i. Access-controlled doors are acceptable as entrances of Groups A, B, E, M, R-1, R-2.

ii. Release by sprinkler, loss of power, alarm or approach sensor, manual device and sign are required. Doors shall unlock from a manual device 40" to 48" (1016 mm to 1219 mm) vertically above floor and within 5′ (1524 mm) of the secured doors, clearly identified "PUSH TO EXIT," with ready access to the device. Operation of the device causes direct interruption of power to the lock—independent of the access control system electronics. Doors must remain unlocked for a minimum of 30 seconds.

iii. Doors in Groups A, B, E, and M cannot be locked from the egress side when the building is open to the public.

l. Doors need to be visually recognizable as doors. They cannot be covered by mirrors, curtains, decorations, etc. (1008.1)

m. Delayed egress locks authorized in Group I-2 if clinical needs require and building sprinkled or has approved smoke or heat detection system. Occupant cannot be required to pass through more than one special egress lock door before entering an exit. Requirements:

i. Doors unlock when sprinklers or fire detection system actuated.

ii. Doors unlock if power lost.

iii. Door locks can be unlocked by a signal fire command center, nursing station or other approved location.

iv. Operating procedures for unlocking system described and approved in emergency planning and preparedness under fire code, Chapter 4.

v. All clinical staff have keys, codes or other operating means.

vi. Emergency lighting provided at the door. Exception: i.-iii. inapplicable to doors to areas for confining or restraining required as part of mental hospital function.

D. Egress lighting (1006)

1. Egress lighting is required in all buildings, including the exit discharge.

2. Not required for Group U, aisle accessways, Group 1 sleeping units, and inside dwelling units.

3. Egress lighting must be provided continuously during occupancy, a minimum of 1 footcandle; or 0.2 footcandle in aisles A and E theaters with restricted access to lighting controls.

4. All means of egress lighting for rooms or buildings required to have more than one means of egress must have emergency back-up power.

E. Hazards in the line of egress

1. Low hanging or protruding items into exit corridors, such as fixtures and closure arms, are unacceptable.

2. All egress floors shall be non-slip. (1003.4)

3. Ramps must be used when change in elevation is less than 12". (1003.5) Alterna-

tives are for maximum 7" step at exterior door (when not required to be accessible) for F, H, S, U and dwelling units.

4. Guards are required beside walks, balconies, landings, porches, and mezzanines which are 30" above a floor or the grade below. Retaining walls are required at 4'. (1012)

    a. No guards required for:

      i. Loading docks, vehicle repair pits, and

      ii. Stages and platforms.

F. Corridors and passageways (1018): Direct access to an exit is required by corridors or passageways with no obstruction and must be conveniently accessible to all occupants. (Note: corridors are not required.)

1. Doors opening into corridors shall not reduce widths more than 50%. When fully opened, the door shall not project more than 7" into the required corridor width. (1021.2)

2. Enclosure

    a. Fire resistance without sprinklers—One hour is required for:

      i. All corridors in H-1, H-2, H-3 and I.

      ii. All corridors in H-4, H-5, A, B, E, F, M, R, S, U serving more than 30.

    b. Fire resistance with sprinklers. No rating is required for:

      i. All corridors in A, B, E, F, M, S, U, I-2, I-4 (and some conditions for I-3s).

      ii. Connecting stories or mezzanines in Group I-3 if all common use areas serving accessible units and all public use areas are on an accessible route.

      iii. Group R-2 with Type A units, an accessible route not required to connect stories or mezzanines if all common use areas serving Type A units and all public use areas on an accessible route.

      iv. In other than Group R-2 dormitories at educational facilities, Group R-2 facilities with accessible units do not require an accessible route to connect stories or mezzanines if accessible units, all common use areas serving accessible units and all public use areas are on an accessible route.

      v. An accessible route is not required to connect Group R-1 stories or mezzanines within individual units, IF accessible level meets requirements for accessible units AND sleeping accommodations for ≥ two persons and a toilet facility available on that level.

      vi. An accessible route not required in Group R-3 and R-4 congregate residences to connect floors or mezzanines if accessible units or Type Bunits, all common use areas serving accessible units, and Type B units and all public use areas serving accessible and Type B units are on an accessible route.

      vii. Multistory dwelling or sleeping units without elevator service in Group I-1, I-2, R-1, R-2, R-3, or R-4 need not be a Type A unit or a Type B unit.

      viii. If multistory unit has external elevator service to only one floor in Group I-1, I-2, R-1, R-2, R-3 or R-4, that floor is primary entry to the unit, and must comply with Type B requirements, with a toilet facility on that floor.

    c. Construction required (708.4)

      i. Continuous from floor to deck or fire-rated assembly for all fire-rated corridors.

     3. Maximum dead end length is 20′ unless the length is less than 2½ times the width of corridor.

        a. For certain I-3 and sprinkled B and F, maximum of 50 feet.

     4. The common path of travel is a maximum of 75′.

        a. Common path of travel is a shared egress route before independent directions are available.

        b. For B, F, and S, allowed to be 100′ when fully sprinkled or tenant space has a maximum of 30 occupants, and for all I-3.

  G. Prohibited corridor use (1018.5)

     1. Exits and access corridors shall not be used as a supply or return air plenum, except in tenant spaces less than 1000 sq. ft.

     2. A corridor ceiling plenum may be used if the ceiling below is a fire-rated assembly, the corridor is not required to be rated, or if it is located within a dwelling unit.

  H. Exit Signs (1011)

     1. Signs are required in all areas when more than one egress route is required (except within sleeping room areas of Group I). Signs must be placed so that every point in an exit access corridor or exit passageway is ≤ 100′ (30 480 mm) or the listed viewing distance for the sign, whichever is less, from the nearest visible exit sign.

     2. Signs must have minimum of 6″ high × ¾″ wide red letters, or other contrasting colors.

     3. If arrows are included, they must be permanently and securely mounted to prevent being changed.

     4. Signs must be illuminated according to the following requirements:

        a. 5 footcandles of illumination.

        b. Power shall be also connected to an emergency source.

        c. Self-luminous signs are acceptable per UL 924.

 I. Maximum travel distances to exits (1016)

     1. The distances are measured from the furthest point of occupancy to the nearest acceptable exit.

     2. Established distances are as follows:

Building Groups	Maximum Travel Distance in Feet	
	Without Sprinklers	With Sprinklers
A, E, F-1, I-1, M, R, S-1	200	250
B	200	300
F-2, S-2, U	300	400
H-1	NP	75
H-2	NP	100
H-3	NP	150
H-4	NP	175
H-5	NP	200
I-2, I-3, I-4	150	200

NP: H and I-2 Use Groups require fire suppression systems. The distance also applies when the H and I-2 fire area is part of the building.

     3. Covered malls require a 200′ maximum travel distance from within tenant space to an exit. (402.4.4)

     4. In Use Groups F-1 and S-1, if building is one story and the minimum height from the finished floor to the bottom of the ceiling or roof slab or deck is 24′ (7315mm) with automatic heat and roof smoke vents and the building has early suppression fire response automatic fire sprinkler system and manually activated smoke exhaust systems, the exit travel distance may be 400′. (1016.3)

5. HPM facilities require a maximum travel distance of 75′.

6. Atriums, except lowest level, require a maximum travel distance of 200′. (404.9)

7. A maximum travel distance of 100′ is allowed in temporary and membrane structures. (See 2403.12.1 International Fire Code 2003.)

8. For Group A-5, maximum travel distance may be 400′ when exit routes are open to exterior.

9. Exterior egress balconies can increase the tabular amount by 100 feet. (1016.2)

J. Interior exit stairs

1. For minimum width requirements (1009.1). See also ACCESSIBILITY GUIDELINES.

2. Headroom is 6′8″ minimum. (6′6″ for spiral stairways.) (1009.2)

3. No projections are permitted except at or below handrails (4$\frac{1}{2}$″), and not limited above the headroom minimum height. (1009.11.7)

4. Maximum vertical rise in any run is 12′. (1009.6)

5. The least dimension of landings and platforms must be equal to the width of the stairs. (This is not required to be greater than 4′ if straight.)

6. Treads and risers (maximum rise and minimum tread) (1009.4)

    a. In Use Groups R-3 and R-2 (dwelling units), stairs may have a maximum 8$\frac{1}{4}$″ rise and a minimum 9″ tread plus nosing of $\frac{3}{4}$″ to 1$\frac{1}{4}$″.

    b. Interior exit stairs must have a maximum 7″ rise and a minimum 11″ run, except:
   i. Winders
   ii. Spiral stairs and alternating tread stairways
   iii. Circular stairs
   iv. Aisles for assembly
   v. Existing stairs, and
   vi. Replaced stairs where added length is not feasible. (3403.4)

    c. A $\frac{3}{8}$″ maximum variation between the highest and lowest rise or depth in any one run is required.

    d. Leading edge of tread has a radius of curvature $\leq$ $\frac{9}{16}$″ (14.3 mm), with beveling of nosings $\leq$ $\frac{9}{16}$″ (14.3 mm). Risers must be solid and vertical or sloped under the tread above from the underside of the nosing above at an angle $\leq$ 30 (0.52 rad) from vertical. Tread nosing shall can project $\leq$ 1$\frac{1}{2}$″ (32 mm) beyond the tread below. Al leading edge projections must have uniform size (including the leading edge of the floor at the top of a flight). Exceptions:
   a. Group I-3 or F, H, and S other than where accessible to public.
   b. Spiral stairways.
   c. Alternating tread devices.

7. Handrails (1012)

    a. Handrails are required on both sides except within a dwelling unit, aisles with seating on only one side, and on spiral stairs.

    b. Stair width greater than 60″ needs intermediate rails spaced so that no part of required width is greater than 30″, with exception for placement at "monumental" stairs.

    c. Vertical height: 34″ is the minimum and 38″ is the maximum from the edge of the nosing.

    d. Must support 50 lbs/foot, and 200 lbs at any one point. (1607.7)

    e. Handrail ends must be 12″ at top and one tread at bottom.

    f. Allow minimum of 1$\frac{1}{2}$″ (38 mm) of clear space between handrail and wall or other surface, with both free of sharp or abrasive elements.

g. Clear width between handrails on ramps is minimum 36" (914 mm). No projections into required width are allowed if > 4½ inches (114 mm) at or below handrail height.

8. Winders (1009.4.3)
   a. Winders are unacceptable except for egress within a dwelling unit.
   b. Minimum tread is 11" at 12" from the narrow end. 6" is the minimum tread.

9. Spiral stairways (1009.9)
   a. Spiral stairs may be used for egress in dwelling units, from mezzanines not more than 250 sq. ft. and with an occupant load of no greater than 5 people, or from catwalks and gridirons.
   b. Minimum width is 26". Tread is 7½" (minimum) at 12" from the narrow side, 9½" is maximum rise, and 6'6" is the minimum headroom.

10. Circular stairways (1009.8)
    a. Circular stairways are acceptable as egress when having conforming riser (7") and tread (11" measured 12" from the inside edge).
    b. Small radius must be equal to twice the stairway width.

11. Alternating tread stairs (1009.10)
    a. Can be used in Groups F, H, S from mezzanines up to 250 sq. ft. and no more than 5 people.
    b. Can be used for I-3 guard towers and control rooms up to 250 sq. ft.
    c. Can be used for roof access.
    d. Minimum tread projection of 5", minimum tread of 8½ ", minimum tread width of 7", maximum riser of 9½".
    e. Handrails required both sides.
    f. Also can be used to any mezzanine up to 250 sq. ft. with 8½" tread projections and 10½" tread depth.

12. Construction (1009.6)
    a. Construction must be consistent with the building type.
    b. Solid treads and platforms with non-slip finish are required, with maximum slope of ¹/₄₈. Groups F, H, S allowed to have 1⅛ diameter holes.
    c. Wood handrails are acceptable for all construction types.
    d. Required strength is 100 lbs./sq. ft. and 300 lb. concentrated load except in Group R-3.

13. Guard rails (1013)
    a. Height—See also BALCONIES, PORCHES, AND DECKS.
       i. Extend 42" above the nosing or adjacent walking surface.
       ii. Inside dwelling units, guards that have a handrail on the top are allowed 34"-38".
       iii. Exception for 26" height at assembly seating. (1028.14)
    b. Maximum openings of 4" in diameter, 6" at tread riser triangle are permitted, and up to 8" opening at top part of 42" rail, exception for assembly aisle ends.
    c. Maximum openings of 21" in diameter in Groups I-3, F, H, and S (except public garages) are permitted.
    d. Solid panels and grilles are acceptable.
    e. Guard rails are required at open-sided floor areas, screened porches, mezzanines, and landings (30" above floor or grade). (1013.4)
    f. Guards required for roof equipment when within 10' of edge (21" opening and 42" height). (1013.6)
    g. Guardrails must support 50 lbs./foot and 200 lbs. at any one point at top plus 50 lbs. on any one sq. ft. of guard.

14. Stair openings (1022.3)
   a. No openings except for egress from occupied rooms—no doors to mechanical rooms, toilet rooms, ducts, or unnecessary pipes.
   b. Sprinklers, standpipes, smoke control, and necessary electric conduit allowed.
   c. Ventilation for stair must come from outside or be enclosed with the stair. (1022.5)
15. Stair enclosures (1022)
   a. Interior exit stairs shall be enclosed, except:
      i.   Group I-3
      ii. Open parking structures
      iii. Inside dwelling units
      iv. Suppl. stairs
      v.   50% of exit stairs connecting only one adjacent floor
      vi. 100% of exit stairs connecting only the first and second floor where sprinkled throughout.
   b. Enclosure shall not be used for any other purpose.
   c. Space under the stairs may be open, or closed with rated construction, but cannot be accessed from stair enclosure except in dwellings.
   d. Only exit doors shall open into stair enclosures.
   e. Fire resistance must be 2 hour fire barriers. If connecting less than 4 floors, fire resistance may be 1 hour.
   f. Exterior walls of enclosure also must be protected. (1020.1.4)

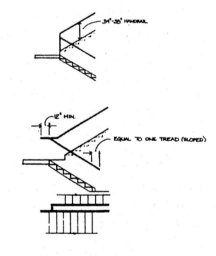

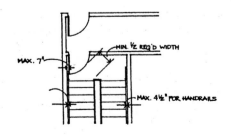

K. Exterior stairs (1026)
1. Exterior stairs are acceptable for floors not more than 6 stories 75' in height, but not for I-2s, I-4s, and child care facilities in E occupancies at any height.
2. Exterior stairs are defined as stairs where at least one side has 35 sq. ft. minimum open at each landing and floor, above the guardrail height. The open area must be not less than 42" above the adjacent floor or landing level.
3. The open side must be to a yard, court, or public way.
4. Construction shall be consistent with the building type.
5. Protect the corridor and stairs from ice and snow.
6. One stairway may be acceptable. (See O. Minimum number of exits, this heading.)
7. Dimensions are the same as interior stairs and corridors.
8. Locate at least 10' from lot line or other buildings unless they have walls and openings that comply for fire separation distance in Section 704.
9. Balcony maximum travel distance is the same as for interior egress.
10. Guards and handrails are required.
11. Fire separations from the exterior stair to the rest of the building (the non-open sides) are the same as for interior stairs with the following exceptions (1023.6):
    a. When the building is no more than 2 stories, but not R-1 or R-2.
    b. When the exterior stair(s) are connected by an exterior balcony. An exterior balcony must be open for 50% of its perimeter and the open sides must be 50% open in the lower 7'.
    c. When the building would not require enclosure for an interior stairway.
    d. When the exterior stairs are connected by open-ended corridors. The building must be fully sprinkled, the corridors must still have any required rating, and additional exterior openings are required if the corridor bends any more than 45 degrees.
12. Stairs may discharge through a protected egress court. (1024.5)

L. Horizontal exits (1025)
1. Horizontal exits are defined as passageway from a building to an area of refuge in either the same or another building on approximately the same floor level; may also be by a vestibule, or through a fire wall.
2. The compartment being evacuated and the one for refuge must be separated by a 2-hour fire barrier or fire wall, across the entire building. No rating required for above-grade pedestrian walkways of $\geq$ 20 feet.
3. Doors in horizontal exits
    a. Doors are required to be self-closing or automatic closing by a smoke detector.
    b. Doors must swing in the direction of travel.
    c. Two-way travel requires double doors.
4. Refuge area (1025.4)
    a. Refuge area must be adequate size for all connecting areas, both from the horizontal exit plus the persons already in the compartment.
    b. Allow 3 sq. ft./person.
    c. In Group I, allow 30 sq. ft./nonambulatory person, 15 sq.ft. for non-bedridden in Use I-2 and 6 sq. ft. for I-3.
    d. The area must be a public space.
5. Exits
    a. Horizontal exits can be up to 50% in number of exits and occupant capacity from the compartment they serve, but up to $^2/_3$ capacity in I-2, 100% in I-3.
    b. The egress route cannot return through the compartment being evacuated.
    c. The exits in the refuge compartment only need to be sized for their original occupants.

       d. Stairs must be within the allowable travel distance to the exit.

M. Ramps (1010 and ADAAG 4.8)

  1. Calculate required width in the same manner as for exits.

  2. Minimum headroom is 6'8".

  3. No projections are permitted into minimum width of 36" (but wider if required for occupant load).

  4. Doors opening onto landings shall not reduce the clear width to less than 42".

  5. Maximum ramp slopes

     a. Slope less than or equal to 1:20 is not a ramp.

     b. Maximum slope shall be 1:12; may be steeper if less than 6" rise, or if not an accessible route maximum 1:8.

     c. Maximum cross-slope is 1:48.

  6. Landings

     a. Landings must be provided at all points of turning, entrance, exits, and at doors.

     b. Maximum rise between landings shall be 30".

     c. Minimum landing is 60" in direction of movement, except 36" in dwelling units.

     d. Pedestrian ramps in parking garage not required to comply, when not required to be accessible route.

  7. Guards are required both sides if over 30" above floor. Minimum height is 42".

  8. Handrails

     a. Handrails are required on both sides of every ramp with a slope greater than 1:20, and rise over 6".

  9. Ramp construction

     a. Ramp must conform to the building type as for stairs.

     b. Non-slip surface is required.

     c. Edge protection by rail at 17"-19" or curb at bottom 4".

N. Smokeproof stair enclosure (smoke tower) (1022.1 and 909.20)

  1. General

     a. Definition: An interior stair exit completely enclosed except for ventilation from the lowest to the highest building point and may include the roof. (909.20)

     b. Smokeproof enclosure is required for occupied floors 75' above fire truck access or more than 30' below exit level. Not required in Group I-2 buildings.

     c. Access to the smoke tower from every story shall be by a vestibule, an open balcony, or to a pressurized stair enclosure.

     d. Exit outlet shall be a street, a 2-hour passageway without any other openings, a pressurized passageway, or the building discharge exit.

     e. Enclosing construction shall be 2-hour walls, without any openings except for required doors and natural ventilation (and balconies per floor construction).

     f. Vestibule walls require 2-hour construction.

  2. Natural ventilation (909.20.3)

     a. Each connecting vestibule requires 16 sq. ft. of opening in a wall facing a 20' minimum open space.

     b. Vestibule/corridor door or balcony must be 1½-hours; tower door must be 20 minutes.

  3. Mechanical ventilation (909.20.4)

     a. Door ratings must be same as natural ventilation. (1½-hour at corridor, 20 minutes to tower with gasketing and sill to minimize air leakage.)

       b. Vestibule must have 60 air changes/hour with exhaust 150% more than supply air quantity. Use separate duct system with supply at the bottom and exhaust at the top, and provide a 20" smoke trap at the ceiling.

       c. Stairs—System shall be activated by smoke detectors in the corridors to the stair, and stair must have 0.10" positive pressure with all doors shut.

       d. Standby power is required for ventilation and detectors.

   4. Stairwell pressurization (909.20.5)—allowed as alternative to smokeproof enclosure balconies and vestibules

       a. Building must be fully sprinkled.

       b. Stairwell pressure minimum 0.10 and maximum 0.35 in-(of water column) with all doors closed.

       c. Activated by smoke detectors in corridor to stair.

   5. Mechanical systems requirements (909.20.6.1)

       a. Must be independent of all other systems.

       b. Equipment and ductwork must be located in one of the following locations:

          i. Outside, with 2-hour fire barrier.

         ii. In the smokeproof enclosure, with 2-hour fire barriers to the outside.

        iii. In the building, with complete enclosure of 2-hours.

       c. Must have standby power system.

O. Location of exits

   1. Egress from a room may be through adjoining accessory rooms, which are not high hazard, and provide a path to an exit. (1014.2)

   2. No exit access is permitted through a kitchen, storeroom, or rest room, provided it is not the only available exit.

   3. An exit shall not pass through a lockable room.

   4. All assembly buildings over 300 people must face on at least one street where the main entrance and exit is located. (1028.2, 1028.3)

   5. Measure the travel distance along the line of occupant travel.

   6. Egress through another tenant or dwelling is not pemitted. (1014.2.1)

   7. If 2 exits are required from an area, room, or building, space the exits equal to at least ½ (⅓ if in sprinklered building) the diagonal distance of the room, area, or building. (1015.2.1)

   8. If 3 or more exits are required from a room or an area, at least 2 shall be spaced by at least ½ the diagonal distance (⅓ if in sprinklered building). (1015.2.2)

   9. Elevators and escalators are unacceptable as a means of egress, except elevators for accessible exists in Section 1007.4.

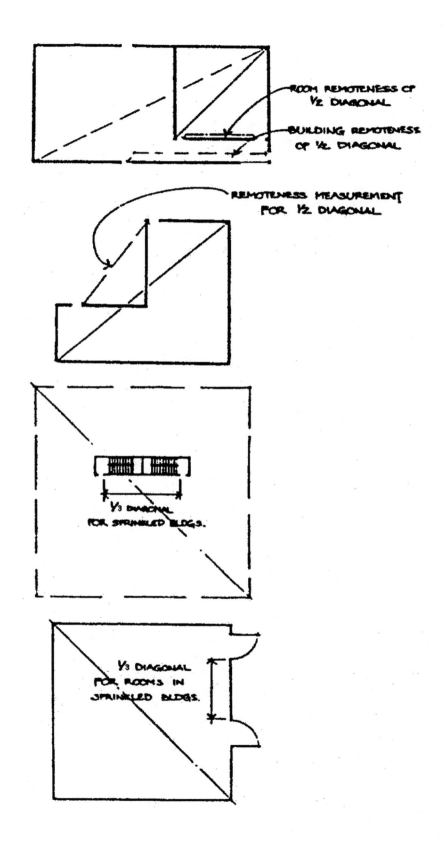

P. Minimum number of exits (1021)
1. Number of exits required per floor for all groups:
    a. Single exit is required for 1 or 2 stories and limited occupants and travel. (Table 1021.1)
    b. Occupant load of 500 or less: 2 exits minimum.
    c. Occupant load of 501 to 1000: 3 exits minimum.
    d. Occupant load of over 1000: 4 exits minimum.
2. In Group I-2, at least 1 exit from each smoke compartment shall lead directly to the exterior, interior exit stairs, exterior exit stairs, exterior ramp, exit passageway, or to a smoke tower without returning to the compartment where exiting began. (407.4.2)
3. Emergency escapes (1029)
    a. In every sleeping room and basement below the fourth floor of Groups R and I-1, one operable window or exterior door is required for egress or rescue, except non-habitable basements ≤ 200 sq. ft.
    b. The sill of the operable window shall not be more than 44" above the floor.
    c. The window shall provide an opening of at least 5.7 sq.ft. with minimum net dimensions of 24" height by 20" width.
    d. Grade floor windows may be 5 sq.ft. with the same minimum dimensions.
    e. Bars, screens, and grilles must be easily removable from the inside (no keys or tools).
    f. Where sleeping rooms open to a corridor with access to remote exits in opposite directions, operable window or exterior door is not required.
    g. Not required if building equipped with automatic sprinkler system throughout, for basements with ceilings at less than 80", or for basements with doors to the exterior.
    h. Emergency escape window is allowed to open to an atrium balcony where the balcony leads to exits.
    i. Window wells can be used for emergency escape windows.
        a. Minimum horizontal area of 9 sq. ft., minimum 36" each way.
        b. If deeper than 44", must have ladder or steps of minimum 12" width and maximum 18" rise per rung.
    j. Exterior exit stairways cannot be used as part of required egress for Groups I-2, I-4 and child care facilities in Group E. Otherwise, allow use for required egress for buildings not exceeding six stories above grade plane or having occupied floors more than 75' (22 860 mm) above lowest level of fire department vehicle access.
4. Open parking structure requires 2 exits for each parking tier. Open stairway acceptable (406.3.11), but car ramp is not acceptable for egress. (406.2.5)
5. Room or Space (1015.1)
    Two exits from room or space required if:
    a. A, B, E, F, M, U > 50 occupants or > 75' travel. (100' for sprinkled B, F, S.)
    b. H > 3 occupants or > 25' travel.
    c. H-4, H-5, I, R > 10 occupants or > 75' travel.
    d. S, > 30 occupants or > 100' travel.
    e. I-2 must have door directly from patient room to corridor or nursing suite. (1014.2)
    f. Minimum 2 exits or exit access from Boiler rooms, refrigeration machinery rooms, and refrigerated rooms depending on size and equipment. (1015.3, 1015.4, 1015.5)

Room or Space (common path of travel)

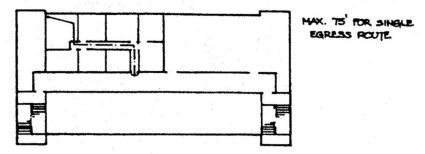

MAX. 75' FOR SINGLE
EGRESS ROUTE.

Q. Discharge of exits (1027)
1. All exits shall discharge directly to a public street, open area, or to a passageway which exits directly to a street.
2. Vestibule as a passageway
   a. Not more than 50% of the exits may discharge into a vestibule.
   b. Vestibule may be the normal egress and ingress of the building facility.
   c. Maximum size for a vestibule is 10' deep × 30' wide.
   d. Vestibules must be separated from the building by self-closing doors and the equivalent of 1/4" wired glass in steel frames. The exit enclosure rating must be applied to separate the vestibule from basements.
3. Lobby as a passageway
   a. Exits may discharge into an interior lobby located at the building exit discharge level providing the lobby is sprinkled.
   b. Adjacent lobby areas must be sprinkled or enclosed, and basement must be separated with the exit stair rating.
   c. Lobby must provide a direct line of travel with no obstructions.

Stairway (exit) (exit discharge)

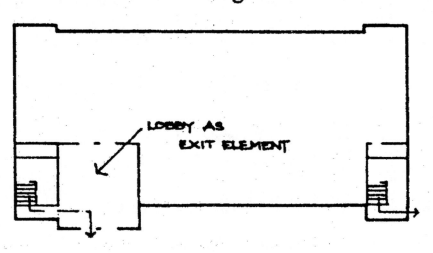

LOBBY AS
EXIT ELEMENT

4. The effective width of any passageway shall not be less than the widths required for the connecting exits.
5. Minimum ceiling height of any passageway is 8'0".
6. Not more than 50% of the exit stairs shall pass through areas on the same level. All others must exit directly to the outside.

R. Fire Escapes—See FIRE ESCAPES.

ELEVATORS (CHAPTER 30 AND ASME A17.1)

A. The Ohio Elevator Code governs the design, construction, installation, alteration and repair of elevators, escalators, vertical and inclined chair lifts, dumbwaiters, moving walks, stair lifts, and belt manlifts, but not material handling conveyors.

B. Cabs and controls
1. Minimum size car is 51" × 80" with center door, 51" × 68" with offset door, 36" door width. (See Figure 22, ADAAG.)
2. For fire departments' use, a car must be able to accommodate a 24" × 84" cot for buildings 4 stories or more in height. (3002.4).

C. Hoistways (3002)
1. 4 or more elevators require 2 hoistways, and not more than 4 elevators per hoistway.
2. Hoistways must be rated as shafts, with rated opening protectives.
3. When elevator travel exceeds 25', smoke detectors must be installed in lobbies and elevator equipment room to send elevator to designated floor or alternate floor.

D. Venting of hoistways (3004)
1. Venting is required when service when hoistway serves more than 3 stories.
2. Venting is not required in sidewalk elevators.
3. In buildings other than Uses R-1, R-2, I-1, I-2, and similar occupancies, a sprinkled building does not require vents.
4. Locate vents below the floor or floors over the shaft.
5. Vent must open directly to the exterior or through non-combustible ducts to the exterior.
6. Holes in cable-elevator machine room floors must have maximum 2" clearance around cable openings.
7. One-third of the vents must be permanently open, unless smoke detectors activate vents.
8. Minimum vent area is 3 sq. ft. per car, or $3\frac{1}{2}\%$ of hoistway, whichever is greater.
9. Mechanical means of venting may be acceptable for other than buildings with sleeping quarters, and hoistway does not go to top of building.
10. Closed portions of vent area may be $\frac{1}{8}$" plain glass.

E. No plumbing or electrical except shaft drain is allowed in hoistways.

F. Machine room enclosure 1 hr. (3006)

F. Dumbwaiters
1. Shaft walls are required.
2. Vent the shafts with $\frac{1}{2}$ sq. ft. per dumbwaiter, or $3\frac{1}{2}\%$ of hoistway area, whichever is greater.

EMERGENCY ELECTRICAL (CHAPTER 27)

A. Compliance with the National Electrical Code is the basis for all electrical code requirements. (NFPA 70, 2701.1, NFPA 110, NFPA 111, 604 Fire code)

B. Emergency power (NFPA 110, NFPA 111, 604 Fire code)
1. Emergency power must pick up loads within 10 seconds or be connected to standby power.

2. Emergency power must be capable of powering exit signs, egress lighting, and door locks. (2702)

3. Emergency power can be battery, generator, separate service, or connection ahead of disconnect when approved.

C. Standby power (UL2200)

1. Standby power must pick up loads within 60 seconds.

2. When required, standby power must carry smoke control, fire pumps, communication equipment, elevators, and lighting.

3. Standby power can be battery, generator, separate service, or connection ahead of the disconnect when approved.

ESCALATORS—FLOOR OPENING

A. Escalators cannot be used as a part of the required means of egress. (1003.7)

B. Delete shaft if every escalator at every floor: (708.2)

1. Is in a 100% sprinkled building, and

2. The area of opening is equal to or less than twice the escalator horizontal projection and connects 4 floors (maximum) except for M and B Uses. Sprinklered draft curtain must be installed or the opening must have a powered automatic fire shutter.

C. Fire shutters (708)

1. Shutters must be automatic power operated.

2. When used, shutters must be installed at each floor.

3. Shutters shall be constructed of material with $1\frac{1}{2}$-hour fire rating.

4. Shall completely close when activated by an approved smoke or fire device.

5. Maximum speed shall be 30'/minute.

6. Stopping safety edge is required.

D. For smoke control see SMOKE CONTROL.

EXHAUST HOODS (AT KITCHENS) (M-505, M-506, M-507)

A. Required locations

1. Restaurant ranges, deep fat fryers, broilers, roasting ovens, candy kettles, grills and all food heating appliances must have exhaust hoods.

2. Exhaust hoods are not required for:

   a. Domestic use (505)

B. Type I—Kitchen hood for grease and smoke vapors

1. Vapors must be confined within the hood.

2. Instead of using code specification, hood may be UL 1978 304.1 listed (factory-built).

3. A Type I hood is not required for single light-duty electric convection, bread, retherm or microwave ovens IF HVAC system accommodates the additional heat and moisture loads so generated.

4. Use Type II hood over ovens not generating grease laden vapors or smoke in hazardous quantities.

TABLE 507.11
MINIMUM DISTANCE BETWEEN THE LOWEST EDGE OF A
GREASE FILTER AND THE COOKING SURFACE OR THE
HEATING SURFACE

TYPE OF COOKING APPLIANCES	HEIGHT ABOVE COOKING SURFACE (feet)
Without exposed flame	0.5
Exposed flame and burners	2
Exposed charcoal and charbroil type	3.5

For SI: 1 foot = 304.8 mm.

C. Type II—Kitchen hood for steam, vapor, heat, or odor
    1. Rigid metallic ducts required.
    2. Must be sealed when positive pressure exists.
D. Hood with canopy must have a 6" minimum overhang on all sides (M-507.12)
    1. Construction (M-507.4, M-507.5)
        a. (Type I hood) Minimum 18 ga. steel or 20 ga. stainless
        b. (Type II hood) Minimum 22 ga. steel, or 24 gal. stainless, or 24 oz/ft. sheet copper
    2. Joints and seams welded liquid tight for Type I, smooth and water-tight for Type II.
E. Non-canopy type hood must have a maximum 3' above the cooking surface with a maximum of 1' setback from the cooking edge. (M-507.14).
F. Exhaust volume is required. (M-507.13)
    1. Extra Heavy-Duty (507.13.1):

Type of Hood	CFM per liner foot of hood
Backshelf/pass-over	Not allowed
Double island canopy (per side)	550
Eyebrow	Not allowed
Single island canopy	700
Wall-mounted canopy	550

    2. Heavy-Duty (507.13.2):

Type of Hood	CFM per liner foot of hood
Backshelf/pass-over	400
Double island canopy (per side)	400
Eyebrow	Not allowed
Single island canopy	600
Wall-mounted canopy	400

For SI: 1 cfm per linear foot = 1.55 L/s per linear meter.

3. Medium-Duty (507.13.3):

Type of Hood	CFM per liner foot of hood
Backshelf/pass-over	300
Double island canopy (per side)	300
Eyebrow	250
Single island canopy	500
Wall-mounted canopy	300

For SI: 1 cfm per linear foot = 1.55 L/s per linear meter.

4. Light-Duty (507.13.4):

Type of Hood	CFM per liner foot of hood
Backshelf/pass-over	250
Double island canopy (per side)	250
Eyebrow	250
Single island canopy	400
Wall-mounted canopy	200

For SI: 1 cfm per linear foot = 1.55 L/s per linear meter.

G. Grease removal filters (M-507-11)
   1. Grease removal is required in Type I exhaust hoods.
   2. Filters must be accessible, and removable for cleaning.
   3. Install at 45° minimum angle and drain grease to collection cup.
   4. All filters must be labeled and listed.
H. Kitchen hood exhaust ducts (M-506)
   1. For Type I (grease vapor) hoods
      a. 16-gauge steel or 18-gage stainless steel ducts.
      b. Steel fan housings, or as labeled for grease ducts.
      c. Joints and seams must be welded or brazed liquid-tight.
      d. Duct supports must be noncombustible, and fasteners cannot penetrate into ducts.
      e. Fan motors must be outside the airstream.
      f. Ducts must slope 2% to collection cup, or a minimum of 8.3% if horizontal length is greater than 75′.
      g. Ducts must be enclosed in shafts with enclosures 18″ from duct, unless firestopped.
      h. Cleanouts must be provided for inaccessible sections, and at every 20′ for horizontal runs.
      i. Air velocity must be 500′ per minute.
      j. All ducts must be independent, except when serving hoods within same or adjoining rooms and do not go through rated assemblies.
      k. Minimum clearance to combustibles in 18″, minimum 3″ gypsum bd. over non-combustible materials.
      l. Termination must be a minimum of 40″ of duct length above the roof and 10′ horizontally from buildings, property lines, air intakes, and above grade. (May be reduced to 5′ when discharging away from items above.)
I. Fire suppression (M-509 and 904.1)

1. Fire suppression is required at cooking surfaces, exhaust systems, hood, and grease removal systems.

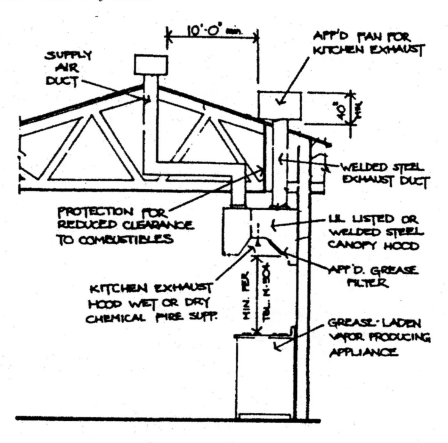

EXHAUST SYSTEMS (CHAPTER M-5)

A. General exhaust (M-501)

  1. Exhaust systems are required whenever dust or airborne particles, heat, odors, fumes, spray, gas or smoke are given off in quantities that are irritating or injurious to health or safety.

  2. Exhaust outlets must not cause nuisance or be drawn back into building.

  3. There must be sufficient make-up air to provide system balance.

B. Hazardous exhaust systems (M-510)

  1. Required use of a hazardous exhaust system applies:

     a. Removal of flammable vapors, gases, fumes, ducts, or mists > 25% of lower flammability limit.

     b. Any concentration of vapor, gas, fume, mist or dust with a health-hazard rating of 4.

     c. Concentrations exceeding 1% of the median lethality for acute inhalation toxicity of vapor, gas, fume, mist, or dust. Exception:

        (1) Laboratories, UNLESS concentrations exceed 1% of the median lethality for vapors, gasses, fumes, mists, or dusts with 1, 2, 3, or 4 health-hazard ratings.

  2. System shall be independent of other systems.

  3. Enclose in fire-rated shafts through fire separations.

  4. Ducts shall not penetrate a fire wall.

  5. Dampers are prohibited.

  6. Ducts require a fire suppression system (except noncombustible/nonflammable fumes).

  7. Construct ducts of galvanized sheet metal with minimum 1" lap joints.

  8. Other materials are acceptable if exhaust is detrimental to sheet metal. Materials must be Class I, labeled, and approved by test agency for specific use Table 510.8.

Minimum Duct Thickness

Diameter	Nonabrasive Exhaust	Nonabrasive/Abrasive Materials	Abrasive Exhaust
0-8"	24 gauge	22 gauge	20 gauge
9-18"	22 gauge	20 gauge	18 gauge
19-30"	20 gauge	18 gauge	16 gauge
Over 30"	18 gauge	16 gauge	14 gauge

  9. Clearance to combustibles

     a. Less than 100°F exhaust temperatures — 1"
     b. 100°F to 600°F — 12"
     c. Flammable vapors — 6"

  10. When temperature is less than 600°F, exhaust must be connected to chimney.

  11. Do not locate mechanical equipment in the airstream.

  12. Support ducts a minimum of 10' o.c., with noncombustible material.

  13. Provide explosion relief per NFPA 69.

C. Clothes dryer exhaust (M-504)

  1. Exhaust must be installed per manufacturer's instructions.

  2. System must be independent of other systems.

  3. Cleanouts must be provided at vertical rise.

4. Multiple dryers require make-up air if use is more than 200 cfm. No mechanicals in the air-stream.

5. For domestic dryer ducts, minimum 4" diameter duct and maximum (per 504.6.4.1 in duct). This length can be increased for certain dryer models, but exact model would have to actually be installed.

6. Commercial dryer ducts are required to have a minimum 6" clearance to combustibles.

D. Vehicle ventilation not required to operate continuously if 25 parts/million maintainable. (M-404.1)

EXISTING BUILDINGS (CHAPTER 34)

A. Alterations and repairs must conform to the code requirements for new construction. Portions of the structure not altered and/or affected by the alteration do not need to comply with the code requirements for a new structure.

B. The building official may require corrections in any existing building if deemed to "endanger public safety and welfare" and may order vacation or demolition. (111.2)

C. Additions
1. For Groups R and I, the height and area must comply for both the existing building and the addition.
2. For all Groups other than R and I, the height and area for the addition must be based on the total area, but the existing building does not need to comply as long as it is separated by a fire barrier or fire wall. (3401.1) If a fire barrier separates the existing building from the addition, the combined height and area of addition AND existing building determines both construction type and fire protection requirements of addition.

D. The building owner or lessee is responsible for maintaining safe means of egress. (3401.2)

E. Minor repairs may be made without application or notice to the building official. (105.2)

F. Change of occupancy requires compliance with requirements for the new occupancy. Change of occupancy is a change in the purpose or level of activity that changes the application of the code. The building official can allow changes in occupancy without total compliance as long as the new use is not less safe.

G. Original building code compliance is acceptable except when a serious hazard or fraud exists.

H. Do not apply any new roofing over wet roofing or existing shakes, slate, clog, or asbestos-cement tile. (1510.3) A maximum of 2 layers of existing shingles is allowed before tearoff is required.

I. Loads used in the original design may be used if public safety is not endangered. (3403.2 and 1510.2) For all structural elements of lateral-force-resisting systems, except Group R occupancies with ≤ five solely residential dwelling/sleeping units that are altered using the OBC's conventional light-frame construction methods or per RCO:
1. A registered design professional must prepare an engineering evaluation and analysis establishing the altered structure's structural adequacy and submit to the code official.
2. If > 30% of structure's total floor and roof areas are in or are proposed to be in structural alteration within a three-year period, the evaluation and analysis must demonstrate that the alteration complies with OBC for wind loading and reduced level seismic forces. 30% includes areas tributary to the vertical loadcarrying components (i.e., joists, beams, columns, walls and other structural components that have been or will be removed, added or altered, plus areas such as mezzanines, penthouses, roof structures, and in-filled courts and shafts).

3. If ≤ 30% of Structure's total floor and roof areas are involved in structural alteration within a three-year period, the evaluation and analysis must demonstrate that the altered structure complies with loads applicable at the original construction or at most recent substantial structural alteration. An existing structural element having a seismic demand-capacity ratio with the alteration that is > 10% greater than its demand-capacity ratio with the alteration/addition ignored must meet the reduced level seismic forces as.

J. Existing buildings may be posted for original design loads, even if nonconforming to current code, if use is not changed and life is not endangered. (3403.3, 3403.3.1)

K. If building loads are increased by more than 5%, the existing structural components must be capable of sustaining the new loads. (3403.3)

L. Historic buildings (3411.9)
   1. To be considered as an historic building, must be classified as an historic building by the state or local authorities, or listed in the National Register of Historic Places.
   2. Building must conform to structural, fire safety, egress, light, ventilation, and sanitary requirements according to the building official.
   3. Accessibility requirements are limited. (3409.8)

M. Existing stairs are not required to meet current code dimensions where limited by the building structure. (3404.1)

N. Moved or relocated structures must comply as if they are new. Replaced glass must comply with new code requirements. (3407 and 3410)

O. Fire escapes are permitted for existing buildings where full stairs cannot be located (above sidewalks or alleys, for example). (3406) Fire escapes permitted in existing adult group homes and where an existing building is proposed for a change of occupancy to an adult group home.

P. Accessibility is required in existing buildings. (3411)
   1. Type B dwellings not required.
   2. Changes of occupancy must provide at least one complying accessible route and entrance, and accessible parking.
   3. All portions of additions and alterations must comply, where feasible.
   4. The route to occupiable areas of alterations must comply on a proportionate basis.
      a. A requirement is disproportionate when the cost exceeds 20% of the cost of alteration to the primary function area. Proportionality is based on costs for:
         (1) Providing accessible entrance and route to the altered area (i.e., widening doorways or installing ramps).
         (2) Making restrooms accessible (i.e., installing grab bars, enlarging toilet stalls, insulating pipes, installing accessible faucet controls).
         (3) Providing accessible telephones (i.e., height, installing amplification devices or telecommunication devices for deaf persons (TDD)).
         (4) Relocating inaccessible water drinking fountains.
   5. There are also partial compliance requirements for:
      a. elevators, lifts, escalators, and ramps
      b. dining, performance, and assembly areas
      c. Type A dwellings
      d. Toilet rooms, dressing and locker rooms, check-out aisles, sales counters, jury boxes, witness stands, and thresholds. R. Seismic compliance see 3401.5.
   6. Disproportionality applies to alterations to provide an accessible path of travel to the altered area if the cost exceeds 20% of the cost of the alteration to the primary function area, using as costs of alteration:
      a. Accessible entrance and accessible route to the altered area (i.e., the cost of widening doorways or installing ramps);

b. Accessible restrooms (i.e., grab bars, enlarging toilet stalls, insulating pipes, accessible faucet controls);

c. Accessible telephones (i.e., relocating telephones to an accessible height, installing amplification devices or a telecommunications device for deaf persons (TDD));

d. Costs associated with relocating an inaccessible drinking fountain. If the travel path costs are found disproportionate, limit the path alterations to those that remain within proportionality, giving priority, in order, to:

    a. An accessible entrance;

    b. An accessible route to the altered area;

    c. At least one accessible restroom per gender or a single unisex restroom;

    d. Accessible telephones;

    e. Accessible drinking fountains;

    f. If possible, parking, storage, and alarms;

    g. Multiple smaller alterations, UNLESS done to avoid providing a single travel path.

If a primary function area has been altered without providing an accessible travel path, and either subsequent alterations to the area or to a different area on the same travel path, are made within three years of the original alteration, the total cost of primary function alterations are considered as to proportionality.

Q. Fire resistance rating of existing assemblies or components can be evaluated per "Resource A, Guidelines on Fire Ratings of Archaic Materials and Assemblies" in the "International Existing Buildings Code," if no other guide available.

R. Allow used materials and products meeting OBC requirements for new materials and products, if approved by the building official.

S. Seismic evaluation and per OBC, ASCE 31 or ASCE 41; allow procedures in "Appendix A, Guidelines for the Seismic Retrofit of Existing Buildings" in the "International Existing Buildings Code."

  1. If 100% OBC compliance required:

    a. "Rfactor" used is that specified for structural systems classified as "Ordinary" per table 12.2-1 of ASCE 7, UNLESS structural system satisfies the proportioning and detailing requirements for systems classified as "Intermediate" or "Special".

    b. If evaluation and design can meet reduced seismic force levels, use 75% of OBC prescribed forces.

    c. If structure or portion of structure complies with requirements in applicable chapter of "Appendix A, Guidelines for the Seismic Retrofit of Existing Buildings" in IBC, Appendix A, in "International Existing Buildings Code" may apply following chapters:

      (1) Evaluation and design of unreinforced masonry bearing wall buildings in occupancy category I or II may follow chapter A1.

      (2) Evaluation and design of wall anchorage system in reinforced concrete and reinforced masonry wall buildings with flexible diaphragms in occupancy category I or II may follow chapter A2.

      (3) Evaluation and design of cripple walls and sill plate anchorage in light frame wood residences in category I or II may follow chapter A3.

      (4) Evaluation and design of soft, weak, or open-front wall conditions in multiunit wood residences in category I or II may follow chapter A4.

(5) Evaluation and design of concrete buildings and concrete with masonry infill buildings in all occupancy categories may follow chapter A5.

    d. ASCE 31 compliance based on applicable performance level per table 3401.5.2. Allow use of "BSE-1" earthquake hazard level as defined in ASCE 41 and subject to compliance with ASCE 41 using both the "BSE-1" hazard level and the performance level in table 3401.5.2. Design spectral response acceleration parameters S_{XS} and S_{X1} in ASCE 41 must be at 75% of respective design spectral response acceleration parameters S_{DS} and S_{D1} in OBC.

  T. Compliance alternatives—see OBC 3412

EXPLOSION HAZARDS (IFC)

A. Every structure, room, or space subject to any explosive materials according to 414.5.1 shall be equipped with automatic pressure relief devices. They can be explosion venting, explosion prevention (per NFPA 69), or barricades (per NFPA 495).

B. Acceptable devices are releasing roof or wall panels, which discharge into an exterior space over 50′ wide on the same lot.

C. The discharge end shall be at least 10′ vertical and 20′ horizontal from any window, door, or exit in the same or adjoining building.

D. Minimum total area of relief vents based on 20 psf interior pressure versus non-venting area. Minimum 100 psf for internal structure to resist explosion pressure.

See also FIREWORKS (OAC 1301:7-7-31).

EXTERIOR TRIM (1406)

A. Noncombustible trim is allowed in any location.

B. Combustible trim
1. Trim must pass heat exposure test except:
    a. Wood
    b. Aluminum
    c. Trim on Type V buildings
    d. Foam plastic with barrier cover except vinyl siding
2. A maximum of 10% of wall may be combustible trim if less than 5′ to lot line. (1406.2.2)

C. In Type I, II, III and IV buildings not more than 3 stories or 40′ above grade, half timbering, wood, or other similar materials may be used provided solid noncombustible backing is used. The trim cannot extend past the top of the exterior wall.

D. Non-egress balconies, porches, decks, and supplemental exterior stairs
1. Non-combustible materials are acceptable on Type I and II buildings.
2. On Types III, IV, V, non-combustible, FRTW, as for floor construction, or Type IV must be used.
3. Total length cannot exceed 50% of building perimeter, except when building and balconies sprinkled.

E. Bay and oriel windows must be of the same construction required for the building, except fire-retardant wood allowed for any Construction Type.

F. Furred combustible solid surface trim (e.g. plywood) can only be furred out up to 1⅝″, and open spaces over 100 sq. ft. must be firestopped. Wood furring must be pressure (decay) treated. (1406.2.4, 717.2.6)

TABLE 1406.2.1.2
MINIMUM FIRE SEPARATION FOR COMBUSTIBLE VENEERS

FIRE SEPARATION DISTANCE (feet)	TOLERABLE LEVEL INCIDENT RADIANT HEAT ENERGY (kW/m^2)	FIRE SEPARATION DISTANCE (feet)	TOLERABLE LEVEL INCIDENT RADIANT HEAT ENERGY (kW/m^2)
5	12.5	16	5.9
6	11.8	17	5.5
7	11.0	18	5.2
8	10.3	19	4.9
9	9.6	20	4.6
10	8.9	21	4.4
11	8.3	22	4.1
12	7.7	23	3.9
13	7.2	24	3.7
14	6.7	25	3.5
15	6.3		

For SI: 1 foot = 304.8 mm, 1 Btu/H2 $\times$ °F = 0.0057 kW/m^2 $\times$ K.

FIBERBOARD (2303.1.5)

A. Fiberboard shall be vermin proof, rot resistant, water repellant, and meet the necessary structural strength of applicable standards (per ASTM C208).
B. Joints shall be square edge, shiplap, bevel, T and G, or U joints.
C. Joints must fit tight in fire-resistant assemblies.
D. Fiberboard may be used as wall insulation on all building types.
E. Fiberboard must be fire treated (Class A) when used as insulation on fire walls or fire separation walls unless it is installed directly to noncombustible base and covered with noncombustible veneer.
F. When used as roof insulation, the board must be covered with an approved roofing.
G. Use 1" minimum thickness when used as roof decking in open-beam construction.

FIRE ALARM SYSTEMS (907)

A. Automatic fire detection systems (activated by a smoke detector)
   1. Required installations
      a. Automatic fire detection systems are required in Groups H, I-1, I-2, I-3, M, R-1, and R-2. (907.2.5-907.2.9)
      b. Group I-1 and R-1 occupancies must have visible alarm notification appliances (activated by in-room and building alarm system), and R-2 occupancies must have capability for visible alarm notification appliances.
      c. Use Group R-1: Automatic fire detection systems are not required when no interior corridors and direct exterior exits from all units exist or single-station detectors are connected to attended location and monitored.
      d. In addition to the required automatic system, single-station smoke detectors are required in all suites, guest rooms, sleeping rooms, and dwelling units. Multiple detectors within units must be interconnected. (907.2.6, 907.2.8)
      e. Automatic fire detection systems are required in Use Group I-3 housing areas except in sleeping rooms occupied by 4 or fewer persons.
   2. Automatic fire detection systems in above Use Groups are not required when building is sprinkled (except Group I-2 and I-3), but manual system (see 5, Manual-pull system, this heading) and single-station alarms must be provided for all Group R.
   3. Special systems, are required for:
      a. Special amusement buildings. (907.2.12)
      b. High-rise and underground buildings HVAC shafts. (907.2.19, 907.2.13)
      c. Atriums. (907.2.14)
      d. Door hold-opens (for rated doors)
      e. Residential aircraft hangars. (907.2.21)
      f. Battery rooms (more than 50 gal. capacity). (907.2.23)
      g. Covered mall buildings. (907.2.20)
      h. Airport traffic control towers. (907.2.22)
   4. Each floor shall be zoned separately. (907.6.3)
      a. Maximum area per zone is 22,500 sq. ft.
      b. Maximum length of any zone is 300' in any direction.
      c. High-rises (over 75') must have separate zones for different device types. (907.2.13)
   5. Manual-pull system (fire protective signaling systems). (907.2, 907.3)
      a. Building locations (907.4.2)

        i.   Manual-pull systems must be installed at every exit, and at maximum travel distance of 200 feet (except sprinkled Group E buildings).

        ii. Locate 5′ from the entry to an exit and 42″–48″ above the floor.

        iii. Pulls must be red, and Building Official can allow covers to prevent damage or false alarms.

    b. Manual alarms required for (907.2.1-907.2.9):

        i.   Group A > 300 occupants, unless sprinkled. If over 1,000 occupants, alarm activates emergency voice/alarm communication system.

        ii. Group B, M > 500 occupants, unless sprinkled (Group B, if more than 100 persons above/below discharge level, or if ambulatory care center).

        iii. Group E ≥ 50, with exception list

        iv. Group F > 500 persons above/below discharge level and over 1 story high

        v.   Group H-5 (highly toxic gases, organic peroxides, oxidizers), I

        vi. Group R-1, with exceptions

        vii. Group R-2 > 2 stores or 16 units

6. System must conform to NFPA 72.

7. Alarm verification is required by cross-zoned detectors or addressable unit with delay according to NFPA 72. (907.2.11.3)

8. System must be supervised except single-station units, and fire suppression in 1 and 2 family buildings.

9. Alarm must be audible above all other noises and heard in all areas (15 decibels above ambient sound level or 5 decibels above maximum sound level lasting 60 seconds). Minimum sound pressure levels are 75 dBA in Groups R, I-1, 90 dBA in mechanical equipment rooms, 60 dBA all other occupancies. Visual recognition of the means of egress and directional marking is required with light of not less than 1 foot-candle (11 lux) at the walking surface level. Emergency voice directions/instructions must be activated when alarm sounds, including live voice (in high rise, minimum of alarmed floor and 1 floor above/below). (907.5.2)

10. A pre-signal system shall be used only with 24-hour supervision and Building Official and Fire Department approval. (907.2.13.2)

11. System must be emergency powered. See (907.2.11.4) ELECTRICAL, B. Emergency power.

FIRE CODE (OAC CHAPTER 1301:7)

A. General

1. The intent of the Ohio Fire Code (OFC) is to determine the minimum requirements and controls necessary to provide the maximum safety of life and property from the hazards of fire, and/or explosions in any building, in addition to storage, use, handling, and manufacture of hazardous materials as well as matters related to the construction, extension, repair, alteration or removal of fire suppression and alarm systems. Also the OFC is intended to provide evacuation plans for high-rise buildings, conduct fire drills, and designate tornado shelters.

2. The Code applies to the construction and design of:

    a. Structures, facilities and conditions arising after the adoption of the Code.

    b. Existing structures, facilities and conditions not legally in existence at the time of the adoption of the Code.

    c. Existing structures, facilities and conditions when identified in specific sections of the Code.

    d. Existing conditions not in strict compliance with the Code that constitute a hazard to life or property in the opinion of the fire code official, if he or she can prove that by a preponderance of the evidence.

3. All persons involved in the installation, servicing, testing, and repair of fire protection systems or firefighting equipment shall be certified by the Fire Marshal in accordance with the OFC requirements.

4. Fire protection systems must be tested prior to acceptance. (901.5)

5. *Please Note that when the Building Code references the International Fire Code for compliance standards, this is not the same as the Ohio Fire Code, which is based on a different model as of this writing.*

6. The NFPA 70 edition in Chapter 35 of the OBC applies to all electrical components, equipment, and system requirements.

B. Enforcement personnel
1. Fire Marshals
2. Assistant Fire Marshals
3. Certified Safety Inspectors
4. Fire chiefs of municipal fire departments
5. Fire chiefs of township fire departments, and
6. Fire prevention officers in areas where there are no established fire departments.

C. Inspections
1. A fire official has the right of entry into all structures and premises.
2. There is no limit on the number of inspections.
3. Coordinated inspections with the building inspector are required when necessary.
4. All fires shall be investigated.
5. When there is a conflict between the building code requirement and the fire code requirement, the building code shall control. (102.4)
6. Permits are required for the structures, facilities and activities listed in Appendix A to the Ohio Fire Code.
7. All violation notices must be issued in writing.

D. Tornado shelters in schools
1. Tornado shelter requirements apply to all private and public primary and secondary schools with an average daily attendance of more than 50 pupils.
2. The designated shelter area does not require special construction or improvements.

E. Permits (varies by jurisdiction)
1. Permits are required for all hazardous operations, storage, and disposal of hazardous materials, and for other special uses of hazardous materials. See USE GROUP CLASSIFICATION, L. Use Group H.
2. A permit does not allow any future violations.
3. Permits are issued by the fire official.
4. Omissions or errors of approved plans are not acceptable as compliance with the OFC.
5. A fire official may revoke a permit.
6. Permits are required for, but not limited to the following:
   a. Airports, air supported structures, tents
   b. Assembly places, bowling establishments
   c. Cellulose nitrate plastics, chemicals of all kinds
   d. Compressed gases
   e. Combustible fibers and materials
   f. Cryogenic liquids
   g. Drying ovens and furnaces
   h. Dry cleaning plants, dust explosion hazards
   i. Explosives of all kinds, and fireworks sale and use
   j. Application of flammable types of finishes

k. Fruit ripening processes
l. Fumigation and insect fogging
m. Gas stations, garages, and heliports
n. Incinerators of all types
o. Junk and waste yards
p. Flammable liquids and above-ground storage of liquids
q. Magnesium and more than 25 cases of matches
r. Manufacture of organic coatings
s. Paint removal by torching
t. Tire recapping, and
u. Disposal of flammable types of wastes.

7. A license is required from the fire official for the operation of a hotel (including extended stay hotel), motel, motor hotel, lodge, inn, bed and breakfast, and any transient lodging business.

FIRE DAMPERS (716 AND M-607)

A. Fire dampers are required in duct systems which penetrate fire walls, fire partition walls, shaft enclosures, or fire separation assemblies. Minimum fire protection ratings are per 607.3.2.1

TABLE 607.3.2.1

FIRE DAMPER RATING

TYPE OF PENETRATION	MINIMUM DAMPER RATING (hour)
Less than 3-hour fire-resistance-rated assemblies	1 ½
3-hour or greater fire-resistance-rated assemblies	3

B. Dampers, when so used, must be labeled and automatically activated.

C. The objective of fire dampers is to prevent the spread of fire to other areas and provide continuity of the rated assembly.

D. Fire dampers are not required in fire barriers where:
1. In ducts which are part of an engineered smoke removal system, and
2. In hazardous exhaust systems. (M-607.2.2)
3. 22" steel subducts extending upward in an exhaust shaft. (M-607.5.5, exception 1)
4. Tested penetrations, as part of the listed assembly, and
5. 1 hr. or less rating, B use, and building is fire-suppressed throughout.
6. For parking garage ventilation shafts—but must be 2-hour separated from other shafts.

E. Fire dampers are not required in fire partitions (tenant and corridor separations) where:
1. The building is fully sprinkled.
2. Ducts of steel that do not open to the corridor, run above the ceiling, are not more than 100 sq. in. of cross-section, and do not end at a register in the rated wall.

FIRE DOORS (715)

A. General requirements

TABLE 715.4
FIRE DOOR AND FIRE SHUTTER FIRE PROTECTION RATINGS

TYPE OF ASSEMBLY	REQUIRED ASSEMBLY RATING (hours)	MINIMUM FIRE DOOR AND FIRE SHUTTER ASSEMBLY RATING (hours)
Fire walls and fire rating	4	3
barriers having a	3	3[a]
required fire-resistance	2	1½
greater than 1 hour	1½	1½
Fire barriers having a required fire-resistance rating of 1 hour:		
Shaft, exit enclosure and exit passage-way walls	1	1
Other fire barriers	1	¾
Fire partitions:		
Corridor walls	1	1/3[b]
Other fire partitions	0.5	1/3[b]
	1	3/4
	0.5	1/3
Exterior walls	3	1½
	2	1½
	1	3
		4
Smoke barriers	1	1/3[b]

a. Two doors, each with a fire protection rating of 1½ hours, installed on opposite sides of the same opening in a fire wall, shall be deemed equivalent in fire protection rating to one 3-hour fire do or.

b. For testing requirements, see Section 715.3.3.

B. A fire door assembly includes the door, frame, and hardware.

C. All fire doors shall be labeled, self-closing, and latching.

D. Automatic closing devices may be acceptable (such as smoke detectors, heat detectors, and fusible links) and must close in 10 seconds.

E. Multiple doors are acceptable in the same opening, except when used as an exit, and doors must swing free of each other. Two 1¹/₂-hour doors, when used together, have a 3-hour rating.

F. Wire glass is acceptable within the allowable wire glass area. (Table 715.4) Non-wired rated glass is limited by NFPA 80.

G. Automatic-closing fire doors must be smoke detector activated
   1. Corridors and fire partitions (708.6)
   2. Incidental use areas (312)
   3. Exits and horizontal exits (1019.1.1)
   4. Smoke barriers (709.5)
   5. Fire walls (705.8)

TABLE 705.8
MAXIMUM AREA OF EXTERIOR WALL OPENINGS BASED ON FIRE
SEPARATION DISTANCE AND DEGREE OF OPENING PROTECTION

FIRE SEPARATION DISTANCE (feet)	DEGREE OF OPENING PROTECTION	ALLOWABLE AREA[a]
0 to less than 3[b, c]	Unprotected, Nonsprinklered (UP, NS)	Not Permitted
	Unprotected, Sprinklered (UP, S)[i]	Not Permitted
	Protected (P)	Not Permitted
3 to less than 5[d, e]	Unprotected, Nonsprinklered (UP, NS)	Not Permitted
	Unprotected, Sprinklered (UP, S)[i]	15%
	Protected (P)	15%
5 to less than 10[e, f]	Unprotected, Nonsprinklered (UP, NS)	10%[h]
	Unprotected, Sprinklered (UP, S)[i]	25%
	Protected (P)	25%
10 to less than 15[e, f, g]	Unprotected, Nonsprinklered (UP, NS)	15%[h]
	Unprotected, Sprinklered (UP, S)[i]	45%

	Protected (P)	45%
15 to less than 20[f, g]	Unprotected, Nonsprinklered (UP, NS)	25%
	Unprotected, Sprinklered (UP, S)[i]	75%
	Protected (P)	75%
20 to less than 25[f, g]	Unprotected, Nonsprinklered (UP, NS)	45%
	Unprotected, Sprinklered (UP, S)[i]	No Limit
	Protected (P)	No Limit
25 to less than 30[f, g]	Unprotected, Nonsprinklered (UP, NS)	70%
	Unprotected, Sprinklered (UP, S)[i]	No Limit
	Protected (P)	No Limit
30 or greater	Unprotected, Nonsprinklered (UP, NS)	No Limit
	Unprotected, Sprinklered (UP, S)[i]	Not Required
	Protected (P)	Not Required

For SI: 1 foot = 304.8 mm.

UP, NS = Unprotected openings in buildings not equipped throughout with an automatic sprinkler system in accordance with Section 903.3.1.1.

UP, S = Unprotected openings in buildings equipped throughout with an automatic sprinkler system in accordance with Section 903.3.1.1.

P = Openings protected with an opening protective assembly in accordance with Section 705.8.2.

a. Values indicated are the percentage of the area of the exterior wall, per story.

b. For the requirements for fire walls of buildings with differing heights, see Section 706.6.1.

c. For openings in a fire wall for buildings on the same lot, see Section 706.8.

d. The maximum percentage of unprotected and protected openings shall be 25 percent for Group R-3 occupancies.

e. Unprotected openings shall not be permitted for openings with a fire separation distance of less than 15 feet for Group H-2 and H-3 occupancies.

f. The area of unprotected and protected openings shall not be limited for Group R-3 occupancies, with a fire separation distance of 5 feet or greater.

g. The area of openings in an open parking structure with a fire separation distance of 10 feet or greater shall not be limited.

h. Includes buildings accessory to Group R-3.

i. Not applicable to Group H-1, H-2 and H-3 occupancies.

FIRE ESCAPES (3406)

A. Fire escapes are not counted as part of the means of egress in new construction.

B. Existing fire escapes continue to be a part of the exit components.

C. New fire escapes on existing buildings are permitted only where exterior stairs cannot be used due to other factors except in existing adult group homes and existing building converted to adult group homes, but ONLY as a means of emergency escape/fire department access.

D. Access by window is not permitted for new fire escapes.

E. Ladders are not permitted on new fire escapes.

F. Fire escapes may not provide more than 50% of the required exits nor more than 50% of the required exit capacity.

G. When located on the front of a building beyond the lot line, the lowest landing shall not be less than 7' nor more than 12' above the grade and provided with a counterbalanced stair to the street.

H. In alleys and streets less than 30' wide, the lowest landing shall be 12' above grade.

I. Construction

   1. Fire escape must support a 100 lb. live load.

   2. Fire escape must be constructed of steel or approved noncombustibles.

   3. 2"-thick wood is allowed in Type V construction.

J. Stairs must be at least 22" wide, with 8" minimum treads, and an 8" maximum rise.

K. Landings must be at least 40" wide × 36" long, and must be no more than 8 below the access window or door.

L. Doors and windows require a ¾-hour opening protective.

FIREPLACES (M-902.1, M-903.1 AND 2113.0)

A. Masonry

   1. Minimum depth of the firebox is 20". Rumford fireplaces minimum 12".

   2. Minimum size chimney connection is 50 sq. in.

   3. Area of the throat shall not be greater than the connector.

   4. Walls shall be a minimum of 8" solid masonry, including the lining, minimum 10" when no lining.

   5. Refractory brick lining must be at least 2" thick.

   6. Unlined walls shall be constructed of minimum 10" solid masonry.

   7. Extend liners at least 4" into the fireplace throat.

   8. Walls of the throat and smoke chamber shall not be less than 8" thick.

   9. The use of a heat exchanger shall not reduce the required thickness of any fireplace wall.

   10. A masonry fireplace foundation shall be noncombustible and carry the fireplace and chimney load to the ground.

   11. Hearth and hearth extensions for masonry fireplaces shall be a minimum of 4" thick.

   12. A metal hood shall extend at least 6" beyond the firebox.

B. Clearances

   1. 6" minimum clearance is required from fireplace opening to combustibles.

   2. 2" minimum clearance to combustibles is required for any portion of a masonry fireplace, front and back.

   3. 4" minimum clearance from the back faces of masonry fireplaces.

C. A metal damper is required. Damper must be 12 gauge minimum.

D. A means of combustion air direct from the building exterior must be provided.

E. Firestop between fireplace and framing at each floor.

F. An approved, labeled, factory-built unit is acceptable. (M-903.1)
G. Chimney flue (Chapter M-8 and 2113.0)
    1. Fireplace flue shall not be used for any other purpose, or with any other fuel.
    2. Extend chimney 3′ above the roof or 2′ above any part of the building within 10′.
    3. A spark arrestor may be required.
    4. Minimum clearance of 2″ combustibles.

TABLE 2113.16(1)
NET CROSS-SECTIONAL AREA OF ROUND FLUE SIZES

FLUE SIZE, INSIDE DIAMETER (inches)	CROSS-SECTIONAL AREA (square inches)
6	28
7	38
8	50
10	78
10 ¾	90
12	113
15	176
18	254

For SI: 1 inch = 25.4 mm, 1 square inch = 645.16 mm^2.
a.   Flue sizes are based on ASTM C 315.

TABLE 2113.16(2)
NET CROSS-SECTIONAL AREA OF SQUARE
AND RECTANGULAR FLUE SIZES

FLUE SIZE, OUTSIDE NOMINAL DIMENSIONS (inches)	CROSS-SECTIONAL AREA (square inches)
4.5 x 8.5	23
4.5 x 13	34
8 x 8	42
8.5 x 8.5	49
8 x 12	67
8.5 x 13	76
12 x 12	102
8.5 x 18	101
13 x 13	127
12 x 16	131
13 x 18	173
16 x 16	181
16 x 20	222
18 x 18	233
20 x 20	298
20 x 24	335
24 x 24	431

For SI: 1 inch = 25.4 mm, 1 square inch = 645.16 mm^2.

FIRE RESISTANCE RATING (601, 602, AND 700)

A. Notes on the rating tables
1. H.T. = Heavy Timber.
2. Fire separation = distance in feet from the building face to the nearest interior lot line, or the center line of a street or public way.
3. No wall openings are allowed when the building separation is less than 3'. (Table 705.8)
4. Fire walls and party walls shall not be less than the applicable highest fire rating in Table 706.4.
5. Exit or shaft enclosures connecting 3 stories or less shall be 1-hour minimum and 2-hours when over 3 stories. (708.2)

TABLE 705.8
MAXIMUM AREA OF EXTERIOR WALL OPENINGS BASED ON FIRE SEPARATION DISTANCE AND DEGREE OF OPENING PROTECTION

FIRE SEPARATION DISTANCE (feet)	DEGREE OF OPENING PROTECTION	ALLOWABLE AREA[a]
0 to less than 3[b, c]	Unprotected, Nonsprinklered (UP, NS)	Not Permitted
	Unprotected, Sprinklered (UP, S)[i]	Not Permitted
	Protected (P)	Not Permitted
3 to less than 5[d, e]	Unprotected, Nonsprinklered (UP, NS)	Not Permitted
	Unprotected, Sprinklered (UP, S)[i]	15%
	Protected (P)	15%
5 to less than 10[e, f]	Unprotected, Nonsprinklered (UP, NS)	10%[h]
	Unprotected, Sprinklered (UP, S)[i]	25%
	Protected (P)	25%
10 to less than 15[e, f, g]	Unprotected, Nonsprinklered (UP, NS)	15%[h]
	Unprotected, Sprinklered (UP, S)[i]	45%

	Protected (P)	45%
15 to less than 20[f, g]	Unprotected, Nonsprinklered (UP, NS)	25%
	Unprotected, Sprinklered (UP, S)[i]	75%
	Protected (P)	75%
20 to less than 25[f, g]	Unprotected, Nonsprinklered (UP, NS)	45%
	Unprotected, Sprinklered (UP, S)[i]	No Limit
	Protected (P)	No Limit
25 to less than 30[f, g]	Unprotected, Nonsprinklered (UP, NS)	70%
	Unprotected, Sprinklered (UP, S)[i]	No Limit
	Protected (P)	No Limit
30 or greater	Unprotected, Nonsprinklered (UP, NS)	No Limit
	Unprotected, Sprinklered (UP, S)[i]	Not Required
	Protected (P)	Not Required

For SI: 1 foot = 304.8 mm.

UP, NS = Unprotected openings in buildings not equipped throughout with an automatic sprinkler system in accordance with Section 903.3.1.1.

UP, S = Unprotected openings in buildings equipped throughout with an automatic sprinkler system in accordance with Section 903.3.1.1.

P = Openings protected with an opening protective assembly in accordance with Section 705.8.2.

a. Values indicated are the percentage of the area of the exterior wall, per story.

b. For the requirements for fire walls of buildings with differing heights, see Section 706.6.1.

c. For openings in a fire wall for buildings on the same lot, see Section 706.8.

d. The maximum percentage of unprotected and protected openings shall be 25 percent for Group R-3 occupancies.

e. Unprotected openings shall not be permitted for openings with a fire separation distance of less than 15 feet for Group H-2 and H-3 occupancies.

f. The area of unprotected and protected openings shall not be limited for Group R-3 occupancies, with a fire separation distance of 5 feet or greater.

g. The area of openings in an open parking structure with a fire separation distance of 10 feet or greater shall not be limited.

h. Includes buildings accessory to Group R-3.

i. Not applicable to Group H-1, H-2 and H-3 occupancies.

TABLE 706.4
FIRE WALL FIRE-RESISTANCE RATINGS

GROUP	FIRE-RESISTANCE RATING (hours)
A, B, E, H-4, I, R-1, R-2, U	3[a]
F-1, H-3[b], H-5, M, S-1	3
H-1, H-2	4[b]
F-2, S-2, R-3, R-4	2

a. In Type II or V construction, walls shall be permitted to have a 2-hour fire-resistance rating.

b. For Group H-1, H-2 or H-3 buildings, also see Sections 415.4 and 415.5.

6. Where omission of fire protection is allowed, the materials used in Type I and II buildings shall be noncombustible or may be Type IV construction.

7. Fire-retardant wood may be used for non-bearing partitions in exit access corridors, vertical separation of tenant spaces, dwelling unit separations, non-bearing partitions, furring, and all roof construction where no rating is required.

TABLE 601
FIRE-RESISTANCE RATING REQUIREMENTS FOR BUILDING ELEMENTS
(hours)

BUILDING ELE-MENT	TYPE I		TYPE II		TYPE III		TYPE IV	TYPE V	
	A	B	A[e]	B	A[e]	B	HT	A[e]	B
Structural frame[a]	3[b]	2[b]	1	0	1	0	HT	1	0
Bearing walls									
Exterior[g]	3	2	1	0	2	2	2	1	0
Interior	3[b]	2[b]	1	0	1	0	1/HT	1	0
Nonbearing walls and partitions Exterior	See Table 602								
Nonbearing walls and partitions Interior[f]	0	0	0	0	0	0	See Section 602.4.6	0	0
Floor construction, including supporting beams and joists	2	2	1	0	1	0	HT	1	0
Roof construction, including supporting beams and joists	1½[c]	1[c, d]	1[c, d]	0[d]	1[c,d]	0[d]	HT	1[c,d]	0

For SI: 1 foot = 304.8 mm.

a. The structural frame shall be considered to be the columns and the girders, beams, trusses and spandrels having direct connections to the columns and bracing members designed to carry gravity loads. The members of floor or roof panels which have no connection to the columns shall be considered secondary members and not a part of the structural frame.

b. Roof supports: Fire-resistance ratings of structural frame and bearing walls are permitted to be reduced by 1 hour where supporting a roof only.

c. Except in Group F-1, H, M and S-1 occupancies, fire protection of structural members shall not be required, including protection of roof framing and decking where every part of the roof construction is 20 feet or more above any floor immediately below. Fire-retardant-treated wood members shall be allowed to be used for such unprotected members.

d. In all occupancies, heavy timber shall be allowed where a 1-hour or less fire-resistance rating is required.

e. An approved automatic sprinkler system in accordance with Section 903.3.1.1shall be allowed to be substituted for 1-hour fire-resistance-rated construction, provided such system is not otherwise required by other provisions of the code or used for an allowable area increase in accordance with Section 506.3 or an allowable height increase in accordance with Section 504.2. The 1-hour substitution for the fire resistance of exterior walls shall not be permitted.

f. Not less than the fire-resistance rating required by other sections of this code.

g. Not less than the fire-resistance rating based on fire separation distance (see Table 602).

TABLE 602
FIRE-RESISTANCE RATING REQUIREMENTS FOR EXTERIOR WALLS BASED ON FIRE SEPARATION DISTANCE[a,e]

FIRE SEPARA-TION DISTANCE = X (feet)	TYPE OF CON-STRUCTION	OCCUPANCY GROUP H	OCCUPANCY GROUP F-1, M, S-1	OCCUPANCY GROUP A, B, E, F-2, I, R, S-2, U[b]
X < 5[c]	All	3	2	1
5 ≤X <10	IA	3	2	1
	Others	2	1	1
10 ≤X< 30	IA, IB	2	1	1[d]
	IIB, VB	1	0	0
	Others	1	1	1[d]

FIRE SEPARA-TION DISTANCE = X (feet)	TYPE OF CON-STRUCTION	OCCUPANCY GROUP H	OCCUPANCY GROUP F-1, M, S-1	OCCUPANCY GROUP A, B, E, F-2, I, R, S-2, U[b]
X ≥ 30	All	0	0	0

For SI: 1 foot = 304.8 mm.

a. Load-bearing exterior walls shall also comply with the fire-resistance rating requirements of Table 601.

b. For special requirements for Group U occupancies see Section 406.1.2

c. See Section 705.1.1 for party walls.

d. Open parking garages complying with Section 406 shall not be required to have a fire-resistance rating.

e. The fire-resistance rating of an exterior wall is determined based upon the fire separation distance of the exterior wall and the story in which the wall is located.

FIRE SEPARATION

A. Plans must designate the type of construction and fire resistance rating of all structural members as required by the code. (106.1.1)

B. Fire resistance applies to party walls, fire walls, fire barriers, and fire partitions as well as horizontal assemblies.

C. Sprinklers throughout reduces fire resistance by 1 hr. but to not less than 1 hr.

D. Non-separated and separated mixed uses are covered under "mixed uses."

TABLE 508.3.3 REQUIRED SEPARATION OF OCCUPANCIES (HOURS)

OCCU-PANCY	A^e,E^e		I		R^d		F-2, S-2^{c,d}, U^d		B^b, F-1, M^b, S-1		H-1		H-2		H-3,H-4,H-5	
	S	NS	S	NS	S	NS	S	NS	S	NS	S	NS	S	NS	S	NS
A^e,E^e	N	N	1	2	1	2	N	1	1	2	NP	NP	3	4	2	3^a
I	—	—	N	N	1	NP	1	2	1	2	NP	NP	3	NP	2	NP
R^d	—	—	—	—	N	N	1	2	1	2	NP	NP	3	NP	2	NP
F-2, S-2^{c,d}, U^d	—	—	—	—	—	—	N	N	1	2	NP	NP	3	4	2	3^a
B^b, F-1, M^b, S-1	—	—	—	—	—	—	—	—	N	N	NP	NP	2	3	1	2^a
H-1	—	—	—	—	—	—	—	—	—	—	N	NP	NP	NP	NP	NP
H-2	—	—	—	—	—	—	—	—	—	—	—	—	N	NP	1	NP
H-3, H-4, H-5	—	—	—	—	—	—	—	—	—	—	—	—	—	—	N	NP

For SI: 1 square foot = 0.0929 m^2.

S = Buildings equipped throughout with an automatic sprinkler system installed in accordance with Section 903.3.1.1.

NS = Buildings not equipped throughout with an automatic sprinkler system installed in accordance with Section 903.3.1.1.

N = No separation requirement.

NP = Not permitted.

a. For Group H-5 occupancies, see Section 903.2.4.2.

b. Occupancy separation need not be provided for storage areas within Groups B and M if the:

1. Area is less than 10% of the floor area;

2. Area is equipped with an automatic fire-extinguishing system and is less than 3,000 square feet; or

3. Area is less than 1,000 square feet.

c. Areas used only for private or pleasure vehicles shall be allowed to reduce separation by 1 hour.

d. See Section 406.1.4.

e. Commercial kitchens need not be separated from the restaurant seating areas that they serve.

E. Specific use areas within buildings require separation and/or a fire suppression system. (Table 508.4)

F. Fire separations can create Fire Areas, which are related to threshold requirements for sprinklers, occupancies, and allowable heights and areas. (See Table 706.4)

FIRESTOPPING/FIREBLOCKING/FIRE-RESISTANT JOINT SYSTEMS (712, 713, 717)

A. Firestopping and fireblocking is required in all building types and must be inspected prior to concealment or closing up a wall. (108.2.7)

B. Fireblocking materials (717.2.1)
   1. All material must be noncombustible, except in wood framing. With staggered or parallel studs, mineral wool or fiberglass batts/blankets are permitted.
   2. In wood framing, nominal 23/32" plywood (or equal) or 2" lumber is acceptable, or if 2 layers, 1" lumber is acceptable.

C. Fireblocking locations
   1. All concealed spaces, furring, and stud walls at floor and ceiling must be firestopped.
   2. Connections between horizontal and vertical space at soffits, drops, and cove ceilings must be firestopped.
   3. Firestopping is required between stair stringers at top and bottom of a run.
   4. Ceiling and floor openings (pipes, ducts) must be firestopped.
   5. Space behind combustible exterior architectural trim 20' o.c. must be firestopped.
   6. Space behind trim on rated walls 10' o.c. must be firestopped, or fill the space full with noncombustible material.
   7. Floor sleepers must be firestopped every 100 sq. ft.
   8. In walls at 10' o.c.

D. Firestopping types (713.3)
   1. Membrane firestopping,
   2. Annular space protection, and
   3. Through penetrations.

E. Fire-resistant joints (714)
   1. Must be tested per ASTM E 1966 (or UL 2079).
   2. Curtain wall voids must pass ASTM E 119.
   3. Not required for:
      a. Floors in dwellings, atriums, malls, open parking structures, mezzanines.
      b. Walls and roofs where openings are allowed.
      c. Control joints up to 5/8" and tested as an assembly per ASTM E 119 or UL 263.

FIRE SUPPRESSION REQUIRED (903)

A. General
   1. Refers to automatic water sprinkler systems for whole building protection, partial buildings by fire area or stories below occupancy, or individual rooms per Ohio Fire Code.
   2. Where a fire suppression system is installed, it must be maintained in full operating condition.
   3. Specific required locations are listed in 903.2.
   4. Pre-approval of installation, alteration, repair or renewal is required for the building official, with review by the local fire official where locally required. Acceptance tests are required in the presence of a certified building or fire protection inspector, if the building official requires.

B. Required in the following groups
1. Use Group A-2: Fire suppression is required in all buildings or portions thereof when more than 5000 sq. ft. when the occupant load is over 100, and when the Group A is on any floor other than at exit discharge level.
2. Use Group A-1, A-3, and A-4: Fire suppression is required in all buildings or portions over 12,000 sq. ft., when the occupant load is over 300 (except A-3), and when the Group A is on any floor other than at exit discharge level. All multi-theaters with fixed seats as well as areas used exclusively for religious worship, also need sprinklers (Group A-1).
3. Use Group A-5: Fire suppression required for concession stands, press boxes, retail areas, and other accessory uses in excess of 1,000 sq. ft.
4. Use Group B: Fire suppression required where 4 or more care recipients are unable to care for themselves, or 1 or more of such recipients are at a level other than the discharge level.
5. Use Group H: Fire suppression required in all buildings or portions.
6. Use Group E: Fire suppression required in all buildings or portions 20,000 sq. ft. or more, and when below the exit discharge level unless the classrooms all have exits to the exterior.
7. Use Group I: Fire suppression required in all buildings.
8. Use Groups M, S-1, and F-1.
   a. Fire suppression is required when fire area is more than 12,000 sq. ft./floor or all fire areas of these Use Groups total over 24,000 sq. ft. in total area.
   b. When the Use Group occupies an area over 3 stories in height.
   c. When woodworking area in excess of 2,500 sq. ft. generates flammable dust (F-1).
   d. When furniture retail in excess of 8,000 sq. ft. (M).
   e. When commercial bus/truck storage area in excess of 5,000 sq. ft. (S-1).
9. Use Group R: Fire suppression required unless R-2 occupancy with single exterior exit and fire separated dwelling units empty directly onto exit. OR:
   (1) The building is not used as an "SRO" occupancy, and
   (2) The exit is an exterior stair, and
   (3) The dwelling units egress directly into an exit, and
   (4) The building is divided into two hour fire barriers with a maximum of two dwelling units per floor and not more than six dwelling units per fire area, and
   (5) All dwelling units in the fire area have separations.
10. All buildings with floors more than 55′ above the lowest level of fire department vehicle access must be suppressed. Exceptions:
   a. Open parking structures
   b. Airport control towers, and
   c. Group F-2
   d. Rubbish and linen chutes through 3 or more floors.
   e. Hazardous exhaust ducts.
   f. Commercial cooking and exhaust system.
C. Enclosed public garages require fire suppression systems (903.2.10)
1. Commercial truck or bus garages over 5000 sq. ft.
2. Repair garages (903.2.9.1)
   a. 10,000 sq. ft. and more than 1 story
   b. 12,000 sq. ft.
   c. Basement repair areas
3. Garages located under other use groups except R-3

    D. Windowless story (applicable to Use Groups R-3 and U) (903.2.11)

      1. A fire suppression system is required in any building floor or basement without sufficient windows or access openings, operable from the exterior by the fire department in excess of 1,500 sq. ft.

      2. The minimum size access is at least 20 sq. ft. above ground per 50 lineal feet of perimeter, on at least one side. Each opening must be a minimum of 30" in either dimension, with no more than 50' between access openings.

      3. Fire suppression is required when there is more than 75' to wall with access openings, or to an additional wall with accessible openings.

      4. Fire suppression is required when the travel distance to any access opening is 75 from any interior point.

    E. Manually activated smoke exhaust system can be used in lieu of smoke and heat vents, if

      1. Fans are evenly spaced in Groups F-1, S-1.

      2. Minimum individual capacity of cubic feet per minute (cfm) and minimum 2 air changes per minute.

      3. Individual manual controls.

      4. Wiring protects against $\geq$ 1,000° F (538 C) for 15 minutes.

      5. Controls are on building exterior, with $\geq$ 1 hour interior fire exposure.

      6. Air for exhaust fans must be near floor level and provide minimum 50% of exhaust.

      7. May combine comfort and smoke exhaust systems, with automatic shutdown of comfort system upon exhaust activation.

    F. Additional Locations—see Table 903.2.11.6 for sprinkler requirements from other code sections.

FIRE SUPPRESSION SYSTEMS (See SPRINKLERS.)

FIREWORKS (OAC 1301:7-7-33)

    A. Equipment, processes, and operations involving the manufacture, processing, sale, transportation, importation, exportation, use, and discharge of every class or kind of fireworks must comply with the Ohio Fire Code (OFC) and the following:

      1. NFPA 160, NFPA 1122-1127

      2. NFPA 495, NFPA 498

      3. DOTn 49 C.F.R. Parts 100–185

      4. DOL 29 CFR Part 1910.1200

      5. DOTy 27 CFR Part 35

    B. Classes of fireworks:

      1. 1.1 G fireworks(UN0333)

      2. 1.2G fireworks (UN0334)

      3. 1.3G fireworks (UN0335)

      4. 1.4G fireworks (UN0336)

      5. 1.4G special effects fireworks (UN0432)

      6. 1.4S fireworks (UN0337)

      7. 1.4S special effects fireworks (UN0432)

    C. Permit required for manufacture, processing or storage of fireworks. No permit is allowed if the applicant has been convicted of or pled guilty to a felony under state or federal law. A permit for fireworks storage requires a state fire marshal civilian background check for criminal history, or a currently valid "Certificate of Clearance" or equivalent from the bureau of alcohol, tobacco, firearms and explosives.

    D. All buildings in which fireworks are manufactured, processed, stored, and offered for sale must comply with OAC 1301:7-7-47 for high hazard occupancies.

E. Manufacturer must install in every building for manufacturing, storage, or display to which the public has access interlinked fire detection, smoke exhaust, and smoke evacuation systems approved by the appropriate fire code official.

FLAME SPREAD RATINGS (800)
A. Interior finishes on walls and ceilings (803.0)
1. Class A = 0-25; Class B = 25-76; Class C = 76-200. If sprinkled, lower requirement one level (but not less than Class C).
2. Class C may be used in any room for trim, if not more than 10% of the wall area except around fire doors and fire windows is trim. (806.5)
3. Maximum smoke-developed rating is 450.
4. Table of maximum flame spread rating chart for walls and ceilings.

TABLE 803.9
INTERIOR WALL AND CEILING FINISH REQUIREMENTS BY OCCUPANCY[k]

GROUP	SPRINKLERED[l]			UNSPRINKLERED		
	Exit enclosures and exit passage ways[a,b]	Corridors	Rooms and enclosed spaces[c]	Exit enclosures and exit passage ways[a,b]	Corridors	Rooms and enclosed spaces[c]
A-1 & A-2	B	B	C	A	A[d]	B[e]
A-3[f], A-4, A-5	B	B	C	A	A[d]	C
B, E, M, R-1, R-4	B	C	C	A	B	C
F	C	C	C	B	C	C
H	B	B	C[g]	A	A	B
I-1	B	C	C	A	B	B
I-2	B	B	B[h,i]	A	A	B
I-3	A	A[j]	C	A	A	B
I-4	B	B	B[h,i]	A	A	B
R-2	C	C	C	B	B	C
R-3	C	C	C	C	C	C
S	C	C	C	B	B	C
U	No restrictions			No restrictions		

For SI: 1 inch = 25.4 mm, 1 square foot = 0.0929 m².

a. Class C interior finish materials shall be permitted for wainscotting or paneling of not more than 1,000 square feet of applied surface area in the grade lobby where applied directly to a noncombustible base or over furring strips applied to a noncombustible base and fireblocked as required by Section 803.4.1.

b. In vertical exits of buildings less than three stories in height of other than Group I-3, Class B interior finish for unsprinklered buildings and Class C interior finish for sprinklered buildings shall be permitted.

c. Requirements for rooms and enclosed spaces shall be based upon spaces enclosed by partitions. Where a fire-resistance rating is required for structural elements, the enclosing partitions shall extend from the floor to the ceiling. Partitions that do not comply with this shall be considered enclosing spaces and the rooms or spaces on both sides shall be considered one. In determining the applicable requirements for rooms and enclosed spaces, the specific occupancy thereof shall be the governing factor regardless of the group classification of the building or structure.

d. Lobby areas in A-1, A-2 and A-3 occupancies shall not be less than Class B materials.

e. Class C interior finish materials shall be permitted in places of assembly with an occupant load of 300 persons or less.

f. For places of religious worship, wood used for ornamental purposes, trusses, paneling or chancel furnishing shall be permitted.

g. Class B material required where building exceeds two stories.

h. Class C interior finish materials shall be permitted in administrative spaces.

i. Class C interior finish materials shall be permitted in rooms with a capacity of four persons or less.

j. Class B materials shall be permitted as wainscotting extending not more than 48 inches above the finished floor in corridors.

k. Finish materials as provided for in other sections of this code.

l. Applies when the exit enclosures, exit passageways, corridors or rooms and enclosed spaces are protected by a sprinkler system installed in accordance with Section 903.3.1.1 or Section 903.3.1.2.

5. Textiles must pass NFPA 286 testing or be Class A in sprinkled building.
6. Alternative to use NFPA 286 test, with listed conditions.

B. Floor interior finish (804.0)
  1. Per NFPA 253:
      a. Class I (high resistance), 0.45 watts/cm^2 or greater;
      b. Class II (medium resistance), 0.22 watts/cm^2 or greater.
  2. Wood, vinyl, terrazzo, and other resilient flooring do not require any rating.
  3. All carpeting shall be labeled or certified as to flame spread rating.
      a. All exits and exit access corridors must be Class II, except Class I in I-2 and I-3, pill test applies to all groups.
      b. Fill all spaces under wood over concrete floors in Type I and II construction with non-combustibles or firestop per 100 sq. ft. (717.2.7) See FIRESTOPPING/FIREBLOCKING.
      c. If sprinkled, lower requirement one class but not lower than pill test. (DOCFF-1 "pill test" (CPSC 16 CFR, Part 1630))

FLOOD RESISTANCE PROTECTION (1612.0)

A. In flood hazard areas (area within flood plain subject to $\geq$ 1% flooding per year), all buildings and structures determined to need flood resistant construction by either the local flood plain administrator under the National Flood Insurance Program (NFIP), or the Ohio Department of Natural Resources for communities in the NFIP, must meet approval under CFR parts 59-77 of NFIP's "Regulations for Floodplain Management and Flood Hazard Identification."

AND

Local authority's flood damage prevention regulations. (1612.3)

B. Design Flood Elevation is design flood (including wave) height, based on community's flood hazard map. For Zone AO, it is elevation of the highest existing grade of a building's perimeter, plus foot depth on flood hazard map. For Zone AO where depth is not specified on the flood hazard map, depth is designated as 2' (610 mm). Floodway is a natural watercourse channel and adjacent land area reserved to discharge floodwaters without increasing cumulative water surface height above a designated level.
  1. If Design Flood Elevations are not included in flood hazard areas OR Floodways are not designated, building official may require applicant to:
      a. Use any available federal, state, or other derived Design Flood Elevation and Floodway data, OR
      b. Use accepted hydrologic and hydraulic engineering practices as to flood hazard areas, relying on registered design professionals who document that technical methods used are current. (1612.3.1)
  2. If riverine flood hazard area and Design Flood Elevations shown but no Floodways designated, applicant must supply Floodway analysis proving planned work will not increase Design Flood Elevation $\geq$ 1' (305 mm) within jurisdiction. (1612.3.2)
  3. Design/construction in all flood hazard areas must be per Ch. 5 of ASCE 7 and with ASCE 24. (1612.4) Application must be documented (prepared/sealed) by registered design professional:
      a. As to flood hazard areas lacking high-velocity wave threat, document elevation of lowest floor (including basement) per registered surveyor.
        (1) If fully enclosed areas below Design Flood Elevation not meeting minimum requirements of Sec. 2.6.2.1 of ASCE 24 per automatic entry/exit of floodwaters, include statement that design provides equalization of hydrostatic flood forces per Sec. 2.6.2.2 of ASCE 24.
        (2) As to dry floodproofed nonresidential buildings, include statement that dry floodproofing is per ASCE 24.

b. As to flood hazard areas with high-velocity wave threat, registered surveyor must provide bottom elevation of lowest horizontal structural member.

4. Include with construction documents statement that building is per ASCE 24, including:

    a. pile or column foundation and building/structure attached thereto is designed to anchor to:

        (1) resist flotation

        (2) collapse

        (3) lateral movement because of simultaneous wind and float loads on all building components.

        (4) Other load requirements of entry for STRUCTURAL LOADS

5. If breakaway walls designed to resist nominal load of < 10 psf (0.48 kN/m^2) OR > 20 psf (0.96 kN/m^2), include with construction documents statement that breakaway wall is designed per ASCE 24. (1612.5)

C. Flood hazard zone A

1. In fully enclosed areas below the design flood elevation allowing for the automatic entry and exit of floodwaters that do not meet the minimum requirements in Section 2.6.2.1 of ASCE 24, the construction documents must state that the design will provide for equalization of hydrostatic flood forces in accordance with Section 2.6.2.2 of ASCE 24.

2. For dry floodproofed nonresidential buildings, construction documents shall must state that the dry floodproofing is designed in accordance with ASCE 24.

3. All basement floors shall be above the base level.

D. High hazard flood zone V

1. These zones are subject to high wave action and high water velocity including erosion damage.

2. Construction documents must state that the building is designed in accordance with ASCE 24, including that the pile or column foundation and building or structure is designed to be anchored to resist flotation, collapse and lateral movement due to the effects of wind and flood loads acting simultaneously on all building components.

3. For breakaway walls designed to resist a nominal load of less than 10 psf or more than 20 psf, construction documents must state that the breakaway wall is designed in accordance with ASCE 24.

E. Base level elevation shall be certified, and plans and construction shall be certified by a registered design professional that all requirements have been met for flood resistance protection. (1612.5)

FLOOR/CEILING AND ROOF/CEILING (700)

Fire Protection Assemblies

A. The aggregate in ceiling openings for metal piping, electrical boxes, and tubes shall not exceed 144 sq. in./100 sq. ft. of ceiling. (713.4.1.2)

B. Lay-in ceiling panels must resist a 1 lb./sq. ft. upward force.

C. Firestop all ceiling penetrations of pipes, ducts, electrical, and wire. (716)

D. In a 1-hour assembly, either the flooring over or the ceiling under an unusable space may be omitted.

E. Fire dampers in a rated assembly ceiling opening may be omitted if they would interfere with a smoke control system. (716)

F. Supporting construction must have the same rating as the horizontal assembly. (705.11.2)

G. Roofs in buildings more than 20' above finished floor may be unrated, noncombustible or fire-retardant wood, except Groups F-1, H, M, S-1. (Table 601, note b)

H. Horizontal assemblies, same as fire barriers for continuity and supported construction (712.3)
    1. Dwelling and sleeping unit ratings can be reduced to ½ hour when sprinkled in Types IIB, IIIB, and VB.
    2. Attics and crawl spaces do not need part of assembly facing unoccupiable space.

FOAM PLASTICS (2603.0)

A. Insulation uses
    1. In foam plastic and foam plastic cores of manufactured assemblies up to 4" thick, maximum flame spread is 75 with maximum smoke rating of 450 when tested per ASTM E84 or UL 723.
    2. A 15-minute thermal barrier is required between the plastic and the building interior with ½" gypsum board or equivalent; 1" concrete or masonry may be used.

B. Walk-in coolers
    1. Coolers not over 400 sq. ft. area must have no more foam plastic than 4" thick if covered with.032" aluminum or.016" steel. No thermal barrier is required. Up to 10" is allowed with a thermal barrier.

C. Roofing
    1. Foam plastic is acceptable as insulation without a thermal barrier if separated from the interior with $^{15}/_{32}$" exterior glue T and G plywood or equivalent.
    2. No flame spread or thermal barrier is required if roof assembly tested as such, when tested per FM 4450 or UL 1256.

D. Doors (core material)
    1. Foam plastic may be used in non-fire rated doors.
    2. Cover foam plastic with.032" aluminum or.016" steel.
    3. In Groups R-2 and R-3, foam plastic may be wood-faced for exterior door.
    4. Garage doors that are not fire-rated can be foam plastic insulated with a metal facing.

E. Attics and crawl spaces: When used in attics and crawl spaces that have utilities within the space, the foam surfaces must be protected from ignition by barriers installed so no plastic is exposed.

F. Siding backer board
    1. Maximum thickness is ½" and foam plastic backer board must be separated from the interior with 2" of mineral wool or equal.
    2. Foam plastic backer board can be applied over existing exterior wall construction.

G. Interior trim (2604.2)
    1. Minimum density for interior trim is 20 lbs./cu. ft., maximum thickness is ½", and maximum width is 8".
    2. Maximum aggregate use shall not exceed 10% of the wall area.

H. Exterior walls
    1. On a one-story building, foam plastic may be used without a thermal barrier if the flame spread is less than 25, the maximum smoke rating is not more than 450, is not over 4" thick, and if protected with.032" aluminum or.016" steel, and the entire building is sprinkled.
    2. Buildings of Type I, II, III, and IV exterior walls
        a. Foam plastic must be a maximum thickness of 4" and flame spread 25 with smoke rating of 450 with barrier on the inside all bonded to building frame, or an approved prefab. aluminium panel.
        b. Foam plastic may be used within exterior rated walls.
        c. Test data per ASTM E84 or UL 723 must be submitted.

I. Tests allowing specific foam use allowed without thermal barrier are acceptable. (FM 4880, UL 1040, UL 1715, or NFPA 286)

FOOTINGS (1809)

A. General
  1. Unless other frost protection is provided, protect footings and other foundations from frost by:
     a. Extending below frost line,
     b. Constructing per ASCE 32,
     c. Construction on solid rock.
     d. Exception: free-standing building that:
        (1) meet Occupancy Category I,
        (2) are $\leq$ 600' square (56 m^2) for light-frame construction
            OR $\leq$ 400' square (37 m^2) for other construction,
        (3) have eave height $\leq$ 10' (3048 mm), and
        (4) able to bear on permanently frozen soil with shallow foundation. (1809.5)
  2. Build shallow foundations on undisturbed soil, compacted fill, or controlled low-strength material (CLSM).
  3. Footings bearing on peat or organic materials are unacceptable, unless supporting data shows otherwise. (1806.2)
  4. Locate footings on granular soil with line between lower edges of adjoining footings having vertical slope > 30° (0.52 rad) UNLESS material supporting higher footing has approved bracing, retaining or other lateral support OR engineering analysis allows greater slope. (1809.6)
  5. Footing top must be level. Bottom may have $\leq$ 10% slope. Step Footings as needed to change top elevation OR if ground slopes $\geq$ 10%. footing or where. (1809.3)
  6. Timber footings are acceptable for Type V. (1809.12)

     Treat per AWPA U1 (Commodity Specification A), Use Category 4B, unless timbers are entirely below permanent water level OR if capping for wood piles projecting above water over submerged/marsh lands. If untreated supported by treated piles, compressive stresses perpendicular to grain $\leq$ 70% of allowable stress timber species and grade per AF & PA NDS.

B. Floating mats on expansive soils need design per CRSI manual.
C. Steel grillages (1809.11)
  1. Beams shall be completely encased in a minimum of 6" concrete at the bottom and 4" on sides with all voids filled.
  2. Space beams with permanent spacers are required.
  3. Rest grillage on 6" minimum concrete.
D. Masonry footings (1809.8)
  1. Use type M or S mortar in masonry footings.
  2. Minimum width for footings is the width of the wall supported plus 8".
  3. Offset footings 1½" maximum for a single course and 3" maximum for a double course.
E. Plain concrete footings supporting walls of other than light frame construction on soil/rock need edge thickness $\geq$ 8" (203 mm). Exception:
  1. If supporting Group R-3, may be 6" inches (152 mm), IF does not extend past distance > thickness of footing on either side of supported wall.
F. 12" (305 mm) minimum depth for footings below undisturbed ground surface, with 12" minimum width.
G. If specific design, concrete/masonry-unit footings for light-frame construction use Table 1809.7

TABLE 1809.7
PRESCRIPTIVE FOOTINGS SUPPORTING WALLS OF LIGHT-FRAME CONSTRUCTION[a, b, c, d, e]

NUMBER OF FLOORS SUPPORTED BY THE FOOTING[f]	WIDTH OF FOOTING (inches)	THICKNESS OF FOOTING (inches)
1	12	6
2	15	6
3	18	8[g]

For SI: 1 inch = 25.4 mm, 1 foot = 304.8 mm.

a. Depth of footings shall be in accordance with Section 1809.4.

b. The ground under the floor shall be permitted to be excavated to the elevation of the top of the footing.

c. Interior stud-bearing walls shall be permitted to be supported by isolated footings. The footing width and length shall be twice the width shown in this table, and footings shall be spaced not more than 6 feet on center.

d. See Section 1908 for additional requirements for concrete footings of structures assigned to Seismic Design Category C, D, E or F.

e. For thickness of foundation walls, see Section 1807.1.6.

f. Footings shall be permitted to support a roof in addition to the stipulated number of floors. Footings supporting roof only shall be as required for supporting one floor.

g. Plain concrete footings for Group R-3 occupancies shall be permitted to be 6 inches thick.

H. Pier and curtain foundations may support light-frame construction ≤ two stories above grade plane, IF:
   1. Load-bearing walls on concrete footings bonded to exterior wall footings.
   2. Load-bearing masonry walls need thickness ≥ 4" (102 mm) nominal, or 3⁵/₈" (92 mm) actual, bonded with 6' (1829 mm) spaced o.c. piers
   3. Pier height unsupported ≤ 10 x least dimension. If structural clay or hollow concrete masonry for piers supporting beams and girders, fill with concrete/Type M or S mortar. Exception:
      Allow unfilled hollow piers if unsupported height ≤ 4 x least dimension. Cap with 4" (102 mm) solid masonry/concrete OR top course cavities with concrete/grout.
   4. 4' (1219 mm) maximum height of 4" (102 mm) load-bearing masonry foundation wall for wood frame walls and floors.
   5. 24" (610 mm) maximum unbalanced fill for foundation walls—12" (305 mm) for hollow masonry.
I. For Seismic Design D, E, or F structures, footings in Site Class E or F soil need interconnection by ties that can carry (tension or compress) force = lesser of larger footing design gravity load x seismic coefficient, SDS, ÷ 10% and 25% of smaller footing design gravity load UNLESS equivalent restraint from reinforced concrete beams within slabs on grade OR reinforced concrete slabs on grade.

FOUNDATION WALLS (1805.5, 1807)

A.
   1. Thickness per Table 1807.1.6.3(1) for plain masonry walls or Table 1807.1.6.3(2), 1807.1.6.3(3) or 1807.1.6.3(4) for masonry walls with reinforcement. Thickness cannot be less than wall supported, except an 8" wall may support brick veneer frame or 10" cavity wall.
   2. Vertical reinforcement needs minimum yield strength of 60,000 psi (414 MPa).
   3. Reinforcement's specified location ≥ effective depth distance, d, noted in Tables 1807.1.6.3(2), 1807.1.6.3(3) and 1807.1.6.3(4), is measured from face of exterior (soil) side of wall to center of vertical reinforcement. Reinforcement meets tolerances of TMS 602/ACI 530.1/ASCE 6, Article 3.3.B.8 of the specified location.
   4. Concrete masonry units meet ASTM C 90.
   5. Clay masonry units meet ASTM C 652 for hollow brick; allow ASTM C 62 or ASTM C 216 where solid masonry units installed per Table 1807.1.6.3(1) for plain masonry.
   6. Lay masonry units in running bond, installed with Type M or S mortar per Section 2103.8.
   7. Unfactored axial load per linear foot of wall ≤ 1.2 tf'm, where t is specified wall thickness in inches, and f'm is specified compressive masonry strength lbs. per square inch.
   8. At least 4" (102 mm) of solid masonry needed at girder supports at top of hollow masonry unit foundation walls.
   9. As an alternative to Table 1807.1.6.3(2), 1807.1.6.3(3) or 1807.1.6.3(4) masonry reinforcement procedures, use alternative reinforcing bar sizes and spacings with equivalent cross-sectional area of reinforcement per linear foot (mm) of wall, IF spacing of reinforcement ≤ 72" (1829 mm) and reinforcing bar sizes ≤ No. 11.
   10. Using structure's seismic design category per EARTHQUAKES, masonry foundation walls following Tables 1807.1.6.3(1)-1807.1.6.3(4), subject to following limitations:
      a. Seismic Design Categories A and B—no additional seismic requirements.

  b. Seismic Design Category C—design using Tables 1807.1.6.3(1)-1807.1.6.3(4) subject to seismic requirements of Section 1.17.4.3 of TMS 402/ACI 530/ASCE 5.

  c. Seismic Design Category D—design using Tables 1807.1.6.3(2)-1807.1.6.3(4) subject to seismic requirements of Section 1.17.4.4 of TMS 402/ACI 530/ASCE 5.

  d. Seismic Design Categories E and F—design using Tables 1807.1.6.3(2)-1807.1.6.3(4) subject to seismic requirements of Section 1.17.4.5 of TMS 402/ACI 530/ASCE 5.

B. Concrete Foundation Walls—if laterally supported at top and bottom:

  1. Table 1807.1.6.2 vertical reinforcement size and spacing based on reinforcement with 60,000 lbs. per sq. in. (414 MPa) minimum yield strength. If 40,000 psi (276 MPa) or 50,000 psi (345 MPa), need same size bar and spacing per table, less spacing x 0.67 or 0.83 respectively.

  2. Put any vertical reinforcement nearest inside wall face at distance, d, from outside (soil). D = wall thickness, t, minus 1.25" (32mm) plus one-half the bar diameter, d_b, [d = t - (1.25 + d_b / 2)]. Reinforcement placement within tolerance of ±³/₈" (9.5 mm), where d ≤ 8" (203 mm) or ±½" (12.7 mm) where d > 8" (203 mm).

  3. Allow smaller size reinforcing bars with closer spacings giving equivalent cross-sectional reinforcement area per unit length instead of Table 1807.1.6.2.

  4. Reinforcement's concrete cover—from inside face of wall ≥ ³/₈" inch (19.1 mm); from outside face of wall, ≥ 1½" (38 mm) for No. 5 bars and smaller, ≥ 2" (51 mm) for larger bars.

  5. Concrete—have specified compressive strength, f'c, ≥ 2,500 psi (17.2 MPa).

  6. Unfactored axial load per linear foot of wall ≤ 1.2 tf '$_c$, where t is specified wall thickness in inches.

TABLE 1807.1.6.2
CONCRETE FOUNDATION WALLS [b, c]

		MINIMUM VERTICAL REINFORCEMENT-BAR SIZE AND SPACING (inches)								
		Design lateral soil load[a] (psf per foot of depth)								
		30[d]			45[d]			60		
MAXIMUM WALL HEIGHT (feet)	**MAXIMUM UNBALANCED BACKFILL HEIGHT[e] (feet)**	Minimum wall thickness (inches)								
		7.5	9.5	11.5	7.5	9.5	11.5	7.5	9.5	11.5
5	4	PC	PC	PC	PC	PC	PC	PC	PC	PC
	5	PC	PC	PC	PC	PC	PC	PC	PC	PC
6	4	PC	PC	PC	PC	PC	PC	PC	PC	PC
	5	PC	PC	PC	PC	PC	PC	PC	PC	PC
	6	PC	PC	PC	PC	PC	PC	PC	PC	PC
7	4	PC	PC	PC	PC	PC	PC	PC	PC	PC
	5	PC	PC	PC	PC	PC	PC	PC	PC	PC
	6	PC	PC	PC	PC	PC	PC	#5 at 48	PC	PC
	7	PC	PC	PC	#5 at 46	PC	PC	#6 at 48	PC	PC
8	4	PC	PC	PC	PC	PC	PC	PC	PC	PC
	5	PC	PC	PC	PC	PC	PC	PC	PC	PC
	6	PC	PC	PC	PC	PC	PC	#5 at 43	PC	PC
	7	PC	PC	PC	#5 at 41	PC	PC	#6 at 43	PC	PC
	8	#5 at 47	PC	PC	#6 at 43	PC	PC	#6 at 32	#6 at 44	PC
9	4	PC	PC	PC	PC	PC	PC	PC	PC	PC
	5	PC	PC	PC	PC	PC	PC	PC	PC	PC
	6	PC	PC	PC	PC	PC	PC	#5 at 39	PC	PC
	7	PC	PC	PC	#5 at 37	PC	PC	#6 at 38	#5 at 37	#4 at 48
	8	#5 at 41	PC	PC	#6 at 38	#5 at 37	PC	#7 at 39	#6 at 39	#6 at 39
	9[d]	#6 at 46	PC	PC	#7 at 41	#6 at 41	PC	#7 at 31	#7 at 41	PC
10	4	PC	PC	PC	PC	PC	PC	PC	PC	PC
	5	PC	PC	PC	PC	PC	PC	PC	PC	PC
	6	PC	PC	PC	PC	PC	PC	#5 at 37	PC	#6 at 45
	7	PC	PC	PC	#6 at 48	PC	PC	#6 at 35	#6 at 48	#7 at 47
	8	#5 at 38	PC	PC	#7 at 47	#6 at 47	PC	#7 at 35	#7 at 47	#7 at 38
	9[d]	#6 at 41	#4 at 48	PC	#7 at 37	#7 at 48	#4 at 48	#6 at 22	#7 at 37	
	10[d]	#7 at 45	#6 at 45	PC	#7 at 31	#7 at 40	#6 at 38	#6 at 22	#7 at 30	

For SI: 1 inch = 25.4 mm, 1 foot = 304.8 mm, 1 pound per square foot per foot = 0.157 kPa/m.
a. For design lateral soil loads, see Section 1610.
b. Provisions for this table are based on design and construction requirements specified in Section 1807.1.6.2.
c. "PC" means plain concrete.
d. Where unbalanced backfill height exceeds 8 feet and design lateral soil loads from Table 1610.1 are used, the requirements for 30 and 45 psf per foot of depth are not applicable (see Section 1610).
e. For height of unbalanced backfill, see Section 1807.1.2.

C.   Other foundation walls
    1.   Rubble stone foundation must be 16" minimum thickness. Do not use rubble stone if structure is Seismic Design Category C, D, E, or F.
    2.   Approved wood foundation systems are acceptable AF&PA PWF. Treat lumber and plywood per AWPA U1 (Commodity Specification A, Use Category 4B and section 5.2). (1807.1.4)

D.   Foundation walls must be drained. (1805.4)

E.   Unbalanced backfill height (height difference of exterior finish ground Level and lower of concrete footing top supporting foundation wall or interior of finish ground level) may run from exterior finish ground level to top of interior concrete slab, if that contacts foundation wall's interior surface.

F.   Design retaining walls for stability against overturning, sliding, excessive foundation pressure and water uplift. If keyway extends wall base for passive pressure and greater sliding stability, consider lateral soil pressures on both sides of keyway in the sliding analysis. Also design retaining walls against lateral soil action per sliding and overturning, with minimum 1.5 safety factor in each case. OBC 1605 inapplicable— use 0.7 x nominal earthquake loads, 1.0 x other nominal loads, and investigation with one or more of variable loads set at zero. Safety factor against lateral sliding is available soil resistance at base of retaining wall foundation ÷ net lateral force applied to retaining wall. Exception:
    a.   If earthquake loads included, minimum safety factor for retaining wall sliding and overturning is 1.1.

G.   Use embedded posts and poles (in earth or concrete footings) to resist both axial and lateral loads allowed, subject to:
    a.   Frictional resistance for structural walls and slabs on silts and clays limited to one-half of normal force imposed on soil by the weight of footing or slab.
    b.   Cannot use posts embedded in earth for lateral support for structural or nonstructural materials, i.e., plaster, masonry or concrete, unless bracing available to develops required limited deflection.
    c.   Treat wood poles per AWPA U1 for sawn timber posts (Commodity Specification A, Use Category 4B); for round timber posts (Commodity Specification B, Use Category 4B).

H.   Lateral load design criteria—determine depth to resist lateral loads per design criteria herein, or by other methods approved by registered design professional.
    a.   If nonconstrained (no lateral constraint at ground surface, i.e., rigid floor or rigid ground surface pavement), and no lateral constraint above ground surface, (i.e., structural diaphragm), determine depth of embedment needed to resist lateral loads per:

$$d = 0.5A\{1 + [1 + (4.36h/A)]^{1/2}\} \qquad \textbf{(Equation 18-1)}$$

where:

$A = \quad 2.34P/S_lb.$

$b =$ Diameter of round post or footing or diagonal dimension of square post or footing, feet (m).

$d =$ Depth of embedment in earth in feet (m) but not over 12 feet (3658 mm) for purpose of computing lateral pressure.

$h =$ Distance in feet (m) from ground surface to point of application of "P."

$P =$ Applied lateral force in pounds (kN).

$S_l =$ Allowable lateral soil-bearing pressure as set forth in Section 1806.2 based on a depth of one-third the depth of embedment in pounds per square foot (psf) (kPa).

b. If constrained, (lateral constraint at ground surface, i.e., rigid floor or pavement) use either of following to determine depth of embedment needed to resist lateral loads:

$$d = \sqrt{\frac{4.25Ph}{S_3 b}} \qquad \text{(Equation 18-2)}$$

or alternatively

$$d = \sqrt{\frac{4.25M_g}{S_3 b}} \qquad \text{(Equation 18-3)}$$

where:

M_g = Moment in the post at grade, in foot-pounds (kN-m).

S_3 = Allowable lateral soil-bearing pressure as set forth in Section 1806.2 based on a depth equal to the depth of embedment in pounds per square foot (kPa).

c. Vertical load resistance per vertical foundation pressure in Table 1806.2

I. Follow one of following methods for backfill in annular space around columns not embedded in poured footings:

   a. Concrete backfill with specified compressive strength ≥ 2,000 psi (13.8 MPa); hole ≥ 4" (102 mm) larger than column diameter at bottom OR 4" larger diagonal dimension of a square or rectangular column.

   b. Clean sand backfill, thoroughly compacted by tamping in layers ≤ 8" (203 mm) in depth.

   c. Controlled low-strength material backfill (CLSM).

TABLE 1806.2
PRESUMPTIVE LOAD-BEARING VALUES

CLASS OF MATERIALS	VERTICAL FOUNDATION PRESSURE (psf)	LATERAL BEARING PRESSURE (psf/f below natural grade)	LATERAL SLIDING RESISTANCE	
			Coefficient of friction[a]	Cohesion (psf)[b]
1. Crystalline bedrock	12,000	1,200	0.70	—
2. Sedimentary and foliated rock	4,000	400	0.35	—
3. Sandy gravel and/or gravel (GW and GP)	3,000	200	0.35	—
4. Sand, silty sand, clayey sand, silty gravel and clayey gravel (SW, SP, SM, SC, GM and GC)	2,000	150	0.25	—
5. Clay, sandy clay, silty clay, clayey silt, silt and sandy silt (CL, ML, MH and CH)	1,500	100	—	130

For SI: 1 pound per square foot = 0.0479 kPa, 1 pound per square foot per foot = 0.157 kPa/m.

a. Coefficient to be multiplied by the dead load.

b. Cohesion value to be multiplied by the contact area, as limited by Section 1806.3.2.

G

GARAGES (406.0)
A. Public (311.2, 311.3)
    1. Group 1 type: Garages used for the care, storage, repair, or dispensing fuel to all motor vehicles, are classified as Use S-1.
    2. Group 2 type: Garages used exclusively for parking vehicles are classified as Use S-2.
B. Structure shall comply with the height and area of the applicable use group.
    1. Open parking garages have separate requirements. (See "Open Parking Garages.")
    2. Group U garages are allowed up to 3000 sq. ft. as part of another building with the mixed use fire barrier.
    3. Carports are not garages when open on at least 2 sides.
    4. Private garages are limited to 1000 sq. ft. and 1-story. (406.1.1) All private garages are Group U.
C. Gasoline dispensing pumps see Ohio Fire Code, OAC 1301: 7-7-22.
D. Floors shall be graded to provide drainage through oil separators or collection traps.
E. All floors shall be concrete or other approved non-combustible and non-absorbent material.
F. Vehicle barriers required for drop off > 1'.
G. Enclosed garage ventilation requires a minimum of .75 cfm/sq. ft. (Table M-403.3, M-404)
H. Minimum 7' clear height.
I. Ramps for vehicles cannot be used for egress.
J. Garages for repairing non-odorized gas vehicles (such as LNG) must have gas-detection systems.

GAS APPLIANCES—COMBUSTION AIR FOR

Use manufacturer's installation instructions for solid fuel-burning appliances. Oil-fired appliances per NFPA 31. Combustion and dilation air for gas-fired appliances per International Fuel Gas Code.

GAS STATIONS (SERVICE STATIONS) (406.5)
A. All equipment per Fire Code
B. Canopies
    1. Minimum 13'-6" clear height.
    2. Constructed of noncombustible, FRTW, Heavy Timber or 1-hour protected.
    3. Combustible materials on the canopy must be:
        a. shielded from pumps,
        b. metal faced, or
        c. plastic 10' from buildings, no panel over 100 sq. ft., and total not over 1000 sq. ft.

GLASS
A. Glazing
    1. All glass shall be marked as to quality and thickness. (2403.1) (See also SKYLIGHTS.)
        a. Tempered glass (except spandrels) must be etched with label.
        b. Glass sloped 8–15° from vertical is designed for wind load. (2404.1)
    2. Areas where safety glass is required (2406.2). (See also 715.3.6, and 715.4 for fire doors.)

       a. Shower and tub enclosures

       b. Framed and unframed swinging doors

       c. Framed doors with large glass areas

       d. Sliding glass doors and storm doors

       e. Glazing in egress and ingress doors

       f. Fixed panels over 9 sq. ft., less than 18" from the floor and top edge more than 36" above floor within 3' of walkways. A bar at least $1^{1}/_{2}$" may be used in lieu of safety glass when at 34"–38" height.

       g. Glass within a 24" arc of either vertical door edge, and less than 60" from the floor, unless the glass and door is separated by solid partition or to a shallow closet.

       h. All glass in railings. (See also 2407.0.)

       i. Glass in walls and fences around pools within 60" of pool edge and bottom edge is less than 60" high.

       j. Glass within 36" of stairs, ramps, and landings, less than 60" above surface. Also, glass within 60" horizontal around bottom tread, except where railing protects. Exceptions are when there is a railing in front of the glass, or the glass > 18" from the stair railing.

       k. Fire Department access panels. (2406.4)

    3. Areas where safety glass is not required

       a. Any door glazing less than 3" in maximum dimension

       b. Mirrors with solid backing, leaded and decorative glass installations (unless on doors).

       c. Curved glass in revolving doors

       d. Glass doors in refrigerated cabinets

       e. Louvered windows and jalousies.

    4. Glass used in sporting areas such as tennis and racquet ball courts is considered a hazardous area and requires special impact tests for acceptance. (2408)

B. Glass block construction in accordance with Ch. 7 of TMS 402/ACI 530/ASCE 4

    1. Minimum average glass face thickness at 3/16". Surface contact mortar must be treated with polyvinyl butyral coating or latex-based paint. (2103.6)

    2. Use Type S or N mortar with noncorrosive ties per ASTM C270. (2103.8)

    3. Provide a $^{3}/_{8}$" expansion joint or caulking at panel perimeter.

    4. Lay the first course in non-hardening waterproof mastic. (1405.12.3)

       a. Glass block is allowed for atrium enclosures. (See also 404.6)

C. Glass veneer panels (1405.12)

    1. Use structural glass of $^{11}/_{32}$" minimum thickness.

    2. Maximum panel area is 10 sq. ft. with a 4' maximum dimension. Only 6 sq. ft. permitted when > 15 feet above grade.

    3. Backing—set glass in a mastic cement with a minimum 50% of glass bonded to minimum $^{1}/_{4}$" thickness mastic.

    4. The bottom of the panel shall rest on a non-corrosive metal frame which is anchored to the backing and caulked with waterproof material.

    5. Provide expansion joints at the ends and intermediate sections.

    6. Use approved bonding agent or device at horizontal joints into masonry.

    7. No other loading shall be applied to the panel.

    8. Minimum joint width of $^{1}/_{16}$".

D. Wired glass (715.5.3)

    1. $^{1}/_{4}$" minimum thickness is required.

    2. Wired glass must be labeled when used for fire protection openings.

3. Minimum $\frac{1}{8}$" thick steel frame.
4. $\frac{1}{4}$" wired glass panels may be used in 1-hour or less fire separation walls.
5. Maximum allowable sizes

TABLE 715.5.4
LIMITING SIZES OF WIRED GLASS PANELS

OPENING FIRE PROTECTION RATING	MAXIMUM AREA (square inches)	MAXIMUM HEIGHT (inches)	MAXIMUM WIDTH (inches)
3 hours	0	0	0
1½ hour doors in exterior walls	0	0	0
1 and 1½ hours	100	33	10
¾ hour	1,296	54	54
20 minutes	Not Limited	Not Limited	Not Limited
Fire window assemblies	1,296	54	54

For SI: 1 inch = 25.4 mm, 1 square inch = 645.2 mm².

GRANDSTANDS AND BLEACHERS (1028 AND ICC 300)

A. Exterior assembly seating qualifies as "smoke-protected seating" for determining requirements.
B. Construction
   1. Footboards and seatboards must support 120 plf (passenger load factor), with sway-bracing of 24 plf parallel and 10 plf perpendicular. (Table 1607.1)
   2. Grandstands and reviewing stands per ICC. (Table 1607.1)
C. Egress for smoke-protected seating
   1. Means of egress route must not hold smoke. Minimum roof height must be 15' above highest aisle.
   2. Any enclosed seating must be sprinkled, unless
      a. Performance floor is low-hazard and roof is a minimum of 50' above the floor, or
      b. Press boxes and storage is less than or equal to 1000 sq. ft. in area with open egress routes.
   3. All seating must have natural or mechanical smoke control (design per 909).
   4. Travel distance can be increased to 200' to vomitory or concourse, and then another 200' from vomitory to exterior exit ramp or stair. Travel distance cannot be measured across seats. For outdoor locations, maximum 400'. For outdoor seating, of Type I and II, unlimited travel. (1028.6.2)
   5. Egress widths are determined by Table 1028.6.2. For outdoor locations, multiply by 80% for aisles and stairs, and 60% for ramps and corridors. (1025.6.3)
   6. Dead ends are allowed to be 21 rows, or longer if travel to aisle is a maximum of 40 seats with increased aisle accessway width. The maximum number of seats per row as covered by Table 1028.10.1 can be exceeded when:
      a. The aisle accessway is increased for each seat by 0.3" for aisles at both ends and 0.6" for aisles at one end beyond the number in the table.
   7. Aisles
      a. The maximum number of seats for rows with aisles at both ends is 100.
      b. The maximum travel distance for rows with an aisle at one end is 50' to point of two egress routes.
      c. Use Table 1028.10.1 for seats per row.
      d. Minimum aisle width = same as for interior.

   D. Egress
      1. For seats with no backrests, a maximum of 16 in a dead-end row is permitted.
      2. Aisles are not required for seating when all of the following exist.
         a. Seats have no backrests and continuous flat seats are at least 11" wide.
         b. Maximum rise per row is 6", and maximum row spacing is 28".
         c. Maximum number of rows is 16.
         d. Egress routes are not obstructed, even by railings.
         e. Lowest seat board is maximum 12" above floor or grade.
      3. Footboards
         a. Footboards are required for all rows above the third row, or where there is 2′ above the aisle/floor/grade.
         b. Footboard can be seatboard where footboard is at least 24" wide and gaps are a maximum of ¼".
         c. Openings between footboards and seatboards more than 30" above ground must have guards with a maximum of 4" openings.
   E. Spaces under grandstands must be 1-hour rated, and open area under seats must not have exits or combustibles. Ed. Note: This requirement does not appear in the OBC. However, it is included in the International Fire Code and should be considered "good practice" when designing grandstands.

GUARD RAILS (1013, 1607, AND 2407)
   A. Guard rail requirements apply to parking garages, ramps, stairs, and open-sided walkways, retaining walls, balconies, and platforms with a drop of more than 30".
   B. Minimum height
      1. In general, guard rails must be at least 42" high.
      2. In dwelling units, guard rails must be at least 34" high and not more than 38" high, measured vertically from the leading edge of the stair tread nosing.
      3. At theatre fascia boxes and balconies, guard rails must be 26" high, except at bottom of aisles where guard rails must be 36" high.
   C. Maximum size openings
      1. In general, guard rail openings must be no larger than 4". Above 34" of rail, maximum opening of 8".
      2. In Use Groups I-3, F, H, and S, guard rail openings may be 21".
      3. For guards at end of balcony aisles, rail above 26" allowed 8" opening.
   D. Design loading (1607.7)
      1. Guard rails must withstand a concentrated load of 200 lbs. at any point and in any direction on top member.
      2. The top rail must resist a lateral load of 50 lbs./lineal foot. (20 lbs/lineal foot for non-public I-3, F, H, and S.)
      3. Guardrail infill must be designed for 50 lbs. on any 1 sq. ft.
   E. Glass is allowed if tempered or laminated, except in parking areas. (2407)

GYPSUM DRYWALL (CHAPTER 25)
   A. The building must be inspected prior to installation, usually with prior notice, for firestopping, and other factors.
   B. Do not use drywall where it will be directly exposed to weather.
   C. All wall areas subject to repeated dampness or moisture conditions such as bathtubs and showers shall be of water-resistant type board unless protected with a moisture-proof covering.
      1. Water-resistant gypsum board not allowed as tile backing when:

a. Over a vapor retarder at showers and tubs
b. Direct exposure to water or high humidity
c. On ceilings where framing > 12" for $1/2$" board or > 16" for $5/8$" board.

D. All gypsum wall materials must conform to appropriate referenced standards and be so marked.

E. References for fire-resistive drywall assemblies are listed in Table 2506.2

TABLE 2506.2
GYPSUM BOARD MATERIALS AND ACCESSORIES

MATERIAL	STANDARD
Accessories for gypsum board	ASTM C 1047
Adhesives for fastening gypsum wallboard	ASTM C 557
Elastomeric joint sealants	ASTM C 920
Exterior soffit board	ASTM C 931
Fiber-reinforced gypsum panels	ASTM C 1278
Glass mat gypsum backing panel	ASTM C 1178
Glass mat gypsum panel	ASTM C 1658
Glass mat gypsum substrate	ASTM C 1177
Gypsum backing board and gypsum shaftliner board	ASTM C 442
Gypsum ceiling board	ASTM C 1395
Gypsum sheathing	ASTM C 79
Gypsum wallboard	ASTM C 36
Joint reinforcing tape and compound	ASTM C 474; C 475
Nails for gypsum boards	ASTM C 514, F 547, F 1667
Predecorated gypsum board	ASTM C 960
Steel screws	ASTM C 954; C 1002
Steel studs, load-bearing	ASTM C 955
Steel studs, nonload-bearing	ASTM C 645
Standard specification for gypsum board	ASTM C 1396
Testing gypsum and gypsum products	ASTM C 22; C 472; C 473
Water-resistant gypsum backing board	ASTM C 630

H

HEATING INSTALLATIONS
(See also International Fuel Gas Code Sections 301, 303, 304)
A. All heating units must be labeled by an approved agency. (M-301.4)
B. Installation (M-304)
    1. Access opening to be not less than the size of the largest component. (M-306)
    2. Minimum 8' above floor in garages (when protected from vehicles).
    3. "Alcove" units must be used when room < 12 times volume of the appliance. (M-303.5)
C. Outdoor installation (M-303.6, M-306)
    1. Equipment must be approved for outdoor use.
    2. Roof shall support the unit load and any dynamic forces.
    3. Installation
        A 10' minimum clearance is required from the roof edge or a 42" high protective rail or parapet must be provided.
D. Appliances in attics and under floors must have switched light and receptacle per NEC.
E. Ductwork (See DUCTS.)
F. Prohibited locations (M-303.3)
    1. Sleeping, toilet, surgical, or bath rooms
    2. Storage closets
    3. Not prohibited for direct-vent and solid fuel-fired appliances with combustion air from outdoors.

HEAVY TIMBER (2304)
A. Timber may be single-piece or laminated solid, stress-grade lumber.
B. Minimum sizes for Type IV construction (nominal)
    1. Columns
        a. 8" × 8" columns are required when supporting floor loads.
        b. 6" width × 8" depth columns are required when supporting ceiling and roof loads.
    2. Floor framing
        a. Beams and girders must be 6" × 10" minimum.
        b. Trusses supporting floors must have 8" × 8" members.
        c. Arches from floor line supporting floors must be 8" × 8".
    3. Roof framing
        a. Arches from floor line must be 6" width × 8" depth lower half and 6" × 6" minimum for the upper half.
        b. Arches from walls must have 4" width × 6" depth minimum size members.
        c. Rafters or other roof framing must be at least 3" thick with solid blocking.
        d. The underside of any concealed roof framing shall be entirely enclosed with 2" material on the underside.
        e. For a fully sprinkled building, framing can be 3" minimum.
C. Flooring
    1. No concealed spaces are allowed.
    2. A 3" splined or T and G plank covered with 1" T and G flooring, $^{15}/_{32}$" plywood, or $^{1}/_{2}$" particle board is required.
    3. A 4"-wide plank set on edge, spiked together and covered with 1" particle board is allowed.

4. Stagger all flooring joints not over a support.
5. Provide a ½" firestopped clearance at perimeter.
D. Roof decking
1. No concealed spaces are allowed.
2. A 2" plank, T and G or splined; 1⅛" exterior glue plywood, or 3" plank set on edge and spiked is required.
E. Interior heavy timber walls
Use 2 layers of 1" matched boards, or 4" thick laminated boards, or 1-hour rated construction.
F. Wood columns and/or arches may be used on the exterior if the fire separation is over 20'.
G. 4" solid masonry at ends of timbers in 2-hour walls is required. (705.7)
H. Exterior walls must be noncombustible, with a minimum 2-hour rating when loadbearing. Fire-retardant treated wood is permitted within exterior assemblies of 2-hours.
I. Connections and bearing per 2304.9.

HIGH HAZARD (See USE GROUP CLASSIFICATION, Use Group H.)

HIGH-RISE BUILDINGS (403, 907, NFPA 70, NFPA 110, NFPA 111)
A. Special requirements
1. Applies to all buildings (except Groups H-1, H-2, H-3, A-5, open parking garages, special industrial uses, and airport traffic control towers) where the floors 75' above fire department access are used for human occupancy.
2. High Rise Occupancy Category II or IV structures—Concrete Frame (vertical loads primarily supported by columns) structures of reinforced or prestressed concrete (cast-in-place or precast) or combination, must meet applicable Sections 7.13, 13.3.8.5, 13.3.8.6, 16.5, 18.12.6, 18.12.7, 18.12.8. If nonprestressed reinforcing or prestressing steel must be present in column reinforced sector, must have minimum nominal tensile strength of ⅔ of required vertical strength (one-way) of floor or roof system connection to column, in each direction of reinforcement. Exception:
   a. If concrete slabs having continuous reinforcement sized ≥ 0.0015 x concrete area running each of 2 orthagonal directions AND monolithic OR equivalently bonded to beams, columns, or girders, nominal tensile strength of longitudinal reinforcing or prestressing steel in column must be ⅓ of required vertical strength of column's floor or roof system connection.
3. If frame structure of structural steel, open wed steel joist, joist girder either with or without structural steel elements, or composite steel or composite steel joist and concrete reinforcement:
   a. All column splices require minimum design strength in tension allowing transferring of design dead/live load tributary to column between splice and splice/base below.
   b. Beam and girder end connections need equal minimum nominal axial tensile strength to required vertical shear strength for allowable stress design (ASD) OR ⅔ required sheer strength for load and resistance factor design (LRFD), but ≥ 10 kips (45 kN). Sheer and axial tensile forces not assumed simultaneously active. Exception:
      a. If concrete slab or slab on metal deck attached to beam or girder with ≥ ⅜" diameter (9.5 mm) headed shear studs, spaced ≤ 12" (305 mm) on center as averaged over length OR other equivalent shear strength attachment, is supported by the beam, girder, open web joist, and joist girders

AND slab has continuous distributed reinforcement in both orthogonal directions, with area $\geq$ 0.0015 x concrete area, THEN nominal axial tension strength may be ½ required vertical shear strength for ASD OR ⅓ required shear strength for LRFD, BUT $\geq$ 10 kips (45 kN).

4. If bearing wall structure (vertical loads primarily supported by walls), require vertical ties in all load-bearing walls, longitudinal ties, transverse ties, and perimeter ties on all floor levels per Figure 1614.4.

   a. Precast bearing wall structures solely of reinforced or prestressed concrete, or those combinations must meet ACI, Sections 7.13, 13.3.8.5, 16.5.

   b. Longitudinal ties (consisting of continuous reinforcement in slabs; continuous/spliced decks or sheathing; continuous/spliced members framing to, within or across walls; connections of continuous framing members to walls) must extend across interior load-bearing walls and connect to exterior load-bearing walls, must be spaced $\leq$ 10 (3038 mm) on center, with minimum nominal tensile strength, TT, from Equation 16-46. Minimum nominal tensile strength for ASD may be 1.5 x allowable tensile stress x tie area.

$$T_T = wLS \leq \alpha_T S \qquad \textbf{(Equation 16-46)}$$

where:

$L =$ The span of the horizontal element in the direction of the tie, between bearing walls, feet (m).

$w =$ The weight per unit area of the floor or roof in the span being tied to or across the wall, psf (N/m^2).

$S =$ The spacing between ties, feet (m).

$\alpha_T =$ A coefficient with a value of 1,500 pounds per foot (2.25 kN/m) for masonry bearing wall structures and a value of 375 pounds per foot (0.6 kN/m) for structures with bearing walls of cold-formed steel light-frame construction.

c. Transverse ties (consisting of continuous reinforcement in slabs; continuous/spliced decks or sheathing; continuous/spliced members framing to, within or across walls; connections of continuous framing members to walls) cannot be placed farther apart than spacing of load-bearing walls, with minimum nominal tensile strength TT, from Equation 16-46. Minimum nominal tensile strength for ASD may be 1.5 x allowable tensile stress x tie area.

d. Perimeter ties (consisting of continuous reinforcement in slabs; continuous/spliced decks or sheathing; continuous/spliced members framing to, within or across walls; connections of continuous framing members to walls) must be within 4' (1219 mm) of the edge, must give nominal strength in tension $\geq T_p$ from Equation 16-47. Minimum nominal tensile strength for ASD may be 1.5 x allowable tensile stress x tie area.

$$T_p = 200w \leq \beta_T \qquad \text{(Equation 16-47)}$$

For SI:

$$T_p = 90.7w \leq \beta_T$$

where:

$w =$ As defined in Section 1614.4.2.1.

$\beta_T =$ A coefficient with a value of 16,000 pounds (7200 kN) for structures with masonry bearing walls and a value of 4,000 pounds (1300 kN) for structures with bearing walls of cold-formed steel light-frame construction.

e. Vertical tension ties (consisting of continuous or spliced reinforcing, continuous or spliced members, wall sheathing or other engineered systems) may be in bearing walls; if so, must be continuous over structure's height, with minimum nominal tensile strength (within bearing wall) equal to weight of wall within that story PLUS weight of diaphragm tributary to wall in story below, with at least two ties for each wall. Individual ties' strength need not exceed 3,000 lbs. per foot (450 kN/m) of wall tributary to tie for masonry walls OR 750 lbs. per foot (140 kN/m) of wall tributary to tie for cold-formed steel light-frame walls.

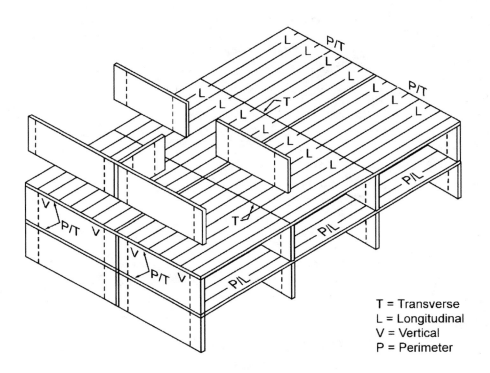

T = Transverse
L = Longitudinal
V = Vertical
P = Perimeter

GURE 1614.4
LONGITUDINAL, PERIMETER, TRANSVERSE AND VERTICAL TIES

5. Sprinklers shall be installed throughout the entire building (except portions which are open parking or telephone equipment, and electrical equipment rooms with smoke detectors, 1-hour walls, and 2-hour floors and ceilings).
6. Alternate sprinkler design
   a. Shut-off valves and flow control are required at each floor.
   b. Allowable building modifications: Type I-A may be I-B, Type I-B may be II-A (except for M, F-1, S-1).
   c. Shafts, except for exits and elevators, can be only 1-hour if sprinklers are at top and alternate floors.
B. A smokeproof tower is required for exit stairs over 75′ unless it is pressurized. (909.20)
C. Smoke detectors are required in every mechanical, electrical, transformer, telephone equipment, and elevator machine room. They are also required for HVAC system returns > 2000 cfm and any duct riser serving multiple stories. (907.2.13)
D. Elevators:
   1. Installation shall be for fire department access to all floors. (3003.2)
   2. At least 1 elevator shall allow for a 24" × 84" cot. (3002.4)
E. Standby electrical power (2702, Ohio Fire Code, OAC 1301:7-7-06)
   1. Locate the generator set in a 2-hour room.
   2. Provide for at least a 2-hour fuel supply.
   3. Piped natural gas may be approved for operation.
   4. Capacity of the standby power supply.
      a. Fire command power and lighting.
      b. Electric fire pumps.
      c. Emergency ventilation and detection for smokeproof enclosures.
      d. Elevators per Section 3003.
F. Emergency Electrical Power (403.4.8.1, 2702, Ohio Fire Code, OAC 1301:7-7-06)
   1. Power must be available in 10 seconds (700.12 NEC)
   2. Capacity of emergency power supply
      a. Exit signs and emergency lights.
      b. Elevator cab lights.
      c. Emergency voice and communication.
      d. Fire detection and alarm systems.
G. Exits
   1. Locked exit doors from the stairway side require an automatic, simultaneous unlocking feature from the fire command station.
   2. A 2-way communication system must be provided on every 5th floor to an emergency service station, which operates on a continuous basis in locked stairwells.
H. Alarm and communications
   1. Voice alarm (907.5)
      a. Voice alarm should be able to be heard throughout building as for public address. System operates with recorded messages, with manual override.
      b. Activation by detector, sprinkler, or manual station is required.
      c. Voice alarms should be located at elevators, elevator lobbies, corridors, exit stairs, rooms and tenant spaces over 1000 sq. ft., and rooms, suites, dwelling units (and guestrooms) of Use Group R.
   2. Fire department communication (907.2.13.2)
      a. A 2-way system is required.
      b. Communication system must operate between fire command station and every elevator, elevator lobby, emergency power and fire pump rooms, and exit stairs.

3. Fire command station (911)
   a. Fire command station is for fire department use.
   b. All readouts and controls for safety systems, including alarms, smoke control, sprinklers, and elevators should be located in the fire command station.
   c. Room to be minimum 200 sq. ft., and enclosed by one-hour.

HPM (415, 1018)

A. General
    1. Hazardous Production Materials (HPM, now designated Group H-5) are materials such as those found in semiconductor fabrication facilities and areas of comparable research and development.
    2. A fabrication area involves hazardous production materials and includes rooms such as dressing rooms and offices that are involved with the area processes.
B. Fabrication area size is determined by dividing quantities of allowed HPM by the density of the material.

TABLE 415.8.2.1.1
QUANTITY LIMITS FOR HAZARDOUS MATERIALS IN A SINGLE FABRICATION AREA IN GROUP H-5[a]

HAZARD CATEGORY		SOLIDS (pounds per square feet)	LIQUIDS (gallons per square feet)	GAS (feet^3 @NTP/square feet)
PHYSICAL-HAZARD MATERIALS				
Combustible dust		Note b	Not Applicable	Not Applicable
Combustible fiber	Loose	Note b		
	Baled	Notes b, c	Not Applicable	Not Applicable
Combustible liquid	II		0.01	
	IIIA		0.02	
	IIIB	Not Applicable	Not Limited	Not Applicable
Combination Class I, II and IIIA			0.04	
Cryogenic gas	Flammable			Note d
	Oxidizing	Not Applicable	Not Applicable	1.25
Explosives		Note b	Note b	Note b
Flammable gas	Gaseous			Note d
	Liquefied	Not Applicable	Not Applicable	Note d
Flammable liquid	IA		0.0025	
	IB		0.025	
	IC	Not Applicable	0.025	Not Applicable
Combination Class IA, IB and IC			0.025	
Combination Class I, II and IIIA			0.04	
Flammable solid		0.001	Not Applicable	Not Applicable
Organic peroxide				
Unclassified detonable		Note b		
	Class I	Note b		
	Class II	0.025	Not Applicable	Not Applicable
	Class III	0.1		
	Class IV	Not Limited		
	Class V	Not Limited		
Oxidizing gas	Gaseous			1.25
	Liquefied			1.25
Combination of gaseous and liquefied		Not Applicable	Not Applicable	1.25
Oxidizer	Class 4	Note b	Note b	
	Class 3	0.003	0.03	
	Class 2	0.003	0.03	Not Applicable

HAZARD CATEGORY		SOLIDS (pounds per square feet)	LIQUIDS (gallons per square feet)	GAS (feet³ @NTP/square feet)
Combination	Class 1	0.003	0.03	
	Class 1, 2, 3	0.003	0.03	
Pyrophoric material		Note b	0.00125	Notes d and e
Unstable reactive	Class 4	Note b	Note b	Note b
	Class 3	0.025	0.0025	Note b
	Class 2	0.1	0.01	Note b
	Class 1	Not Limited	Not Limited	Not Limited
Water reactive	Class 3	Note b	0.00125	
	Class 2	0.25	0.025	Not Applicable
	Class 1	Not Limited	Not Limited	
HEALTH-HAZARD MATERIALS				
Corrosives		Not Limited	Not Limited	Not Limited
Highly toxic		Not Limited	Not Limited	Note d
Toxics		Not Limited	Not Limited	Note d

For SI: 1 pound per square foot = 4.882 kg/m², 1 gallon per square foot = 40.7 L/m², 1 cubic foot @ NTP/square foot = 0.305 m³ @ NTP/m², 1 cubic foot = 0.02832 M³.

a. Hazardous materials within piping shall not be included in the calculated quantities.

b. Quantity of hazardous materials in a single fabrication shall not exceed the maximum allowable quantities per control area in Tables 307.1(1) and 307.1(2).

c. Densely packed baled cotton that complies with the packing requirements of ISO 8115 shall not be included in this material class.

d. The aggregate quantity of flammable, pyrophoric, toxic and highly toxic gases shall not exceed 9,000 cubic feet at NTP.

e. The aggregate quantity of pyrophoric gases in the building shall not exceed the amounts set forth in Table 415.3.2.

C. Egress (415.8.4.4)
   1. Two means of egress in any fabrication area or HPM area.
   2. One means of egress may pass through an adjacent fabrication area.
   3. Only the ground floor and one level above are permitted to be occupied fabrication areas. (415.8.2.3)

D. Separation (415.8.2.2)
   1. 1-hour assemblies shall separate fabrication areas from:
       a. Other fabrication areas
       b. Egress corridors, and
       c. Remainder of building.

E. Floors (415.8.2.4)
   1. Floors within fabrication areas shall be non-combustible.
   2. Floors must be liquid-tight at fabrication area separations.
   3. Unprotected openings are allowed solely for mechanical equipment for fabrication areas.
   4. Mechanical, ducts, and piping permitted (415.8.2.5)
       a. Mechanical, ducts, and piping may not penetrate more than two floors.
       b. Draftstops are required at floors.
       c. Interconnected areas are considered to be one fire area.

F. Ventilation (415.8.2.6)
   1. 1 cfm/sq. ft. minimum is required.
   2. Independent exhaust and return is required for each fabrication area. Exhaust ducts cannot go through fire walls. They require shaft enclosures and cannot use fire dampers.
   3. Continuous gas-monitoring devices connected to the emergency control station are required.

G. Electrical (415.8.2.8.1)

      1. Electrical equipment and devices shall comply with Chapter 27 and NFPA 70.

      2. The requirements for hazardous locations need not apply when:

         a. Average rate of air changes is 4 cfm/sq. ft. of area, and

         b. Rate of air change is 3 cfm/sq. ft. in any location.

H. Egress corridors (415.8.3)

      1. Egress corridors shall comply with requirements for corridors in 1018.

      2. Egress corridors must be separated from fabrication areas by 1-hour.

      3. Egress corridors are not used for transporting HPM except in piping.

      4. Existing corridors adjacent to the fabrication area under alteration may be used for transport of HPM when:

         a. A 1-hour fire separation is provided.

         b. The fire separation is the length of the common wall and the fabrication area, and the distance to the point of entry of the HPM into the egress corridor serving that fabrication area. (1018)

I. Service passages (415.8.4)

      1. Service passages must be part of the HPM use facilities.

      2. Service passages shall be separated from corridors by 1-hour.

      3. Service passages must be ventilated, minimum 6 air changes per hour or 1 cfm/sq. ft. (whichever is more).

      4. Two means of egress are required.

      5. Not more than 50% of the required exits may lead into the fabrication area.

      6. Self-closing doors are required and must swing in the direction of egress.

      7. Maximum of 75′ travel to an exit or a fabrication area is permitted.

      8. A 4′ maximum dead end is permitted.

      9. Emergency alarm system required (See Section 414.7.)

      10. Minimum width of 5 ft.

J. Storage of HPM (415.8.5)

      1. 2-hour rating required for rooms over 300 sq. ft., 1-hour when 300 sq. ft. or less. Rooms must be at perimeter of building, and minimum 30′ to property lines.

      2. Storage room doors must be ³/₄ hour, self-closing, and if two egress doors are required, one must go to exterior.

      3. Each workstation using HPM liquids must have the following.

         a. Drainage piping systems connected to a compatible disposition system.

         b. The work surface sloped or otherwise channeled for funneling liquids into disposition system.

         c. An approved means for draining the liquids into the disposition system.

      4. HPM materials must be separated from each other by 1-hour walls if up to 150 sq. ft. and 2- hour walls if more than 150 sq. ft. (Ohio Fire Code, OAC 1301:7-7-18, Section 707, 712)

      5. The storage rooms must be ventilated by 1 cfm/sq. ft. or 6 air changes/hour.

      6. Emergency alarm signal and gas detector system are required.

K. Piping and tubing (415.8.6)

      1. General

         a. Piping and tubing shall be metallic unless incompatible.

         b. Gas pipes shall be welded when using hazardous gas.

         c. Piping must be exposed in service passages.

         d. Piping and tubing must comply with all applicable ASME provisions with the responsibility for compliance on the owner.

      2. Installation in egress corridors or above other use groups

         a. Sprinklers are required in egress corridors where 6″ is the least dimension in concealed spaces.

  b. Ventilation of spaces is required at 6 changes/hr. with independent system.

  c. Liquids require drain receptors and cannot be a part of wall rating.

  d. Enclosure must be at least 1-hour.

  e. Emergency shut-off valves are required on supply lines at branch connections in fabrication areas and entrance into egress corridors.

  f. Gas requires fail-safe shut-off in pressurized pipes.

  g. Gas requires gas detection protective. (Ohio Fire Code, OAC 1301:7-7-18)

  h. Electric wiring shall be approved for Class I—Division 2.

 3. Across corridors, use metal sleeves coaxially closed. Corridors may be open to fabrication areas.

 4. All piping, tubing, and waste lines shall be identified per ANSI A13.1.

L. Emergency systems

 1. Manual alarm system required. (415.8.8)

 2. An emergency control station, outside the HPM fabrication area, is required for control of all fire safety systems. (415.8.9)

 3. Emergency power is required for all alarm and detection systems, exhaust systems, except that exhaust can run at half-rate. (415.8.10)

M. Sprinklers

 1. All H-5 occupancies are required to be sprinkled (903.2.5.2), with most areas at Ordinary Hazard Group 2 density. (Table 903.2.5.2)

 2. Exhaust ducts must have sprinklers—top and bottom and at every other floor level for vertical ducts, 12 ft. on center for horizontal ducts. Required for all ducts where largest dimension is 10" or more. If ducts are metal, they only need sprinklers if 10" or more, in the building enclosure, and have flammable fumes. (415.8.11)

INCINERATORS (M-907)

A. General: Incinerators must meet established emission limits. (O.R.C Section 3745-105-02)

B. Design of commercial and industrial types must be listed and labeled per UL 791 and installed per manufacturer's recommendations. (M-907.1)

INSTITUTIONAL

(See NURSING HOMES AND HOSPITALS; DAY CARE CENTERS; USE GROUP CLASSIFICATION, M. Use Group I-1, N. Use Group I-2, and O. Use Group I-3.)

L

LATHING AND PLASTERING (2500)

A. Lathing and furring (2510)
1. Metal lath must be corrosion-resistant.
2. Gypsum lath not to be used for cement plaster unless covered with weather barrier and self-furring lath.
3. Weather barriers must be vapor permeable when used over wood-based sheathing.

B. Interior plaster (2511)
1. Minimum 3 coats on metal/wire lath, 2 coats over solid lath.
2. Do not apply plaster to fiber insulation board.
3. Showers and lavatory splash areas must have moisture barrier over framing behind. (1210.2, 1210.3)
4. Minimum thickness of plaster must comply with ASTM C 842 and ASTM C 926. Plaster thickness is measured from the face of lath and other bases.

C. Exterior plaster (2512)
1. Minimum 3 coats on metal/wire, 2 coats on masonry.
2. Weep screeds required at sill, minimum 4" above grade.
3. The temperature must be 40°F for application, and not be exposed to freezing for 24 hours after set.

LIGHT (1205, 2600)

A. General (See also EGRESS AND EXITS, C. Egress lighting.)
1. All spaces used for human occupancy require artificial or natural light. A minimum of 10 footcandles at 30" above the floor.
2. All habitable rooms requiring natural light must have 8% of the floor area in glazing.
3. Adjoining room spaces may use the natural light from the main room if the connecting opening is over 25 sq. ft. but not less than 10% of the adjoining area. The combined area shall be used to determine the minimum glass area required. A sunroom can also be an adjoining room if the opening is 10%, but at least 20 sq. ft.
4. Stairways (for dwelling units)
    a. Both interior and exterior stairways require minimum of 1 foot-candle.
    b. Lighting outlets at each floor level (210.70 NEC) in dwelling units.
5. Natural light may be from courts and yards, or roofed porch with minimum dimensions.

B. Light transmitting plastics (2606)
1. Materials
    a. Class CC1 or Class CC2 is acceptable.
    b. Plastic panels must be identified.
    c. All plastic assemblies must sustain required load.
2. Light transmitting plastics are acceptable in openings as follows. (2608)
    a. Panel area does not exceed 25% of the wall area for each story.
    b. If sprinkled may be 50% of the wall area.
    c. Maximum size of a single pane above the first floor is 16 sq. ft. and a 4' maximum vertical dimension and minimum 3' spandrel between stories.
    d. Maximum height use is 75', unless sprinkled building.

C. Plastic wall panels (2607)
1. Light-transmitting plastics cannot be exterior wall panels in Groups A-l, A-2, H, I-2 and I-3. All other groups, panels can be used if no fire-resistance rating

required. Panels must be anchored on a foundation, waterproofed, and sealed with a coat of mastic or other approved waterproof coating.

2. The use of plastic panels does not change the building type.
3. Unless fire suppressed, plastic panels cannot be used above 75'.
4. See Table 2607.4 for allowable areas based on plastic Class. Greenhouses are excluded.
5. Allowable areas may be increased 100%, up to 50% of wall area when building is sprinkled.

Table 2607.4
AREA LIMITATION AND SEPARATION REQUIREMENTS FOR LIGHT-TRANSMITTING PLASTIC WALL PANELS[a]

FIRE SEPARATION DISTANCE (feet)	CLASS OF PLASTIC	MAXIMUM PERCENTAGE AREA OF EXTERIOR WALL IN PLASTIC WALL PANELS	MAXIMUM SINGLE AREA OF PLASTIC WALL PANELS (square feet)	MINIMUM SEPARATION OF PLASTIC WALL PANELS (feet)	
				Vertical	Horizontal
Less than 6	—	Not Permitted	Not Permitted	—	—
6 or more but less than 11	CC1	10	50	8	4
	CC2	Not Permitted	Not Permitted	—	—
11 or more but less than or equal to 30	CC1	25	90	6	4
	CC2	15	70	8	4
Over 30	CC1	50	Not Limited	3[b]	0
	CC2	50	100	6[b]	3

For SI: 1 foot = 304.8 mm, 1 square foot = 0.0929 m².

a. For combinations of plastic glazing and plastic wall panel areas permitted, see Section 2607.6.

b. For reductions in vertical separation allowed, see Section 2607.4.

D. Plastic roof panels (2609)
1. Plastic roof panels may be used in all buildings except Groups H, I-3, or I-2 with one of the following.
   a. The building is completely sprinkled.
   b. The roof is not required to have a rating.
   c. Panels meet the same requirements of the roof covering.
2. Spacing
   a. Space individual panels 4 horizontally (minimum).
   b. Space panels 0' if building is sprinkled, or greenhouses, or shelters < 5000 sq. ft.
   c. Space panels 6' from rated exterior.
3. Area limits

TABLE 2609.4
AREA LIMITATIONS FOR LIGHT-TRANSMITTING PLASTIC ROOF PANELS

CLASS OF PLASTIC	MAXIMUM AREA OF INDIVIDUAL ROOF PANELS (square feet)	MAXIMUM AGGREGATE AREA OF ROOF PANELS (percent of floor area)
CC1	300	30
CC2	100	25

For SI: 1 square foot = 0.0929 m².

MAXIMUM ALLOWABLE RATES

Plastic Class	Maximum Unit Area	Total Aggregate Area in % of Roof Area
C-1	300 sq. ft.	30%
C-2	100 sq. ft.	25%

4. Exceptions
   a. Areas may be increased 100% with sprinklers.
   b. For low hazard uses such as swimming pool shelters or greenhouses, there is no limit if the building is less than 5000 sq. ft. with at least a 4' fire separation.
   c. There is no area limit when used over patios or terraces in Use Group R-3.
E. Use of plastic in skylight assemblies (2610)
   1. Mount on a 4" curb and protect edge with metal unless skylight passes flame-resistance test, or if roof is not classified.
   2. Slope a flat panel 4:12 minimum.
   3. Dome height must be equal to 10% of the maximum span, but not less than 3".
   4. Curb is not required on an unclassified roof, or in Use Group R-3, or with a minimum 3:12 roof slope.
   5. Maximum unit area is 100 sq. ft. No limit applies if building is sprinkled.
   6. Aggregate must be 33% if C1 or 25% if C2 (may be increased 100% if building is sprinkled, or if the building has smoke vents).
   7. Assembly separation of 4' minimum is required. No separation is required if building is sprinkled. Group R-3 can have multiple skylights in one room if aggregate doesn't exceed maximum.
   8. Locate more than 6' from any exterior rated wall where openings must be protected.
   9. When used in combination with roof panels, use roof panel area requirements.
F. Lighting outlets required in dwellings for all habitable areas, hotel/motel guest rooms, and HVAC equipment in attics and crawl spaces. (210.70 NEC)

LINTELS
A. Steel lintels have allowable stress and strength design per 2107, 2108.

LOADS (See STRUCTURAL LOADS.)

M

MANUFACTURED HOMES

A. Manufactured homes used a single-family dwellings are governed exclusively by 24 C.F.R. 3280.

B. Manufactured homes other than single-family dwellings, or used for temporary travel, recreation or vacation are governed by the OBC.

MARQUEES (3106)

A. Marquees must be able to bear a minimum uniformly distributed live load of 75 psf (Table 1607.1).

B. Marquees shall be constructed of noncombustible material and be supported entirely by the building.

C. Marquees must not impede the clear passage of stairs or exits.

D. Marquees must not interfere with the operation of exterior standpipes, and installation or maintenance of exterior street lights.

E. Marquee roof
   1. Roof must not drain over the sidewalk.
   2. Slope roof to a downspout drain.
   3. Any part of a marquee which acts as a skylight needs to also comply with Chapter 24.

F. The design must withstand all wind and snow loads.

G. Marquee signs (3107.13)
   1. Must be of noncombustible materials.
   2. Cannot project beyond perimeter of marquee.
   3. Cannot extend beyond more than 6' above or 1' below the marquee. Maximum height of marquee signage is 8' in all cases.

MASONRY WALLS (CH. 21, 1405, 720)

A. General
   1. Wall ties per TMS 602/ACI 530.1/ASCE 6 as allowed in 2104.1.1.
   2. "Prism" testing of units is required when "unit strength" design method is not sampled and tested. (2105.2.2)

B. Installation (2104)
   1. Masonry cannot be wood-supported, except: (2304.12)
   2. Lintel design per 2107, 2108.
   3. Corbeling per 1.12 of TMS 402/ACI 530/ASCE 5.
   4. Chases and recesses need a lintel when opening is over 12" wide.
   5. Cold-weather procedures (per TMS 602/ACI 530.1/ASCE 6, Article 1.8D) must be followed when ambient temperature of < 40°F. Hot-weather construction procedures (per TMS 602/ACI 530.1/ASCE 6, Article 1.8D) when ambient temperature is < 100°F or < 90°F with wind over 8 mph.

C. Masonry veneer (1405.6.1)
   1. Can be supported on wood per Article 3.3 G1 of ACI TMS 602/530.1/ASCE 6/TMS 602.
   2. Flashing and weepholes required at first course above grade and points of support. (1405.3, 1405.4)

D. Fire resistance
   1. Prescriptive per Table 720.1.
   2. Anchored at points of support (structural floors, shelf angles, lintels) per Tables 721.1, 721.2, 721.3, and 721.4 for brick and tile.

3. Steel column protection prescriptive—Table 721.5.

TABLE 720.1(1)
MINIMUM PROTECTION OF STRUCTURAL PARTS BASED ON TIME PERIODS
FOR VARIOUS NONCOMBUSTIBLE INSULATING MATERIALS[m]

STRUCTURAL PARTS TO BE PROTECTED	ITEM NUMBER	INSULATING MATERIAL USED	MINIMUM THICKNESS OF INSULATING MATERIAL FOR THE FOLLOWING FIRE-RESISTANCE PERIODS (inches)			
			4 hour	3 hour	2 hour	1 hour
1. Steel columns and all of primary trusses	1-1.1	Carbonate, lightweight and sand-lightweight aggregate concrete, members 6"x 6" or greater (not including sandstone, granite and siliceous gravel).[a]	2½	2	1½	1
	1-1.2	Carbonate, lightweight and sand-lightweight aggregate concrete, members 8"x 8" or greater (not including sandstone, granite and siliceous gravel).[a]	2	1½	1	1
	1-1.3	Carbonate, lightweight and sand-lightweight aggregate concrete, members 12"x 12" or greater (not including sandstone, granite and siliceous gravel).[a]	1½	1	1	1
	1-1.4	Siliceous aggregate concrete and concrete excluded in Item 1-1.1, members 6"x 6" or greater.[a]	3	2	1½	1
	1-1.5	Siliceous aggregate concrete and concrete excluded in Item 1-1.1, members 8"x 8" or greater.[a]	2½	2	1	1
	1-1.6	Siliceous aggregate concrete and concrete excluded in Item 1-1.1, members 12"x 12" or greater.[a]	2	1	1	1
	1-2.1	Clay or shale brick with brick and mortar fill.[a]	3¾	—	—	2¼
	1-3.1	4" hollow clay tile in two 2" layers, ½" mortar between tile and column; ³/₈" metal mesh 0.046" wire diameter in horizontal joints; tile fill.[a]	4	—	—	—
	1-3.2	2" hollow clay tile; ¾" mortar between tile and column; ³/₈" metal mesh 0.046" wire diameter in horizontal joints; limestone concrete fill;[a] plastered with ¾" gypsum plaster.	3	—	—	—
	1-3.3	2" hollow clay tile with outside wire ties 0.08" diameter at each course of tile or ³/₈" metal mesh 0.046" diameter wire in horizontal joints; limestone or trap-rock concrete fill[a] extending 1" outside column on all sides.	—	—	3	—
	1-3.4	2" hollow clay tile with outside wire ties 0.08" diameter at each course of tile with or without concrete fill; ¾" mortar between tile and column.	—	—	—	2
	1-4.1	Cement plaster over metal lath wire tied to ¾" cold-rolled vertical channels with 0.049" (No. 18 B.W. gage) wire ties spaced 3" to 6" on center. Plaster mixed 1.2 ½ by volume, cement to sand.	—	—	2½[b]	⁷/₈
	1-5.1	Vermiculite concrete, 1:4 mix by volume over paperbacked wire fabric lath wrapped directly around column with additional 2"x 2" 0.065"/0.065" (No. 16/16 B.W. gage) wire fabric placed ¾" from outer concrete surface. Wire fabric tied with 0.049" (No. 18 B.W. gage) wire spaced 6" on center for inner layer and 2" on center for outer layer.	2	—	—	—
	1-6.1	Perlite or vermiculite gypsum plaster over metal lath wrapped around column and furred 1¼" from column flanges. Sheets lapped at ends and tied at 6" intervals with 0.049" (No. 18 B.W. gage) tie wire. Plaster pushed through to flanges.	1½	1	—	—
	1-6.2	Perlite or vermiculite gypsum plaster over self-furring metal lath wrapped directly around column, lapped 1" and tied at 6" intervals with 0.049" (No. 18 B.W. gage) wire.	1¾	1³/₈	1	—
	1-6.3	Perlite or vermiculite gypsum plaster on metal lath applied to ¾" cold-rolled channels spaced 24" apart vertically and wrapped flatwise around column.	1½	—	—	—

1. Steel columns and all of primary trusses (continued)	1-6.4	Perlite or vermiculite gypsum plaster over two layers of ½" plain full-length gypsum lath applied tight to column flanges. Lath wrapped with 1" hexagonal mesh of No. 20 gage wire and tied with doubled 0.035" diameter (No. 18 B.W. gage) wire ties spaced 23" on center. For three-coat work, the plaster mix for the second coat shall not exceed 100 pounds of gypsum to 2½ cubic feet of aggregate for the 3-hour system.	2½	2	—	—
	1-6.5	Perlite or vermiculite gypsum plaster over one layer of ½" plain full-length gypsum lath applied tight to column flanges. Lath tied with doubled 0.049" (No. 18 B.W. gage) wire ties spaced 23" on center and scratch coat wrapped with 1" hexagonal mesh 0.035" (No. 20 B.W. gage) wire fabric. For three-coat work, the plaster mix for the second coat shall not exceed 100 pounds of gypsum to 2½ cubic feet of aggregate.	—	2	—	—
	1-7.1	Multiple layers of ½" gypsum wallboard[e] adhesively[d] secured to column flanges and successive layers. Wallboard applied without horizontal joints. Corner edges of each layer staggered. Wallboard layer below outer layer secured to column with doubled 0.049" (No. 18 B.W. gage) steel wire ties spaced 15" on center. Exposed corners taped and treated.	—	—	2	1
	1-7.2	Three layers of ⁵/₈" Type X gypsum wallboard.[e] First and second layer held in place by ⅛" diameter by 1³/₈" long ring shank nails with ⁵/₁₆" diameter heads spaced 24" on center at corners. Middle layer also secured with metal straps at mid-height and 18" from each end, and by metal corner bead at each corner held by the metal straps. Third layer attached to corner bead with 1" long gypsum wallboard screws spaced 12" on center.	—	—	1⁷/₈	—
	1-7.3	Three layers of ⁵/₈" Type X gypsum wallboard,[e] each layer screw attached to 1⅝" steel studs 0.018" thick (No. 25 carbon sheet steel gage) at each corner of column. Middle layer also secured with 0.049" (No. 18 B.W. gage) double-strand steel wire ties, 24" on center. Screws are No. 6 by 1" spaced 24" on center for inner layer, No. 6 by 1³/₈" spaced 12" on center for middle layer and No. 8 by 2¼" spaced 12" on center for outer layer.	—	1⁷/₈	—	—
	1-8.1	Wood-fibered gypsum plaster mixed 1:1 by weight gypsum-to-sand aggregate applied over metal lath. Lath lapped 1" and tied 6" on center at all end, edges and spacers with 0.049" (No. 18 B.W. gage) steel tie wires. Lath applied over ½" spacers made of ¾" furring channel with 2" legs bent around each corner. Spacers located 1" from top and bottom of member and a maximum of 40" on center and wire tied with a single strand of 0.049" (No. 18 B.W. gage) steel tie wires. Corner bead tied to the lath at 6" on center along each corner to provide plaster thickness.	—	—	1⁵/₈	—
	1-9.1	Minimum W8x35 wide flange steel column (w/d ≥ 0.75) with each web cavity filled even with the flange tip with normal weight carbonate or siliceous aggregate concrete (3,000 psi minimum compressive strength with 145 pcf ± 3 pcf unit weight) Reinforce the concrete in each web cavity with a minimum No. 4 deformed reinforcing bar installed vertically and centered in the cavity, and secured to the column web with a minimum No. 2 horizontal deformed reinforcing bar welded to the web every 18" on center vertically. As an alternative to the No. 4 rebar, ¾" diameter by 3" long headed studs, spaced at 12" on center vertically, shall be welded on each side of the web midway between the column flanges.	—	—	—	See Note n
2. Webs or flanges of steel beams and girders	2-1.1	Carbonate, lightweight and sand-lightweight aggregate concrete (not including sandstone, granite and siliceous gravel) with 3" or finer metal mesh placed 1" from the finished surface anchored to the top flange and providing not less than 0.025 square inch of steel area per foot in each direction.	2	1½	1	1

	2-1.2	Siliceous aggregate concrete and concrete excluded in Item 2-1.1 with 3" or finer metal mesh placed 1" from the finished surface anchored to the top flange and providing not less than 0.025 square inch of steel area per foot in each direction.	2½	2	1½	1
	2-2.1	Cement plaster on metal lath attached to ¾" cold-rolled channels with 0.04" (No. 18 B.W. gage) wire ties spaced 3" to 6" on center. Plaster mixed 1:2½ by volume, cement to sand.	—	—	2½[b]	7/8
	2-3.1	Vermiculite gypsum plaster on a metal lath cage, wire tied to 0.165" diameter (No. 8 B.W. gage) steel wire hangers wrapped around beam and spaced 16" on center. Metal lath ties spaced approximately 5" on center at cage sides and bottom.	—	7/8	—	—
	2-4.1	Two layers of 5/8" Type X gypsum wallboard[c] are attached to U-shaped brackets spaced 24" on center. 0.018" thick (No. 25 carbon sheet steel gage) 1 5/8" deep by 1" galvanized steel runner channels are first installed parallel to and on each side of the top beam flange to provide a ½" clearance to the flange. The channel runners are attached to steel deck or concrete floor construction with approved fasteners spaced 12" on center. U-shaped brackets are formed from members identical to the channel runners. At the bent portion of the U-shaped bracket, the flanges of the channel are cut out so that 1 5/8" deep corner channels can be inserted without attachment parallel to each side of the lower flange. As an alternate, 0.021" thick (No. 24 carbon sheet steel gage) 1"x 2" runner and corner angles may be used in lieu of channels, and the web cutouts in the U-shaped brackets may be omitted. Each angle is attached to the bracket with ½"-long No. 8 self-drilling screws. The vertical legs of the U-shaped bracket are attached to the runners with one ½" long No. 8 self-drilling screw. The completed steel framing provides a 2 1/8" and 1½" space between the inner layer of wallboard and the sides and bottom of the steel beam, respectively. The inner layer of wallboard is attached to the top runners and bottom corner channels or corner angles with 1¼"-long No. 6 self-drilling screws spaced 16" on center. The outer layer of wallboard is applied with 1¾"-long No. 6 self-drilling screws spaced 8" on center. The bottom corners are reinforced with metal corner beads.	—	—	1¼	—
	2-4.2	Three layers of 5/8" Type X gypsum wallboard[c] attached to a steel suspension system as described immediately above utilizing the 0.018" thick (No. 25 carbon sheet steel gage) 1"x 2" lower corner angles. The framing is located so that a 2 1/8" and 2" space is provided between the inner layer of wallboard and the sides and bottom of the beam, respectively. The first two layers of wallboard are attached as described immediately above. A layer of 0.035" thick (No. 20 B.W. gage) 1" hexagonal galvanized wire mesh is applied under the soffit of the middle layer and up the sides approximately 2". The mesh is held in position with the No. 6 1 5/8"-long screws installed in the vertical leg of the bottom corner angles. The outer layer of wallboard is attached with No. 6 2¼"-long screws spaced 8" on center. One screw is also installed at the mid-depth of the bracket in each layer. Bottom corners are finished as described above.	—	1 7/8	—	—
3. Bonded pretensioned reinforcement in prestressed concrete[e]	3-1.1	Carbonate, lightweight, sand-lightweight and siliceous[f] aggregate concrete Beams or girders	4[g]	3[g]	2½	1½
		Solid slabs[h]		2	1½	1

Item	Ref.	Description				
4. Bonded or unbonded post-tensioned tendons in prestressed concrete[e, i]	4-1.1	Carbonate, lightweight, sand-lightweight and siliceous[f] aggregate concrete. Unrestrained members:				
		Solid slabs[h]	—	2	1½	—
		Beams and girders[j]				
		8" wide		4½	2½	1¾
		greater than 12" wide	3	2½	2	1½
	4-1.2	Carbonate, lightweight, sand-lightweight and siliceous aggregate. Restrained members:[k]				
		Solid slabs[h]	1¼	1	¾	—
		Beams and girders[j]				
		8" wide	2½	2	1¾	—
		greater than 12" wide	2	1¾	1½	—
5. Reinforcing steel in reinforced concrete columns, beams girders and trusses	5-1.1	Carbonate, lightweight and sand-lightweight aggregate concrete, members 12" or larger, square or round. (Size limit does not apply to beams and girders monolithic with floors.)	1½	1½	1½	1½
		Siliceous aggregate concrete, members 12" or larger, square or round. (Size limit does not apply to beams and girders monolithic with floors.)	2	1½	1½	1½
6. Reinforcing steel in reinforced concrete joists[l]	6-1.1	Carbonate, lightweight and sand-lightweight aggregate concrete. Siliceous aggregate concrete.	1¼	1¼	1	¾
	6-1.2		1¾	1½	1	¾
7. Reinforcing and tie rods in floor and roof slabs[l]	7-1.1	Carbonate, lightweight and sand-lightweight aggregate concrete. Siliceous aggregate concrete.	1	1	¾	¾
	7-1.2		1¼	1	1	¾

For SI: 1 inch = 25.4 mm, 1 square inch = 645.2 mm², 1 cubic foot = 0.0283 m³, 1 pound per cubic foot = 16.02 kg/m³.

a. Reentrant parts of protected members to be filled solidly.

b. Two layers of equal thickness with a ¾-inch airspace between.

c. For all of the construction with gypsum wallboard described in Table 720.1(1), gypsum base for veneer plaster of the same size, thickness and core type shall be permitted to be substituted for gypsum wallboard, provided attachment is identical to that specified for the wallboard and the joints on the face layer are reinforced, and the entire surface is covered with a minimum of $\frac{1}{16}$-inch gypsum veneer plaster.

d. An approved adhesive qualified under ASTM E 119 or UL 263.

e. Where lightweight or sand-lightweight concrete having an oven-dry weight of 110 pounds per cubic foot or less is used, the tabulated minimum cover shall be permitted to be reduced 25 percent, except that in no case shall the cover be less than ¾ inch in slabs or 1 ½ inches in beams or girders.

f. For solid slabs of siliceous aggregate concrete, increase tendon cover 20 percent.

g. Adequate provisions against spalling shall be provided by U-shaped or hooped stirrups spaced not to exceed the depth of the member with a clear cover of 1 inch.

h. Prestressed slabs shall have a thickness not less than that required in Table 720.1(3) for the respective fire-resistance time period.

i. Fire coverage and end anchorages shall be as follows: Cover to the prestressing steel at the anchor shall be ½ inch greater than that required away from the anchor. Minimum cover to steel-bearing plate shall be 1 inch in beams and ¾ inch in slabs.

j. For beam widths between 8 inches and 12 inches, cover thickness shall be permitted to be determined by interpolation.

k. Interior spans of continuous slabs, beams and girders shall be permitted to be considered restrained.

l. For use with concrete slabs having a comparable fire endurance where members are framed into the structure in such a manner as to provide equivalent performance to that of monolithic concrete construction.

m. Generic fire-resistance ratings (those not designated as PROPRIETARY* in the listing) in GA 600 shall be accepted as if herein listed.

n. No additional insulating material is required on the exposed outside face of the column flange to achieve a 1-hour fire-resistance rating.

TABLE 720.1(2)
RATED FIRE-RESISTANCE PERIODS FOR
VARIOUS WALLS AND PARTITIONS [a, o, p]

MATERIAL	ITEM NUMBER	CONSTRUCTION	MINIMUM FINISHED THICKNESS FACE-TO-FACE[b] (inches)			
			4 hour	3 hour	2 hour	1 hour
1. Brick of clay or shale	1-1.1	Solid brick of clay or shale[c].	6	4.9	3.8	2.7
	1-1.2	Hollow brick, not filled.	5.0	4.3	3.4	2.3
	1-1.3	Hollow brick unit wall, grout or filled with perlite vermiculite or expanded shale aggregate.	6.6	5.5	4.4	3.0
	1-2.1	4" nominal thick units at least 75 percent solid backed with a hat-shaped metal furring channel ¾" thick formed from 0.021" sheet metal attached to the brick wall on 24" centers with approved fasteners, and ½" Type X gypsum wallboard attached to the metal furring strips with 1"-long Type S screws spaced 8" on center.	—	—	5[d]	—
2. Combination of clay brick and load-bearing hollow clay tile.	2-1.1	4" solid brick and 4" tile (at least 40 percent solid).	—	8	—	—
	2-1.2	4" solid brick and 8" tile (at least 40 percent solid).	12	—	—	—
3. Concrete masonry units	3-1.1[f, g]	Expanded slag or pumice.	4.7	4.0	3.2	2.1
	3-1.2[f, g]	Expanded clay, shale or slate.	5.1	4.4	3.6	2.6
	3-1.3[f]	Limestone, cinders or air-cooled slag.	5.9	5.0	4.0	2.7
	3-1.4[f, g]	Calcareous or siliceous gravel.	6.2	5.3	4.2	2.8
4. Solid concrete[h, i]	4-1.1	Siliceous aggregate concrete.	7.0	6.2	5.0	3.5
		Carbonate aggregate concrete.	6.6	5.7	4.6	3.2
		Sand-lightweight concrete.	5.4	4.6	3.8	2.7
		Lightweight concrete.	5.1	4.4	3.6	2.5
5. Glazed or unglazed facing tile, nonloadbearing	5-1.1	One 2" unit cored 15 percent maximum and one 4" unit cored 25 percent maximum with ¾" mortar-filled collar joint. Unit positions reversed in alternate courses.	—	6³/₈	—	—
	5-1.2	One 2" unit cored 15 percent maximum and one 4" unit cored 40 percent maximum with ¾" mortar-filled collar joint. Unit positions side with ¾" gypsum plaster. Two wythes tied together every fourth course with No. 22 gage corrugated metal ties.	—	6¾	—	—
	5-1.3	One unit with three cells in wall thickness, cored 29 percent maximum.	—	—	6	—
	5-1.4	One 2" unit cored 22 percent maximum and one 4" unit cored 41 percent maximum with ¼" mortar-filled collar joint. Two wythes tied together every third course with 0.030" (No. 22 galvanized sheet steel gage) corrugated metal ties.	—	—	6	—
	5-1.5	One 4" unit cored 25 percent maximum with ¾" gypsum plaster on	—	—	4¾	—

Item	Reference	Construction				
		one side.				
	5-1.6	One 4" unit with two cells in wall thickness, cored 22 percent maximum.	—	—	—	4
	5-1.7	One 4" unit cored 30 percent maximum with ¾" vermiculite gypsum plaster on one side.	—	—	4½	—
	5-1.8	One 4" unit cored 39 percent maximum with ¾" gypsum plaster on one side.	—	—	—	4½
6. Solid gypsum plaster	6-1.1	¾" by 0.055" (No. 16 carbon sheet steel gage) vertical cold-rolled channels, 16" on center with 2.6-pound flat metal lath applied to one face and tied with 0.049" (No. 18 B.W. Gage) wire at 6" spacing. Gypsum plaster each side mixed 1:2 by weight, gypsum to sand aggregate.	—	—	—	2[d]
	6-1.2	¾" by 0.05" (No. 16 carbon sheet steel gage) cold-rolled channels 16" on center with metal lath applied to one face and tied with 0.049" (No. 18 B.W. gage) wire at 6" spacing. Perlite or vermiculite gypsum plaster each side. For three-coat work, the plaster mix for the second coat shall not exceed 100 pounds of gypsum to 2½ cubic feet of aggregate for the 1-hour system.	—	—	2½ [d]	2[d]
	6-1.3	¾" by 0.055" (No. 16 carbon sheet steel gage) vertical cold-rolled channels, 16" on center with ³⁄₈" gypsum lath applied to one face and attached with sheet metal clips. Gypsum plaster each side mixed 1:2 by weight, gypsum to sand aggregate.	—	—	—	2[d]
	6-2.1	Studless with ½" full-length plain gypsum lath and gypsum plaster each side. Plaster mixed 1:1 for scratch coat and 1:2 for brown coat, by weight, gypsum to sand aggregate.	—	—	—	2[d]
	6-2.2	Studless with ½" full-length plain gypsum lath and perlite or vermiculite gypsum plaster each side.	—	—	2½ [d]	2[d]
	6-2.3	Studless partition with ³⁄₈" rib metal lath installed vertically adjacent edges tied 6" on center with No. 18 gage wire ties, gypsum plaster each side mixed 1:2 by weight, gypsum to sand aggregate.	—	—	—	2[d]
7. Solid perlite and portland cement	7-1.1	Perlite mixed in the ratio of 3 cubic feet to 100 pounds of portland cement and machine applied to stud side of 1½" mesh by 0.058-inch (No. 17 B.W. gage) paper-backed woven wire fabric lath wire-tied to 4"-deep steel trussed wire[f] studs 16" on center. Wire ties of 0.049" (No. 18 B.W. gage) galvanized steel wire 6" on center vertically.	—	—	3⅛[d]	—
8. Solid neat wood fibered gypsum plaster	8-1.1	¾" by 0.055-inch (No. 16 carbon sheet steel gage) cold-rolled channels, 12" on center with 2.5-pound flat metal lath applied to one face and tied with 0.049" (No. 18 B.W. gage) wire at 6" spacing. Neat gypsum plaster applied each side.	—	—	2[d]	—
9. Solid wallboard partition	9-1.1	One full-length layer ½" Type X gypsum wallboard[c] laminated to each side of 1" full-length V-edge gypsum coreboard with approved laminating compound. Vertical joints of face layer and coreboard staggered at least 3".	—	—	2[d]	—
10. Hollow (studless) gypsum wallboard partition	10-1.1	One full-length layer of ⅝" Type X gypsum wallboard[c] attached to both sides of wood or metal top and bottom runners laminated to each side of 1"x 6" full-length gypsum coreboard ribs spaced 2" on center with approved laminating compound. Ribs centered at vertical joints of face plies and joints staggered 24" in opposing faces. Ribs may be recessed 6" from the top and bottom.	—	—	—	2¼ [d]

Item	Ref.	Construction				
	10-1.2	1" regular gypsum V-edge full-length backing board attached to both sides of wood or metal top and bottom runners with nails or 1⅝" drywall screws at 24" on center. Minimum width of rumors 1⅝". Face layer of ½" regular full-length gypsum wallboard laminated to outer faces of backing board with approved laminating compound.	—	—	4⅝ d	—
11. Noncombustible studs—interior partition with plaster each side	11-1.1	3¼" x 0.044" (No. 18 carbon sheet steel gage) steel studs spaced 24" on center. ⅝" gypsum plaster on metal lath each side mixed 1:2 by weight, gypsum to sand aggregate.	—	—	—	4¾ d
	11-1.2	3 3/8" x 0.055" (No. 16 carbon sheet steel gage) approved nailablek studs spaced 24" on center. ⅝" neat gypsum wood-fibered plaster each side over ⅜" rib metal lath nailed to studs with 6d common nails, 8" on center. Nails driven 1¼" and bent over.	—	—	5⅝	—
	11-1.3	4" x 0.044" (No. 18 carbon sheet steel gage) steel studs at 16" on center. On each side approved resilient clips pressed onto stud flange at 16" vertical spacing, ¼" pencil rods snapped into or wire tied onto outer loop of clips, metal lath wire-tied to pencil rods at 6" intervals, 1" perlite gypsum plaster, each side.	—	7⅝ d	—	—
	11-1.4	2½" x 0.044" (No. 18 carbon sheet steel gage) steel studs spaced 16" on center. Wood fibered gypsum plaster mixed 1:1 by weight gypsum to sand aggregate applied on ¾-pound metal lath wire tied to studs, each side. ¾" plaster applied over each face, including finish coat.	—	—	4¼ d	—
12. Wood studs interior partition with plaster each side	12-1.1 [l, m]	2" x 4" wood studs 16" on center with ⅝" gypsum plaster on metal lath. Lath attached by 4d common nails bent over or No. 14 gage by 1¼" by ¾" crown width staples spaced 6" on center. Plaster mixed 1:1½ for scratch coat and 1:3 for brown coat, by weight, gypsum to sand aggregate.	—	—	—	5⅛
	12-1.2 [l]	2" x 4" wood studs 16" on center with metal lath and ⅞" neat wood-fibered gypsum plaster each side. Lath attached by 6d common nails, 7" on center. Nails driven 1¼" and bent over.	—	—	5½ d	—
	12-1.3 l	2" x 4" wood studs 16" on center with ⅜" perforated or plain gypsum lath and ½" gypsum plaster each side. Lath nailed with 1⅛" by No. 13 gage by 19/64" head plasterboard blued nails, 4" on center. Plaster mixed 1:2 by weight, gypsum to sand aggregate.	—	—	—	5¼
	12-1.4 l	2" x 4" wood studs 16" on center with ⅜" Type X gypsum lath and ½" gypsum plaster each side. Lath nailed with 1 1/8" by No. 13 gage by 19/64" head plasterboard blued nails, 5" on center. Plaster mixed 1:2 by weight, gypsum to sand aggregate.	—	—	—	5 ¼
13. Noncombustible studs — interior partition with gypsum wallboard each side	13-1.1	0.018" (No. 25 carbon sheet steel gage) channel-shaped studs 24" on center with one full-length layer of ⅝" Type X gypsum wallboard° applied vertically attached with 1" long No. 6 drywall screws to each stud. Screws are 8" on center around the perimeter and 12" on center on the intermediate stud. The wallboard may be applied horizontally when attached to 3⅝" studs and the horizontal joints are staggered with those on the opposite side. Screws for the horizontal application shall be 8" on center at vertical edges and 12" on center at intermediate studs.	—	—	—	2⅞ d

	13-1.2	0.018" (No. 25 carbon sheet steel gage) channel-shaped studs 25" on center with two full-length layers of ½" Type X gypsum wallboard[e] applied vertically each side. First layer attached with 1"-long, No. 6 drywall screws, 8" on center around the perimeter and 12" on center on the intermediate stud. Second layer applied with vertical joints offset one stud space from first layer using $1^3/_8$" long, No. 6 drywall screws spaced 9" on center along vertical joints, 12" on center at intermediate studs and 24" on center along top and bottom runners.	=	=	$3^5/_8$ [d]	=
	13-1.3	0.055" (No. 16 carbon sheet steel gage) approved nailable metal studs[e] 24" on center with full-length $^5/_8$" Type X gypsum wallboard[e] applied vertically and nailed 7" on center with 6d cement-coated common nails. Approved metal fastener grips used with nails at vertical butt joints along studs.	=	=	=	$4^7/_8$
14. Wood studs—interior partition with gypsum wallboard each side	14-1.1 [h, m]	2"x 4" wood studs 16" on center with two layers of $^3/_8$" regular gypsum wallboard[e] each side, 4d cooler[n] or wallboard[n] nails at 8" on center first layer, 5d cooler[n] or wallboard[n] nails at 8" on center second layer with laminating compound between layers, joints staggered. First layer applied full length vertically, second layer applied horizontally or vertically.	=	=	=	5
	14-1.2 [l, m]	2"x 4" wood studs 16" on center with two layers ½" regular gypsum wallboard[e] applied vertically or horizontally each side[k], joints staggered. Nail base layer with 5d cooler[n] or wallboard[n] nails at 8" on center face layer with 8d cooler[n] or wallboard[n] nails at 8" on center.	=	=	=	5½
	14-1.3 [l, m]	2"x 4" wood studs 24" on center with $^5/_8$" Type X gypsum wallboard[e] applied vertically or horizontally nailed with 6d cooler[n] or wallboard[n] nails at 7" on center with end joints on nailing members. Stagger joints each side.	=	=	=	4¾
	14-1.4 [l]	2"x 4" fire-retardant-treated wood studs spaced 24" on center with one layer of $^5/_8$" Type X gypsum wallboard[e] applied with face paper grain (long dimension) parallel to studs. Wallboard attached with 6d cooler[n] or wallboard[n] nails at 7" on center.	=	=	=	4¾ [d]
	14-1.5 [l, m]	2"x 4" wood studs 16" on center with two layers $^5/_8$" Type X gypsum wallboard[e] each side. Base layers applied vertically and nailed with 6d cooler[n] or wallboard[n] nails at 9" on center. Face layer applied vertically or horizontally and nailed with 8d cooler[n] or wallboard[n] nails at 7" on center. For nail-adhesive application, base layers are nailed 6" on center. Face layers applied with coating of approved wallboard adhesive and nailed 12" on center.	=	=	6	=
	14-1.6 [l]	2"x 3" fire-retardant-treated wood studs spaced 24" on center with one layer of $^5/_8$" Type X gypsum wallboard[e] applied with face paper grain (long dimension) at right angles to studs. Wallboard attached with 6d cement-coated box nails spaced 7" on center.	=	=	=	$3^5/_8$ [d]
15. Exterior or interior walls	15-1.1 [l, m]	Exterior surface with ¾" drop siding over ½" gypsum sheathing on 2"x 4" wood studs at 16" on center, interior surface treatment as required for 1-hour-rated exterior or interior 2"x 4" wood stud partitions. Gypsum sheathing nailed with 1¾" by No. 11 gage by $^7/_{16}$" head galvanized nails at 8" on center. Siding nailed with 7d galvanized smooth box nails.	=	=	=	Varies
	15-1.2 [l, m]	2"x 4" wood studs 16" on center with metal lath and ¾" cement plaster on each side. Lath attached with 6d common nails 7" on center driven to 1" minimum penetration and bent over. Plaster mix 1:4 for scratch coat and 1:5 for brown coat, by volume, cement to sand.	=	=	=	$5^3/_8$

	15-1.3 [l, m]	2"x 4" wood studs 16" on center with $\frac{7}{8}$" cement plaster (measured from the face of studs) on the exterior surface with interior surface treatment as required for interior wood stud partitions in this table. Plaster mix 1:4 for scratch coat and 1:5 for brown coat, by volume, cement to sand.	—	—	—	Varies
	15-1.4	$3\frac{5}{8}$" No. 16 gage noncombustible studs 16" on center with $\frac{7}{8}$" cement plaster (measured from the face of the studs) on the exterior surface with interior surface treatment as required for interior, nonbearing, noncombustible stud partitions in this table. Plaster mix 1:4 for scratch coat and 1:5 for brown coat, by volume, cement to sand.	—	—	—	Varies [d]
	15-1.5 [m]	$2\frac{1}{4}$"x $3\frac{3}{4}$" clay face brick with cored holes over $\frac{1}{2}$" gypsum sheathing on exterior surface of 2"x 4" wood studs at 16" on center and two layers $\frac{5}{8}$" Type X gypsum wallboard [e] on interior surface. Sheathing placed horizontally or vertically with vertical joints over studs nailed 6" on center with $1\frac{3}{4}$"x No. 11 gage by $\frac{7}{16}$" head galvanized nails. Inner layer of wallboard placed horizontally or vertically and nailed 8" on center with 6d cooler [n] or wallboard [n] nails. Outer layer of wallboard placed horizontally or vertically and nailed 8" on center with 8d cooler [n] or wallboard [n] nails. All joints staggered with vertical joints over studs. Outer layer joints taped and finished with compound. Nail heads covered with joint compound. 0.035 inch (No. 20 galvanized sheet gage) corrugated galvanized steel wall ties $\frac{3}{4}$" by $6\frac{3}{8}$" attached to each stud with two 8d cooler [n] or wallboard [n] nails every sixth course of bricks.	—	—	10	—
15. Exterior or interior walls (continued)	15-1.6 [l, m]	2"x 6" fire-retardant-treated wood studs 16" on center. Interior face has two layers of $\frac{3}{8}$" Type X gypsum with the base layer placed vertically and attached with 6d box nails 12" on center. The face layer is placed horizontally and attached with 8d box nails 8" on center at joints and 12" on center elsewhere. The exterior face has a base layer of $\frac{5}{8}$" Type X gypsum sheathing placed vertically with 6d box nails 8" on center at joints and 12" on center elsewhere. An approved building paper is next applied, followed by self-furred exterior lath attached with $2\frac{1}{2}$", No. 12 gage galvanized roofing nails with a $\frac{3}{8}$" diameter head and spaced 6" on center along each stud. Cement plaster consisting of a $\frac{1}{2}$" brown coat is then applied. The scratch coat is mixed in the proportion of 1:3 by weight, cement to sand with 10 pounds of hydrated lime and 3 pounds of approved additives or admixtures per sack of cement. The brown coat is mixed in the proportion of 1:4 by weight, cement to sand with the same amounts of hydrated lime and approved additives or admixtures used in the scratch coat.	—	—	$8\frac{1}{4}$	—
	15-1.7 [l, m]	2"x 6" wood studs 16" on center. The exterior face has a layer of $\frac{5}{8}$" Type X gypsum sheathing placed vertically with 6d box nails 8" on center at joints and 12" on center elsewhere. An approved building paper is next applied, followed by 1" by No. 18 gage self-furred exterior lath attached with 8d by $2\frac{1}{2}$" long galvanized roofing nails spaced 6" on center along each stud. Cement plaster consisting of a $\frac{1}{2}$" scratch coat, a bonding agent and a $\frac{1}{2}$" brown coat and a finish coat is then applied. The scratch coat is mixed in the proportion of 1:3 by weight, cement to sand with 10 pounds of hydrated lime and 3 pounds of approved additives or admixtures per sack of cement. The brown coat is mixed in the proportion of 1:4 by weight, cement to sand with the same amounts of hydrated lime and approved additives or admixtures used in the scratch coat. The interior is covered with $\frac{3}{8}$" gypsum lath with 1" hexagonal mesh of 0.035 inch (No. 20 B.W. gage) woven wire lath furred out $\frac{5}{16}$" and 1" perlite or vermiculite gypsum plaster. Lath nailed with $1\frac{1}{8}$" by No. 13 gage by $\frac{19}{64}$" head plasterboard glued nails spaced 5" on center. Mesh attached by $1\frac{3}{4}$" by No. 12 gage by $\frac{3}{8}$" head nails with $\frac{3}{8}$" furrings, spaced 8" on center. The plaster mix shall not exceed 100 pounds of gypsum to $2\frac{1}{2}$ cubic feet of aggregate.	—	—	$8\frac{3}{8}$	—
	15-1.8 [l, m]	2"x 6" wood studs 16" on center. The exterior face has a layer of $\frac{5}{8}$" Type X gypsum sheathing placed vertically with 6d box nails 8" on center at joints and 12" on center elsewhere. An approved building paper is next applied, followed by $1\frac{1}{2}$" by No. 17 gage self-furred exterior lath attached with 8d by $2\frac{1}{2}$" long galvanized roofing nails spaced 6" on center along each stud. Cement plaster consisting of a $\frac{1}{2}$" scratch coat, and a $\frac{1}{2}$" brown coat is then applied. The plaster may be placed by machine. The scratch coat is mixed in the proportion of 1:4 by weight, plastic cement to sand. The brown coat is mixed in the proportion of 1:5 by weight, plastic cement to sand. The interior is covered with $\frac{3}{8}$" gypsum lath with 1" hexagonal mesh of No. 20 gage woven wire lath furred out $\frac{5}{16}$" and 1" perlite or vermiculite gypsum plaster. Lath nailed with $1\frac{1}{8}$" by No. 13 gage by $\frac{19}{64}$" head plasterboard glued nails spaced 5" on center. Mesh attached by $1\frac{3}{4}$" by No. 12 gage by $\frac{3}{8}$" head nails with $\frac{3}{8}$" furrings, spaced 8" on center. The plaster mix shall not exceed 100 pounds of gypsum to $2\frac{1}{2}$ cubic feet of aggregate.	—	—	$8\frac{3}{8}$	—
	15-1.9	4" No. 18 gage, nonload-bearing metal studs, 16" on center, with 1" portland cement lime plaster [measured from the back side of the $\frac{3}{4}$-pound expanded metal lath] on the exterior surface. Interior surface to be covered with 1" of gypsum plaster on $\frac{3}{4}$-pound expanded metal lath proportioned by weight—1:2 for scratch coat, 1:3 for brown, gypsum to sand. Lath on one side of the partition fastened to $\frac{1}{4}$" diameter pencil rods supported by No. 20 gage metal clips, located 16" on center vertically, on each stud. 3" thick mineral fiber insulating batts friction fitted between the studs.	—	—	$6\frac{1}{2}$ [d]	—

15. Exterior or interior walls (continued)	15-1.10	Steel studs 0.060" thick, 4" deep or 6" at 16" or 24" centers, with ½" Glass Fiber Reinforced Concrete (GFRC) on the exterior surface. GFRC is attached with flex anchors at 24" on center, with 5" leg welded to studs with two ½"-long flare-bevel welds, and 4" foot attached to the GFRC skin with $^5/_8$" thick GFRC bonding pads that extend 2½" beyond the flex anchor foot on both sides. Interior surface to have two layers of ½" Type X gypsum wallboard.[e] The first layer of wallboard to be attached with 1"-long Type S buglehead screws spaced 24" on center and the second layer is attached with $1^5/_8$"-long Type S screws spaced at 12" on center. Cavity is to be filled with 5" of 4 pcf (nominal) mineral fiber batts. GFRC has 1½" returns packed with mineral fiber and caulked on the exterior.	=	=	6½	=
	15-1.11	Steel studs 0.060" thick, 4" deep or 6" at 16" or 24" centers, respectively, with ½" Glass Fiber Reinforced Concrete (GFRC) on the exterior surface. GFRC is attached with flex anchors at 24" on center, with 5" leg welded to studs with two ½"-long flare-bevel welds, and 4" foot attached to the GFRC skin with $^5/_8$"-thick GFRC bonding pads that extend 2 ½" beyond the flex anchor foot on both sides. Interior surface to have one layer of $^5/_8$" Type X gypsum wallboard[e], attached with 1¼"-long Type S buglehead screws spaced 12" on center. Cavity is to be filled with 5" of 4 pcf (nominal) mineral fiber batts. GFRC has 1½" returns packed with mineral fiber and caulked on the exterior.	=	=	=	$6^1/_8$
	15-1.12[q]	2"x 6" wood studs at 16" with double top plates, single bottom plate; interior and exterior sides covered with $^5/_8$" Type X gypsum wallboard, 4" wide, applied horizontally or vertically with vertical joints over studs, and fastened with 2¼" Type S drywall screws, spaced 12" on center. Cavity to be filled with 5½" mineral wool insulation.	=	=	=	6¾
	15-1.13[q]	2"x 6" wood studs at 16" with double top plates, single bottom plate; interior and exterior sides covered with $^5/_8$" Type X gypsum wallboard, 4" wide, applied vertically with all joints over framing or blocking and fastened with 2¼" Type S drywall screws, spaced 12" on center. R-19 mineral fiber insulation installed in stud cavity.	=	=	=	6¾
	15-1.14[q]	2"x 6" wood studs at 16" with double top plates, single bottom plate; interior and exterior sides covered with $^5/_8$" Type X gypsum wallboard, 4" wide, applied horizontally or vertically with vertical joints over studs, and fastened with 2¼" Type S drywall screws, spaced 7" on center.	=	=	=	6¾
	15-1.15[q]	2"x 4" wood studs at 16" with double top plates, single bottom plate; interior and exterior sides covered with $^5/_8$" Type X gypsum wallboard and sheathing, respectively, 4" wide, applied horizontally or vertically with vertical joints over studs, and fastened with 2¼" Type S drywall screws, spaced 12" on center. Cavity to be filled with 3½" mineral wool insulation.	=	=	=	4¾
	15-1.16[q]	2"x 6" wood studs at 24" centers with double top plates, single bottom plate; interior and exterior side covered with two layers of $^5/_8$" Type X gypsum wallboard, 4" wide, applied horizontally with vertical joints over studs. Base layer fastened with 2¼" Type S drywall screws, spaced 24" on center and face layer fastened with Type S drywall screws, spaced 8" on center, wallboard joints covered with paper tape and joint compound, fastener heads covered with joint compound. Cavity to be filled with 5½" mineral wool insulation.	=	=	7¾	=

	15-2.1[d]	3⁵⁄₈" No. 16 gage steel studs at 24" on center or 2"x 4" wood studs at 24" on center. Metal lath attached to the exterior side of studs with minimum 1" long No. 6 drywall screws at 6" on center and covered with minimum ¾" thick portland cement plaster. Thin veneer brick units of clay or shale complying with ASTM C 1088, Grade TBS or better, installed in running bond in accordance with Section 1405.10. Combined total thickness of the portland cement plaster, mortar and thin veneer brick units shall be not less than 1¾". Interior side covered with one layer of ⁵⁄₈" thick Type X gypsum wallboard attached to studs with 1" long No. 6 drywall screws at 12" on center.				6
	15-2.2[d]	3⁵⁄₈" No. 16 gage steel studs at 24" on center or 2"x 4" wood studs at 24" on center. Metal lath attached to the exterior side of studs with minimum 1" long No. 6 drywall screws at 6" on center and covered with minimum ¾" thick portland cement plaster. Thin veneer brick units of clay or shale complying with ASTM C 1088, Grade TBS or better, installed in running bond in accordance with Section 1405.10. Combined total thickness of the portland cement plaster, mortar and thin veneer brick units shall be not less than 2". Interior side covered with two layers of ⁵⁄₈" thick Type X gypsum wallboard. Bottom layer attached to studs with 1" long No. 6 drywall screws at 24" on center. Top layer attached to studs with 1⁵⁄₈" long No. 6 drywall screws at 12" on center.				6⁷⁄₈
	15-2.3[d]	3⁵⁄₈" No. 16 gage steel studs at 16" on center or 2"x 4" wood studs at 16" on center. Where metal lath is used, attach to the exterior side of studs with minimum 1" long No. 6 drywall screws at 6" on center. Brick units of clay or shale not less than 2⁵⁄₈" thick complying with ASTM C 216 installed in accordance with Section 1405.6 with a minimum 1" air space. Interior side covered with one layer of ⁵⁄₈" thick Type X gypsum wallboard attached to studs with 1" long No. 6 drywall screws at 12" on center.				7⁷⁄₈
	15-2.4[d]	3⁵⁄₈" No. 16 gage steel studs at 16" on center or 2"x 4" wood studs at 16" on center. Where metal lath is used, attach to the exterior side of studs with minimum 1" long No. 6 drywall screws at 6" on center. Brick units of clay or shale not less than 2⁵⁄₈" thick complying with ASTM C 216 installed in accordance with Section 1405.6 with a minimum 1" air space. Interior side covered with two layers of ⁵⁄₈" thick Type X gypsum wallboard. Bottom layer attached to studs with 1" long No. 6 drywall screws at 24" on center. Top layer attached to studs with 1⁵⁄₈" long No. 6 drywall screws at 12" on center.				8½
16. Exterior walls rated for fire resistance from the inside only in accordance with Section 705.5.	16-1.1[q]	2"x 4" wood studs at 16" centers with double top plates, single bottom plate, interior side covered with ⁵⁄₈" Type X gypsum wallboard, 4" wide, applied horizontally unblocked, and fastened with 2¼" Type S drywall screws, spaced 12" on center, wallboard joints covered with paper tape and joint compound, fastener heads covered with joint compound. Exterior covered with ³⁄₈" thick wood structural panels, applied vertically, horizontal joints blocked and fastened with 6d common nails (bright) — 12" on center in the field, and 6" on center panel edges. Cavity to be filled with 3½" mineral wool insulation. Rating established for exposure from interior side only.	—	—	—	4½

16-1.2[q]	2"x 6" (51mm x 152 mm) wood studs at 16" centers with double top plates, single bottom plate; interior side covered with $^5/_8$" Type X gypsum wallboard, 4" wide, applied horizontally or vertically with vertical joints over studs and fastened with 2¼" Type S drywall screws, spaced 12" on center, wallboard joints covered with paper tape and joint compound, fastener heads covered with joint compound, exterior side covered with $^7/_{16}$" wood structural panels fastened with 6d common nails (bright) spaced 12" on center in the field and 6" on center along the panel edges. Cavity to be filled with 5½" mineral wool insulation. Rating established from the gypsum-covered side only.	—	—	—	6 $^9/_{16}$
16-1.3	2"x 6" wood studs at 16" centers with double top plates, single bottom plates; interior side covered with $^5/_8$" Type X gypsum wallboard, 4" wide, applied vertically with all joints over framing or blocking and fastened with 2¼" Type S drywall screws spaced 7" on center. Joints to be covered with tape and joint compound. Exterior covered with $^3/_8$" wood structural panels, applied vertically with edges over framing or blocking and fastened with 6d common nails (bright) at 12" on center in the field and 6" on center on panel edges. R-19 mineral fiber insulation installed in stud cavity. Rating established from the gypsum-covered side only.	—	—	—	6½

For SI: 1 inch = 25.4 mm, 1 square inch = 645.2 mm², 1 cubic foot = 0.0283 m³.

a. Staples with equivalent holding power and penetration shall be permitted to be used as alternate fasteners to nails for attachment to wood framing.

b. Thickness shown for brick and clay tile is nominal thicknesses unless plastered, in which case thicknesses are net. Thickness shown for concrete masonry and clay masonry is equivalent thickness defined in Section 721.3.1 for concrete masonry and Section 721.4.1.1 for clay masonry. Where all cells are solid grouted or filled with silicone-treated perlite loose-fill insulation; vermiculite loose-fill insulation; or expanded clay, shale or slate lightweight aggregate, the equivalent thickness shall be the thickness of the block or brick using specified dimensions as defined in Chapter 21. Equivalent thickness may also include the thickness of applied plaster and lath or gypsum wallboard, where specified.

c. For units in which the net cross-sectional area of cored brick in any plane parallel to the surface containing the cores is at least 75 percent of the gross cross-sectional area measured in the same plane.

d. Shall be used for nonbearing purposes only.

e. For all of the construction with gypsum wallboard described in this table, gypsum base for veneer plaster of the same size, thickness and core type shall be permitted to be substituted for gypsum wallboard, provided attachment is identical to that specified for the wallboard, and the joints on the face layer are reinforced and the entire surface is covered with a minimum of $^1/_{16}$-inch gypsum veneer plaster.

f. The fire-resistance time period for concrete masonry units meeting the equivalent thicknesses required for a 2-hour fire-resistance rating in Item 3, and having a thickness of not less than 7$^5/_8$ inches is 4 hours when cores which are not grouted are filled with silicone-treated perlite loose-fill insulation; vermiculite loose-fill insulation; or expanded clay, shale or slate lightweight aggregate, sand or slag having a maximum particle size of $^3/_8$ inch.

g. The fire-resistance rating of concrete masonry units composed of a combination of aggregate types or where plaster is applied directly to the concrete masonry shall be determined in accordance with ACI 216.1/TMS 0216. Lightweight aggregates shall have a maximum combined density of 65 pounds per cubic foot.

h. See also Note b. The equivalent thickness shall be permitted to include the thickness of cement plaster or 1.5 times the thickness of gypsum plaster applied in accordance with the requirements of Chapter 25.

i. Concrete walls shall be reinforced with horizontal and vertical temperature reinforcement as required by Chapter 19.

j. Studs are welded truss wire studs with 0.18 inch (No. 7 B.W. gage) flange wire and 0.18 inch (No. 7 B.W. gage) truss wires.

k. Nailable metal studs consist of two channel studs spot welded back to back with a crimped web forming a nailing groove.

l. Wood structural panels shall be permitted to be installed between the fire protection and the wood studs on either the interior or exterior side of the wood frame assemblies in this table, provided the length of the fasteners used to attach the fire protection is increased by an amount at least equal to the thickness of the wood structural panel.

m. The design stress of studs shall be reduced to 78 percent of allowable $F'c$ with the maximum not greater than 78 percent of the calculated stress with studs having a slenderness ratio L/d of 33.

n. For properties of cooler or wallboard nails, see ASTM C 514, ASTM C 547 or ASTM F 1667.

o. Generic fire-resistance ratings (those not designated as PROPRIETARY* in the listing) in the GA 600 shall be accepted as if herein listed.

p. NCMA TEK 5-8A shall be permitted for the design of fire walls.

q. The design stress of studs shall be equal to a maximum of 100 percent of the allowable $F'c$ calculated in accordance with Section 2306.

TABLE 720.1(3)
MINIMUM PROTECTION FOR FLOOR AND ROOF SYSTEMS[a, q]

FLOOR OR ROOF CONSTRUCTION	ITEM NUMBER	CEILING CONSTRUCTION	THICKNESS OF FLOOR OR ROOF SLAB (inches)				MINIMUM THICKNESS OF CEILING (inches)			
			4 hour	3 hour	2 hour	1 hour	4 hour	3 hour	2 hour	1 hour
1. Siliceous aggregate concrete	1-1.1	Slab (no ceiling required). Minimum cover over nonprestressed reinforcement shall not be less than ¾" [b].	7.0	6.2	5.0	3.5	—	—	—	—
2. Carbonate aggregate concrete	2-1.1		6.6	5.7	4.6	3.2	—	—	—	—
3. Sand-lightweight concrete	3-1.1		5.4	4.6	3.8	2.7	—	—	—	—
4. Lightweight concrete	4-1.1		5.1	4.4	3.6	2.5	—	—	—	—
5. Reinforced concrete	5-1.1	Slab with suspended ceiling of vermiculite gypsum plaster over metal lath attached to ¾" cold-rolled channels spaced 12" on center. Ceiling located 6" minimum below joists.	3	2	—	—	1	¾	—	—
	5-2.1	3/8" Type X gypsum wallboard[c] attached to 0.018 inch (No. 25 carbon sheet steel gage) by $^7/_8$" deep by $2^5/_8$" hat-shaped galvanized steel channels with 1"-long No. 6 screws. The channels are spaced 24" on center, span 35" and are supported along their length at 35" intervals by 0.033" (No. 21 galvanized sheet gage) galvanized steel flat strap hangers having formed edges that engage the lips of the channel. The strap hangers are attached to the side of the concrete joists with $^5/_{32}$" by 1¼" long power-driven fasteners. The wallboard is installed with the long dimension perpendicular to the channels. All end joints occur on channels and supplementary channels are installed parallel to the main channels, 12" each side, at end joint occurrences. The finished ceiling is located approximately 12" below the soffit of the floor slab.	—	—	2½	—	—	—	$^5/_8$	—

6. Steel joists constructed with a poured reinforced concrete slab on metal lath forms or steel form units[d, e].	6-1.1	Gypsum plaster on metal lath attached to the bottom cord with single No. 16 gage or doubled No. 18 gage wire ties spaced 6" on center. Plaster mixed 1:2 for scratch coat, 1:3 for brown coat, by weight, gypsum-to-sand aggregate for 2-hour system. For 3-hour system plaster is neat.	=	=	2½	2¼	=	=	¾	5/8
	6-2.1	Vermiculite gypsum plaster on metal lath attached to the bottom chord with single No. 16 gage or doubled 0.049-inch (No. 18 B.W. gage) wire ties 6" on center.	=	2	=	=	=	5/8	=	=
	6-3.1	Cement plaster over metal lath attached to the bottom chord of joists with single No. 16 gage or doubled 0.049" (No. 18 B.W. gage) wire ties spaced 6" on center. Plaster mixed 1:2 for scratch coat, 1:3 for brown coat for 1-hour system and 1:1 for scratch coat, 1:1½ for brown coat for 2-hour system, by weight, cement to sand.	=	=	=	2	=	=	=	5/8 f
	6-4.1	Ceiling of 5/8" Type X wallboard[c], attached to 7/8" deep by 2 5/8" by 0.021 inch (No. 25 carbon sheet steel gage) hat-shaped furring channels 12" on center with 1" long No. 6 wallboard screws at 8" on center. Channels wire tied to bottom chord of joists with doubled 0.049 inch (No. 18 B.W. gage) wire or suspended below joists on wire hangers.[g]	=	=	2½	=	=	=	5/8	=
	6-5.1	Wood-fibered gypsum plaster mixed 1:1 by weight gypsum to sand aggregate applied over metal lath. Lath tied 6" on center to ¾" channels spaced 13½" on center. Channels secured to joists at each intersection with two strands of 0.049 inch (No. 18 B.W. gage) galvanized wire.	=	=	2½	=	=	=	¾	=
7. Reinforced concrete slabs and joists with hollow clay tile fillers laid end to end in rows 2½" or more apart; reinforcement placed between rows and concrete cast around and over tile.	7-1.1	5/8" gypsum plaster on bottom of floor or roof construction.	=	=	8[h]	=	=	=	5/8	=
	7-1.2	None	=	=	=	5½[i]	=	=	=	=

8. Steel joists constructed with a reinforced concrete slab on top poured on a ½" deep steel deck.[e]	8-1.1	Vermiculite gypsum plaster on metal lath attached to ¾" cold-rolled channels with 0.049" (No. 18 B.W. gage) wire ties spaced 6" on center.	2½[j]	—	—	—	¾	—	—	—
9. 3" deep cellular steel deck with concrete slab on top. Slab thickness measured to top.	9-1.1	Suspended ceiling of vermiculite gypsum plaster base coat and vermiculite acoustical plaster on metal lath attached at 6" intervals to ¾" cold-rolled channels spaced 12" on center and secured to 1½" cold-rolled channels spaced 36" on center with 0.065" (No. 16 B.W. gage) wire. 1½" channels supported by No. 8 gage wire hangers at 36" on center. Beams within envelope and with a 2½" airspace between beam soffit and lath have a 4-hour rating.	2½	—	—	—	1⅛[k]	—	—	—
10. 1½"-deep steel roof deck on steel framing. Insulation board, 30 pcf density, composed of wood fibers with cement binders of thickness shown bonded to deck with unified asphalt adhesive. Covered with a Class A or B roof covering.	10-1.1	Ceiling of gypsum plaster on metal lath. Lath attached to ¾" furring channels with 0.049" (No. 18 B.W. gage) wire ties spaced 6" on center. ¾" channel saddle tied to 2" channels with doubled 0.065" (No. 16 B.W. gage) wire ties. 2" channels spaced 36" on center suspended 2" below steel framing and saddle-tied with 0.165" (No. 8 B.W. gage) wire. Plaster mixed 1:2 by weight, gypsum-to-sand aggregate.	—	—	1⅞	1	—	—	¾[l]	¾[l]
11. 1½"-deep steel roof deck on steel-framing wood fiber insulation board, 17.5 pcf density on top applied over a 15-lb asphalt-saturated felt. Class A or B roof covering.	11-1.1	Ceiling of gypsum plaster on metal lath. Lath attached to ¾" furring channels with 0.049" (No. 18 B.W. gage) wire ties spaced 6" on center. ¾" channels saddle tied to 2" channels with doubled 0.065" (No. 16 B.W. gage) wire ties. 2" channels spaced 36" on center suspended 2" below steel framing and saddle tied with 0.165" (No. 8 B.W. gage) wire. Plaster mixed 1:2 for scratch coat and 1:3 for brown coat, by weight, gypsum-to-sand aggregate for 1-hour system. For 2-hour system, plaster mix is 1:2 by weight, gypsum-to-sand aggregate.	—	—	1½	1	—	—	⅞[g]	¾[l]
12. 1½"deep steel roof deck on steel-framing insulation of rigid board consisting of expanded perlite and fibers impregnated with integral asphalt waterproofing; density 9 to 12 pcf secured to metal roof deck by ½" wide ribbons of waterproof, cold-process liquid adhesive spaced 6" apart. Steel joist or light steel construction with	12-1.1	Gypsum-vermiculite plaster on metal lath wire tied at 6" intervals to ¾" furring channels spaced 12" on center and wire tied to 2" runner channels spaced 32" on center. Runners wire tied to bottom chord of steel joists.	—	—	1	—	—	—	⅞	—

Item	Ref.	Ceiling Construction								
metal roof deck, insulation, and Class A or B built-up roof covering.[e]										
13. Double wood floor over wood joists spaced 16" on center.[m,n]	13-1.1	Gypsum plaster over $\frac{3}{8}$" Type X gypsum lath. Lath initially applied with not less than four $1\frac{1}{8}$" by No. 13 gage by $\frac{19}{64}$" head plasterboard blued nails per bearing. Continuous stripping over lath along all joist lines. Stripping consists of 3" wide strips of metal lath attached by $1\frac{1}{2}$"by No. 11 gage by $\frac{1}{2}$" head roofing nails spaced 6" on center. Alternate stripping consists of 3" wide 0.049" diameter wire stripping weighing 1 pound per square yard and attached by No.16 gage by $1\frac{1}{2}$" by $\frac{1}{4}$" crown width staples, spaced 4" on center. Where alternate stripping is used, the lath nailing may consist of two nails at each end and one nail at each intermediate bearing. Plaster mixed 1:2 by weight, gypsum-to-sand aggregate.	=	=	=	=	=	=	=	$\frac{7}{8}$
	13-1.2	Cement or gypsum plaster on metal lath. Lath fastened with $1\frac{1}{2}$" by No. 11 gage by $\frac{7}{16}$" head barbed shank roofing nails spaced 5" on center. Plaster mixed 1:2 for scratch coat and 1:3 for brown coat, by weight, cement to sand aggregate.	=	=	=	=	=	=	=	$\frac{5}{8}$
	13-1.3	Perlite or vermiculite gypsum plaster on metal lath secured to joists with $1\frac{1}{2}$" by No. 11 gage by $\frac{7}{16}$" head barbed shank roofing nails spaced 5" on center.	=	=	=	=	=	=	=	$\frac{5}{8}$
	13-1.4	$\frac{1}{2}$" Type X gypsum wallboard[o] nailed to joists with 5d cooler[o] or wallboard[o] nails at 6" on center. End joints of wallboard centered on joists.	=	=	=	=	=	=	=	$\frac{1}{2}$
14. Plywood stressed skin panels consisting of $\frac{5}{8}$" - thick interior C-D (exterior glue) top stressed skin on 2"x 6" nominal (minimum) stringers. Adjacent panel edges joined with 8d common wire nails spaced 6"on center. Stringers spaced 12"maximum on center.	14-1.1	$\frac{1}{2}$"-thick wood fiberboard weighing 15 to 18 pounds per cubic foot installed with long dimension parallel to stringers or $\frac{3}{8}$" C-D (exterior glue) plywood glued and/or nailed to stringers. Nailing to be with 5d cooler[o] or wallboard[o] nails at 12" on center. Second layer of $\frac{1}{2}$" Type X gypsum wallboard[o] applied with long dimension perpendicular to joists and attached with 8d cooler[o] or wallboard[o] nails at 6" on center at end joints and 8" on center elsewhere. Wallboard joints staggered with respect to fiberboard joints.	=	=	=	=	=	=	=	1
15. Vermiculite concrete slab proportioned 1:4 (portland cement to vermiculite aggregate) on a $1\frac{1}{2}$"-deep steel deck supported on individually protected steel framing. Maximum span of deck 6'-10" where deck is less than 0.019 inch (No. 26 carbon steel sheet gage) or greater. Slab reinforced with 4"x 8" 0.109/0.083" (No. 12/14 B.W. gage) welded wire mesh.	15-1.1	None	=	=	=	3^{j}	=	=	=	=
16. Perlite concrete slab proportioned 1:6 (portland cement to perlite aggregate) on a $1\frac{1}{4}$"-deep steel deck supported on individually protected steel framing. Slab reinforced with 4"x 8" 0.109/0.083" (No. 12/14 B.W. gage) welded wire mesh.	16-1.1	None	=	=	=	$3\frac{1}{2}^{j}$	=	=	=	=
17. Perlite concrete slab proportioned 1:6 (portland cement to perlite aggregate) on a $\frac{9}{16}$"-deep steel deck supported by steel joists 4" on center. Class A or B roof covering on top.	17-1.1	Perlite gypsum plaster on metal lath wire tied to $\frac{3}{4}$" furring channels attached with 0.065" (No. 16 B.W. gage) wire ties to lower chord of joists.	=	2^{p}	2^{p}	=	=	$\frac{7}{8}$	$\frac{3}{4}$	=

Item	No.	Membrane								
18. Perlite concrete slab proportioned 1:6 (portland cement to perlite aggregate) on 1¼"-deep steel deck supported on individually protected steel framing. Maximum span of deck 6'-10" where deck is less than 0.019" (No. 26 carbon sheet steel gage) and 8'-0" where deck is 0.019" (No. 26 carbon sheet steel gage) or greater. Slab reinforced with 0.042" (No. 19 B.W. gage) hexagonal wire mesh. Class A or B roof covering on top.	18-1.1	None	=	2¼^p	2¼^p	=	=	=	=	=
19. Floor and beam construction consisting of 3"-deep cellular steel floor unit mounted on steel members with 1:4 (proportion of portland cement to perlite aggregate) perlite-concrete floor slab on top.	19-1.1	Suspended envelope ceiling of perlite gypsum plaster on metal lath attached to ¾" cold-rolled channels, secured to 1½" cold-rolled channels spaced 42" on center supported by 0.203 inch (No. 6 B.W. gage) wire 36" on center. Beams in envelope with 3" minimum airspace between beam soffit and lath have a 4-hour rating.	2^p	=	=	=	1^1	=	=	=
20. Perlite concrete proportioned 1:6 (portland cement to perlite aggregate) poured to ⅛" thickness above top of corrugations of 5/16"-deep galvanized steel deck maximum span 8'-0" for 0.024" (No. 24 galvanized sheet gage) or 6'-0" for 0.019" (No. 26 galvanized sheet gage) with deck supported by individually protected steel framing. Approved polystyrene foam plastic insulation board having a flame spread not exceeding 75 (1" to 4" thickness) with vent holes that approximate 3 percent of the board surface area placed on top of perlite slurry. A 2" by 4" insulation board contains six 2¾" diameter holes. Board covered with 2¼" minimum perlite concrete	20-1.1	None	=	=	Varies	=	=	=	=	=

slab.										
20. Slab reinforced with mesh consisting of 0.042" (No. 19 B.W. gage) galvanized steel wire twisted together to form 2" hexagons with straight 0.065" (No. 16 B.W. gage) galvanized steel wire woven into mesh and spaced 3". Alternate slab reinforcement shall be permitted to consist of 4"x 8", 0.109/0.238" (No. 12/4 B.W. gage), or 2"x 2", 0.083/0.083" (No. 14/14 B.W. gage) welded wire fabric. Class A or B roof covering on top.	20-1.1	None	—	—	Varies	—	—	—	—	—
21. Wood joists, wood I-joists, floor trusses and flat or pitched roof trusses spaced a maximum 24" o.c. with ½" wood structural panels with exterior glue applied at right angles to top of joist or top chord of trusses with 8d nails. The wood structural panel thickness shall not be less than nominal ½" nor less than required by Chapter 23.	21-1.1	Base layer $^5/_8$" Type X gypsum wallboard applied at right angles to joist or truss 24" o.c. with 1¼" Type S or Type W drywall screws 24" o.c. Face layer $^5/_8$" Type X gypsum wallboard or veneer base applied at right angles to joist or truss through base layer with $1^5/_8$"Type S or Type W drywall screws 12" o.c. at joints and intermediate joist or truss. Face layer Type G drywall screws placed 2" back on either side of face layer end joints, 12" o.c.	—	—	—	Varies	—	—	—	1¼
22. Steel joists, floor trusses and flat or pitched roof trusses spaced a maximum 24" o.c. with ½" wood structural panels with exterior glue applied at right angles to top of joist or top chord of trusses with No. 8 screws. The wood structural panel thickness shall not be less than nominal ½" nor less than required by Chapter 23.	22-1.1	Base layer $^5/_8$" Type X gypsum board applied at right angles to steel framing 24" on center with 1" Type S drywall screws spaced 24" on center. Face layer $^5/_8$" Type X gypsum board applied at right angles to steel framing attached through base layer with $1^5/_8$" Type S drywall screws 12" on center at end joints and intermediate joints and 1½"Type G drywall screws 12 inches on center placed 2" back on either side of face layer end joints. Joints of the face layer are offset 24" from the joints of the base layer.	—	—	—	Varies	—	—	—	1¼
23. Wood I-joist (minimum joist depth 9¼" with a minimum flange depth of $^{15}/_{16}$" and a minimum flange cross-sectional area of 2.3 square inches) at 24" o.c. spacing with 1 inch by 4 inch (nominal) wood furring strip spacer applied parallel to and covering the bottom of the bottom flange of each member, tacked in place. 2" mineral wool insulation, 3.5 pcf (nominal) installed adjacent to the bottom flange of the I-joist and supported by the 1"x 4" furring strip spacer.	23-1.1	½" deep single leg resilient channel 16" on center (channels doubled at wallboard end joints), placed perpendicular to the furring strip and joist and attached to each joist by $1^7/_8$" Type S drywall screws. $^5/_8$" Type C gypsum wallboard applied perpendicular to the channel with end joints staggered at least 4" and fastened with $1^1/_8$" Type S drywall screws spaced 7" on center. Wallboard joints to be taped and covered with joint compound.	—	—	—	Varies	—	—	—	$^5/_8$
24. Wood I-joist (minimum I-joist depth 9¼" with a minimum flange depth of 1½" and a minimum flange cross-sectional area of 5.25 square inches; minimum web thickness of $^3/_8$") @ 24" o.c., 1½" mineral wool insulation (2.5 pcf—nominal) resting on hat-shaped furring channels.	24-1.1	Minimum 0.026" thick hat-shaped channel 16" o.c. (channels doubled at wallboard end joints), placed perpendicular to the joist and attached to each joist by $1^5/_8$" Type S drywall screws. $^5/_8$" Type C gypsum wallboard applied perpendicular to the channel with end joints staggered and fastened with $1^1/_8$" Type S drywall screws spaced 12" o.c. in the field and 8" o.c. at the wallboard ends. Wallboard joints to be taped and covered with joint compound.	—	—	—	Varies	—	—	—	$^5/_8$
25. Wood I-joist (minimum I-joist depth 9¼" with a minimum flange depth of 1½" and a minimum flange cross-sectional area of 5.25 square inches; minimum web thickness of $^7/_{16}$") @ 24" o.c., 1½" mineral wool insulation (2.5 pcf—nominal) resting on resilient channels.	25-1.1	Minimum 0.019" thick resilient channel 16" o.c. (channels doubled at wallboard end joints), placed perpendicular to the joist and attached to each joist by $1^5/_8$" Type S drywall screws. $^5/_8$" Type C gypsum wallboard applied perpendicular to the channel with end joints staggered and fastened with 1" Type S drywall screws spaced 12" o.c. in the field and 8" o.c. at the wallboard ends. Wallboard joints to be taped and covered with joint compound.	—	—	—	Varies	—	—	—	$^5/_8$

26. Wood I-joist (minimum I-joist depth 9¼" with a minimum flange thickness of 1½" and a minimum flange cross-sectional area of 2.25 square inches; minimum web thickness of $^{3}/_{8}$") @ 24" o.c.	26-1.1	Two layers of ½" Type X gypsum wallboard applied with the long dimension perpendicular to the I-joists with end joints staggered. The base layer is fastened with $1^{5}/_{8}$" Type S drywall screws spaced 12" o.c. and the face layer is fastened with 2" Type S drywall screws spaced 12" o.c. in the field and 8" o.c. on the edges. Face layer end joints shall not occur on the same I-joist as base layer end joints and edge joints shall be offset 24" from base layer joints. Face layer to also be attached to base layer with 1½" Type G drywall screws spaced 8" o.c. placed 6" from face layer end joints. Face layer wallboard joints to be taped and covered with joint compound.	—	—	—	Varies	—	—	—	1
27. Wood I-joist (minimum I-joist depth 9½" with a minimum flange depth of $1^{5}/_{16}$" and a minimum flange cross-sectional area of 1.95 square inches; minimum web thickness of $^{3}/_{8}$") @ 24" o.c.	27-1.1	Minimum 0.019" thick resilient channel 16" o.c. (channels doubled at wallboard end joints), placed perpendicular to the joist and attached to each joist by $1^{5}/_{8}$" Type S drywall screws. Two layers of ½" Type X gypsum wallboard applied with the long dimension perpendicular to the I-joists with end joints staggered. The base layer is fastened with 1¼" Type S drywall screws spaced 12" o.c. and the face layer is fastened with $1^{5}/_{8}$" Type S drywall screws spaced 12" o.c. Face layer end joints shall not occur on the same I-joist as base layer end joints and edge joints shall be offset 24" from base layer joints. Face layer to also be attached to base layer with 1½" Type G drywall screws spaced 8" o.c. placed 6" from face layer end joints. Face layer wallboard joints to be taped and covered with joint compound.	—	—	—	Varies	—	—	—	1
28. Wood I-joist (minimum I-joist depth 9¼" with a minimum flange depth of 1½" and a minimum flange cross-sectional area of 2.25 square inches; minimum web thickness of $^{3}/_{8}$") @ 24" o.c. Unfaced fiberglass insulation is installed between the I-joists supported on the upper surface of the flange by stay wires spaced 12" o.c.	28-1.1	Base layer of $^{5}/_{8}$" Type C gypsum wallboard attached directly to I-joists with $1^{5}/_{8}$" Type S drywall screws spaced 12" o.c. with ends staggered. Minimum 0.0179" thick hat-shaped $^{7}/_{8}$-inch furring channel 16" o.c. (channels doubled at wallboard end joints), placed perpendicular to the joist and attached to each joist by $1^{5}/_{8}$" Type S drywall screws after the base layer of gypsum wallboard has been applied. The middle and face layers of $^{5}/_{8}$" Type C gypsum wallboard applied perpendicular to the channel with end joints staggered. The middle layer is fastened with 1" Type S drywall screws spaced 12" o.c. The face layer is applied parallel to the middle layer but with the edge joints offset 24" from those of the middle layer and fastened with $1^{5}/_{8}$" Type S drywall screws 8" o.c. The joints shall be taped and covered with joint compound.	—	—	—	Varies	—	—	2¾	—
29. Channel-shaped 18 gage steel joists (minimum depth 8") spaced a maximum 24" o.c. supporting tongue-and-groove wood structural panels (nominal minimum ¾" thick) applied perpendicular to framing members. Structural panels attached with 1-$^{5}/_{8}$" Type S-12 screws spaced 12" o.c.	29-1.1	Base layer $^{5}/_{8}$" Type X gypsum board applied perpendicular to bottom of framing members with $1^{1}/_{8}$" Type S-12 screws spaced 12" o.c. Second layer $^{5}/_{8}$" Type X gypsum board attached perpendicular to framing members with $1^{5}/_{8}$" Type S-12 screws spaced 12" o.c. Second layer joints offset 24" from base layer. Third layer $^{5}/_{8}$" Type X gypsum board attached perpendicular to framing members with $2^{3}/_{8}$" Type S-12 screws spaced 12" o.c. Third layer joints offset 12" from second layer joints. Hat-shaped 7/8-inch rigid furring channels applied at right angles to framing members over third layer with two $2^{3}/_{8}$" Type S-12 screws at each framing member. Face layer $^{5}/_{8}$" Type X gypsum board applied at right angles to furring channels with $1^{1}/_{8}$" Type S screws spaced 12" o.c.	—	—	Varies	—	—	—	$3^{3}/_{8}$	—

For SI: 1 inch = 25.4 mm, 1 foot = 304.8 mm, 1 pound = .454 kg, 1 cubic foot = 0.0283m^{3}, 1 pound per square inch = 6.895 kPa, 1 pound per lineal foot = 1.4882 kg/m.

a. Staples with equivalent holding power and penetration shall be permitted to be used as alternate fasteners to nails for attachment to wood framing.

b. When the slab is in an unrestrained condition, minimum reinforcement cover shall not be less than $1^{5}/_{8}$ inches for 4-hour (siliceous aggregate only); $1^{1}/_{4}$ inches for 4- and 3-hour; 1 inch for 2-hour (siliceous aggregate only); and $^{3}/_{4}$ inch for all other restrained and unrestrained conditions.

c. For all of the construction with gypsum wallboard described in this table, gypsum base for veneer plaster of the same size, thickness and core type shall be permitted to be substituted for gypsum wallboard, provided attachment is identical to that specified for the wallboard, and the joints on the face layer are reinforced and the entire surface is covered with a minimum of $^{1}/_{16}$-inch gypsum veneer plaster.

d. Slab thickness over steel joists measured at the joists for metal lath form and at the top of the form for steel form units.

e. (a) The maximum allowable stress level for H-Series joists shall not exceed 22,000 psi.

  (b) The allowable stress for K-Series joists shall not exceed 26,000 psi, the nominal depth of such joist shall not be less than 10 inches and the nominal joist weight shall not be less than 5 pounds per lineal foot.

f. Cement plaster with 15 pounds of hydrated lime and 3 pounds of approved additives or admixtures per bag of cement.

g. Gypsum wallboard ceilings attached to steel framing shall be permitted to be suspended with $1^1/_2$-inch cold-formed carrying channels spaced 48 inches on center, which are suspended with No. 8 SWG galvanized wire hangers spaced 48 inches on center. Cross-furring channels are tied to the carrying channels with No.18 SWG galvanized wire hangers spaced 48 inches on center. Cross-furring channels are tied to the carrying channels with No. 18 SWG galvanized wire (double strand) and spaced as required for direct attachment to the framing. This alternative is also applicable to those steel framing assemblies recognized under Note q.

h. Six-inch hollow clay tile with 2-inch concrete slab above.

i. Four-inch hollow clay tile with $1^1/_2$-inch concrete slab above.

j. Thickness measured to bottom of steel form units.

k. Five-eighths inch of vermiculite gypsum plaster plus $^1/_2$ inch of approved vermiculite acoustical plastic.

l. Furring channels spaced 12 inches on center.

m. Double wood floor shall be permitted to be either of the following:

(a) Subfloor of 1-inch nominal boarding, a layer of asbestos paper weighing not less than 14 pounds per 100 square feet and a layer of 1-inch nominal tongue-and-groove finished flooring; or

  (b) Subfloor of 1-inch nominal tongue-and-groove boarding or $^{15}/_{32}$-inch wood structural panels with exterior glue and a layer of 1-inch nominal tongue-and-groove finished flooring or $^{19}/_{32}$-inch wood structural panel finish flooring or a layer of Type 1 Grade M-1 particleboard not less than $^5/_8$-inch thick.

n. The ceiling shall be permitted to be omitted over unusable space, and flooring shall be permitted to be omitted where unusable space occurs above.

o. For properties of cooler or wallboard nails, see ASTM C 514, ASTM C 547 or ASTM F 1667.

p. Thickness measured on top of steel deck unit.

q. Generic fire-resistance ratings (those not designated as PROPRIETARY* in the listing) in the GA 600 shall be accepted as if herein listed.

MEMBRANE STRUCTURES (3102 AND CHAP. 24 INTERNATIONAL FIRE CODE 2003)

A. General
   1. Requirements for membrane structures apply to air-supported, air-inflated, covered cables, covered frames, tents, and tensioned membrane structures. This includes circus tents, entertainment, and food service establishments.
   2. Exception: Over water greenhouses, treatment, water storage, and sewage treatment areas not used for human occupancy, only material and engineering design requirements apply.
   3. Flame-resistance or flame-retardance treatment certificates required to show NFPA 701 compliance.
   4. Maximum exit travel distance for temporary structures is 100 ft. (2403.12.1 IFC 2003)
B. Building classification type (3102.3)
   1. Membrane structures with noncombustible or flame-resistant fabric over noncombustible frame are Type IIB.
   2. Membrane structures with combustible frame use Type V, heavy timber Type IV.
   3. Plastic less than 30' above the floor for non-public greenhouses and aquaculture pond covers does not need flame resistance.
   4. Noncombustible membranes allowed as roof or skylight if at least 20' above floor, balcony, or gallery. (3102.6.1)
   5. Flame-resistant membranes allowed same as for non-combustible membranes, but only for IIB, III, IV, and V construction, and if at least 20' above floor, balcony or gallery. (3102.6.1.1)
C. Floor area and height allowable if per Table 503.
D. Inflation (3102.8)
   1. Inflation of membrane structures requires a primary and auxiliary air system.
   2. Auxiliary system must be capable of automatically maintaining the structure inflated.
   3. Blowers shall be housed in a weatherproof building.
   4. Standby power is required with an auxiliary system.
   5. Standby power must reach maximum in 60 seconds with a 4-hour duration period.
   6. Envelope design and building anchoring in accordance with 2403.10.2 IFC 2003.
E. Supports: Provide a support system in case of deflation where the load is more than 50 people or for any swimming pool. (3102.8.3)
   1. Support shall maintain the membrane at least 7' above floor, seating, and/or water.
   2. If used as a roof for Type I construction, support must be 20' minimum above any floor or seating.
F. Assembly occupancies (2403 IFC 2003)
   1. Minimum open perimeter of 20' measured from tent supports and ropes, without guys, stakes, ropes, other tents, building, or lot lines.
   2. If not used for cooking and less than 15,000 sf, separation not required. Area can be aggregate area of tents and/or membrane structures.
   3. Separation not required from buildings when all of below are met:
      a. Aggregate floor area less than 10,000 sf and not over allowable for construction type.
      b. Building and adjacent tent have complying egress, with travel distance under tent included.
      c. Fire apparatus access roads required.
   4. When membrane structures or tents are over 15,000 sf:

a. Minimum 50′ open perimeter, measure to tent wall.

b. Option to have enclosed walkways between membrane structures with exit doors at each end and 12′ openings at the middle on each side.

5. Egress

a. Number of exits and exit width determined per Table 2403.12.2 IFC 2003.

b. Maximum travel distance is 100′.

c. Exits open, or with contrasting curtain at 80″ minimum height.

d. Doors must swing in direction of egress.

e. Exit signs required for 50 or more, and signs must be illuminated.

f. Emergency egress lighting required.

6. Cooking tents (2404.15 IFC)

a. Minimum 20′ open perimeter.

b. Minimum 20′ to fuel-fired power appliances.

MEZZANINES (505)

A. Mezzanines are defined as intermediate level(s) between the floor and ceiling of a story. (505.1)

B. A mezzanine is considered to be a part of the floor below.

C. A mezzanine does not add to the building area or number of stories.

D. Area limits

1. Aggregate area of the mezzanine(s) shall not exceed $1/2$ of the area of the room where the mezzanine is located.

2. Special industrial occupancies in Type I and II buildings may use $2/3$ of the area of the room below.

E. Two independent means of egress are required when the common path of travel in 1004.2.5 requires them. When travel distance is measured from a stair it shall be measured from the bottom. (505.3)

F. Openness to room below, except for 42″ railings and support columns

1. Mezzanines may have enclosed areas if occupant load is 10 or less.

2. Mezzanines with two exit routes, with one being an enclosed exit, need not be open.

3. Up to 10% of a mezzanine can be enclosed.

4. Control rooms in factories can be glass-enclosed.

5. In other than Groups H and I no higher than two stories and having two or more means of egress, can be enclosed if sprinkled (505.4).

6. Industrial equipment platforms are not mezzanines. (See 505.5.) They must be sprinkled above and below in fully sprinkled buildings.

MIXED USES (508)

A. Mixed use options

1. No separation: Requirements for all uses in a building are applied to construction type, high-rise, and fire protection. All other provisions apply to only the requirements for the use of that space.

2. Separated by fire separation assemblies: Requirements of each occupancy are applied only to the occupancies within the area that is separated. Height (508.3.1) and area also apply to each use group in the building (508.3.2). The separation rating must be the highest fire resistance required for the use groups being separated. (See Table 508.2.5) Each use is restricted to the height limits independent of the other uses in a building. Building area is determined by the proportion of the building occupied by each use, using the "unity" formula for each fire area (508.4).

$$\frac{\text{Area A}}{\text{Allowable A}} \quad + \quad \frac{\text{Area B}}{\text{Allowable B}} \quad + \quad \cdots \quad \frac{\text{Area N}}{\text{Allowable N}} \quad \leq \quad 1$$

3. Separated by fire walls: The areas are separate buildings and no common requirements are applied. The fire wall rating must be based on the highest fire grading of the uses.

TABLE 508.2.5
INCIDENTAL ACCESSORY OCCUPANCIES

ROOM OR AREA	SEPARATION AND/OR PROTECTION
Furnace room where any piece of equipment is over 400,000 Btu per hour input	1 hour or provide automatic fire-extinguishing system
Rooms with boilers where the largest piece of equipment is over 15 psi and 10 horsepower	1 hour or provide automatic fire-extinguishing system
Refrigerant machinery room	1 hour or provide automatic sprinkler system
Hydrogen cutoff rooms, not classified as Group H	1 hour in Group B, F, M, S and U occupancies; 2 hours in Group A, E, I and R occupancies.
Incinerator rooms	2 hours and automatic sprinkler system
Paint shops, not classified as Group H, located in occupancies other than Group F	2 hours; or 1 hour and provide automatic fire-extinguishing system
Laboratories and vocational shops, not classified as Group H, located in a Group E or I-2 occupancy	1 hour or provide automatic fire-extinguishing system
Laundry rooms over 100 square feet	1 hour or provide automatic fire-extinguishing system
Group I-3 cells equipped with padded surfaces	1 hour
Group I-2 waste and linen collection rooms	1 hour
Waste and linen collection rooms over 100 square feet	1 hour or provide automatic fire-extinguishing system
Stationary storage battery systems having a liquid electrolyte capacity of more than 50 gallons, or a lithium-ion capacity of 1,000 pounds used for facility standby power, emergency power or uninterrupted power supplies	1 hour in Group B, F, M, S and U occupancies; 2 hours in Group A, E, I and R occupancies.
Rooms containing fire pumps in nonhigh-rise buildings	2 hours; or 1 hour and provide automatic sprinkler system throughout the building
Rooms containing fire pumps in high-rise buildings	2 hours

For SI: 1 square foot = 0.0929 m², 1 pound per square inch (psi) = 6.9 kPa, 1 British thermal unit (Btu) per hour = 0.293 watts, 1 horsepower = 746 watts, 1 gallon = 3.785 L.

TABLE 508.4
REQUIRED SEPARATION OF OCCUPANCIES (HOURS)

OCCUPANCY	A[d], E		I-1, I-3, I-4		I-2		R		F-2, S-2[b], U		B, F-1, M, S-1		H-1		H-2		H-3, H-4, H-5	
	S	NS	S	NS	S	NS	S	NS	S	NS	S	NS	S	NS	S	NS	S	NS
A[d], E	N	N	1	2	2	NP	1	2	N	1	1	2	NP	NP	3	4	2	3a
I-1, I-3, I-4	—	—	N	N	2	NP	1	NP	1	2	1	2	NP	NP	3	NP	2	NP
I-2	—	—	—	—	N	N	2	NP	2	NP	2	NP	NP	NP	3	NP	2	NP
R	—	—	—	—	—	—	N	N	1[c]	2[c]	1	2	NP	NP	3	NP	2	NP
F-2, S-2[b], U	—	—	—	—	—	—	—	—	N	N	1	2	NP	NP	3	4	2	3[a]
B, F-1, M, S-1	—	—	—	—	—	—	—	—	—	—	N	N	NP	NP	2	3	1	2[a]
H-1	—	—	—	—	—	—	—	—	—	—	—	—	N	NP	NP	NP	NP	NP
H-2	—	—	—	—	—	—	—	—	—	—	—	—	—	—	N	NP	1	NP
H-3, H-4, H-5	—	—	—	—	—	—	—	—	—	—	—	—	—	—	—	—	1[c, f]	NP

For SI: 1 square foot = 0.0929 m².

S = Buildings equipped throughout with an automatic sprinkler system installed in accordance with Section 903.3.1.1.

NS = Buildings not equipped throughout with an automatic sprinkler system installed in accordance with Section 903.3.1.1.

N = No separation requirement.

NP = Not permitted.

a. For Group H-5 occupancies, see Section 903.2.5.2.

b. The required separation from areas used only for private or pleasure vehicles shall be reduced by 1 hour but to not less than 1 hour.

c. See Section 406.1.4.

d. Commercial kitchens need not be separated from the restaurant seating areas that they serve.

e. Separation is not required between occupancies of the same classification.

f. For H-5 occupancies, see Section 415.8.2.2.

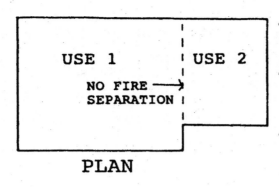

| USE 1 | USE 2 |

NO FIRE →
SEPARATION

PLAN

- HT. & AREA IS SMALLEST
  OF ALLOWABLE FOR
  USE 1 OR 2

- **ALL** AREAS SUBJECT
  TO MOST RESTRICTIVE
  CONSTRUCTION TYPE
  REQ'MTS. OF USE 1 OR 2

- HEIGHT & AREA FIRE
  SUPP. & HIGH RISE

  SPECIFIC REQ. FOR 1 & 2
  APPLY ONLY TO 1 & 2

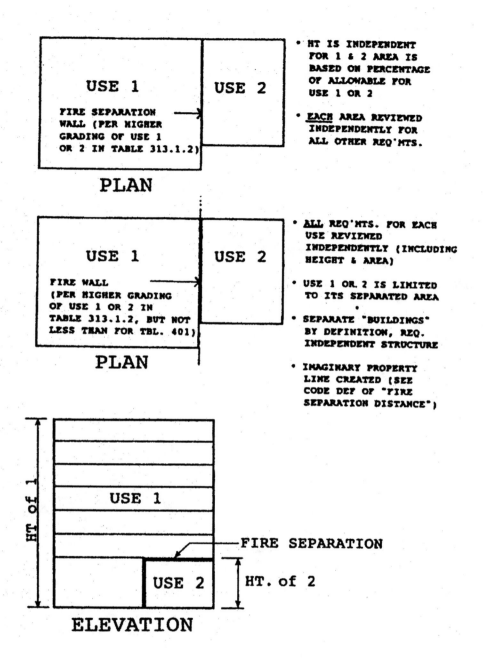

- HT IS INDEPENDENT
  FOR 1 & 2 AREA IS
  BASED ON PERCENTAGE
  OF ALLOWABLE FOR
  USE 1 OR 2

- EACH AREA REVIEWED
  INDEPENDENTLY FOR
  ALL OTHER REQ'MTS.

USE 1

USE 2

FIRE SEPARATION
WALL (PER HIGHER
GRADING OF USE 1
OR 2 IN TABLE 313.1.2)

PLAN

- ALL REQ'MTS. FOR EACH
  USE REVIEWED
  INDEPENDENTLY (INCLUDING
  HEIGHT & AREA)

- USE 1 OR. 2 IS LIMITED
  TO ITS SEPARATED AREA

- SEPARATE "BUILDINGS"
  BY DEFINITION, REQ.
  INDEPENDENT STRUCTURE

- IMAGINARY PROPERTY
  LINE CREATED (SEE
  CODE DEF OF "FIRE
  SEPARATION DISTANCE")

USE 1

USE 2

FIRE WALL
(PER HIGHER GRADING
OF USE 1 OR 2 IN
TABLE 313.1.2, BUT NOT
LESS THAN FOR TBL. 401)

PLAN

HT. OF 1

USE 1

FIRE SEPARATION

USE 2

HT. of 2

ELEVATION

B. Accessory use areas—no sep. req'd. if: (508.3.1)
1. Not Use Group H-2, H-3, H-4, H-5.
2. Not I-1, R-1, R-2, R-3 dwelling/sleeping units.
3. Not open parking structure. (406.3, 509.2)
4. Is a separate building with only a 2-hour fire separation to malls. (402.7.1)
5. Open parking structures above enclosed garages. (509.3)
   1. Can be considered separate buildings with mixed use formula of ratios, minimum Type I or Type II construction type.
6. Parking garages under Use Group R. (509.4)
   1. Maximum one-story garage (enclosed or open).
   2. Garages must be Type I or Type IV.
   3. Mixed use separation required.
   4. Number of stories for R Use counted from top of garage.
7. A mixed use with Use Group H in buildings must be separated per Table 508.3.3.1. H-1 uses must be in a separate building.

NAILING/SCREWING/STAPLING SCHEDULE (TABLE 2304)

A. Power-driven staples, screws, and nails are acceptable per table.

B. In all cases the fasteners must be capable of transferring all the applied loads.

C. Typical framing schedule

Stud to sole plate	8d common	4 toenails
	16d common	2 direct
Stud to cap plate	16d common	2 direct
Sole plate to joists	16d common	16" o.c.
Double plate	16d common	16" o.c. direct
Roof rafter to plate	8d common	3 toenails
Roof rafter to ridge	16d common	2 toenails or direct
Floor joists to sill	8d common	3 toenails
Ledger strip	16d common	3 at each joist, direct
Ceiling joists to plate	8d common	3 toenails
Ceiling joists rafters	16d common	3 direct
Built-up beams	20d common	32" o.c., direct
Built-up corner studs	16d common	24" o.c.

D. Particle board wall sheathing

   1. For $1/2$ and $3/8$" sheathing and other uses 6d, 4"o.c. edges and 8" o.c. field should be used.

   2. For $5/8$ and $3/4$" sheathing 8d, 4" o.c. edges and 12" o.c. field should be used Crown must be flush with the surface of the sheathing.

E. Fiberboard sheathing and wood structural panels

   1. $1/2$", 11 gage galvanized roofing nails or 16 gage staples or 6d common, 3" o.c. edges and 6 o.c. in the field should be used.

   2. $25/32$", $1^{3}/4$" galvanized roofing nails or $1^{1}/2$" staples or 8d common, 3" o.c. edges and 6" o.c. field should be used.

F. For wood shingles, 2 for each shingle, galvanized, no. 14 B & S gage should be used.

TABLE 2304.9.1
FASTENING SCHEDULE

CONNECTION	FASTENINGa, m	LOCATION
1. Joist to sill or girder	3 - 8d common (2 ½" x 0.131") 3 – 3" x 0.131" nails 3 – 3" 14 gage staples	toenail
2. Bridging to joist	2 - 8d common (2 ½" x 0.131") 2 – 3" x 0.131" nails 2 – 3" 14 gage staples	toenail each end
3. 1" x 6" subfloor or less to each joist	2 - 8d common (2 ½" x 0.131")	face nail
4. Wider than 1" x 6" subfloor to each joist	3 - 8d common (2 ½" x 0.131")	face nail
5. 2" subfloor to joist or girder	2 - 16d common (3 ½" x 0.162")	blind and face nail

6. Sole plate to joist or blocking Sole plate to joist or blocking at braced wall panel	16d (3 ½" x 0.135") at 16"o.c. 3" x 0.131" nails at 8"o.c. 3" 14 gage staples at 12" o.c. 3 - 16d (3 ½" x 0.135") at 16" o.c. 4 – 3" x 0.131" nails at 16"o.c. 4 – 3" 14 gage staples at 16"o.c.	typical face nail braced wall panels
7. Top plate to stud	2 - 16d common (3 ½" x 0.162") 3 – 3" x 0.131" nails 3 - 3" 14 gage staples	end nail
8. Stud to sole plate	4 - 8d common (2 ½" x 0.131") 4 – 3" x 0.131" nails 3 – 3" 14 gage staples 2 - 16d common (3 ½" x 0.162") 3 – 3" x 0.131" nails 3 – 3" 14 gage staples	toenail end nail
9. Double studs	16d (3 ½" x 0.135") at 24"o.c. 3" x 0.131" nail at 8" o.c. 3" 14 gage staple at 8" o.c.	face nail
10. Double top plates Double top plates	16d (3 ½" x 0.135") at 16"o.c. 3" x 0.131" nail at 12" o.c. 3" 14 gage staple at 12"o.c. 8 - 16d common (3 ½" x 0.162") 12 – 3" x 0.131" nails 12 – 3" 14 gage staples	typical face nail lap splice
11. Blocking between joists or rafters to top plate	3 - 8d common (2 ½" x 0.131") 3 – 3" x 0.131" nails 3 – 3" 14 gage staples	toenail
12. Rim joist to top plate	8d (2 ½" x 0.131") at at 16" o.c. 3" x 0.131" nail at 6" o.c. 3" 14 gage staple at 6" o.c.	toenail
13. Top plates, laps and intersections	2 - 16d common (3 ½" x 0.162") 3 – 3" x 0.131" nails 3 – 3" 14 gage staples	face nail
14. Continuous header, two pieces	16d common (3 ½" x 0.162")	16◆o.c. along edge
15. Ceiling joists to plate	3 - 8d common (2 ½" x 0.131") 5 – 3" x 0.131" nails 5 – 3"14 gage staples	toenail
16. Continuous header to stud	4 - 8d common (2 ½" x 0.131")	toenail
17. Ceiling joists, laps over partitions (see Section 2308.10.4.1, Table 2308.10.4.1)	3 - 16d common (3 ½" x 0.162") minimum, Table 2308.10.4.1 4 – 3" x 0.131" nails 4 – 3" 14 gage staples	face nail
18. Ceiling joists to parallel rafters (see Section 2308.10.4.1, Table 2308.10.4.1)	3 - 16d common (3 ½" x 0.162") minimum, Table 2308.10.4.1 4 – 3" x 0.131" nails 4 – 3" 14 gage staples	face nail

19. Rafter to plate (see Section 2308.10.1, Table 2308.10.1)	3 - 8d common (2 ½" x 0.131") 3 – 3" x 0.131" nails 3 – 3" 14 gage staples	toenail
20. 1" diagonal brace to each stud and plate	2 - 8d common (2 ½" 0.131") 2 – 3" x 0.131" nails 3 – 3" 14 gage staples	face nail
21. 1" x 8" sheathing to each bearing	3 - 8d common (2 ½" x 0.131")	face nail
22. Wider than 1" x 8" sheathing to each bearing	3 - 8d common (2 ½" x 0.131")	face nail
23. Built-up corner studs	16d common (3 ½" x 0.162") 3" x 0.131" nails 3" 14 gage staples	24" o.c. 16" o.c. 16" o.c.
24. Built-up girder and beams	20d common (4" x 0.192") 32" o.c. 3" x 0.131" nail at 24"o.c. 3" 14 gage staple at 24" o.c. 2 - 20d common (4" x 0.192") 3 – 3" x 0.131" nails 3 – 3" 14 gage staples	face nail at top and bottom staggered on opposite sides face nail at ends and at each splice
25. 2" planks	16d common (3 ½" x 0.162")	at each bearing
26. Collar tie to rafter	3 - 10d common (3" x 0.148") 4 – 3" x 0.131" nails 4 – 3" 14 gage staples	face nail
27. Jack rafter to hip	3 - 10d common (3" x 0.148") 4 – 3" x 0.131" nails 4 – 3" 14 gage staples 2 - 16d common (3 ½" x 0.162") 3 – 3" x 0.131" nails 3 – 3" 14 gage staples	toenail face nail
28. Roof rafter to 2-by ridge beam	2 - 16d common (3 ½" x 0.162") 3 – 3" x 0.131" nails 3 – 3" 14 gage staples 2 -16d common (3 ½" x 0.162") 3 – 3" x 0.131" nails 3 – 3" 14 gage staples	toenail face nail
29. Joist to band joist	3 - 16d common (3 ½" x 0.162") 4 – 3" x 0.131" nails 4 – 3" 14 gage staples	face nail
30. Ledger strip	3 - 16d common (3 ½" x 0.162") 4 – 3" x 0.131" nails 4 – 3" 14 gage staples	face nail at each joist

31. Wood structural panels and particleboard[b] Subfloor, roof and wall sheathing (to framing)	$\frac{1}{2}$" and less	6d[c, l]
		2 3/8" x 0.113" nail[n]
		1 3/4" 16 gage[o]
	$\frac{19}{32}$" to $\frac{3}{4}$"	8d[d] or 6d[e]
		2 3/8" x 0.113" nail[p]
		2" 16 gage[p]
	$\frac{7}{8}$" to 1"	8d[c]
	$1\frac{1}{8}$" to 1 $\frac{1}{4}$"	10d[d] or 8d[e]
Single floor (combination subfloor-underlayment to framing)	$\frac{3}{4}$" and less	6d[e]
	$\frac{7}{8}$" to 1"	8d[e]
	$1\frac{1}{8}$" to 1 $\frac{1}{4}$"	10d[d] or 8d[e]
32. Panel siding (to framing)	$\frac{1}{2}$" or less	6d[f]
	$\frac{5}{8}$"	8d[f]
33. Fiberboard sheathing[g]	$\frac{1}{2}$"	No. 11 gage roofing nail[h]
		6d common nail (2" x 0.113")
		No. 16 gage staple[i]
	$\frac{25}{32}$"	No. 11 gage roofing nail[h]
		8d common nail (2 $\frac{1}{2}$" x 0.131")
		No. 16 gage staple[i]
34. Interior paneling	$\frac{1}{4}$"	4d[j]
	$\frac{3}{8}$"	6d[k]

For SI: 1 inch = 25.4 mm.

a. Common or box nails are permitted to be used except where otherwise stated.

b. Nails spaced at 6 inches on center at edges, 12 inches at intermediate supports except 6 inches at supports where spans are 48 inches or more. For nailing of wood structural panel and particleboard diaphragms and shear walls, refer to Section 2305. Nails for wall sheathing are permitted to be common, box or casing.

c. Common or deformed shank (6d – 2" x 0.113"; 8d – 2 $\frac{1}{2}$" x 0.131"; 10d – 3" x 0.148").

d. Common (6d – 2" x 0.113"; 8d – 2 $\frac{1}{2}$" x 0.131"; 10d – 3" x 0.148").

e. Deformed shank (6d – 2" x 0.113"; 8d – 2 $\frac{1}{2}$" x 0.131"; 10d – 3" x 0.148").

f. Corrosion-resistant siding (6d - 1 $\frac{7}{8}$" x 0.106"; 8d - 2 $\frac{3}{8}$" x 0.128") or casing (6d – 2" x 0.099"; 8d – 2 $\frac{1}{2}$" x 0.113") nail.

g. Fasteners spaced 3 inches on center at exterior edges and 6 inches on center at intermediate supports, when used as structural sheathing. Spacing shall be 6 inches on center on the edges and 12 inches on center at intermediate supports for nonstructural applications.

h. Corrosion-resistant roofing nails with $\frac{7}{16}$-inch-diameter head and 1 $\frac{1}{2}$ -inch length for $\frac{1}{2}$ -inch sheathing and 1 $\frac{3}{4}$ -inch length for $\frac{25}{32}$ -inch sheathing.

i. Corrosion-resistant staples with nominal $\frac{7}{16}$-inch crown or 1-inch crown and 1 $\frac{1}{4}$ -inch length for $\frac{1}{2}$ -inch sheathing and 1 $\frac{1}{2}$ -inch length for $\frac{25}{32}$ -inch sheathing. Panel supports at 16 inches (20 inches if strength axis in the long direction of the panel, unless otherwise marked).

j. Casing (1 $\frac{1}{2}$" x 0.080") or finish (1 $\frac{1}{2}$" x 0.072") nails spaced 6 inches on panel edges, 12 inches at intermediate supports.

k. Panel supports at 24 inches. Casing or finish nails spaced 6 inches on panel edges, 12 inches at intermediate supports.

l. For roof sheathing applications, 8d nails (2 $\frac{1}{2}$" x 0.113") are the minimum required for wood structural panels.

m. Staples shall have a minimum crown width of $\frac{7}{16}$ inch.

n. For roof sheathing applications, fasteners spaced 4 inches on center at edges, 8 inches at intermediate supports.

o. Fasteners spaced 4 inches on center at edges, 8 inches at intermediate supports for subfloor and wall sheathing and 3 inches on center at edges, 6 inches at intermediate supports for roof sheathing.

p. Fasteners spaced 4 inches on center at edges, 8 inches at intermediate supports.

NURSING HOMES AND HOSPITALS (407, 709, 900)

Nursing homes receive and care for individuals needing skilled nursing care because of illness or physical or mental impairment, and for individuals needing personal care but not skilled nursing care. Nursing homes must be licensed by the Ohio Department of Health to provide personal care services and skilled nursing care, and are subject to periodic inspection by the Department of Health. Both nursing homes and hospitals are subject to inspection by the state for compliance with NFPA 101.

A. Doors (minimum size)
1. Patient room, or any door through which beds may pass must be at least 41½" clear width. (1008.1.1)
2. For other doors, 32" clear, but doors must not be less than the calculated load width.
3. Locks on doors in patient rooms shall not restrict egress from room, except in mental health rooms. (407.3.2)

B. Fire protection
1. Nursing homes and hospitals cannot be Type VB or IIIB construction. (Table 503)
2. Automatic sprinklers are required. (903.3.1.1)
    a. Patient sleeping rooms require quick response heads. (407.5)
3. Each patient sleeping or treatment floor with 50 occupants or more shall be divided into at least 2 smoke compartments of not more than 22,500 sq. ft. and 200′ travel distance. (407.4)
4. Smoke barriers (709)
    a. Minimum 1 hour, smoke-tight membrane from deck-to-deck is required.
    b. Barriers may stop at ceiling when ceiling is a smoke barrier and fire barrier and has interstitial space above.
    c. A pair of 20-minute doors, in corridors each 34" wide (44" wide for beds) one swinging in each direction, or sliding doors is required. Center mullions are prohibited. Vision panels, ¼" wire glass (labeled) are required.
    d. Smoke damper at ducts through barrier are required, unless part of smoke control system, or ducts are steel and serve only one compartment.
    e. Each compartment in I-2 Use Groups must provide common areas with 30 sq. ft./person for refuge of adjacent compartments. For floors without beds, common areas of 6 sq. ft./person may be provided. (407.4.1)
    f. In I-2 Use Groups, each compartment must have an egress route out of the compartment without returning through it. (407.4.2)
5. Flame spread rating is Class B. (Table 803.5)
6. Fire alarm system
    a. Manual system is required. (907.2.6)
    b. An automatic fire detection system is required in corridors of nursing homes, detox facilities, and spaces permitted to be open to the corridors. (907.2.6.1)

C. Halls and corridors
1. Minimum width is 8′ in halls and corridors used by patients in beds; other corridors must be at least 44" when occupant load is greater than 50. (1014.2)
2. Maximum travel distance (Table 1016.1)
    a. Maximum travel distance is 150′ from any point within a room. If sprinkled, maximum travel distance is 200′.
3. Corridor walls must provide barrier to smoke, to deck above or to the ceiling which serves as barrier.
4. No rooms allowed to be open to corridors except waiting rooms with the smoke detection, nurses stations, mental health treatment areas < 1,500 sq. ft., and gift shops < 500 sq. ft. (407.2)

181

D. Plumbing fixtures (Table 2902.1)
   1. Each patient room must have water closet and lavatory, or with privacy may be shared.
   2. One shower/tub per 15 patients is required.
E. Ventilation (Table M-403.3)
   1. Patient rooms require natural ventilation of 4% of floor area (M-402.2), or mechanical ventilation of 25 cfm per person.
   2. Patient toilet rooms require a 50 cfm/water closet and urinal.

O

OCCUPANT LOAD (1004)

A. General

1. Plans must indicate the number of occupants (except Use Groups R-2, R-3, and I-1).
2. Occupant load is used for determining the minimum size of corridors, exits, refuge areas, stairs, minimum number of doors, and toilet fixtures (egress). Ventilation is based on a different occupant load basis. (See Table M-403.3.)
3. Minimum floor area per person is 7 sq. ft.
4. With fixed seats, the load is the number of seats: 18/person for bench seats; 24"/person for booths.
5. Mezzanine load is added to the floor load below to determine total exit load.
6. Maximum allowable floor area allowances per person are calculated by the building official as follows.

TABLE 1004.1.1
MAXIMUM FLOOR AREA ALLOWANCES PER OCCUPANT

FUNCTION OF SPACE	FLOOR AREA IN SQ. FT. PER OCCUPANT
Accessory storage areas, mechanical equipment room	300 gross
Agricultural building	300 gross
Aircraft hangars	500 gross
Airport terminal	
Baggage claim	20 gross
Baggage handling	300 gross
Concourse	100 gross
Waiting areas	15 gross
Assembly	
Gaming floors (keno, slots, etc.)	11 gross
Assembly with fixed seats	See Section 1004.7
Assembly without fixed seats	
Concentrated (chairs only—not fixed)	7 net
Standing space	5 net
Unconcentrated (tables and chairs)	15 net
Bowling centers, allow 5 persons for each lane including 15 feet of runway, and for additional areas	7 net
Business areas	100 gross
Courtrooms—other than fixed seating areas	40 net
Day care	35 net
Dormitories	50 gross
Educational	
Classroom area	20 net
Shops and other vocational room areas	50 net
Exercise rooms	50 gross
H-5 Fabrication and manufacturing areas	200 gross
Industrial areas	100 gross
Institutional areas	

FUNCTION OF SPACE	FLOOR AREA IN SQ. FT. PER OCCU-PANT
Inpatient treatment areas	240 gross
Outpatient areas	100 gross
Sleeping areas	120 gross
Kitchens, commercial	200 gross
Library	
Reading rooms	50 net
Stack area	100 gross
Locker rooms	50 gross
Mercantile	
Areas on other floors	60 gross
Basement and grade floor areas	30 gross
Storage, stock, shipping areas	300 gross
Parking garages	200 gross
Residential	200 gross
Skating rinks, swimming pools	
Rink and pool	50 gross
Decks	15 gross
Stages and platforms	15 net
Warehouses	500 gross

For SI: 1 square foot = 0.0929 m².

B. To determine occupant load, use the largest of the following numbers:
1. Proposed number of occupants,
2. Occupant load as determined by floor area using Table 1004.1.2, or
3. Occupant load as determined by combination of 1 and 2 with addition of any occupants egressing through the area.
4. Actual number of occupants may be used in determining load if building official approves.
5. Outdoor areas per building official. (1004.8)
6. Wheelchair spaces counted as additional to number of fixed seats, with occupant load calculated as one occupant for each wheelchair space and one occupant for the associated companion seat.
C. Occupant load must be posted in all assembly spaces. (1004.3)

ONE-, TWO-, AND THREE-FAMILY DWELLING CODE
See **RESIDENTIAL CODE OF OHIO**

OPEN PARKING GARAGES (406, 500, 1000)
A. General
1. Structure may be for ramp or mechanical type parking.
2. Structure must be Type I, II, or IV construction.
3. Structure must have two sides open, which are at least 40% of total perimeter, and total open area must be 20% of total wall area per level.
B. No gasoline dispensing
C. Construction height and area limitations (Table 406.3.5)

TABLE 406.3.5
OPEN PARKING GARAGES AREA AND HEIGHT

TYPE OF CON-STRUCTION	AREA PER TIER (square feet)	HEIGHT (in tiers)		
		Ramp access	Mechanical access	
			Automatic sprinkler system	
			No	Yes
IA	Unlimited	Unlimited	Unlimited	Unlimited
IB	Unlimited	12 tiers	12 tiers	18 tiers
IIA	50,000	10 tiers	10 tiers	15 tiers
IIB	50,000	8 tiers	8 tiers	12 tiers
IV	50,000	4 tiers	4 tiers	4 tiers

For SI: 1 square foot = 0.0929 m^2.

D. Egress
   1. 2 exits are required from each tier for ramp-type parking. (1021.1.1)
   2. 1 exit is required from each tier for a mechanical-type parking.
   3. Maximum travel distance to an exit is 300′, 400′ if sprinkled (as for Use Group S-2). (Table 1016.1)
   4. Open ramp with separate walk space is acceptable for an exit. (406.2.5)
   5. Exits may be open. (1020.1, exception 5)

E. Mixed uses
   1. When under A, I, B, M, and R Uses, the open parking structure shall not exceed height and area allowed by Table 406.3.5.
   2. Height and area limitations for use above parking structure is regulated by Table 503. Total height is regulated by 504.
   3. Required fire separation is by highest fire grading of uses. (Table 508.2.5)
   4. Each part can have different construction types, but structure in garage supporting use above must be to higher of construction type requirements. (506.4.1)
   5. Exits must be sized for uses involved, and stairwells from use above must be enclosed in 2-hour fire resistance-rated fire wall going through garage. (509.7, 509.8, 509.9)

TABLE 508.2.5
INCIDENTAL ACCESSORY OCCUPANCIES

ROOM OR AREA	SEPARATION AND/OR PROTECTION
Furnace room where any piece of equipment is over 400,000 Btu per hour input	1 hour or provide automatic fire-extinguishing system
Rooms with boilers where the largest piece of equipment is over 15 psi and 10 horsepower	1 hour or provide automatic fire-extinguishing system
Refrigerant machinery room	1 hour or provide automatic sprinkler system
Hydrogen cutoff rooms, not classified as Group H	1 hour in Group B, F, M, S and U occupancies, 2 hours in Group A, E, I and R occupancies.
Incinerator rooms	2 hours and automatic sprinkler system
Paint shops, not classified as Group H, located in occupancies other than Group F	2 hours; or 1 hour and provide automatic fire-extinguishing system
Laboratories and vocational shops, not classified as Group H, located in a Group E or I-2 occupancy	1 hour or provide automatic fire-extinguishing system
Laundry rooms over 100 square feet	1 hour or provide automatic fire-extinguishing system
Group I-3 cells equipped with padded surfaces	1 hour
Group I-2 waste and linen collection rooms	1 hour
Waste and linen collection rooms over 100 square feet	1 hour or provide automatic fire-extinguishing system
Stationary storage battery systems having a liquid electrolyte capacity of more than 50 gallons, or a lithium-ion capacity of 1,000 pounds used for facility standby power, emergency power or uninterrupted power supplies	1 hour in Group B, F, M, S and U occupancies; 2 hours in Group A, E, I and R occupancies.
Rooms containing fire pumps in nonhigh-rise buildings	2 hours, or 1 hour and provide automatic sprinkler system throughout the building
Rooms containing fire pumps in high-rise buildings	2 hours

For SI: 1 square foot = 0.0929 m^2, 1 pound per square inch (psi) = 6.9 kPa, 1 British thermal unit (Btu) per hour = 0.293 watts, 1 horsepower = 746 watts, 1 gallon = 3.785 L.

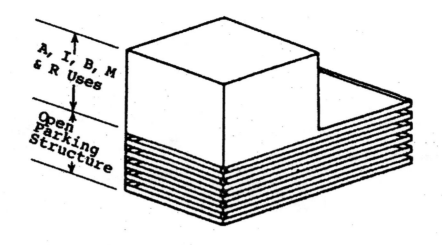

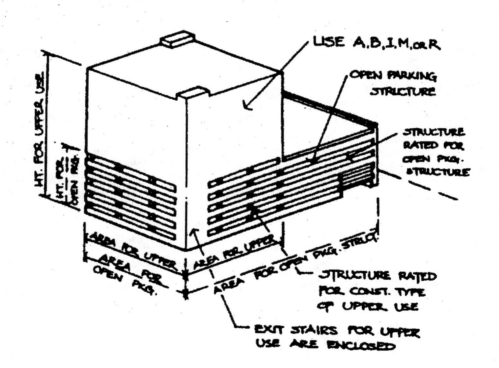

PAINT SPRAYING (416)

A. General
   1. Construction and equipment must comply with the Ohio Fire Code.
   2. Requirements apply to all flammable spraying.
   3. Sprinklers are required in all spray areas, storage rooms, and exhaust ducts.
   4. Interlock the spray equipment with the exhaust system. (M-502.7.3.1)
   5. Use non-sparking electrical control and ground all fan motor rotating elements. (M-502.7.3.6) (NEC)

B. Spray areas
   1. Approved enclosures by non-combustible curtains are required.
   2. Spray booths require non-combustible walls.
   3. Spray rooms require 1-hour partitions within the room; floors must be waterproof with a drain not directly connected to the building sewer.

C. Storage rooms per Ohio Fire Code.

D. Ventilation (M-502.7, M-510)
   1. Exhaust duct must not be less than 6" from combustibles, nor less than 10' from any lot lines for discharge. (Table M-510.8.2, M-511.1.1)
   2. Discharge must not be a nuisance to adjoining property nor to the public.
   3. Provide adequate makeup air.
   4. Provide minimum thickness as required by Table 510.8, and allow no penetrations of rated assemblies without shafts. (M-510.6)
   5. Flammable or combustible paint storage must have minimum 1 cfm/sq. ft. of floor area. (M-502.8.1.1)
   6. An independent system from other exhausts must be provided.

PARAPET WALLS (705.11 AND 706.6)

A. On all exterior walls with rating due to fire separation, a distance of 2'6" above the roof is required, with the following exceptions. (705.11)
   1. Building roof with a slope of more than 16.7 degrees (2:12), exterior wall may be less than the required distance, but the height cannot be less than 30".
   2. If the exterior wall extends to the underside of noncombustible roof construction, or to roofs of 2-hour construction, or 4' of ⁵/₈" Type X gypsum board beneath combustible sheathing on 2" ledgers and roof cover is Class C or better, or 4' of fire-retardant wood roof deck from wall for Uses R-2 and R-3.
   3. In Use Group R-2 and R-3 buildings with not less than a Class B roof covering.
   4. In any building less than 1000 sq. ft.
   5. When rating is only 1-hour and supporting construction for roof is 1-hour for 10' (4' for Uses R and U). No openings allowed 10' from wall (5' for Uses R and U). Minimum Class B roof.

B. All fire walls are required to extend 2' 6" above the roof, with the following exceptions. (706.6)
   1. Fire walls which extend to the underside of noncombustible roof construction, buildings with Class B roofs and no roof openings within 4' of fire wall, are not required to extend above the roof.
   2. Fire walls of Type III, IV, or V construction where roof deck is fire-retardant wood for 4' either side (or 4' of ⁵/₈" Type X gypsum board beneath combustible sheathing on 2" ledges and there are no openings within 4' of fire wall), and combustible material does not go through fire wall are not required to extend above the roof.

3. Fire walls up to 2 hours can terminate at roof deck when a lower roof has 1-hour rating for 4', no openings within 4' of the wall, and both buildings have minimum Class B roof.

PARKING (ADAAG AND OBC WHERE NOTED)

A. Minimum width for a parking space is 8' (vans 11' unless the access aisle is 8'). (ADAAG 502.2)
B. Provide spaces for use by the disabled near the building entry. (1106.6)
C. Maximum parking slope is 2%. (ADAAG 502.4)
D. Dimensions (ADAAG 502.3)
   1. Access route must be at least 5' wide.
   2. Loading access aisle must be 5' × 20'. (ADAAG 503.3)
E. Number per Table 1106.1 (approx. 2% up to 500)
   a. 2% for R-2 and R-3
   b. 10% for outpatient hospitals
   c. 20% for rehab and physical therapy
   d. minimum 1/6 must be van spaces
F. Signage—including fine—must be on signposts for accessible parking.

TABLE 1106.1
ACCESSIBLE PARKING SPACES

TOTAL PARKING SPACES PROVIDED	REQUIRED MINIMUM NUMBER OF ACCESSIBLE SPACES
1 to 25	1
26 to 50	2
51 to 75	3
76 to 100	4
101 to 150	5
151 to 200	6
201 to 300	7
301 to 400	8
401 to 500	9
501 to 1,000	2% of total
1,001 and over	20, plus one for each 100, or fraction thereof, over 1,000

PARTICLEBOARD (2303.1.7)

A. Particleboard is acceptable as an underlayment, subfloor, roof and wall sheathing, and as exterior siding.

B. Particleboard must be labeled as to Type (M-S or M-2).

C. Lay particleboard continuous over 2 or more joists, rafters, or studs. (2308.9.3, Table 2308.9.3(4))

D. Minimum underlayment thickness is ¼". (2308.9.3.1)

E. Use wood structural panel tables for spans. (Table 2308.9.3.1)

PIERS: ISOLATED FOUNDATION (1809.10)

A. Minimum dimension is 4" in width.

B. Maximum height is 10 times the least dimension unless reinforced.

C. Belled -- if structured clay tile or hollow masonry pier, fill cellular spaces with concrete or Type M/S mortar.

D. If hollow, the unsupported height cannot exceed 4 times the smallest width dimension.

E. Vertical masonry foundation elements not piers per 2102.1 are piers per TMS 402/ ACI 530/ASCE 5.

PILES (1808, 1810)

A. Pile foundations (per ASTM standards for each type)

1. Subsurface exploration, pile type, pile capacity, location, driving criteria, load test, durability, and required inspections must be indicated. (1810.2)

2. Special piles may be acceptable. (1808.2.3)

3. A pile location plan is required, with the pile spacing as recommended in the soils report. (1808.6) Special inspections are required by Section 1704.8.

4. Lateral support (1808.9)

   a. Soil other than fluid is considered adequate.

   b. Piles without any lateral support shall be considered structurally as columns.

5. Lateral bracing (1810.2.2)

   a. Lateral bracing is required in all directions.

   b. 3 or more piles may be braced by a rigid cap with piles spaced over 60° apart.

   c. Two piles with a rigid cap along the cap axis are acceptable.

   d. As a wall support, drive piles alternately and space at least 1' apart. Keep piles symmetrical under the footing.

   e. A single rows of piles without lateral bracing may be used in Use Group R and other light buildings up to 35' provided pile center is within foundation width.

6. Pile splices (1810.3.1.2, 1810.3.1.3)

   a. Splices must transmit all loads.

   b. Offset any mislocation by no less than 3", compressive overload to 110%.

7. Pile caps (1808.8)

   a. Use reinforced concrete, and embed piles into caps 3" minimum and project 4" minimum past edges.

   b. No bearing allowance is required for soil under a cap. Seismic connections by embedment are determined per ACI 318.

   c. Cut tops of piles to sound material before capping.

8. Existing piles may be used in some cases if load tested and redriven to load capacity. (1810.1.2)

B. Maximum allowable (1810.3.3)

1. 40 tons per pile is the maximum allowable load.
2. Higher loads may be permitted in some foundations with supporting data from test piles.
3. Piles shall develop twice the design load in load test (1810.3.1.2)

C. Caisson piles (1810.3.5.3.2)
1. Caisson piles consist of a concrete-filled pipe attached to bedrock with an uncased socket drilled into the rock, filled with concrete and having a steel core.
2. Minimum Nominal outside pile diameter is 18".
3. Minimum wall thickness of the pipe is $^3/8$".
4. Minimum concrete strength is 4000 psi with a 4" to 6" slump.
5. Socket
    a. Depth shall equal or exceed one pipe diameter.
    b. Maximum area of the steel core is $^1/4$ the caisson area.
    c. Spliced cores shall be welded full depth.
    d. A 2" minimum clearance between pipe and core is required.
    e. Diameter of the socket must be equal to the inside diameter of the pile.
6. Allowable design stresses as set forth in Table 1810.3.2.6

a.	Concrete	$.33f_c$
b.	Steel pipe	$.35 f_y$
c.	Steel core	$.5 f_y$

7. Remove all foreign matter prior to pour.

D. Cast-in-place piles (1810.3.5.2)
1. With permanent casing, diameter of not less than 8".
2. Without permanent casing, diameter of not less than 12".
3. Pour all concrete through a funnel hopper or tremie.

E. Uncased driven piles (1810.4.1.3, 1810.3.5.2.2)
1. Design for 25% of compressive strength.
2. Maximum length is 30 times the diameter; the minimum diameter is 12".
3. Minimum cover of rebars is 2$^1/2$".
4. Do not drive within 6 diameters of adjacent piles in granular soils within 48 hours unless directed by a design professional.

F. Steel-cased cast-in-place piles 16" minimum in diameter. (1810.3.2.7)
1. Element ratio yield strength to compressive strength of not less than 6.
2. Concrete design shall be 33% of compressive strength.
3. Mandrel drive the entire length of the pile.
4. Thickness not less than 14 gage standard.
5. Concrete-filled steel pipe and tube piles maximum aggregate size is $^3/4$" (zero slump). (1810.3.2.1)

G. Composite piles (1810.3.6)
1. Composite piles consist of 2 or more different pile types.
2. Maximum load allowed is the capacity of the weakest section.
3. Splice shall not separate and shall be able to carry the full compression load as well as at least 50% of the tension and bending of the weaker section.
4. Splices must be capable of sustaining upheaval forces.

H. Pre-cast concrete piles (1810.3.5.1)
1. Minimum lateral dimension is 8".
2. Non-prestressed piles must be minimum 3000 psi concrete and 0.8% steel cross-section.

3. Longitudinal steel (1810.3.8.1)
   a. Steel must be tied maximum 4" o.c. for 2' from ends of pile and maximum 6" elsewhere.
   b. First 5 ties must be a maximum of 1" o.c. each end.
4. Prestressed piles minimum 5000 psi concrete (1810.3.8.2.2)
   a. Minimum 1¼" concrete cover ≤ 12" square.
   b. Minimum 1½" concrete cover > 12" square.

I. Timber piles (1810.3.2.4)
   1. All piles shall be treated as piles per AF&PA NDS. Round timber per ASTM D 25. Sawn timber per DOC PS-20.
   2. Cutoffs shall be treated.
   3. A sudden drop in resistance must be investigated for damage.

J. Steel piles (allowable stress is per 1810.3.2.3 and Table 1810.3.2.6)
   1. Steel pipe (driven, open-ended) per 1810.3.5.3.2
      a. An 8" minimum diameter is required.
      b. Minimum thickness is 0.179".
      c. Thinner walls are acceptable with suitable cutting shoe.

PLASTER (718)

A. Fire-resistive requirements (718)
   1. Thickness is measured from the face of the gypsum to the metal lath.
   2. In Type I and II buildings, furring must be noncombustible.
   3. Plaster more than 1 thick must be reinforced with additional lath.
   4. ½" of unsanded plaster is the equivalent of ¾" of sanded plaster or 1 of portland cement sand plaster.
   5. Plaster may be alternative for up to ½" of required concrete cover for reinforcing steel.

PLENUMS (M-602)

A. Where permitted: Plenums are only allowed in attics, crawl spaces, areas above a ceiling and below a floor, and mechanical equipment rooms.
   1. Plenums cannot extend beyond fire area.
   2. Fuel-fired appliances are not permitted.

B. All material exposed in a plenum must be noncombustible except: (M-602.2.1)
   1. Combustible electrical or electronic wiring, optical fiber cable, and optical fiber raceway with a peak optical density of.5, average optical density of.15 and flame spread 5 ft. per NFPA 262. Use only type OFNP (plenum rated nonconductive optical fiber cable) in plenum-rated optical fiber raceways. Exception:
      a. Wiring methods per section 645.5 of NFPA 70 are permitted for plenums of information technology equipment areas or rooms per NFPA 75 and Article 645 of NFPA 70, separated by ≥ 1-hour barrier.
   2. Fire sprinkler piping (per UL 1887; and only within wet pipe systems) and pneumatic tubing (per UL 1820) with a peak optical density ≤ 0.50, average optical density ≤ 0.15, and flame spread ≤ 5 feet
   3. Ceiling and building insulation of 25 flame spread and 50 smoke development finish rating (M-602.2)
   4. Duct insulation with 25 flame spread and 50 smoke development finish rating (M-604.3), and
   5. Combustible electrical equipment with a peak rate of heat release ≤ 100 kilowatts, peak optical density ≤ 0.50 and average optical density ≤ 0.15 per UL 2043. Equipment must be labeled.

6. Foam plastic insulation (M-602.2.1.5)
    a. Flame spread $\leq$ 75
    b. Smoke developed rating $\leq$ 450
    c. Thermal barrier (2603.8) or 16 gauge metal cover
7. No restrictions for smoke detectors in plenum.

C. Stud and joist spaces (M-602.3)
1. Stud and joist spaces can be used for return but not supply air, from one floor only.
2. Space must not be part of the rated fire-resistive assembly.
3. All connections must be fire- and draft-stopped.

D. Exits and exit access corridors cannot be used as plenums except as listed for exhausted spaces, above ceilings, in dwelling units, and in tenant spaces of 1000 sq. ft. or less. (1018.5) The space above ceiling must be for:
    a. a non-rated corridor
    b. rated separation of the plenum
    c. the HVAC system shuts down with smoke detection or sprinklers
    d. the plenum is part of a smoke control system

PLUMBING

A. Sewers
1. Sanitary sewers
    a. Starts inside the building, to 30 inches of piping beyond the exterior wall. (See definition of "Building Drain" in P-202.)
    b. All buildings covered by OBC/OPC must be connected to a sewer, with an independent connection, unless approved by OEPA. (P-701.2, P-701.3)
2. Storm water sewers
    a. Starts on roof planes, yards and courts, and paved areas on the building, to 30 inches of piping beyond the exterior wall. (See definition of "Building Drain" in P-202.)
    b. Storm water not permitted in sanitary sewers. (P-1101.3)
    c. Storm and sanitary sewers can be combined only if the connection is exterior to the building.
3. Potable water
    a. Starts at the "water service pipe," which is defined as the piping connected to a water main or water meter (when the meter is in the right-of-way) through all piping to the plumbing fixtures. (See definitions of "Water Pipe" and "Water Supply System" in P-202.)
    b. Every structure with plumbing fixtures and used for human habitation must have potable water. (P-602.1)
4. Lead content (605.2)
    a. Pipes, pipe fittings, valves and faucets limited to 8% lead content.
    b. Drinking water pipes, fittings, joints, valves, faucets, and fixture fittings must meet NSF 372, with weighted average lead content of $\leq$ 0.25% lead.
    c. Exceptions to lead content restrictions (although potable water supply pipe serving fixture or supplying nonpotable water system is not exempt):
        1. Pipes, pipe fittings, plumbing fittings, or fixtures, (e.g., backflow preventers used exclusively for nonpotable services—process piping, irrigation piping, and outdoor watering piping.
        2. Toilets, bidets, urinals, fill valves, flushometer valves, tub fillers, shower valves, and service saddles.
        3. Water distribution main gate valves $\geq$ 2".

B. Backwater valve (P-715.2)
   1. Use only non-corrodible parts in backwater valves.
   2. Backwater valves must be the same capacity as the drain.
   3. Backwater valves must be readily accessible.
   4. Only when required by Ohio EPA or by local jurisdiction.
C. Cleanouts (P-708)
   1. Cleanouts must be maximum 100′ center for horizontal drains.
   2. All cleanouts shall be accessible.
   3. Install cleanouts at drain direction changes of more than 45°, but only one per 40′ of length.
   4. Provide cleanouts at the base of each stack.
   5. A cleanout is required near the building drain and the main sewer, except 3" or longer can be 10′ away in pipe length.
   6. Use the same size of the drain up to 4" and 4" minimum when sewer is more than 4". There are exceptions for P-traps with slip-joints of 1½" and 2" pipe. (P-708.7)
   7. A 36" minimum clearance is required for working on 8" drains or larger. (P-708.8)
   8. An 18" minimum clearance is required for working on drains 6" or smaller. (P-708.8)
   9. Cannot be used for new fixture installation. (P-708.6)
D. Fixture flushing—each plumbing fixture that depends on trap siphonage to discharge the contents to the drainage system requires a flushometer valve, tank, or flush tank. Flushometer valves and tanks comply with ASSE 1037. Vacuum breakers on flushometer valves comply with ASSE 1001 or CSA B64.1.1.
   1. Chemical non-flushing water closets are unacceptable.
   2. Each flushing fixture must have its own flushing device.
E. Fixture walls and floor finish
   1. Urinals require a smooth washable surface a minimum of 4′ high and 2′ wide at the sides at 2′ in front of the lip. (P-419.3)
   2. Showers and tub showers require watertight joints, and a smooth washable surface 6′ from the floor on all sides, and ≤ 70" from the compartment floor at the drain. (P-417.4) Shower compartments minimum dimension must be ≥ 30" (762 mm) from finished compartment interior, exclusive of fixture valves, showerheads, soap dishes, and safety grab bars or rails. Minimum size of shower compartments is 900" square. 417.4.1 Use smooth, noncorrosive, nonabsorbent waterproof materials in wall area above built-in tubs with installed shower heads and in shower compartments, with height ≥ 6′ feet (1829 mm) above floor, and ≥ 70" measured from compartment floor at the drain. Minimum clear width of 22" for shower compartment and egress opening.
   3. Shower floors must be permanently waterproof. (P-417.5)
F. Fixture units traps and drains (P-709)
   1. Drains, stacks, and branches are sized to accommodate a certain number of fixture units.
   2. Each fixture is assigned a unit number and minimum trap size. These units are totaled to arrive at the required drain size.
   3. Typical unit and trap size:

TABLE 709.2
DRAINAGE FIXTURE UNITS FOR FIXTURES AND GROUPS

FIXTURE TYPE	DRAINAGE FIXTURE UNIT VALUE AS LOAD FACTORS	MINIMUM SIZE OF TRAP (inches)
Automatic clothes washers, commercial[a,g]	3	2
Automatic clothes washers, residential[g]	2	2
Bathroom group as defined in Section 202 (1.6 gpf water closet)[f]	5	—
Bathroom group as defined in Section 202 (water closet flushing greater than 1.6 gpf)[f]	6	—
Bathtub (with or without overhead shower or whirlpool attachments)	2	$1^1/_2$
Bidet	1	$1^1/_4$
Combination sink and tray	2	$1^1/_2$
Dental lavatory	1	$1^1/_4$
Dental unit or cuspidor	1	$1^1/_4$
Dishwashing machine[c], domestic	2	$1^1/_2$
Drinking fountain	$^1/_2$	$1^1/_4$
Emergency floor drain	0	2
Floor drains	2	2
Kitchen sink, domestic	2	$1^1/_2$
Kitchen sink, domestic with food waste grinder and/or dishwasher	2	$1^1/_2$
Laundry tray (1 or 2 compartments)	2	$1^1/_2$
Lavatory	1	$1^1/_4$
Shower	2	$1^1/_2$
Service sink	2	$1^1/_2$
Sink	2	$1^1/_2$
Urinal	4	Note d
Urinal, 1 gallon per flush or less	2[e]	Note d
Urinal, nonwater supplied	0.5	Note d
Wash sink (circular or multiple) each set of faucets	2	$1^1/_2$
Water closet, flushometer tank, public or private	4[e]	Note d
Water closet, private (1.6 gpf)	3[e]	Note d
Water closet, private (flushing greater than 1.6 gpf)	4[e]	Note d
Water closet, public (1.6 gpf)	4[e]	Note d
Water closet, public (flushing greater than 1.6 gpf)	6[e]	Note d

For SI: 1 inch = 25.4 mm, 1 gallon = 3.785 L (gpf = gallon per flushing cycle).

a. For traps larger than 3 inches, use Table 709.2.

b. A showerhead over a bathtub or whirlpool bathtub attachment does not increase the drainage fixture unit value.

c. See Sections 709.2 through 709.4 for methods of computing unit value of fixtures not listed in this table or for rating of devices with intermittent flows.

d. Trap size shall be consistent with the fixture outlet size.

e. For the purpose of computing loads on building drains and sewers, water closets and urinals shall not be rated at a lower drainage fixture unit unless the lower values are confirmed by testing.

f. For fixtures added to a dwelling unit bathroom group, add the dfu value of those additional fixtures to the bathroom group fixture count.

g. See Section 406.3 for sizing requirements for fixture drain, branch drain, and drainage stack for an automatic clothes washer standpipe.

4. Estimation of other fixtures use fixture drain or trap size (Table 709.2)

Drain		Units	Drain		Units
$1^1/_4$"	—	1	$2^1/_2$"	—	4

Drain		Units	Drain		Units
1½	—	2	3	—	5
2	—	3	4	—	6

5. For a continuous flow into a drain such as a pump, figure 1 gpm = 2 fixture units.

6. Typical stack capacity using fixture units.

TABLE 710.1(1)
BUILDING DRAINS AND SEWERS

DIAMETER OF PIPE (inches)	MAXIMUM NUMBER OF DRAINAGE FIXTURE UNITS CONNECTED TO ANY PORTION OF THE BUILDING DRAIN OR THE BUILDING SEWER, INCLUDING BRANCHES OF THE BUILDING DRAIN[a]			
	Slope per foot			
	1/16 inch	1/8 inch	1/4 inch	1/2 inch
1¼	—	—	1	1
1½	—	—	3	3
2	—	—	21	26
2½	—	—	24	31
3	—	36	42	50
4	—	180	216	250
5	—	390	480	575
6	—	700	840	1,000
8	1,400	1,600	1,920	2,300
10	2,500	2,900	3,500	4,200
12	3,900	4,600	5,600	6,700
15	7,000	8,300	10,000	12,000

For SI: 1 inch = 25.4 mm, 1 inch per for = 83.3 mm/m.

a. The minimum size of any building drain serving a water closet shall be 3 inches.

TABLE 710.1(2)
HORIZONTAL FIXTURE BRANCHES AND STACKS[a]

DIAMETER OF PIPE (inches)	MAXIMUM NUMBER OF DRAINAGE FIXTURE UNITS (dfu)			
		Stacks[b]		
	Total for horizontal branch	Total discharge into one branch interval	Total for stack of three branch intervals or less	Total for stack greater than three branch intervals
1½	3	2	4	8
2	6	6	10	24
2½	12	9	20	42
3	20	20	48	72
4	160	90	240	500
5	360	200	540	1,100
6	620	350	960	1,900
8	1,400	600	2,200	3,600
10	2,500	1,000	3,800	5,600

| DIAMETER OF PIPE (inches) | MAXIMUM NUMBER OF DRAINAGE FIXTURE UNITS (dfu) | | | |
| | Total for horizontal branch | Stacks[b] | | |
		Total discharge into one branch interval	Total for stack of three branch intervals or less	Total for stack greater than three branch intervals
12	2,900	1,500	6,000	8,400
15	7,000	Note c	Note c	Note c

For SI: 1 inch = 25.4 mm.

a. Does not include branches of the building drain. Refer to Table 710.1(1).

b. Stacks shall be sized based on the total accumulated connected load at each story or branch interval. As the total accumulated connected load decreases, stacks are permitted to be reduced in size. Stack diameters shall not be reduced to less than one-half of the diameter of the largest stack size required.

c. Sizing load based on design criteria.

G. Floor drains (P-412)
1. All floor drains require a removable strainer. (P-412.2)
2. Minimum 2" drain outlet, 3" minimum at public laundries.

H. Hangers and support (P-308)
1. Hangers cannot be material that would promote galvanic deterioration.
2. Sway bracing required at 45° or more turns for 4" and larger pipe.
3. Bases of stacks must be supported with concrete, masonry, or metal brackets.

TABLE 308.5
HANGER SPACING

PIPING MATERIAL	MAXIMUM HORIZONTAL SPACING (feet)	MAXIMUM VERTICAL SPACING (feet)
ABS pipe	4	10[b]
Aluminum tubing	10	15
Brass pipe	10	10
Cast-iron pipe	5[a]	15
Copper or copper-alloy pipe	12	10
Copper or copper-allow tubing, 1¼-inch diameter and smaller	6	10
Copper or copper-alloy tubing, 1½-inch diameter and larger	10	10
Cross-linked polyethylene (PEX) pipe	2.67 (32 inches)	10[b]
Cross-linked polyethylene/aluminum/cross-linked polyethylene (PEX-AL-PEX) pipe	2.67 (32 inches)	4
CPVC pipe or tubing, 1 inch and smaller	3	10[b]
CPVC pipe or tubing, 1¼ inches and larger	4	10[b]
Steel pipe	12	15
Lead pipe	Continuous	4
PB pipe or tubing	2.67 (32 inches)	4

PIPING MATERIAL	MAXIMUM HORIZONTAL SPACING (feet)	MAXIMUM VERTICAL SPACING (feet)
Polyethylene/aluminum/polyethylene (PE-AL-PE) pipe	2.67 (32 inches)	4
Polypropylene (PP) pipe or tubing, 1 inch and smaller	2.67 (32 inches)	10[b]
Polypropylene (PP) pipe or tubing, 1¼ inches and larger	4	10[b]
PVC pipe	4	10[b]
Stainless steel drainage systems	10	10[b]

For SI: 1 inch = 25.4 mm, 1 foot = 304.8 mm.

a. The maximum horizontal spacing of cast-iron pipe hangers shall be increased to 10 feet where 10-foot lengths of pipe are installed.

b. Midstory guide for sizes 2 inches and smaller.

I. Vents (P-901)
1. Required to permit admission or emission of air so as to limit pneumatic pressure differential on fixture trap to ≤ 1" of water column.
2   At least one vent pipe or extension (but not an island fixture) per vent system must reach outdoors through and above roof. Vent stacks required for 5 or more branch intervals. Any vent stack connections to building drain should be downstream of stack and at distance < 10x diameter of stack.
3   Where common vent header, number of fixture units is sum of all units on all connected stacks, with length that of longest vent length from intersection at base of farthest stack to vent terminal, as direct extension of one stack. (249 Pa.) (P-901.2, 903.1, .2, .4, .5.)
4. Chemical wastes vent to roof must be independent of sanitary vent. (P-901.3)
5. Use sheet copper per ASTM B 152, weighing ≥ 8 oz. per sq. ft (2.5 kg/m^2), and sheet lead weighing ≥ 3 lbs. per sq. ft. (15 kg/m^2) for field-constructed flashings and ≥ 2 lbs. per sq. ft. (12 kg/m^2) for fabricated flashings. (P-902.2, 3)
6. Vent terminals (P-904)
    a. Must terminate ≥ 12" (304.8 mm) above the roof. If roof is used for other than weather protection, terminate vent extensions ≥ 7' (2134 mm) above the roof. For frost protection, vent extensions are 3" (76 mm) minimum diameter. An increase in vent size can only be within the structure, at a minimum of 1' (305 mm) below the roof or inside the wall. Make vent pipe junctures with roof water-tight with flashing. (P-904.1,-.3)
    b. Cannot use vent terminal to support flag poles, TV aerials, etc. except with approved anchoring. (P-901.4)
    c. No vent terminal directly beneath door, openable window, or air intake, and not horizontally within 10' (3048 mm) of an opening unless ≥ 2' (610 mm) above opening. Terminals through walls must be 10' minimum both from the lot line and above ground level. Never terminate under the overhang of a structure with soffit vents. If on side wall, vent termination must be protected from bird/rodent entry/blockage. Where the climate's 97.6% value for outside design temperature is < 0°F (-18°C), protect exterior vent pipes by insulation and/or heat. (P-904.-.7)
7. Vent connections (P-905)
    a. All vents must connect to vent stacks, stack vents, extend to open air, or connect to an air admittance valve, and graded for gravity drainage to drainage pipe. (P-905.1,.2)

b. Dry vents must connect to horizontal drain above the center line of pipe, and have vertical rise $\geq$ 6" (152 mm) above flood level rim of highest trap or fixture vented UNLESS vent for interceptor outside. (P-905.3,.4)

c. Make connection between vent pipe and stack vent or vent stack $\geq$ 6" above flood level rim of highest fixture served by vent. Same applies to horizontal vent pipe forming branch, relief, or loop vents. (P-905.5)

d. If drainage piping roughed-in for future fixtures, install identified rough-in for vent, sized at $\geq$ $\frac{1}{2}$ diameter of rough-in drain served, to connect to vent system. (P-905.6)

8. Fixture vents(P-906)

a. Per Table 906.1, EXCEPT do not limit developed length of fixture drain from trap weir to vent fitting for self-siphoning fixtures (e.g., water closets) for individual, common, and wet vent systems. (P-906.1)

b. Fixture drain pipe's total fall because of pipe slope cannot exceed fixture drain's diameter. Vent connection to fixture drain UNLESS water closet, cannot be below weir of trap. (P-906.2)

c. No crown vent < two pipe diameters of trap weir. (P-906.3)

TABLE 906.1
MAXIMUM DISTANCE OF FIXTURE TRAP FROM VENT

SIZE OF TRAP (inches)	SLOPE (inch per foot)	DISTANCE FROM TRAP (feet)
1 $\frac{1}{4}$	$\frac{1}{4}$	5
1 $\frac{1}{2}$	$\frac{1}{4}$	6
2	$\frac{1}{4}$	8
3	1/8	12
4	1/8	16

9. Individual common vent (double pattern fitting) can vent two traps or trapped fixtures on same floor level, with connection at fixture drains or downstream of intersection. If drains connect at different levels, vent is vertical extension of vertical drain, which is considered vent for the lower fixture drain; upper fixture cannot be water closet. Size common vent per Table 908.3.

TABLE 908.3
COMMON VENT SIZES

PIPE SIZE (inches)	MAXIMUM DISCHARGE FROM UPPER FIXTURE DRAIN (dfu)
1 ½	1
2	4
2 ½ to 3	6

10. Wet vent (P-909)
    a. Either horizontal or vertical wet vent can vent combination of fixtures within two bathroom groups on same floor level. Wet vent runs from dry vent connection along direction of drain pipe flow to most downstream fixture drain connection. All fixture drains connects independently to wet vent. If vertical, connect water closet drains at same elevation, while other fixture drains connect above or at same elevation as water closet drains. (P-909.1)
    b. Dry vent connection for horizontal wet vent is either individual or common vent for bathroom group fixture EXCEPT emergency floor drain. Dry vent connection to water closet fixture drain is site of horizontal connection to horizontal wet vent system (only one allowed). (P-909.2.1)
    c. Dry vent connection for vertical wet vent is either individual or common vent for most upstream fixture drain. (P-909.2.2)
    d. Dry vent minimum size per Table 909.3. Maximum size per largest required diameter of pipe in wet vent system served. (P-909.3)

TABLE 909.3
WET VENT SIZE

WET VENT PIPE SIZE (inches)	DRAINAGE FIXTURE UNIT LOAD (dfu)
1 ½	1
2	4
2 ½	6
3	12

11. Waste stack vents (P-910)
    a. Waste stacks must be vertical, with both horizontal and vertical offsets barred between lowest and highest fixture drain connections. Water closet or urinal discharges are disallowed. (P-910.1,.2)
    b. Stack vents required for waste stacks, sized at not less than waste stacks, with offsets permitted ≥ 6" above flood level of highest fixture. (P-910.3)
    c. Waste stacks sized per Table 910.4 (P-910.4)

TABLE 910.4
WASTE STACK VENT SIZE

STACK SIZE (inches)	MAXIMUM NUMBER OF DRAINAGE FIXTURE UNITS (dfu)	
	Total discharge into one branch interval	Total discharge for stack
1 ½	1	2
2	2	4
2 ½	No limit	8
3	No limit	24
4	No limit	50
5	No limit	75
6	No limit	100

12. Circuit vents (P-911)
    a. Eight fixtures maximum connected to horizontal branch drain can be a separate circuit vent. Soil or waste discharge is barred. (P-911.1,2.)
    b. Circuit vent connection is between two most upstream fixture drains. Maximum slope is one vertical unit per 12 horizontal (8%). Size the downstream circuit vented horizontal branch for total discharge into branch, inclusive of upstream branches and fixtures. (P-911.3)
    c. Use relief vent for circuit vents receiving discharge from $\geq$ 4 water closets and connecting to drainage stack receiving soil or waste discharge from upper horizontal branches. Maximum discharge to a relief vent is four fixture units. (P-911.4)
13. Combined drain and vent systems are limited to floor drains, sinks, lavatories, and drinking fountains—cannot receive food waste grinder or clinical sink discharge. (P-912.1)
    a. Vertical pipe $\leq$ 8′ (2438 mm) connects fixture drain with horizontal drain/vent combination, which has maximum slope of ½ unit vertical per 12 units horizontal (4%). (P-912.2)
    b. Combination requires either dry vent or horizontal drain connection. Vent connection has minimum vertical extension of 6" (1152 mm) above flood level rim of highest fixture before horizontal offsetting. Fixture branch or fixture drain connects to the combined system per table 906.1 (P-912.2)
    c. Size combined drain/vent system per Table 912.3. (P-912.3)

TABLE 912.3
SIZE OF COMBINATION DRAIN AND VENT PIPE

DIAMETER PIPE (inches)	MAXIMUM NUMBER OF DRAINAGE FIXTURE UNITS (dfu)	
	Connecting to a horizontal branch or stack	Connecting to a building drain or building subdrain
2	3	4
2 ½	6	26
3	12	31
4	20	50
5	160	250
6	360	575

14. Island fixture venting is limited to sinks and lavatories, including residential kitchen sinks with dishwasher waste and/or food waste grinder connections with sink waste. Vent rises vertically 6" to above drainage outlet of fixture before offsetting downward, horizontally or vertically. Island fixture vent connects to either of a vertical drain pipe or top half of a horizontal drain pipe. Use cleanouts in island fixture vent to allow rodding (both directions) of all vent piping below flood level rim of fixtures. (P-913)

15. Relief vents at each 10th interval installed required in buildings with > 10 branch intervals, starting at top floor. Relief vents sized to connecting vent stack, with lower end through wye below horizontal branch serving the floor, and upper end through wye $\geq$ 3′ (914 mm) above the floor. (P-914)

16. If five or more branch intervals above the offset, vent horizontal offsets. Upper section vented as separate stack, while lower section has yoke vent (can be vertical extension of drainage stack) connecting between offset and next lower horizontal branch. Yoke vent and connection are sized to minimum required for vent stack of drainage stack. (P-915)

17. Sizes of stack vents/vent stacks (P-916)
    a. Minimum required diameter per Table 916.1, but always $\geq$ ½ diameter of drain served and < 1 ¼" (43 mm). (P-916.1)

TABLE 916.1
SIZE AND DEVELOPED LENGTH OF STACK VENTS AND VENT STACKS

DIAMETER OF SOIL OR WASTE STACK (inches)	TOTAL FIXTURE UNITS BEING VENTED (dfu)	MAXIMUM DEVELOPED LENGTH OF VENT (feet)[a] DIAMETER OF VENT (inches)										
		1¼	1½	2	2½	3	4	5	6	8	10	12
1¼	2	30	-	-	-	-	-	-	-	-	-	-
1½	8	50	150	-	-	-	-	-	-	-	-	-
1½	10	30	100	-	-	-	-	-	-	-	-	-
2	12	30	75	200	-	-	-	-	-	-	-	-
2	20	26	50	150	-	-	-	-	-	-	-	-
2½	42	-	30	100	300	-	-	-	-	-	-	-
3	10	-	42	150	360	1040	-	-	-	-	-	-
3	21	-	32	110	270	810	-	-	-	-	-	-
3	53	-	27	94	230	680	-	-	-	-	-	-
3	102	-	25	86	210	620	-	-	-	-	-	-
4	43	-	-	35	85	250	980	-	-	-	-	-
4	140	-	-	27	65	200	750	-	-	-	-	-
4	320	-	-	23	55	170	640	-	-	-	-	-
4	540	-	-	21	50	150	580	-	-	-	-	-
5	190	-	-	-	28	82	320	990	-	-	-	-
5	490	-	-	-	21	63	250	760	-	-	-	-
5	940	-	-	-	18	53	210	670	-	-	-	-
5	1400	-	-	-	16	49	190	590	-	-	-	-
6	500	-	-	-	-	33	130	400	1000	-	-	-
6	1100	-	-	-	-	26	100	310	780	-	-	-
6	2000	-	-	-	-	22	84	260	660	-	-	-
6	2900	-	-	-	-	20	77	240	600	-	-	-
8	1800	-	-	-	-	-	31	95	240	940	-	-
8	3400	-	-	-	-	-	24	73	199	720	-	-
8	5600	-	-	-	-	-	20	62	160	610	-	-
8	7600	-	-	-	-	-	18	56	140	560	-	-
10	4000	-	-	-	-	-	-	31	78	310	960	-
10	7200	-	-	-	-	-	-	24	60	240	740	-
10	11,000	-	-	-	-	-	-	20	51	200	630	-
10	15,000	-	-	-	-	-	-	18	46	180	570	-
12	7300	-	-	-	-	-	-	-	31	120	380	940
12	13,000	-	-	-	-	-	-	-	24	94	300	720
12	20,000	-	-	-	-	-	-	-	20	79	250	610
12	26,000	-	-	-	-	-	-	-	18	72	230	500
15	15,000	-	-	-	-	-	-	-	-	40	130	310
15	25,000	-	-	-	-	-	-	-	-	31	96	240
15	38,000	-	-	-	-	-	-	-	-	26	81	200
15	50,000	-	-	-	-	-	-	-	-	24	74	180

b. Individual, branch, circuit, and relief vents are $\geq$ $\frac{1}{2}$ diameter of drain served (per Table 710.1(2)). Vent pipes are $\geq$ 1 $\frac{1}{4}$" (32 mm) in diameter. If $\geq$ 40' (12,192 mm) in developed length, increase by one nominal pipe size for entire developed length. Developed length is measured from farthest point of vent connection to drainage system to point of connection to vent stack, stack vent, or outside termination. Multiple branch vents sized based on size of common horizontal drainage branch required to serve total drainage fixture unit (dfu) load vented. If branch vent over 40' in developed length, increase by one nominal size for entire developed length of vent pipe. (P-916.2,3,.4)

c. Building sump vents for sumps with sewage pumps or sewage ejectors, other than pneumatic, per table 916.5.1. If pneumatic sewage ejector, connect air pressure relief pipe to an independent vent stack terminating through roof, with relief pipe sized to relieve air pressure inside ejector to atmospheric pressure, but $\geq$ 1 $\frac{1}{4}$" (32 mm) in size. (P-916.5)

TABLE 916.5.1
SIZE AND LENGTH OF SUMP VENTS

DISCHARGE CAPACITY OF PUMP (gpm)	MAXIMUM DEVELOPED LENGTH OF VENT (feet)[a]					
	Diameter of vent (inches)					
	1 ¼	1 ½	2	2 ½	3	4
10	No limit[b]	No limit	No limit	No limit	No limit	No limit
20	270	No limit	No limit	No limit	No limit	No limit
40	72	160	No limit	No limit	No limit	No limit
60	31	75	270	No limit	No limit	No limit
80	16	41	150	380	No limit	No limit
100	10[c]	25	97	250	No limit	No limit
150	Not permitted	10[c]	44	110	370	No limit
200	Not permitted	Not permitted	20	60	210	No limit
250	Not permitted	Not permitted	10	36	132	No limit
300	Not permitted	Not permitted	10[c]	22	88	380
400	Not permitted	Not permitted	Not permitted	10[c]	44	210
500	Not permitted	Not permitted	Not permitted	Not permitted	24	130

18. Air admittance valves comply with ASSE 1050 (stack type) or ASSE 1051 (branch type), and require DWV testing before installation. Allowed as termination for individual, branch, and circuit vents. Individual and branch type air admittance valves vent only to fixtures on same floor level and connect to a horizontal branch drain (connected to drainage stack or building drain a maximum of four branch intervals from top of stack. (P-917.1,.2,.3)

   a. Relief vent to vent stack, stack vent or outside required where horizontal branch more than four branch, but less than six, intervals from top of stack. Relief vent connects to horizontal branch drain between stack and most downstream fixture drain connected to horizontal branch drain. (P-917.3.2)

   b. Locate individual and branch type air admittance valve a minimum of 4" (102 mm) above horizontal branch or fixture drain being vented, stack type ≥ 6" above the flood level rim of highest fixture being vented. All air admittance valves are a minimum of 6" above insulation materials. Access to and ventilation for valves is necessary. (P-917.4,.5)

   c. No air admittance valves allowed in nonneutralized special waste systems. No installation of valves in supply or return air plenums or as limited by manufacturer. Cannot use to vent sumps or tanks unless valve has engineered design. (P-917.7,.8)

19. Engineered vents have a maximum developed length for individual fixture vents to vent branches and vent headers per Table 918.2 for minimum pipe diameters at vent airflow rates in Equation 9-1. (P-918.2)

$$Q_{h,b} = N_{n,b} \, Q_v \qquad \textbf{(Equation 9-1)}$$

For SI: $Q_{h,b} = N_{n,b} \, Q_v \, (0.4719 \text{ L/s})$

where:

$N_{n,b}$ = Number of fixtures per header (or vent branch) ÷ total number of fixtures connected to vent stack.

$Q_{h,b}$ = Vent branch or vent header airflow rate (cfm).

Q_v = Total vent stack airflow rate (cfm).

$Q_v \text{ (gpm)} = 27.8 \, r_s^{2/3} \, (1 - r_s) \, D^{8/3}$

$Q_v \text{ (cfm)} = 0.134 \, Q_v \text{ (gpm)}$

where:

D = Drainage stack diameter (inches).

Q_w = Design discharge load (gpm).

r_s = Waste water flow area to total area.

$\qquad = Q_w / 27.8 \, D^{8/3}$

TABLE 918.2
MINIMUM DIAMETER AND MAXIMUM LENGTH OF INDIVIDUAL BRANCH FIXTURE VENTS AND INDIVIDUAL FIXTURE HEADER VENTS FOR SMOOTH PIPES

DIAMETER OF VENT PIPE (inches)	INDIVIDUAL VENT AIRFLOW RATE (cubic feet per minute)																			
	Maximum developed length of vent (feet)																			
	1	2	3	4	5	6	7	8	9	10	11	12	13	14	15	16	17	18	19	20
½	95	25	13	8	5	4	3	2	1	1	1	1	1	1	1	1	1	1	1	1
¾	100	88	47	30	20	15	10	9	7	6	5	4	3	3	3	2	2	2	2	1
1	-	-	100	94	65	48	37	29	24	20	17	14	12	11	9	8	7	7	6	6
1 ¼	-	-	-	-	-	-	-	100	87	73	62	53	46	40	36	32	29	26	23	21
1 ½	-	-	-	-	-	-	-	-	-	-	-	100	96	84	75	65	60	54	49	45
2	-	-	-	-	-	-	-	-	-	-	-	-	-	-	-	-	-	-	-	100

J. Interceptors (P-1003)

1. Interceptors are required when detrimental wastes are harmful to the sewerage system. Grease interceptors and automatic grease removal devices required to catch grease in food preparation areas (i.e., restaurants, hotel kitchens, hospitals, school kitchens, bars, factory cafeterias and clubs), including from pot sinks, prerinse sinks; soup kettles or similar; work stations; floor drains or sinks; automatic hood wash units and dishwashers lacking prerinse sinks. Interceptors and automatic grease removal devices only receive waste from fixtures and equipment allowing discharge of fats, oils or grease. Require solids interceptor if food waste grinders connect to grease interceptors. Disallow emulsifiers, chemicals, enzymes and bacteria discharge into the food waste grinder.

2. Wastes from industrial processes such as meat packing, food processing, and septic systems, are regulated by the health departments and the OEPA.

3. Grease traps must provide 2 lbs. of capacity for every gpm of flow-through rating. (Table P-1003.3.4.1)

4. Separators for service stations must have 6 cu. ft. for first 100 sq. ft. of area, then 1 cu. ft. for every additional 100 sq. ft.

5. Parking garages without repair or fuel dispensing do not require separators but must have sediment receivers and traps. Drains in open parking garages are considered to be storm drains. (P-1003.4.2.2)

TABLE 1003.3.4.1
CAPACITY OF GREASE INTERCEPTORS[a]

TOTAL FLOW-THROUGH RATING (gpm)	GREASE RETENTION CAPACITY (pounds)
4	8
6	12
7	14
9	18
10	20
12	24
14	28
15	30
18	36
20	40
25	50
35	70
50	100
75	150
100	200

For SI: 1 gallon per minute = 3.785 L/m, 1 pound = 0.454 kg.
a. For total flow-through ratings greater than 100 (gpm), double the flow-through rating to determine the grease retention capacity (pounds).

K. Joints for drainage (P-705)
   1. Compression type joints for cast iron are acceptable.
   2. Hubless cast iron joints are acceptable.
   3. Caulked cast iron requires 1" of lead not less than 1/8" below the rim.
   4. Use slip joints on the inlet side of traps. (P-705.17 and P-405.8)
   5. Concrete, mastic, and solvent-cement joints between different types of plastic and saddle-type fittings are prohibited. (P-705.16 and P-707)

L. Pipe material for drainage (P-702 Sanitary, P-1102 Storm)

   Most of the materials on the market today are acceptable for their intended use and should be supported, properly joined, and installed with the recommended fittings.

M. Roof leaders (P-1105)
   1. Install roof leaders separate from the building drains. Strainers extend ≥ 4" (102 mm) above roof surface immediately adjacent to roof drain, and have available inlet area, above roof level, of ≥ one and one-half times the area of the conductor or leader to which the drain is connected.
   2. Use the same piping materials as for drains.
   3. Emergency roof drains required where capable of ponding when drains are blocked. (P-1101.7 and P-1107)
   4. Vertical leader sizes based on 100-year hourly rainfall or 4 inches per hour. (1106.1)

TABLE 1106.2(1)
SIZE OF CIRCULAR VERTICAL CONDUCTORS AND LEADERS

DIAMETER OF LEADER (inches)[a]	HORIZONTALLY PROJECTED ROOF AREA (square feet)											
	Rainfall rate (inches per hour)											
	1	2	3	4	5	6	7	8	9	10	11	12
2	2,880	1,440	960	720	575	480	410	360	320	290	260	240
3	8,800	4,400	2,930	2,200	1,760	1,470	1,260	1,100	980	880	800	730
4	18,400	9,200	6,130	4,600	3,680	3,070	2,630	2,300	2,045	1,840	1,675	1,530
5	34,600	17,300	11,530	8,650	6,920	5,765	4,945	4,325	3,845	3,460	3,145	2,880
6	54,000	27,000	17,995	13,500	10,800	9,000	7,715	6,750	6,000	5,400	4,910	4,500
8	116,000	58,000	38,660	29,000	23,200	19,315	16,570	14,500	12,890	11,600	10,545	9,600

For SI: 1 inch = 25.4 mm, 1 square foot = 0.0929 m².

a. Sizes indicated are the diameter of circular piping. This table is applicable to piping of other shapes provided the cross-sectional shape fully encloses a circle of the diameter indicated in this table.

TABLE 1106.2(2)
SIZE OF RECTANGULAR VERTICAL CONDUCTORS AND LEADERS

DIMENSIONS OF COMMON LEADER SIZES width x length (inches)[a]	HORIZONTALLY PROJECTED ROOF AREA (square feet)											
	Rainfall rate (inches per hour)											
	1	2	3	4	5	6	7	8	9	10	11	12
1 ¾ × 2 ½	3,410	1,700	1,130	850	680	560	480	420	370	340	310	280
2 × 3	5,540	2,770	1,840	1,380	1,100	920	790	690	610	550	500	460
2 ¾ × 4 ¼	12,830	6,410	4,270	3,200	2,560	2,130	1,830	1,600	1,420	1,280	1,160	1,060
3 × 4	13,210	6,600	4,400	3,300	2,640	2,200	1,880	1,650	1,460	1,320	1,200	1,100
3 ½ × 4	15,900	7,950	5,300	3,970	3,180	2,650	2,270	1,980	1,760	1,590	1,440	1,320
3 ½ × 5	21,310	10,650	7,100	5,320	4,260	3,550	3,040	2,660	2,360	2,130	1,930	1,770
3 ¾ × 4 ¾	21,960	10,980	7,320	5,490	4,390	3,660	3,130	2,740	2,440	2,190	1,990	1,830

3 ¾ × 5 ¼	25,520	12,760	8,500	6,380	5,100	4,250	3,640	3,190	2,830	2,550	2,320	2,120
3 ½ × 6	27,790	13,890	9,260	6,940	5,550	4,630	3,970	3,470	3,080	2,770	2,520	2,310
4 × 6	32,980	16,490	10,990	8,240	6,590	5,490	4,710	4,120	3,660	3,290	2,990	2,740
5 ½ × 5 ½	44,300	22,150	14,760	11,070	8,860	7,380	6,320	5,530	4,920	4,430	4,020	3,690
7 ½ × 7 ½	100,500	50,250	33,500	25,120	20,100	16,750	14,350	12,560	11,160	10,050	9,130	8,370

a. Sizes indicated are nominal width × length of the opening for rectangular piping.

b. For shapes not included in this table, Equation 11-1 shall be used to determine the equivalent circular diameter, D_e, of rectangular piping for use in interpolation using the data from Table 1106.2(1).

$$D_e = [\text{width} \times \text{length}]^{1/2} \hspace{3cm} \textbf{(Equation 11-1)}$$

where:

D_e = equivalent circular diameter and D_e, width and length are in inches.

TABLE 709.1
DRAINAGE FIXTURE UNITS FOR FIXTURES AND GROUPS

FIXTURE TYPE	DRAINAGE FIXTURE UNIT VALUE AS LOAD FACTORS	MINIMUM SIZE OF TRAP (inches)
Automatic clothes washers, commercial[a,g]	3	2
Automatic clothes washers, residential[g]	2	2
Bathroom group as defined in Section 202 (1.6 gpf water closet)[f]	5	—
Bathroom group as defined in Section 202 (water closet flushing greater than 1.6 gpf)[f]	6	—
Bathtub[b] (with or without overhead shower or whirpool attachments)	2	1 ½

Bidet	1	1 ¼
Combination sink and tray	2	1 ½
Dental lavatory	1	1 ¼
Dental unit or cuspidor	1	1 ¼
Dishwashing machine,c domestic	2	1 ½
Drinking fountain	½	1 ¼
Emergency floor drain	0	2
Floor drainsh	2h	2
Floor sinks	Note h	2
Kitchen sink, domestic	2	1 ½
Kitchen sink, domestic with food waste grinder and/or dishwasher	2	1 ½
Laundry tray (1 or 2 compartments)	2	1 ½
Lavatory	1	1 ¼
Shower (based on the total flow rate through showerheads and body sprays) Flow rate:		
5.7 gpm or less	2	1 ½
Greater than 5.7 gpm to 12.3 gpm	3	2
Greater than 12.3 gpm to 25.8 gpm	5	3
Greater than 25.8 gpm to 55.6 gpm	6	4
Service sink	2	1 ½
Sink	2	1 ½
Urinal	4	Note d
Urinal, 1 gallon per flush or less	2e	Note d
Urinal, nonwater supplied	½	Note d
Wash sink (circular or multiple) each set of faucets	2	1 ½
Water closet, flushometer tank, public or private	4e	Note d
Water closet, private (1.6 gpf)	3e	Note d
Water closet, private (flushing greater than 1.6 gpf)	4e	Note d
Water closet, public (1.6 gpf)	4e	Note d
Water closet, public (flushing greater than 1.6 gpf)	6e	Note d

For SI: 1 inch = 25.4 mm, 1 gallon = 3.785 L, gpf = gallon per flushing cycle, gpm = gallon per minute.

a. For traps larger than 3 inches, use Table 709.2.

b. A showerhead over a bathtub or whirlpool bathtub attachment does not increase the drainage fixture unit value.

c. See Sections 709.2 through 709.4.1 for methods of computing unit value of fixtures not listed in this table or for rating of devices with intermittent flows.

d. Trap size shall be consistent with the fixture outlet size.

e. For the purpose of computing loads on building drains and sewers, water closets and urinals shall not be rated at a lower drainage fixture unit unless the lower values are confirmed by testing.

f. For fixtures added to a dwelling unit bathroom group, add the dfu value of those additional fixtures to the bathroom group fixture count.

g. See Section 406.3 for sizing requirements for fixture drain, branch drain, and drainage stack for an automatic clothes washer standpipe.

h. See Sections 709.4 and 709.4.1.

TABLE 710.1(1)
BUILDING DRAINS AND SEWERS

DIAMETER OF PIPE (inches)	MAXIMUM NUMBER OF DRAINAGE FIXTURE UNITS CONNECTED TO ANY PORTION OF THE BUILDING DRAIN OR THE BUILDING SEWER, INCLUDING BRANCHES OF THE BUILDING DRAINa

	Slope per foot			
	1/16 inch	1/8 inch	1/4 inch	1/2 inch
1 ¼	—	—	1	1
1 ½	—	—	3	3
2	—	—	21	26
2 ½	—	—	24	31
3	—	36	42	50
4	—	180	216	250
5	—	390	480	575
6	—	700	840	1,000
8	1,400	1,600	1,920	2,300
10	2,500	2,900	3,500	4,200
12	3,900	4,600	5,600	6,700
15	7,000	8,300	10,000	12,000

For SI: 1 inch = 25.4 mm, 1 inch per foot = 83.3 mm/m.

a. The minimum size of any building drain serving a water closet shall be 3 inches.

TABLE 710.1(2)
HORIZONTAL FIXTURE BRANCHES AND STACKS[a]

	MAXIMUM NUMBER OF DRAINAGE FIXTURE UNITS (dfu)			
		Stacks[b]		
DIAMETER OF PIPE (inches)	Total for horizontal branch	Total discharge into one branch interval	Total for stack of three branch Intervals or less	Total for stack greater than three branch intervals
1 ½	3	2	4	8
2	6	6	10	24
2 ½	12	9	20	42
3	20	20	48	72
4	160	90	240	500
5	360	200	540	1,100
6	620	350	960	1,900
8	1,400	600	2,200	3,600
10	2,500	1,000	3,800	5,600
12	3,900	1,500	6,000	8,400
15	7,000	Note c	Note c	Note c

For SI: 1 inch = 25.4 mm.

a. Does not include branches of the building drain. Refer to Table 710.1(1).

b. Stacks shall be sized based on the total accumulated connected load at each story or branch interval. As the total accumulated connected load decreases, stacks are permitted to be reduced in size. Stack diameters shall not be reduced to less than one-half of the diameter of the largest stack size required.

c. Sizing load based on design criteria.

TABLE 1106.3
SIZE OF HORIZONTAL STORM DRAINGE PIPING

SIZE OF HOR-IZONTAL PIP-ING (inches)	HORIZONTALLY PROJECTED ROOF AREA (square feet)					
	Rainfall rate (inches per hour)					
	1	2	3	4	5	6
1/8 unit vertical in 12 units horizontal (1-percent slope)						
3	3,288	1,644	1,096	822	657	548
4	7,520	3,760	2,506	1,800	1,504	1,253
5	13,360	6,680	4,453	3,340	2,672	2,227
6	21,400	10,700	7,133	5,350	4,280	3,566
8	46,000	23,000	15,330	11,500	9,200	7,600
10	82,800	41,400	27,600	20,700	16,580	13,800
12	133,200	66,600	44,400	33,300	26,650	22,200
15	218,000	109,000	72,800	59,500	47,600	39,650
1/4 unit vertical in 12 units horizontal (2-percent slope)						
3	4,640	2,320	1,546	1,160	928	773
4	10,600	5,300	3,533	2,650	2,120	1,766
5	18,880	9,440	6,293	4,720	3,776	3,146
6	30,200	15,100	10,066	7,550	6,040	5,033
8	65,200	32,600	21,733	16,300	13,040	10,866
10	116,800	58,400	38,950	29,200	23,350	19,450
12	188,000	94,000	62,600	47,000	37,600	31,350
15	336,000	168,000	112,000	84,000	67,250	56,000
1/2 unit vertical in 12 units horizontal (4-percent slope)						
3	6,576	3,288	2,295	1,644	1,310	1,096
4	15,040	7,520	5,010	3,760	3,010	2,500
5	26,720	13,360	8,900	6,680	5,320	4,450
6	42,800	21,400	13,700	10,700	8,580	7,140
8	92,000	46,000	30,650	23,000	18,400	15,320
10	171,600	85,800	55,200	41,400	33,150	27,600
12	266,400	133,200	88,800	66,600	53,200	44,400
15	476,000	238,000	158,800	119,000	95,300	79,250

For SI: 1 inch = 25.4 mm, 1 square foot = 0.0929 m².

N. Safety devices (domestic and other hot water supply) (P-504)
1. Antisiphon devices required, backflow prevention at hose bibbs and sprinkler systems.
2. Vacuum relief devices are required for bottom-fed tanks.
3. Energy cutoff devices are required, for 210°F. Device is in addition to temperature and pressure-relief valves. (P-504.5) (pressure setting cannot exceed manufacturer's rated pressure or 150 psi, whichever is less)
4. Air gaps are required on all relief and overflow pipes.
5. No valves are allowed in overflow relief piping.
6. Maximum temperature for tankless water heaters is 140°F. (P-501.6)
7. All valves shall be easily accessible.
8. Safety valves are required on all boilers and heaters.
9. Where tank leaks can cause damage, water heaters must be in metal pan at least 1 1/2" deep (P-504.7), draining through an indirect waste pipe with a minimum diameter of 3/4" (19 mm).

O. Sumps (P-712)
1. Pumps must eject to building sewer or to a wye fitting a minimum of 10' from base of stack.
2. Sumps must be vented.
3. A water- and air-tight cover is required.

4. A sump discharge requires gate and check valves (only check valve required in buildings under Residential Code of Ohio).

5. Storm water sumps shall be connected to storm sewers. (P-1113)

6. Access for repairs to sump system is required.

7. Pumps or ejectors receiving water closet discharge must handle spherical solids with a diameter $\leq$ 2". Other pumps or ejectors must handle spherical solids with a diameter $\leq$ 1". Pump minimum capacity based on the discharge pipe diameter is per Table 712.4.2.

8. Sump pit is $\geq$ 18" in diameter and 24" deep, unless otherwise approved. Pit must be of tile construction, must be accessible and drain by gravity.

P. Stacks, drains, and sewers (Chapter P-7)

1. Building drain with a water closet must be 3" minimum.

2. Required size is based on the number of fixture units with a fall of ⅛"/ft. for pipes 3" or larger, ¼"/ft. for smaller pipes. Greater or lesser fall will increase or decrease the number of allowable fixture units connected to the drain. (Table P-710.1(1))

3. All drains shall be by gravity.

4. Sump only those portions below the sewer. Sanitary sumps shall be sealed and vented. (See Sumps, N. above.)

TABLE 709.1
DRAINAGE FIXTURE UNITS FOR FIXTURES AND GROUPS

FIXTURE TYPE	DRAINAGE FIXTURE UNIT VALUE AS LOAD FACTORS	MINIMUM SIZE OF TRAP (inches)
Automatic clothes washers, commercial[a,g]	3	2
Automatic clothes washers, residential[g]	2	2
Bathroom group as defined in Section 202 (1.6 gpf water closet)[f]	5	—
Bathroom group as defined in Section 202 (water closet flushing greater than 1.6 gpf)[f]	6	—
Bathtub[b] (with or without overhead shower or whirlpool attachments)	2	1 ½

Bidet	1	1 ¼
Combination sink and tray	2	1 ½
Dental lavatory	1	1 ¼
Dental unit or cuspidor	1	1 ¼
Dishwashing machine,ᶜ domestic	2	1 ½
Drinking fountain	½	1 ¼
Emergency floor drain	0	2
Floor drainsʰ	2ʰ	2
Floor sinks	Note h	2
Kitchen sink, domestic	2	1 ½
Kitchen sink, domestic with food waste grinder and/or dishwasher	2	1 ½
Laundry tray (1 or 2 compartments)	2	1 ½
Lavatory	1	1 ¼
Shower (based on the total flow rate through showerheads and body sprays) Flow rate: 5.7 gpm or less Greater than 5.7 gpm to 12.3 gpm Greater than 12.3 gpm to 25.8 gpm Greater than 25.8 gpm to 55.6 gpm	2 3 5 6	1 ½ 2 3 4
Service sink	2	1 ½
Sink	2	1 ½
Urinal	4	Note d
Urinal, 1 gallon per flush or less	2ᵉ	Note d
Urinal, nonwater supplied	½	Note d
Wash sink (circular or multiple) each set of faucets	2	1 ½
Water closet, flushometer tank, public or private	4ᵉ	Note d
Water closet, private (1.6 gpf)	3ᵉ	Note d
Water closet, private (flushing greater than 1.6 gpf)	4ᵉ	Note d
Water closet, public (1.6 gpf)	4ᵉ	Note d
Water closet, public (flushing greater than 1.6 gpf)	6ᵉ	Note d

For SI: 1 inch = 25.4 mm, 1 gallon = 3.785 L, gpf = gallon per flushing cycle, gpm = gallon per minute.
a. For traps larger than 3 inches, use Table 709.2.
b. A showerhead over a bathtub or whirlpool bathtub attachment does not increase the drainage fixture unit value.
c. See Sections 709.2 through 709.4.1 for methods of computing unit value of fixtures not listed in this table or for rating of devices with intermittent flows.
d. Trap size shall be consistent with the fixture outlet size.
e. For the purpose of computing loads on building drains and sewers, water closets and urinals shall not be rated at a lower drainage fixture unit unless the lower values are confirmed by testing.
f. For fixtures added to a dwelling unit bathroom group, add the dfu value of those additional fixtures to the bathroom group fixture count.
g. See Section 406.3 for sizing requirements for fixture drain, branch drain, and drainage stack for an automatic clothes washer standpipe.
h. See Sections 709.4 and 709.4.1.

TABLE 710.1(1)
BUILDING DRAINS AND SEWERS

DIAMETER OF PIPE (inches)	MAXIMUM NUMBER OF DRAINAGE FIXTURE UNITS CONNECTED TO ANY PORTION OF THE BUILDING DRAIN OR THE BUILDING SEWER, INCLUDING BRANCHES OF THE BUILDING DRAINᵃ

	Slope per foot			
	1/16 inch	1/8 inch	1/4 inch	1/2 inch
1 ¼	—	—	1	1
1 ½	—	—	3	3
2	—	—	21	26
2 ½	—	—	24	31
3	—	36	42	50
4	—	180	216	250
5	—	390	480	575
6	—	700	840	1,000
8	1,400	1,600	1,920	2,300
10	2,500	2,900	3,500	4,200
12	3,900	4,600	5,600	6,700
15	7,000	8,300	10,000	12,000

For SI: 1 inch = 25.4 mm, 1 inch per foot = 83.3 mm/m.
a. The minimum size of any building drain serving a water closet shall be 3 inches.

TABLE 710.1(2)
HORIZONTAL FIXTURE BRANCHES AND STACKS[a]

DIAMETER OF PIPE (inches)	MAXIMUM NUMBER OF DRAINAGE FIXTURE UNITS (dfu)			
	Total for horizontal branch	Stacks[b]		
		Total discharge into one branch interval	Total for stack of three branch Intervals or less	Total for stack greater than three branch intervals
1 ½	3	2	4	8
2	6	6	10	24
2 ½	12	9	20	42
3	20	20	48	72
4	160	90	240	500
5	360	200	540	1,100
6	620	350	960	1,900
8	1,400	600	2,200	3,600
10	2,500	1,000	3,800	5,600
12	3,900	1,500	6,000	8,400
15	7,000	Note c	Note c	Note c

For SI: 1 inch = 25.4 mm.
a. Does not include branches of the building drain. Refer to Table 710.1(1).
b. Stacks shall be sized based on the total accumulated connected load at each story or branch interval. As the total accumulated connected load decreases, stacks are permitted to be reduced in size. Stack diameters shall not be reduced to less than one-half of the diameter of the largest stack size required.
c. Sizing load based on design criteria.

Q. Tests (P-312)
1. Sanitary and storm systems
   a. Building sewers, building drains, and vents are included in sanitary systems.
   b. Use 10′ of water head or 5 psi air for 15 minutes, for initial test prior to covering is permitted and air test of 5 psi for 15 minutes.
   c. For final drainage and vent test, use air pressure of 1″ water for 15 minutes inside building only.
2. All backflow prevention assemblies must be tested at installation and annually. (P-312.10.1)
3. Water supply: Air test at 50 psi for 1 minute except for plastic, or 110% of design working pressure. (P-312.5)
R. Toilet rooms (See PLUMBING FIXTURES.)
S. Traps (Chapter P-10)
1. A 2″ minimum and 4″ maximum water seal is required, and trap must be self-cleaning.
2. Building underground traps not permitted in general.
3. Drum traps are unacceptable.
4. A 24″ maximum vertical distance from a fixture is required, no double traps are permitted.
5. A series of drains from the same fixture may discharge into one trap. (P-1002.1)
6. Traps no larger than drain it serves.
7. A laundry tub or washing machine cannot dischange into a kitchen sink trap. (P-1003.3.1)
8. Bell, crown-vented, "S" traps are prohibited.
9. Slip joints required. (P-1002.2)
T. Fixture supply pipe sizes (Table P-604.5)
1. A ³/₈″ supply pipe must be used for drinking fountains, lavatories, and tank toilets.
2. A ¹/₂″ supply pipe must be used for bathtubs, sinks, domestic dishwashers, showers, laundry trays, hose bibs, and tank urinals.
3. A ³/₄″ supply pipe must be used for flush urinals and flush sinks.
4. A 1″ supply pipe must be used for flush valve water closets.
5. Water service and water distribution pipe materials per Tables 605.3 and 605.4, respectively.

TABLE 605.3
WATER SERVICE PIPE

MATERIAL	STANDARD
Acrylonitrile butadiene styrene (ABS) plastic pipe	ASTM D 1527; ASTM D 2282
Asbestos-cement pipe	ASTM C 296
Brass pipe	ASTM B 43
Chlorinated polyvinyl chloride (CPVC) plastic pipe	ASTM D 2846; ASTM F 441; ASTM F 442; CSA B137.6
Copper or copper-alloy pipe	ASTM B 42; ASTM B 302
Copper or copper-alloy tubing (Type K, WK, L, WL, M or WM)	ASTM B 75; ASTM B 88; ASTM B 251; ASTM B 447
Cross-linked polyethylene (PEX) plastic tubing	ASTM F 876; ASTM F 877; CSA B137.5
Cross-linked polyethylene/aluminum/cross-linked polyethylene (PEX-AL-PEX) pipe	ASTM F 1281; CSA B137.10M
Cross-linked polyethylene/aluminum/high-density polyethylene (PEX-AL-HDPE)	ASTM F 1986
Ductile iron water pipe	AWWA C151; AWWA C115
Galvanized steel pipe	ASTM A 53

MATERIAL	STANDARD
Polybutylene (PB) plastic pipe and tubing	ASTM D 2662; ASTM D 2666; ASTM D 3309; CSA B137.8M
Polyethylene (PE) plastic pipe	ASTM D 2239; CSA B137.1
Polyethylene (PE) plastic tubing	ASTM D 2737; CSA B137.1
Polyethylene/aluminum/polethylene (PE-AL-PE) pipe	ASTM F 1282; CSA B137.9
Polypropylene (PP) plastic pipe or tubing	ASTM F 2389; CSA B137.11
Polyvinyl chloride (PVC) plastic pipe	ASTM D 1785; ASTM D 2241; ASTM D 2672; CSA B137.3
Stainless steel pipe (Type 304/304L)	ASTM A 312; ASTM A 778
Stainless steel pipe (Type 316/316L)	ASTM A 312; ASTM A 778

TABLE 605.4
WATER DISTRIBUTION PIPE

MATERIAL	STANDARD
Brass pipe	ASTM B 43
Chlorinated polyvinyl chloride (CPVC) plastic pipe and tubing	ASTM D 2846; ASTM F 441; ASTM F 442; CSA B137.6
Copper or copper-alloy pipe	ASTM B 42; ASTM B 302
Copper or copper-alloy tubing (Type K, WK, L, WL, M or WM)	ASTM B 75; ASTM B 88; ASTM B 251; ASTM B 447
Cross-linked polyethylene (PEX) plastic tubing	ASTM F 877; CSA B137.5
Cross-linked polyethylene/aluminum/cross-linked polyethylene (PEX-AL-PEX) pipe	ASTM F 1281; CSA B137.10M
Cross-linked polyethylene/aluminum/high-density polyethylene (PEX-AL-HDPE)	ASTM F 1986
Galvanized steel pipe	ASTM A 53
Polybutylene (PB) plastic pipe and tubing	ASTM D 3309; CSA B137.8M
Polyethylene/Aluminum/Polyethylene (PE-AL-PE) composite pipe	ASTM F 1282
Polypropylene (PP) plastic pipe or tubing	ASTM F 2389; CSA B137.11
Stainless steel pipe (Type 304/304L)	ASTM A 312; ASTM A 778
Stainless steel pipe (Type 316/316L)	ASTM A 312; ASTM A 778

TABLE 605.5
PIPE FITTINGS

MATERIAL	STANDARD
Acrylonitrile butadiene styrene (ABS) plastic	ASTM D 2468
Cast-iron	ASME B16.4; ASME B16.12
Chlorinated polyvinyl chloride (CPVC) plastic	ASTM F 437; ASTM F 438; ASTM F 439; CSA B137.6
Copper or copper alloy	ASME B16.15; ASME B16.18; ASME B16.22; ASME B16.23; ASME B16.26; ASME B16.29
Cross-linked polyethylene/aluminum/high-density polyethylene (PEX-AL-HDPE)	ASTM F 1986
Fittings for cross-linked polyethylene (PEX) plastic tubing	ASTM F 877; ASTM F 1807; ASTM F 1960; ASTM F 2080; ASTM F 2159; CSA B137.5
Gray iron and ductile iron	AWWA C110; AWWA C153
Malleable iron	ASME B16.3
Metal (brass) insert fittings for Polyethylene/Aluminum/Polyethylene (PE-AL-PE) and Cross-linked Polyethylene/Aluminum/Polyethylene (PEX-AL-PEX)	ASTM F 1974
Polybutylene (PB) plastic	CSA B137.8

MATERIAL	STANDARD
Polyethylene (PE) plastic	ASTM D 2609; CSA B137.1
Polypropylene (PP) plastic pipe or tubing	ASTM F 2389; CSA B137.11
Polyvinyl chloride (PVC) plastic	ASTM D 2464; ASTM D 2466; ASTM D 2467; CSA B137.2
Stainless steel (Type 304/304L)	ASTM A 312; ASTM A 778
Stainless steel (Type 316/316L)	ASTM A 312; ASTM A 778
Steel	ASME B16.9; ASME B16.11; ASME B16.28

6. Hot water is required to fixtures for bathing, washing, cooking, cleaning, and laundry. Public hand-sinks require "tempered" water. (P-607.1) Water must be provided through water temperature limiting device per ASSE 1070 that limits temperature to a maximum of 110°F (43°C).

TABLE 604.5
MINIMUM SIZES OF FIXTURE WATER SUPPLY PIPES

FIXTURE	MINIMUM PIPE SIZE (inch)
Bathtubs[a] (60" x 32" and smaller)	1/2
Bathtubs[a] (larger than 60" x 32")	1/2
Bidet	3/8
Combination sink and tray	1/2
Dishwasher, domestic[a]	1/2
Drinking fountain	3/8
Hose bibbs	1/2
Kitchen sink[a]	1/2
Laundry, 1, 2 or 3 compartments[a]	1/2
Lavatory	3/8
Shower, single head[a]	1/2

Sinks, flushing rim	3/4
Sinks, service	1/2
Urinal, flush tank	1/2
Urinal, flush valve	3/4
Wall hydrant	1/2
Water closet, flush tank	3/8
Water closet, flush valve	1
Water closet, flushometer tank	3/8
Water closet, one piece[a]	1/2

For SI: 1 inch = 25.4 mm

1 foot = 304.8 mm

1 pound per square inch = 6.895 kPa.

a. Where the developed length of the distribution line is 60 feet or less, and the available pressure at the meter is a minimum of 35 psi, the minimum size of an individual distribution line supplied from a manifold and installed as part of a parallel water distribution system shall be one nominal tube size smaller than the sizes indicated.

PLUMBING FIXTURES (FROM OHIO PLUMBING CODE)

See also ACCESSIBILITY GUIDELINES.

A. General
  1. Assume an equal number of male and female occupants. (2902.3)
  2. Separate restrooms for each sex are required except in private residential and with 15 or fewer employees and mercantile establishments with 50 occupants or less. (2902.2)
  3. All public restrooms must be marked as to sex.
  4. For employees and public in occupancies other then covered malls, facilities up to 1 story above or below and within 500'.
  5. In covered malls, facilities up to 1 story above or below and within 300'. Facilities based on total square footage, and must be installed in each individual store or in a central toilet area. Travel distance is measured from the main entrance of any store or tenant space. If employees' facilities are not provided in the individual store, travel distance is measured from the employees' work area.
  6. Required fixtures must be free (not pay toilets).

B. Water supply (2903.1)
  1. Backflow protection is required.

C. Adequate space is required around water closets, lavs, and bidets: (2904.31)
  1. 15" minimum to wall or 30" c/c.
  2. 21" minimum clearance at front.
  3. Minimum 30" × 60" stall size.
  4. Minimum 20" clearance in front of lavatory to any wall, fixture or door.

D. Fixture wall and floor connections must be sealed with galvanized or brass bolts or screws.

E. Fixture joints at walls and floors must be water-tight. Flanges are required at all floor connections.

F. Wall-hung water closets must be supported on carriers, not by piping (2904.4.3).

G. Overflows must drain completely, and drain into system on fixture side of the trap or into fixture served if flush tank (2904.7).

H. Toilet rooms cannot open into room for food preparation. (1210.5)

I. Walls at public water closets and urinals must be nonabsorbent to 4' above floor. (1210.2)

J. Showers must have nonabsorbent walls to 70" above the drain inlet. (1210.3)

PLYWOOD (WOOD STRUCTURAL PANELS)

A. General (2304.6—walls, 2304.7—floors)
  1. Exterior type plywood may be used on all interior work. (2304.6.1)
  2. Exterior use
    a. Exposed plywood shall be of exterior waterproof type.
    b. Roof sheathing exposed to the weather on the underside may be interior plywood attached with exterior glue.
    c. Exterior type plywood may be applied to framing as siding if not less than 3/8" thick with thickness measured to bottom of grooves.
    d. If plywood is used as lap siding without sheathing, corner bracing is required.
    e. All spans indicated are with outer layer perpendicular to supports. Spans must be reduced when the outer face grain is parallel to the supports. (Table 2304.7(3))
  3. Each sheet shall be labeled. (2303.1.4)

B. The following chart applies to allowable spans and loads for wood structural panel sheathing and single-floor grades continuous over two or more spans with strength axis perpendicular to supports.

TABLE 2304.7(3)
ALLOWABLE SPANS AND LOADS FOR WOOD STRUCTURAL PANEL SHEATHING AND SINGLE-FLOOR GRADES CONTINUOUS OVER TWO OR MORE SPANS WITH STRENGTH AXIS PERPENDICULAR TO SUPPORTS[a,b]

SHEATHING GRADES		ROOF[c]				FLOOR[d]
Panel span rating roof/floor span	Panel thickness (inches)	Maximum span (inches)		Load[e] (psf)		Maximum span (inches)
		With edge support[f]	Without edge support	Total load	Live load	
12/0	5/16	12	12	40	30	0
16/0	5/16, 3/8	16	16	40	30	0
20/0	5/16, 3/8	20	20	40	30	0
24/0	3/8, 7/16, 1/2	24	20[g]	40	30	0
24/16	7/16, 1/2	24	24	50	40	16
32/16	15/32, 1/2, 5/8	32	28	40	30	16[h]
40/20	19/32, 5/8, 3/4, 7/8	40	32	40	30	20[h,i]
48/24	23/32, 3/4, 7/8	48	36	45	35	24
54/32	7/8, 1	54	40	45	35	32
60/32	7/8, 1-1/8	60	48	45	35	32
SINGLE FLOOR GRADES		ROOF[c]				FLOOR[d]
Panel span rating	Panel thickness (inches)	Maximum span (inches)		Load[e] (psf)		Maximum span (inches)
		With edge support[f]	Without edge support	Total load	Live load	
16 o.c.	1/2, 19/32, 5/8	24	24	50	40	16[h]
20 o.c.	19/32, 5/8, 3/4	32	32	40	30	20[h,i]
24 o.c.	23/32, 3/4	48	36	35	25	24
32 o.c.	7/8, 1	48	40	50	40	32
48 o.c.	13/32, 11/8	60	48	50	40	48

For SI: 1 inch = 25.4 mm, 1 pound per square foot = 0.0479kN/m².

a. Applies to panels 24 inches or wider.

b. Floor and roof sheathing conforming with this table shall be deemed to meet the design criteria of Section 2304.7.

c. Uniform load deflection limitations 1/180 of span under live load plus dead load, 1/240 under live load only.

d. Panel edges shall have approved tongue-and-groove joints or shall be supported with blocking unless 1/4-inch minimum thickness underlayment or 1 1/2 inches of approved cellular or lightweight concrete is placed over the subfloor, or finish floor is 3/4-inch wood strip. Allowable uniform load based on deflection of 1/360 of span is 100 pounds per square foot except the span rating of 48 inches on center is based on a total load of 65 pounds per square foot.

e. Allowable load at maximum span.

f. Tongue-and-groove edges, panel edge clips (one midway between each support, except two equally spaced between supports 48 inches on center), lumber blocking or other. Only lumber blocking shall satisfy blocked diaphragm requirements.

g. For 1/2-inch panel, maximum span shall be 24 inches.

h. Span is permitted to be 24 inches on center where 3/4-inch wood strip flooring is installed at right angles to joist.

i. Span is permitted to be 24 inches on center for floors where 1 1/2 inches of cellular or lightweight concrete is applied over the panels.

C.   Combination subfloor/underlayment
1. Space nails a minimum of 6" o.c. at edges and 12" o.c. in the field for floors and roofs.
2. Minimum 6d nails for flooring, 8d nails for roofs. Minimum 8d for plywood over 1/2" up to 3/4", 6d if screen-shank. Minimum 8d for over 3/4" up to 1". (Table 2304.9.1)

D.   Stud spacing for plywood sheathing (Table 2308.9.1)
1. Space studs a maximum of 16" o.c. with 5/16" thickness.
2. If plywood is 3/8" to 7/16" thick, space studs 24" o.c. if exterior covering is nailed to the studs; space studs 16" o.c. if the exterior covering is nailed to the sheathing. Studs may be spaced 24" o.c. if the face grain is nailed perpendicular to the studs.
3. Blocking of horizontal joints is not required.

PREFABRICATED CONSTRUCTION

A. Scope (Section 113—Industrialized Units)
   1. Requirements apply to all prefabricated buildings, sub-assemblies, and building units either open or closed which do not allow for normal, on-site inspection.
   2. Closed construction requires prior approval of the Board of Building Standards.
B. General requirements
   1. Plans must be approved by Ohio Board of Building Standards, and copies turned in for permit.
   2. Plant inspection is required.
   3. Every unit receives an insignia.
   4. A permit from the local building department for siting utilities and foundations is required.

PRISONS AND RESTRAINED INSTITUTIONS (408 AND USE GROUP I-3)

See USE GROUP CLASSIFICATION, O. Use Group I-3 (restrained institutional).

PROJECTION ROOMS (409)

A. Permanent projection rooms
   1. Requirements apply to rooms using ribbon-type safety film with electric arc or xenon light sources.
   2. A sign is required on door noting safety film only.
   3. Construction shall be of the building's type, but opening protectives are not required.
   4. Minimum area for a projection room is 80 sq. ft., and minimum of 40 sq. ft. per machine.
   5. Minimum ceiling height is 7′6″, including any adjoining rooms.
   6. Provide a 30″ × 30″ working area on each side of and to the rear of each projector (30″ between adjacent machines is acceptable).
   7. Total openings in the wall facing the auditorium shall not exceed 25% of the wall area.
   8. All openings shall be solid, with glass or equivalent.
   9. Rewind and film storage is required.
   10. Auditorium light control system is required in the projection room and one other convenient location in the building.
   11. Exhaust Systems (Chapter M-5)
       a. Provide at least 200 cfm/electric arc light, and 300 cfm/xenon lamp with a maximum 130°F at lamp. (M-502.11)
       b. Exhaust direct to the exterior.
       c. Lamp and projection systems may be combined, but must be independent of all other exhaust. (409.3.3)

PROJECTIONS INTO STREET OR YARD (3200)

A. Street projection (3202)
   1. All projections below 8′ subject to local jurisdiction judgment.
   2. Belt courses, lintels, sills, balconies, cornices, and similar architectural features may project 4″ when less than 8′ high; then 1″ of projection allowed per inch over 8′, up to total of 48″. Projections above 15′ are not limited.
   3. Columns and pilasters may project 12″.
   4. Steps may project 12″ with 3′ high guards.
   5. Doors and windows cannot open or swing into right-of-way.
   6. Pedestrian walkways allowed (see 3104) subject to local jurisdiction and minimum 15′ clear.

      7. Temporary vestibules and awnings allowed with conditions (3202.4)

B.   See also MARQUEES, and AWNINGS AND CANOPIES.

RADIO AND TV TOWERS (3108)

A. Radio and TV towers (3108)
  1. Tower access is required by step bolts or ladder. (3108.2)
  2. Guy wires and other accessory supports shall not cross any street, public place, or electric lines. (3108.2)
  3. Construction (3108.2)
    a. Use noncombustible corrosion-resistant materials if ≤75'.
    b. Design towers to resist both wind and ice loads, per Electronics Industries Association Standard TIA/EIA-222. (3108.2)
  4. All towers must be permanently grounded.

REFRIGERATION (M-11)

A. General
  1. Codes classify refrigerants as Group A (1-3) or Group B (102) according to their hazard quality and limits the amount used as related to the building group.
  2. Factory-built equipment must be labeled.
  3. All piping must be compatible to the refrigerant.
B. Refrigerant classification (per ASHRAE 34) listed in Table 1103.1.
C. Refrigeration systems
  1. High-probability systems (M-1103.3.2)
    a. direct
    b. indirect with open-spray
  2. Low-probability systems (M-1103.3.1)
    a. double-indirect open-spray
    b. indirect closed
    c. indirect vented
  3. Direct is defined as a single condenser, compressor, and evaporator which are the least hazardous in small amounts.
  4. Double direct is defined as two separate direct systems in series, where one pre-cools the condenser of the other. Each circuit is treated as a direct system.
  5. Indirect is defined as a primary unit which cools liquids which are circulated to various converters for cooling. The indirect liquid is usually a brine mixture. System may be an open spray, closed system, or vented closed system.
D. Allowable amounts
  1. Occupancy Classification of Types 1 through 7 (M-1103.2) determines system application in Section 1104 and maximum permissible quantities. (See Table 1104.3.2.)
  2. Note that quantity of refrigerant is unlimited in industrial occupancies when:
    a. Machinery room is enclosed by tight construction.
    b. Room has door to exterior.
    c. Maximum occupant load above first floor is 100 sq. ft./person, or with direct exits.
    d. Refrigerant detectors are provided.
E. A permanent tag is required indicating the type of system and refrigerant.
F. All systems which are not factory assembled are to be pressure-tested. (M-1108.0)
G. Machinery rooms (M-1105, M-1106)
  1. Ventilation is required, interlocked with the refrigeration system based on the amount of refrigerant. Vents must be 15' above grade and 20' from openings. (M-1105.7)

2. Openings shall not permit refrigerants to other parts of the building. (M-1105.6.2)
3. Emergency remote control to stop refrigerant action is required outside of the room. (M-1106.5)
4. Refrigerant detector is required. (M-1105.3)

REHAB (COMPLIANCE ALTERNATIVES) (3400)

Chapter 34 provides an alternative to compliance with Sections 3403 to 3407 for buildings that were built prior to the adoption of the Ohio Building Code effective July 1, 1979 (OAC 4101:2-1-13). Chapter 34 was designed to allow the use of existing buildings which cannot be altered sufficiently without appeal hearings, based upon the evaluation of the building against 18 areas of compliance in the code.

Building Height	Communications
Building Area	Smoke Control
Compartment Area	Exit Capacity
Space Division	Dead Ends
Corridor Partitions/Walls	Maximum Travel Distance
Vertical Opening	Elevator Control
HVAC System	Egress Lighting
Automatic Alarms	Mixed Use
Sprinklers	Incidental Use Areas

A. Administration: Chapter 34 requires that the safety of the building not be reduced.
 1. Disabled access is necessary where required for structures according to Section 3411.
 2. Structural analysis must be done to determine that the new loads can be sustained.
 3. Additions must comply with Section 3403.
 4. Serious hazards must be made safe by complying with Chapters 2 through 33.
 5. Compliance with fire prevention code still required. (3401.2)
 6. *Not* applicable to Use Groups H and I (except I-1).
B. Safety evaluation: Each category is evaluated to determine level of compliance and scores assigned. A great deal of judgment must be used by the designer and the building official in determining that there is not a serious hazard created by the alterations and changes. The judgment is no different from other judgments that are made in many areas of the code, only the implications are relative to receiving a score.
 1. Building height calculation: Base height on Formula at 3412.6.1.1.
    a. Modifications permitted: suppression.
 2. Building area calculation: Base area on formulas at 3412.6.2.1. and 3412.6.2.2.
    a. Modifications permitted: suppression and open perimeter taken per building area.
    b. Score based upon the relation to the 1,200 sq. ft. area factor used in formulas at 3412.6.2.1. and 3412.6.2.2.
    c. Maximum positive score is half of Fire Safety score.
 3. Fire area must be based upon high-rise compartmentation per Table 3412.6.3 (2-hour fire resistance).
 4. Separations must be based upon additional compartmentation between dwelling units and tenants per Table 3412.6.4.
 5. Corridor partitions/walls must be based upon additional compartmentation per table 3412.6.5 (fire rated).
 6. Vertical opening must be based upon the formula at 3412.6.6.

7. HVAC systems must be based upon categories at 3412.6.7.1.

8. Automatic alarms must be based upon the level of alarms as required in the Mechanical Code per Table 3412.6.8.

9. Communications must be based upon the ability to notify the occupants of a fire per Table 3412.6.9.

10. Smoke control must be based upon the ability to open windows in the building, stairways, provide a smokeproof enclosure, or conforming smoke control system per Table 3412.6.10.

11. Exit capacity must be based upon the concept that additional capacity of exits will provide additional safety per Table 3412.6.11.

12. Dead ends are based on their length relative to that allowed for the Use Group per Table 3412.6.12.

13. Maximum travel distance should be based upon the advantages due to the ability to egress the building quickly per formula at 3412.6.13.

14. Elevator control should be based upon the safety provided by recall controls and the aid to fire fighter access per Table 3412.6.14.

15. Egress lighting should be based upon the need to know where and how to exit a building per Table 3412.6.15.

16. Mixed use should be based upon compliance with mixed use requirements of the code per Table 3412.16.

17. Sprinklers should be based upon sprinklers throughout fire areas or entire building per Table 3412.6.17.

18. Compliance for incidental use areas (boiler rooms, storage rooms, etc.) is covered as hazard per 508.2 and Table 3412.6.18.

C. Scoring: after determining the individual scores from Sections 3412.6, enter data in Table 3412.7 and total the building score. Subtract the mandatory safety score from the building score for each category per 3412.8. If the final score for any category equals zero or more, the building is compliant for that category. If the final score for any category is less than zero, the building is not compliant.

TABLE 3412.8
MANDATORY SAFETY SCORES[a]

OCCUPANCY	FIRE SAFETY (MFS)	MEANS OF EGRESS (MME)	GENERAL SAFETY (MGS)
A-1	16	27	27
A-2	19	30	30
A-3	18	29	29
A-4, E	23	34	34
B	24	34	34
F	20	30	30
M	19	36	36
R	17	34	34
S-1	15	25	25
S-2	23	33	33

a. MFS = Mandatory Fire Safety;
MME = Mandatory Means of Egress;
MGS = Mandatory General Safety.

RESIDENTIAL CARE/ASSISTED LIVING AND GROUP HOMES

Residential care/assisted living facilities house on a 24-hour basis individuals requiring personal care in a licensed supervised residential environment because of age, mental illness, severe mental disability, infirmity, or other reason. The residents must be capable of capable of responding to emergency situations without physical assistance from staff. Included are residential care facilities holding themselves out as: board and care facilities, assisted living facilities, halfway houses, adult care or mental health group homes, congregate care facilities, social rehabilitation facilities, alcohol and drug abuse centers, and convalescent facilities housing no more than 16 residents.

RETAINING WALLS (1610)

A. Basement, foundation and retaining walls must be designed to resist soil lateral loads per Table 1610.1.

TABLE 1610.1
SOIL LATERAL LOAD

DESCRIPTION OF BACKFILL MATERIAL[c]	UNIFIED SOIL CLASSIFICA-TION	DESIGN LATERAL SOIL LOAD[a] (pound per square foot per foot of depth)	
		Active pressure	At-rest pressure
Well-graded, clean gravels; gravel-sand mixes	GW	30	60
Poorly graded clean gravels; gravel-sand mixes	GP	30	60
Silty gravels, poorly graded gravel-sand mixes	GM	40	60
Clayey gravels, poorly graded gravel-and-clay mixes	GC	45	60
Well-graded, clean sands; gravelly sand mixes	SW	30	60
Poorly graded clean sands; sand-gravel mixes	SP	30	60
Silty sands, poorly graded sand-silt mixes	SM	45	60
Sand-silt clay mix with plastic fines	SM-SC	45	100
Clayey sands, poorly graded sand-clay mixes	SC	60	100
Inorganic silts and clayey silts	ML	45	100
Mixture of inorganic silt and clay	ML-CL	60	100
Inorganic clays of low to medium plasticity	CL	60	100
Organic silts and silt clays, low plasticity	OL	Note b	Note b
Inorganic clayey silts, elastic silts	MH	Note b	Note b
Inorganic clays of high plasticity	CH	Note b	Note b
Organic clays and silty clays	OH	Note b	Note b

For SI: 1 pound per square foot per foot of depth = 0.157kPa/m, 1 foot = 304.8 mm.

a. Design lateral soil loads are given for moist conditions for the specified soils at their optimum densities. Actual field conditions shall govern. Submerged or saturated soil pressures shall include the weight of the buoyant soil plus the hydrostatic loads.

b. Unsuitable as backfill material.

c. The definition and classification of soil materials shall be in accordance with ASTM D 2487.

B. Guard rails are required when there is over a 30" drop with a walk, drive, or parking on the high side. (1013.1)

ROOFS (1500)

A. Roof stairway access (1009.13)
1. Stairway access is required on buildings of more than 4 stories if the roof pitch is less than 4:12. Access must be through penthouse.
2. Stairs, or alternating tread stair, with 16 sq. ft. trap door is acceptable when roof is unoccupied.
3. If roof is used as occupiable or habitable space, provide typical exit facilities.

B. Roof covering (Chapter 15)
1. Classifications (1505)
    a. Class A for severe fire exposure is acceptable on all building types (concrete, slate, and tile, for example).
    b. Class B for moderate fire exposure is the minimum required on all protected construction types.
    c. Class C for light fire exposure is the minimum required on all unprotected construction types.
2. Use of non-classified roofing
    a. Non-classified roofing may be used on detached R-3 and U buildings and their accessory buildings when the fire separation distance is not less than 6'.
3. Roof insulation materials and required standards are as follows

TABLE 1508.2
MATERIAL STANDARDS FOR ROOF INSULATION

Cellular glass board	ASTM C 552
Composite boards	ASTM C 1289, Type III, IV, V or VI
Expanded polystyrene	ASTM C 578
Extruded polystyrene board	ASTM C 578
Perlite board	ASTM C 728
Polyisocyanurate board	ASTM C 1289, Type I or Type II
Wood fiberboard	ASTM C 208

4. Asphalt shingles (1507.2)
    a. $^2/_{12}$ to $^4/_{12}$ slope—double layer underlayment required;
    b. less than $^2/_{12}$ slope—not allowed;
    c. cannot re-roof over 2 existing layers. (1510.3)
5. Tile, metal panels, roll roofing, wood shingles and shakes, built-up roofs, EDPM (single-ply), and slate, bitumen, thermoset, coated roofs are all detailed. (1507.4 to 1507.15)

ROOF STRUCTURES (1500, 2400)

A. All towers, spires, domes or cupolas exceeding 60' height above the roof, or exceeding 200 sq ft, or intended for other than a belfry or architectural embellishment must be noncombustible, separated by fire-rated < 1.5 hours. Structures must be noncombustible except aerial supports ≤ 12', flagpoles, water tanks and cooling towers exceeding 50' height.
B. Cooling towers (1509.4)
1. Must be noncombustible when more than 50' high, and over 250 sq. ft. or 15" in height of equipment.
2. Cooling drip bars may be constructed of wood.
3. Limited to $^1/_3$ of roof area.
C. Penthouses (1509.2)
1. Must not be occupied (or penthouse becomes additional story).
2. Maximum 28' height above roof (except Type I building).
3. Maximum $^1/_3$ of roof (including other rooftop structures in ratio).
4. Must be constructed as for rest of building except:
    a. If 5' to 20' from lot line on Type I or II, minimum 1-hour and non-combustible construction required; if over 20', just noncombustible.

      b. If 5′ to 20′ from lot line on Types III, IV, V, minimum 1-hour construction required; if over 20′, then Type IV or noncombustible.

      c. If less than 5′, same as for building.

      d. Combustible mechanical screens (no roof) allowed up to 4 high on one-story buildings, minimum 20′ from lot line.

D. Roof scuttles

  1. Minimum size of roof scuttles is 16 sq. ft. (1009.11.1, exception)

E. Skylights (2405.5)

  1. Requirements apply to glazing 15° or more from vertical. (2405.1)

  2. If part of the roof system, the skylight must meet the roof's structural requirements.

  3. Fire retardant wood is acceptable if subject to acids, or acid fumes; but sash and frame must be noncombustible on Type I and II buildings.

  4. Mounting (2405.4)

      a. All glass less than 45° and plastic must have 4″ curbs.

      b. When roof pitch exceeds 45°, pitch glass may be in plane of roof.

      c. For Use Group R-3, glass can be in plane of roof 3:12 or steeper.

  5. Glazing may be laminated glass, wire glass, annealed, tempered, heat strengthened, glass block, or approved plastics.

  6. Required screens (2405.3)

      a. Install below tempered or heat-strengthened glass.

      b. Use a minimum of 1″ × 1″ mesh #12 gauge or equal.

      c. Keep the screen within 4″ of glass.

  7. Screens not required for:

      a. Tempered glass at 30° or less from vertical and up to 10′ above the floor

      b. Any glazing allowed, when permanent protection of walking surfaces is installed, and

      c. In R-2, R-3 and R-4 dwellings for tempered glass when each piece is 16 sq. ft. or less, up to 12′ above floor, and maximum $^3/_{16}$″ thick.

      d. Non-public greenhouses.

F. Towers, spires, domes, and cupolas (1509.5)

  1. Towers, spires, domes, and cupolas require the same construction as the building.

  2. When more than 60′ above grade, or more than 200 sq. ft. base when used for other than a belfry, or ornamental, it shall be construction of Type I or II.

G. Water tanks (1509.3)

  1. Tanks which hold more than 500 gallons require support on a noncombustible base or Type IV. When supports are in building and above lowest story, they must be IA.

  2. Provide an emergency drain.

  3. Locate away from stairs or elevator shafts unless built over a solid concrete roof.

  4. All roof tanks must have sloped covers.

ROOM SIZES AND CEILING HEIGHTS (1208)

A. Dwelling unit areas

  1. Dwelling unit areas: 1 room shall be 120 sq. ft. minimum; other habitable rooms except kitchens shall be 70 sq. ft. minimum.

  2. Minimum habitable room except kitchen must have a minimum dimension of 7′.

  3. Non-accessible kitchens in dwellings need minimum 3′ clear passages.

  4. "Efficiency" units must have living room of at least 220 sq. ft., and 100 sq. ft./person more after first 2 people. Units must have own kitchens and bathrooms, and closet.

B. Ceiling heights
 1. In occupiable and habitable rooms, ceilings must be 7′6″.
 2. The average ceiling height of sloped ceilings must be the minimum ceiling height, and must be at least 5′0″ high.
 3. Two-thirds of rooms with furred ceilings must be the minimum ceiling height and at least 7′0″.
 4. Bathrooms, kitchens, storage, and laundry—minimum 7′0″.

SEWAGE—EPA

A. General
1. All sewerage treatment and disposal systems where public sewers are not available must be approved by the Ohio EPA, except for private residences.
2. Public sewers shall be used where feasible.
3. No storm or clean water shall drain into the private systems.
4. Always contact the Ohio EPA district office assigned to proposed area.

DISTRICT OFFICES

District Office	Address	Phone/Fax
Central District Office	Physical Address: Lazarus Government Center 50 W. Town St., Suite 700 Columbus, Ohio 43215 Mailing Address Ohio EPA—CDO P.O. Box 1049 Columbus, Ohio 43216-1049	Telephone: (614) 728-3778 Fax: (614) 728-3898

Counties served: Delaware, Fairfield, Fayette, Franklin, Knox, Licking, Madison, Morrow, Pickaway and Union.

Northeast District Office	2110 East Aurora Road Twinsburg, Ohio 44087	Telephone: (330) 963-1200 Fax: (330) 487-0769

Counties served: Ashtabula, Carroll, Columbiana, Cuyahoga, Geauga, Holmes, Lake, Lorain, Mahoning, Medina, Portage, Stark, Summit, Trumbull and Wayne.

Northwest District Office	347 N. Dunbridge Road Bowling Green, Ohio 43402	Telephone: (419) 352-8461 Fax: (419) 352-8468

Counties served: Allen, Ashland, Auglaize, Crawford, Defiance, Erie, Fulton, Hancock, Hardin, Henry, Huron, Lucas, Marion, Mercer, Ottawa, Paulding, Putnam, Richland, Sandusky, Seneca, Van Wert, Williams, Wood and Wyandot.

Southeast District Office	2195 Front Street Logan, Ohio 43138	Telephone: (740) 385-8501 Fax: (740) 385-6490

Counties served: Adams, Athens, Belmont, Coshocton, Gallia, Guernsey, Harrison, Hocking, Jackson, Jefferson, Lawrence, Meigs, Monroe, Morgan, Muskingum, Noble, Perry, Pike, Ross, Scioto, Tuscarawas, Vinton and Washington.

Southwest District Office	401 East Fifth Street Dayton, Ohio 45402	Telephone: (937) 285-6357 Fax: (937) 285-6249

Counties served: Brown, Butler, Champaign, Clark, Clermont, Clinton, Darke, Greene, Hamilton, Highland, Logan, Miami, Montgomery, Preble, Shelby and Warren.

Non-Emergency Complaints

To submit a complaint or report a non-emergency environmental situation, please use the following toll-free numbers to contact the appropriate Ohio EPA district office during business hours.

Central District Office: 1-800-686-2330

Northeast District Office: 1-800-686-6330

Northwest District Office: 1-800-686-6930

Southeast District Office: 1-800-686-7330

Southwest District Office: 1-800-686-8930

SHAFTS, VERTICAL (708)

A. Vertical enclosures (708)

    1. These requirements are for shafts such as stairs, chutes, elevators, hoistways, and dumbwaiters.

    2. Shafts connecting 3 stories or less must be rated 1 hour. All others must be rated 2 hours.

3. Ducts and pipe shafts required when:
   a. Ducts penetrate 3 or more floors in unprotected construction.
   b. Combustible pipes (PVC) penetrate 2 or more floors in unprotected construction.
4. Shafts not through the roof shall be closed with the same rating as the floor but not less than the minimum shaft rating.
5. Shaft bottom construction shall be the same as the floor but not less than the shaft rating.
6. Shaft openings shall be by approved fire shutters, fire doors, fire dampers, or fire windows.
7. Floor penetrations and shaftwall penetrations may use special firestopping which allows use of PVC through floors instead of shafts or coming out of rated shafts.
8. Ducts and pipes cannot go into exit shafts (even with fire damper).
9. Each floor must have enclosed elevator lobby if more than three stories. Lobby separates elevator shaft enclosure doors from each floor by partitions rated as the corridor and required opening protection. Lobbies require at least one means of egress. Exception:
   a. Other than Group I-3 and buildings with occupied floors more than 75′ above lowest level of fire department vehicle access, no enclosed elevator lobbies if building sprinkled.

B. Enclosure exceptions
1. Within dwelling units up to 4 stories.
2. Non-egress stairs and escalators in sprinkled buildings.
   a. Area of opening $\leq$ 2 times the horizontal projection of the stair or escalator with draft curtains and sprinklers per NFPA 13 and maximum of 4 stories except B and M Uses.
   b. Power operated shutters at every floor within 1½ hour rating and operated by smoke detection.
3. Pipes, tubes, conduit, wire, cable and vents with protection based on "floor ceiling assembly" and "walls" penetration requirements.
4. Covered malls and atriums.
5. Floor opening or open wall.
   a. Not in I-2 or I-3 use.
   b. Connects only two stories.
   c. Not part of means of egress.
   d. Cannot open to a corridor on floors that are not sprinkled.
   e. Cannot be open to a corridor in I or R uses.
   f. Must be separated from other floor openings by a shaft enclosure.
   g. Not concealed within the building construction.
6. Car ramps in parking garages.
7. Mezzanines.

SIGNS (3107)

A. Exterior signs: A building permit is not required under the following circumstances (Local zoning rules which may affect size, height, and location supersede the building code):
1. Signs painted on exterior walls.
2. Temporary yard-type for sale signs.
3. Accessibility signage.
4. Sign is a street sign.

5. Projecting signs not more than 2½ sq. ft.
6. Signs undergoing minor repair.
   B. General sign requirements:
1. Design structurally for wind and earthquake loads.
2. Cannot obstruct exit signs, means of egress, or fire escapes.
3. Only electrical illumination is allowed, and only ≤ 200.
4. Plastic allowed as material if burning rate ≤ 2.5" per minute, per ASTM D 635.
5. Roof signs ≥ 40 square feet must be of metal or other approved noncombustible material allowing ≤ 6' between sign and roof level, with 5' clearance between vertical supports.
6. Marquee signs ≥ 40 square feet must metal or approved noncombustible material, and cannot extend > 6' above, nor 1' below marquee, UNLESS building official approves.

SMOKE AND HEAT VENTS (910)

   A. Required where:
1. Their use applies to Use Groups F-1 and S in sprinkled one-story buildings to increase the allowable travel distance to 400'. (1016.2)
2. All S-1 and F-1 with over 50,000 sq. ft. of open space.
3. H-1, H-2 and H-3 requirements per 415.4 and 2005 Ohio Fire Code.
4. High-piled storage. (413)
   B. Vents shall open automatically (100° to 220°F above ambient temperature in non-sprinkled buildings or drop-out vents at 500°F) and shall be operable by an approved manual system.
   C. Curtain boards are required to subdivide the areas of a large vented building per Table 910.3.
   D. Vents minimum 16 sq. ft., with minimum dimension of 4'.
   E. Vents must be minimum 20' from lot lines and 10' from fire barriers.
   F. Mechanical smoke control is option to replace vents. (910.4)

SMOKE BARRIERS (700, 400)

   A. Smoke barriers are required in Use Groups I-2 and I-3. (407.4 and 408.6)
   B. Construction is required to be 1-hour or 0.10" steel in I-3.
   C. Doors must be 20-minute with closers (715.4.8.3), except for opposite-swing door sets in I-2. (710.5)
   D. Ducts must have smoke dampers. (716.5.5)
   E. Provide an effective membrane from exterior walls to floor and ceiling, continuous through concealed spaces, except as above-ceiling where ceiling is designed to be smoke barrier.
   F. Use Group I-2 (407.4)
1. Smoke barrier is required to divide each floor of 50 or more occupants into 2 compartments, each with a maximum area of 22,500 sq. ft. and a maximum travel distance from any place in a compartment of 200'.
2. Provide 30 sq. ft./occupant on each side of the smoke barrier for patient floors, 6 sq. ft. per occupant on other floors.
3. An independent egress in each compartment is required.
   G. Use Group I-3 (408.6)
1. Smoke barrier is required to divide floors of 50 or more occupants; except for spaces with direct exit to public way, court 50' away, or separate building, for sleeping.

2. Maintain a maximum occupant load of 200 per compartment.
3. Limit travel to 150' from any room door.
4. Limit travel to 200' in any room.
5. Provide 6 sq. ft./occupant on each side of the smoke barrier.
6. An independent egress in each compartment is required.

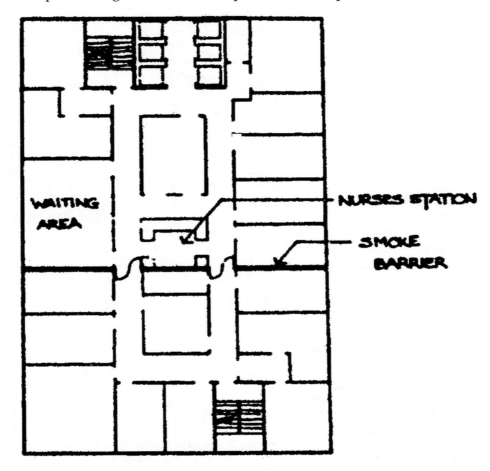

SMOKE CONTROL (909)

Smoke control is required in sections of the code. Smoke control as specified in section 909 is only required for atriums connecting three or more floors (404.4), underground buildings (405.5), covered malls (402.9), stages (410.3.7.2), high-rise exits (1021.1.7), smoke-protected assembly seating (1025.6.2.1), and existing buildings under 3410.6.10.1 category e.

A. Volume is defined by smoke barriers.
B. Need smoke detection system activation.
C. By active or passive systems, using exhaust, pressurization, or airflow designs.
D. Standby power is required. (909.11 and 2702.2)
E. Thorough identification and testing requirements.

SMOKE DETECTORS (907)

A. Single and multiple station (907.2.11)
  1. Smoke detectors are required in every guest room suite, or sleeping areas in Use Groups R-1, SRO (Single room occupancy) facilities (i.e., facilities with > 5 sleeping rooms open to the public, with each sleeping room intended as a permanent residence for a single occupant) and in the egress route of the suite in R-1 (except I-1 with auto-fire detection).
  2. Install smoke detectors near bedrooms and in bedrooms in Use Groups R-2, R-3, R-4 and I-1.
  3. Install smoke detectors in all different levels of a living unit, including basements.
  4. Multiple detectors in one living unit shall be wired together to sound simultaneously.
  5. Battery back-up is required for hard-wired units.
B. Automatic fire detection (907.2)
  1. High rise
    a. Automatic fire detection system is required in machine room, electrical, transformer, telephone, elevator, and air plenums.
  2. Automatic fire detection system is required in all Use Group I-1 unless sprinkled throughout.
  3. In Use Group I-2, an automatic fire detection system is required except:
    a. fully fire suppressed building, and
    b. if room is a patient sleeping room door with door closers activated by room side detector and visual and audible alarm at nursing station, or closers to patient rooms have integral detectors.
  4. An automatic fire detection system is required in Use Group I-3 housing areas (except sleeping rooms with four or less occupants), or sleeping rooms in Conditions II and III.
  5. An automatic fire detection system is required in Use Group R-1 except units that have direct grade exit access and no interior corridors, or sprinkled building with audible alarms.
  6. H Uses with toxic gases, peroxides or oxidizers (as required by the Fire Code).
  7. Special amusement buildings.
  8. Where smoke control is required. (909)
  9. For high-piled storage. (Table 2306.2 International Fire Code 2003)
  10. For egress-control devices (door hold-opens).
  11. Underground buildings.
  12. Residential aircraft hangars (one required).
  13. Battery rooms (over 50 gallons).
  14. Lumber, wood structural panel and veneer mills.

15. Aerosol storage buildings.
16. Mechanical equipment, electrical, transformer, telephone equipment, elevator machine or similar rooms.
17. Elevator lobbies.
18. Covered mall buildings.

SMOKEPROOF STAIRS (See EGRESS AND EXITS, M. Smokeproof stair enclosure (smoke tower))

SNOW LOADS

(See STRUCTURAL LOADS)

SOILS (1803)

A. Soil borings are required for all buildings unless waived by the building official.
B. Soils reports required for all pile or pier foundations.
C. Typical minimum bearing values per Table 1806.2.

Crystalline bedrock	12,000 psf
Sedimentary rock	4,000 psf
Sandy gravel or gravel	3,000 psf
Sand, silty sand, clayey sand, gravel, and clayey gravel	2,000 psf
Clay, sandy clay, silty clay, and clayey silt	1,500 psf

D. Soils report must include (1803.6)
1. Boring locations and results.
2. Water table.
3. Bearing capacity.
4. Remedies and recommendations.
5. Compacted fill data.

SOLAR ENERGY (M-14)

A. Install system per manufacturer's instructions for use in space heating or cooling, domestic hot water heating, process heating, or swimming pool heating (M-1401.1 and M-1401.4)
  a. Protect potable water supplies against contamination per the plumbing code. Exception:
    1. If potable distribution system includes all system piping per the plumbing code, and all piping system components are listed for potable water use, no requirement for cross-connection protection measures. (1401.2)
  b. Heat exchangers for domestic water heater require approval, and adequate protection to ensure proper water potability and distribution. (1401.3)
  c. Install ducts per entry for DUCTS. (1401.5)
  d. List factory-built collectors and label (pertaining solely to collectors) as to manufacturer's name and address, model number, dry weight, maximum allowable operating/nonoperating temperatures and pressures, minimum allowable temperatures, and heat transfer fluids with which they are compatible. (1404.1)
  e. List pressurized thermal storage units and label (pertaining solely to collectors) as to manufacturer's name and address, model and serial numbers, storage unit maximum/minimum allowable operating pressures and temperatures, and heat transfer fluids with which they are compatible. The label shall clarify that these specifications apply only to the thermal storage unit. (1404.2)

B. Installation is per the following (1402)
   a. Maintenance access to equipment and appliances is required. Solar systems and appurtenances cannot obstruct or interfere with operation or access to doors, windows or any other building components. (1402.1)
   b. If solar equipment is exposed to vehicular traffic, it must be installed ≥ 6′ (1829mm) over the finished floor, UNLESS the equipment is protected from vehicular impact. (1402.2)
   c. If a passive solar system includes attics or structural spaces, no ventilation is required where condensation is controlled by other approved methods. (1402.3)
   d. A roof-mounted solar collector also functioning as a roof covering must be of noncombustible materials or fire-retardant wood to meet OBC roof coverings requirements for the subject roof EXCEPT that plastic solar collector covers can only be those approved plastics approved as plastic panels in the OBC. (1402.4)
   e. Flash and seal roof and wall penetrations to bar water, rodent, and insect entry. (1402.6)
   f. Filter air from heat storage system to occupied spaces through rock or dust-producing materials other than by natural convection.
C. Protection of solar system equipment (1402.5)
   a. Relief valves for pressure and temperature are required to protect system components containing pressurized fluids from pressures and temperatures exceeding design limitations. Every section susceptible to developing excessive pressures needs access to a relief device that cannot be valved off from. (1402.5.1)
   b. Vacuum relief valves are necessary to protect system components subjected to vacuum in either operation or shutdown OR components must be designed to tolerate vacuum. (1402.5.2)
   c. Protection of system components is required from damage by freezing of heat transfer liquids. Protection must cover lowest ambient temperatures encountered during system operation. (1402.5.3)
   d. Heat transfer fluid flash point must be ≥ 50 F the design maximum nonoperating temperature attained by fluid in the collector. (1403)
      1. Flammable liquid or gas is barred as heat transfer fluid.
      2. Do not use lower flash point for liquids used in Group H or F occupancies UNLESS approved.
   e. Include expansion tanks with liquid single-phase systems, sized per OMC. (1402.5.4)
D. Other required items
   1. Expansion tank is required with a single phase system. (M-1402.5.4)
   2. Collectors must be able to sustain high stagnation temperature, and be protected from freezing of heat transfer liquid. (M-1402.5.3)

SOUND TRANSMISSION (1207)

A. Requirements generally apply to only walls, partitions, and floor/ceilings of Use Group R between dwelling units as well as adjacent common areas.
B. Airborne is not less than 50 STC (Sound Transmission Class). Not for dwelling unit entry doors—only tight fitting is required.
C. Structure borne (floor/ceiling and walls) is not less than 50 impact (IIC) (Impact Insulation Class).
D. Field-tested assemblies are acceptable for only 45 STC and 45 IIC.

SPACE HEATERS

A. Space heaters must be in a ventilated area designed to prevent accumulation of carbon monoxide. (See R.C. 3701.82 for portable, unvented kerosene heaters.)

SPECIAL INSPECTIONS (1704)

A. Statement of special inspections is required as part of the plan review prior to permit approval.

B. Special inspectors must be able to provide records of all inspections and corrections.

C. Special inspections *not* required:
1. Minor work;
2. Building components not required to be designed by an architect or engineer.

D. Special inspection required for:
1. Shop-fabricated structural assemblies (of any material)
   a. At fabricator's shop, and
   b. Fabricator inspected by independent agency.
2. Steel—bolting, welding materials, and bracing except that the special inspector need not be continuously present during welding of shop-fabricated structural assemblies, provided the materials, procedures and qualifications of welders are verified prior to the start of the work. (Table 1704.3)
3. Required verification and inspection concrete construction is per Table 1704.4

TABLE 1704.4

REQUIRED VERIFICATION AND INSPECTION OF CONCRETE CONSTRUCTION				
1. Inspection of reinforcing steel, including prestressing tendons, and placement.	—	X	ACI 318: 3.5, 7.1-7.7	1913.4
2. Inspection of reinforcing steel welding in accordance with Table 1704.3, Item 5b.	—	—	AWS D1.4 ACI 318: 3.5.2	—
3. Inspect bolts to be installed in concrete prior to and during placement of concrete where allowable loads have been increased.	X	—	—	1911.5
4. Verifying use of required design mix.	—	X	ACI 318: Ch. 4, 5.2-5.4	1904.2.2, 1913.2, 1913.3
5. At the time fresh concrete is sampled to fabricate specimens for strength tests, perform slump and air content tests, and determine the temperature of the concrete.	X	—	ASTM C 172 ASTM C 31 ACI 318: 5.6, 5.8	1913.10
6. Inspection of concrete and shotcrete placement for proper application techniques.	X	—	ACI 318: 5.9, 5.10	1913.6, 1913.7, 1913.8
7. Inspection for maintenance of specified curing temperature and techniques.	—	X	ACI 318: 5.11-5.13	1913.9
8. Inspection of prestressed concrete: a. Application of prestressing forces. b. Grouting of bonded prestressing tendons in the seismic-force-resisting system.	X X	—	ACI 318: 18.20 ACI 318: 18.18.4	—
9. Erection of precast concrete members.	—	X	ACI 318: Ch. 16	—
10. Verification of in-situ concrete strength, prior to stressing of tendons in posttensioned concrete and prior to removal of shores and forms from beams and structural slabs.	—	X	ACI 318: 6.2	—
11. Inspect formwork for shape, location and dimensions of the concrete member being formed.	—	X	ACI 318: 6.1.1	—

For SI: 1 inch = 25.4 mm

a. Where applicable, see also Section 1707.1, Special inspection for seismic resistance.

4. Masonry has 2 levels of special inspection:
    a. Level 1 Table 1704.5.1 for "essential facilities" such as hospitals and fire stations.
    b. Level 2 Table 1704.5.3 for "non-essential" buildings.
5. Spray fireproofing
6. EIFS (Exterior insulation and finish system)
7. Smoke control systems.

TABLE 1704.5.1
LEVEL 1 REQUIRED VERIFICATION AND INSPECTION OF
MASONRY CONSTRUCTION

VERIFICATION AND INSPECTION	FREQUENCY OF INSPECTION		REFERENCE FOR CRITERIA		
	CONTINUOUS	PERIODIC	OBC SECTION	TMS 402/ACI 530/ASCE 5[a]	TMS 602/ACI 530.1/ASCE 6[a]
1. Compliance with required inspection provisions of the construction documents and the approved submittals shall be verified.	—	X	—	—	Art. 1.5

				REFERENCE FOR CRITERIA
2. Verification of f'_m and f'_{AAC} prior to construction except where specifically exempted by this code.	—	X	—	—	Art. 1.4B
3. Verification of slump flow and VSI as delivered to the site for self-consolidating grout.	X	—	—	—	Art. 1.5B.1.b.3
4. As masonry construction begins, the following shall be verified to ensure compliance:					
a. Proportions of site-prepared mortar.	—	X	—	—	Art. 2.6A
b. Construction of mortar joints.	—	X	—	—	Art. 3.3B
c. Location of reinforcement, connectors, prestressing tendons and anchorages.	—	X	—	—	Art. 3.4, 3.6A
d. Prestressing technique.	—	X	—	—	Art. 3.6B
e. Grade and size of prestressing tendons and anchorages.	—	X	—	—	Art. 2.4B, 2.4H
5. During construction the inspection program shall verify:					
a. Size and location of structural elements.	—	X	—	—	Art. 3.3F
b. Type, size and location of anchors, including other details of anchorage of masonry to structural members, frames or other construction.	—	X	—	Sec. 1.2.2(e), 1.16.1	—
c. Specified size, grade and type of reinforcement, anchor bolts, prestressing tendons and anchorages.	—	X	—	Sec. 1.15	Art. 2.4, 3.4
d. Welding of reinforcing bars.	X	—	—	Sec. 2.1.9.7.2, 3.3.3.4(b)	—
e. Preparation, construction and protection of masonry during cold weather (temperature below 40°F) or hot weather (temperature above 90°F).	—	X	Sec. 2104.3, 2104.4	—	Art. 1.8C, 1.8D
f. Application and measurement of prestressing force.	X	—	—	—	Art. 3.6B
6. Prior to grouting, the following shall be verified to ensure compliance:					
a. Grout space is clean.	—	X	—	—	Art. 3.2D
b. Placement of reinforcement and connectors, and prestressing tendons and anchorages.	—	X	—	Sec. 1.13	Art. 3.4
c. Proportions of site-prepared grout and prestressing grout for bonded tendons.	—	X	—	—	Art. 2.6B
d. Construction of mortar joints.	—	X	—	—	Art. 3.3B
7. Grout placement shall be verified to ensure compliance.	X	—	—	—	Art. 3.5
a. Grouting of prestressing bonded tendons.	X	—	—	—	Art. 3.6C
8. Preparation of any required grout specimens, mortar specimens and/or prisms shall be observed.	—	X	Sec. 2105.2.2, 2105.3	—	Art. 1.4

For SI: °C = [(°F) - 32]/1.8.
a. The specific standards referenced are those listed in Chapter 35.

TABLE 1704.5.3
LEVEL 2 REQUIRED VERIFICATION AND INSPECTION OF MASONRY CONSTRUCTION

VERIFICATION AND INSPECTION	CONTINUOUS	PERIODIC	OBC SECTION	TMS 402/ACI 530/ASCE 5	TMS 602/ACI 530.1/ASCE 6
1. Compliance with required inspection provisions of the construction documents and the approved submittals.	—	X	—	—	Art. 1.5
2. Verification of f'_m and f'_{AAC} prior to construction and for every 5,000 square feet during construction.	—	X	—	—	Art. 1.4B
3. Verification of proportions of materials in premixed or preblended mortar and grout as delivered to the site.	—	X	—	—	Art. 1.5B
4. Verification of slump flow and VSI as delivered to the site for self-consolidating grout.	X	—	—	—	Art. 1.5B.1.b.3
5. The following shall be verified to ensure compliance:					
a. Proportions of site-prepared mortar, grout and prestressing grout for bonded tendons.	—	X	—	—	Art. 2.6A
b. Placement of masonry units and construction of mortar joints.	—	X	—	—	Art. 3.3B

c. Placement of reinforcement, connectors and prestressing tendons and anchorages.	=	X	=	Sec. 1.15	Art. 3.4, 3.6A
d. Grout space prior to grout.	X	=	=	=	Art. 3.2D
e. Placement of grout.	X	=	=	=	Art. 3.5
f. Placement of prestressing grout.	X	=	=	=	Art. 3.6C
g. Size and location of structural elements.	=	X	=	=	Art. 3.3F
h. Type, size and location of anchors, including other details of anchorage of masonry to structural members, frames or other construction.	X	=	=	Sec. 1.2.2(e), 1.16.1	=
i. Specified size, grade and type of reinforcement, anchor bolts, prestressing tendons and anchorages.	=	X	=	Sec. 1.15	Art. 2.4, 3.4
j. Welding of reinforcing bars.	X	=	=	Sec. 2.1.9.7.2, 3.3.3.4 (b)	=
k. Preparation, construction and protection of masonry during cold weather (temperature below 40°F) or hot weather (temperature above 90°F).	=	X	Sec. 2104.3, 2104.4	=	Art. 1.8C, 1.8D
l. Application and measurement of prestressing force.	X	=	=	=	Art. 3.6B
6. Preparation of any required grout specimens and/or prisms shall be observed.	X	=	Sec. 2105.2.2, 2105.3	=	Art. 1.4

For SI: °C = [(°F) - 32]/1.8, 1 square foot = 0.0929 m^2.
a. The specific standards referenced are those listed in Chapter 35.

245

SPRINKLERS (900, 1000)

A. Where required (903.2)

1. in Use group A-1 fire areas in excess of 12,000 sq. ft., an occupant load of 300 or more, the fire area contains a multitheater complex, or whenever the fire area is a level different from the ground floor.

2. in Use Group A-2 fire areas in excess of 5,000 sq. ft., an occupant load of 100 or more, or whenever the fire area is a level different from the ground floor.

3. in Use Group A-3 fire areas in excess of 12,000 sq. ft. Exception:
   a. Area is used exclusively for religious services with fixed seating.
   b. Occupant load is 300 or more.

4. in Use Group A-4 fire areas in excess of 12,000 sq. ft., an occupant load of 300 or more, or whenever the fire area is a level different from the ground floor. Exception:
   a. Participant sports areas where the main floor area is at the same level as the main entrance and exit.

5. in Use Group A-5 fire areas in concession stands, retail areas, press boxes and other accessory use areas in excess of 1,000 sq. ft.

6. in Use Group B ambulatory health care facilities whenever four or more care recipients need self-preservation care, or one or more such care recipients are located at other than the level of exit discharge for the occupancy.

7. in Use Group E fire areas in excess of 20,000 sq. ft. and below grade, except when all classrooms exit directly to grade.

8. in Use Group H in all high hazard buildings, with a special Table (903.2.5.2) for H-5.

9. in Use Group I.

10. For all Use Group R, except R-3 using option for IRC compliance.
    a. NFPA 13D for 1-, or 2-family dwellings.
    b. NFPA 13R allowed for residential up to 4 stories.
    c. NFPA 13 for all others.

11. Use Groups M, F-1, S-1: (903.2.7, 903.2.4, 903.2.9)
    a. Sprinklers are required when one fire area is larger than 12,000 sq. ft., or if the total area of all fire areas exceeds 24,000 sq. ft.
    b. Sprinklers are required when building is more than 3 stories tall. (M-1)
    c. Sprinklers required when F-1 has woodworking over 2500 sq. ft.
    d. All repair garages in basement; or one-story and > 12,000 sq. ft., or two or more stories and > 10,000 sq. ft. fire areas. (S-1)
    e. Bulk tire storage over 20,000 cubic feet. (S-1)

12. Use Group S-2 when enclosed or beneath other use groups except R-3, and also when storing over 5,000 sq. ft. of trucks or buses.

13. High rise: Sprinklers are required in all high rises with occupied floors 55' above the lowest level of fire department vehicle access.

14. Sprinklers are required in unlimited area buildings except: (507.1)
    a. Special industrial buildings, and
    b. Sport/recreation areas which have exits opening directly outdoors and have a signaling system with manual alarm devices. (507.3)

15. All covered malls require sprinklers. (402.7)

16. Atriums (404.3)
    Exception:
    a. The area of a building adjacent to or above the atrium need not be sprinklered, if separated from the atrium by not less than 2-hour fire-rated barrier or horizontal assembly, or both.

b. The ceiling of the atrium is more than 55′ above the floor.
17. Underground buildings (405.3)
18. High-piled storage (413)
B. Where required partially:
1. Windowless stories over 1,500 sq. ft. (except R-3 and U). (903.2.11)
2. Incidental use areas (Table 508.2.5)
   a. Waste rooms
   b. Furnace and boiler rooms (or 1-hour enclosure)
   c. Paint shops (or 2-hour enclosure)
   d. Incinerator rooms
   e. Storage rooms, laundry rooms, and waste or linen collection rooms over 100 sq. ft. (or 1-hour), and
   f. Battery rooms over 100 gallons.
3. Fuel dispensing areas in public garages
4. Trash and linen chutes (903.2.11.2)
5. Stages (410.6)
6. Level of exit discharge lobbies. (1023)
C. Where sprinklers allow a tradeoff:
1. Mixed use fire resistance rating reduction. (509 exception)
2. As a substitute for 1-hour construction other than exterior walls (Table 601, footnote d), but cannot *also* take height or area increases.
3. Increased percentage of unprotected openings for separation distance. (705.8.1)
4. Corridor exit access travel distance modified with sprinkler for some uses.

TABLE 1016.1
EXIT ACCESS TRAVEL DISTANCE[a]

OCCUPANCY	WITHOUT SPRINKLER SYSTEM (feet)	WITH SPRINKLER SYSTEM (feet)
A, E, F-1, I-1, M, R, S-1	200	250[b]
B	200	300[c]
F-2, S-2, U	300	400[c]
H-1	Not Permitted	75[c]
H-2	Not Permitted	100[c]
H-3	Not Permitted	150[c]
H-4	Not Permitted	175[c]
H-5	Not Permitted	200[c]
I-2, I-3, I-4	150	200[c]

For SI: 1 foot = 304.8 mm.

a. See the following sections for modifications to exit access travel distance requirements:
Section 402: For the distance limitation in malls.
Section 404: For the distance limitation through an atrium space.
Section 1016.2: For increased limitations in Groups F-1 and S-1.
Section 1025.7: For increased limitation in assembly seating.
Section 1025.7: For increased limitation for assembly open-air seating.
Section 1019.2: For buildings with one exit.
Chapter 31: For the limitation in temporary structures.

b. Buildings equipped throughout with an automatic sprinkler system in accordance with Section 903.3.1.1 or 903.3.1.2. See Section 903 for occupancies where automatic sprinkler systems in accordance with Section 903.3.1.2 are permitted.

c. Buildings equipped throughout with an automatic sprinkler system in accordance with Section 903.3.1.1.

5. Allowed building area increase (except for H uses) (506.3):

      a. 300% increase is allowed for 1-story buildings.

      b. 200% increase is allowed for buildings of 2 or more stories.

6. Allowed height increase (except for H uses) is 1 story and 20'. (504.2)

7. Sprinklers allow increased distance between exits (from $\frac{1}{3}$ to $\frac{1}{2}$ the diagonal). (1014.3)

8. Sprinklers allow increased capacity of egress elements (stair, door, ramp, corridor). (1007)

9. Eliminate emergency escape windows from sleeping rooms. (1029.1)

10. Use of special locking arrangements to delay exit is allowed. (1008.1.9.6)

11. Reduce to one the number of exits in R-2 buildings with 4 dwelling units, and 3 stories tall. (Table 1021.1, exception 4)

12. Eliminate smokeproof enclosure with stair pressurization. (909.20.5)

13. Increase size of fire wall openings. (705.8)

14. Reduce interior finish rating by one classification. (Table 803.9, note b)

15. Eliminate smoke detector system in I-3 (907.2.6.3.3), R-1 (907.2.8.1), and R-2 (907.2.9.1) when using single-station systems.

16. Eliminate the fire resistance required for walls separating buildings from pedestrian walkways if buildings connected are 10 apart. (3104.5., exception 1)

17. Increase allowed area of plastic in the following:

      a. Skylights (2610.4, 2610.5, and 2610.6)

      b. Wall, ceiling, and roof panels (2606.7.4, 2607.5, 2608.2, exception 1, and 2609.4, exception 1)

      c. Foam plastic insulation that is part of the roof assembly. (2603.3)

D. Supervision of sprinklers required

  1. Electronic—supervision is required in all uses. (903.4)

  2. Not required for 13R systems where sprinklers use domestic main supply and share same shutoff valve.

  3. Not required for limited area systems. (System is limited to 20 heads per fire area by 903.3.5.1.1.)

E. Sprinklers must be designed by Ohio Board of Building Standards certified designers, architects, or professional engineers.

F. Sprinklers must be installed by installers licensed by the Ohio Fire Marshal.

G. Sprinkler system types

  1. NFPA 13 (903.3.1.1) is a standard system throughout buildings including combustible spaces.

  2. NFPA 13R (903.3.1.2) is a reduced coverage system for groups I-1, I-4, and R (maximum 4 stories that qualifies for fewer tradeoffs).

  3. NFPA 13D (903.3.1.3) is a reduced coverage system qualifying for no tradeoffs, and intended for Groups I-1, R-3, and R-4.

STADIUMS AND GRANDSTANDS (See GRANDSTANDS AND BLEACHERS.)

STANDPIPES (905)

A. Required locations (905.3)

  1. During construction (3311)

      a. For building 4 stories or more, must be installed when height reaches 40' and stay within one floor of top of construction.

      b. For building with standpipes being demolished, must be maintained to one floor below top.

  2. Building height (905.3.1)

  a. When 30′ above or below (highest or lowest) level of fire department access.
  b. The 1½″ connections are not required in fully sprinkled buildings and open parking structures.
  c. Open parking structures are allowed dry standpipes.
3. Occupancy—in nonsprinklered Group A buildings having an occupant load exceeding 1,000 persons (905.3.2).
4. Covered malls (905.3.3)
5. Stages over 1,000 sq. ft.
6. Underground buildings
B. Outlet locations (905.3, 905.4)
  1. At the intermediate landing of every exit stair and passageway.
  2. On each side of horizontal exit.
  3. In covered malls, at all public entrances and all exits and exit corridors.
  4. On the roof (if sloped less than ⁴/₁₂).
  5. Additional outlets if areas of the building cannot be reached:
    a. Within 150′ if not sprinkled;
    b. Within 200′ if sprinkled.
  6. Both sides of stages.
C. Standpipe class definition of "standpipe system" (902.1)
  1. Classes
    a. Class I—2½″ only (for use by fire department).
    b. Class II—1½″ only (for use by occupants).
    c. Class III—*both* 2½″ and 1½″.
  2. The height threshold and stages require Class III, except Class I if sprinkled.
  3. The area threshold for malls, stages, and underground buildings requires Class I.
D. All Class I and III standpipes must have all piping enclosed in rated shaft or stair, except horizontal runs in sprinkled buildings.
E. All Class I and III standpipes must be interconnected.
F. See NFPA 14 for water supply requirements.

STEEL (CHAPTER 22)

A. Structural steel design (2205)
  1. Must use AISC 360 for structural steel design in buildings.
  2. Seismic design
    a. Seismic Design Category A, B or C—an R factor in Section 12.2.1 of ASCE 7 for the appropriate steel system allowed if the structure is designed per AISC 341, Part I. Other systems must use the R factor in Section 12.2.1 of ASCE 7 designated for "structural steel systems not specifically detailed for seismic resistance."
    b. Seismic Design Category D, E or F—must be designed per AISC 341, Part I.
B. Formed steel design (2209, 2210, 2211)
  1. Cold-formed carbon and low-alloy steel structural members is per AISI-NAS.
    a. Cold-formed stainless-steel structural members is per ASCE 8.
    b. Composite slabs on steel decks is per ASCE 3.
    c. Cold-formed carbon or low-alloy steel, structural and nonstructural steel framing is per AISI-General and AISI-NAS.
  2. Cold-formed steel box headers, back-to-back headers and single and double L-headers used in single-span conditions for load-carrying purposes is per AISI-S212 or AISI S100.
  3. Design, QA, installation and testing of cold-formed steel trusses is per AISI-S214.

4. Cold-formed steel studs for structural and nonstructural walls is per AISI-S211 or AISI S100.
5. Design of light-framed cold-formed steel walls and diaphragms to resist wind and seismic loads is per AISI-S213.
C. Open web steel (bar joist) joists (2206)
　　Must use SJI specifications and load tables for joists and girders. (2206.1)
D. Other types of steel materials (2207 and 2208)
1. Steel cable structures must be designed according to ASCE 19 (2207).
2. Steel racks must be designed according to RMI (2208).

STRUCTURAL LOADS (CHAPTER 16)

A. Design and construct buildings and parts of buildings to:
1. support the factored loads in load combinations per OBC without exceeding appropriate strength limit states for construction materials OR
2. support the nominal loads in load combinations per the OBC without exceeding appropriate allowable stresses for construction materials. (1604.2)
B. Design structural systems members for adequate stiffness against deflections and lateral drift. (1604.3)
1. Drift limits for earthquake loading, see ASCE 7 Sec. 12.12.1.
2. Deflections ≤ more restrictive limitations of 1604.3.2-3.5 OR as permitted by Table 1604.3.
   a. Reinforced concrete deflection ≤ ACI 318 limits.
   b. Steel deflection ≤ AISC 360, AISI S100, ASCE 3, ASCE 8, SJI CJ-1.0, SJI JG-1.1, SJI K-1.1 or SJI LH/DLH-1.1 limits as applicable.
   c. Masonry deflection ≤ TMS 402/ACI 530/ASCE 5 limits.
   d. Aluminum deflection ≤ AA ADMI limits.
   e. Structural member deflection over span, 1, ≤ Table 1604.3 limits.
C. Load analysis on structural members must use well-established principles of mechanics, and take into account equilibrium, general stability, geometric compatibility and short/long term material properties.
1. If members accumulating residual deformations in repeated service loads, add additional eccentricities expected during service life.
2. Analysis results in complete load path to transfer loads from origin point to load-resisting elements.
3. Distribute total lateral force to various vertical elements of lateral-force-resisting system, proportionate to their rigidities, given rigidity of the horizontal bracing system or diaphragm.
4. Rigid elements not assumed part of lateral-force-resisting system are incorporated in buildings IF consider effect on system action and provide for in design.
5. Allow for increased forces induced on structural system resisting elements due to torsion from eccentricity between center of application of lateral forces and center of rigidity of lateral-force-resisting system EXCEPT if diaphragms flexible, or can be analyzed as flexible.
6. Design structures to resist lateral forces overturning effects (wind load, lateral soil loads, earthquake loads). (1604.4)
D. Occupancy categories assigned per Table 1604.5.
1. If building/structure has 2+ occupancies in different categories, assign highest occupancy category to each.
2. If building/structure with 2+ portions structurally separated, classify each separately.
3. If separated portion of building/structure gives required access to, egress from, or

shares life safety components with separate portion having higher occupancy category, assign both to higher occupancy category. (1604.5)

E. If question of safety for intended occupancy, building official may require engineering analysis, load test, or both in situ. (1604.6)

F. Preconstruction load tests required if materials/methods cannot be designed by approved engineering analysis, or do not comply with applicable material design standards. (1604.7)

G. Require anchorage of roof to walls and columns, and of walls and columns to foundations, to resist uplift and sliding forces from prescribed load application.

    1. Anchor walls to floors, roofs and any structural elements giving lateral support. Positive direct connection must resist horizontal forces of stated in 1604 but $\geq$ minimum strength design horizontal force per ASCE 7, Sec. 11.7.3 (substituted for "E" in Sec. 1605.2 or 1605.3)

    2. Concrete and masonry walls must resist bending between anchors if anchor spacing > 4′ (1219 mm). Imbed anchors in hollow or cavity masonry walls in reinforced grouted structural element of the wall. Special requirements for wind/earthquake design.

    3. Deck requirements

        a. If supported by attachment to exterior wall, positively anchor to primary structure and design for applicable vertical and lateral loads.

        b. Do not use toenails or other withdrawable nails.

        c. If cannot verify positive connections to primary structure during inspection, decks must be self-supporting.

        d. Design deck connections with cantilevered framing members per both (acting on all parts of deck):

            (1) Either dead and live load reactions per Table 1607.1 OR snow load

            (2) Either dead and live load reactions per Table 1607.1 OR snow load (acting on cantilevered part of deck, with no live or snow load on remainder of deck). (1604.8)

    4. Design structural members, systems, components, and cladding to resist earthquake/wind, considering overturning, sliding, and uplift. Provide continuous load paths for transmitting earthquake/wind forces to foundation. If using sliding to isolate elements, include effects of friction between elements as a force. (1604.9)

    5. Wind and seismic lateral force resisting must meet ASCE 7 (except Ch. 14 and Appendix 11A), even if wind effects exceed seismic load effects. (1604.10)

TABLE 1604.5
OCCUPANCY CATEGORY OF BUILDINGS AND OTHER STRUCTURES

OCCUPANCY CATEGORY	NATURE OF OCCUPANCY
I	Buildings and other structures that represent a low hazard to human life in the event of failure, including but not limited to: • Agricultural facilities. • Certain temporary facilities. • Minor storage facilities.
II	Buildings and other structures except those listed in Occupancy Categories I, III and IV.
III	Buildings and other structures that represent a substantial hazard to human life in the event of failure, including but not limited to: • Buildings and other structures whose primary occupancy is public assembly with an occupant load greater than 300. • Buildings and other structures containing elementary school, secondary school or day care facilities with an occupant load greater than 250. • Buildings and other structures containing adult education facilities, such as colleges and universities, with an occupant load greater than 500. • Group I-2 occupancies with an occupant load of 50 or more resident patients but not having surgery or emergency treatment facilities. • Group I-3 occupancies. • Any other occupancy with an occupant load greater than 5,000[a]. • Power-generating stations, water treatment facilities for potable water, waste water treatment facilities and other public utility facilities not included in Occupancy Category IV. • Buildings and other structures not included in Occupancy Category IV containing sufficient quantities of toxic or explosive substances to be dangerous to the public if released.
IV	Buildings and other structures designated as essential facilities, including but not limited to: • Group I-2 occupancies having surgery or emergency treatment facilities. • Fire, rescue, ambulance and police stations and emergency vehicle garages. • Designated earthquake, hurricane or other emergency shelters. • Designated emergency preparedness, communications and operations centers and other facilities required for emergency response. • Power-generating stations and other public utility facilities required as emergency backup facilities for Occupancy Category IV structures. • Structures containing highly toxic materials as defined by Section 307 where the quantity of the material exceeds the maximum allowable quantities of Table 307.1(2). • Aviation control towers, air traffic control centers and emergency aircraft hangars. • Buildings and other structures having critical national defense functions. • Water storage facilities and pump structures required to maintain water pressure for fire suppression.

a. For purposes of occupant load calculation, occupancies required by Table 1004.1.1 to use gross floor area calculations shall be permitted to use net floor areas to determine the total occupant load.

H. Typical design dead loads
   Note: These loads are no longer a part of the current code. We have retained this information for the convenience of the code user.
   1. Concrete Slabs Per Inch of Thickness:

a. Plain concrete	—	12 lbs./sq. ft.
b. Lightweight concrete	—	8½ lbs./sq. ft.
c. Both with reinforcement add	—	1½ lbs./sq. ft.

   2. Floor Finishes:

a. 1" hardwood flooring	—	4 lbs./sq. ft.
b. 1" Underlayment	—	3 lbs./sq. ft.
c. Linoleum or tile	—	2 lbs./sq. ft.
d. Brick pavers	—	10 lbs./sq. ft.

   3. Wood Joists: (at 16" o.c.)

a. 2 × 6	—	5 lbs./sq. ft.
b. 2 × 8	—	6 lbs./sq. ft.
c. 2 × 10	—	6 lbs./sq. ft.
d. 2 × 12	—	7 lbs./sq. ft.

   4. Roofing:

a. 5 ply with gravel	—	6 lbs./sq. ft.
b. Asphalt shingles	—	2 lbs./sq. ft.
c. Rigid insulation/inch of thickness	—	1½ lbs./sq. ft.
d. Slate (¼")	—	10 lbs./sq. ft.
e. Spanish Tile	—	20 lbs./sq. ft.
f. Roof sheathing/per inch thickness	—	3 lbs./sq. ft.

   5. Materials:

a. Haydite	—	90 lbs./cu. ft.
b. Gravel/Stone	—	144 lbs./cu. ft.
c. Sand (dry)	—	96 lbs./cu. ft.
d. Concrete (gravel)	—	150 lbs./cu. ft.
e. Concrete (lightweight)	—	84 lbs./cu. ft.
f. Earth (damp)	—	108 lbs./cu. ft.
g. Cork	—	15 lbs./cu. ft.
h. Granite	—	153 lbs./cu. ft.
i. Terra Cotta (solid)	—	120 lbs./cu. ft.
j. Timbers (hardwood)	—	45 lbs./cu. ft.
k. Timbers (softwood)	—	35 lbs./cu. ft.

   6. Walls:

a. 4" brick	—	40 lbs./sq. ft.
b. 4" hollow lightweight concrete block	—	20 lbs./sq. ft.
c. 8" hollow lightweight concrete block	—	38 lbs./sq. ft.
d. 12" hollow lightweight concrete block	—	55 lbs./sq. ft.
e. 4" glass block	—	18 lbs./sq. ft.
f. Partitions with ⁵/₈" drywall both sides	—	10 lbs./sq. ft.

I. Load combinations (1605)

1. For buildings and other structures use not only those in the OBC, but also those in ASCE 7 Sec. 12.4.3.2 (if required by Secs. 12.2.5.2, 12.3.3.3, or 12.10.2.1) (1605).

2. If simplified procedure under ASCE Sec. 12.14, use load combinations with overstrength factor in ASCE 7 Sec. 12.14.3.2.

   a. Use overstrength factor instead of Equations 16-5, 16-7 for basic combinations for strength design.

   b. Use overstrength factor instead of Equations 16-12, 16-13, 16-15 for basic combinations for allowable stress design.

   c. Use overstrength factor instead of Equations 16-20, 16-21 for basic combinations for allowable stress design. (1605.1)

3. Calculate also for earthquake and wind loads, and set each load combination to one or more variables set to zero. (1605.1)

4. For any load combination, assuming verification of overall structure stability is the goal, use either of strength or allowable stress design. If strength design load combinations used, registered design professional must provide strength reduction factors applicable to soil resistance. (1605.1)

5. Strength design and resistance factor design load combinations (from OBC):

   Basic load combinations. Where strength design or load and resistance factor design is used, structures and portions thereof shall resist the most critical effects from the following combinations of factored loads:

   $1.4(D + F)$ (Equation 16-1)

   $1.2(D + F + T) + 1.6(L + H) + 0.5(Lr \text{ or } S \text{ or } R)$ (Equation 16-2)

   $1.2D + 1.6(Lr \text{ or } S \text{ or } R) + (f1L \text{ or } 0.8W)$ (Equation 16-3)

   $1.2D + 1.6W + f1L + 0.5(Lr \text{ or } S \text{ or } R)$ (Equation 16-4)

   $1.2D + 1.0E + f1L + f2S$ (Equation 16-5)

   $0.9D + 1.6W + 1.6H$ (Equation 16-6)

   $0.9D + 1.0E + 1.6H$ (Equation 16-7)

   where:

   $f_1 = 1$ for floors in places of public assembly, for live loads in excess of 100 pounds per square foot (4.79 kN/m^2), and for parking garage live load, and $= 0.5$ for other live loads.

   $f_2 = 0.7$ for roof configurations (such as saw tooth) that do not shed snow off the structure, and $= 0.2$ for other roof configurations.

   Exception: Where other factored load combinations are specifically required by the provisions of this code, such combinations shall take precedence. (1605.2.1)

   (If flood loads (Fa) are involved in the design, use load combinations in ASCE 7, Sec. 2.3.3)

6. Allowable stress design load combinations (from OBC):

   Basic load combinations. Where allowable stress design (working stress design), as permitted by this code, is used, structures and portions thereof shall resist the most critical effects resulting from the following combinations of loads:

D + F (Equation 16-8)

D + H + F + L + T (Equation 16-9)

D + H + F + (Lr or S or R) (Equation 16-10)

D + H + F + 0.75(L + T) + 0.75(Lr or S or R) (Equation 16-11)

D + H + F + (W or 0.7E) (Equation 16-12)

D + H + F + 0.75(W or 0.7E) + 0.75L +

0.75(Lr or S or R) (Equation 16-13)

0.6D + W + H (Equation 16-14)

0.6D + 0.7E + H (Equation 16-15)

Exceptions:

1. Crane hook loads need not be combined with roof live load or with more than three-fourths of the snow load or one-half of the wind load.

2. Flat roof snow loads of 30 psf (1.44 kN/m^2) or less and roof live loads of 30 psf or less need not be combined with seismic loads. Where flat roof snow loads exceed 30 psf (1.44 kN/m^2), 20% shall be combined with seismic loads. (1605.3.1) Increases in allowable stresses specified in the appropriate material chapter or the referenced standards shall not be used with the load combinations of Section 1605.3.1, except that increases shall be permitted in accordance with Chapter 23. (1605.3.1.1)

(If flood loads (Fa) are involved in the design, use ASCE 7 Sec. 2.4.2 load combinations)

7. Use alternative basic load combinations as follows:

In lieu of the basic load combinations specified in Section 1605.3.1, structures and portions thereof shall be permitted to be designed for the most critical effects resulting from the following combinations. When using these alternative basic load combinations that include wind or seismic loads, allowable stresses are permitted to be increased or load combinations reduced where permitted by the material chapter of this code or the referenced standards. For load combinations that include the counteracting effects of dead and wind loads, only two-thirds of the minimum dead load likely to be in place during a design wind event shall be used. Where wind loads are calculated in accordance with Chapter 6 of ASCE 7, the coefficient ω in the following equations shall be taken as 1.3. For other wind loads, ω shall be taken as 1. When using these alternative load combinations to evaluate sliding, overturning and soil bearing at the soil-structure interface, the reduction of foundation overturning from Section 12.13.4 in ASCE 7 shall not be used. When using these alternative basic load combinations for proportioning foundations for loadings, which include seismic loads, the vertical seismic load effect, Ev, in Equation 12.4-4 of ASCE 7 is permitted to be taken equal to zero.

D + L + (Lr or S or R) (Equation 16-16)

D + L + (ω W) (Equation 16-17)

D + L + ω W + S/2 (Equation 16-18)

D + L + S + ω W/2 (Equation 16-19)

D + L + S + E/1.4 (Equation 16-20)

0.9D + E/1.4 (Equation 16-21)

Exceptions:

Crane hook loads need not be combined with roof live loads or with more than three-fourths of the snow load or one-half of the wind load.

Flat roof snow loads of 30 psf (1.44 kN/m^2) or less and roof live loads of 30 psf or less need not be combined with seismic loads. Where flat roof snow loads exceed 30 psf (1.44 kN/m^2), 20% shall be combined with seismic loads. Other loads. Where F, H or T are to be considered in the design, each applicable load shall be added to the combinations specified in Section 1605.3.2.

8. Design heliports and helistops for the following loads:

a. Dead load, D, plus gross weight of helicopter,

b. Dead load, D, plus two single concentrated impact loads, L, app. 8′ (2438 mm) apart applied anywhere on the touchdown pad (for each of helicopter's two main, either skid or wheeled type), with a magnitude 0.75 X gross weight of the helicopter.

   c. Dead load, D, plus uniform live load, L, of 100 psf (4.79 kN/m^2). Exception: Landing areas for helicopters with gross weights ≤ 3,000 lbs. (13.34 kN) per a. and b. may be designed using 40 psf (1.92 kN/m^2—nonreducable) uniform live load inc., IF landing area is identified with a 3,000 lb. (13.34 kN) weight limitation. Landing area weight limitation is indicated by the numeral "3" (kips) in the bottom right corner of the landing area as viewed from the primary approach path. The indication for landing area weight limitation must be ≥ 5′ (1524 mm) high. (1605.4)

J.   Dead loads are considered permanent loads. Use actual weights of materials of construction and fixed service equipment for design purposes. (1606)

K.   Live loads not specified in Table 1607.1 determined per generally accepted engineering practice. For buildings and other structures, use anticipated maximum loads for intended occupancy, but ≥ minimum uniformly distributed unit live loads per Table 1607.1.

   1. Design floors and related surfaces to support uniformly distributed live loads OR the concentrated load in lbs. (kilonewtons) per Table 1607.1, whichever causes greater load effects. Assume concentration to be uniformly distributed over 2½′ x 2½′ [6¼′ (0.58 m^2)], and placed to produce maximum load effects in structural members.

   2. If partition locations subject to change (e.g., office buildings), allow for partition weight on construction documents, even if partitions not depicted UNLESS live loads specified are > 80 psf (3.83 kN/m^2). Partition load must be > 15 psf (0.74 kN/m^2) uniformly distributed live load.

   3. Truck and bus garage minimum live loads per Table 1607.6, but 50 psf (2.40kN/m^2), unless other loads specified. Use actual loads if > table-specified loads. Uniformly distribute concentrated load and uniform load over 10′ (3048 mm) width on a line normal to centerline of the lane, placed within 12′ (3568 mm) wide lane. Place loads within their individual lanes to cause maximum stress for each structural member. Design single spans for Table 1607.6 uniform load, and one simultaneous concentrated load to produce maximum effect. Design multiple spans for table 1607.6 uniform load on spans, and two simultaneous concentrated loads on two spans to cause maximum negative moment effect. For other effects—same for multiple span design loads as for single spans. (1607.6)

   4. Design and construct handrail, guard, grab bar, accessible seats/benches and vehicle barrier systems as follows (include allowance for impact conditions):

      i. Design handrails and guards to resist ≥ 50 lbs. per linear foot (plf) (0.73 kN/m) applied at top, in any direction, and transfer load through supports to structure. Exceptions:

         1. For Group I-3, F, H, S occupancy areas not accessible to general public and with occupant load < 50, minimum load is 20 lbs. per foot (0.29 kN/m). (1607.7.1)

      ii. Glass handrail assemblies/guards also per entry for GLASS. (1607.7.7.1)

      iii. Handrails and guards must resist single concentrated load of 200 lbs. (0.89 kN) applied along top in any direction, and to transfer load through supports to structure—need not be concurrent with K.4.i.1. loads above.

      iv. Design intermediate rails (except handrail), balusters, and panel fillers to resist horizontally applied 50 lbs. (0.22 kN) normal load on area equal to 1 square foot (0.093 m^2), to include openings and space between rails—need not superimpose reactions with K.4.i.1. or K.4.iii. (1607.7.1.2)

      v. Design grab bars, shower seats, and dressing room bench seats to resist 250 lbs. (1.11 kN) single concentrated load applied in any direction, at any point. (1607.7.2)

   vi. Design passenger car vehicle barrier systems to resist 6,000 lbs. (26.70 kN) single load horizontally in any direction to barrier system, and with attachment that can transmit load to the structure. Two required loading conditions, with more severe to govern design:

     (a) Apply load at height of 1′6″ (457 mm) above floor or ramp surface.

     (b) Apply load at height of 2′3″ (686 mm) above floor or ramp surface.

Assume load to act on area $\leq$ 1 square foot (0.0929 m²)—need not act concurrently with handrail or guard loadings. Design garages accommodating buses and trucks per method providing for traffic railings. (1607.7.3)

  5. Increase elevator loads by 100% for impact. Design structural Supports within ASME A17.1 limits. (1607.8.1)

  6. Increase weight of machinery and moving loads for impact for design purposes as follows:

    i. Elevator machinery—100%

    ii. Shaft or motor-driven light machinery—20%

    iii. Reciprocating machinery or power-driven units—50%

    iv. Floor or balcony hangers—33% (1607.8.2)

  7. Reduction in minimum uniformly distributed live loads (Below in Table 1607.1 and the succeeding 5 pages of text containing boldface type) allowed as follows:

TABLE 1607.9.1
LIVE LOAD ELEMENT FACTOR, K_{LL}

ELEMENT	K_{LL}
Interior columns	4
Exterior columns without cantilever slabs	4
Edge columns with cantilever slabs	3
Corner columns with cantilever slabs	2
Edge beams without cantilever slabs	2
Interior beams	2

All other members not identified above including:
    Edge beams with cantilever slabs
    Cantilever beams
    One-way slabs
    Two-way slabs
    Members without provisions for continuous
       shear transfer normal to their span
	1

1607.9.1.1 One-way slabs. The tributary area, A_T, for use in Equation 16-22 for one-way slabs shall not exceed an area defined by the slab span times a width normal to the span of 1.5 times the slab span.

1607.9.1.2 Heavy live loads. Live loads that exceed 100 psf (4.79 kN/m^2) shall not be reduced.

Exceptions:

1. The live loads for members supporting two or more floors are permitted to be reduced by a maximum of 20%, but the live load shall not be less than L as calculated in Section 1607.9.1.

2. For uses other than storage, where approved, additional live load reductions shall be permitted where shown by the registered design professional that a rational approach has been used and that such reductions are warranted.

1607.9.1.3 Passenger vehicle garages. The live loads shall not be reduced in passenger vehicle garages.

Exception: The live loads for members supporting two or more floors are permitted to be reduced by a maximum of 20%, but the live load shall not be less than L as calculated in Section 1607.9.1.

1607.9.1.4 Group A occupancies. Live loads of 100 psf (4.79 kN/m^2) and at areas where fixed seats are located shall not be reduced in Group A occupancies.

1607.9.1.5 Roof members. Live loads of 100 psf (4.79 kN/m^2) or less shall not be reduced for roof members except as specified in Section 1607.11.2.

1607.9.2 Alternate floor live load reduction. As an alternative to Section 1607.9.1, floor live loads are permitted to be reduced in accordance with the following provisions. Such reductions shall apply to slab systems, beams, girders, columns, piers, walls and foundations.

1. A reduction shall not be permitted in Group A occupancies.

2. A reduction shall not be permitted where the live load exceeds 100 psf (4.79 kN/m^2) except that the design live load for members supporting two or more floors is permitted to be reduced by 20%.

   Exception: For uses other than storage, where approved, additional live load reductions shall be permitted where shown by the registered design professional that a rational approach has been used and that such reductions are warranted.

3. A reduction shall not be permitted in passenger vehicle parking garages except that the live loads for members supporting two or more floors are permitted to be reduced by a maximum of 20%.

4. For live loads not exceeding 100 psf (4.79 kN/m^2), the design live load for any structural member supporting 150 square feet (13.94 m^2) or more is permitted to be reduced in accordance with Equation 16-23.

5. For one-way slabs, the area, A, for use in Equation 16-23 shall not exceed the product of the slab span and a width normal to the span of 0.5 times the slab span.

$$R = 0.08(A - 150) \qquad \text{(Equation 16-23)}$$

For SI: $R = 0.861(A - 13.94)$

Such reduction shall not exceed the smallest of:

1. 40 percent for horizontal members;
2. 60 percent for vertical members; or
3. R as determined by the following equation.

$$R = 23.1(1 + D/L_o) \qquad \text{(Equation 16-24)}$$

where:

A = Area of floor supported by the member, square feet (m^2).

D = Dead load per square foot (m^2) of area supported.

L_o = Unreduced live load per square foot (m^2) of area supported.

R = Reduction in percent.

1607.10 Distribution of floor loads. Where uniform floor live loads are involved in the design of structural members arranged so as to create continuity, the minimum applied loads shall be the full dead loads on all spans in combination with the floor live loads on spans selected to produce the greatest effect at each location under consideration. It shall be permitted to reduce floor live loads in accordance with Section 1607.9.

1607.11 Roof loads. The structural supports of roofs and marquees shall be designed to resist wind and, where applicable, snow and earthquake loads, in addition to the dead load of construction and the appropriate live loads as prescribed in this section, or as set forth in Table 1607.1. The live loads acting on a sloping surface shall be assumed to act vertically on the horizontal projection of that surface.

1607.11.1 Distribution of roof loads. Where uniform roof live loads are reduced to less than 20 psf (0.96 kN/m^2) in accordance with Section 1607.11.2.1 and are applied to the design of structural members arranged so as to create continuity, the reduced roof live load shall be applied to adjacent spans or to alternate spans, whichever produces the most unfavorable load effect. See Section 1607.11.2 for reductions in minimum roof live loads and Section 7.5 of ASCE 7 for partial snow loading.

1607.11.2 Reduction in roof live loads. The minimum uniformly distributed live loads of roofs and marquees, Lo, in Table 1607.1 are permitted to be reduced in accordance with Section 1607.11.2.1 or 1607.11.2.2.

1607.11.2.1 Flat, pitched and curved roofs. Ordinary flat, pitched and curved roofs, and awnings and canopies other than of fabric construction supported by lightweight rigid skeleton structures, are permitted to be designed for a reduced roof live load as specified in the following equations or other controlling combinations of loads in Section 1605, whichever produces the greater load. In structures such as greenhouses, where special scaffolding is used as a work surface for workers and materials during maintenance and repair operations, a lower roof load than specified in the following equations shall not be used unless approved by the building official. Such structures shall be designed for a minimum roof live load of 12 psf (0.58 kN/m^2).

$$L_r = L_o R_1 R_2 \qquad \textbf{(Equation 16-25)}$$

where: $12 \leq L_r \leq 20$

For SI: $Lr = L_o R_1 R_2$

where: $0.58 \leq L_r \leq 0.96$

L_r = Reduced live load per square foot (m2) of horizontal projection in pounds per square foot (kN/m2).

The reduction factors R_1 and R_2 shall be determined as follows:

$R_1 = 1$ for $A_t \leq 200$ square feet

$(18.58$ m^2) $\qquad$ **(Equation 16-26)**

$R_1 = 1.2 - 0.001 A_t$ for 200 square feet $< A_t < 600$ square feet $\qquad$ **(Equation 16-27)**

For SI: $1.2 - 0.011 A_t$ for 18.58 square meters $< A_t < 55.74$ square meters

$R_1 = 0.6$ for $A_t \geq 600$ square feet

$(55.74$ m^2) $\qquad$ **(Equation 16-28)**

where:

A_t = Tributary area (span length multiplied by effective width) in square feet (m^2) supported by any structural member, and

$R_2 = 1$ for $F \leq 4$ $\qquad$ **(Equation 16-29)**

$R_2 = 1.2 - 0.05 F$ for $4 < F < 12$ $\qquad$ **(Equation 16-30)**

$R_2 = 0.6$ for $F \geq 12$ $\qquad$ **(Equation 16-31)**

where:

F = For a sloped roof, the number of inches of rise per foot (for SI: $F = 0.12$ x slope, with slope expressed as a percentage), or for an arch or dome, the rise-to-span ratio multiplied by 32.

1607.11.2.2 Special-purpose roofs. Roofs used for promenade purposes, roof gardens, assembly purposes or other special purposes, and marquees, shall be designed for a minimum live load, L_o, as specified in Table 1607.1. Such live loads are permitted to be reduced in accordance with Section 1607.9. Live loads of 100 psf (4.79 kN/m^2) or more at areas of roofs classified as Group A occupancies shall not be reduced.

1607.11.3 Landscaped roofs. Where roofs are to be landscaped, the uniform design live load in the landscaped area shall be 20 psf (0.958 kN/m^2). The weight of the landscaping materials shall be considered as dead load and shall be computed on the basis of saturation of the soil.

1607.11.4 Awnings and canopies. Awnings and canopies shall be designed for uniform live loads as required in Table 1607.1 as well as for snow loads and wind loads as specified in Sections 1608 and 1609.

TABLE 1607.6
UNIFORM AND CONCENTRATED LOADS

LOADING CLASS[a]	UNIFORM LOAD (pounds/linear foot of lane)	CONCENTRATED LOAD (pounds)[b]	
		For moment design	For shear design
H20-44 and HS20-44	640	18,000	26,000
H15-44 and HS15-44	480	13,500	19,500

For SI: 1 pound per linear foot = 0.01459 kN/m, 1 pound = 0.004448 kN, 1 ton = 8.90 kN.

a. An H loading class designates a two-axle truck with a semitrailer. An HS loading class designates a tractor truck with a semitrailer. The numbers following the letter classification indicate the gross weight in tons of the standard truck and the year the loadings were instituted.

b. See Section 1607.6.1 for the loading of multiple spans.

8. Rated capacity of crane is crane live load. For moving bridge cranes and monorail cranes, runway beams design loads, including connections and support brackets, must include maximum wheel loads of crane as well as vertical impact, lateral, and longitudinal forces that the moving crane induces. (1607.12)

   i. Maximum wheel loads are those caused by weight of bridge + sum of rated capacity and weight of trolley as on its runway at spot where that effect is greatest.

   ii. Increase maximum wheel loads of crane to determine induced vertical impact or vibration force:

      (a) Monorail cranes (powered)—25%

      (b) Cab-operated or remotely operated bridge cranes (powered)—25%

      (c) Pendant-operated bridge cranes (powered)—10%

      (d) Bridge cranes or monorail cranes with hand -geared bridge trolley and hoist—0%

   iii. Calculate lateral force on crane runway beams having electrically powered trolleys at 20% of sum of rated capacity of crane and weight of hoist + trolley. Assume lateral force to act horizontally at traction surface of runway beam, operating perpendicular to beam in either direction. Distribute lateral force per lateral stiffness of runway beam and supporting structure.

   iv. Calculate longitudinal force on crane runway beams (except for bridge cranes on hand-geared bridges) at 10% of maximum wheel loads of crane. Assume longitudinal force to act horizontally at traction surface of runway beam, operating parallel to beam in either direction.

9. If interior walls and partitions (including finish materials) exceed 6' (1829 mm) height, they must resist subjected loads but $\geq$ horizontal load of 5 psf (0.24 kN/m^2). Exception: Fabric partitions meet either test of:

   i. Apply horizontally distributed load of 5 psf (0.24 kN/m^2) to partition framing. Area used for determining distributed load is fabric face between framing members to which fabric attached, with distributed load applied uniformly to framing members in proportion to each member's length. (1607.13)

   ii. Apply concentrated load of 40 lbs. (0.176 kN) to 50.3" square (1372 mm)—8" (203 mm) diameter of fabric face, 54" (1372 mm) above floor.

L. Design snow loads per ASCE 7, Ch. 7, but $\geq$ Sec. 1607—calculate from ground snow loads per ASCE 7 or Figure 1608.2 (use site-specific case studies in areas designated "CS" on Figure 1608.2). Approval for ground snow loads at elevations above Figure 1608.2 limits, and at sites within "CS" areas. If values inadequate due to record snowfall or experience, local jurisdiction must calculate higher ground snow loads. (1608)

FIGURE 1608.2
GROUND SNOW LOADS, p_g, FOR THE UNITED STATES (psf)

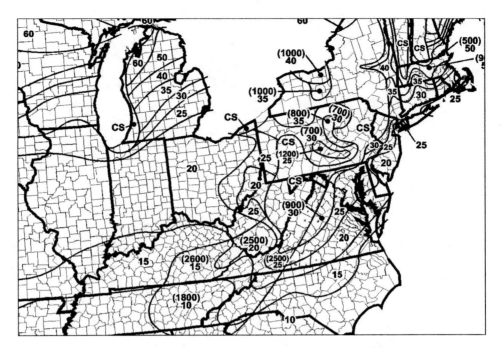

In CS areas, site-specific Case Studies are required to establish ground snow loads. Extreme local variations in ground snow loads in these areas preclude mapping at this scale.

Numbers in parentheses represent the upper elevation limits in feet for the ground snow load values presented below. Site -specific case studies are required to establish ground snow loads at elevations not covered.

To convert lb/sq ft to kNm², multiply by 0.0479.

To convert feet to meters, multiply by 0.3048.

M. Lateral Soil Loads (1610)—must be resisted at-rest by foundation and retaining walls (i.e., all walls where horizontal movement restricted at top). Table 1610.1 provides minimum lateral soil loads that control unless controverted by geotechnical investigation. Add lateral pressure from surcharge loads to lateral loads. If soils expansive, increase design lateral pressure.

1. If retaining wall allows movement and rotation at top, may design for active pressure.

2. Design foundation walls to support full hydrostatic pressure of undrained backfill unless drainage system installed. Exception:

   a. If wall extends $\leq 8'$ (2438 mm) below grade and laterally supported at top by flexible diaphragms, may design for active pressure.

TABLE 1610.1
LATERAL SOIL LOAD

DESCRIPTION OF BACKFILL MATERIAL[c]	UNIFIED SOIL CLASSIFICATION	DESIGN LATERAL SOIL LOAD[a] (pound per square foot per foot of depth)	
		Active pressure	At-rest pressure
Well-graded, clean gravels; gravel-sand mixes	GW	30	60
Poorly graded clean gravels; gravel-sand mixes	GP	30	60
Silty gravels, poorly graded gravel-sand mixes	GM	40	60
Clayey gravels, poorly graded gravel-and-clay mixes	GC	45	60
Well-graded, clean sands; gravelly sand mixes	SW	30	60
Poorly graded clean sands; sand-gravel mixes	SP	30	60
Silty sands, poorly graded sand-silt mixes	SM	45	60
Sand-silt clay mix with plastic fines	SM-SC	45	100
Clayey sands, poorly graded sand-clay mixes	SC	60	100
Inorganic silts and clayey silts	ML	45	100
Mixture of inorganic silt and clay	ML-CL	60	100
Inorganic clays of low to medium plasticity	CL	60	100
Organic silts and silt clays, low plasticity	OL	Note b	Note b
Inorganic clayey silts, elastic silts	MH	Note b	Note b
Inorganic clays of high plasticity	CH	Note b	Note b
Organic clays and silty clays	OH	Note b	Note b

For SI: 1 pound per square foot per foot of depth = 0.157 kPa/m, 1 foot = 304.8 mm.

a. Design lateral soil loads are given for moist conditions for the specified soils at their optimum densities. Actual field conditions shall govern. Submerged or saturated soil pressures shall include the weight of the buoyant soil plus the hydrostatic loads.

b. Unsuitable as backfill material.

c. The definition and classification of soil materials shall be in accordance with ASTM D 2487.

N. Rain Loads (1611)—Design for rainwater load if primary drainage system is blocked PLUS uniform load from water rising above inlet of secondary drainage system at design flow. Design for roof portions. Base Design Rainfall on 100-year hourly rainfall rate in Figure 1611.1 or approved local weather data.

1. If roof slopes < $1/4$" per foot [1.19° (0.0208 rad)], include in design calculations a verification of adequate stiffness to prevent deflection per ASCE 7, Section 8.4.

2. Controlled drainage roofs need secondary drainage system at higher elevation to limit accumulation. Design to sustain rainwater load accumulation to level of secondary drainage system PLUS uniform load from water rising over secondary drainage system inlet at Table 1611.1 design flow. Also check for ponding.

$$R = 5.2(d_s + d_h) \hspace{4cm} \textbf{(Equation 16-35)}$$

For SI: $R = 0.0098(d_s + d_h)$

where:

$d_h =$ Additional depth of water on the undeflected roof above the inlet of secondary drainage system at its design flow (i.e., the hydraulic head), in inches (mm).

$d_s =$ Depth of water on the undeflected roof up to the inlet of secondary drainage system when the primary drainage system is blocked (i.e., the static head), in inches (mm).

$R =$ Rain load on the undeflected roof, in psf (kN/m2). When the phrase "undeflected roof" is used, deflections from loads (including dead loads) shall not be considered when determining the amount of rain on the roof.

[P] FIGURE 1611.1
100-YEAR, 1-HOUR RAINFALL (INCHES) EASTERN UNITED STATES

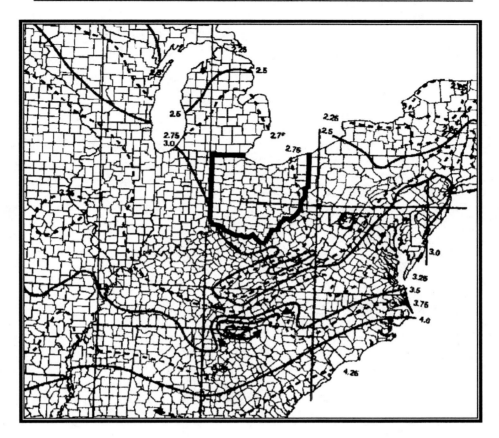

SWIMMING POOLS (3109)

A. Classification
1. Private: for use only in connection with 1-, 2-, or 3-family dwellings and not for public use, and not regulated by the OBC.
2. Public: a permit is required prior to construction from the local authority in accordance with the state Department of Health rules for pools with a capacity of > 150 gallons. (RC 3749.03)

B. Typical basic requirements
1. Plans must show construction details, distance from any building and lot line, walks, fences, water supply, and drainage.
2. Pool barrier requirements are minimum 48" high with 4" opening. Gates must be self-closing and self-latching. Maximum 2" vertical clearance between grade and bottom of barrier. If top of pool structure is above grade, barrier may be at ground level, and 4' maximum vertical clearance between top of structure and bottom of barrier.
3. Chain link fence must be ≤ 2 ¼" UNLESS slats fastened at top or bottom leave only ≤1 ¾" openings.
4. Horizontal members:
   a. Closely spaced (< 45") members on swimming pool side of fence, with vertical spacing ≤ 4".
   b. Widely spaced (< 45"), with vertical spacing ≤ 4".
5. Diagonal members allowed maximum opening of ≤ 1 ¾".
6. If dwelling wall is part of barrier:
   a. Doors with direct pool access require audible alarm per UL 2017. If accessible unit, deactivation switch must be 54" above threshold of door. If nonaccessible unit, switch must be 48"-54" above threshold of door.
   b. Self-closing doors with approved self-latching required.
7. All pools shall be supplied with a potable water supply according to the Plumbing Code.
8. Cross connections with the pool and pool equipment are unacceptable. (Plumbing Code)
9. All accessory structures such as showers, dressing rooms, buildings housing equipment, plumbing, heating, and other facilities must comply with the applicable Building Code requirements.
10. Interior pools must be properly ventilated. (Table M-403.3)
11. All pool accessories shall be designed and installed so as not to be a safety hazard.
12. Equipment shall be enclosed and accessible only to authorized personnel.
13. Accumulation of water in the vicinity of any electrical equipment is unacceptable.
14. Access gates must have a locking device, opening outward away from the pool, self-closing and self-latching. Gates other than pedestrian access gates must have self-latching devices. If the release mechanism is < 54" inches (1372 mm) above the finished surface, place the release mechanism on the pool side of the door/gate ≥ 3" (76 mm) below the top of the door/gate. Gate cannot have opening > ½" (12.7 mm) within 18" (457 mm) of the release mechanism.
15. Pools require a power safety cover that complies with ASTM F 1346.
16. Suction outlets required per ANSI/ANSP-7 and Ohio Department of Health rules.
17. Water drainage goes to storm water system or otherwise disposed of. Indoor pools require separate leak drainage UNLESS exempted by the Ohio Department of Health.

T

TEMPORARY STRUCTURES (107, 3102, AND Chapter 24 International Fire Code 2003)

A. "Temporary" means a structure which will stand for less than 180 days, and usually refers to tents and other membrane structures.

B. A permit is required from the fire or building official if the structure is larger than 120 square feet. Approval requirement covers tents ≥ 400 square feet, or multiple tents aggregating ≥ 400 square feet, when within 10′ of each other, including connecting areas or areas with common egress or entrance, used for ≥ 10 persons.

C. Plastic <30′ above the floor in greenhouses need not meet fire performance criteria of NFPA 701. Exception:

   1. Recreational tents.
   2. Tents open on all sides ≤ 700 square feet.
   3. Multiple tents open on all sides, side by side, without fire break clearance of 12′, ≤ 700 square feet.
   4. Minimum clearance of 12′ to all structures and other tents.

D. See MEMBRANE STRUCTURES.

E. Temporary structures need to comply with Table 602 for fire separation distance based on exterior wall rating.

F. Maximum travel distance to an exit is 100′. (2403.12.1 IFC 2003)

THEATRES (410)

A. Dressing rooms, storage, and similar rooms (410.3.1)

   1. Enclose with at least 1-hour construction from the stage and other rooms, with 2-hour to stage when stage height is over 50′.
   2. No door opening to the stage from such rooms except at stage level.

B. Exits

   1. Theatre exits and egress

      a. Aisles shall be designed depending on "smoke-protected" seating. (1028.6.2)
      b. Lighting (1006.2)

         i. Lighting in seating aisles must be at least 0.2 footcandles.
         ii. Lighting in all other egress must be at least 1 footcandle.

      c. In Group A and group E occupancies over 300, a main entrance and exit that face a street and accommodate at least 50% of the total occupant load are required. Multiple main entrances/exits are also permitted. (1028.2)
      d. Each different level of Group A and Group E occupancies shall have at least one access to the main exit; other exits shall accommodate ½ of that level load. (1028.3)
      e. Balconies and galleries with over 50 seats must have an egress from each side, and one of them directly to an exit. (1028.5)
      f. Egress stairs for balconies in theaters, churches, and auditoriums do not need rated enclosures. (1028.5.1)

   2. Stages and spaces under stages require one exit on each side.
   3. Fly galleries and gridirons must have at least one complying means of egress.
   4. A steel ladder from the gridiron to a roof scuttle is permitted.

C. Foyer for theatrical use (1028.4)

   1. Foyer area shall not include required exit space.
   2. The waiting portions must be separated from the exit routes by walls or permanent railings 42" high.

3. Foyer must be adjacent to main entrances/exits or be connected to them with corridors.

D. Proscenium opening (410.3.4)
1. The proscenium wall of a legitimate stage over 50′ in height shall be completely separated from the auditorium seating, extending from the foundation to the roof with a 2-hour wall.
2. Proscenium curtain for stages over 50′ in height shall be noncombustible or fire retardant and protect against flame and smoke for 20 minutes, or have a water curtain-type sprinkler system. The curtain must close in 30 seconds, and be activated by rate-of-rise heat detection and manual operation.
3. The curtain must have tested material and a bottom pocket with at least 4 lbs./foot weight.
4. All combustible sets and scenery must be flame-resistant treated. (410.3.6)

E. Railings (mezzanine, balcony, boxes) (1028.14)
1. At facia of balconies and boxes, railing must be 26" high.
2. Railings must be 42" high at the ends of aisles and must be the full width at the aisle.
3. Railings must be 42" high at the end of steps and must be the full width of the steps, but above 26" can have 8" openings.
4. At cross aisles, seat backs 24" high are allowed instead of guards.

F. Stage classification Insert (410.2)
1. Stage—a space for entertainment or presentations.
2. Platform—a raised area for presentation with no scenery, curtains, or drops.
3. A temporary platform is a platform erected for 30 days or less.

G. Stage construction (410.3.1)
1. Per floor requirements for type of construction except:
   a. Type IIB or IV with 2" wood deck and 2 hours as for proscenium wall.
   b. Non-rated floor in Types IIA, IIIA, or VA when sprinkled below stage.
   c. Finish floor allowed to be wood with solid wood trap doors.
2. Platform (lectures and similar platforms) (410.4)
   a. A temporary platform can be any approved construction if it is not used for more than 30 days, and the concealed space underneath can only be for electrical and plumbing.
   b. All other permanent platforms must be constructed per building floor construction requirements.
   c. Fire-retardant wood is allowed for Type I, II, and IV construction when platform height is 30" or less, not more than 1/3 of the overall room, and not more than 3,000 sq. ft.
   d. When space under the platform stage is used for other than electric wiring or plumbing, platform shall be 1-hour construction.

H. Combustible scenery materials must be flame-treated. (See 410.3.6 also Section 805 and Section 800 of the Ohio Fire Code, OAC 1301:7-7-08.)

I. General (stages)
1. Rigging, loft, and gridiron shall correspond to the construction type, but not rated. Fly galleries and catwalks are not restricted. (410.3.2)
2. Ventilation (410.3.7)
   a. Ventilation is required for all stages which are more than 1000 sq. ft. or over 50 ft. in height.
   b. Provide heat-activated vents directly to the exterior. Vents must also have manual activation.
   c. Aggregate area of the vents shall be at least 5% of the stage area.

       d. Smoke control per Section 909 required.

J.   Fire suppression (410.6)

1. Fire extinguishers must be provided as required by the fire department or fire marshal.
2. All A-1 over 300 people or 12,000 sq. ft. are to be sprinkled. (903.2.1.1)
3. Stages over 1000 sq. ft. must have standpipes on each side of the stage. (905.3.4)
4. Sprinklers not required under stages used only for table and chair storage and less than 4 ft. high, but need Type X drywall. (410.6)
5. Sprinklers not required for stages 1,000 sq. ft. or less, 50 ft. high or less, and single combustible backdrop.

UNDERGROUND STRUCTURES (405)

A. Where applicable: All buildings with a floor level more than 30′ below the exit floor. (405.1)
   1. Exceptions
      a. Fully sprinkled public garages
      b. Fixed guideway transit systems.
      c. Where only one story is 30′ underground, and that story has a maximum of 1,500 sq. ft. and 10 people.
      d. Pumping stations and similar spaces intended for periodic use by service personnel.
B. Construction
   1. Underground portion must be at least Type I construction. (405.2)
   2. When underground stories are 60′ or more below the exit floor, all underground and exit levels must have 1-hour smoke barriers with separate HVAC in each compartment. (405.4)
      a. Each compartment must have direct elevator access and an exit.
      b. Each compartment must have a smoke exhaust system. (405.5)
      c. Smoke barriers are not required in the lowest story if it is a maximum of 1500 sq. ft. or has an occupancy of no more than 10 people. (405.4.1)
   3. All underground floor levels must have two exits (405.7.1)
C. Fire protection systems
   1. All underground stories and their exit levels must be sprinkled.
   2. For underground stories more than 60′ in ground, pull stations with emergency voice and alarm communications, and a public address system are required. (907.2.19)
   3. Smokeproof enclosures for the exits are required.
   4. Standby power is required for smoke control, fire pump, smokeproof enclosure ventilation, and elevators per Section 2702.
   5. Emergency power is required for alarm and communiction systems, exit signs, egress lighting, and elevator cabs. (405.9)
   6. Underground buildings must have standpipes. (405.10)

USE GROUP CLASSIFICATION (CH. 3, USE AND OCCUPANCY)

A. General
   1. All buildings shall be classified as to use group and degree of fire hazard rating in hours and fraction of hours.
   2. A doubtful use shall be classified by the building official.
   3. Accessory rooms which are used as assembly with an occupant load of less than 50 or have an area of 750 sq. ft. or less and are part of another use are considered part of that use, not assembly occupancies. (303.1)
   4. Rooms used as assembly that are not accessory with less than 50 are Group B.
B. Use Group A-1 (theatres) include: (303.1)
   1. All buildings used for motion picture performances with fixed seats
   2. Theatres, including movie theatres
   3. Studios admitting audiences, and
   4. Symphony and concert halls
C. Use Group A-2 places of assembly. (303.1)
   1. A-2 Uses are for food and drink and include:

   a. Banquet halls

   b. Night clubs (definition of "nightclub" is found in R.C. 4301.01.)

   c. Taverns and bars, and

   d. Restaurants

 D. Use Group A-3 includes all buildings used for worship, recreation, amusement and other assembly not in other categories, including:

  1. Art galleries

  2. Exhibition halls

  3. Museums

  4. Lecture halls and courtrooms

  5. Libraries

  6. Community halls

  7. Bowling alleys

  8. Airline, train, or bus terminal waiting rooms

  9. Places of religious worship

  10. Dance halls (without food or drink)

  11. Funeral parlors

  12. Gyms, pools, and tennis courts without spectator seating

  13. Pool parlors

  14. Amusement arcades

 E. Use Group A-4 is indoor sports with seating, including:

  1. Arenas

  2. Skating rinks

  3. Swimming pools and tennis courts

 F. Use Group A-5 involves outdoor assembly structures where height and area limitations are not practical, such as:

  1. Grandstands

  2. Bleachers

  3. Stadiums, and

  4. Amusement park structures

 G. Use Group B (business buildings) (304)

  1. Buildings used for business and professional services, such as:

Airport control towers
Animal hospitals
Animal kennels
Animal pounds
Banks
Barber shops
Beauty shops
Car showrooms
Car wash
Civic administration buildings
Educations occupancies for students
above the 12th grade
Electronic data processing
Laboratories: research
Laboratories: testing

Laundries: pick-up and self-service
Out-patient clinics when staff is adequate to assure the safe evacuation
of patients in an emergency
Post offices
Print shops
Professional services
architects, doctors, dentists,
engineers, lawyers, etc.
Radio and TV stations
Self-service dry cleaning
Telephone exchanges

H. Use Group E (educational) (305)
1. All buildings or parts thereof used for education purposes by 6 or more up through the 12th grade are classified as Use Group E.
2. Education through K-12 used by no more than 6 students is considered Use Group A-3.
3. Religious educational rooms and auditoriums which are accessory to places of worship and have occupant loads of less than 100 are A-3 occupancies.
4. A building or structure, or portion thereof used for educational, supervision or personal care services for more than five but no more than one hundred children two and one-half years or less of age is a Group E occupancy when the children are cared for in rooms on the level of exit and each such room has an exit door directly to the exterior.

I. Use Group F-1 (moderate hazard industrial) (306.2)
1. All buildings used as factories, assembly plants, industrial laboratories, fabrication, and processing with only moderate fire hazards are classified as Use Group F-1, such as:

Aircraft products (> 12%)
Appliances
Automobiles
Bakeries

Bicycles
Boats
Brushes and brooms
Business machines
Cameras and film
Canvas and fabric
Carpets and rugs
Clothing
Construction equipment
Disinfectants
Dry cleaning—low hazard
Electric power plants

Laundries (non-public)
Machinery
Metals
Motion pictures and TV filming
Motored and recreational vehicles Beverages > 12% alcohol
Musical instruments
Optical goods
Paper mills and products
Photographic uses
Plastic products
Printing and binding
Refuse incinerators

Shoes and boots
Soaps and detergents
Sporting equipment
Trailers

Electronics
Engines
Food processing and milk products
Furniture and upholstery
Hemp and jute

Textiles
Tobacco
Trailers
Woodworking

2. Group F does not allow use or storage of highly combustible, flammable, or explosive materials. (See K. Use Group H (high hazard), this heading.)

3. Fire suppression systems may be waived in unlimited area buildings if detrimental to use or occupancy. (903.3.1.1.1)

J. Use Group F-2 (low industrial hazard) (306.3)

1. This group includes the fabrication and manufacturing of noncombustible materials which during finishing, processing, and packing do not produce any significant fire hazard, such as:

   a. Nonalcoholic beverages (and alcohol $\leq$ 12%)
   b. Brick and masonry
   c. Ceramic products
   d. Glass products
   e. Gypsum and gypsum products
   f. Ice plants
   g. Metal fabrication, and
   h. Foundries.

2. Industrial low hazard buildings which require large areas and unusual heights, such as electric plants and steel mills, are exempt from height and area requirements. (503.1.1)

K. Use Group H (high hazard) includes the following (307):

   H-1. (307.3)—Detonation hazards, such as:

   Explosives
   Organic peroxides (unclassified)
   Class 4 oxidizers
   Class 3 and 4 detonable unstable materials, and
   Pyrophoric materials.

   H-2. (307.4)—Deflagration hazards such as:

   Combustible dusts
   Flammable and combustible liquids, class I, II or IIIA in open containers
   Cryogenic liquids
   Flammable gases
   Class I organic peroxides
   Class 3 oxidizers
   Pyrophoric materials, (nondetonable)
   Class III reactives (nondetonable)
   Water-reactive materials, class 3

   H-3. (307.5)—Combustion or physical hazards, such as:

   Flammable and combustible liquids, Class I, II, or III-A in closed, unpressurized containers
   Combustible fibers
   Flammable solids

Class II and III organic peroxides

Class 2 and 3 oxidizers

Bulk tire storage (10,000 or more)

Class 2 unstable materials

Water-reactive Class 2

Consumer fireworks

Oxidizing gases

H-4. (307.6)—Health hazards, such as:

Corrosives

Highly toxic materials

Toxics

H-5. (307.7)—Hazardous production in semiconductor fabrication facilities (HPMs)

1. Exceptions (not classified as Group H) (307.1)

    a. Buildings, or control areas per 414.2, with less than the maximum allowable amount of hazardous materials are not classified as Use Group H, but must still meet the requirements of the Ohio Fire Code (OFC). (Table 307.7(1) and (2))

    b. Flammable finish rooms meeting 416 and the OFC are not classified as Group H.

    c. Rooms with sealed 1-gallon containers in amounts not more than 2 gal./sq. ft. for retail or private use are not classified as Group H.

    d. Buildings using control areas per 414.2 and containing not more than the maximum allowable quantities per control area of hazardous materials per Tables 307.1(1) and 307.1(2).

    e. Wholesale and retail stores: when stored per the Ohio Fire Code.

    f. Liquor stores and distributors with no bulk storage are not classified as Group H.

    g. Buildings housing agricultural material for use on the premises are not classified as Group H.

    h. Buildings housing closed machinery using hazardous materials are not classified as Group H.

    i. Cleaning establishments using combustible liquid solvents having a flash point of 140°F (60°C) or higher in closed systems employing state-approved equipment with a 1-hour separation are not classified as Group H.

    j. Buildings housing cleaning systems with flash points of 200F or higher are not classified as Group H.

    k. Buildings housing refrigeration systems are not classified as Group H.

    l. Buildings housing batteries for emergency power provided the batteries have safety venting caps and ventilation is per the Ohio Mechanical Code are not classified as Group H.

    m. Buildings housing personal and household products in original packaging are not classified as Group H.

    n. Black powder in M and R-3, and indust. explosives in B, F, M, and S where stored according to Fire Code.

    o. Aerosol manufacturers meeting the Ohio Fire Code are F-1 and/or S-1 and are not classified as Group H.

    p. Buildings and structures for the application of flammable finishes, if they conform to 416 and the Ohio Fire Code.

TABLE 307.1(1)
MAXIMUM ALLOWABLE QUANTITY PER CONTROL AREA OF
HAZARDOUS MATERIALS POSING A PHYSICAL HAZARD [a, j, m, n, p]

MATERIAL	CLASS	GROUP WHEN THE MAXIMUM ALLOWABLE QUANTITY IS EXCEEDED	STORAGE[b]			USE-CLOSED SYSTEMS[b]			USE-OPEN SYSTEMS[b]	
			Solid pounds (cubic feet)	Liquid gallons (pounds)	Gas (cubic feet at NTP)	Solid pounds (cubic feet)	Liquid gallons (pounds)	Gas (cubic feet at NTP)	Solid pounds (cubic feet)	Liquid gallons (pounds)
Combustible liquid[c,j]	II	H-2 or H-3	N/A	$120^{d,\,e}$	N/A	N/A	120^{d}	N/A	N/A	30^{d}
	IIIA	H-2 or H-3		$330^{d,e}$			330^{d}			80^{d}
	IIIB	N/A		$13,200^{e,\,f}$			$13,200^{f}$			$3,300^{f}$
Combustible fiber	Loose Baled[o]	H-3	(100) (1,000)	N/A	N/A	(100) (1,000)	N/A	N/A	(20) (200)	N/A
Consumer fireworks(Class C, Common)	1.4G	H-3	0	N/A	N/A	N/A	N/A	N/A	N/A	N/A
Cryogenics, flammable	N/A	H-2	N/A	45^{d}	N/A	N/A	45^{d}	N/A	N/A	10^{d}
Cryogenics, inert	N/A	N/A	N/A	N/A	NL	N/A	N/A	NL	N/A	N/A
Cryogenics, oxidizing	N/A	H-3	N/A	45^{d}	N/A	N/A	45^{d}	N/A	N/A	10^{d}
Explosives	Division 1.1	H-1	$1^{e,\,g}$	$(1)^{e,\,g}$	N/A	0.25^{g}	$(0.25)^{g}$	N/A	0.25^{g}	$(0.25)^{g}$
	Division 1.2	H-1	$1^{e,\,g}$	$(1)^{e,\,g}$	N/A	0.25^{g}	$(0.25)^{g}$	N/A	0.25^{g}	$(0.25)^{g}$
	Division 1.3	H-1 or H-2	$5^{e,\,g}$	$(5)^{e,\,g}$	N/A	1^{g}	$(1)^{g}$	N/A	1^{g}	$(1)^{g}$
	Division 1.4	H-3	$50^{e,\,g}$	$(50)^{e,\,g}$	N/A	50^{g}	$(50)^{g}$	N/A	N/A	N/A
	Division 1.4G	H-3	$125^{d,\,e,\,l}$	N/A	N/A	N/A	N/A	N/A	N/A	N/A
	Division 1.5	H-1	$1^{e,\,g}$	$(1)^{e,\,g}$	N/A	0.25^{g}	$(0.25)^{g}$	N/A	0.25^{g}	$(0.25)^{g}$
	Division 1.6	H-1	$1^{d,\,e,\,g}$	N/A	N/A	N/A	N/A	N/A	N/A	N/A
Flammable gas	Gaseous Liquefied	H-2	N/A	N/A $(150)^{d,\,e}$	$1,000^{d,\,e}$ N/A	N/A	N/A $(150)^{d,\,e}$	$1,000^{d,\,e}$ N/A	N/A	N/A

Material	Class	Group								
Flammable liquid[c]	1A 1B and 1C	H-2 or H-3	N/A	30 [d,e] 120 [d,e]	N/A	N/A	30 [d] 120 [d]	N/A	N/A	10 [d] 30 [d]
Flammable liquid,combination (1A, 1B, 1C)	N/A	H-2 or H-3	N/A	120 [d,e,h]	N/A	N/A	120 [d,h]	N/A	N/A	30 [d,h]
Flammable solid	N/A	H-3	125 [d,e]	N/A	N/A	125 [d]	N/A	N/A	25 [d]	N/A
Inert gas	Gaseous Liquefied	N/A N/A	N/A N/A	N/A N/A	NL NL	N/A N/A	N/A N/A	NL NL	N/A N/A	N/A N/A
Organic peroxide	UD I II III IV V	H-1 H-2 H-3 H-3 N/A N/A	1 [e,g] 5 [d,e] 50 [d,e] 125 [d,e] NL NL	(1) e, g (5) d, e (50)d, e (125)d, e NL NL	N/A N/A N/A N/A N/A N/A	0.25 [g] 1 [d] 50 [d] 125 [d] NL NL	(0.25) [g] (1) (50) [d] (125) [d] NL NL	N/A N/A N/A N/A NL NL	0.25 [g] 1 [d] 10 [d] 25 [d] NL NL	(0.25) [g] (1) [d] (10) [d] (25) [d] NL NL
Oxidizer	4 3 [k] 2 1	H-1 H-2 or H-3 H-3 N/A	1 [e,g] 10 [d,e] 250 [d,e] 4,000 [e,f]	(1) [e,g] (10) [d,e] (250) [d,e] (4,000) [e,f]	N/A N/A N/A N/A	0.25 [g] 2 [d] 250 [d] 4,000 [f]	(0.25) [g] (2) [d] (250) [d] (4,000) [f]	N/A N/A N/A N/A	0.25 [g] 2 [d] 50 [d] 1,000 [f]	(0.25) [g] (2) [d] (50) [d] (1,000) [f]
Oxidizing gas	Gaseous Liquefied	H-3	N/A N/A	N/A (150) [d,e]	1,500 [d,e] N/A	N/A N/A	N/A (150) [d,e]	1,500 [d,e] N/A	N/A N/A	N/A N/A
Pyrophoric material	N/A	H-2	4 [e,g]	(4) [e,g]	50 [e,g]	1 [g]	(1) [g]	10 [g]	0	0
Unstable (reactive)	4 3 2 1	H-1 H-1 or H-2 H-3 N/A	1 [e,g] 5 [d,e] 50 [d,e] NL	(1) [e,g] (5) [d,e] (50) [d,e] NL	10 [g] 50 [d,e] 250 [d,e] NL	0.25 [g] 1 [d] 50 [d] NL	(0.25) [g] (1) [d] (50) [d] NL	2 [e,g] 10 [d,e] 250 [d,e] NL	0.25 [g] 1 [d] 10 [d] NL	(0.25) [g] (1) [d] (10) [d] NL
Water reactive	3 2 1	H-2 H-3 N/A	5 [d,e] 50 [d,e] NL	(5) [d,e] (50) [d,e] NL	N/A N/A N/A	5 [d] 50 [d] NL	(5) [d] (50) [d] NL	N/A N/A N/A	1 [d] 10 [d] NL	(1) [d] (10) [d] NL

For SI: 1 cubic foot = 0.028 m³, 1 pound = 0.454 kg, 1 gallon = 3.785 L. NL = Not Limited; N/A = Not Applicable; UD = Unclassified Detonable

a. For use of control areas, see Section 414.2.

b. The aggregate quantity in use and storage shall not exceed the quantity listed for storage.

c. The quantities of alcoholic beverages in retail and wholesale sales occupancies shall not be limited providing the liquids are packaged in individual containers not exceeding 1.3 gallons. In retail and wholesale sales occupancies, the quantities of medicines, foodstuffs, consumer or industrial products, and cosmetics containing not more than 50 percent by volume of water-miscible liquids with the remainder of the solutions not being flammable, shall not be limited, provided that such materials are packaged in individual containers not exceeding 1.3 gallons.

d. Maximum allowable quantities shall be increased 100 percent in buildings equipped throughout with an automatic sprinkler system in accordance with Section 903.3.1.1. Where Note e also applies, the increase for both notes shall be applied accumulatively.

e. Maximum allowable quantities shall be increased 100 percent when stored in approved storage cabinets, day boxes, gas cabinets or exhausted enclosures or in listed safety cans in accordance with Section 2703.9.10 of the fire code. Where Note d also applies, the increase for both notes shall be applied accumulatively.

f. The permitted quantities shall not be limited in a building equipped throughout with an automatic sprinkler system in accordance with Section 903.3.1.1.

g. Permitted only in buildings equipped throughout with an automatic sprinkler system in accordance with Section 903.3.1.1.

h. Containing not more than the maximum allowable quantity per control area of Class IA, IB or IC flammable liquids.

i. The maximum allowable quantity shall not apply to fuel oil storage complying with Section 603.3.2 of the *fire code.*

j. Quantities in parenthesis indicate quantity units in parenthesis at the head of each column.

k. A maximum quantity of 200 pounds of solid or 20 gallons of liquid Class 3 oxidizers is allowed when such materials are necessary for maintenance purposes, operation or sanitation of equipment. Storage containers and the manner of storage shall be approved.

l. Net weight of the pyrotechnic composition of the fireworks. Where the net weight of the pyrotechnic composition of the fireworks is not known, 25 percent of the gross weight of the fireworks, including packaging, shall be used.

m. For gallons of liquids, divide the amount in pounds by 10 in accordance with Section 2703.1.2 of the *fire code.*

n. For storage and display quantities in Group M and storage quantities in Group S occupancies complying with Section 414.2.5, see Tables 414.2.5(1) and 414.2.5(2).

o. Densely packed baled cotton that complies with the packing requirements of ISO 8115 shall not be included in this material class.

p. The following shall not be included in determining the maximum allowable quantities:

    1. Liquid or gaseous fuel in fuel tanks on vehicles.

    2. Liquid or gaseous fuel in fuel tanks on motorized equipment operated in accordance with this code.

    3. Gaseous fuels in piping systems and fixed appliances regulated by the *fuel gas code.*

    4. Liquid fuels in piping systems and fixed appliances regulated by the *mechanical code.*

TABLE 307.1(2)

MAXIMUM ALLOWABLE QUANTITY PER CONTROL AREA OF HAZARDOUS MATERIAL POSING A HEALTH HAZARD [a, b, c, i]

MATERIAL	STORAGE[d]			USE-CLOSED SYSTEMS[d]			USE-OPEN SYSTEMS[d]	
	Solid pounds (cubic feet)	Liquid gallons (pounds)[e, f]	Gas (cubic feet at NTP)[e]	Solid pounds[e]	Liquid gallons (pounds)[e]	Gas (cubic feet at NTP)[e]	Solid pounds[e]	Liquid gallons (pounds)[e]
Corrosive	5,000	500	Gaseous 810[f] Liquefied (150)[h]	5,000	500	Gaseous 810[f] Liquefied (150)[h]	1,000	100
Highly toxic	10	(10)[h]	Gaseous 20[g] Liquefied (4)[g, h]	10	(10)[i]	Gaseous 20[g] Liquefied (4)[g, h]	3	(3)[i]
Toxic	500	(500)[h]	Gaseous 810[f] Liquefied (150)[f, h]	500	(500)[i]	Gaseous 810[f] Liquefied (150)[f, h]	125	(125)

For SI: 1 cubic foot = 0.028 m³, 1 pound = 0.454 kg, 1 gallon = 3.785 L.

a. For use of control areas, see Section 414.2.

b. In retail and wholesale sales occupancies, the quantities of medicines, foodstuffs, consumer or industrial products, and cosmetics, containing not more than 50 percent by volume of water-miscible liquids and with the remainder of the solutions not being flammable, shall not be limited, provided that such materials are packaged in individual containers not exceeding 1.3 gallons.

c. For storage and display quantities in Group M and storage quantities in Group S occupancies complying with Section 414.2.5, see Tables 414.2.5(1) and 414.2.5(2).

d. The aggregate quantity in use and storage shall not exceed the quantity listed for storage.

e. Maximum allowable quantities shall be increased 100 percent in buildings equipped throughout with an approved automatic sprinkler system in accordance with Section 903.3.1.1. Where Note f also applies, the increase for both notes shall be applied accumulatively.

f. Maximum allowable quantities shall be increased 100 percent when stored in approved storage cabinets, gas cabinets or exhausted enclosures as specified in the *fire code*. Where Note e also applies, the increase for both notes shall be applied accumulatively.

g. Allowed only when stored in approved exhausted gas cabinets or exhausted enclosures as specified in the *fire code*.

h. Quantities in parenthesis indicate quantity units in parenthesis at the head of each column.

i. For gallons of liquids, divide the amount in pounds by 10 in accordance with Section 2703.1.2 of the *fire code*.

2. No increase in height or area with sprinklers for Use Groups H-1, H-2, H-3, or H-5 (for height) is permitted.

3. Control areas—up to 100% of exempt amount is allowed in each control area depending on the number of control areas per floor and fire separation. (414.2)

4. Use Group H-1 is only permitted in one-story separate buildings with no basements. (415.4)

5. Use Group H-2 (415.6)

    a. Grain elevators may be unlimited height.

    b. Storage tanks shall be noncombustible and protected from physical damage. Fire barrier walls or horizontal assemblies or are permitted as protection.

    c. Storage tanks are per the "Ohio Fire Code." Sprinklers are required. A liquid-tight containment area compatible with the stored liquid must be provided, with method of spill control, drainage control and secondary containment. Exception:

        (1) Rooms where only double-wall storage tanks conforming to 415.6.2.3 used to store Class I, II and IIIA flammable and combustible liquids do not required a leakage containment area.

    d. An approved automatic audible alarm for leaks in a storage tank and room is required, 15 dBa above the ambient sound level, at every entry point into tank is located. An approved sign is required on every entry door to the room indicating the potential hazard, or shall state: WARNING, WHEN ALARM SOUNDS, THE ENVIRONMENT WITHIN THE ROOM MAY BE HAZARDOUS. The alarm is supervised per Chapter 9 to transmit a trouble signal.

    e. Storage tank vents for Class I, II or IIIA liquids must terminate to the outdoor air per the Ohio Fire Code. Tank areas must have mechanical ventilation, per the Ohio Mechanical Code and the Ohio Fire Code. Where Class I liquids are stored, explosion venting is required per the Ohio Fire Code. Tank openings other than vents from tanks inside buildings must ensure that liquids or vapor concentrations are not released inside the building.

6. Groups H-3 and H-4 (415.7 and Ohio Fire Code)

    a. Gas rooms must have not less than a 1-hour fire barrier. Floors in storage areas for corrosive liquids and highly toxic or toxic materials must be liquid-tight, noncombustible.

    b. Highly toxic solids and liquids not stored in approved hazardous materials cabinets must be isolated from other hazardous materials storage by a fire barrier having of not less than 1 hour.

    c. Consumer fireworks facilities are covered by the OAC and the Ohio Fire Code. Areas used for display and sale of consumer fireworks, must be $\leq$ 5,000 sq. ft., and be separated consumer fireworks storage areas per OBC 706.

    d. A smoke control system must be provided throughout all display and sales areas per OBC 909 and fire separation per OBC 706.

    e. Awnings, tents and canopies cannot be used for display, sale or storage of consumer fireworks.

    f. No horizontal exits used as required exits from display and sale areas.

7. Use Group H-5 (415.8)

    a. Fabrication areas need 1-hour separation.

    b. Minimum ventilation of 1 cfm/sq. ft.

    c. Service corridors egress travel maximum 75'.

    d. Sprinklers required in exhausts.

e. The aggregate quantities of hazardous materials stored and used in a single fabrication area must not exceed the quantities in Table 415.8.2.1.1.

f. Emergency alarms must be placed in corridors, liquid storage rooms, HPM rooms and gas rooms, activating a local alarm and transmitting a signal to the emergency control station. An approved emergency telephone system, local alarm manual pull stations, or other approved alarm-initiating devices may be used as emergency alarm devices.

g. Per O.R.C. 4104.42, owner is responsible for ensuring ASME code compliance.

TABLE 415.8.2.1.1

QUANTITY LIMITS FOR HAZARDOUS MATERIALS IN A SINGLE

FABRICATION AREA IN GROUP H-5[a]

HAZARD CATEGORY	SOLIDS (pounds per square feet)	LIQUIDS (gallons per square feet)	GAS (feet^3 @ NTP/square feet)
PHYSICAL-HAZARD MATERIALS			
Combustible dust	Note b	Not Applicable	Not Applicable

Combustible fiber Loose Baled	Note b Notes b, c	Not Applicable	Not Applicable

Combustible liquid   II
          IIIA
          IIIB
Combination Class I, II and IIIA
	Not Applicable	0.01
		0.02
		Not Limited
		0.04
			Not Applicable

Cryogenic gas Flammable Oxidizing	Not Applicable	Not Applicable	Note d 1.25
Explosives	Note b	Note b	Note b
Flammable gas Gaseous Liquefied	Not Applicable	Not Applicable	Note d Note d

Flammable liquid   IA
          IB
          IC
Combination Class IA, IB and IC
Combination Class I, II and IIIA
	Not Applicable	0.0025
		0.025
		0.025
		0.025
		0.04
			Not Applicable

Flammable solid	0.001	Not Applicable	Not Applicable

Organic peroxide
Unclassified detonable
          Class I
          Class II
          Class III
          Class IV
          Class V
	Note b
	Note b
	0.025
	0.1
	Not Limited
	Not limited
		Not Applicable	Not Applicable

Oxidizing gas Gaseous Liquefied Combination of gaseous and liquefied	Not Applicable	Not Applicable	1.25 1.25 1.25

Oxidizer   Class 4
          Class 3
          Class 2
          Class 1
Combination   Class 1, 2, 3
	Note b
	0.003
	0.003
	0.003
	0.003
		Note b
		0.03
		0.03
		0.03
		0.03
			Not Applicable

Pyrophoric material	Note b	0.00125	Notes d and e

Unstable reactive   Class 4
          Class 3
          Class 2
          Class 1
	Note b
	0.025
	0.1
	Not Limited
		Note b
		0.0025
		0.01
		Not Limited
			Note b
			Note b
			Note b
			Not Limited

Water reactive   Class 3
          Class 2
          Class 1
	Note b
	0.25
	Not Limited
		0.00125
		0.025
		Not Limited
			Not Applicable

HEALTH-HAZARD MATERIALS			
Corrosives	Not Limited	Not Limited	Not Limited
Highly toxic	Not Limited	Not Limited	Note d
Toxics	Not Limited	Not Limited	Note d

For SI: 1 pound per square foot = 4.882 kg/m^2, 1 gallon per square foot = 40.7 L/m^2, 1 cubic foot @ NTP/square foot = 0.305 m^3 @ NTP/m^2, 1 cubic foot = 0.02832 m^3.

a. Hazardous materials within piping shall not be included in the calculated quantities.

b. Quantity of hazardous materials in a single fabrication shall not exceed the maximum allowable quantities per control area in Tables 307.1(1) and 307.1(2).

c. Densely packed baled cotton that complies with the packing requirements of ISO 8115 shall not be included in this material class.

d. The aggregate quantity of flammable, pyrophoric, toxic and highly toxic gases shall not exceed 9,000 cubic feet at NTP.

e. The aggregate quantity of pyrophoric gases in the building shall not exceed the amounts set forth in Table 415.3.2.

h. HPM piping and tubing must comply with ASME, and be identifiable to OBC and Ohio Fire Code, as determined by registered design professional, as opposed to building official.

L. Use Group I-1 (residential care-type housing) (308.2)

1. Use Group I-1 includes buildings or parts thereof for housing more than 16 individuals on a 24-hour daily basis under supervision but who are physically able and can respond to emergencies. The following uses are all classified as Use Group I-1:

   a. Residential board and care type housing
   b. Room and board care type housing
   c. Half-way houses
   d. Group homes
   e. Social rehabilitation facilities
   f. Alcohol and drug centers
   g. Assisted living facilities
   h. Convalescent and congregate care facilities

2. A facility such as the above with five or fewer persons is classified as a Group R-3. When housing at least six and not more than 16, it is classified as Group R-4. I-1 also includes residential care facilities if more than 16 reside and supervision and personal care services are provided for 3 or more and when no more than 5 need physical assistance in response to an emergency.

M. Use Group I-2 (institutions for the incapacitated) (308.3)

1. Use Group I-2 includes housing for 5 or more individuals on a 24-hour daily basis who require full supervision and are not able to respond to emergencies without help, such as:

   a. Residential care type housing for more than 16 persons, where 3 or more require personal care and more than 5 need physical help in an emergency
   b. Hospitals and mental hospitals
   c. Detoxification facilities
   d. Nursing homes, both intermediate and skilled service, housing 3 or more individuals
   e. Child care facilities for more than 5 children less than 2½ years old.
   f. Does not include child care for up to 100 under 2½ when rooms have direct exit doors to exterior. (Group E)
   g. Does not include clinics/outpatient surgery where staffing is adequate for each patient. (Group B)

2. The allowable height increase for sprinklers does not apply to building Types IIB, III, IV, or V. (504.2)

3. A smoke barrier is required in all Use Group I-2 buildings. (407.4)

   a. Every sleeping floor and all other floors where treatment occurs shall be divided into at least 2 smoke compartments.
   b. The smoke barrier shall be a continuous wall of 1-hour minimum rating which extends from outside wall to outside wall and from floor to bottom of floor above. (710)
   c. Compartment size
      i. Compartment may be a maximum of 22,500 sq. ft. (407.4)
      ii. A 200′ maximum travel distance to smoke barrier is permitted.
      iii. Minimum: Each compartment requires space for its occupants plus those of the adjoining compartment, based on 30 sq. ft. for bed patients and 6 sq. ft. for all others. (407.4.1)
   d. Doors in smoke barriers (715)

      i. Double swinging doors are required between compartments. Doors must swing in opposite directions.

     ii. Minimum size: Doors must be at least 44" wide for bed movement; 32" for others.

    iii. Rated at least 20 minutes, with closures.

    iv. Double doors require vision panels.

     v. All doors shall be fitted to prevent smoke passage.

e. Automatic smoke dampers are required in ducts serving both compartments activated by a smoke detector.

f. Use Group I-2 day care uses of less than 150′ in either dimension are exempt from smoke barrier.

TABLE 715.4
FIRE DOOR AND FIRE SHUTTER FIRE PROTECTION RATINGS

TYPE OF ASSEMBLY	REQUIRED ASSEMBLY RATING (hours)	MINIMUM FIRE DOOR AND FIRE SHUTTER ASSEMBLY RATING (hours)
Fire walls and fire barriers having a required fire-resistance rating greater than 1 hour	4 3 2 1 ½	3 3[a] 1 ½ 1 ½
Fire barriers having a required fire-resistance rating of 1 hour: Shaft, exit enclosure and exit passageway walls Other fire barriers	1 1	1 ¾

Fire partitions:
  Corridor walls
 	
  Other fire partitions
	1
	0.5
	1
	0.5
		$1/_3$ [b]
		$1/_3$ [b]
		¾
		$1/_3$

Exterior walls	3 2 1	1 ½ 1 ½ ¾
Smoke barriers	1	$1/_3$ [b]

a. Two doors, each with a fire protection rating of 1 ½ hours, installed on opposite sides of the same opening in a fire wall, shall be deemed equivalent in fire protection rating to one 3-hour fire door.

b. For testing requirements, see Section 715.4.3.

4. Corridors in I-2 must: (407.3)
   a. Limit smoke movement.
   b. Be constructed from floor to deck or smoke proof ceiling.
   c. Doors—no rating is required,
      – no closers,
      – no roller latches.
   d. Gift shops <500 square feet can be open to corridor if fully sprinkled.
   e. Cooking facilities can be open to corridor if:
      i. One facility per smoke compartment.
      ii. Serving ≤ 30 persons, uses only ovens with hoods equipped with fire suppression systems, and manual activation and interlock devices, cooktops, ranges, warmers, and microwaves.
      iii. Clearly defined space does not obstruct exit.
      iv. Fuel and electrical cutoff for cooking equipment.
      v. Timer shutoff for cooking appliances after 120 minutes.
      vi. Fire extinguisher present.
   f. Projections of furniture into corridor allowed only if affixed to wall or floor, allow clear movement of < 72", on one side only of corridor, arrangements are 50 square feet maximum, with 10′ separations.

N. Use Group I-3 (restrained institutional) (308.4, 408)
   1. Use Group I-3 includes confined housing (for 5 or more) for security reasons such as:
      a. Prisons and jails
      b. Reformatories
      c. Detention centers
      d. Correctional centers, and
      e. Pre-release centers.
   2. Conditions I to V (308.4.1 through 308.4.5)
      a. Condition I: When occupants are free to move about and exit without restraint, use is classified as Use Group R.
      b. Condition II: Exit from building is restricted.
      c. Condition III: Limited movement within one smoke compartment is permitted.
      d. Condition IV: Limited movement within sleeping rooms is permitted.
         e.Condition V: Staff-controlled, manually controlled movement.
      e. Condition V: Staff-controlled, manually controlled movement.
   3. Smoke barriers are required in sleeping areas and floors with more than 50 occupants. (408.6)
   4. Special locks are permitted. (408.4)
   5. Communicating floors are permitted in residential housing. (408.5)
   6. Separation walls between residential areas and other occupancies. (408.7)
   7. Windowless buildings defined as buildings with non-operable windows. (408.8)
   8. Padded cells must have 1-hour separations. (Table 302.1.1)

O. Use Group I-4 (day care facilities) (308.5)
   1. Use Group I-4 includes day-care facilities for both children and the elderly, when care is for less than 24 hours for six or more.
   2. Adult day-care facility
      a. Provides supervision and personal care to more than five unrelated adults.
      b. If the occupants are capable of exiting without assistance, then R-3.
   3. Child day-care facility

a. Care for more than five children 2½ years of age or less.

b. Does *not* include care for more than five, but not more than 100 where all classrooms have exits at grade (Use Group E).

P. Use Group M (mercantile) (309)

1. Use Group M includes buildings or parts used for sales and displays open to the public, and involving stocks of goods, wares, and merchandise incidental to such purposes, such as:

   a. Department stores
   b. Retail shops
   c. Wholesale stores
   d. Gas stations
   e. Sales rooms
   f. Retail markets
   g. Discount marts and drug stores
   h. Super markets

2. Highly combustible goods shall be limited to small quantities if not hazardous. (See Table 414.2.2.)

3. If the quantity of combustibles are above the exception for hazardous, the building classification shall be Group H.

4. Plumbing fixtures to serve the public are not required in stores with an occupant number under 50 and food and drink is not served. (2902.2)

Q. Use Group R-1 (transient residency) (310.1)

1. Guests are primarily transient if less than 30-day occupancy.

2. Structures include hotels, motels, and boarding houses.

3. The Residential Code of Ohio for One-, Two-, or Three- Family Dwellings applies to one-, two-, or three-family dwellings and accessory structures in jurisdictions where a residential department is board certified. If no residential department is certified in a jurisdiction, construction documents for such structures need not be submitted for approval.

R. Use Group R-2 (primarily permanent residents) (310.1)

1. This group applies to the following multi-family buildings:

   a. Buildings with more than 3 dwelling units, apartments, condominiums, or vacation time-shares.

   b. Dormitories, boarding houses, lodging houses, convents and monasteries, fraternities and sororities, non-transient hotels for more than 5 individuals—occupants stay longer than 30 days.

   c. Dwelling units attached to any use group shall conform to Group R-2 requirements unless all Group R-3 requirements are satisfied.

S. Use Group R-3 (multiple single family dwellings) (310.1)

1. Buildings containing more than 3 dwelling units with private and independent means of egress, i.e., row or townhouse types are classified as Use Group R-3.

2. Use "Residential Code of Ohio for One-, Two-, and Three-Family Dwellings" (RCO) in place of the OBC for R-3 occupancies in buildings three stories or less, that are exclusively dwelling units where each unit has an independent means of egress if:

   a. No more than 1 dwelling unit may be located above another unit. Fire separation between units within a grouping of two units including a unit located partially or totally above another is per code section R317.1. Fire separation between any grouping of two units and other adjacent units is per code sections R317.2 through R317.3.2.

3. The OBC shall apply when installing non-required components, equipment and systems for which there revised code provisions (i.e., elevators and fire protection systems).

T. Use Group R-4 (310.1)

    Residential care and assisted living for more than 5 and up to 16 residents. All R-4s to comply with R-3 construction requirements.

U. Use Group S-1 (moderate-hazard storage) (311.2)

1. Buildings used primarily for the storage of goods, wares, merchandise (except those of Use Group H) of moderate hazard and includes warehouses, storehouses, and freight depots are classified as Use Group S-1.

2. Moderate hazards are contents which burn but do not produce poisonous fumes, gases, or explosions such as:

Aerosols, levels 2 and 3	Buttons
Bags: cloth, paper, burlap	Canvas
Bamboo and rattan baskets	Cardboard—boxes
Belting	Clothing, woolens
Books, paper rolls	Cordage, threads
Boots, shoes	Dry boat storage
Bulk tire storage	Furniture
Glue, paste, size	Furs
Grain silos	Resilient flooring
Leather	Silk
Linoleum	Soap
Lumber yards	Sugars, Tires, Bulk storage
Mattresses	Tobacco products
Motor vehicle repair shops and aircraft repair	Upholstery
	Wax products

    Note: Above is only a guide, many other products fall within the above categories.

3. A public garage in this Group is for care, storage, repair, or painting of motor vehicles. (For definition of "Garage, Public," see 202.0.)

V. Use Group S-2 (low-hazard storage) (311.3)

1. Use Group S-2 includes buildings used for storage of noncombustibles or items which do not burn rapidly, such as:

	Glass
Asbestos	Ivory
Beer and wine up to 16% in metal cabinets or glass	Masonry materials
	Metals
Cement and lime in bags	Oil-filled and other types of
Chalk and crayons	distribution transformers
Dairy products in coated paper	Parking garages (see Section 406)
Dry cell batteries	Porcelain
Empty cans	Stoves
Electric motors, coils, and distribution transformers	Talc, soapstone, and gypsum
	Washers, dryers, and stoves
Fresh food products, frozen foods	Gypsum Board, Mirrors

    Use group includes products on wood pallets or in paper cartons without combustible wrappings other than plastic knobs, handles, or film wrapping.

W. Use Group U (312)

1. Use Group U includes utility and miscellaneous structures that cannot be classified in any particular use group, such as:

          a. Greenhouses

          b. Tanks

          c. Detached private garages and all carports

          d. Barns and sheds

          e. Retaining walls

          f. Stables

          g. Towers

          h. Fences more than 6 feet high

          i. Agricultural buildings, livestock shelters (not used for agricultural purposes as defined in code Aircraft hangars, residential 3781.06)

    2. All buildings and structures in this group must meet fire and life safety hazards.

X. Specific Use buildings (Chapter 4)

    The following uses are considered special and have specific sections in Chapter 4:

    1. Rooftop heliports

    2. Air traffic control towers

    3. Hazardous occupancies

    4. Covered malls

    5. High-rise buildings

    6. Underground buildings

    7. Special amusement buildings

V

VENEERS (1400)

A. Glass veneers: See GLASS.
B. Metal veneers (1405.11)
   1. Veneer must be corrosion-resistant on both sides.
   2. Caulk all joints and ventilate all panels. (1405.11.2)
   3. Fasteners maximum 24" o.c.
   4. Minimum veneer thickness of 0.0149".
   5. Bonding and grounding must comply with Chapter 27. (1405.11.4)
   6. Metal attachments cross-sectional area ≤ that provided by W 1.7 wire, and able with their supports to resist horizontal force per WIND LOADS, but in no case less than 20 psf (0.958 kg/m^2).
C. Plastic veneers (light transmitting wall panels) (2607)
   1. Plastic veneers are not allowed in Use Groups A-1, A-2, I-2, or I-3.
   2. Plastic veneers are not allowed in a wall which is required to be rated.
   3. Cannot use more than 75' above grade. (2607.3)
   4. Plastic area is limited, depending on plastic type (C1 or C2), and fire separation distance, except Type V. (2607.4)
   5. Minimum spandrel of 3' for C2 is permitted.
   6. When building sprinkled, may double allowable areas up to 50% of wall area, and height is not limited. (2607.5)
D. Wood
   1. Minimum ³/₈" structural panel, ⁷/₁₆" hardboard or nominal 1" solid material.
   2. Maximum 40', except FRTW to 60'.
   3. Maximum 24" out from building wall.
E. 15 lb. felt paper required behind brick, clay tile, concrete, and stone veneers. (1404.2)

TABLE 1405.2
MINIMUM THICKNESS OF WEATHER COVERINGS

COVERING TYPE	MINIMUM THICKNESS (inches)
Adhered masonry veneer	0.25
Aluminum siding	0.019
Anchored masonry veneer	2.625
Asbestos-cement boards	0.125
Asbestos shingles	0.156
Cold-rolled copper[d]	0.0216 nominal
Copper shingles[d]	0.0162 nominal
Exterior plywood (with sheathing)	0.313
Exterior plywood (without sheathing)	See Section 2304.6
Fiber cement lap siding	0.25[c]
Fiber cement panel siding	0.25[c]
Fiberboard siding	0.5
Glass-fiber reinforced concrete panels	0.375
Hardboard siding[c]	0.25
High-yield copper[d]	0.0162 nominal
Lead-coated copper[d]	0.0216 nominal
Lead-coated high yield copper	0.0162 nominal

COVERING TYPE	MINIMUM THICKNESS (inches)
Marble slabs	1
Particleboard (with sheathing)	See Section 2304.6
Particleboard (without sheathing)	See Section 2304.6
Precast stone facing	0.625
Steel (approved corrosion resistant)	0.0149
Stone (cast artificial)	1.5
Stone (natural)	2
Structural glass	0.344
Stucco or exterior portland cement plaster	
Three-coat work over:	
Metal plaster base	0.875[b]
Unit masonry	0.625[b]
Cast-in-place or precast concrete	0.625[b]
Two coat work over:	
Unit masonry	0.5[b]
Cast-in-place or precast concrete	0.375[b]
Terra cotta (anchored)	1
Terra cotta (adhered)	0.25
Vinyl siding	0.035
Wood shingles	0.375
Wood siding (without sheathing)[a]	0.5

For SI: 1 inch = 25.4 mm.

a. Wood siding of thicknesses less than 0.5 inch shall be placed over sheathing that conforms to Section 2304.6.

b. Exclusive of texture.

c. As measured at the bottom of decorative grooves.

d. 16 ounces per square foot for cold-rolled copper and lead-coated copper, 12 ounces per square for copper shingles, high-yield copper and lead-coated high-yield copper.

VENTILATION (1203 AND CHAPTER 28, CHAPTER M-4)

  A. General
1. Ventilation is required in all areas with human occupancy. (M-401.2)
2. Balance exhaust and supply by infiltration or make-up air. (M-403.3.3)
3. Systems shall operate during occupancy periods. (M-401.3)
4. The system may be natural or mechanical. (M-401.2)
5. The occupant load shall be determined based on Table M-403.3 for purposes of ventilation minimum designs.
6. Outdoor air inflow per ASHRAE 62.2, if registered design professional demonstrates compliance with ASHRAE standard.

  B. Required exhaust direct to the exterior: Any air which is detrimental to a person's health must be exhausted to the exterior. (M-401.6)

  C. Prohibited recirculation of ventilating air (M-403.2.1)
1. Between dwellings, or dwellings to other occupancies.
2. For swimming pools, unless dehumidified to maintain a relative humidity of 60% or less and returned only to pool.
3. Where mechanical exhaust is required.

  D. Natural ventilation (M-402 and 1203.4)
1. Natural ventilation must provide uncontaminated air.

2. Openable areas shall not be less than 4% of the floor area unless some is by mechanical means.
3. Windows, doors, louvres, monitors, and ventilating skylights may be used.
4. Window wells are acceptable if the perpendicular distance from the openings is $1^1/_2$ times the depth.
5. Courts may be used as a source of natural ventilation if properly sized. (See YARDS.)
6. Rooms without openings may use the adjoining room area with not less than a 25 sq. ft. opening and not less than 8% of room area and the ventilating area is based on the total area of both rooms.
7. Bathrooms must be mechanically exhausted.

TABLE 403.3
MINIMUM VENTILATION RATES

OCCUPANCY CLASSIFICATION	ESTIMATED MAXIMUM OCCUPANT LOAD, PERSONS PER 1,000 SQUARE FEET[a]	OUTDOOR AIR [Cubic feet per minute (cfm) per person] UNLESS NOTED[e]
Correctional facilities		
Cells		
without plumbing fixtures	20	20
with plumbing fixtures[g,h]	20	20
Dining halls	100	15
Guard stations	40	15
Dry cleaners, laundries		
Coin-operated dry cleaner	20	15
Coin-operated laundries	20	15
Commercial dry cleaner	30	30
Commercial laundry	10	25
Storage, pick up	30	35
Education		
Auditoriums	150	15
Classrooms	50	15
Corridors	—	0.10 cfm/ft^2
Laboratories	30	20
Libraries	20	15
Locker rooms[h]	—	0.50 cfm/ft^2
Music rooms	50	15
Smoking lounges[b,g]	70	60
Training shops	30	20
Food and beverage service		
Bars, cocktail lounges	100	30
Cafeteria, fast food	100	20
Dining rooms	70	20
Kitchens (cooking)[f,g]	20	15
Hospitals, nursing and convalescent homes		
Autopsy rooms[b]	—	0.50 cfm/ft^2
Medical procedure rooms	20	15
Operating rooms	20	30
Patient rooms	10	25
Physical therapy	20	15
Recovery and ICU	20	15

OCCUPANCY CLASSIFICATION	ESTIMATED MAXIMUM OCCUPANT LOAD, PERSONS PER 1,000 SQUARE FEET[a]	OUTDOOR AIR [Cubic feet per minute (cfm) per person] UNLESS NOTED[e]
Hotels, motels, resorts and dormitories		
Assembly rooms	120	15
Bathrooms[g,h]	—	35
Bedrooms	—	30 cfm per room
Conference rooms	50	20
Dormitory sleeping areas	20	15
Gambling casinos	120	30
Living rooms	—	30 cfm per room
Lobbies	30	15
Offices		
Conference rooms	50	20
Office spaces	7	20
Reception areas	60	15
Telecommunication centers and data entry	60	20
Private dwellings, single and multiple		
Garages, common for multiple units[b]	—	1.5 cfm/ft^2
Garages, separate for each dwelling	—	100 cfm per car
Kitchens[g]	—	100 cfm intermittent or 25 cfm continuous
Living areas[c]	Based upon number of bedrooms. First bedroom: 2; each additional bedroom: 1	0.35 air changes per hour[a] or 15 cfm per person, whichever is greater
Toilet rooms and bathrooms[g,h]	—	Mechanical exhaust capacity of 50 cfm intermittent or 20 cfm continuous
Public spaces		
Corridors and utilities	—	0.05 cfm/ft^2
Elevator car[g]	—	1.00 cfm/ft^2
Locker rooms[h]	—	0.5 cfm/ft^2
Shower rooms (per shower head)[g,h]	—	50 cfm intermittent or 20 cfm continuous
Smoking lounges[b,h]	70	60
Toilet rooms[g,h]	—	75 cfm per water closet or urinal
Retail stores, sales floors and showroom floors		
Basement and street	—	0.30 cfm/ft^2
Dressing rooms	—	0.20 cfm/ft^2
Malls and arcades	—	0.20 cfm/ft^2
Shipping and receiving	—	0.15 cfm/ft^2
Smoking lounges[b]	70	60
Storage rooms	—	0.15 cfm/ft^2
Upper floors	—	0.20 cfm/ft^2
Warehouses	—	0.05 cfm/ft^2
Specialty shops		
Automotive motor-fuel-dispensing stations	—	1.5 cfm/ft^2
Barber	25	15
Beauty	25	25
Clothiers, furniture	—	0.30 cfm/ft^2
Embalming room[b]	—	2.0 cfm/ft^2
Florists	8	15

OCCUPANCY CLASSIFICATION	ESTIMATED MAXIMUM OCCUPANT LOAD, PERSONS PER 1,000 SQUARE FEET[a]	OUTDOOR AIR [Cubic feet per minute (cfm) per person] UNLESS NOTED[e]
Hardware, drugs, fabrics	8	15
Nail salon[b,i]	—	50 cfm intermittent or 20 cfm continuous per station
Pet Shops	—	1.00 cfm/ft^2
Reducing salons	20	15
Supermarkets	8	15
Sports and amusement		
Ballrooms and discos	100	25
Bowling alleys (seating areas)	70	25
Game rooms	70	25
Ice arenas	—	0.50 cfm/ft^2
Playing floors (gymnasiums)	30	20
Spectator areas	150	15
Swimming pools (pool and deck area)	—	0.50 cfm/ft^2
Storage		
Repair garages, enclosed parking garages[d]	—	1.5 cfm/ft^2
Warehouses	—	0.05 cfm/ft^2
Theaters		
Auditoriums	150	15
Lobbies	150	20
Stages, studios	70	15
Ticket booths	60	20
Transportation		
Platforms	100	15
Vehicles	150	15
Waiting rooms	100	15
Workrooms		
Bank vaults	5	15
Darkrooms	—	0.50 cfm/ft^2
Duplicating, printing	—	0.50 cfm/ft^2
Meat processing[c]	10	15
Pharmacy	20	15
Photo studios	10	15

For SI: 1 cubic foot per minute = 0.0004719 m^3/s, 1 ton = 908 kg,

1 cubic foot per minute per square foot = 0.00508 m^3/(s • m^2), °C = [(°F) -32]/1.8, 1 square foot = 0.0929 m^2

a. Based upon net floor area.

b. Mechanical exhaust required and the recirculation of air from such spaces as permitted by Section 403.2.1 is prohibited. (See Section 403.2.1, Items 1 and 3.)

c. Spaces unheated or maintained below 50°F are not covered by these requirements unless the occupancy is continuous.

d. Ventilation systems in enclosed parking garages shall comply with Section 404.

e. Where the ventilation rate is expressed in cfm/ft^2, such rate is based upon cubic feet per minute per square foot of the floor area being ventilated.

f. The sum of the outdoor and transfer air from adjacent spaces shall be sufficient to provide an exhaust rate of not less than 1.5 cfm/ft^2.

g. Transfer air permitted in accordance with Section 403.2.2.

h. Mechanical exhaust is required and recirculation is prohibited except that recirculation shall be permitted where the resulting supply airstream consists of not more than 10% air recirculated from these spaces (see Section 403.2.1, Items 2 and 4).

i. The required exhaust system shall capture the contaminants and odors at their source.

E.   Miscellaneous

1. Openings in louvers, grilles and screens must be sized per Table 401.5. Outdoor air

exhaust and intake openings located in exterior walls must meet the exterior wall opening requirements of the OBC.

2. Exhaust outlets cannot create nuisance or go into walkways.
3. Exhaust and intake openings must have weather and corrosion protective screens. (M-401.6)

WALLS (700)

A. Fire resistance requirements—Exterior walls (special requirements) (704)

    1. Requirements do not apply to the exterior walls of buildings facing each other on the same lot when the combined areas are within the group area and height limitations. (704.3, exception)

    2. Imaginary line representing lot line for two buildings on same lot. (705.3)

    3. Minimum exterior wall ratings (hours): In no case shall the rating of bearing walls be less than indicated in the fire resistive chart in Table 601, nor less than the fire separation from Table 602.

TABLE 601
FIRE-RESISTANCE RATING REQUIREMENTS FOR BUILDING ELEMENTS (hours)

BUILDING ELEMENT	TYPE I A	TYPE I B	TYPE II A[d]	TYPE II B	TYPE III A[d]	TYPE III B	TYPE IV HT	TYPE V A[d]	TYPE V B
Primary structural frame[g] (see Section 202)	3[a]	2[a]	1	0	1	0	HT	1	0
Bearing walls Exterior[f,g]	3	2	1	0	2	2	2	1	0
Interior	3[a]	2[a]	1	0	1	0	1/HT	1	0
Nonbearing walls and partitions Exterior	See Table 602								
Nonbearing walls and partitions Interior[e]	0	0	0	0	0	0	See Section 602.4.6	0	0
Floor construction and secondary members (see Section 202)	2	2	1	0	1	0	HT	1	0
Roof construction and secondary members (see Section 202)	1½[b]	1[b,c]	1[b,c]	0[c]	1[b,c]	0	HT	1[b,c]	0

For SI: 1 foot = 304.8 mm.

a. Roof supports: Fire-resistance ratings of primary structural frame and bearing walls are permitted to be reduced by 1 hour where supporting a roof only.

b. Except in Group F-1, H, M and S-1 occupancies, fire protection of structural members shall not be required, including protection of roof framing and decking where every part of the roof construction is 20 feet or more above any floor immediately below. Fire-retardant-treated wood members shall be allowed to be used for such unprotected members.

c. In all occupancies, heavy timber shall be allowed where a 1-hour or less fire-resistance rating is required.

d. An approved automatic sprinkler system in accordance with Section 903.3.1.1 shall be allowed to be substituted for 1-hour fire-resistance-rated construction, provided such system is not otherwise required by other provisions of the code or used for an allowable area increase in accordance with Section 506.3 or an allowable height increase in accordance with Section 504.2. The 1-hour substitution for the fire resistance of exterior walls shall not be permitted.

e. Not less than the fire-resistance rating required by other sections of this code.

f. Not less than the fire-resistance rating based on fire separation distance (see Table 602).

g. Not less than the fire-resistance rating as referenced in Section 704.10.

TABLE 602
**FIRE-RESISTANCE RATING REQUIREMENTS FOR EXTERIOR WALLS BASED
ON FIRE SEPARATION DISTANCE[a, e]**

FIRE SEPARATION DISTANCE = X (feet)	TYPE OF CONSTRUCTION	OCCUPANCY GROUP H	OCCUPANCY GROUP F-1, M, S-1	OCCUPANCY GROUP A, B, E, F-2, I, R, S-2, U[b]
X < 5[c]	All	3	2	1
5 ≤ X < 10	IA	3	2	1
	Others	2	1	1
10 ≤ X < 30	IA, IB	2	1	1[d]
	IIB, VB	1	0	0
	Others	1	1	1[d]
X ≥ 30	All	0	0	0

For SI: 1 foot = 304.8 mm.

a. Load-bearing exterior walls shall also comply with the fire-resistance rating requirements of Table 601.

b. For special requirements for Group U occupancies see Section 406.1.2.

c. See Section 705.1.1 for party walls.

d. Open parking garages complying with Section 406 shall not be required to have a fire-resistance rating.

e. The fire-resistance rating of an exterior wall is determined based upon the fire separation distance of the exterior wall and the story in which the wall is located.

4. See also PARAPET WALLS.

B.   Wall openings (Table 705.8)

1. Maximum area of wall openings

TABLE 705.8
MAXIMUM AREA OF EXTERIOR WALL OPENINGS[a]

CLASSIFICATION OF OPENING	FIRE SEPARATION DISTANCE (feet)							
	0 to 3[f,j]	Greater than 3 to 5[c,g]	Greater than 5 to 10[c,e,g,h]	Greater than 10 to 15[d,e,g]	Greater than 15 to 20[d,g]	Greater than 20 to 25[d,g]	Greater than 25 to 30[d,g]	Greater than 30
Unprotected	Not permitted	Not permitted[c]	10%[i]	15%	25%[i]	45%[i]	70%[i]	No Limit
Protected	Not permitted	15%	25%	45%	75%	No Limit	No Limit	No Limit

For SI: 1 foot = 304.8 mm.

a. Values given are percentage of the area of the exterior wall.

b. Deleted.

c. For occupancies in Group R-3, the maximum percentage of unprotected and protected exterior wall openings shall be 25%.

d. The area of openings in an open parking structure with a fire separation distance of greater than 10 feet shall not be limited.

e. For occupancies in Group H-2 or H-3, unprotected openings shall not be permitted for openings with a fire separation distance of 15 feet or less.

f. For requirements for fire walls for buildings with differing roof heights, see Section 705.6.1.

g. The area of unprotected and protected openings is not limited for occupancies in Group R-3, with a fire separation distance greater than 5 feet.

h. For special requirements for Group U occupancies, see Section 406.1.2

i. Buildings whose exterior bearing wall, exterior nonbearing wall and exterior structural frame are not required to be fire-resistance rated by Table 601 or 602 shall be permitted to have unlimited unprotected openings.

j. Includes accessory buildings to Group R-3.

2. Group R-3 permits 25% unprotected and protected openings for 3' to 15' distance.

3. In buildings completely sprinkled, use protected area percentage for unprotected openings except in Groups H-1, H-2, and H-3. (The code does not specify what percentage of protected openings can be used with suppression.) (705.8.1)

4. Unlimited unprotected openings are permitted in the first story of a building facing a street with more than 15' separation or 30' of open space (with fire lane) except in Group H.

5. Vertical separation for buildings of more than 3 stories and not fire suppressed, must be 5' horizontally and 3' vertically unless protected as prescribed. (705.8.5)

6. Openings less than 15' above and within 15' horizontally of adjacent buildings and/or roofs must be protected unless lower roof has 1-hour rating. (705.10)

C. Party and fire walls (706)

1. Party and fire walls must completely separate the building from the foundation through the roof and must be structurally sound under fire conditions including the collapse of adjacent construction on either side. (706.1, 706.2)

2. Fire ratings in Table 706.4:

    a. H-1, H-2—4 hours

    b. F-2, S-2, R-3, R-4—2 hours

    c. All others—3 hours, but can be 2 hours in Type II or V construction for some Use Groups

3. All fire walls must be noncombustible except for Type V construction. (706.3)

4. Hollow walls (712.2, 706.7)

    a. Wood framing must be completely surrounded by a minimum of 4" solid noncombustible material.

5. Horizontal continuity

    a. Horizontal extension of fire wall 18" out from exterior wall. (706.5)

       i. Extension not required when exterior wall has 1-hour rating and ³/₄-hour opening protectives for 4' each side.

       ii. Extension not required when exterior siding and sheathing is noncombustible for 4' each side.

       iii. Extension not required where buildings on both sides of fire wall are fully sprinkled.

       iv. Exterior walls next to fire wall must be 1-hour with ³/₄-hour opening protectives for 4' each side, unless intersection of exterior walls at fire wall is 180 or more. (Flat plane exterior wall perpendicular to fire wall is an example.) (705.5.1)

       v. Fire walls must extend as far as balconies, canopies, roof overhangs, etc., within 4' of the fire wall unless wall behind and below is 1-hour rated.

6. Vertical continuity (706.6)

    a. Vertical extension of fire wall to 30" above roof.

       i. 2-hour walls allowed to stop at roof deck when lower roof within 4' is 1-hour with no openings and Class B roof. (1-hour area needs 1-hour supports.)

       ii. Fire walls allowed to stop at noncombustible roof deck where Class B roof and no openings within 4'.

       iii. For Types III, IV, V, fire wall can stop at roof deck where Class B roof and no openings within 4' where roof deck is noncombustible or FRT wood for 4', or roof deck has ⁵/₈" Type X drywall on 2" ledgers for 4' each side.

    b. Offset roofs, options to:

      i. Fire wall extends 30" above lower roof and wall of taller building is 1-hour with ³/₄-hour protectives for 15' above lower roof, or

      ii. The lower roof is 1-hour rated with no openings for 10' horizontally from fire wall (1-hour area needs 1-hour supports).

7. Penetrations (713)

    a. Combustible wires, cables, and pipes must be protected to conform with ASTM E814 with UL 1479.01 pressure and "F" equal to wall rating. (713.3.1.2)

    b. Noncombustible construction requires the same protection as combustible or grout or mortar in a maximum opening of 144 sq. in. around a 6" and maximum copper, iron, or steel pipe penetrating a concrete or masonry assembly. (713.3.1)

8. Fire wall openings (706.8, 711)

    a. Maximum size of each opening is 156 sq. ft. and not more than ¹/₄ the wall length.

    b. Doors must be labeled and rated.

    c. Exit doors require closures or smoke-activated closures.

    d. Opening size unlimited when building on both sides sprinkled.

    e. No openings in party walls.

    f. No openings in fire wall on lot line.

    g. Ducts and air openings must be figured into 25% maximum openings in a fire wall.

D. Fire barriers (707)

1. These walls are used to separate mixed uses, fire areas, areas of refuge, exit stair enclosures, and incidental use areas.

2. When separating mixed uses, the wall shall provide fire resistance to comply with the more stringent hazard rating of the groups involved.

3. Any portion of a separated wall which is exposed to the exterior shall equal the rating for exterior walls only unless at an exit stair. (707)

4. Supporting construction shall equal or exceed the wall supported except for incidental use areas and smoke barrier walls in building Types IIB, IIIB, and VB. (707.4, 705)

5. Openings in the wall (706.8)

    a. 156 sq. ft. maximum area for a single opening. Openings are not limited when both areas have sprinklers.

    b. Total openings shall not exceed ¹/₄ of the wall length.

    c. Doors in the openings shall be labeled and rated.

    d. Opening size not limited when adjacent areas are sprinkled, for exit stair doors, or when protective meets wall test and rating (not door test).

6. Continuity of the wall (706)

    a. Wall must be completely closed between floors and fire walls.

    b. Close all concealed spaces and seal all penetrations same as fire walls.

    c. Separation walls must continue through concealed spaces to the floor or roof deck.

    d. Shafts allowed a top enclosure with at least rating of floor or shaft. (708.1)

7. Wired glass panels (Table 715.5.4)

    a. 0 sq. in.—3 hour opening protection

    b. 0 sq. in.—1¹/₂-hour *exterior* wall opening

    c. 100 sq. in.—1 and 1¹/₂-hour opening protection, all other locations

    d. 1,296 sq. in.—³/₄-hour opening protection or fire windows

    e. Not limited—¹/₃-hour opening protection

E. Fire partitions (709)
  1. Fire partitions are 1-hour and are required for tenant and dwelling unit separations, corridors, atriums ($\frac{1}{2}$ hour if sprinkled both sides in Types IIB, IIIB, and VB for residential units).
  2. Do not require rated supporting construction in Types IIB, IIIB, VB. (709.4)
  3. Fire partitions must be continuous from floor to assembly above. Partition may terminate at ceiling if part of rated assembly. (709.4)
  4. Fire partitions do not need to extend into crawl spaces when 1-hour floor.
  5. Rated corridor walls can stop at the top membrane of a wall-like ceiling.
  6. Rated corridor can be enclosed by single layer of wall assembly above ceiling when corridor ceiling is material from a rated design.
  7. Mall tenant separations not required above ceiling line.
F. Smoke barriers (710) (See SMOKE BARRIERS.)
G. Fire-rated joints (713)
  1. Must be tested (ASTM E119 or UL263) and securely installed.
  2. Not required for floors of malls, open garages, mezzanines, inside dwelling units, in atriums, and control joints up to $\frac{5}{8}$".
H. Penetrations (713)
  1. Through penetrations maximum 6" diameter noncombustible pipe in maximum 144 sq. in. opening with grout or concrete.
  2. Firestop systems meeting ASTM E814 and UL 1479.
  3. Hole fill that passes same test as wall or floor. (ASTM E119)
  4. Membrane-only penetrations allow recessed, tested devices, like electrical boxes.

WATERPROOFING (1805)

A. Required for areas where hydrostatic pressure exists and not a ground water control system in design.
B. Floors need membrane of rubber, 6-mil PVC or other approved system.
C. Walls need membrane of double hot-applied felts, 6-mil PVC, 40-mil asphalt system, or other approved systems.

WIND LOADS

A. Wind load design calculated per ASCE 7, Ch. 6 OR Sec. 1609.6 alternate all-height method (based on type of opening protection needed, basic wind speed, and site exposure category). Assume wind from any horizontal direction. Assume wind pressures to act normal to any surface. Do not decrease wind load for shielding effect of other structures. Exceptions:
  1. ICC 600 applicable to Group R-2, R-3 buildings, subject to Sec. 1609.1.1.1.
  2. Designs per NAAMM FP 1001.
  3. Designs per TIA-222 for antennas, antenna-supporting structures.
  4. Sec. 6.6 ASCE 7 wind tunnel tests, subject to Sec. 1609.1.1.2. (1609.1.1)
B. Wind load—ICC 600 applies only to Sec. 1609.4 Exposure B or C buildings. ICC 600 inapplicable to buildings on upper half of isolated hill, ridge, or escarpment if:
  1. Land feature is $\geq$ 60' (18,288 mm) for Exposure B; 30' $\geq$ (9,144 mm) for Exposure C AND
  2. Maximum average slope of hill $\geq$ 10% AND
  3. Land feature unobstructed upwind by similar features EITHER from high point thereof of 50 x hill height OR 1 mile (1.61 km). (1609.1.1.1)
C. Wind force-resisting system, components, and cladding lower limit based on wind tunnel testing must be $\geq$ 80% of design base overturning moments per Sec. 6.5 of

ASCE 7 UNLESS specific test shows lower value caused by building's aerodynamic coefficient and NOT by shielding by other structures. May adjust 80% limit by ratio of frame load at critical wind directions per wind tunnel testing (including appropriate upwind roughness, not specific adjacent buildings) TO ration per ASCE 7, Sec. 6.5.

1. Design pressures for components/cladding for walls/roofs is GREATER OF wind tunnel test results OR 80% of pressure for Zone 4 (walls) and Zone 1 (roofs) per ASCE 7, Sec. 6.5 UNLESS specific testing shows lower value caused by building's aerodynamic coefficient and NOT by shielding by other structures.

   (a) Alternative method—limited tests at a few wind directions without specific adjacent buildings, but with appropriate wind roughness, may show lower pressures caused by building shape, not shielding. (1609.1.1.2)

D. Glazing protection of openings in wind-borne debris regions must be Impact-resistant per approved standard or ASTM E 1996 and ASTM E 1886 as follows:

1. Openings < 30' (9144 mm) of grade must meet ASTM E 1996 large missile test.

2. Openings > 30' (9144 mm) above grade must meet ASTM E 1996 small missile test.

Louvers protecting intake/exhaust ventilation ducts not assumed open and < 30' (9144 mm) of grade must meet EITHER approved impact-resistant standard OR ASTM E 1996 large missile test. Garage door glazed opening protection for wind-borne debris must meet EITHER approved impact-resisting standard OR ANSI/DASMA 115. Exceptions:

1. Allow wood structural panels with minimum thickness of 7/16 (11.1 mm) and maximum panel span of 8' (2438 mm) in one- and two-story buildings in Group R-3, R-4 Occupancies. Precut panels to attach to framing of glazed product opening. Predrill panels for anchorage, secure with attachment hardware. Design attachments to resist component/cladding loads per ASCE 7, using corrosion-resistant attachment hardware and anchors permanently installed on building. Allow attachment per Table 1609.1.2 with corrosion-resistant attachment hardware and anchors permanently installed on building if building has mean roof height $\leq$ 45' (13,716 mm AND wind speed $\leq$ 140 mph (63 m/s).

2. If Occupancy Category I building (including production or research greenhouses without public access), allow unprotected glazing per entry on GLASS.

3. No need to protect Occupancy Category II, III, or IV buildings that are > 60' (18,288 mm) above ground AND > 30' (9144 mm) above aggregate surface roofs < 1,500' (458 mm) of buildings. (1609.1.2)

E. Wind Speed is per Table 1609, calculated at $\geq$ wind speed associated with annual probability 0.02 (50-year mean recurrence interval). Adjust estimate for equivalence to 3-second gust wind speed at 33' (10 m) above ground in Exposure Category C. Calculations follow ASCE 7, Section 6.5.4.2 If special wind region (mountains, gorges), check local jurisdiction requirements per ASCE 7, Section 6.5.4.

1. Convert Figure 1609 3-second gust basic wind speeds as necessary to fastest-mile wind speeds (Vfm) per Table 1609.3.1 or Equation 16-32. (1609.3)

TABLE 1609.1.2
WIND-BORNE DEBRIS PROTECTION FASTENING
SCHEDULE FOR WOOD STRUCTURAL PANELS[a, b, c, d]

FASTENER TYPE	FASTENER SPACING (inches)		
	Panel Span ≤ 4 feet	4 feet < Panel Span ≤ 6 feet	6 feet < Panel Span ≤ 8 feet
No. 8 wood-screw-based anchor with 2-inch embedment length	16	10	8
No. 10 wood-screw-based anchor with 2-inch embedment length	16	12	9
1/4-inch diameter lag-screw-based anchor with 2-inch embedment length	16	16	16

For SI: 1 inch = 25.4 mm, 1 foot = 304.8 mm, 1 pound = 4.448 N, 1 mile per hour = 0.447 m/s.

a. This table is based on 140 mph wind speeds and a 45-foot mean roof height.

b. Fasteners shall be installed at opposing ends of the wood structural panel. Fasteners shall be located a minimum of 1 inch from the edge of the panel.

c. Anchors shall penetrate through the exterior wall covering with an embedment length of 2 inches minimum into the building frame.

Fasteners shall be located a minimum of 2 ½ inches from the edge of concrete block or concrete.

d. Where panels are attached to masonry or masonry/stucco, they shall be attached using vibration-resistant anchors having a minimum ultimate withdrawal capacity of 1,500 pounds.

$$V_{fm} = \frac{(V_{3S} - 10.5)}{1.05}$$ **(Equation 16-32)**

where:

V_{3S} = 3-second gust basic wind speed from Figure 1609.

TABLE 1609.3.1
EQUIVALENT BASIC WIND SPEEDS[a, b, c]

V_{3S}	85	90	100	105	110	120	125	130	140	145	150	160	170
V_{fm}	71	76	85	90	95	104	109	114	123	128	133	142	152

For SI: 1 mile per hour = 0.44 m/s.
a. Linear interpolation is permitted.
b. V_{3S} is the 3-second gust wind speed (mph).
c. V_{fm} is the fastest mile wind speed (mph).

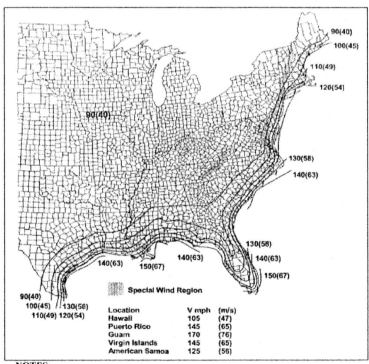

Location	V mph	(m/s)
Hawaii	105	(47)
Puerto Rico	145	(65)
Guam	170	(76)
Virgin Islands	145	(65)
American Samoa	125	(56)

NOTES:
1. Values are nominal design 3-second gust wind speeds in miles per hour (m/s) at 33 ft (10m) above ground for Exposure C category.
2. Linear Interpolation between wind contours is permitted.
3. Islands and coastal areas outside the last contour shall use the last wind speed contour of the coastal area.
4. Deleted.

F. Exposure Categories exist for each wind direction to show ground surface irregularities (topography, vegetation, and man-made) at structure site. At each direction, structure exposure for the two upwind sectors 45° (0.79 rad) either side of selected direction. Exposure causing highest wind loads represents wind in from that direction. Surface Roughness Categories for each sector can be:
   1. B—urban/suburban areas, woodlands or other areas with closely-spaced obstructions sized as single-family dwellings or larger.
   2. C —open terrain with scattered obstructions < 30' (9144 mm).
   3. D —flat, unobstructed areas and water surfaces, mud flats, salt flats, unbroken ice.
   Surface Exposure Categories:
   1. B—surface roughness prevails upwind for ≥ 2,600' (792 m) OR 20 x height of structure, whichever is greater. Exception: if structure's mean roof height is ≤ 30' (9,144 mm) reduce permissible upwind distance to 1,500' (457 m).
   2. Exposure C applies wherever B or D do not.
   3. D—surface roughness prevails upwind for ≥ 5,000' OR 20 x structure height, whichever is greater. If shoreline, extend inland for 600' OR 20 x structure height, whichever is greater. (1609.4)

G. Roof Deck—withstand wind pressures per ASCE 7.
   1. Rigid tile roof coverings per equation 16-33(1609.5):

$$M_a = q_h C_L b L L_a [1.0 - GC_p] \qquad \text{(Equation 16-33)}$$

For SI: $M_a = \dfrac{q_h C_L b L L_a [1.0 - GC_p]}{1,000}$

where:

b = Exposed width, feet (mm) of the roof tile.

C_L = Lift coefficient. The lift coefficient for concrete and clay tile shall be 0.2 or shall be determined by test in accordance with Section 1716.2.

GC_p = Roof pressure coefficient for each applicable roof zone determined from Chapter 6 of ASCE 7. Roof coefficients shall not be adjusted for internal pressure

L = Length, feet (mm) of the roof tile.

L_a = Moment arm, feet (mm) from the axis of rotation to the point of uplift on the roof tile. The point of uplift shall be taken at $0.76L$ from the head of the tile and the middle of the exposed width. For roof tiles with nails or screws (with or without a tail clip), the axis of rotation shall be taken as the head of the tile for direct deck application or as the top edge of the batten for battened applications. For roof tiles fastened only by a nail or screw along the side of the tile, the axis of rotation shall be determined by testing. For roof tiles installed with battens and fastened only by a clip near the tail of the tile, the moment arm shall be determined about the top edge of the batten with consideration given for the point of rotation of the tiles based on straight bond or broken bond and the tile profile.

M_a = Aerodynamic uplift moment, feet-pounds (N-mm) acting to raise the tail of the tile.

q_h = Wind velocity pressure, psf (kN/m^2) determined from Section 6.5.10 of ASCE 7.

H. Alternate wind designs per ASCE 7—Analytical Procedure, allowed on regularly-shaped structures if following conditions (apply wind pressures simultaneously and in direction normal to all structure envelope wall/roof surfaces). (1609.4)

1. Structure $\leq$ 75' (22,860 mm) high, height-to-least width ratio of 4 or less, OR structure has fundamental frequency $\geq$ 1 hertz.
2. Structure not sensitive to dynamic effects.
3. Structure not on site channeling or buffeting from upwind obstructions needs special consideration.
4. Simple diaphragm structure per ASCE 7, Section 6.2, transmitting wind loads solely to main wind-force-resisting system (MWFRS) at diaphragms.
5. If open structure, multispan gable roof, stepped roof, sawtooth roof, domed roof, roof sloped > 45° (0.79 rad), solid free-standing wall and solid signs, rooftop equipment—ASCE 7 applies.

Apply symbols and notations for alternate designs as follows per OBC 1609.6.2:

C_{net} = Net-pressure coefficient based on K_d $[(G)(C_p)—(GC_{pi})]$, in accordance with Table 1609.6.2(2).

G = Gust effect factor for rigid structures in accordance with ASCE 7 Section 6.5.8.1.

K_d = Wind directionality factor in accordance with ASCE 7 Table 6-4.

P_{net} = Design wind pressure to be used in determination of wind loads on structures or other structures or their components and cladding, in psf (kN/m^2). 4101:1-16-01 38

q_s = Wind stagnation pressure in psf (kN/m^2) in accordance with Table 1609.6.2(1).

Apply equation 16-34 for alternative method to MFWRS, components, cladding of structures to resist wind pressure effects on structure envelope:

P_{net} = q_s K_z C_{net} $[IK_{zt}]$.

1. MWFRS wind forces $\leq$ 10 psf (0.48 kN/m^2) x structure area on plane normal to assumed wind direction per ASCE 7.
2. Component/cladding wind pressure $\geq$ 10 psf (0.48kN/m^2), either Direction to surface. (1609.6.3)

Design procedure for MFWRS, components, cladding for all structures

1. Check MRWRS for torsional effects per ASCE 7, Figure 6-9.
2. Determine velocity pressure exposure coefficient K_z per ASCE 7, Section 6.5.6.6; topographic factor K_{zt} per ASCE 7, Section 6.5.7
   a. Windward side of structure, base K_z, K_{zt} on height $_z$.
   b. Leeward side, sidewalls, windward, leeward roofs—base on mean roof height h.

Apply wind pressure for each components/cladding element using Cnet value calculated on: effective wind area, A, in zones of discontinuity of width and/or length "a," "2a," or "4a" for—roof/wall corners, edge strips on ridges, rakes, eaves and field areas on walls or roofs per Table 1609.6.2(2) referencing ASCE 7 based on:

1. a. calculated pressures for local discontinuities at edge strips or corner boundaries
2. b. Zone 1, 2, or 4 pressures included outside discontinuity areas.
   c. if necessary, combine calculated pressures for discontinuities in Zones 2, 3) with design pressures specific to rakes or eave overhangs.

TABLE 1609.6.2(1)

BASIC WIND SPEED (mph)	85	90	100	105	110	120	125	130	140	150	160	170
PRESSURE, q_s (psf)	18.5	20.7	25.6	28.2	31.0	36.9	40.0	43.3	50.2	57.6	65.5	74.0

WIND VELOCITY PRESSURE (q_s) AT STANDARD HEIGHT OF 33 FEET[a]

For SI: 1 foot = 304.8 mm, 1 mph = 0.44 m/s, 1 psf = 47.88 Pa.

a. For basic wind speeds not shown, use $q_s = 0.00256 \ V^2$.

TABLE 1609.6.2(2)
NET PRESSURE COEFFICIENTS, C_{net}[a, b]

STRUCTURE OR PART THEREOF	DESCRIPTION	C_{net} FACTOR	
1. Main wind-force-	**Walls:**	**Enclosed**	**Partially enclosed**

resisting frames and systems			+ Internal pressure	- Internal pressure	+ Internal pressure	- Internal pressure
	Windward wall		0.43	0.73	0.11	1.05
	Leeward wall		-0.51	-0.21	-0.83	0.11
	Sidewall		-0.66	-0.35	-0.97	-0.04
	Parapet wall	Windward	1.28		1.28	
		Leeward	-0.85		-0.85	
	Roofs:		**Enclosed**		**Partially enclosed**	
	Wind perpendicular to ridge		+ Internal pressure	- Internal pressure	+ Internal pressure	- Internal pressure
	Leeward roof or flat roof		-0.66	-0.35	-0.97	-0.04
	Windward roof slopes:					
	Slope ≤ 2:12 (10°)	Condition 1	-1.09	-0.79	-1.41	-0.47
		Condition 2	-0.28	0.02	-0.60	0.34
	Slope = 4:12 (18°)	Condition 1	-0.73	-0.42	-1.04	-0.11
		Condition 2	-0.05	0.25	-0.37	0.57
	Slope = 5:12 (23°)	Condition 1	-0.58	-0.28	-0.90	0.04
		Condition 2	0.03	0.34	-0.29	0.65
	Slope = 6:12 (27°)	Condition 1	-0.47	-0.16	-0.78	0.15
		Condition 2	0.06	0.37	-0.25	0.68
	Slope = 7:12 (30°)	Condition 1	-0.37	-0.06	-0.68	0.25
		Condition 2	0.07	0.37	-0.25	0.69
	Slope 9:12 (37°)	Condition 1	-0.27	0.04	-0.58	0.35
		Condition 2	0.14	0.44	-0.18	0.76
	Slope 12:12 (45°)		0.14	0.44	-0.18	0.76
	Wind parallel to ridge and flat roofs		-1.09	-0.79	-1.41	-0.47
	Nonbuilding Structures: Chimneys, Tanks and Similar Structures:					
			h/D			
			1	**7**	**25**	
	Square (Wind normal to face)		0.99	1.07	1.53	
	Square (Wind on diagonal)		0.77	0.84	1.15	
	Hexagonal or Octagonal		0.81	0.97	1.13	
	Round		0.65	0.81	0.97	
	Open signs and lattice frameworks		Ratio of solid to gross area			
			≤ 0.1	0.1 to 0.29	0.3 to 0.7	
	Flat		1.45	1.30	1.16	

	Round		0.87	0.94	1.08
	Roof elements and slopes		**Enclosed**		**Partially enclosed**
	Gable of hipped configurations (Zone 1)				
	Flat < Slope < 6:12 (27°) See ASCE 7 Figure 6-11C Zone 1				
	Positive	10 square feet or less	0.58		0.89
		100 square feet or more	0.41		0.72
	Negative	10 square feet or less	-1.00		-1.32
		100 square feet or more	-0.92		-1.23
	Overhang: Flat < Slope < 6:12 (27°) See ASCE 7 Figure 6-11B Zone 1				
	Negative	10 square feet or less		-1.45	
		100 square feet or more		-1.36	
		500 square feet or more		-0.94	
2. Components and cladding not in areas of discontinuity—roofs and overhangs	6:12 (27°) < Slope < 12:12 (45°) See ASCE 7 Figure 6-11D Zone 1				
	Positive	10 square feet or less	0.92		1.23
		100 square feet or more	0.83		1.15
	Negative	10 square feet or less	-1.00		-1.32
		100 square feet or more	-0.83		-1.15
	Monosloped configurations (Zone 1)		**Enclosed**		**Partially enclosed**
	Flat < Slope < 7:12 (30°) See ASCE 7 Figure 6-14B Zone 1				
	Positive	10 square feet or less	0.49		0.81
	-	100 square feet or more	0.41		0.72
	Negative	10 square feet or less	-1.26		-1.57
		100 square feet or more	-1.09		-1.40
	Tall flat-topped roofs h > 60'		**Enclosed**		**Partially enclosed**
	Flat < Slope < 2:12 (10°) (Zone 1) See ASCE 7 Figure 6-17 Zone 1				
	Negative	10 square feet or less	-1.34		-1.66
		500 square feet or more	-0.92		-1.23
3. Components and cladding in areas of discontinuity— roofs and overhangs (continued)	**Roof elements and slopes**		**Enclosed**		**Partially enclosed**
	Gable or hipped configurations at ridges, eaves and rakes (Zone 2)				
	Flat < Slope < 6:12 (27°) See ASCE 7 Figure 6-11C Zone 2				
	Positive	10 square feet or less	0.58		0.89

		Enclosed	Partially enclosed
	100 square feet or more	0.41	10.72
Negative	10 square feet or less	-1.68	-2.00
	100 square feet or more	-1.17	-1.49

Overhang for Slope Flat < Slope < 6:12 (27°) See ASCE 7 Figure 6-11C Zone 2

Negative	10 square feet or less	-1.87	
	100 square feet or more	-1.87	

6:12 (27°) < Slope < 12:12 (45°) Figure 6-11D

		Enclosed	Partially enclosed
Positive	10 square feet or less	0.92	1.23
	100 square feet or more	0.83	1.15
Negative	10 square feet or less	-1.17	-1.49
	100 square feet or more	-1.00	-1.32

Overhang for 6:12 (27°) < Slope < 12:12 (45°) See ASCE 7 Figure 6-11D Zone 2

Negative	10 square feet or less	-1.70	
	500 square feet or more	-1.53	

Monosloped configurations at ridges, eaves and rakes (Zone 2)

Flat < Slope < 7:12 (30°) See ASCE 7 Figure 6-14B Zone 2

		Enclosed	Partially enclosed
Positive	10 square feet or less	0.49	0.81
	100 square feet or more	0.41	0.72
Negative	10 square feet or less	-1.51	-1.83
	100 square feet or more	-1.43	-1.74

Tall flat topped roofs $h > 60'$ — Enclosed — Partially enclosed

Flat < Slope < 2:12 (10°) (Zone 2) See ASCE 7 Figure 6-17 Zone 2

		Enclosed	Partially enclosed
Negative	10 square feet or less	-2.11	-2.42
	500 square feet or more	-1.51	-1.83

Gable or hipped configurations at corners (Zone 3) See ASCE 7 Figure 6-11C Zone 3

Flat < Slope < 6:12 (27°)

		Enclosed	Partially enclosed
Positive	10 square feet or less	0.58	0.89
	100 square feet or more	0.41	0.72
Negative	10 square feet or less	-2.53	-2.85
	100 square feet or more	-1.85	-2.17

Overhang for Slope Flat < Slope < 6:12 (27°) See ASCE 7 Figure 6-11C Zone 3

Negative	10 square feet or less	-3.15	
	100 square feet or more	-2.13	

	6:12 (27°) < 12:12 (45°) See ASCE 7 Figure 6-11D Zone 3			
	Positive	10 square feet or less	0.92	1.23
		100 square feet or more	0.83	1.15
	Negative	10 square feet or less	-1.17	-1.49
		100 square feet or more	-1.00	-1.32
	Overhang for 6:12 (27°) < Slope < 12:12 (45°)		**Enclosed**	**Partially enclosed**
	Negative	10 square feet or less	-1.70	
		100 square feet or more	-1.53	
	Monosloped Configurations at corners (Zone 3) See ASCE 7 Figure 6-14B Zone 3			
	Flat < Slope < 7:12 (30°)			
	Positive	10 square feet or less	0.49	0.81
		100 square feet or more	0.41	0.72
	Negative	10 square feet or less	-2.62	-2.93
		100 square feet or more	-1.85	-2.17
	Tall flat topped roofs $h > 60'$		**Enclosed**	**Partially enclosed**
	Flat < Slope < 2:12 (10°) (Zone 3) See ASCE 7 Figure 6-17 Zone 3			
	Negative	10 square feet or less	-2.87	-3.19
		500 square feet or more	-2.11	-2.42
4. Components and cladding not in areas of discontinuity—walls and parapets	Wall Elements: $h = 60'$ (Zone 4) Figure 6-11A		**Enclosed**	**Partially enclosed**
	Positive	10 square feet or less	1.00	1.32
		500 square feet or more	0.75	1.06
	Negative	10 square feet or less	-1.09	-1.40
		500 square feet or more	-0.83	-1.15
	Wall Elements: $h > 60'$ (Zone 4) See ASCE 7 Figure 6-17 Zone 4			
	Positive	20 square feet or less	0.92	1.23
		500 square feet or more	0.66	0.98
	Negative	20 square feet or less	-0.92	-1.23
		500 square feet or more	-0.75	-1.06
	Parapet Walls			
	Positive		2.87	3.19
	Negative		-1.68	-2.00

	Wall elements: $h \leq 60'$ (Zone 5) Figure 6-11A		**Enclosed**	**Partially enclosed**
5. Components and cladding in areas of discontinuity— walls and parapets	Positive	10 square feet or less	1.00	1.32
		500 square feet or more	0.75	1.06
	Negative	10 square feet or less	-1.34	-1.66
		500 square feet or more	-0.83	-1.15
	Wall elements: $h > 60'$ (Zone 5) See ASCE 7 Figure 6-17 Zone 4			
	Positive	20 square feet or less	0.92	1.23
		500 square feet or more	0.66	0.98
	Negative	20 square feet or less	-1.68	-2.00
		500 square feet or more	-1.00	-1.32
	Parapet walls			
	Positive		3.64	3.95
	Negative		-2.45	-2.76

For SI: 1 foot = 304.8 mm, 1 square foot = 0.0929 m^2, 1 degree = 0.0175 rad.
a. Linear interpolation between values in the table is permitted.
b. Some C_{net} values have been grouped together. Less conservative results may be obtained by applying ASCE 7 provisions.

Determine net pressure coefficients Cnet as sum of internal and external net pressure.
1. For walls, roofs, base Cnet on Table 1609.6.2(2).
2. If Cnet has more than one value, use more severe wind load condition.

WINDOWS, DOORS, AND OTHER OPENINGS (700, 602, 2300)

A. Fire protection (705.8, 706.8, 707.8, 708.7)
   1. Openings are doors, windows, ventilators, storefronts, light transmitting plastic or glass, ducts and transfer grilles.
   2. Opening protectives are fire doors, fire shutters, fire dampers, fire windows, glass or glass block which is fire resistant, or wire glass. Protectives must be labeled or approved.
   3. Outside sprinklers may be used as protection with an automatic sprinkler system in the building instead of exterior opening protectives. (704.12)
   4. Opening protective assemblies shall be fixed, self-closing or have an automatic closing device.

B. Fire windows (715.5)
   1. A ³/₄-hour window assembly is ¹/₈" steel frame with ¹/₄" wired glass.
   2. Mullions more than 12' high require the same rating as the wall with the opening.
   3. Other types of fire-rated glazing must meet NFPA 252 and NFPA 257 (and impact safety testing in doors and sidelights).

C. Fire shutters (715.4.9)
   1. Swinging fire shutters: Every 3rd row of openings must be operable from exterior and have 6" identifying letters.
   2. Rolling fire shutters must be automatic-closing (usually fusible link).

D. Fire doors (715.4) (See also DOORS.) (715.4)
   1. Testing requirements differ for locations in corridors and smoke barriers, exits, and all other locations. Installations per NFPA 80.
   2. Size of glass in door limited, depending on rating (from zero to not limited).
   3. Positive latching required.
   4. Rated doors in the following locations must be smoke-activated when automatic-closing:
      a. Corridors, exits, horizontal exits
      b. Incidental use areas
      c. Smoke barriers, fire partitions, fire walls

TABLE 715.4
FIRE DOOR AND FIRE SHUTTER FIRE PROTECTION RATINGS

TYPE OF ASSEMBLY	REQUIRED ASSEMBLY RATING (hours)	MINIMUM FIRE DOOR AND FIRE SHUTTER ASSEMBLY RATING (hours)
Fire walls and fire barriers having a required fire-resistance rating greater than 1 hour	4 3 2 1 ½	3 3[a] 1 ½ 1 ½
Fire barriers having a required fire-resistance rating of 1 hour: Shaft, exit enclosure and exit passageway walls Other fire barriers	1 1	1 ¾
Fire partitions: Corridor walls	1 0.5	$^1/_3$ [b] $^1/_3$ [b]
Other fire partitions	1 0.5	¾ $^1/_3$
Exterior walls	3 2 1	1 ½ 1 ½ ¾
Smoke barriers	1	$^1/_3$ [b]

a. Two doors, each with a fire protection rating of 1 ½ hours, installed on opposite sides of the same opening in a fire wall, shall be deemed equivalent in fire protection rating to one 3-hour fire door.

b. For testing requirements, see Section 715.4.3.

E. Fire dampers (716 and M-607)
1. Tested to UL 555.
2. For 3-hours or more rated assembly—3-hour damper; for all less than 3-hours—1½-hour rating.
3. Smoke dampers must be smoke detector-activated.

FIRE SEPARATION DISTANCE AND OPENINGS

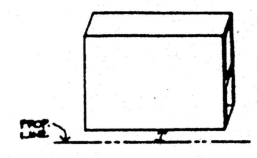

__0% OPENINGS__

- 0 - 3 FT. - NO OPENINGS ALLOWED

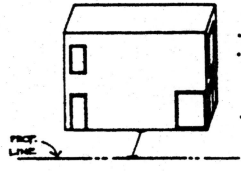

__14% OPENINGS__

- PROTECTED OPNGS. - MIN. 3'-1"
- UNPROTECTED OPNGS. - MIN 10'-1" (OR 5'-1" FOR SPRINKLED BLDGS.)
- UNIFORM DISTRIBUTION OF OPENINGS IS REQUIRED

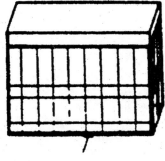

__85% OPENINGS__

- PROTECTED OPNGS. - MIN. 20'-1"
- UNPROTECTED OPNGS. - MIN. 30'-1" (OR 20'-1" FOR SPRINKLED BUILDINGS)

WOOD (CHAPTER 23)

A. Where permitted: Wood frame construction is permitted in every type of construction.
  1. Fire-retardant treated wood is permitted in Types I and II for: (603.1)
      a. Exterior non-bearing unrated walls.
      b. Non-bearing partitions where rating is up to 2 hours.
      c. Roof construction which is 20 or more to lowest member except Use Groups F-1, S-1, M, H. (Table 601, footnote c)
      d. In roofs of Types I and II construction, for buildings not over 2 stories.
  2. Heavy timber construction can be used for roof construction in all types where rating is 1-hour or less.
  3. Type III construction requires exterior masonry walls or approved noncombustible materials and floors, roofs and interior framing permitted to be combustible. All exterior bearing walls must have a 2-hour rating. (602.3)
  4. Type IV construction requires exterior walls of noncombustible construction and interior structural members to be of solid or laminated wood without concealed spaces. (602.4, 2308.2)
      a. Columns are required to be 8" nominal supporting floors loads 6" × 8" nominal when supporting roof and ceiling only. (602.4.1)
      b. Floor framing: 6" ×10" nominal for beams and girders is required
          i. 8" for arches springing from the floor, and
          ii. 8" for framed trusses. (602.4.2)
      c. Roof framing: 6" × 8" on bottom half and 6" × 6" for upper half for arches springing from floor or grade without floor loads. (602.4.3)
      d. Flooring: No concealed spaces. 3" nominal plank + 1" T&G flooring or nominal 1/2" plywood or particle board. (602.4.4)
      e. Roofs: No concealed spaces, 2" nominal plank + 1 1/8" interior plywood (exterior glue). (602.4.5)
      f. Walls: Two one-inch matched boards or laminated construction 4" thick or one-hour fire resistance rating (not the exterior walls). (602.4.6)
  5. Type V construction can be an entirely wood constructed structure.
B. Foundations: Wood foundations are permitted where appropriate for the type of construction. (1807.1.4)

  Footings, foundations, and piles shall be treated to prevent deterioration based on member and exposure.
C. Lumber sizing: Wood materials used in construction must be sized in accordance with the specifications referenced in 2303.1.
  1. Design stress capability
  2. Certificates of inspection accepted in lieu of grade on appearance materials
  3. Dimensions are nominal
  4. Fabrication of structural members may require special inspection
  5. Notch dimensions: (2308.8.2)
      a. 1/6 member depth top and bottom in outer thirds of span
      b. 1/4 member depth at end, and
      c. Studs up to 1/4 width for bearing, and 40% for non-bearing (2308.9.10)
  6. Hole dimensions
      a. Joists: 2" minimum from top diameter should be equal to or less than 1/3 the member depth.
      b. Studs up to 40% for bearing, and 60% for non-bearing and doubled studs. (2308.9.11)
D. Type IV construction: Heavy timber construction has several specific requirements that are outlined in the code: (2304.10)

        1. Grade

        2. Substitution of other structural materials

        3. Columns

        4. Floors, heavy timber

        5. Clearances, beams, and girders

        6. Girders, and

        7. Clearances of ½" minimum to exterior walls (2304.10.4)

E. General framing: Standard framing practices

        1. Design for wood shear walls and diaphragms (2305)

        2. Floor joists (2308.8) with span tables

        3. Bearing walls (2308.8.1)

        4. Nonbearing walls (2308.9.2.3), and

        5. Bracing (2308.9.3)

            a. 8 methods available, depending on height and seismic design category (from 1615).

            b. Cripple walls minimum 14" or solid blocking; when over 4, must be framed as additional story.

            c. Generally, 1 × 4 diagonals, ⅝" boards, wood-based sheathing, gypsum sheathing, plaster walls with mesh.

        6. Headers (2308.9.5)

        7. Sheathing (2308.6, 2304.7.1)

        8. Fasteners and nailing (Table 2304.9.1)

        9. Anchorage: Design for wind uplift must be 1-1 minimum: (2308.6)

            a. To foundation by 2 × 4 sill plates with ½" anchor bolts

            b. Two anchor bolts per section of sill plate

            c. Bolts shall be 12" from each end of plate, spaced a maximum of 4'0" o.c.

            d. CABO requires a 2 × 4 plate anchored with ½" diameter bolts at 6'0" o.c. embedded 7" into the foundation.

                i. Embedded 8" into concrete, and

                ii. Embedded 15" into grouted masonry.

F. Termites and decay use the following options. (2302, 2304)

        1. Naturally durable wood (2302)

            a. Decay-resistant woods include redwood, cedar, black locust, and black walnut.

            b. Termite-resistant woods include redwood and eastern red cedar.

        2. Preservative-treated wood (2302, 2304.11.6)

            a. American Wood Preservers Association (AWPA) Standards for preservatives (Chapter 35)

                i. P1: Creosote

                ii. P2: Coal tar

                iii. P5: Water borne

                iv. P8: Oil borne, and

                v. P9: Organic preservatives.

            b. AWPA Standards for preservative treatments (Chapter 35)

                i. C1: General requirements for pressure treatment of all lumber

                ii. C2: Pressure treatment for lumber, timber, bridge ties, and mine ties, and

                iii. C9: Pressure treatment for plywood.

        3. Treatment is required when clearances from earth are as follows: (2304.11.2)

      a. Siding < 6"

      b. Joists < 18"

      c. Girders < 12"

      d. Studs and sheathing < 8", and

      e. Posts < 1" above slab; < 6" above ground.

G. Fire resistance: Fire safety and the use of wood construction is addressed in the code restrictions on the size of structure that can be built using the material. Additionally, the treatment of the material to retard the surface burning characteristics is allowed, providing additional uses within the code as elements of fire resistive construction.

  1. Fire-retardant-treated wood (2303.2)

      a. ASTM E84 (Steiner tunnel test) 25 flame spread (select red oak = 100) + $10\frac{1}{2}$ feet beyond the centerline of the burner

      b. Standards

         i. ASTM D 5664 is the standard for fire-retardant-treated wood, structural.

        ii. ASTM D 5516 is the standard for fire-retardant-treated wood, plywood.

      c. See Table 601 and Section 603 for permitted substitutions for noncombustible materials.

  2. Fireblocking (717.2)

      a. Materials

         i. 2 thicknesses of 1" lumber

        ii. $^{23}/_{32}$" plywood, and

        iii. 2" lumber with tight joints.

      b. Fireblocking is required in:

         i. Concealed wall spaces at floor and roof

        ii. Connections with coves or soffits

        iii. Between 2 stair stringers (if there are two)

        iv. Openings in the floor or roof, and

        v. Architectural trim

            a. 20'0" intervals, and

            b. 4" separation of sections if discontinuous.

      c. Combustible trim

         i. No openspace exceeding 100 sq. ft. horizontally.

        ii. Filled solid with noncombustibles.

      d. Sleeper spaces

         i. 100 sq. ft., or

        ii. Filled solid with noncombustibles.

      e. Fireblocking around penetrations through floors for chimneys is required.

  4. Draftstopping (717.3)

      a. Material

         i. $\frac{1}{2}$" gypsum board

        ii. $^{3}/_{8}$" plywood

        iii. $^{3}/_{8}$" particleboard

        iv. 1" nominal lumber

        v. Cement fiberboard, batts or blankets of mineral wool or glass fiber, or other approved materials.

      b. Draftstopping is required for floors with suspended ceilings below wood joists or open web wood trusses.

         i. Use Group R: Align with tenant separation walls.

        ii. Other Uses: 1,000 sq. ft. area maximum is permitted.

    c. Required for attic spaces (717.4)

        i. Use Groups R-1, R-2: Draftstopping is required in attics, mansards and overhangs in line with tenant separation walls.

        ii. Other uses: 3,000 sq. ft. area maximum is permitted.

    d. Exceptions: Fire suppression above and below the ceiling negates the need for draftstopping in floors and attics.

Y

YARDS (1206)

A. When required for light and ventilation, yards and courts must meet the following standards.
1. Yards
   a. Yards cannot be less than 3′ in width for one- and two-story buildings.
   b. For buildings more than two stories, the minimum width of the yard can be increased 1′ for each additional story.
   c. For buildings over 14 stories, yard width is limited to that for 14 stories.
2. Courts
   a. Courts cannot be less than 3′ in width.
   b. With windows opening on opposite sides, cannot be less than 6′ in width.
   c. Courts cannot be less than 10′ in length unless bounded on one end by a public way or yard.
   d. For buildings of more than two stories, court is increased 1′ in width and 2′ in length for each additional story.
   e. For buildings exceeding 14 stories, the required dimensions are limited to those for 14 stories.
3. Access must be provided to court bottoms for cleaning.
4. Drainage: Bottom must be sloped and drained to sewer.
5. Courts over 2 stories must have a horizontal air intake at the bottom not less than 10 sq. ft. in area leading to the exterior of the building, unless abutting a yard or public way.

Part 2

RESIDENTIAL CODE OF OHIO (4101:8)
RESIDENTIAL CODE OF OHIO (4101:8)

ADJUDICATIONS

1. Departments or political subdivisions must issue a written adjudication order under ORC 119.06 to 119.13, or a stop work order, prior to attempting to enforce the RCO through civil or criminal proceedings. **All** work ceases on the project pending a hearing under ORC 3781.19, appeals therefrom, or the release from an order. The owner must resubmit plans, drawings, and specifications for approval prior to continuing work on the construction, erection, alteration, or equipment of a structure. (113.1-3)

2. The Residential Building Official (RBO) is responsible for serving the adjudication order on the owner or owner's agent for a structure. The order must state that the work or equipment does not comply with approved construction documents and/or with specific statutes or BBS rules, and detail the lack of complicity as to the appliances, site preparations, additions, or alterations to structures, plans, materials, assemblages or procedures involved. The order must specify a reasonable time in which to achieve compliance. It must give notice to a party of the procedure for appeal and of the right to a hearing if requested, within 30 days of mailing of the notice. It must also inform a party of the right to representation by counsel, to the presentation of arguments orally or in writing, and to the presentation of evidence and the examination of witnesses. (113.1-3)

3. If the owner fails to file construction documents required by the RCO, does not comply with an adjudication order, AND the time for appeal has expired, the owner may be prosecuted; subject to fine of not more than $500 per ORC 3791.04. (113.4, 5)

ALTERNATIVE MATERIALS, APPLIANCES, EQUIPMENT AND METHODS OF CONSTRUCTION

1. The RCO is not intended to bar the installation of any material or the use of any appliance, equipment or method of construction, IF such is not specifically barred, and IF such alternative has been approved per this section. The Residential Code is intended for dwellings resided in by a family and ≤ 5 lodgers or boarders. Shared means of egress is limited to those rooms open to the exterior. Otherwise: all appliances must be listed and labeled per the approved agency. Exception:
   a. Industrialized units constructed per OBC. (116.1, 1302)

2. Any such alternative material, appliance, equipment or method of construction, requires valid research report from an evaluation service listed in appendix P of OBC and is deemed to be approved if it complies with the conditions listed in report, meets intent of the RCO, and does not conflict with the applicable BBS rules. (116.1.1)

3. The BBS may approve alternative materials, appliances, equipment or methods of construction upon application per OBC 118.2.2. (116.1.2)

4. An alternative engineered system design must conform to the intent of the RCO and provide an equivalent level of quality, strength, effectiveness, fire resistance, durability and safety. Materials, equipment or components must be designed and installed per the manufacturer's installation instructions.
   a. A registered design professional is responsible for indicating on the application that the system is an alternative engineered design; approval and permanent approval records must indicate that alternative engineered design was part of approved installation.

    b. A registered design professional is responsible for providing sufficient technical data to substantiate the proposed alternative design and to prove that performance meets RCO intent. In special circumstances, the Residential Building Official) may require additional construction documents from the design professional. (116.2)

APPLIANCES

1. Do not place, or obtain combustion air from, appliances in sleeping rooms, bathrooms, toilet rooms, or storage closets. Exceptions:

    a. Direct-vent appliances obtaining all combustion air directly from outdoors.

    b. Vented room heaters, wall furnaces, vented decorative appliances and decorative appliances installed in vented solid fuel-burning fireplaces, if the room meets the required volume criteria of ORC 2407.5.

    c. A single wall-mounted unvented room heater equipped with an oxygen depletion safety shutoff system and installed in bathroom, if the input rating $\leq$ 6,000 Btu/h (1.76kW) AND the bathroom meets ORC 2407.5 volume criteria.

    d. A single wall-mounted unvented room heater equipped with an oxygen depletion safety shutoff system and installed in bedroom, if the input rating $\leq$ 10,000 Btu/h (2.93 kW) AND the bedroom meets ORC 2407.5 volume criteria.

    e. Appliances installed in enclosure drawing all combustion air from outdoors per ORC 2407.6, with access through a solid weather-stripped door having an approved self-closing device. (2406.2)

APPLICABILITY

1. The Residential Code of Ohio (RCO) is mandatory for one, two and three family dwellings. It covers all construction, alteration, movement, enlargement, replacement, repair, equipment, use, occupancy, location, maintenance, removal and demolition of residential buildings or structures, including all appurtenances and accessory structures thereto. Exceptions:

    a. Manufactured homes.

    b. Multiple single-family dwelling structures > 3 stories high.

    c. Residential structures if no independent egress for each dwelling unit exists.

    d. OBC structural requirements or ORC 116.2 apply to residential structures of detached 1, 2 and 3-family dwellings > 3 stories high.

    e. Residential buildings with attached occupancies covered by the OBC. (101.2)

2. The RCO's intent is to standardize construction practices, methods, equipment, materials and techniques, to maximize energy conservation, safety and sanitation. (101.3)

3. Additional municipal, township and county regulation is allowed if the BBS finds such is compatible with the RCO. If a conflict is found and:

    a. The BBS determines local regulation is unnecessary for public health and safety, the BBS shall bar enforcement.

    b. If the BBS determines such regulation is necessary for public health and safety, it shall draft rule incorporating such into ORC, and grant a variance allowing interim enforcement of regulation. (101.3)

4. The RCO supersede rules issued by the division of fire marshal or industrial compliance if found to be conflicting, unless the fire marshal rules are issued per ORC 3743. (102.2.1)

APPROVALS

1. An owner or authorized agent seeking to do work that is regulated by the RCO as to the following must first apply to the Residential Building Official (RBO) for approval (the actual review is made by the residential plans examiner):

    a. Construct, enlarge, alter, repair, move, or change the occupancy of a residential building or structure, or portion thereof, or

    b. Erect, install, enlarge, alter, repair, remove, convert or replace any electrical, gas, mechanical, plumbing system, other residential building service equipment, or piping system. (105.1, 105.3)

2. Exceptions to approval requirement:

    a. One-story detached accessory structures if floor area ≤ 200′ square (18.58 m$_2$).

    b. Fences ≤ 6′ (1829 mm) high.

    c. Retaining walls ≤ 4′ feet (1219 mm) high, measured from bottom of the footing to top of the wall (unless supporting surcharge).

    d. Water tanks supported directly upon grade if capacity ≤ 5,000 gallons (18927 L) and height/diameter ratio or width ≤ 2 to 1.

    e. Sidewalks and driveways ≤ 30″ (762 mm) above adjacent grade, and without basement or story below.

    f. Finish work (i.e., painting, papering, tiling, carpet, cabinets, counter tops).

    g. Prefabricated swimming pools < 24″ (610 mm) deep.

    h. Swings/playground equipment accessory to 1, 2, or 3-family dwelling.

    i. Exterior wall-supported window awnings projecting ≤ 54″ (1372 mm) from the exterior wall and without need of additional support.

    j. Minor electrical repairs and maintenance (i.e., replacement of lamps, connection of approved portable electrical equipment to approved permanently installed receptacles).

    k. The following items involving the use of natural gas:

        (1) Portable heating, cooking or clothes drying appliances.

        (2) Minor part replacement not altering equipment approval or making such equipment unsafe.

        (3) Portable fuel cell appliances not connected to fixed piping system and that are not interconnected to any power grid.

    l. The following items involving the use of mechanical devices:

        (1) Portable heating, ventilation appliances and cooling units.

        (2) Steam, hot or chilled water piping within RCO-regulated heating or cooling equipment regulated by the RCO.

        (3) Minor part replacement not altering equipment approval or making such equipment unsafe.

        (4) Portable evaporative cooler.

        (5) Self-contained refrigeration systems with < 10 lbs (4.54 kg) refrigerant OR that are actuated by motors ≤ 1 horsepower (746 W).

        (6) Portable fuel cell appliances not connected to fixed piping system and that are not interconnected to any power grid.

    m. The following plumbing usages:

        (1) Stoppage of leaks in drains, water, soil, waste or vent pipe. Exception:

           (a) If a concealed trap, drainpipe, water, soil, waste or vent pipe becomes defective and must be removed and replaced with new material, such work is considered new work, requiring approval and inspection.

           (b) Clearing of stoppages or repairing of leaks in pipes, valves or fixtures, and the removal and reinstallation of water closets, UNLESS such repairs involve the replacement or rearrangement of valves, pipes or fixtures. (105.2)

3. Emergency repairs/equipment replacement require submission of an approval application to the RBO by the following business day. (105.2.1)

4. Minor repairs to residential structures do not require application or notice to the RBO. Exception:

    a. Cutting away of any wall, partition or portion thereof,

b. The removal or cutting of any structural beam or load bearing support,

c. The removal, change or rearrangement of structure affecting required means of egress,

d. The addition/alteration/replacement/relocation of standpipe, water supply, sewer, drainage, drain leader, gas, soil, waste, vent, or similar piping affecting public health or general safety

e. The addition, alteration, replacement, or relocation of electrical wiring, mechanical, or any other work affecting public health or general safety. (105.2.2)

5. An applicant for plan approval must filing a written application, using form the provided by the residential building department, that:

a. Identifies and describes the work.

b. Describes the property where the proposed work is to be done, using street address or similar description.

c. Is supplemented by residential construction documents and any other pertinent information in 2 or more sets, in dimensioned form and drawn on suitable material. Electronic media are permissible if approved by the RBO. All documents must have clarity and detail sufficient to show building, plumbing, and fire protection code compliance, and also:

   (1) An index of drawings on first sheet.

   (2) Site plan scaling size and location of new and existing structures on site, such as setback and side yard dimensions, property and interior lot lines, distances from lot lines, and locations of nearest streets. If demolition work is involved, the construction to be demolished and location and size of the remaining structures and construction must be shown on the site plan. The plan can be waived or modified by the RBO if the application is for alteration or repair, or is otherwise warranted. (105.3, 106.1)

   (3) If residential buildings or structures are in communities with identified flood hazard areas, the documents must include the current FEMA "Flood Hazard Boundary Map" (FHBM), "Flood Insurance Rate Map" (FIRM) or "Flood Boundary Floodway Map" (FBFM) for location. The site plan must show building elevations based on same datum as the flood hazard map. The owner is responsible for providing additional critical elevation information for project site. (105.3, 106.2.2)

   (4) Complete structural description of building, including the size and location of all structural elements used in design. (105.3, 106.2.6)

   (5) Complete floor plans, including full/partial basements, full/ partial attics, door swings, stairs and ramps, windows, shafts, all parts of means of egress, etc., with sufficient dimension to describe all relevant space sizes. Describe wall materials by cross-hatching (with explanatory key), notation, or other clearly understandable method. Identify spaces by function. (105.3, 106.2.3)

   (6) Details of the exterior wall envelope such as flashing, intersections with dissimilar materials, corners, end details, control joints, intersections at roof, eaves, parapets, means of drainage, water-resistive membrane, necessary elevations for description of exterior including floor to floor dimensions, and details around openings. Include cross and wall sections, and details necessary to fully describe the wall, ceiling, floor and roof materials. All details must be in sufficient detail to show compliance with the RCO. (105.3, 106.2.4, 106.2.5)

   (7) Fire-resistance ratings and substantiating data for all structural elements, with details demonstrating penetrations to be made for electrical, mechanical, plumbing, and communication conduits, pipes, and systems,

and materials and methods for maintaining required structural integrity, fire-resistance rating, and firestopping. (105.3, 106.2.7)

(8) Mechanical, plumbing and electrical systems descriptions (i.e., materials, location and type of fixtures and equipment; materials and sizes of ductwork; location and type of heating, ventilation, air conditioning and other mechanical equipment; and lighting and power equipment); (105.3, 106.2.8)

(9) Any additional graphic or text information necessary for the RBO to review special/extraordinary construction methods or equipment. (105.3, 106.2.9)

(10) Substantive changes to building contemplated after the initial document submission or during construction must be submitted to the RBO for review and approval prior to execution; this requirement is subject to waiver if the work is in the nature of emergency repair. (105.3, 106.2)

d. Is signed by owner or owner's authorized agent.

e. Provides any other information requested by the RBO. (105.3)

f. If the work involves a residential fire protection system, supporting documents submitted by an individual certified per ORC 3781.105 must conform to ORC statutory rules per design loads, stresses, strength, stability, or other requirements involving technical analysis, just as would those from a registered design professional. The plans must name the individual, certified by the fire marshal, who is installing the fire protection system; if the installer not known at time of submission, the plans are granted partial approval only, subject to full approval when the installer known, which must be prior to installation. (105.3.1.1.3)

g. BBS-approved industrialized units or alternative materials, designs and methods of construction or equipment must be documented to the RBO with descriptions of their proposed use, prior to installation or use, including:

(1) A copy of construction documents approved by the BBS

(2) Details of on-site interconnection of modules/assemblies.

(Exception to documentation requirement: None is required for industrialized units that are to be used for 1-, 2-, and 3- family dwellings and their accessory structures IF no residential department is certified in jurisdiction. (105.3, 106.2.10)

h. Submit construction documents for fire protection system(s) indicating RCO conformance for approval prior to the start of system installation. (105.3, 106.1.1.1)

i. If approval is denied (which denial must specify the reasons), or if the plans are not approved within 30 days of filing, that constitutes an "adjudication order denying the issuance of a license," and an "adjudication hearing" is required per ORC 119.07-119.13, as modified by ORC 3781.031 and 3781.19. If the owner does not exercise the right to appeal, the application is deemed invalid 6 months after date of adjudication order. (105.3.2)

j. If the residential work has not started within 12 months of approval of the residential construction documents, that approval is deemed invalid, subject to 1 12-month extension if fee ≤ $100 paid by owner ≥ 10 days prior to approval's expiration. Work delays or suspensions of > 6 months require extensions; up to a total of 2 for 6 months each may be granted if the owner requests ≥ 10 days in advance of the expiration of approval and pays fee of ≤ $100. (105.5, .6; 106.3.2)

k. Once the construction documents are approved, the RBO endorses or stamps such plans as approved. The owner receives a certificate of plan approval, providing the serial number, property/equipment address, the owner's name and address, the signature of the issuing RBO, and any other necessary information. The certificate is to be posted on the site until the work is completed, so far as practical. 1 set of construction documents is kept by the RBO, the other is returned to the applicant to keep at the work site, open for inspection by the RBO or his or her representative. (105.7.2, 106.3.1)

l. Nonconforming construction documents may be approved by RBO if the nonconformance will not result in a serious hazard, AND the owner or owner's representative subsequently submits revised documents evidencing compliance with the applicable BBS rules. If such revised documents are not received within 30 days, the RBO must order an adjudication revoking the plan approval. (106.3.1.1)

m. Construction documents that cannot be approved otherwise may be given conditional approval by the RBO at the request of owner or owner's representative, where a portion of the documents conflict with RCO interpretations, OR if compliance requires only minor building design or construction modifications. Such approval is not allowed if the RBO's objection is to the application of SPECIFIC technical requirements of the RCO, or if correction would cause extensive changes in building design or construction. Conditional approvals are conditional licenses to proceed with work up to the point where the objected-to construction or materials are to be incorporated into building. Objections must be in writing from the RBO; and serve as an appealable adjudication order denying the issuance of the license. Items previously examined are presumed to comply with ORC Chapters 3781 and 3791 and RCO in the absence of fraud or a serious safety or sanitation hazard. Reexamination of construction documents is limited to items in the adjudication order. Conditional plan approvals are not considered phased plan approvals. (106.3.1.2)

n. The RBO may issue a **phased** approval of construction of foundations or other part of structure, or for any other stage in construction sequence, prior to the submission of construction documents for the remainder of the structure, subject to the filing of information and detailed statements complying with pertinent RCO provisions. The holder of a phased plan approval may proceed only to the point for which approval has been given. The holder proceeds at his or her own risk with building operation, and without assurance that approval for entire structure will be granted. (106.3.3; 110.4)

o. 105.8 Systems or portions thereof not RCO-required may be installed partially or fully if they meet the RCO requirements to extent of installation. (105.8)

BUILDING DEPARTMENTS

A. Structure

1. BBS rules require the certification of municipal, county, and township building departments and their personnel to accept and approve plans under ORC 3781.03 and 3791.04, per ORC 38.10. That certification does not confer authority over lands owned by the state or by state agencies. (103.1)

2. The local board of health enforces the RCO if the municipality's residential building department is not certified to enforce the plumbing provisions. (103.2.1.1)

3. A political subdivision may enforce the RCO if the nonresidential building department is certified to enforce the OBC, IF the subdivision submits an application for an additional certification to the BBS. (103.2.2.2)

4. All personnel of residential building departments (municipal, township, county) with authority for RCO enforcement, approval of construction documents, and the making of inspections, and persons and employees of persons, firms, or corporations with RCO enforcement authority, must be certified prior to exercising that authority. (103.2, 103.3) Specified certified personnel include:

a. One residential building official (RBO, either employed directly or under contract), who is responsible for overall departmental administration and for RCO enforcement, residential plans examination and residential building inspections;

b. At least one residential plans examiner (employed directly or under contract), who is certified as such or is otherwise qualified under BBS rules, to examine residential construction documents for compliance with the RCO;

c. Electrical plans examiners (employed directly or under contract), to examine construction documents as to electrical systems for compliance with the RCO. If the department lacks such persons, then the residential plans examiner performs that function.

d. At least one residential building inspector, certified as such or otherwise qualified under BBS rules, to examine compliance with approved residential construction documents per the RCO;

e. Residential mechanical inspectors (employed directly or under contract), certified as such to determine compliance with approved heating, ventilating, air conditioning (HVAC) systems construction documents, and associated refrigeration, fuel gas, and heating piping systems, per the RCO. If the department lacks such persons, then the residential building inspector performs that function;

f. The residential building department of the municipality may choose to enforce the RCO's plumbing provisions. If so, then the department must employ or have under contract at least one person who is certified as a residential plumbing inspector, to determine compliance with approved residential construction documents per the RCO;

g. At least one electrical safety inspector (employed directly or under contract), who is certified as such to determine compliance with approved residential construction documents as to electrical systems per the RCO;

h. Alternate personnel (employed directly or under contract) meeting certification requirements herein, to serve in the event of a conflict of interest or the unavailability of above personnel;

i. Permanent replacement personnel that are needed within 120 days of personnel required above leaving the employment of the department;

j. Municipalities, townships, or counties may contract with certified residential building departments, health districts, or persons, firms, or corporations, in lieu of themselves exercising RCO enforcement authority, administering RCO rules, approving residential plans and specifications and performing field inspections, IF that is done by contract with such entities AND the BBS approves. (103.2)

5. A residential building department certification application must include (103.2.1):

a. A copy of the law creating the department, and a copy of the resolution requesting certification of the department to enforce RCO rules.

b. A proposed budget and organizational chart for department.

c. Data showing the population and size of area to be served.

d. The number and qualifications of departmental staff.

e. The names, addresses and qualifications of any persons, firms or corporations contracted with to furnish architectural, engineering, or inspection services per the RCO.

f. The names of other municipalities, townships, counties, health districts, or other political subdivisions, or their officers or employees, that are contracting to furnish architectural or engineering services to the municipality, township, or county.

g. A copy of the ordinance or resolution authorizing the residential building department to contract with other municipalities, townships, counties, health districts, or other political subdivisions, persons, firms or corporations for plan approval and inspections, and a copy of the contract(s) for such.

h. The department within the jurisdiction's governmental structure that is responsible for plumbing inspection, if that is not handled by the residential building department.

     i. Any other charts, maps, statistical data or other information, which the department feels, may benefit the BBS in considering the certification application.

     j. Amendments to an application, made prior to formal action being taken by the BBS, if the jurisdiction requests leave in writing, and the amendments conform to the RCO.

     k. The proposed procedure for residential plan approval, a copy of the residential plan review application, and a copy of the residential department's approval stamp.

     l. An original and 6 copies of all documents, papers and charts provided per paragraphs **a-k** above. Copies can be reproduced if they are clear and readable.

     m. The signature of the authorized representative of the board of township trustees in townships, the board of county commissioners in counties, or the appropriate official in municipalities. (The latter should consult the legal advisor to determine the appropriate municipal officer or body with authority to authorize the application preparation and filing.)

6. After the application is filed and the BBS reviews it, the BBS holds a public hearing per ORC 3781.101 and ORC Chapter 119. The hearing will be attended by the proposed RBO for the municipality, the board of township trustees, or the board of county commissioners, or the appropriate legal counselor, or other authorized representative, to answer questions posed by the BBS; or, such officials may present their positions in writing. All interested persons have a right to be heard at the hearing, after being duly sworn or affirmed. The BBS must record the proceeding. (103.2.2)

7. The BBS approval must state those subject matters for which the department is certified, and any limitations on its powers. (103.2.3)

8. If the BBS denies an application in whole or in part, the appropriate official in either municipalities, boards of township trustees, or boards of county commissioners, must be notified in writing of the denial, the reason for denial, and of the right to appeal. (103.2.5.1)

9. The BBS assesses fees of 1% in addition to any fees that are imposed by political subdivisions for the approvals and acceptance of plans and specifications, and inspections per ORC 3781.102. The fee is collected by those subdivisions, and includes fees from residential departments under contract. The RBO remits assessments by monthly check, payable to the treasurer of the state of Ohio. (103.2.4.2)

B. Personnel

1. An applicant for RBO certification must be either:

     a. Registered in Ohio as an architect or professional engineer;

     b. With at least 5 years experience as a residential or nonresidential contractor, or superintendent responsible for obtaining approvals and inspections of structures regulated per ORC, or

     c. Experienced as a residential plans examiner. (103.3.3.1)

2. An applicant for a residential plans examiner certification must be either:

     a. Registered in Ohio as an architect or professional engineer;

     b. With at least 5 years experience in building design and construction of residential or non-residential buildings or structures; or

     c. The graduate of an RCO trainee program. (103.3.3.2)

3. An applicant for electrical plans examiner certification must have at least 5 years experience as a full-time electrical safety inspector in a certified building department. (103.3.3.2.1)

4. An applicant for residential building inspector certification must be either:

     a. With at least 3 years experience as a contractor or supervisor for residential or non-residential buildings or structures, or experienced as a residential plans examiner; or

     b. With at least 3 years experience as a skilled tradesman for work that is subject to inspection under a code adopted per either the RCO or OBC; or,

     c. The graduate of an RCO trainee program. (103.3.3.3)

5.   An applicant for residential plumbing inspector certification must be either:

     a. With at least 7 years experience as a plumbing contractor or supervisor for residential or non-residential buildings or structures, or experienced as a residential building inspector; or

     b. With at least 7 years experience as a skilled tradesman for plumbing work that is subject to inspection under a code adopted per either the RCO or OBC; or,

     c. The graduate of an RCO trainee program. (103.3.3.4)

6.   An applicant for residential mechanical inspector certification must be either:

     a. With at least 3 years experience as an HVAC systems contractor or as the supervisor of residential or non-residential buildings, or experienced as a residential plans examiner; or

     b. With at least 3 years experience as a skilled tradesman for HVAC systems and associated refrigeration, fuel gas, and heating piping; or

     c. The graduate of an RCO trainee program. (103.3.3.5)

7.   Certificate holders under 1-6 above must complete at least 30 hours of BBS-approved continuing education in their respective classifications prior to the expiration of their certificates, and attend all BBS-required and sponsored continuing education courses. A failure to complete the required number of hours results in certification forfeiture. The certificate holder is responsible for providing the BBS with proof of successful course completion. (103.3.6)

8.   Certifications must be renewed every 3 years. The requirements are the payment of a $30 fee and proof of completion of the required number of course hours. An expired certification may be renewed within 1 year of the expiration date if all the prerequisites for renewal have been met. (103.3.7)

9.   The BBS may investigate a certification holder on its own motion or on the written complaint of any person affected by plan approval or enforcement if there is an allegation of:

     a. Fraud or deceit in the obtaining of the certificate;

     b. A felony or crime involving moral turpitude;

     c. Gross negligence, incompetence, or misconduct by the holder in performing his or her duties; or

     d. A failure to complete continuing education requirements prior to the expiration of the certificate. (103.3.8)

10.   In the event of an investigation under 9. above:

     a. The BBS notifies the certification holder of the charges, that a hearing before the BBS must be requested by the holder within 30 days from the date of mailing of the notice, and that the applicant is allowed representation by counsel. Notification is made by certified mail, return receipt requested. Even if the certificate holder fails to request a hearing, the BBS must still hold one before ordering the revocation or suspension of a certification.

     b. The BBS schedules the hearing within 7-15 days after receipt of the request for such, unless the parties agree on another date. The hearing may be continued or postponed by the BBS either upon application by the holder or on its own motion.

     c. The adjudication hearing is conducted per ORC 3781.10, 3781.101, and Chapter 119.09. After the hearing, the BBS may either dismiss the complaint or order either the revocation or suspension of the certification.

     d. The BBS must send an affected party a certified copy of its order, return receipt requested, and inform the party that it may appeal order within 15 days to court of common pleas in Franklin county per ORC 3781.10, 3781.101, and Chapter 119.12. (103.3.8)

11. No employee, or person contracting to perform RCO services within a residential department's jurisdictional area, may perform such services for a department in which **that employee or person exercises RCO authority over** any work, or evaluation of such, that is furnished by the employee or person, or by a private contractor employing him, (full or part-time) or on an incidental basis. In addition, no conflict of interest is allowed by that person or employee under ORC 102.03 and 102.04. (103.2.3)

C. *Powers*

1. The RBO of a BBS-certified department is authorized to enforce the RCO, ORC Chapters 3781. and 3791, and all other codes and standards referenced in the RCO, to the extent they are referenced for design data, facts, figures, requirements, criteria, conditions, measures, and information, as to construction of residential buildings or parts thereof. Exceptions:

    a. The Fire marshal, or fire chief of municipal corporations or townships having fire departments, enforces all provisions of BBS rules concerning fire prevention. The RBO enforces design and construction requirements and other requirements in fire prevention code to which the RCO refers, to extent of the reference. (104.1.1)

    b. City or general health district boards of health, or the residential building departments of municipal corporations, enforce provisions as to sanitary construction. (104.1.2)

    c. The department of the city engineer, in cities having such, supervises and regulates the city's entire sewerage and drainage system, including house drain, house sewer, and all laterals draining into street sewers. Such departments control and supervise the installation and construction of all drains and sewers becoming part of the city sewerage system. They issue all necessary approvals and licenses for constructing and installing all house drains, house sewers, and all other lateral drains emptying into main sewers. The department maintains a permanent record of the installation/location of every drain and sewerage system of the city. (104.3.3)

    d. Any officer or department may enforce any provision of the RCO **if necessary**, notwithstanding the above. (104.4.4)

2. RBO tasks:

    a. Receive applications.

    b. Review of required construction documents as they are submitted.

    c. Issue plan approvals for the erection, alteration, demolition, or moving of residential buildings and structures

    d. Inspect premises where approvals are issued and enforce compliance with the RCO. If the work or equipment is contrary to approved plans and the RCO, RBO must send written notice to the owner or owner's agent, indicating where and how the nonconformity exists, and specifying a reasonable time within which to achieve that conformity. (104.2, 104.3)

CERTIFICATES OF OCCUPANCY

1. A Certificate of Occupancy issued by the Residential Building Official (RBO) indicates the allowable conditions for the use or occupation of a new residential structure, or the enlargement, extension, or partial or total alteration of an existing structure. The use of spaces in an existing structure which are unaffected by alteration work may continue if the RBO determines that they are safe for use. The structure and all approved building service equipment must be maintained per the certificate. The certificate should be issued in a timely manner when construction is conducted per the approved construction documents, the final tests and inspections are completed, and no building official orders are outstanding. The certificate's validity is conditional upon

the maintenance and testing of building systems and equipment per the approval and per applicable equipment and systems schedules. (110.1)

a. If for an existing structure, a certificate is granted upon request from the owner where there are no pending violations of law or BBS orders, and inspection and investigation indicates that the alleged occupancy has in fact previously existed. Unless necessary to protect public safety and welfare, the RCO does not require the removal, alteration, or abandonment of the property, or prevent the continuation of lawful occupancy. (110.3)

b. Partial occupancy is allowed by issuance of a certificate before completion of the work, upon the request of the owner or owner's representative, if the RBO finds that the space can be safely occupied without endangering life or public welfare. The certificate must indicate the areas that are approved for occupancy and the time limits for completion of work. (110.4)

c. If a structure changed in part from one occupancy to another, the RBO may issue a time-limited occupancy, assuming:

(1) No legal violations or RBO orders are pending;

(2) Inspection and investigation establishes that the proposed use does not endanger public safety and welfare safely;

(3) The RBO approves the use for an alternative purpose on a temporary basis;

(4) A certificate is issued indicating any special conditions for the time-limited alternative purpose use. (110.1.5)

2. The certificate must contain:

a. The plan approval application number.

b. Property address.

c. The name and address of owner.

d. A description of those portions of the structure for which the certificate is issued.

e. The signature of all RBOs with jurisdiction over the property (i.e., if a certification of a given building department is limited for systems as plumbing or piping systems). Each must sign the certificate, stating the scope of their individual approvals.

f. The RCO edition under which plan approval was issued.

g. The type and description of the automatic sprinkler system, if one is provided.

h. Any special stipulations and conditions for plan approval, including any variances granted to the RCO. (110.3)

3. The RBO may suspend or revoke a certificate if it is issued in error, on the basis of incorrect information supplied, or if the structure or a portion thereof violates any ordinance or regulation or any RCO provisions. (110.5)

4. If work that is regulated by the RCO (including site preparations, construction, appliance use, materials, assemblage, or manufactured product) is found after inspection to have been performed contrary to the RCO, or in a dangerous or unsafe manner (per ORC Chapters 3781 and 3791), the RBO may issue a written stop work order, limited to the specific subject of order, providing the reason for the order, and the conditions under which the resumption of work may occur. The stop work order is given to the owner, or to the owner's agent, and the person performing the work. Once the order is issued, the cited work must immediately cease, except for that necessary to remove the violation or unsafe condition. Failure to cease work otherwise is deemed a public nuisance. (114)

CLIMATE DESIGN

1. Ohio has established or adopted various climate and geographical design criteria, supplemented as necessary by local jurisdictions, which are to be observed in construction. These criteria are referenced as follows:

a. TABLE 301.2(1) Climatic and Geographic Design Criteria
b. TABLE 301.2(2) Component and Cladding Loads for a Building with a Mean Roof Height of 30 Feet Located In Exposure B (Psf)
c. TABLE 301.2(3) Height and Exposure Adjustment Coefficients for Table 301.2(2)
d. FIGURE 301.2(1) Isolines of The 971/2 Percent Winter (December, January and February) Design Temperatures (& 176;F)
e. Figure 301.2(2) Seismic Design Categories — Site Class D
f. FIGURE 301.2(3) Weathering Probability Map for Concrete
g. FIGURE 301.2(4) Basic Wind Speeds for 50-Year Mean Recurrence Interval
h. FIGURE 301.2(5) Ground Snow Loads, Pg, for the United States (lb/ft2)
i. FIGURE 301.2(6) Termite Infestation Probability Map
j. FIGURE 301.2(7) Decay Probability Map
k. FIGURE 301.2(8) Component and Cladding Pressure Zones
   [Tables and Figures are available at: http://www.com.ohio.gov/documents/dico__Re sidentialCode10412.pdf]

CONCRETE

1. Concrete must meet the minimum specified compressive strength per Table R402.2. If subject to weathering per Table R301.2(1), concrete must be air entrained per Table R402.2. Do not exceed the percentages of total weight of cementitious materials specified in ACI 318 for maximum weight of fly ash, other pozzolans, silica fume, or slag included in concrete mixtures for garage floor slabs and for exterior porches, carport slabs, and for steps exposed to deicing chemicals. ACI 318-listed standards apply to materials used in producing/testing concrete. Allow the use of cements permitted by ACI 318 and ASTM C 1157. (402.2)
   a. TABLE R402.2 MINIMUM SPECIFIED COMPRESSIVE STRENGTH OF CONCRETE
      [Table is available at: http://www.com.state.oh.us/dic/Documents/ResidentialCodeb oardchangestotheOBOA2004ResidentialCodeofOhio.pdf]
3. Concrete slab-on-ground floors are to be a minimum 3.5" (89 mm) thick. (If soils are expansive, see 403.1.8). Concrete requires a specified compressive strength per **WALLS, STUDS AND GIRDERS**. (506.1)

ENERGY STANDARDS

1. Energy efficiency for the design and construction of RCO-regulated buildings comprised of detached 1, 2, and 3 family dwellings must meet (and may exceed) the International Energy Conservation Code, where the local jurisdiction adopts such per RCO 101.3(3). In the alternative, they must meet either paragraphs 1-3 below, OR paragraph 4 below. If they are comprised of R-3 occupancies, the building must comply with OBC 13 as to energy efficiency. Use Figure 1101.1 or Table 1101.2 to determine the appropriate climate zone for establishing the applicable requirements paragraphs 1-3 below. Identify all materials, systems, and equipment to indicate they are in compliance with **APPLIANCES**. Exceptions from these requirements:
   a. Building envelope portions not enclosing conditioned space. (1101.1, .2, .3, .7)
   b. FIGURE 1101.1 — CLIMATE ZONES
   c. TABLE 1101.2 — CLIMATE ZONES BY STAES AND COUNTIES
      OHIO is in Zone 5 except for following counties in Zone 4:
      Adams, Brown, Clermont, Gallia, Hamilton, Lawrence, Pike, Scioto, Washington
      [Tables and Figures are available at: http://www.registerofohio.state.oh.us/pdfs/ 4101/8/11/4101$8-11-01__PH__FF__A__RU__20081222__0836.pdf]
2. The manufacturer of the building's thermal envelope insulation must indicate the R-value identification marking on all insulation pieces ≥ 12" (305 mm) wide, OR the

insulation installers must provide a certification indicating the type, manufacturer and R-value of insulation for each installed element of the thermal envelope.

    a. If the insulation is blown or sprayed (fiberglass and cellulose, the certification must show the initial installed and settled thickness, the settled R-value, installed density, coverage area and the number of bags installed.

    b. If the insulation is sprayed polyurethane foam (SPF), the certification must show the installed thickness of the area covered and the R-value. The certificate must be signed, dated and posted conspicuously on job site, in readily observable form. (1101.4)

    c. The thickness of blown in or sprayed roof/ceiling (fiberglass or cellulose must be written in inches (mm) on markers that are spaced at least 1 per 300' (28 mm) in attic space, facing the access opening). They must also be affixed to trusses or joists, showing the minimum initial installed thickness in numbers at least 1" (25 mm) high. (1101.4.1)

3. U-factors for fenestration products (windows, doors and skylights) must be labeled or certified by the manufacturer after a determination of compliance with NFRC 100 is made by an accredited, independent laboratory.

    a. If lacking a labeled U-factor, products must be assigned a default U-factor from Tables 1101.5(1) and 1101.5(2). The Solar Heat Gain Coefficient (SHGC) of glazed fenestration products (windows, glazed doors and skylights) must be labeled or certified by the manufacturer after a determination of compliance with NFRC 200 is made by an accredited, independent laboratory.

    b. If lacking a labeled SHGC, products must be assigned a default SHGC from Table 1101.5(3). (1105.5)

    c. TABLE 1101.5(1) — DEFAULT GLAZED FENESTRATION U-FACTORS

    d. TABLE 1101.5(2) — DEFAULT DOOR U-FACTORS

    e. TABLE 1101.5(3) — DEFAULT GLAZED FENESTRATION SHGC

      [Tables are available at: http://www.registerofohio.state.oh.us/pdfs/4101/8/11/ 4101$8-11-01__PH__FF__A__RU__20081222__0836.pdf]

4. Install all materials, systems and equipment per the manufacturer's installation instructions and RCO provisions. NOTE: Install a rigid, opaque, and weather-resistant protective covering on insulation that is applied to basement wall exteriors, crawl space walls, and the perimeter of slab-on-grade floors, to prevent thermal performance degradation. This covers exposed exterior insulation, and extends a minimum of 6" (152 mm) below grade. (1101.6)

5. The builder or a registered design professional must post a permanent certificate on or in the electrical distribution panel, listing the predominant R-values of insulation that is installed in or on the ceiling, roof, walls, foundation (slab, basement wall, crawlspace wall and/or floor) and ducts outside conditioned spaces. A certification posting requirement also applies for U-factors for fenestration; the solar heat gain coefficient (SHGC) of fenestration; and the type and efficiency of all heating, cooling and service water heating equipment. If a component has more than 1 value, the certificate must list the value covering the largest area. (1101.8)

6. Building Thermal Envelope (1102)

    a. Must meet Table 1102.1 requirements for the building thermal envelope, using the climate zone per Table 1101.2. Take the sum of insulation material used in layers (i.e., framing cavity insulation and insulation sheathing) to determine the component R-value. If blown insulation, use the manufacturer's settled R-value. Do not include the R-value for other building materials or air films in computing the R-values. (1102.1)

    b. Allow assembly with U-factor ≤ Table 1102.1.2 value as an alternative to Table 1102.1 R-value. Exception:

(1) In mass walls not meeting insulation location criterion per 6.e. below, allow the U-factor to be:

    (i)   U-factor of 0.17 in Climate Zone 1

    (ii)   U-factor of 0.14 in Climate Zone 2

    (iii)   U-factor of 0.12 in Climate Zone 3

    (iv)   U-factor of 0.l0 in Climate Zone 4 except Marine

    (v)   U-factor of 0.082 in Climate Zone 5 and Marine 4 (1102.1.2)

c. If the total thermal envelope UA (U-factor x assembly area) is ≤ total UA, based on Table 1102.1.2 U-factors, (multiplied by assembly area of proposed building), the building is deemed to be in compliance with Table 1102.1. Use a method consistent with the ASHRAE Handbook of Fundamentals to compute the UA and include the thermal bridging effects of framing materials. Must meet SHGC requirements also. (1102.1.3)

d. If R-38 in the ceiling is required by paragraph 6.a. hereof, R-30 satisfies that R-38 requirement where the full height of uncompressed R-30 extends over the wall top plate at the eaves. R-38 satisfies an R-49 requirement where the full height of uncompressed R-38 extends over the wall top plate at the eaves. If the insulation levels required is above R-30, but the roof or ceiling assembly design does not have sufficient space, R-30 is the minimum required insulation, limited to 500' sq (46 sq m) of the ceiling area. (1102.2)

e. TABLE 1102.1 — INSULATION AND FENESTRATION REQUIREMENTS BY COMPONENT

f. TABLE 1102.1.2 — EQUIVALENT U-FACTORS

    [Tables are available at: http://www.registerofohio.state.oh.us/pdfs/4101/8/11/ 4101$8-11-01__PH__FF__A__RU__20081222__0836.pdf]

g. Mass walls are concrete block, concrete, insulated concrete form (ICF), masonry cavity, brick (other than brick veneer), earth (adobe, compressed earth block, rammed earth) and solid timber/log walls. Paragraph 6 provisions above for mass walls apply if at least 50% of the required insulation R-value is either exterior of, or integral to, the wall. Otherwise, walls must meet the wood frame wall insulation requirements of paragraph 6. Exception:

    (1) If walls do not meet above criterion per insulation, the minimum added insulation R-value is:

        (i)   R-value of 4 in Climate Zone 1

        (ii)   R-value of 6 in Climate Zone 2

        (iii)   R-value of 8 in Climate Zone 3

        (iv.)   R-value of 10 in Climate Zone 4, except Marine

        (v)   R-value of 13 in climate Zone 5 and Marine 4 (1102.2.3)

h. Steel-frame ceilings, walls and floors must meet Table 1102.2.4 insulation requirements OR Table 1102.1.2 U-factor requirements. Use a series-parallel path calculation method to calculate the U-factor for the steel-frame envelope assembly. (1102.2.4)

    (i) TABLE 1102.2.4 — STEEL-FRAME CEILING, WALL AND FLOOR INSULATION (R-VALUE)

       [Table is available at: http://www.registerofohio.state.oh.us/pdfs/4101/8/11/ 4101$8-11-01__PH__FF__A__RU__20081222__0836.pdf]

i. Floor insulation must maintain permanent contact with the subfloor decking underside. Insulate slab-on-grade floors with a surface < 12" below grade per Table 1102.1, with the insulation extending downward from top of slab, outside or inside of the foundation wall. Extend insulation below grade the distance required per Table 1102.1, using any combination of vertical insulation, insulation extending under slab, or insulation extending out from the building. Protect insulation extending from the building by pavement, or by a minimum of 10" (254 mm) of soil. The top edge of the insulation between the exterior wall and the edge of the interior slab may be cut at 45 (0.79 rad) angle from the exterior wall. If the jurisdiction is designated as one with a very heavy termite infestation, slab-edge insulation is not required. (1102.2.5, .7)

j. Insulate exterior walls for conditioned basements from the top of the wall to 10′ (3048 mm) below grade or to the basement floor, whichever is less. Unconditioned basement walls must meet the same requirement UNLESS the floor overhead is insulated per paragraphs 6.a. and 6.i hereof. (1102.2.6)

k. Allow insulation of crawl space walls if the crawl space is not vented to the outside, as an alternative to insulating floors over crawl spaces. Permanently fasten crawl space insulation to the wall, and extend downward from the floor to the finished grade level, then vertically and/or horizontally ≥ 24" (610 mm) more. Cover all exposed earth in unvented crawl space foundations with a continuous vapor retarder, extending the retarder edges ≥ 6" (152 mm) up, and attached to, the stem wall. Overlap all joints of the retarder by 6" (152 mm), and seal or tape. (1102.2.8)

l. No insulation is required on the horizontal portion of the foundation supporting a masonry veneer. (1102.2.9)

m. The minimum ceiling insulation R-values is R-19 in zones 1-4 and R-24 in zones 5-8. In all other zones, the minimum wall R-value is R-13. Where a sunroom is separated from conditioned space by new wall(s), the latter must meet building thermal envelope requirements. (1102.2.10)

7. Fenestration (1102.3)

a. Allow an area-weighted average of fenestration products to satisfy U-factor requirements. If > 50% is glazed, the area-weighted average meets solar gain coefficient (SHGC) requirements. Exempt up to 15′ sq (1.4 m₂) of glazed fenestration from the U-factor and SHGC requirements. 1 opaque door assembly per unit is exempted from the U-factor requirement. (1102.3.1, .2, .3, .4)

b. The maximum fenestration U-factor is 0.50, and the maximum skylight U-factor is 0.75, for zones 4-8. New windows/doors separating the sunroom from conditioned space must meet the building thermal envelope requirements. (1102.3.5)

c. If replacing some or all of an existing fenestration unit with a new fenestration product, including sash and glazing, the replacement unit must meet the applicable U-factor and SHGC requirements in Table 1102.1. (1102.3.6)

8. Air Leakage (1102.4)

a. Durably seal the building thermal envelope to limit air infiltration, using sealing methods between dissimilar materials that allow for differential expansion and contraction. Caulk, gasket, weather-strip or otherwise seal with an air barrier material, suitable film or solid material the following:

   (1) All joints, seams and penetrations.
   (2) Site-built windows, doors and skylights.
   (3) Openings between window and door assemblies and their respective jambs and framing.
   (4) Utility penetrations.
   (5) Dropped ceilings or chases adjacent to the thermal envelope.
   (6) Knee walls.
   (7) Walls and ceilings separating a garage from conditioned spaces.
   (8) Behind tubs and showers on exterior walls.
   (9) Common walls between dwelling units.
   (10) Other sources of infiltration. (1102.4.1)

b. The air infiltration rate for windows, skylights and sliding glass doors must be $\leq$ 0.3 cubic foot per minute per square foot [1.5(L/s)/m$_2$], and for swinging doors $\leq$ 0.5 cubic foot per minute per square foot [2.5(L/s)/m$_2$]. Testing must be done by an accredited independent laboratory, and windows, skylights, and doors must be labeled by the manufacturer to NFRC 400 or AAMA/WDMA/CSA 101/IS.2/A440. Exception:

    (1) site-built windows, skylights, and doors. (1102.4.2)

c. Seal recessed luminaries in building thermal envelope to limit air leakage between conditioned and unconditioned spaces to be either:

    (1) IC-rated and labeled with sealed or gasketed enclosures that prevent air leakage to the ceiling cavity or any unconditioned space; or,

    (2) IC-rated and labeled as meeting ASTM E 283 (tested at 1.57 lbs. per square foot (75 Pa) pressure differential with $\leq$ 2.0′ cubic per minute (0.944 L/s) of air movement from any conditioned space to the ceiling cavity; or placed inside an airtight sealed box with clearances of $\geq$ 0.5″ (13 mm) from any combustible material and 3″ (76 mm) from the insulation). (1102.4.3)

9.   Moisture Control (1102.5)

a. The building design cannot create or allow accelerated deterioration due to moisture condensation. Provide an approved vapor retarder in above-grade frame walls, floors and ceilings that are not ventilated to allow moisture to escape, installed on the warm-in-winter side of thermal insulation. Exceptions:

    (1) Construction situations if moisture/freezing will not damage materials.

    (2) Frame walls, floors and ceilings in Zones 1, 2, 3, 4A, and 4B. Do not exempt crawl space floor vapor retarders.

    (3) If other approved means to avoid condensation are available.

b. Allow a area weighted average maximum fenestration U-factor using tradeoffs per paragraph 6.c above in Zones 6 through 8 of 0.55.

c. The maximum U-factor for skylights is 0.75 in zones 6 through 8, for purposes of paragraph 9.

10.   Heating and Cooling Systems (1103)

a. Each separate heating and cooling system requires a separate thermostat. Heat pumps with supplementary electric-resistance heat require controls that disallow such supplemental operation if the heat pump compressor can handle the heating load (except during defrost). (1103.1)

b. Seal all ducts, air handlers, filter boxes and building cavities used as ducts. Joints/seams compliance is required with OBC 1601.3.l. Do not use building cavities as supply ducts. Insulate ducts for supply and return to a minimum of R-38. Insulate ducts in floor trusses to a minimum of R-6. Exception:

    (1) Ducts or portions thereof that are totally within the thermal envelope. (1103.2)

c. Insulate mechanical system piping capable of carrying fluids above 105 & 176 F (40 & 176;C) or below 55 & 176 F (13 & 176;C) to a minimum of R-2. (1103.3)

d. Insulate all circulating service hot water piping to at least R-2. Circulating hot water systems include an automatic or readily accessible manual switch that can stop the hot water circulating pump when the system is not in use. (1103.4)

e. Install automatic or gravity dampers that close if the ventilation system is not operating in outdoor air intakes and exhausts. (1103.5)

f. Size heating and cooling equipment per OBC M1401.3. (1103.6)

11.   Energy Prescriptive Requirements (1104)

a. RCO energy compliance is demonstrated by compliance with the prescriptive requirements in Tables 1, 2, and 3 below.

b. TABLE 1 — Ohio Residential Prescriptive Energy Requirements Table a

    c. TABLE 2 — Zone A Zone B

    d. TABLE 3 — AIR INFILTRATION REQUIREMENTS

      [Tables are available at: http://www.registerofohio.state.oh.us/pdfs/4101/8/11/ 4101$8-11-01__PH__FF__A__RU__20081222__0836.pdf]

EXISTING STRUCTURES

1. The RCO is applicable to buildings constructed per plans approved prior to the code's effective date. The occupancy of structures in existence at the date of RCO adoption may continue without change if the alleged occupancy can be demonstrated, no order of the RBO is pending, and there is no evidence of fraud, or of serious safety or sanitation hazard. (102.6)

2. If an existing residential building undergoes alteration, repair, addition and change of occupancy (change in purpose or level of activity within the structure involving a change in code requirement application):

    a. The owner must maintain the structures and equipment in a safe and sanitary condition per current and previous plan approvals and certificates of occupancy; and, maintain RCO-required devices/safeguards per the code edition to which they are installed. This does not require the removal or abrogation of existing fire protection and safety systems or devices without the RBO's approval. Maintenance responsibility is placed on the owner or the owner's designated agent. (115.2, .3)

    b. The owner must conform any additions or alterations with the RCO, subject to approval by the RBO, without causing the existing structure to be in violation of the RCO. Structural portions not altered or affected by the alteration need not comply with RCO's new structure requirements. Exception:

        (1) If the building or structure is in a flood hazard area, all additions, alterations or repairs substantially improving the existing structure must meet the flood design requirements for new construction, including ALL PARTS of the existing structure. (115.4)

    c. The owner must conform any alterations to an existing system (egress, fire protection, mechanical, plumbing, etc.), and materials or building components, not otherwise provided for in the RCO, to new construction requirements to the extent of the alteration. Existing systems/materials/components must meet the RCO only to the extent that they are affected by such alteration; however, alterations must not cause them to become unsafe, hazardous, overloaded or less effective than when they were originally installed, constructed and/or approved. (115.5)

    d. The owner must replace all building components, and repair existing systems and materials or building components, not otherwise provided for in the RCO, to the standard in place at the time when they were **originally** installed, not to the current RCO standard, if the work is done per the conditions of and in the same manner and arrangement as was done for a system installed at the time, is not less safe than at the time of original installation, and is approved by the RBO. Allow minor reductions in the clear opening dimensions of replacement doors and windows due to different materials, regardless of the RCO standard. Allow used materials, equipment, appliances, and devices meeting current RCO requirements for new materials, if they are approved by the RBO. (115.6)

3. The owner may make no change of use or purpose to a residential building, space within, or accessory structure, unless the change complies with the RCO requirements for such use and the RBO approves. However, no approval is required if the RCO requirements are the same for both uses. (CHANGE OF OCCUPANCY IS DEFINED AS: a change in purpose or level of activity within a structure involving a change in the application of RCO requirements) Similarly, the owner must make no change to uses within the scope of the OBC for existing residential building, spaces within, or

accessory structures, unless such comply with OBC requirements for such occupancy and the RBO approves. (115.7)

4. Residential buildings intended to be used in whole or in part as licensed Type A family day-care home must pass Type A family day-care home checklist (available from BBS). The RBO reports his or her findings to the Ohio Department of Jobs and Family Services. (115.7.2)

5. Moved structures must be safe and sanitary, and repairs, alterations, or changes in occupancy must comply with RCO provisions per new structures (including field work, building location, foundations and foundation connections, wind loads, seismic loads, snow loads, and flood loads). The RBO may inspect, or require inspection at the owner's expense of, various components of relocated building to verify they have not sustained damage; building service equipment, mechanical, plumbing, and fire protection systems must be tested to assure proper operating condition. All such repairs/alterations are subject to approval and completion prior to the issuance of the certificate of occupancy. (115.8)

6. The owner may install components, building elements, equipment, systems, or portions thereof NOT required by the RCO IF they are constructed or installed per the RCO to the extent of the installation. Exceptions: (102.7)

   a. Install non-required fire protection systems per Chapter 9 of OBC to extent of the intended installation. (102.7.1)

   b. A non-required elevator must be designed and installed per residential elevator provisions in Chapter 10 of ANSI A117.1 (Chapter 35 of OBC). (102.7.1)

   c. A non-required platform (wheelchair) lifts must be designed and installed per ASME A18.1 (Chapter 35 of OBC). (102.7.2)

7. RCO provisions per the construction, repair, alteration, addition, restoration and movement of structures, and change of occupancy, are not mandatory for historic buildings if the RBO determines the structure does not constitute a distinct life safety hazard. However, if within an established flood hazard area, the building must comply with 2.b.1 under **EXISTING STRUCTURES** herein. (115.9)

   a. Historic residential buildings must be either:

      (1) Listed or preliminarily determined to be eligible for listing in the "National Register of Historic Places"; or

      (2) Determined by secretary of U.S. department of interior as contributing to the historical significance of a registered historic district, or a district preliminarily determined to qualify as an historic district; or

      (3) Designated as historic under state or local historic preservation program approved by U.S. department of interior.

INSPECTIONS

1. The RBO is responsible for authorizing inspections of properties that are subject to inspection concerning erection, construction, repair, alteration, relocation, or equipment, to determine if the work conformed to approved plans, and if the work meets safety and sanitation requirements. Testing and reports from qualified inspection agencies are acceptable, but the testing must be done in the presence of department personnel if the party being inspected so requests. All required testing is done at the owner's expense or that of owner's representative. Testing is required of any unit that has been altered, repaired, renovated, or extended. (104.4; 109.2, .3, .5; .8)

2. The owner or owner's representative responsible for notifying the RBO that property is ready for inspection. The RBO or a designated representative may enter the structure or premises at reasonable times for inspection, if he or she shows proper identification upon request. The residential building inspector may use remedies provided by law to gain access if permission to enter is denied, or if he or she has

probable cause to believe that the premises harbor a serious hazard. The owner or his or her representative has a duty to allow accessibility and exposure for the inspector to any work required, but if the inspector fails to reinspect within 3 days after the work is redone, exclusive of Saturdays, Sundays, and legal holidays, the work is deemed accepted. (104.5, .6; 109.1, .5)

3. No work is allowed past the point of approval in a prior inspection without the approval of the RBO, who either approves that portion of construction that is satisfactorily completed, or notifies owner or owner's agent as to how that portion does not comply with the RCO. Noncompliant portions constitute code violations and must be corrected. (109.6; 109.8.3)

4. If the inspector finds nonconforming work that the owner fails or refuses to bring into RCO conformity, the inspector must make a written report of those finding to the RBO, documenting the relevant rule and nonconformity, and such other information the RBO requires, or that is considered important by the inspector. (109.7)

5. The inspector may approve industrial units, alternative materials, design, and methods of construction and equipment, not specifically prescribed by the RCO, if they are approved by the RBO.

   a. If the inspector has insufficient evidence that an alternative method or material complies with the RCO, the RBO may require testing at no cost to jurisdiction per the RCO or other recognized test standards, performed by an approved agency. (104.9, 106.2.10)

   b. All manufacturer's installation instructions are to be available on the job site at the time of inspection. (106.2.10)

   c. Inspections include the following items:

      (1) Footings and foundations (109.3.1)

      (2) Concrete slab and underfloors - conducted after in-slab or under-floor reinforcing steel and building service equipment, conduit, piping accessories and ancillary equipment items are installed, and prior to the installing of concrete or floor sheathing (including subfloor). (109.3.2)

      (3) Elevation certificate — lowest floor elevation. (109.3.3)

      (4) Framing inspections, after the completion of roof deck/sheathing, framing, fire blocking/bracing, and pipes, chimneys, proper concealment of venting, and rough electrical, plumbing, heating wires, pipes and ducts is approved. Allow the viewing of joints and penetrations in fire-resistance rated assemblies until inspection/approval. (109.3.4, 109.3.8)

      (5) If fire-resistance rating construction is required between dwelling units or as a function of property location, inspection is required either after lathing/wallboarding, or before the wallboards or joints/fasteners are taped and finished. (109.3.5)

      (6) Industrial unit inspection results are reported by the inspector to the RBO, who in turn notifies the BBS. Units cannot be occupied until any BBS-mandated corrective action is taken. Inspections of industrial units includes:

         (i) Connections to on-site construction, module interconnection, utility connections. Inspection and testing does not require factory constructed BBS-authorized component to be destroyed or disassembled.

         (ii) Inspection for transportation, improper weather exposure or other damage.

         (iii) Inspection of the unit for the presence of BBS-furnished insignia.

         (iv) The floor plan, exterior elevations, and exposed details must conform to approved plans. (109.3.6.1, 109.7.1)

(7) The inspection must occur after the exterior and interior lath/gypsum board in place, but before plastering or gypsum board joints, and fasteners are taped and finished. Exception:

    (i) Gypsum board not part of fire-resistance assembly or shear assembly. (109.3.7)

(8) The RBO must approve utility, source of energy, fuel, or power connections to any RCO-regulated structure or system for which approval is required (including temporary connections). (111)

(9) Energy efficiency (i.e., envelope insulation R and U value, infiltration, fenestration U value, duct system R value, HVAC/water heating equipment efficiency). (109.3.9)

(10) A final inspection after all plan approval work is completed. (109.3.10)

MULTI-UNIT STRUCTURES

1. Separate dwelling units in two-family dwelling structures by wall and/or floor assemblies with ≥ 1-hour fire-resistance rating per ASTM E 119 testing. Extend fire-resistance-rated floor-ceiling and wall assemblies tightly to the exterior wall, and wall assemblies to the underside of roof sheathing. Exception:

    a. ½ hour fire resistance rating is permitted in buildings equipped throughout with an automatic sprinkler system installed per NFPA 13. (317.1)

2. If more than 2 dwelling units:

    a. Separate dwelling units in structures of more than 2 dwelling units from an adjacent unit by 2 1-hour fire-resistance-rated wall assemblies, or by common 2-hour fire-resistance rated wall if such wall does not contain plumbing, mechanical equipment, ducts, or vents in a common wall cavity. Treat penetrations of electrical outlet boxes per 4 below.

3. Within 2-unit groupings:

    a. Separate units by 1-hour fire-resistance rated wall and/or floor assemblies, if that grouping is separated from adjacent units or other 2-unit groupings by 2 1-hour fire-resistance rated wall assemblies, or 1 2-hour wall constructed as above. If assemblies must be fire-resistance-rated, the supporting construction must have an equal or greater fire-resistive rating. (317.2)

4. If ≥ 4 dwelling/sleeping units in a single structure:

    a. OBC 11 provisions apply. Non-required accessibility components must comply with ANSI A117.1 per OBC 35, to the extent of the installation. (322.1)

TEMPORARY STRUCTURES

1. The Residential Building Official (RBO) may approve temporary residential structures and occupancies for limited times of service ≤ 180 days, with extensions allowed for demonstrated cause. Such structures and occupancies must conform to the structural strength, fire safety, means of egress, accessibility, light, ventilation and sanitary requirements of the RCO to ensure public health, safety and general welfare. (107.1, 2)

2. Approvals of temporary residential structures or occupancies may be terminated if the use of such facilities is discontinued at the order of the RBO. (107.3)

UNSAFE BUILDINGS

1. Serious hazards (i.e., unsafe or unsanitary structures or existing equipment due to inadequate egress facilities, inadequate light, and ventilation, or constituting fire hazards, or otherwise endangering human life) must be eliminated, or the building vacated, at the written direction of the Residential Building Official. If a vacant building remains a serious hazard, it must be razed. (117.1)

2. If the RBO deems a structure or equipment to be a serious hazard and the owner fails to eliminate such, or to vacate or raze the building within a specified time, the RBO must proceed under **ADJUDICATION** and ORC section 3781.15. (117.2)

3. Unsafe structure may be restored to a safe condition. All repairs, alterations or additions or changes of occupancy occurring during restoration must comply with the requirements of **EXISTING STRUCTURES**.

WALLS, STUDS, AND GIRDERS

1. Girders fabricated of dimension lumber may not have allowable spans exceeding the values in Tables 502.5(1) and 502.5(2). (502.5)
   a. TABLE R502.5(1) GIRDER SPANS AND HEADER SPANS FOR EXTERIOR BEARING WALLS
   b. TABLE 502.5(2) GIRDER SPANS AND HEADER SPANS FOR INTERIOR BEARING WALLS

   [Tables are available at: http://www.com.state.oh.us/dic/Documents/Residential CodeboardchangestotheOBOA2004ResidentialCodeofOhio.pdf]

2. All sizing, height and spacing of studs is per Table 602.3.(5). Exception:
   a. Space utility grade studs ≤ 16" (406 mm) on center, not supporting more than the roof and ceiling, and ≤ 8′ (2438 mm) high for exterior and load-bearing walls or 10′ (3048 mm) for interior nonload-bearing walls.
   b. Studs > 10′ (3048 mm) high are per Table 602.3.1. (602.3.1)

3. TABLE 602.3.1 Maximum Allowable Length of Wood Wall Studs Exposed To Wind Speeds of 100 Mph or Less In Seismic Design Categories

   [Table is available at: ttp://www.com.state.oh.us/dic/Documents/ResidentialCodeboar dchangestotheOBOA2004ResidentialCodeofOhio.pdf]

4. Design and construct exterior wood-frame walls per **ENERGY STANDARDS** and Figures 602.3(1) and 602.3(2), or per AF&PA's NDS. Fasten exterior wall components per Tables 602.3(1) through 602.3(4). Brace exterior walls covered with foam plastic sheathing per **ENERGY STANDARDS**. Fasten structural sheathing directly to structural framing members. (602.3)
   a. TABLE 602.3(1) Fastener Schedule for Structural Members
   b. TABLE 602.3(2) ALTERNATE ATTACHMENTS SPACING OF FASTENERS
   c. TABLE 602.3(3) ALLOWABLE STUD SPACING FOR WOOD STRUCTURAL PANEL WALL SHEATHING
   d. TABLE 602.3(4) ALLOWABLE SPANS FOR PARTICLEBOARD WALL SHEATHING
   e. TABLE 602.3(5) SIZE, HEIGHT AND SPACING OF WOOD STUDS
   f. FIGURE 602.3(1) Typical Wall, Floor and Roof Framing
   g. FIGURE 602.3(2) Framing Details

   [Tables and Figures are available at: http://www.com.state.oh.us/dic/Document s/ResidentialCodeboardchangestotheOBOA2004ResidentialCodeofOhio.pdf]

5. If continuous wood structural panel sheathing is present per Method 3 of R602.10.3 on all sheathable areas with ≥ 1 exterior wall lines, AND on any required interior braced wall lines, including areas above and below openings, install braced wall panel for such walls lengths per Table R602.10.5. Install wood structural panel sheathing at corners per Figure R602.10.5, if such corners are at both ends of each wall line that is subject to **ENERGY STANDARDS**. May multiply bracing amounts in Table R602.10.1 for Method 3 by a factor of 0.9 for walls with maximum opening height ≤ 85% of wall height, or by a factor of 0.8 for walls with a maximum opening height ≤ 67% of wall height. (602.10.5)
   a. TABLE R602.10.5 LENGTH REQUIREMENTS FOR BRACED WALL PANELS IN A CONTINUOUSLY SHEATHED WALL

b. FIGURE R602.10.5 EXTERIOR CORNER FRAMING
[Table and Figure are available at: http://www.com.state.oh.us/dic/Documents/
ResidentialCodeboardchangestotheOBOA2004ResidentialCodeofOhio.pdf]

APPLIANCE DEFINITIONS

Following are the appliance definitions as set forth in RCO 2406.

AIR CONDITIONING, GAS FIRED. A gas-burning, automatically operated appliance for supplying cooled and/or dehumidified air or chilled liquid.

AIR, EXHAUST. Air being removed from any space or piece of equipment and conveyed directly to the atmosphere by means of openings or ducts.

AIR-HANDLING UNIT. A blower or fan used for the purpose of distributing supply air to a room, space or area.

AIR, MAKEUP. Air that is provided to replace air being exhausted.

ALTERATION. A change in a system that involves an extension, addition or change to the arrangement, type or purpose of the existing installation.

ANODELESS RISER. A transition assembly in which plastic piping is installed and terminated above ground outside of a building.

APPLIANCE (EQUIPMENT). Any apparatus or equipment that utilizes gas as a fuel or raw material to produce light, heat, power, refrigeration or air conditioning.

APPLIANCE, FAN-ASSISTED COMBUSTION. An appliance equipped with an integral mechanical means to either draw or force products of combustion through the combustion chamber or heat exchanger.

APPLIANCE, AUTOMATICALLY CONTROLLED. Appliances equipped with an automatic burner ignition and safety shut-off device and other automatic devices, which accomplish complete turn-on and shut-off of the gas to the main burner or burners, and graduate the gas supply to the burner or burners, but do not affect complete shut-off of the gas.

APPLIANCE, UNVENTED. An appliance designed or installed in such a manner that the products of combustion are not conveyed by a vent or chimney directly to the outside atmosphere.

APPLIANCE, VENTED. An appliance designed and installed in such a manner that all of the products of combustion are conveyed directly from the appliance to the outside atmosphere through an approved chimney or vent system.

ATMOSPHERIC PRESSURE. The pressure of the weight of air and water vapor on the surface of the earth, approximately 14.7 pounds per square inch (psia) (101 kPa absolute) at sea level.

AUTOMATIC IGNITION. Ignition of gas at the burner(s) when the gas controlling device is turned on, including re-ignition if the flames on the burner(s) have been extinguished by means other than by the closing of the gas controlling device.

BAROMETRIC DRAFT REGULATOR. A balanced damper device attached to a chimney, vent connector, breeching or flue gas manifold to protect combustion equipment by controlling chimney draft. A double-acting barometric draft regulator is one whose balancing damper is free to move in either direction to protect combustion equipment from both excessive draft and backdraft.

BOILER, LOW-PRESSURE. A self-contained gas-fired appliance for supplying steam or hot water.

Hot water heating boiler. A boiler in which no steam is generated, from which hot water is circulated for heating purposes and then returned to the boiler, and that operates at water pressures not exceeding 160 psig (1100 kPa gauge) and at water temperatures not exceeding 250 & 176;F (121 & 176;C) at or near the boiler outlet.

Hot water supply boiler. A boiler, completely filled with water, which furnishes hot water to be used externally to itself, and that operates at water pressures not exceeding 160 psig (1100 kPa gauge) and at water temperatures not exceeding 250 & 176;F (121 & 176;C) at or near the boiler outlet.

Steam heating boiler. A boiler in which steam is generated and that operates at a steam pressure not exceeding 15 psig (100 kPa gauge).

BRAZING. A metal joining process wherein coalescence is produced by the use of a nonferrous filler metal having a melting point above 1,000 & 176;F (538 & 176;C), but lower than that of the base metal being joined. The filler material is distributed between the closely fitted surfaces of the joint by capillary action.

BTU. Abbreviation for British thermal unit, which is the quantity of heat required to raise the temperature of 1 pound (454 g) of water 1 & 176;F (0.56 & 176;C) (1 Btu = 1055 J).

BURNER. A device for the final conveyance of the gas, or a mixture of gas and air, to the combustion zone.

Induced-draft. A burner that depends on draft induced by a fan that is an integral part of the appliance and is located downstream from the burner.

Power. A burner in which gas, air or both are supplied at pressures exceeding, for gas, the line pressure, and for air, atmospheric pressure, with this added pressure being applied at the burner.

CHIMNEY. A primarily vertical structure containing one or more flues, for the purpose of carrying gaseous products of combustion and air from an appliance to the outside atmosphere.

Factory-built chimney. A listed and labeled chimney composed of factory-made components, assembled in the field in accordance with manufacturer's instructions and the conditions of the listing.

Masonry chimney. A field-constructed chimney composed of solid masonry units, bricks, stones or concrete.

CLEARANCE. The minimum distance through air measured between the heat producing surface of the mechanical appliance, device or equipment and the surface of the combustible material or assembly.

CLOTHES DRYER. An appliance used to dry wet laundry by means of heated air. Type 1. Factory-built package, multiple production. Primarily used in the family living environment. Usually the smallest unit physically and in function output.

CODE. The Ohio residential code.

CODE OFFICIAL. An individual who has received and maintains a certification of "Residential Building Official" in accordance with rules of the board of building standards.

COMBUSTION. In the context of this code, refers to the rapid oxidation of fuel accompanied by the production of heat or heat and light.

COMBUSTION AIR. Air necessary for complete combustion of a fuel, including theoretical air and excess air.

COMBUSTION CHAMBER. The portion of an appliance within which combustion occurs.

COMBUSTION PRODUCTS. Constituents resulting from the combustion of a fuel with the oxygen of the air, including the inert gases, but excluding excess air.

CONCEALED LOCATION. A location that cannot be accessed without damaging permanent parts of the building structure or finish surface. Spaces above, below or behind readily removable panels or doors shall not be considered as concealed.

CONCEALED PIPING. Piping that is located in a concealed location (see "Concealed location").

CONDENSATE. The liquid that condenses from a gas (including flue gas) caused by a reduction in temperature or increase in pressure.

CONNECTOR. The pipe that connects an approved appliance to a chimney, flue or vent.

CONTROL. A manual or automatic device designed to regulate the gas, air, water or electrical supply to, or operation of, a mechanical system.

CONVERSION BURNER. A unit consisting of a burner and its controls for installation in an appliance originally utilizing another fuel.

CUBIC FOOT. The amount of gas that occupies 1 cubic foot (0.02832 m3) when at a temperature of 60 & 176;F (16 & 176;C), saturated with water vapor and under a pressure equivalent to that of 30 inches of mercury (101 kPa).

DAMPER. A manually or automatically controlled device to regulate draft or the rate of flow of air or combustion gases.

DECORATIVE GAS APPLIANCE, VENTED. A vented appliance wherein the primary function lies in the aesthetic effect of the flames.

DECORATIVE GAS APPLIANCES FOR INSTALLATION IN VENTED FIREPLACES. A vented appliance designed for installation within the fire chamber of a vented fireplace, wherein the primary function lies in the aesthetic effect of the flames.

DEMAND. The maximum amount of gas input required per unit of time, usually expressed in cubic feet per hour, or Btu/h (1 Btu/h = 0.2931 W).

DESIGN FLOOD ELEVATION. The elevation of the "design flood," including wave height, relative to the datum specified on the community's legally designated flood hazard map.

DILUTION AIR. Air that is introduced into a draft hood and is mixed with the flue gases.

DIRECT-VENT APPLIANCES. Appliances that are constructed and installed so that all air for combustion is derived directly from the outside atmosphere and all flue gases are discharged directly to the outside atmosphere.

DRAFT. The pressure difference existing between the equipment or any component part and the atmosphere, that causes a continuous flow of air and products of combustion through the gas passages of the appliance to the atmosphere.

Mechanical or induced draft. The pressure difference created by the action of a fan, blower or ejector that is located between the appliance and the chimney or vent termination.

Natural draft. The pressure difference created by a vent or chimney because of its height, and the temperature difference between the flue gases and the atmosphere.

DRAFT HOOD. A nonadjustable device built into an appliance, or made as part of the vent connector from an appliance, that is designed to (1) provide for ready escape of the flue gases from the appliance in the event of no draft, backdraft, or stoppage beyond the draft hood, (2) prevent a backdraft from entering the appliance, and (3) neutralize the effect of stack action of the chimney or gas vent upon operation of the appliance.

DRAFT REGULATOR. A device that functions to maintain a desired draft in the appliance by automatically reducing the draft to the desired value.

DRIP. The container placed at a lowpoint in a system of piping to collect condensate and from which the condensate is removable.

DUCT FURNACE. A warm-air furnace normally installed in an air-distribution duct to supply warm air for heating. This definition shall apply only to a warm-air heating appliance that depends for air circulation on a blower not furnished as part of the furnace.

EQUIPMENT. See "Appliance."

FIREPLACE. A fire chamber and hearth constructed of noncombustible material for use with solid fuels and provided with a chimney.

Masonry fireplace. A hearth and fire chamber of solid masonry units such as bricks, stones, listed masonry units or reinforced concrete, provided with a suitable chimney.

Factory-built fireplace. A fireplace composed of listed factory-built components assembled in accordance with the terms of listing to form the completed fireplace.

FLAME SAFEGUARD. A device that will automatically shut off the fuel supply to a main burner or group of burners when the means of ignition of such burners becomes inoperative, and when flame failure occurs on the burner or group of burners.

FLOOD HAZARD AREA. The greater of the following two areas:

1. The area within a floodplain subject to a 1 percent or greater chance of flooding in any given year.
2. This area designated as a flood hazard area on a community's flood hazard map, or otherwise legally designated.

FLOOR FURNACE. A completely self-contained furnace suspended from the floor of the space being heated, taking air for combustion from outside such space and with means for observing flames and lighting the appliance from such space.

FLUE, APPLIANCE. The passage(s) within an appliance through which combustion products pass from the combustion chamber of the appliance to the draft hood inlet opening on an appliance equipped with a draft hood or to the outlet of the appliance on an appliance not equipped with a draft hood.

FLUE COLLAR. That portion of an appliance designed for the attachment of a draft hood, vent connector or venting system.

FLUE GASES. Products of combustion plus excess air in appliance flues or heat exchangers.

FLUE LINER (LINING). A system or material used to form the inside surface of a flue in a chimney or vent, for the purpose of protecting the surrounding structure from the effects of combustion products and or conveying combustion products without leakage to the atmosphere.

FUEL GAS. Fuel gases include: a natural gas, manufactured gas, liquefied petroleum gas, hydrogen gas and mixtures of these gases.

FUEL GAS UTILIZATION EQUIPMENT. See "Appliance."

FURNACE. A completely self-contained heating unit that is designed to supply heated air to spaces remote from or adjacent to the appliance location.

FURNACE, CENTRAL FURNACE. A self-contained appliance for heating air by transfer of heat of combustion through metal to the air, and designed to supply heated air through ducts to spaces remote from or adjacent to the appliance location.

FURNACE PLENUM. An air compartment or chamber to which one or more ducts are connected and which forms part of an air distribution system.

GAS CONVENIENCE OUTLET. A permanently mounted, manually operated device that provides the means for connecting an appliance to, and disconnecting an appliance from, the gas supply piping. The device includes an integral, manually operated valve with a non-displaceable valve member and is designed so that disconnection of an appliance only occurs when the manually operated valve is in the closed position.

GAS PIPING. An installation of pipe, valves or fittings installed on a premises or in a building and utilized to convey fuel gas.

GAS UTILIZATION EQUIPMENT. An appliance that utilizes gas as a fuel or raw material or both.

HAZARDOUS LOCATION. Any location considered to be a fire hazard for flammable vapors, dust, combustible fibers or other highly combustible substances. The location is not necessarily categorized in the Ohio Building Code as a high-hazard use group classification.

HOUSE PIPING. See "Piping system."

IGNITION PILOT. A pilot that operates during the lighting cycle and discontinues during main burner operation.

IGNITION SOURCE. A flame spark or hot surface capable of igniting flammable vapors or fumes. Such sources include appliance burners, burner igniters and electrical switching devices.

INFRARED RADIANT HEATER. A heater which directs a substantial amount of its energy output in the form of infrared radiant energy into the area to be heated. Such heaters are of either the vented or unvented type.

JOINT, FLARED. A metal-to-metal compression joint in which a conical spread is made on the end of a tube that is compressed by a flare nut against a mating flare.

JOINT, MECHANICAL. A general form of gas-tight joints obtained by the joining of metal parts through a positive holding mechanical construction, such as flanged joint, threaded joint, flared joint or compression joint.

JOINT, PLASTIC ADHESIVE. A joint made in thermoset plastic piping by the use of an adhesive substance which forms a continuous bond between the mating surfaces without dissolving either one of them.

LIQUEFIED PETROLEUM GAS or LPG (LP-GAS). Liquefied petroleum gas composed predominately of propane, propylene, butanes or butylenes, or mixtures thereof that is gaseous under normal atmospheric conditions, but is capable of being liquefied under moderate pressure at normal temperatures.

LIVING SPACE. Space within a dwelling unit utilized for living, sleeping, eating, cooking, bathing, washing and sanitation purposes.

LOG LIGHTER, GAS-FIRED. A manually operated solid-fuel ignition appliance for installation in a vented solid-fuel-burning fireplace.

MAIN BURNER. A device or group of devices essentially forming an integral unit for the final conveyance of gas or a mixture of gas and air to the combustion zone, and on which combustion takes place to accomplish the function for which the appliance is designed.

MANUFACTURED HOME. A dwelling complying with 24 C.F.R. Part 3280, usually built on a steel chassis, with 1 1/2" × 3" metal plate inscribed with HUD reference number on an exterior end wall.

MECHANICAL EXHAUST SYSTEM. Equipment installed in and made a part of the vent, which will provide a positive induced draft.

METER. The instrument installed to measure the volume of gas delivered through it.

MODULATING. Modulating or throttling is the action of a control from its maximum to minimum position in either predetermined steps or increments of movement as caused by its actuating medium.

OFFSET (VENT). A combination of approved bends that make two changes in direction, bringing one section of the vent out of line, but into a line parallel with the other section.

OUTLET. A threaded connection or bolted flange in a pipe system to which a gas-burning appliance is attached.

OXYGEN DEPLETION SAFETY SHUTOFF SYSTEM (ODS). A system designed to act to shut off the gas supply to the main and pilot burners if the oxygen in the surrounding atmosphere is reduced below a predetermined level.

PILOT. A small flame that is utilized to ignite the gas at the main burner or burners.

PIPING. Where used in this code, "piping" refers to either pipe or tubing, or both.

  Pipe. A rigid conduit of iron, steel, copper, brass or plastic.

  Tubing. Semi-rigid conduit of copper, aluminum, plastic or steel.

PIPING SYSTEM. All fuel piping, valves, and fittings from the outlet of the point of delivery to the outlets of the equipment shutoff valves.

PLASTIC, THERMOPLASTIC. A plastic that is capable of being repeatedly softened by increase of temperature and hardened by decrease of temperature.

POINT OF DELIVERY. For natural gas systems, the point of delivery is the outlet of the service meter assembly, or the outlet of the service regulator or service shutoff valve where a meter is not provided. Where a valve is provided at the outlet of the service meter assembly, such valve shall be considered to be downstream of the point of delivery. For undiluted liquefied petroleum gas systems, the point of delivery shall be considered the outlet of the first-stage pressure regulator that provides utilization pressure, exclusive of line gas regulators, in the system.

PRESSURE DROP. The loss in pressure due to friction or obstruction in pipes, valves, fittings, regulators and burners.

PRESSURE TEST. An operation performed to verify the gas-tight integrity of gas piping following its installation or modification.

READY ACCESS (TO). That which enables a device, appliance or equipment to be directly reached, without requiring the removal or movement of any panel, door or similar obstruction. (See "Access.")

REGULATOR. A device for controlling and maintaining a uniform gas supply pressure, either pounds-to-inches water column (MP regulator) or inches-to-inches water column (appliance regulator).

REGULATOR, GAS APPLIANCE. A pressure regulator for controlling pressure to the manifold of gas equipment.

REGULATOR, LINE GAS PRESSURE. A device placed in a gas line between the service pressure regulator and the equipment for controlling, maintaining or reducing the pressure in that portion of the piping system downstream of the device.

REGULATOR, PRESSURE. A device placed in a gas line for reducing, controlling and maintaining the pressure in that portion of the piping system downstream of the device.

REGULATOR, SERVICE PRESSURE. A device installed by the serving gas supplier to reduce and limit the service line gas pressure to delivery pressure.

RELIEF OPENING. The opening provided in a draft hood to permit the ready escape to the atmosphere of the flue products from the draft hood in the event of no draft, backdraft or stoppage beyond the draft hood, and to permit air into the draft hood in the event of a strong chimney updraft.

RELIEF VALVE (DEVICE). A safety valve designed to forestall the development of a dangerous condition by relieving either pressure, temperature or vacuum in the hot water supply system.

RELIEF VALVE, PRESSURE. An automatic valve which opens and closes a relief vent, depending on whether the pressure is above or below a predetermined value.

RELIEF VALVE, TEMPERATURE

Reseating or self-closing type. An automatic valve which opens and closes a relief vent, depending on whether the temperature is above or below a predetermined value.

Manual reset type. A valve which automatically opens a relief vent at a predetermined temperature and which must be manually returned to the closed position.

RELIEF VALVE, VACUUM. A valve that automatically opens and closes a vent for relieving a vacuum within the hot water supply system, depending on whether the vacuum is above or below a predetermined value.

REPAIR, MINOR. Any reconstruction or renewal with limited impact on access, safety, or health. They do not include additions to, alterations of, replacement or relocation of standpipes, water supply, sewer, drainage, drain leader, gas, soil, waste, vent, or similar piping, electrical wiring or mechanical or fire protection equipment.

RISER, GAS. A vertical pipe supplying fuel gas.

ROOM HEATER, UNVENTED. See "Unvented room heater."

ROOM HEATER, VENTED. A freestanding gas-fired heating unit used for direct heating of the space in and adjacent to that in which the unit is located. [See also "Vented room heater."]

SAFETY SHUTOFF DEVICE. See "Flame safeguard."

SHAFT. An enclosed space extending through one or more stories of a building, connecting vertical openings in successive floors, or floors and the roof.

SPECIFIC GRAVITY. As applied to gas, specific gravity is the ratio of the weight of a given volume to that of the same volume of air, both measured under the same condition.

THERMOSTAT

Electric switch type. A device that senses changes in temperature and controls electrically, by means of separate components, the flow of gas to the burner(s) to maintain selected temperatures.

Integral gas valve type. An automatic device, actuated by temperature changes, designed to control the gas supply to the burner(s) in order to maintain temperatures between predetermined limits, and in which the thermal actuating element is an integral part of the device.

1. Graduating thermostat. A thermostat in which the motion of the valve is approximately in direct proportion to the effective motion of the thermal element induced by temperature change.

2. Snap-acting thermostat. A thermostat in which the thermostatic valve travels instantly from the closed to the open position, and vice versa.

TRANSITION FITTINGS, PLASTIC TO STEEL. An adapter for joining plastic pipe to steel pipe. The purpose of this fitting is to provide a permanent, pressure-tight connection between two materials that cannot be joined directly one to another.

UNIT HEATER

High-static pressure type. A self-contained, automatically controlled, vented appliance having integral means for circulation of air against 0.2" (15mmH2O) or greater static pressure. Such appliance is equipped with provisions for attaching an outlet air duct and, where the appliance is for indoor installation remote from the space to be heated, is also equipped with provisions for attaching an inlet air duct.

Low-static pressure type. A self-contained, automatically controlled, vented appliance, intended for installation in the space to be heated without the use of ducts, having integral means for circulation of air. Such units are allowed to be equipped with louvers or face extensions made in accordance with the manufacturer's specifications

UNVENTED ROOM HEATER. An unvented heating appliance designed for stationary installation and utilized to provide comfort heating. Such appliances provide radiant heat or convection heat by gravity or fan circulation directly from the heater and do not utilize ducts.

VALVE. A device used in piping to control the gas supply to any section of a system of piping or to an appliance.

Automatic. An automatic or semiautomatic device consisting essentially of a valve and operator that control the gas supply to the burner(s) during operation of an appliance. The operator shall be actuated by application of gas pressure on a flexible diaphragm, by electrical means, by mechanical means or by other approved means.

Automatic gas shutoff. A valve used in conjunction with an automatic gas shutoff device to shut off the gas supply to a water heating system. It shall be constructed integrally with the gas shutoff device or shall be a separate assembly.

Equipment shutoff. A valve located in the piping system, used to isolate individual equipment for purposes such as service or replacement. Individual main burner. A valve that controls the gas supply to an individual main burner.

Main burner control. A valve that controls the gas supply to the main burner manifold.

Manual main gas-control. A manually operated valve in the gas line for the purpose of completely turning on or shutting off the gas supply to the appliance, except to pilot or pilots that are provided with independent shutoff.

Manual reset. An automatic shutoff valve installed in the gas supply piping and set to shut off when unsafe conditions occur. The device remains closed until manually reopened.

Service shutoff. A valve, installed by the serving gas supplier between the service meter or source of supply and the customer piping system, to shut off the entire piping system.

VENT. A pipe or other conduit composed of factory-made components, containing a passageway for conveying combustion products and air to the atmosphere, listed and labeled for use with a specific type or class of appliance.

Special gas vent. A vent listed and labeled for use with listed Category II, III and IV gas appliances.

Type B vent. A vent listed and labeled for use with appliances with draft hoods and other Category I appliances that are listed for use with Type B vents.

Type BW vent. A vent listed and labeled for use with wall furnaces.

Type L vent. A vent listed and labeled for use with appliances that are listed for use with Type L or Type B vents.

VENT CONNECTOR. (See "Connector.")

VENTED GAS APPLIANCE CATEGORIES. Appliances that are categorized for the purpose of vent selection are classified into the following four categories:

Category I.	An appliance that operates with a non-positive vent static pressure and with a vent gas temperature that avoids excessive condensate production in the vent.

Category II.	An appliance that operates with a non-positive vent static pressure and with a vent gas temperature that is capable of causing excessive condensate production in the vent.

Category III.	An appliance that operates with a positive vent static pressure and with a vent gas temperature that avoids excessive condensate production in the vent.

Category IV.	An appliance that operates with a positive vent static pressure and with a vent gas temperature that is capable of causing excessive condensate production in the vent.

VENTED ROOM HEATER. A vented self-contained, free-standing, non-recessed appliance for furnishing warm air to the space in which it is installed, directly from the heater without duct connections.

VENTED WALL FURNACE. A self-contained vented appliance complete with grilles or equivalent, designed for incorporation in or permanent attachment to the structure of a building, mobile home or travel trailer, and furnishing heated air circulated by gravity or by a fan directly into the space to be heated through openings in the casing. This definition shall exclude floor furnaces, unit heaters and central furnaces as herein defined.

VENTING SYSTEM. A continuous open passageway from the flue collar or draft hood of an appliance to the outside atmosphere for the purpose of removing flue or vent gases. A venting system is usually composed of a vent or a chimney and vent connector, if used, assembled to form the open passageway.

WALL HEATER, UNVENTED-TYPE. A room heater of the type designed for insertion in or attachment to a wall or partition. Such heater does not incorporate concealed venting arrangements in its construction and discharges all products of combustion through the front into the room being heated.

WATER HEATER. Any heating appliance or equipment that heats potable water and supplies such water to the potable hot water distribution system.

LIST OF STANDARDS AND ISSUING AGENCIES

Following are the standards referenced in the RCO, listed by issuing agency and address, standard identification, and title, per RCO 4301.2.

American Architectural Manufacturers Association
1827 Walden Office Square, Suite 550
Schaumburg, IL 60173

AAMA Standard reference number	**Title**
AAMA/WDMA/CSA	
101/I.S.2/A440—08	North American Fenestration Standards/ Specifications for Windows, Doors and Skylights
450—*10*	Voluntary Performance Rating Method for Mulled Fenestration Assemblies
506—*08*	Voluntary Specifications for Hurricane Impact and Cycle Testing of Fenestration Products
711—07	Voluntary Specification for Self Adhering Flashing Used for Installation of Exterior Wall Fenestration Products.

Air Conditioning Contractors of America
2800 Shirlington Road, Suite 300
Arlington, VA 22206

ACCA Standard reference number	**Title**
Manual D—*09*	Residential Duct Systems
Manual J— *04*	Residential Load Calculation—Eighth Edition
Manual S—04	Residential Equipment Selection

American Concrete Institute
38800 Country Club Drive
Farmington Hills, MI 48331

ACE Standard reference number	**Title**
318—08	Building Code Requirements for Structural Concrete
332—08	Code Requirements for Residential Concrete Construction
530—08	Building Code Requirements for Masonry Structures
530.1—08	Specification for Masonry Structures

American Forest and Paper Association
1111 19th Street, NW, Suite 800
Washington, DC 20036

American Forest Products Association (Currently the American Wood Council)
803 Sycolin Road, Suite 201
Leesburg, VA 20175
http://www.awc.org/index.html

AFPA Standard reference number

AFPA Standard reference number	Title
NDS—05	National Design Specification (NDS) for Wood Construction—with 2005 Supplement
WFCM-01	Wood Frame Construction Manual for One- and Two- family Dwellings
AFPA—93	Span Tables for Joists and Rafters
PWF—07	Permanent Wood Foundation Design Specification

American Iron and Steel Institute
1140 Connecticut Ave, Suite 705
Washington, DC 20036

AISI Standard reference number

AISI Standard reference number	Title
AISI S100—07	North American Specification for the Design of Cold-formed Steel Structural Members
AISI S230—07	Standard for Cold-formed Steel Framing- prescriptive Method for One- and Two-family Dwellings

American Institute of Timber Construction
7012 S. Revere Parkway, Suite 140
Centennial, CO 80112

AITC Standard reference number

AITC Standard reference number	Title
ANSI/AITC A 190.1—07	Structural Glued Laminated Timber

American National Standards Institute
25 West 43rd Street, Fourth Floor
New York, NY 10036

ANSI Standard reference number

ANSI Standard reference number	Title
A108.1A—09	Installation of Ceramic Tile in the Wet-set Method, with Portland Cement Mortar
A108.1B—09	Installation of Ceramic Tile, Quarry Tile on a Cured Portland Cement Mortar Setting Bed with Dry-set or Latex-Portland Mortar
A108.4—09	Installation of Ceramic Tile with Organic Adhesives or Water Cleanable Tile-setting Epoxy Adhesive
A108.5—09	Installation of Ceramic Tile with Dry-set Portland Cement Mortar or Latex-Portland Cement Mortar
A108.6—09	Installation of Ceramic Tile with Chemical- resistant, Water-cleanable Tile-setting and -grouting Epoxy
A108.11—09	Interior Installation of Cementitious Backer Units A118.1—10.1 American National Standard Specifications for Dry- set Portland Cement Mortar

A118.3—*10.1*	American National Standard Specifications for Chemical-resistant, Water-cleanable Tile-setting and Grouting Epoxy and Water-cleanable Tile- setting Epoxy Adhesive
A118.10—*10.1*	Specification for Load Bearing, Bonded, Waterproof Membranes for Thin-set Ceramic Tile and Dimension Stone Installation
A136.1—*10.1*	American National Standard Specifications for Organic Adhesives for Installation of Ceramic Tile
A137.1—*08*	American National Standard Specifications for Ceramic Tile
A208.1—*09*	Particleboard
LC1—*05*	Interior Fuel Gas Piping Systems Using Corrugated Stainless Steel Tubing
LC4—*07*	Press-connect Copper and Copper Alloy Fittings for use in Fuel Gas Distribution Systems
Z21.1—*05*	Household Cooking Gas Appliances
Z21.5.1—*06*	Gas Clothes Dryers—Volume I—Type I Clothes Dryers
Z21.8—94 (R2002)	Installation of Domestic Gas Conversion Burners
Z21.10.1—*09*	Gas Water Heaters—Volume I—Storage Water Heaters with Input Ratings of 75,000 Btu per hour or Less
Z21.10.3—*07*	Gas Water Heaters—Volume III—Storage Water Heaters with Input Ratings above 75,000 Btu per hour, Circulating and Instantaneous Water Heaters
Z21.11.2—*07*	Gas-fired Room Heaters—Volume II—Unvented Room Heaters
Z21.13—*10*	Gas-fired Low-Pressure Steam and Hot Water Boilers
Z21.15—*09*	Manually Operated Gas Valves for Appliances, Appliance Connector Valves and Hose End Valves
Z21.24—*06*	Connectors for Gas Appliances
Z21.40.1—96 (R2002)	Gas-fired, Heat-activated Air Conditioning and Heat Pump Appliances—with Z21.40.1a-97 (R2002)
Z21.40.2—96 (R2002)	Gas-fired, Work-activated Air Conditioning and Heat Pump Appliances (Internal Combustion) — with Z21.40.2a-1997 (R2002)
Z21.42—*04*	Gas-fired Illuminating Appliances
Z21.47—*06*	Gas-fired Central Furnaces
Z21.50—*07*	Vented Gas Fireplaces
Z21.56—*06*	Gas-fired Pool Heaters
Z21.58—*08*	Outdoor Cooking Gas Appliances
Z21.60—*03*	Decorative Gas Appliances for Installation in Solid Fuel Burning Fireplaces—with Addenda Z21.60a-2003
Z21.75/CSA6.27—*07*	Connectors for Outdoor Gas Appliances Z21.80—*03* Line Pressure Regulators
Z21.83—98	Fuel Cell Power Plants.

Z21.84—02	Manually Listed, Natural Gas Decorative Gas Appliances for Installation in Solid Fuel-burning Fireplaces—with Addenda Z21.84a -2003
Z21.86—08	Gas-fired Vented Space Heating Appliances
Z21.88—09	Vented Gas Fireplace Heaters
Z21.91—07	Ventless Firebox Enclosures for Gas-fired Unvented Decorative Room Heaters
Z83.6—90 (R1998)	Gas-fired Infrared Heaters
Z83.8—09	Gas-fired Unit Heaters and Gas-fired Duct Furnaces
Z97.1—09	Safety Glazing Materials Used in Buildings— Safety Performance Specifications and Methods of Test

APA-The Engineered Wood Association
7011 South 19th
Tacoma, WA 98466

APA Standard reference number	**Title**
APA E30—07	Engineered Wood Construction Guide

American Society of Civil Engineers Structural Engineering Institute
1801 Alexander Bell Drive
Reston, VA 20191

ASCE/SEI Standard reference number	**Title**
5—08	Building Code Requirements for Masonry Structures
6—08	Specification for Masonry Structures
7—05	Minimum Design Loads for Buildings and Other Structures
24—05	Flood-resistant Design and Construction.
32—01	Design and Construction of Frost-protected Shallow Foundations

American Society of Heating, Refrigerating and Air-Conditioning Engineers, Inc.
1791 Tullie Circle, NE
Atlanta, GA 30329

ASHRAE Standard reference number	**Title**
34—10	Designation and Safety Classification of Refrigerants
ASHRAE—09	ASHRAE Fundamentals Handbook—2009

American Society of Mechanical Engineers
Three Park Avenue
New York, NY 10016-5990

ASME Standard reference number	**Title**

A17.1/CSA B44—*04*	Safety Code for Elevators and Escalators
A18.1—*03*	Safety Standard for Platforms and Stairway Chair Lifts
B1.20.1—1983 (R2006)	Pipe Threads, General Purpose (Inch)
B16.33—2002 (R*2007*)	Manually Operated Metallic Gas Valves for Use in Gas Piping Systems up to 125 psig (Sizes 1/2 through 2)
B16.44—02	Manually Operated Metallic Gas Valves For Use in Above-ground Piping Systems up to 5 psi.
B36.10M—2004	Welded and Seamless Wrought-steel Pipe
BPVC—2004	ASME Boiler and Pressure Vessel Code
CSD-1—*09*	Controls and Safety Devices for Automatically Fired Boilers

American Society of Sanitary Engineering
901 Canterbury, Suite A
Westlake, OH 44145

ASTM International
100 Barr Harbor Drive
West Conshohocken, PA 19428

ASTM Standard reference number	**Title**
A 36/A 36M—*08*	Specification for Carbon Structural Steel
A 53/A 53M—*10a*	Specification for Pipe, Steel, Black and Hot-dipped, Zinc-coated Welded and Seamless
A 82/A 82M—*07*	Specification for Steel Wire, Plain, for Concrete Reinforcement
A 106/A 106M—*10*	Specification for Seamless Carbon Steel Pipe for High Temperature Service
A 153/A 153M—*09*	Specification for Zinc Coating (Hot Dip) on Iron and Steel Hardware
A 167—*09*	Specification for Stainless and Heat-resisting Chromium-nickel Steel Plate, Sheet and Strip
A 240/A 240M—*10a*	Standard Specification for Chromium and Chromium-nickel Stainless Steel Plate, Sheet and Strip for Pressure Vessels and for General Applications
A 254—*9707*	Specification for Copper Brazed Steel Tubing
A 307—*07b*	Specification for Carbon Steel Bolts and Studs, 6000 psi Tensile Strength
A 463/A 463M—*09a*	Standard Specification for Steel Sheet, Aluminum-coated by the Hot-dip Process.
A 510—*08*	Specification for General Requirements for Wire Rods and Coarse Round Wire, Carbon Steel
A 539—99	Specification for Electric-resistance-welded Coiled Steel Tubing for Gas and Fuel Oil Lines

A 615/A 615M—*09b*	Specification for Deformed and Plain Billet-steel Bars for Concrete Reinforcement
A 641/A 641M—*09b*	Specification for Zinc-coated (Galvanized) Carbon Steel Wire
A 653/A 653M—*09a*	Specification for Steel Sheet, Zinc-coated (Galvanized) or Zinc-iron Alloy-coated (Galvanized) by the Hot-dip Process
A 706/A 706/M—*09b*	Specification for Low-alloy Steel Deformed and Plain Bars for Concrete Reinforcement
A 755/A 755M—*03 (2008)*	Specification for Steel Sheet, Metallic Coated by the Hot-dip Process and Prepainted by the Coil- coating Process for Exterior Exposed Building Products
A 778—*01 (2009)e1*	Specification for Welded Unannealed Austenitic Stainless Steel Tubular Products
A 792/A 792M—*09a*	Specification for Steel Sheet, 55% Aluminum-zinc Alloy-coated by the Hot-dip Process
A 875/A 875M—*09a*	Specification for Steel Sheet, Zinc-5%, Aluminum Alloy-coated by the Hot-dip Process
A 924/A 924M—*10*	Standard Specification for General Requirements for Steel Sheet, Metallic-coated by the Hot-Dip Process
A 951—*06*	Specification for Steel Wire Masonry Joint Reinforcement
A 996/A 996M—*09b*	Specifications for Rail-steel and Axel-steel Deformed Bars for Concrete Reinforcement
A 1003/A 1003M—*10*	Standard Specification for Steel Sheet, Carbon, Metallic and Nonmetallic-coated for Cold-formed Framing Members
B 42—*10*	Specification for Seamless Copper Pipe, Standard Sizes
B 43—*09*	Specification for Seamless Red Brass Pipe, Standard Sizes
B 75—*02*	Specification for Seamless Copper Tube
B 88—*09*	Specification for Seamless Copper Water Tube
B 101—*07*	Specification for Lead-coated Copper Sheet and Strip for Building Construction.
B 135—*10*	Specification for Seamless Brass Tube
B 209—*07*	Specification for Aluminum and Aluminum-alloy Sheet and Plate
B 227—*10*	Specification for Hard-drawn Copper-clad Steel Wire
B 251—*10*	Specification for General Requirements for Wrought Seamless Copper and Copper-alloy Tube
B 302—*07*	Specification for Threadless Copper Pipe, Standard Sizes
B 306—*09*	Specification for Copper Drainage Tube (DWV)
B 370—*09*	Specification for Copper Sheet and Strip for Building Construction
B 447—*07*	Specification for Welded Copper Tube
B 695—*04 (2009)*	Standard Specification for Coatings of Zinc Mechanically Deposited on Iron and Steel

B 813—*10*	Specification for Liquid and Paste Fluxes for Soldering Applications of Copper and Copper Alloy Tube
C 5—*10*	Specification for Quicklime for Structural Purposes
C 27—98 (*2008*)	Specification for Standard Classification of Fireclay and High-alumina Refractory Brick
C 28/C 28M—*10*	Specification for Gypsum Plasters
C 33—*08*	Specification for Concrete Aggregates
C 34—*08*	Specification for Structural Clay Load-bearing Wall Tile C 35—01(2005) Specification for Inorganic Aggregates for Use in Gypsum Plaster
C 36/C 36M—03	Specification for Gypsum Wallboard
C 37/C 37M—01	Specification for Gypsum Lath
C 55—*09*	Specification for Concrete Building Brick
C 59/C 59M—00 (2006)	Specification for Gypsum Casting and Molding Plaster
C 61/C 61M—00 (2006)	Specification for Gypsum Keene's Cement
C 62—*10*	Specification for Building Brick (Solid Masonry Units Made from Clay or Shale)
C 73—05	Specification for Calcium Silicate Face Brick (Sand Lime Brick)
C 79—04a	Specification for Treated Core and Nontreated Core Gypsum Sheathing Board
C 90—*09*	Specification for Load-bearing Concrete Masonry Units
C 91—05	Specification for Masonry Cement
C 94/C 94M—*10*	Specification for Ready-mixed Concrete
C 129—06	Specification for Nonload-bearing Concrete Masonry Units
C 143/C 143M—*10a*	Test Method for Slump or Hydraulic Cement Concrete
C 145—85	Specification for Solid Load-bearing Concrete Masonry Units
C 150—*09*	Specification for Portland Cement
C 199—84 (2005)	Test Method for Pier Test for Refractory Mortar
C 203—05a	Standard Test Methods for Breaking Load and Flexural Properties of Block-type Thermal Insulation
C 207—06	Specification for Hydrated Lime for Masonry Purposes
C 208—*08a*	Specification for Cellulosic Fiber Insulating Board
C 216—*10*	Specification for Facing Brick (Solid Masonry Units Made from Clay or Shale)
C 270—*10*	Specification for Mortar for Unit Masonry
C 272—01 (*2007*)	Standard Test Method for Water Absorption of Core Materials for Structural Sandwich Constructions
C 273—*07a*	Standard Test Method for Shear Properties of Sandwich Core Materials
C 315—07	Specification for Clay Flue Liners and Chimney Pots
C 406—*10*	Specifications for Roofing Slate

C 411—05	Test Method for Hot-surface Performance of High-temperature Thermal Insulation
C 475/C 475—02(2007)	Specification for Joint Compound and Joint Tape for Finishing Gypsum Wallboard
C 476—10	Specification for Grout for Masonry
C 514—04 (2009)e1	Specification for Nails for the Application of Gypsum Wallboard
C 552—07	Standard Specification for Cellular Glass Thermal Insulation
C 557—03 (2009)e1	Specification for Adhesives for Fastening Gypsum Wallboard to Wood Framing
C 578—10	Specification for Rigid, Cellular Polystyrene Thermal Insulation
C 587—04 (2009)	Specification for Gypsum Veneer Plaster
C 588/C 588M—03e1	Specification for Gypsum Base for Veneer Plasters
C 595—10	Specification for Blended Hydraulic Cements
C 630/C 630M—03	Specification for Water-resistant Gypsum Backing Board
C 631—09	Specification for Bonding Compounds for Interior Gypsum Plastering
C 645—09a	Specification for Nonstructural Steel Framing Members
C 652—10	Specification for Hollow Brick (Hollow Masonry Units Made from Clay or Shale)
C 685—10	Specification for Concrete Made by Volumetric Batching and Continuous Mixing
C 728—05 (2010)	Standard Specification for Perlite Thermal Insulation Board
C 836/C836M-10	Specification for High Solids Content, Cold Liquid-applied Elastomeric Waterproofing Membrane for Use with Separate Wearing Course
C 843—99 (2006)	Specification for Application of Gypsum Veneer Plaster
C 844—10	Specification for Application of Gypsum Base to Receive Gypsum Veneer Plaster
C 847—10a	Specification for Metal Lath
C 887—05 (2010)	Specification for Packaged, Dry, Combined Materials for Surface Bonding Mortar
C 897—05 (2009)	Specification for Aggregate for Job-mixed Portland Cement-based Plasters
C 920—10	Standard Specification for Elastomeric Joint Sealants
C 926—06	Specification for Application of Portland Cement-based Plaster
C 931/C 931M—04	Specification for Exterior Gypsum Soffit Board
C 933—09	Specification for Welded Wire Lath
C 954—10	Specification for Steel Drill Screws for the Application of Gypsum Panel Products or Metal Plaster Bases to Steel Studs from 0.033 in. (0.84 mm) to 0.112 in. (2.84 mm) in Thickness

C 955—*09a*	Specification for Load-bearing (Transverse and Axial) Steel Studs, Runners (Tracks), and Bracing or Bridging for Screw Application of Gypsum Panel Products and Metal Plaster Bases
C 957—*10*	Specification for High-solids Content, Cold Liquid-applied Elastomeric Waterproofing Membrane for Use with Integral Wearing Surface
C 960—04	Specification for Predecorated Gypsum Board
C 1002—*07*	Specification for Steel Drill Screws for the Application of Gypsum Panel Products or Metal Plaster Bases
C 1029—*10*	Specification for Spray-applied Rigid Cellular Polyurethane Thermal Insulation
C 1032—06	Specification for Woven Wire Plaster Base
C 1047—*10a*	Specification for Accessories for Gypsum Wallboard and Gypsum Veneer Base
C 1063—*08*	Specification for Installation of Lathing and Furring to Receive Interior and Exterior Portland Cement-based Plaster.
C 1107—*08*	Standard Specification for Packaged Dry, Hydraulic-cement Grout (Nonshrink)
C 1116—*10*	Standard Specification for Fiber-reinforced Concrete and Shotcrete
C 1167—03 *(2009)*	Specification for Clay Roof Tiles
C 1177/C 1177M—*08*	Specification for Glass Mat Gypsum Substrate for Use as Sheathing
C 1178/C 1178M—*08*	Specification for Glass Mat Water-resistant Gypsum Backing Panel
C 1186—*08*	Specification for Flat Nonasbestos Fiber Cement Sheets
C 1261—*10*	Specification for Firebox Brick for Residential Fireplaces
C 1278/C 1278M—*07a*	Specification for Fiber-reinforced Gypsum Panels C 1283—*07a* Practice for Installing Clay Flue Lining
C 1288—99(*2010*)	Standard Specification for Discrete Nonasbestos Fiber-cement Interior Substrate Sheets
C 1289—*10*	Standard Specification for Faced Rigid Cellular Polyisocyanurate Thermal Insulation Board
C 1325—*08b*	Standard Specification for Nonasbestos Fiber-mat Reinforced Cement Interior Substrate Sheets.
C 1328—05	Specification for Plastic (Stucco) Cement.
C *1395 / C 1395M*—06a	Specification for Gypsum Ceiling Board
C 1396/C 1396M—*09a*	Specification for Gypsum Board.
C 1492—03(*2009*)	Specification for Concrete Roof Tile
C 1513—*10*	Standard Specification for Steel Tapping Screws for Cold-formed Steel Framing Connections
C 1658/C 1658M—06	Standard Specification for Glass Mat Gypsum Panels
D 41—05 *(2010)*	Specification for Asphalt Primer Used in Roofing, Dampproofing and Waterproofing

D 43—00(2006)	Specification for Coal Tar Primer Used in Roofing, Dampproofing and Waterproofing
D 225—07	Specification for Asphalt Shingles (Organic Felt) Surfaced with Mineral Granules
D 226/D 226M—09	Specification for Asphalt-saturated (Organic Felt) Used in Roofing and Waterproofing
D 227—03	Specification for Coal Tar Saturated (Organic Felt) Used in Roofing and Waterproofing
D 312—00(2006)	Specification for Asphalt Used in Roofing.
D 422—63 (2007)	Test Method for Particle-size Analysis of Soils
D 449—03 (2008)	Specification for Asphalt Used in Dampproofing and Waterproofing.
D 450—07	Specification for Coal-tar Pitch Used in Roofing, Dampproofing and Waterproofing
D 1227—95(2007)	Specification for Emulsified Asphalt Used as a Protective Coating for Roofing
D 1248—05	Specification for Polyethylene Plastics Extrusion Materials for Wire and Cable
D 1622—08	Standard Test Method for Apparent Density of Rigid Cellular Plastics
D 1623—09	Standard Test Method for Tensile and Tensile Adhesion Properties of Rigid Cellular Plastics
D 1693—08	Test Method for Environmental Stress-cracking of Ethylene Plastics
D 1784—08	Standard Specification for Rigid Poly (Vinyl Chloride) (PVC) Compounds and Chlorinated Poly (Vinyl Chloride) (CPVC) Compounds
D 1863—05	Specification for Mineral Aggregate Used in Built-up Roofs
D 1970—09	Specification for Self-adhering Polymer Modified Bitumen Sheet Materials Used as Steep Roofing Underlayment for Ice Dam Protection
D 2126—09	Standard Test Method for Response of Rigid Cellular Plastics to Thermal and Humid Aging
D 2178—04	Specification for Asphalt Glass Felt Used in Roofing and Waterproofing
D 2412—10	Test Method for Determination of External Loading Characteristics of Plastic Pipe by Parallel-plate Loading
D 2447—03	Specification for Polyethylene (PE) Plastic Pipe Schedules 40 and 80, Based on Outside Diameter
D 2513—09a	Specification for Thermoplastic Gas Pressure Pipe, Tubing and Fittings
D 2559—10a	Standard Specification for Adhesives for Structural Laminated Wood Products for Use Under Exterior (West Use) Exposure Conditions
D 2626—04	Specification for Asphalt-saturated and Coated Organic Felt Base Sheet Used in Roofing
D 2683—10	Specification for Socket-type Polyethylene Fittings for Outside Diameter-controlled Polyethylene Pipe and Tubing

D 2822—05	Specification for Asphalt Roof Cement
D 2823—05	Specification for Asphalt Roof Coatings
D 2824—06	Specification for Aluminum-pigmented Asphalt Roof Coatings, Nonfibered, Asbestos Fibered and Fibered without Asbestos
D 2837—08	Test Method for Obtaining Hydrostatic Design Basis for Thermoplastic Pipe Materials or Pressure Design Basis for Thermoplastic Pipe Products
D 2846/D 2846M—09b	Specification for Chlorinated Poly (Vinyl Chloride) (CPVC) Plastic Hot- and Cold-water Distribution Systems
D 2898—10	Test Methods for Accelerated Weathering of Fire-retardant-treated Wood for Fire Testing
D 3019—08	Specification for Lap Cement Used with Asphalt Roll Roofing, Nonfibered, Asbestos Fibered and Nonasbestos Fibered.
D 3035—08	Specification for Polyethylene (PE) Plastic Pipe (DR-PR) Based On Controlled Outside Diameter
D 3161—09	Test Method for Wind Resistance of Asphalt Shingles (Fan Induced Method)
D 3201—08ae1	Test Method for Hygroscopic Properties of Fire-retardant Wood and Wood-base Products
D 3309—96a (2002)	Specification for Polybutylene (PB) Plastic Hot- and Code-water Distribution System
D 3350—10	Specification for Polyethylene Plastic Pipe and Fitting Materials
D 3462/D 3462M—10a	Specification for Asphalt Shingles Made From Glass Felt and Surfaced with Mineral Granules.
D 3468—99 (2006)e01	Specification for Liquid-applied Neoprene and Chlorosulfanated Polyethylene Used in Roofing and Waterproofing
D 3679—09a	Specification for Rigid Poly (Vinyl Chloride) (PVC) Siding
D 3737—09	Practice for Establishing Allowable Properties for Structural Glued Laminated Timber (Glulam)
D 3747—79 (2007)	Specification for Emulsified Asphalt Adhesive for Adhering Roof Insulation
D 3909—97b (2004)e01	Specification for Asphalt Roll Roofing (Glass Felt) Surfaced with Mineral Granules
D 3957—09	Standard Practices for Establishing Stress Grades for Structural Members Used in Log Buildings
D 4022—07	Specification for Coal Tar Roof Cement, Asbestos Containing
D 4318—10	Test Methods for Liquid Limit, Plastic Limit and Plasticity Index of Soils
D 4434/D 4434—09	Specification for Poly (Vinyl Chloride) Sheet Roofing
D 4479—07	Specification for Asphalt Roof Coatings-asbestos-free
D 4586—07	Specification for Asphalt Roof Cement-asbestos- free
D 4601—04	Specification for Asphalt-coated Glass Fiber Base Sheet Used in Roofing

D 4637/D 4637M—10	Specification for EPDM Sheet Used in Single-ply Roof Membrane
D 4829—08a	Test Method for Expansion Index of Soils
D 4869—05e01	Specification for Asphalt-saturated (Organic Felt) Underlayment Used in Steep Slope Roofing
D 4897/D 4897M—01(2009)	Specification for Asphalt Coated Glass-fiber Venting Base Sheet Used in Roofing
D 4990—97a (2005)e01	Specification for Coal Tar Glass Felt Used in Roofing and Waterproofing
D 5019—07a	Specification for Reinforced Nonvulcanized Polymeric Sheet Used in Roofing Membrane
D 5055—10	Specification for Establishing and Monitoring Structural Capacities of Prefabricated Wood I-joists
D 5516—09	Test Method for Evaluating the Flexural Properties of Fire-retardant-treated Softwood Plywood Exposed to the Elevated Temperatures
D 5643—06	Specification for Coal Tar Roof Cement Asbestos-free
D 5664—10	Test Methods For Evaluating the Effects of Fire-retardant Treatments and Elevated Temperatures on Strength Properties of Fire-retardant-treated Lumber
D 5665—99a(2006)	Specification for Thermoplastic Fabrics Used in Cold-applied Roofing and Waterproofing
D 5726—98(2005)	Specification for Thermoplastic Fabrics Used in Hot-applied Roofing and Waterproofing
D 6083—05e01	Specification for Liquid-applied Acrylic Coating Used in Roofing
D 6162—08	Specification for Styrene Butadiene Styrene (SBS) Modified Bituminous Sheet Materials Using a Combination of Polyester and Glass Fiber Reinforcements
D 6163—00 (2008)	Specification for Styrene Butadiene Styrene (SBS) Modified Bituminous Sheet Materials Using Glass Fiber Reinforcements
D 6164—05e1	Specification for Styrene Butadiene Styrene (SBS) Modified Bituminous Sheet Materials Using Polyester Reinforcements
D 6222—08	Specification for Atactic Polypropelene (APP) Modified Bituminous Sheet Materials Using Polyester Reinforcement.
D 6223/D 6223M—02(2009)e01	Specification for Atactic Polypropelene (APP) Modified Bituminous Sheet Materials Using a Combination of Polyester and Glass Fiber Reinforcement
D 6298—05 e1	Specification for Fiberglass-reinforced Styrene Butadiene Styrene (SBS) Modified Bituminous Sheets with a Factory Applied Metal Surface
D 6305—08	Practice for Calculating Bending Strength Design Adjustment Factors for Fire-retardant-treated Plywood Roof Sheathing
D 6380—03(2008)	Standard Specification for Asphalt Roll Roofing (Organic Felt)

D 6694—*08*	Standard Specification Liquid-applied Silicone Coating Used in Spray Polurethane Foam Roofing
D 6754/*D 6754M—10*	Standard Specification for Ketone-ethylene-ester-based Sheet Roofing2
D 6757—07	Standard Specification for Inorganic Underlayment for Use with Steep Slope Roofing Products.
D 6841—*08*	Standard Practice for Calculating Design Value Treatment Adjustment Factors for Fire-retardant-treated Lumber
D 6878—*08e1*	Standard Specification for Thermoplastic- polyolefin-based Sheet Roofing.
D 6947—07	Standard Specification for Liquid Applied Moisture Cured Polyurethane Coating Used in Spray Polyurethane Foam Roofing System
D 7032—*10a*	Standard Specification for Establishing Perfomance Ratings for Wood-plastic Composite Deck Boards and Guardrail Systems (Guards or Handrails).
D 7158—*08d*	Standard Test Method for Wind Resistance of Sealed Asphalt Shingles (Uplift Force/ Uplift Resistance Method
E 84—*10b*	Test Method for Surface Burning Characteristics of Building Materials
E 90—04	Test Method for Laboratory Measurement of Airborne Sound Transmission Loss of Building Partitions and Elements
E 96/E 96M—05	Test Method for Water Vapor Transmission of Materials
E 108—*10a*	Test Methods for Fire Tests of Roof Coverings
E 119—*10b*	Test Methods for Fire Tests of Building Construction and Materials
E 136—*09b*	Test Method for Behavior of Materials in a Vertical Tube Furnace at 750°C
E 283—04	Test Method for Determining the Rate of Air Leakage through Exterior Windows, Curtain Walls and Doors Under Specified Pressure Differences Across the Specimen
E 330—02 *(2010)*	Test Method for Structural Performance of Exterior Windows, Curtain Walls and Doors by Uniform Static Air Pressure Difference
E 331—00 *(2009)*	Test Method for Water Penetration of Exterior Windows, Skylights, Doors and Curtain Walls by Uniform Static Air Pressure Difference
E 492—*09*	Specification for Laboratory Measurement of Impact Sound Transmission through Floor-ceiling Assemblies Using the Tapping Machine
E 814—*10*	Test Method for Fire Tests of Through-penetration Firestops
E 970—*10*	Test Method for Critical Radiant Flux of Exposed Attic Floor Insulation Using a Radiant Heat Energy Source
E 1509—04	Standard Specification for Room Heaters, Pellet Fuel-burning Type

E 1602—03*(2010)e1*	Guide for Construction of Solid Fuel Burning Masonry Heaters
E 1886—*05*	Test Method for Performance of Exterior Windows, Curtain Walls, Doors and Storm Shutters Impacted by Missles and Exposed to Cyclic Pressure Differentials
E 1996—*09*	Standard Specification for Performance of Exterior Windows, Curtain Walls, Doors and Impact Protective Systems Impacted by Windborne Debris in Hurricanes
E 2178—03	Standard Test Method for Air Permeance of Building Materials
E 2231—*09*	Standard Practice for Specimen Preparation and Mounting of Pipe and Duct Insulation Materials to Assess Surface Burning Characteristics
E 2273—03	Standard Test Method for Determining the Drainage Efficiency of Exterior Insulation and Finish Systems (EIFS) Clad Wall Assemblies
E 2568—*09e1*	Standard Specification for PB Exterior Insulation and Finish Systems (EIFS)
E 2570—07	Standard Test Methods for Evaluating Water- resistive Barrier (WRB) Coatings Used Under Exterior Insulation and Finish Systems (EIFS) or EIFS with Drainage
F 876—*10*	Specification for Cross-linked Polyethylene (PEX) Tubing
F 877—07	Specification for Cross-linked Polyethylene (PEX) Plastic Hot-and Cold-water Distribution Systems
F 1055—98(2006)	Specification for Electrofusion Type Polyethylene Fittings for Outside Diameter Controlled Polyethylene Pipe and Fittings
F 1281—07	Specification for Cross-linked Polyethylene/Aluminum/Cross-linked Polyethylene (PEX-AL-PEX) Pressure Pipe
F 1282—*10*	Specification for Polyethylene/Aluminum/Polyethylene (PE-AL-PE) Composite Pressure Pipe
F 1554—*07a*	Specification for Anchor Bolts, Steel, 36, 55 and 105-ksi Yield Strength
F 1667—*10*	Specification for Driven Fasteners, Nails, Spikes and Staples
F 1807—*10e1*	Specification for Metal Insert Fittings Utilizing a Copper Crimp Ring for SDR9 Cross-linked Polyethylene (PEX) Tubing
F 1960—*10*	Specification for Cold Expansion Fittings with PEX Reinforcing Rings for Use with Cross-linked Polyethylene (PEX) Tubing
F 1973—*08*	Standard Specification for Factory Assembled Anodeless Risers and Transition Fittings in Polyethylene (PE) and Polyamide 11 (PA 11) Fuel Gas Distribution Systems

F 2090—*10*	Specification for Window Fall Prevention Devices— with Emergency Escape (Egress) Release Mechanisms
F 2098—*08*	Standard Specification for Stainless Steel Clamps for SDR9 PEX Tubing to Metal Insert Fittings
F 2389—*10*	Standard for Pressure-rated Polypropylene (PP) Piping Systems
F 2623—*08*	Standard Specification for Polyethylene of Raised Temperature (PE-RT) SDRG Tubing

American Wood Protection Association
P.O. Box 361784
Birmingham, AL 35236-1784

AWPA Standard reference number	**Title**
C1—03	All Timber Products—Preservative Treatment by Pressure Processes
M4—06	Standard for the Care of Preservative-treated Wood Products
U1—*10*	USE CATEGORY SYSTEM: User Specification for Treated Wood Except Section 6 Commodity Specification H

Canadian General Standards Board
Place du Portage 111, 6B1 11 Laurier Street
Gatineau, Quebec, Canada KIA 1G6

CGSB Standard reference number	**Title**
37-GP—52M—(1984)	Roofing and Waterproofing Membrane, Sheet Applied, Elastomeric
37-GP—56M—(*1985*)	Membrane, Modified Bituminous, Prefabricated and Reinforced for Roofing—with December 1985 Amendment
CAN/CGSB-37.54—95	Polyvinyl Chloride Roofing and Waterproofing Membrane

Composite Panel Association
19465 Deerfield Avenue, Suite 306
Leesburg, VA 20176

CPA Standard reference number	**Title**
ANSI A135.4—04	Basic Hardboard
ANSI A135.5—04	Prefinished Hardboard Paneling
ANSI A135.6—*06*	Hardboard Siding

Consumer Product Safety Commission

4330 East West Highway
Bethesda, MD 20814-4408

CPSC Standard reference number	Title
16 C.F.R. Part 1201—(1977)	Safety Standard for Architectural Glazing
16 CFR Part 1209—(1979)	Interim Safety Standard for Cellulose Insulation
16 CFR Part 1404—(1979)	Cellulose Insulation

Canadian Standards Association
5060 Spectrum Way
Mississauga, Ontario, Canada L4N 5N6

CSA Standard reference number	Title
CSA Requirement 3—88	Manually Operated Gas Valves for Use in House Piping Systems
CSA 8-93	Requirements for Gas Fired Log Lighters for Wood Burning Fireplaces—with Revisions through January 1999
O325—07	Construction Sheathing
O437-Series—93	Standards on OSB and Waferboard (Reaffirmed 2006)
101/I.S.2/A440—08	Specifications for Windows, Doors and Unit Skylights
CAN/CSA B137.10M—09	Cross-linked Polyethylene/Aluminum/Polyethylene Composite Pressure Pipe Systems

Cedar Shake & Shingle Bureau
P. O. Box 1178
Sumas, WA 98295-1178

CSSB Standard reference number	Title
CSSB—97	Grading and Packing Rules for Western Red Cedar Shakes and Western Red Shingles of the Cedar Shake and Shingle Bureau

Door and Access Systems Manufacturers Association International
1300 Summer Avenue
Cleveland, OH 44115-2851

DASMA Standard reference number	Title
108—05	Standard Method for Testing Garage Doors: Determination of Structural Performance Under Uniform Static Air Pressure Difference

United States Department of Commerce

1401 Constitution Avenue, NW
Washington, DC 20230

**DOC Standard reference
number**

	Title
PS 1—07	Structural Plywood
PS 2—04	Performance Standard for Wood-based Structural-use Panels
R803.2.1/ PS 20—05	American Softwood Lumber Standard

Department of Transportation
1200 New Jersey Avenue SE East Building, 2nd floor
Washington, DC 20590

**DOTn Standard reference
number**

	Title
49 CFR, Parts 192.281(e) & 192.283 (b)	Transportation of Natural and Other Gas by Pipeline: Minimum Federal Safety Standards

Federal Emergency Management Agency
500 C Street, SW
Washington, DC 20472

**FEMA Standard reference
number**

	Title
TB-2—*08*	Flood Damage-Resistant Materials Requirements
FIA-TB-11—01	Crawlspace Construction for Buildings Located in Special Flood Hazard Area

Factory Mutual Global Research Standards Laboratories
Department 1301 Atwood Avenue, P. O. Box 7500
Johnson, RI 02919

FM Standard reference number

	Title
4450—(1989)	Approval Standard for Class 1 Insulated Steel Deck Roofs—with Supplements through July 1992
4880—(*2010*)	American National Standard for Evaluating Insulated Wall or Wall and Roof/Ceiling Assemblies, Plastic Interior Finish Materials, Plastic Exterior Building Panels, Wall/Ceiling Coating Systems, Interior or Exterior Finish Systems

Gypsum Association
810 First Street, Northeast, Suite 510
Washington, DC 20002-4268

GA Standard reference number

	Title
GA-253—07	Application of Gypsum Sheathing

Hardwood Plywood & Veneer Association
1825 Michael Faraday Drive
Reston, Virginia 20190-5350

**HPVA Standard reference
number**

Title

HP-1—*2009*

The American National Standard for Hardwood and
Decorative Plywood

International Code Council, Inc.
500 New Jersey Avenue, NW 6th Floor
Washington, DC 20001

ICC Standard reference number	**Title**
ICC/ANSI A117.1 — *09*	Accessible and Usable Buildings and Facilities
ICC 400 — *07*	Standard on the Design and Construction of Log Structures
ICC 500 — 08	ICC/NSSA Standard on the Design and Construction of Storm Shelters
ICC 600 — 08	Standard for Residential Construction in High Wind Regions
IEBC-09	International Existing Buildings Code
IECC — 09	International Energy Conservation Code (*adoption includes only section 101 of chapter 1 and chapters 2 through 6*)
IFGC — 09	International Fuel Gas Code (*including ICC Emergency Amendment changing section 406.7*)

International Organization for Standardization
1, ch. de la Voie -Creuse Case postale 56 CH-1211
Geneva 20, Switzerland

ISO Standard reference number	**Title**
15874—*03*	Polypropylene Plastic Piping Systems for Hot and Cold Water Installations

Manufacturers Standardization Society of the Valve and Fittings Industry
127 Park Street, Northeast
Vienna, VA 22180

**MSS Standard reference
number**

Title

SP-58—*09*

Pipe Hangers and Supports—Materials, Design and
Manufacture

North American Insulation Manufacturers Association
44 Canal Center Plaza, Suite 310

Alexandria, VA 22314

**NAIMA Standard reference
number**   **Title**
AH 116—02   Fibrous Glass Duct Construction Standards, Fifth Edition

National Concrete Masonry Association
13750 Sunrise Valley Drive
Herndon, VA 20171-4662

**NCMA Standard reference
number**   **Title**
TR 68-A—75   Design and Construction of Plain and Reinforced Concrete Masonry and Basement and Foundation Walls

National Fire Protection Association
1 Batterymarch Park
Quincy, MA 02269

**NFPA Standard reference
number**   **Title**

Number	Title
13—*10*	Installation of Sprinkler Systems *(including TIA 10-2)*
13D—*10*	Standard for the Installation of Sprinkler Systems in One- and Two-family Dwellings and Manufactured Homes *(including TIA 10-2)*
13R-10	*Standard for the Installation of Sprinkler Systems in Residential Occupancies up to and Including Four Stories in Height (including TIA 10-2)*
31—06	Installation of Oil-burning Equipment
58—*11*	Liquefied Petroleum Gas Code
70—*11*	National Electrical Code *(including TIA 11-1)*
72—*10*	National Fire Alarm Code
85—07	Boiler and Construction Systems Hazards Code
211—*10*	Chimneys, Fireplaces, Vents and Solid Fuel Burning Appliances
259—08	Test Method for Potential Heat of Building Materials
286—06	Standard Methods of Fire Tests for Evaluating Contribution of Wall and Ceiling Interior Finish to Room Fire Growth
501—05	Standard on Manufactured Housing
853—*10*	Standard for the Installation of Stationary Fuel Cell Power Systems

National Fenestration Rating Council Inc.
8484 Georgia Avenue, Suite 320

Silver Spring, MD 20910

NFRC Standard reference number

	Title
100—*10*	Procedure for Determining Fenestration Product U-factors
200—*10*	Procedure for Determining Fenestration Product Solar Heat Gain Coefficients and Visible Transmittance at Normal Incidence
400—*10*	Procedure for Determining Fenestration Product Air Leakage

Portland Cement Association
5420 Old Orchard Road
Skokie, IL 60077

PCA Standard reference number

	Title
100—07	Prescriptive Design of Exterior Concrete Walls for One- and Two-family Dwellings (Pub. No. EB241)

Sheet Metal & Air Conditioning Contractors National Assoc. Inc.
4021 Lafayette Center Road
Chantilly, VA 22021

SMACNA Standard reference number

	Title
SMACNA—03	Fibrous Glass Duct Construction Standards (2003)

The Masonry Society
3970 Broadway, Suite 201-D
Boulder, CO 80304

TMS Standard reference number

	Title
302—07	Standard Method for Determining the Sound Transmission Class Rating for Masonry Walls
402—*08*	Building Code Requirements for Masonry Structures
602—*08*	Specification for Masonry Structures

Truss Plate Institute
583 D'Onofrio Drive, Suite 200
Madison, WI 53719

TPI Standard reference number

	Title
TPI 1—*2007*	National Design Standard for Metal-plate-connected Wood Truss Construction

Underwriters Laboratories, Inc.
333 Pfingsten Road
Northbrook, IL 60062

UL Standard reference number	Title
17—*08*	Vent or Chimney Connector Dampers for Oil-fired Appliances
58—96	Steel Underground Tanks for Flammable and Combustible Liquids—with Revisions through July 1998
80—*07*	Steel Tanks for Oil-burner Fuel
103—*10*	Factory-built Chimneys for Residential Type and Building Heating Appliances
127—*08*	Factory-built Fireplaces
174—04	Household Electric Storage Tank Water Heaters—with Revisions through November 2005
181—05	Factory-made Air Ducts and Air Connectors
181A—05	Closure Systems for Use with Rigid Air Ducts and Air Connectors
181B—05	Closure Systems for Use with Flexible Air Ducts and Air Connectors
217—06	Single- and Multiple-station Smoke Alarms
263—03	Standards for Fire Test of Building Construction and Materials
325—02	Standard for Door, Drapery, Gate, Louver and Window Operations and Systems—with Revisions through February 2006
343—*08*	Pumps for Oil-burning Appliances
441—*10*	Gas Vents
508—99	Industrial Control Equipment—with Revisions through July 2005
536—97	Flexible Metallic Hose—with Revisions through June 2003 641—95 Type L, Low-temperature Venting Systems—with Revisions through August 2005
651—05	Schedule 40 and Schedule 80 Rigid PVC Conduit and Fittings
723—*08*	Standard for Test for Surface Burning Characteristics of Building Materials
726—95	Oil-fired Boiler Assemblies—with Revisions through March 2006
727—06	Oil-fired Central Furnaces
729—03	Oil-fired Floor Furnaces
730—03	Oil-fired Wall Furnaces
732—95	Oil-fired Storage Tank Water Heaters
737—07	Fireplaces Stoves
790—04	Standard Test Methods for Fire Tests of Roof Coverings
795—06	Commercial-industrial Gas Heating Equipment.
834—04	Heating, Water Supply and Power Boilers-Electric

896—93	Oil-burning Stoves—with Revisions through May 2004
923—08	Microwave Cooking Appliances
959—01	Medium Heat Appliance Factory-built Chimneys—with Revisions through September 2006
1040—96	Fire Test of Insulated Wall Construction—with Revisions through June 2001
1256—02	Fire Test of Roof Deck Construction.
1261—01	Electric Water Heaters for Pools and Tubs—with Revisions through June 2004
1453—04	Electronic Booster and Commercial Storage Tank Water Heaters
1479—03	Fire Tests of Through-penetration Firestops
1482—10	Solid-fuel-type Room Heaters
1715—97	Fire Test of Interior Finish Material—with Revisions through March 2004
1738—10	Venting Systems for Gas-burning Appliances, Categories II, III and IV
1777—07	Standard for Chimney Liners
1995—05	Heating and Cooling Equipment.
2017—08	Standard for General-purpose Signaling Devices and Systems—with Revisions through June 2004
2034—08	Standard for Single- and Multiple-station Carbon Monoxide Alarms.
2158A—10	Outline of Investigation for Clothes Dryer Transition Duct

Underwriters' Laboratories of Canada
7 Underwriters Road Toronto,
Ontario, Canada M1R 3B4

| **ULC Standard reference number** | **Title** |
| CAN/ULC S 102—10 | Standard Methods for Test for Surface Burning Characteristics of Building Materials and Assemblies |

United States — Federal Trade Commission
600 Pennsylvania Avenue NW
Washington, DC 20580

| **US-FTC Standard reference number** | **Title** |
| CFR Title 16 Part 460 | R-value Rule |

Window & Door Manufacturers Association
1400 East Touhy Avenue, Suite 470
Des Plaines, IL 60018

WDMA Standard reference number

AAMA/WDMA/CSA

101/I.S2/A440—08

Title

Specifications for Windows, Doors and Skylights

APPENDICES

Appendix 1

Use Group Classifications

The following are typical group classifications as related to the occupancy. When the occupancy is not clearly defined, the building official shall establish the use group.

A-1

        Motion picture theaters
        Radio stations (w/audience)
        Symphony and concert halls
        Television stations (w/audience)
        Theaters

A-2

        Banquet halls
        Night clubs
        Restaurants
        Taverns and bars

A-3

        Amusement arcades
        Art galleries
        Bowling alleys
        Churches
        Community halls
        Courtrooms
        Dance halls (w/o food or drink)
        Exhibition halls
        Funeral parlors
        Gymnasiums (w/o spectator seating)
        Indoor swimming pools (w/o spectator seating)
        Indoor tennis courts (w/o spectator seating)
        Lecture halls
        Libraries
        Museums
        Pool and billiard parlors
        Waiting areas in transportation terminals

A-4

        Arenas
        Skating rinks
        Swimming pools (w/ spectator seating)
        Tennis courts

A-5

        Amusement park structures
        Bleachers (outdoor)

Grandstands (outdoor)
Stadiums

B

Airport traffic control towers
Animal hospitals, kennels and pounds
Banks
Barber and beauty shops
Car wash
Civic administration
Clinic-outpatient (adequate staff for safe evacuation of patients in an emergency)
Dry cleaning and laundries (pick-up and delivery stations and self-service)
Educational occupancies (students above K-12)
Electronic data processing
Laboratories: testing and research
Motor vehicle showrooms
Post offices
Print shops
Professional services (architects, attorneys, dentists, physicians, engineers, etc.)
Radio and television stations (w/o audience)
Telephone exchanges
Training and skill development not within a school or academic program

E

Day-care (children less then 2½)
Education (up to K-12)

F-1

Aircraft Appliances
Athletic equipment
Automobiles and other motor vehicles
Bakeries
Beverages; over 12-percent alcohol content
Bicycles
Boats
Brooms or brushes
Business machines
Cameras and photo equipment
Canvas or similar fabric
Carpets and rugs (includes cleaning)
Clothing
Construction and agricultural machinery
Disinfectants
Dry cleaning and dyeing
Electric generation plants
Electronics
Engines (including rebuilding)
Food processing
Furniture

Hemp products
Jute products
Laundries
Leather products
Machinery
Metals
Millwork (sash & door)
Motion pictures and television filming (without spectators)
Musical instruments
Optical goods
Paper mills or products
Photographic film
Plastic products
Printing or publishing
Recreational vehicles
Refuse incineration
Shoes
Soaps and detergents
Textiles
Tobacco
Trailers
Upholstering
Wood; distillation
Woodworking (cabinet)

F-2

Beverages; up to and including 12-percent alcohol content
Brick and masonry
Ceramic products
Foundries
Glass products
Gypsum
Ice
Metal products (fabrication and assembly)

H-1

Explosives
Organic peroxides, unclassified detonable
Oxidizers, Class 4
Unstable (reactive) materials, Class 3 detonable and Class 4 Detonable pyrophoric materials

H-2

Combustible dusts
Cryogenic fluids, flammable
Flammable gases
Flammable or combustible liquids, Class I, II, IIA (used or stored in open or closed containers pressurized at more than 15 psi gage)
Organic peroxides, Class I Oxidizers, Class 3 (used or stored in open or closed containers pressurized at more than 15 psi gage)

Pyrophoric liquids, solids and gases, nondetonable Unstable (reactive) materials, Class 3, nondetonable

Water-reactive materials, Class 3

H-3

Combustible fibers, other than densely packed baled cotton

Consumer fireworks, 1.4G (Class C, Common)

Cryogenic fluids, oxidizing

Flammable or combustible liquids, Class I, II, IIIA (used or stored in closed containers pressurized at 15 psi gauge or less)

Flammable solids

Organic peroxides, Class II and III

Oxidizers, Class 2

Oxidizers, Class 3 (used or stored in closed containers pressurized at 15 lbs. psi gauge or less)

Oxidizing gases

Unstable (reactive) materials, Class 2

Water-reactive materials, Class 2

H-4

Corrosives

Highly toxic materials

Toxic materials

H-5

Research and development for hazardous material

Semiconductor fabrication facilities

I-1

Alcohol and drug centers

Assisted living facilities

Congregate care facilities

Convalescent facilities

Group homes

Halfway houses

Residential board and care facilities

Social rehabilitation facilities

I-2

Day-care facilities (more than 5 children, more than 24 hours)

Jails

Nursing homes (more then 3 patients)

Prerelease centers

Prisons

Reformatories

I-3

Correctional centers

Detention centers

Jails

Pre-release centers

Prisons

Reformatories

I-4

Day-care facilities (less than 24-hour care, children and adult)

M

Department stores
Markets
Retail stores
Sales rooms
Service stations (no repair)
Trade Centers
Wholesale stores

R-1

Boarding houses (transient)
Hotels (transient)
Motels (transient)

R-2

Apartments
Boarding house (non-transient)
Condominiums
Convalescent facilities (less then 5)
Convents
Dormitories
Fraternities and Sororities
Hotels (non-transient)
Monasteries
Motels (non-transient)
Vacation Time-shares

R-3

Apartments (shared exits)
Condominiums (shared exits)
Pre-manufactured housing
Row/townhouse housing
Townhouses

R-4

Convalescent care (6-16 patients)
Residential care/assisted living

S-1

Aerosols
Airplane repair
Bamboo
Bags
Baskets
Belting
Book storage
Boots and Shoes
Burlap, cloth and paper bag storage

Button storage
Canvas storage
Cardboard
Cloth and clothing storage
Cordage
Dry boat storage
Grains
Furniture storage
Fur storage
Garage (repair)
Glue
Horns and combs
Leather storage
Motor vehicle repair per Table 307.1(1)
Oil storage
Paper storage
Photoengraving storage
Resilient flooring and linoleum
Soap storage
Sugar
Tires (bulk)
Tobacco storage
Upholstery and mattresses
Wax and candle storage

S-2

Cement Manufacturing and Products
Cement Storage
Chalk
Dairy (in coated paper containers)
Dry-cell battery manufacturers
Electrical motor and coil storage
Fresh fruits and vegetables
Food in non-combustible containers
Frozen foods
Garages (public)
Glass and mirror storage
Glass bottles
Gypsum storage
Insert pigments
Ivory products
Masonry storage
Metal cabinets and desks (w/plastic/wood trim)
Metal parts
Meats
Parking garages (open and closed0
Porcelain and pottery

Washers, dryers, stoves

U

Aircraft hangars (residential)
Barns
Fences more than 6' high
Garages (private)
Greenhouses (non-public)
Grain silos, accessory to residences
Livestock shelters (non-residential)
Retaining Walls
Sheds
Stables
Tanks
Towers

Appendix 2

Table of Sources and Referenced Documents

a. Ohio Building Code

AA
Aluminum Association
1525 Wilson Boulevard, Suite 600
Arlington, VA 22209

- ADM1—*10* Aluminum Design Manual: Part 1-A Specification for Aluminum Structures, Allowable Stress Design; and Part 1-B—Aluminum Structures, Load and Resistance Factor Design
- ASM 35—00 Aluminum Sheet Metal Work in Building Construction (Fourth Edition)

AAMA
American Architectural Manufacturers Association
1827 Waldon Office Square,
Suite 550
Schaumburg, IL 60173

- 1402—*09* Standard Specifications for Aluminum Siding, Soffit and Fascia
- AAMA/WDMA/CSA101/I.S.2/A440—08 North American Fenestration Standard/Specifications for Windows, Doors and Skylights

ACI
American Concrete Institute
38800 Country Club Dive
Farmington Hills, MI 48331

- 216.1—07 Standard Method for Determining Fire Resistance of Concrete and Masonry Construction Assemblies
- 318—08 Building Code Requirements for Structural Concrete
- 530—08 Building Code Requirements for Masonry Structures
- 530.1—08 Specifications for Masonry Structures

AF&PA
American Forest & Paper Association
1111 19th St, NW Suite 800
Washington, DC 20036

- WCD No. 4—*03* Wood Construction Data—Plank and Beam Framing for Residential NDS 05 National Design Specification (NDS) for Wood Construction with 2005 Supplement

- AF&PA—93 Span Tables for Joists and Rafters
- ANSI/AF&PA PWF—07 Permanent Wood Foundation Design Specification
- ANSI/AF&PA SDPWS—08 Special Design Provisions for Wind and Seismic

AISC

American Institute of Steel Construction
One East Wacker Drive, Suite 3100
Chicago, IL 60601-2001

- 341—05 Seismic Provisions for Structural Steel Buildings, including Supplement No. 1 dated 2005
- 360—05 Specification for Structural Steel Buildings

AISI

American Iron and Steel Institute
1140 Connecticut Avenue
Suite 705
Washington, DC 20036

- S100—07 North American Specification for the Design of Cold-formed Steel Structural Members
- S200—*08* North American Standard for Cold-formed Steel Framing—General
- S210—*08* North American Standard for Cold-formed Steel Framing—Floor and Roof System Design
- S211—*08* North American Standard for Cold-formed Steel Framing—Wall Stud
- S212—*08* North American Standard for Cold-formed Steel Framing—Header Design
- S213—*08* North American Standard for Cold-formed Steel Framing—Lateral Design
- S214—*08* North American Standard for Cold-formed Steel Framing—Truss Design, with Supplement 2, dated 2008

AITC

American Institute of Timber Construction
Suite 140
7012 S. Revere Parkway
Englewood, CO 80112

- AITC Technical Note 7—96 Calculation of Fire Resistance of Glued Laminated Timbers
- AITC 104—03 Typical Construction Details
- AITC 110—01 Standard Appearance Grades for Structural Glued Laminated
- AITC 113—01 Standard for Dimensions of Structural Glued Laminated Timber
- AITC 117—04 Standard Specifications for Structural Glued Laminated Timber of Softwood Species
- AITC 119—96 Standard Specifications for Structural Glued Laminated Timber of Hardwood
- AITC200—*09* Manufacturing Quality Control Systems Manual for Structural Glued Laminated Timber

- ANSI/AITCA 190.1—07 Structural Glued Laminated Timber

ALI
Automotive Lift Institute
P.O. Box 85
Courtland, NY 13045

- ALI ALCTV—*2007* Standard for Automobile Lifts—Safety Requirements for Construction, Testing and Validation (ANSI)

ANSI
American National Standards Institute
25 West 43rd Street, Fourth Floor
New York, NY 10036

- A13.1—*07* Scheme for the Identification of Piping Systems A108.1A—*09* Installation of Ceramic Tile in the Wet-set Method, with Portland Cement
- A108.1B—*09* Installation of Ceramic Tile, Quarry Tile on a Cured Portland Cement Mortar Setting Bed with Dry-set or Latex-
- A108.4—*09* Installation of Ceramic Tile with Organic Adhesives or Water-cleanable Tile-setting Epoxy Adhesive
- A108.5—*09* Installation of Ceramic Tile with Dry-set Portland Cement Mortar or Latex-Portland Cement Mortar
- A108.6—*09* Installation of Ceramic Tile with Chemical-resistant, Water Cleanable Tile-setting and -grouting Epoxy
- A108.8—*09* Installation of Ceramic Tile with Chemical-resistant Furan Resin Mortar and Grout
- A108.9—*09* Installation of Ceramic Tile with Modified Epoxy Emulsion Mortar/Grout
- A108.10—*09* Installation of Grout in Tilework
- A118.1—*10.1* American National Standard Specifications for Dry-set Portland Cement
- A118.3—*10.1* American National Standard Specifications for Chemical-resistant, Water-cleanable Tile-setting and -grouting Epoxy and Water Cleanable Tile-setting Epoxy
- A118.4—*10.1* American National Standard Specifications for Latex Portland Cement
- A118.5—*10.1* American National Standard Specifications for Chemical Resistant Furan Mortar and Grouts for Tile
- A118.8—*10.1* American National Standard Specifications for Modified Epoxy Emulsion Mortar/Grout
- A136.1—*10.1* American National Standard Specifications for Organic Adhesives for Installation of Ceramic Tile
- A137.1—*08* American National Standard Specifications for Ceramic Tile
- A208.1—*09* Particleboard Z
- A97.1—*09* Safety Glazing Materials Used in Buildings—Safety Performance Specifications and Methods of Test

APA—Engineered Wood Association

7011 South 19th
Tacoma, WA 98466

- APA PDS—*08* Panel Design Specification
- APA PDS Supplement 1—*90* Design and Fabrication of Plywood Curved Panels (revised 1995)
- APA PDS Supplement 2—*92* Design and Fabrication of Plywood-lumber Beams (revised 1998)
- APA PDS Supplement 3—*96* Design and Fabrication of Plywood Stressed-skin Panels (revised 1996)
- APA PDS Supplement 4—*93* Design and Fabrication of Plywood Sandwich Panels (revised 1993)
- APA PDS Supplement 5—*95* Design and Fabrication of All-plywood Beams (revised 1995)
- EWS R540—*07* Builders Tips: Proper Storage and Handling of Glulam Beams
- EWS S475—*07* Glued Laminated Beam Design Tables
- EWS S560—*10* Field Notching and Drilling of Glued Laminated Timber Beams
- EWS T300—*07* Glulam Connection
- EWS X440—*08* Product Guide—Glulam
- EWS X450—*01* Glulam in Residential Construction—Western Edition

APSP

The Association of Pool & Spa Professionals
2111 Eisenhower Avenue
Alexandria, VA 22314

- ANSI/APSP 7—*06* Standard for Suction Entrapment Avoidance in Swimming Pools, Wading Pools, Spas, Hot Tubs and Catch Basins

ASABF

American Society of Agricultural and Biological Engineers
2950 Niles Road
St. Joseph, MI 49085

- EP 484.2—*98* Diaphragm Design of Metal-clad, Post-frame Rectangular Buildings
- EP 486.1—*99* Shallow-post Foundation Design
- EP 559—*03* Design Requirements and Bending Properties for Mechanically Laminated Columns

ASCE

American Society of Civil Engineers
Structural Engineering Institute
1801 Alexander Bell Drive
Reston, VA 20191-4400

- 3—*91* Structural Design of Composite Slabs
- 5—*08* Building Code Requirements for Masonry
- 6—*08* Specification for Masonry Structures

- 7—05 Minimum Design Loads for Buildings and Other Structures including Supplements No. 1 and 2, excluding Chapter 14 and Appendix 11A
- 8—02 Standard Specification for the Design of Cold-formed Stainless Steel Structural Members
- 19—*10* Structural Applications of Steel Cables for Buildings
- 24—05 Flood Resistant Design and Construction
- 29—05 Standard Calculation Methods for Structural Fire Protection
- 32—01 Design and Construction of Frost Protected Shallow Foundations

ASHRAE

American Society of Heating, Refrigerating and Air-Conditioning Engineers, Inc.
1791 Tullie Circle, NE
Atlanta, GA 30329-2305

- ASHRAE 90.1—2007 Energy Standard for Buildings Except Low-Rise Residential Buildings

ASME

American Society of Mechanical Engineers
Three Park Avenue
New York, NY 10016-5990

- A17.1/CSA B44—*2004 2010* Safety Code for Elevators and Escalators
- A18.1—*2003 2008* Safety Standard for Platform Lifts and Stairway Chairlifts
- A90.1—03 *2009* Safety Standard for Belt Manlifts
- B16.18—2001 (Reaffirmed 2005) Cast Copper Alloy Solder Joint Pressure Fittings
- B16.22—2001 (Reaffirmed 2005) Wrought Copper and Copper Alloy Solder Joint Pressure Fittings
- B20.1—*2009* Safety Standard for Conveyors and Related Equipment
- B31.3—*2008* Process Piping

ASTM

American Society Testing Materials
International
100 Barr Harbor Drive
West Conshohocken, PA 19428-2959

- A 36/A 36M—*08* Specification for Carbon Structural Steel
- A 153/A 153M—*09* Specification for Zinc Coating (Hot-dip) on Iron and Steel Hardware
- A 240/A 240M—*10a* Standard Specification for Chromium and Chromium-nickel Stainless Steel Plate, Sheet and Strip for Pressure Vessels and for General Applications
- A 252—*10* Specification for Welded and Seamless Steel Pipe Piles
- A 283/A 283M—03 *(2007)* Specification for Low and Intermediate Tensile Strength Carbon Steel Plates
- A 307—*07b* Specification for Carbon Steel Bolts and Studs, 60,000 psi Tensile Strength

- A 416/A 416M—*10* Specification for Steel Strand, Uncoated Seven-wire for Prestressed Concrete
- A 463/A 463M—*09a* Standard Specification for Steel Sheet, Aluminum coated, by the Hot-dip Process
- A 572/A 572M—07 Specification for High-strength Low-alloy Columbium-vanadium Structural Steel
- A 588/A 588M—*10* Specification for High-strength Low-alloy Structural Steel with 50 ksi (345 Mpa) Minimum Yield Point to 4 inches (100 mm) Thick
- A 615/A 615M—*09b* Specification for Deformed and Plain Billet-steel Bars for Concrete Reinforcement
- A 653/A 653M—*09a* Specification for Steel Sheet, Zinc-coated Galvanized or Zinc-iron Alloy-coated Galvannealed by the Hot-dip Process
- A 690/A 690M—07 Standard Specification for High-strength Low-alloy Nickel, Copper, Phosphorus Steel H-piles and Sheet Piling with Atmospheric Corrosion Resistance for Use in Marine Environments
- A 706/A 706M—*09b* Specification for Low-alloy Steel Deformed and Plain Bars for Concrete Reinforcement
- A 722/A 722M—07 Specification for Uncoated High-strength Steel Bar for Prestressing
- A 755/A 755M—*03 (2008)* Specification for Steel Sheet, Metallic-coated by the Hot-dip Process and Prepainted by the Coil-coating Process for Exterior Exposed Building Products
- A 792/A 792M—*09a* Specification for Steel Sheet, 55% Aluminum-zinc Alloy-coated by the Hot-dip Process
- A 875/A 875M—*09a* Standard Specification for Steel Sheet Zinc-5 percent, Aluminum Alloy-coated by the Hot-dip Process
- A 913/A 913M—07 Specification for High-strength Low-alloy Steel Shapes of Structural Quality, Produced by Quenching and Self-tempering Process (QST)
- A 924/A 924M—*10* Standard Specification for General Requirements for Steel Sheet, Metallic-coated by the Hot-dip Process
- A 992/A 992M—06a Standard Specification for Structural Shapes
- B 42—*10* Specification for Seamless Copper Pipe, Standard
- B 43—*09* Specification for Seamless Red Brass Pipe, Standard Sizes
- B 68—02 Specification for Seamless Copper Tube, Bright Annealed (Metric)
- B 88—*09* Specification for Seamless Copper Water Tube
- B 101—*07* Specification for Lead-coated Copper Sheet and Strip for Building Construction
- B 209—*07* Specification for Aluminum and Aluminum Alloy Steel and Plate
- B 251—*10* Specification for General Requirements for Wrought Seamless Copper and Copper-alloy Tube
- B 280—*08* Specification for Seamless Copper Tube for Air Conditioning and Refrigeration Field Service
- B 370—*09* Specification for Cold-rolled Copper Sheet and Strip for Building Construction
- B 695—04 *(2009)* Standard Specification for Coatings of Zinc Mechanically Deposited on Iron and Steel
- C 5—*10* Specification for Quicklime for Structural
- C 22/C 22M—00 (2005)e01 Specification for Gypsum
- C 27—98 *(2008)* Specification for Standard Classification of Fireclay and High-alumina Refractory Brick

- C 28/C 28M—*10* Specification for Gypsum
- C 31/C 31M—*10* Practice for Making and Curing Concrete Test Specimens in the Field
- C 33—*08* Specification for Concrete Aggregates
- C 34—*10* Specification for Structural Clay Load-bearing Wall Tile
- C 35—*01* (2009) Specification for Inorganic Aggregates for Use in Gypsum Plaster
- C 36/C 36M—03 Specification for Gypsum Wallboard
- C 37/C 37M—01 Specification for Gypsum Lath
- C 55—*09* Specification for Concrete Building Brick
- C 56—*10* Specification for Structural Clay NonloadBearing Tile
- C 59/C 59M—00 (2006) Specification for Gypsum Casting and Molding Plaster
- C 61/C 61M—00 (2006) Specification for Gypsum Keene's
- C 62—*10* Specification for Building Brick (Solid Masonry Units Made from Clay or Shale)
- C 67—*09* Test Methods of Sampling and Testing Brick and Structural Clay
- C 73—05 Specification for Calcium Silicate Face Brick (Sand-lime Brick)
- C 79—04a Specification for Treated Core and Nontreated Core Gypsum Sheathing Board
- C 90—*09* Specification for Loadbearing Concrete Masonry Units
- C 91—05 Specification for Masonry Cement
- C 94/C 94M—*10* Specification for Ready-mixed
- C 126—*10* Specification for Ceramic Glazed Structural Clay Facing Tile, Facing Brick and Solid Masonry Units
- C 140—*10* Test Method Sampling and Testing Concrete Masonry Units and Related Units
- C 150—*09* Specification for Portland Cement
- C 172—*10* Practice for Sampling Freshly Mixed
- C 199—84 (2005) Test Method for Pier Test for Refractory Mortars
- C 206—03 (2009) Specification for Finishing Hydrated Lime
- C 208—*08a* Specification for Cellulosic Fiber Insulating Board
- C 212—*10* Specification for Structural Clay Facing Tile
- C 216—*10* Specification for Facing Brick (Solid Masonry Units Made from Clay or Shale)
- C 270—*10* Specification for Mortar for Unit Masonry
- C 315—07 Specification for Clay Flue Liners and Chimney Pots
- C 317/C 317M—00 (2005) Specification for Gypsum Concrete
- C 330—*09* Specification for Lightweight Aggregates for Structural Concrete
- C 331—05 Specification for Lightweight Aggregates for Concrete Masonry Units
- C 406—*10* Specification for Roofing Slate
- C 442/C 442M—04 Specification for Gypsum Backing Board and Coreboard and Gypsum Shaftliner Board
- C 472—99 (2009) Specification for Standard Test Methods for Physical Testing of Gypsum, Gypsum Plasters and Gypsum Concrete
- C 473—*10* Test Method for Physical Testing of Gypsum Panel Products
- C 474—05 Test Methods for Joint Treatment Materials for Gypsum Board Construction

- C 475—*02 (2007)* Specification for Joint Compound and Joint Tape for Finishing Gypsum Wallboard
- C 503—*10* Specification for Marble Dimension Stone (Exterior)
- C 514—04 *(2009)e1* Specification for Nails for the Application of Gypsum
- C 516—*08* Specifications for Vermiculite Loose Fill Thermal
- C 547—*07e1* Specification for Mineral Fiber Pipe Insulation
- C 549—*06* Specification for Perlite Loose Fill
- C 552—*07* Standard Specification for Cellular Glass Thermal Insulation
- C 557—*03(2009)e01* Specification for Adhesives for Fastening Gypsum Wallboard to Wood Framing
- C 568—*10* Specification for Limestone Dimension Stone
- C 578—*10* Standard Specification for Rigid, Cellular Polystyrene Thermal Insulation
- C 587—04 *(2009)* Specification for Gypsum Veneer Plaster
- C 588/C 588M—01 Specification for Gypsum Base for Veneer Plasters
- C 595—*10* Specification for Blended Hydraulic Cements
- C 615—*10* Specification for Granite Dimension
- C 616—*10* Specification for Quartz Dimension Stone
- C 629—*10* Specification for Slate Dimension
- C 630/C 630M—03 Specification for Water-resistant Gypsum Backing Board
- C 631—*09* Specification for Bonding Compounds for Interior Gypsum Plastering
- C 635/*C 635M—07* Specification for the Manufacture, Performance and Testing of Metal Suspension Systems for Acoustical Tile and Lay-in Panel
- C 636/C 636M—*08* Practice for Installation of Metal Ceiling Suspension Systems for Acoustical Tile and Lay-in Panels
- C 645—*09a* Specification for Nonstructural Steel Framing Members
- C 652—*10* Specification for Hollow Brick (Hollow Masonry Units Made from Clay or Shale)
- C 728—05 *(2010)* Standard Specification for Perlite Thermal Insulation Board
- C 744—*10* Specification for Prefaced Concrete and Calcium Silicate Masonry
- C 754—*09a* Specification for Installation of Steel Framing Members to Receive Screw-attached Gypsum Panel Products
- C 836/*C 836M—10* Specification for High-solids Content, Cold Liquid applied Elastomeric Waterproofing Membrane for Use with Separate Wearing Course
- C 840—*08* Specification for Application and Finishing of Gypsum Board
- C 841—03 *(2008)e1* Specification for Installation of Interior Lathing and Furring
- C 842—*05* Specification for Application of Interior Gypsum Plaster
- C 843—99 (2006) Specification for Application of Gypsum Veneer Plaster
- C 844—*10* Specification for Application of Gypsum Base to Receive Gypsum Veneer Plaster
- C 847—*10a* Specification for Metal Lath
- C 887—05 *(2010)* Specification for Packaged, Dry Combined Materials for Surface Bonding Mortar
- C 897—05 *(2009)* Specification for Aggregate for Job-mixed Portland Cement-based Plaster
- C 920—*10* Standard for Specification for Elastomeric Joint Sealants
- C 926—*06* Specification for Application of Portland Cement based Plaster
- C 931/C 931M—04 Specification for Exterior Gypsum Soffit Board

- C 932—06 Specification for Surface-applied Bonding Compounds Agents for Exterior Plastering
- C 933—09 Specification for Welded Wire Lath
- C 946—10 Specification for Practice for Construction of Drystacked, Surface-bonded Walls
- C 954—10 Specification for Steel Drill Screws for the Application of Gypsum Panel Products or Metal Plaster Bases to Steel Studs from 0.033 inch (0.84 mm) to 0.112 inch (2.84 mm) in Thickness
- C 955—09a Standard Specification for Load-bearing Transverse and Axial Steel Studs, Runners Tracks, and Bracing or Bridging, for Screw Application of Gypsum Panel Products and Metal Plaster Bases
- C 956—04 (2010) Specification for Installation of Cast-in-place Reinforced Gypsum
- C 957—10 Specification for High-solids Content, Cold Liquid applied Elastomeric Waterproofing Membrane with Integral Wearing Surface
- C 960—04 Specification for Predecorated Gypsum Board
- C 1002—07 Specification for Steel Self-piercing Tapping Screws for the Application of Gypsum Panel Products or Metal Plaster Bases to Wood Studs or Steel Studs
- C 1007—08a Specification for Installation of Load Bearing (Transverse and Axial) Steel Studs and Related Accessories
- C 1019—09 Test Method of Sampling and Testing Grout
- C 1029—10 Specification for Spray-applied Rigid Cellular Polyurethane Thermal Insulation
- C 1032—06 Specification for Woven Wire Plaster Base
- C 1047—10a Specification for Accessories for Gypsum Wallboard and Gypsum Veneer
- C 1063—08 Specification for Installation of Lathing and Furring to Receive Interior and Exterior Portland Cement based Plaster
- C 1088—10 Specification for Thin Veneer Brick Units Made from Clay or Shale
- C 1167—03 (2009) Specification for Clay Roof Tiles
- C 1177/C 1177M—08 Specification for Glass Mat Gypsum Substrate for Use as Sheathing
- C 1178/C 1178M—08 Specification for Coated Glass Mat Water-resistant Gypsum Backing Panel
- C 1186—08 Specification for Flat-Fiber Cement Sheets
- C 1261—10 Specification for Firebox Brick for Residential Fireplaces
- C 1278/C 1278M—07a Specification for Fiber-reinforced Gypsum Panels
- C 1280—09 Specification for Application of Gypsum Sheathing
- C 1283—07a Practice for Installing Clay Flue Lining.
- C 1288—99 (2010) Standard Specification for Discrete Nonasbestos Fiber-cement Interior Substrate Sheets
- C 1289—10 Standard Specification for Faced Rigid Cellular Polyisocyanurate Thermal Insulation Board
- C 1314—10 Test Method for Compressive Strength of Masonry Prisms
- C 1325—08b Standard Specification for Nonasbestos Fiber-mat Reinforced Cement Interior Substrate Sheets
- C 1328—05 Specification for Plastic (Stucco Cement)
- C 1386—07 Specification for Precast Autoclaved Aerated Concrete (AAC) Wall Construction

- C 1395/C 1395M—06a Specification for Gypsum Ceiling Board
- C 1396M—*09a* Specification for Gypsum Board
- C 1405—*10* Standard Specification for Glazed Brick (Single Fired, Solid Brick Units)
- C 1492—03 *(2009)* Standard Specification for Concrete Roof
- C 1629/C 1629M—06 Standard Classification for Abuse-resistant Nondecorated Interior Gypsum Panel Products and Fiber-reinforced Cement Panels
- C 1658/C 1658M—06 Standard Specification for Glass Mat Gypsum Panels
- D 25—99 (2005) Specification for Round Timber Piles
- D 41—05 *(2010)* Specification for Asphalt Primer Used in Roofing, Dampproofing and Waterproofing
- D 43—00 (2006) Specification for Coal Tar Primer Used in Roofing, Dampproofing and Waterproofing
- D 56—05 Test Method for Flash Point By Tag Closed Tester
- D 86—*10a* Test Method for Distillation of Petroleum Products at Atmospheric Pressure
- D 93—*10* Test Method for Flash Point By Pensky-MartensClosed Cup Tester
- D 225—*07* Specification for Asphalt Shingles (Organic Felt) Surfaced with Mineral Granules
- *D 226/D 226M—09* Specification for Asphalt-saturated Organic Felt Used in Roofing and Waterproofing
- D 227—03 Specification for Coal-tar-saturated Organic Felt Used in Roofing and Waterproofing
- D 312—00 (2006) Specification for Asphalt Used in
- D 422—63 *(2007)* Test Method for Particle-size Analysis of Soils
- D 448—*08* Standard Classification for Sizes of Aggregate for Road and Bridge
- D 450—07 Specification for Coal-tar Pitch Used in Roofing, Dampproofing and Waterproofing
- D 635—*10* Test Method for Rate of Burning and/or Extent and Time of Burning of Self-supporting Plastics in a Horizontal Position
- D 1143/D 1143M—*07e1* Test Method for Piles Under Static Axial Compressive Load
- D 1227—95 (2007) Specification for Emulsified Asphalt Used as a Protective Coating for Roofing
- D 1557—*09* Test Method for Laboratory Compaction Characteristics of Soil Using Modified Effort[56,000 ft-lb/ft3(2,700 KN m/m3)]
- D 1586—*08a* Specification for Penetration Test and Split-barrel Sampling of Soils
- D 1761—06 Test Method for Mechanical Fasteners in Wood
- D 1863—05 Specification for Mineral Aggregate Used on Builtup Roofs
- D 1929—96 (2001)e01 Test Method for Determining Ignition Properties of Plastics
- D 1970—*09* Specification for Self-adhering Polymer Modified Bituminous Sheet Materials Used as Steep Roof Underlayment for Ice Dam Protection
- D 2166—06 Test Method for Unconfined Compressive Strength of Cohesive Soil
- D 2178—04 Specification for Asphalt Glass Felt Used in Roofing and Waterproofing
- D 2216—*10* Test Method for Laboratory Determination of Water (Moisture) Content of Soil and Rock by Mass

- D 2487—*10* Practice for Classification of Soils for Engineering Purposes (Unified Soil Classification System)
- D 2626—04 Specification for Asphalt Saturated and Coated Organic Felt Base Sheet Used in Roofing
- D 2822—05 Specification for Asphalt Roof Cement
- D 2823—05 Specification for Asphalt Roof Coatings
- D 2843—*10* Test for Density of Smoke from the Burning or Decomposition of Plastics
- D 2850—03a *(2007)* Test Method for Unconsolidated, Undrained Triaxial Compression Test on Cohesive Soils
- D 2898—*10* Test Methods for Accelerated Weathering of Fireretardant-treated Wood for Fire Testing
- D 3019—*08* Specification for Lap Cement Used with Asphalt Roll Roofing, Nonfibered, Asbestos Fibered and Nonasbestos-Fibered
- D 3161—*09* Test Method for a Wind Resistance of Asphalt Shingles (Fan Induced Method)
- D 3200—74 (2005) Standard Specification and Test Method for Establishing Recommended Design Stresses for Round Timber Construction Poles
- D 3201—*08ae1* Test Method for Hygroscopic Properties of Fireretardant-treated Wood and Wood-based Products
- D 3278—*96*(2004)e01 Test Methods for Flash Point of Liquids by Small Scale Closed-cup Apparatus
- D 3462/ *D3462M—10a* Specification for Asphalt Shingles Made from Glass Felt and Surfaced with Mineral Granules
- D 3468—99 (2006)e1 Specification for Liquid-applied Neoprene and Chlorosulfonated Polyethylene Used in Roofing and Waterproofing
- D 3679—*09a* Specification for Rigid Poly [Vinyl Chloride (PVC) Siding]
- D 3689—*07* Method for Testing Individual Piles Under Static Axial Tensile Load
- D 3737—*09* Practice for Establishing Allowable Properties for Structural Glued Laminated Timber (Glulam)
- D 3746—85 *(2008)* Test Method for Impact Resistance of Bituminous Roofing Systems
- D 3747—79 (2007) Specification for Emulsified Asphalt Adhesive for Adhering Roof Insulation
- D 3909—97b (2004)e01 Specification for Asphalt Roll Roofing (Glass Felt) Surfaced with Mineral Granules
- D 3957—*09* Standard Practices for Establishing Stress Grades for Structural Members Used in Log Buildings
- D 4022—07 Specification for Coal Tar Roof Cement, Asbestos Containing
- D 4272—*09* Test Method for Total Energy Impact of Plastic Films by Dart Drop
- D 4318—*10* Test Methods for Liquid Limit, Plastic Limit and Plasticity Index of Soils
- D 4434/D 4434M—09 Specification for Poly (Vinyl Chloride) Sheet Roofing
- D 4479—*07* Specification for Asphalt Roof Coatings—Asbestos-free
- D 4586—*07* Specification for Asphalt Roof Cement—Asbestos-free
- D 4601—04 Specification for Asphalt-coated Glass Fiber Base Sheet Used in Roofing
- D 4637/*D 4637M—10* Specification for EPDM Sheet Used in Single-ply Roof Membrane
- D 4829—*08a* Test Method for Expansion Index of Soils

- D 4869—05e01 Specification for Asphalt-saturated (Organic Felt) Underlayment Used in Steep Slope Roofing
- D 4897/*D 4897M—01(2009)* Specification for Asphalt-coated Glass Fiber Venting Base Sheet Used in Roofing
- D 4945—*08* Test Method for High-strain Dynamic Testing of Piles
- D 4990—97a (2005)e1 Specification for Coal Tar Glass Felt Used in Roofing and Waterproofing
- D 5019—07a Specification for Reinforced Nonvulcanized Polymeric Sheet Used in Roofing Membrane
- D 5055—*10* Specification for Establishing and Monitoring Structural Capacities of Prefabricated Wood I-joists
- D 5456—*10* Specification for Evaluation of Structural Composite Lumber Products
- D 5516—*09* Test Method of Evaluating the Flexural Properties of Fire-retardant-treated Softwood Plywood Exposed to the Elevated Temperatures
- D 5643—06 Specification for Coal Tar Roof Cement, Asbestos-free
- D 5664—*10* Test Methods for Evaluating the Effects of Fireretardant Treatment and Elevated Temperatures on Strength Properties of Fire-retardant-treated Lumber
- D 5665—99a (2006) Specification for Thermoplastic Fabrics Used in Cold-applied Roofing and Waterproofing
- D 5726—98 (2005) Specification for Thermoplastic Fabrics Used in Hot-applied Roofing and Waterproofing
- D 6083—05e01 Specification for Liquid Applied Acrylic Coating Used in Roofing
- D 6162—00a *(2008)* Specification for Styrene-butadiene-styrene (SBS) Modified Bituminous Sheet Materials Using a Combination of Polyester and Glass Fiber Reinforcements
- D 6163—00 *(2008)* Specification for Styrene-butadiene-styrene (SBS) Modified Bituminous Sheet Materials Using Glass Fiber Reinforcements
- D 6164—05 e1 Specification for Styrene-butadiene-styrene (SBS) Modified Bituminous Sheet Metal Materials Using Polyester Reinforcements
- D 6222—*08* Specification for Atactic Polypropylene (APP) Modified Bituminous Sheet Materials Using Polyester Reinforcements
- D 6223/D6223M—02(2009)e1 Specification for Atactic Polypropylene (APP) Modified Bituminous Sheet Materials Using a Combination of Polyester and Glass Fiber Reinforcements
- D 6298—05e1 Specification for Fiberglass Reinforced Styrenebutadiene-styrene (SBS) Modified Bituminous Sheets with a Factory Applied Metal Surface
- D 6305—*08* Practice for Calculating Bending Strength Design Adjustment Factors for Fire-retardant-treated Plywood Roof Sheathing
- D 6380—03 *(2009)* Standard Specification for Asphalt Roll Roofing (Organic) Felt
- D 6509/*D6509M—09* Standard Specification for Atactic Polypropylene (APP) Modified Bituminous base Sheet Materials Using Glass Fiber Reinforcements
- D 6694—*08* Standard Specification for Liquid-applied Silicone Coating Used in Spray Polyurethane Foam Roofing
- D 6754/*D6754M—10* Standard Specification for Ketone Ethylene Ester Based Sheet Roofing
- D 6757—07 Standard Specification for Inorganic Underlayment for Use with Steep Slope Roofing Products

- D 6841—*08* Standard Practice for Calculating Design Value Treatment Adjustment Factors for Fire-retardant treated Lumber
- D 6878—*08e1* Standard Specification for ThermoplasticPolyolefinBased Sheet Roofing
- D 6947—07 Standard Specification for Liquid Applied Moisture Cured Polyurethane Coating Used in Spray Polyurethane Foam Roofing System
- D 7158—*08d* Standard Test Method for Wind Resistance of Sealed Asphalt Shingles (Uplift Force/Uplift Resistance Method)
- E 84—*10b* Test Methods for Surface Burning Characteristics of Building Materials
- E 90—*09* Test Method for Laboratory Measurement of Airborne Sound Transmission Loss of Building Partitions and Elements
- E 96/E 96M—05 Test Method for Water Vapor Transmission of Materials
- E 108—*10a* Test Methods for Fire Tests of Roof Coverings
- E 119—*10b* Test Methods for Fire Tests of Building Construction and Materials
- E 136—*09b* Test Method for Behavior of Materials in a Vertical Tube Furnace at 750°C
- E 330—02 (2010) Test Method for Structural Performance of Exterior Windows, Curtain Walls and Doors by Uniform Static Air Pressure Difference
- E 331—00 *(2009)* Test Method for Water Penetration of Exterior Windows, Skylights, Doors and Curtain Walls by Uniform Static Air Pressure Difference
- E 492—*09* Test Method for Laboratory Measurement of Impact Sound Transmission Through Floor-ceiling Assemblies Using the Tapping Machine
- E 605—93 (2006) Test Method for Thickness and Density of Sprayed Fire-resistive Material (SFRM) Applied to Structural Members
- E 681—*09* Test Methods for Concentration Limits of Flammability of Chemical Vapors and Gases
- E 736—00 (2006) Test Method for Cohesion/Adhesion of Sprayed Fire-resistive Materials Applied to Structural Members
- E 814—*10* Test Method of Fire Tests of Through-penetration Firestops
- E 970—*10* Test Method for Critical Radiant Flux of Exposed Attic Floor Insulation Using a Radiant Heat Energy Source
- E 1300—*09a* Practice for Determining Load Resistance of Glass in Buildings
- E 1354—*10a* Standard Test Method for Heat and Visible Smoke Release Rates for Materials and Products Using an Oxygen Consumption Calorimeter
- E 1592—*05* Test Method for Structural Performance of Sheet Metal Roof and Siding Systems by Uniform Static Air Pressure Difference
- E 1602—03 *(2010)e1* Guide for Construction of Solid Fuel-burning Masonry Heaters
- E 1886—*05* Test Method for Performance of Exterior Windows, Curtain Walls, Doors and Storm Shutters Impacted by Missiles and Exposed to Cyclic Pressure Differentials
- E 1966—*07* Test Method for Fire-resistant Joint Systems
- E 1996—*09* Specification for Performance of Exterior Windows, Glazed Curtain Walls, Doors and Impact Protective Systems Impacted by Windborne Debris in Hurricanes
- E 2072—*10* Standard Specification for Photoluminescent (Phosphorescent) Safety Markings
- E 2273—03 Standard Test Method for Determining the Drainage Efficiency of Exterior Insulation and Finish Systems (EIFS) Clad Wall Assemblies

- E 2307—*10* Standard Test Method for Determining Fire Resistance of Perimeter Fire Barrier Systems Using Intermediate-scale, Multistory Test Apparatus
- E 2404—*10* Standard Practice for Specimen Preparation and Mounting of Textile, Paper or Vinyl Wall or Ceiling Coverings to Assess Surface Burning Characteristics
- E 2568—*09e1* Standard Specification for PB Exterior Insulation and Finish Systems (EIFS)
- E 2570—07 Standard Test Method for Evaluating Water-resistive Barrier (WRB) Coatings Used Under Exterior Insulation and Finish Systems (EIFS) for EIFS with Drainage
- E 2573—*07a* Standard Practice for Specimen Preparation and Mounting of Site-fabricated Stretch Systems to Assess Surface Burning Characteristics
- F 547—*06* Terminology of Nails for Use with Wood and Wood-based Materials
- F 1346—91 (2003) Performance Specification for Safety Covers and Labeling Requirements for All Covers for Swimming Pools, Spas and Hot Tubs
- F 1667—*10* Specification for Driven Fasteners: Nails, Spikes and Staples
- F 2006—*10* Standard/Safety Specification for Window Fall Prevention Devices for Nonemergency Escape (Egress) and Rescue (Ingress) Windows
- F 2090—*10* Specification for Window Fall Prevention Devices with Emergency Escape (Egress) Release Mechanisms
- F 2200—05 Standard Specification for Automated Vehicular Gate Construction
- G 152—*06* Practice for Operating Open Flame Carbon Arc Light Apparatus for Exposure of Nonmetallic Materials
- G 154—*06* Practice for Operating Fluorescent Light Apparatus for UV Exposure of Nonmetallic Materials
- G 155—05a Practice for Operating Xenon Arc Light Apparatus for Exposure of Nonmetallic Materials

AWCI

The Association of the Wall and Ceiling Industries International
513 West Broad Street, Suite 210
Falls Church, VA 22046

- 12-B—*05* Technical Manual 12-B Standard Practice for the Testing and Inspection of Field Applied Thin Film Intumescent Fire-resistive Materials; an Annotated Guide, *Second* Edition

AWPA

American Wood Protection Association
P.O. Box 361784
Birmingham, AL 35236-1784

- C1—03 All Timber Products—Preservative Treatment by Pressure Processes
- M4—06 Standard for the Care of Preservative-treated Wood Products
- U1—*10* USE CATEGORY SYSTEM: User Specification for Treated Wood Except Section 6, Commodity Specification H

AWS

American Welding Society
550 N.W. LeJeune Road
Miami, FL 33126

- D1.1—*10* Structural Welding Code—Steel
- D1.3—*08* Structural Welding Code—Sheet Steel
- D1.4—*05* Structural Welding Code—Reinforcing Steel

BHMA
Builders Hardware Manufacturers' Association
355 Lexington Avenue, 17th Floor
New York, NY 10017-6603

- A 156.10—*05* Power Operated Pedestrian Doors
- A 156.19—*07* Standard for Power Assist and Low Energy Operated Doors

CGSB
Canadian General Standards Board
Place du Portage 111, 6B1
11 Laurier Street
Gatineau, Quebec, Canada KIA 1G6

- 37-GP-52M (1984) Roofing and Waterproofing Membrane, Sheet Applied, Elastomeric
- 37-GP-56M *(1985)* Membrane, Modified, Bituminous, Prefabricated and Reinforced for Roofing—with December 1985 Amendment
- CAN/CGSB 37.54—95 Polyvinyl Chloride Roofing and Waterproofing Membrane

CPA
Composite Panel Association
19465 Deerfield Avenue, Suite 306
Leesburg, VA 20176

- ANSI A135.4—*2004* Basic Hardboard
- ANSI A135.5—*2004* Prefinished Hardboard Paneling
- ANSI A135.6—*2006* Hardboard Siding

CPSC
Consumer Product Safety Commission
4330 East West Highway
Bethesda, MD 20814-4408

- 16 CFR Part 1201 (1977) Safety Standard for Architectural Glazing Material
- 16 CFR Part 1209 (1979) Interim Safety Standard for Cellulose Insulation
- 16 CFR Part 1404 (1979) Cellulose Insulation
- 16 CFR Part 1500 (1991) Hazardous Substances and Articles; Administration and Enforcement Regulations
- 16 CFR Part 1500.44 (2001) Method for Determining Extremely Flammable and Flammable Solids

- 16 CFR Part 1507 (2001) Fireworks Devices
- 16 CFR Part 1630 (2000) Standard for the Surface Flammability of Carpets and Rugs

CSA

Canadian Standards Association
5060 Spectrum Way, Suite 100
Mississauga, Ontario, L4W 5N6 Canada

- 101/I.S.2/A440—08 Specifications for Windows, Doors and Unit Skylights

CSSB

Cedar Shake and Shingle Bureau
P.O. Box 1178
Sumas, WA 98295-1178

- CSSB—97 Grading and Packing Rules for Western Red Cedar Shakes and Western Red Shingles of the Cedar Shake and Shingle Bureau Door and Access Systems Manufacturers Association International

DASMA

Door and Access Systems Manufacturers Association International
1300 Summer Avenue
Cleveland, OH 44115-2851

- ANSI/DASMA 107—1997 (R2004) Room Fire Test Standard for Garage Doors Using Foam Plastic Insulation
- 108—05 Standard Method for Testing Sectional Garage Doors and Rolling Doors: Determination of Structural Performance Under Uniform Static Air Pressure Difference
- 115—05 Standard Method for Testing Sectional Garage Doors and Rolling Doors: Determination of Structural Performance Under Missile Impact and Cyclic Wind Pressure

DOC

U.S. Department of Commerce
National Institute of Standards and Technology
1401 Constitution Avenue, NW
Washington, DC 20230

- PS-1—07 Structural Plywood
- PS-2—04 Performance Standard for Wood-based Structural-use Panels
- PS 20—05 American Softwood Lumber Standard

DOJ

U.S. Department of Justice,
950 Pennsylvania Avenue, NW,
Civil Rights Division,
Disability Rights Section-NYA
Washington, DC 20530

DOL

U.S. Department of Labor
c/o Superintendent of Documents
U.S. Government Printing Office
Washington, DC 20402-9325

- 29 CFR Part 1910.1000 (1974) Air Contaminants

DOT

U.S. Department of Transportation
c/o Superintendent of Documents
1200 New Jersey Avenue, SE
Washington, DC 20402-9325

- 49 CFR Parts 100-185-2005 Hazardous Materials Regulations
- 49 CFR Parts 173.137 (2005) Shippers—General Requirements for Shipments and Packaging—Class 8—Assignment of Packing Group
- 49 CFR—1998 Specification of Transportation of Explosive and Other Dangerous Articles, UN 0335, UN 0336 Shipping Containers

EN

European Committee for Standardization (EN)
Central Secretariat
Rue de Stassart 36
B-10 50 Brussels

- EN 1081—98 Resilient Floor Coverings—Determination of the Electrical Resistance

FEMA

Federal Emergency Management Agency
Federal Center Plaza
500 C Street S.W.
Washington, DC 20472

- FIA-TB11—01 Crawlspace Construction for Buildings Located in Special Flood Hazard Areas

FM

Factory Mutual Global Research
Standards Laboratories Department
1301 Atwood Avenue, P.O. Box 7500
Johnson, RI 02919

- 4450 (1989) Approval Standard for Class 1 Insulated Steel Deck Roofs—with Supplements through July 1992
- 4470 *(2010)* Approval Standard for Class 1 Roof Covers

- 4474 (04) Evaluating the Simulated Wind Uplift Resistance of Roof Assemblies Using Static Positive and/or Negative Differential Pressures
- 4880 *(2010)* American National Standard for Evaluating Insulated Wall or Wall and Roof/ Ceiling Assemblies, Plastic Interior Finish Materials, Plastic Exterior Building Panels, Wall/Ceiling Coating Systems, Interior and Exterior Finish Systems

GA

Gypsum Association
810 First Street N.E. #510
Washington, DC 20002-4268

- GA 216—*10* Application and Finishing of Gypsum Panel Products
- GA 600—*09* Fire-resistance Design Manual, 18th Edition

HPVA

Hardwood Plywood Veneer Association
1825 Michael Faraday Drive
Reston, VA 20190-5350

- HP-1—*2009* Standard for Hardwood and Decorative Plywood

HUD

U.S. Department of Housing and Urban Development
451 7th Street, SW,
Washington, DC 20410

- HUD 24 CFR Part 3280 (1994) Manufactured Home Construction and Safety Standards

ICC

International Code Council, Inc.
500 New Jersey Ave, NW 6th Floor
Washington, DC 20001

- ICC/ANSI A117.1—03 *09* Accessible and Usable Buildings and Facilities
- ICC 300—07 ICC Standard on Bleachers, Folding and Telescopic Seating
- ICC 400—07 Standard on Design and Construction of Log Structures
- ICC 500—08 ICC/NSSA Standard on the Design and Construction of Storm
- ICC 600—08 Standard for Residential Construction in High Wind Regions
- IEBC—09 International Existing Buildings Code
- IECC—09 International Energy Conservation Code *(adoption includes only section 101 of chapter 1 and chapters 2 through 6)*
- IFC—09 International Fire Code
- IFGC—09 International Fuel Gas Code *(including ICC Emergency Amendment changing IFGC Sections 406.7)*
- SBCCI SSTD 11—*99* Test Standard for Determining Wind Resistance of Concrete or Clay Roof Tiles

ISO

International Organization for Standardization
ISO Central Secretariat,
1 ch, de la Voie-Creuse,
Case Postale 56
CH-1211 Geneva 20, Switzerland

- ISO 8115—86 Cotton Bales–Dimensions and Density

NAAMM

National Association of Architectural Metal Manufacturers,
800 Roosevelt Road,
Bldg. C, Suite 312
Glen Ellyn, IL 60137

- FP 1001—07 Guide Specifications for Design of Metal Flag Poles

NCMA

National Concrete Masonry Association,
13750 Sunrise Valley,
Herndon, VA 22071-4662

- TEK5—08 Details for Concrete Masonry Fire Walls

NFPA

National Fire Protection Association
1 Batterymarch Park
Quincy, MA 02269-9101

- 10—10 Portable Fire Extinguishers
- 11—10 Low Expansion Foam
- 12—08 Carbon Dioxide Extinguishing Systems
- 12A—04 Halon 1301 Fire Extinguishing Systems
- 13—10 Installation of Sprinkler Systems (including TIA 10-12)
- 13D—10 Installation of Sprinkler Systems in One- and Two family Dwellings and Manufactured Homes (including TIA 10-2)
- 13R—10 Installation of Sprinkler Systems in Residential Occupancies Up to and Including Four Stories in Height (including TIA 10-2)
- 14—10 Installation of Standpipe and Hose System
- 16—07 Installation of Foam-water Sprinkler and Foamwater Spray Systems
- 17—09 Dry Chemical Extinguishing Systems
- 17A—09 Wet Chemical Extinguishing
- 20—10 Installation of Stationary Pumps for Fire Protection
- 30—08 Flammable and Combustible Liquids Code
- 31—06 Installation of Oil-burning Equipment
- 32—07 Dry Cleaning Plants
- 40—11 Storage and Handling of Cellulose Nitrate Film
- 58—11 Liquefied Petroleum Gas Code

- 61—08 Prevention of Fires and Dust Explosions in Agricultural and Food Product Facilities
- 70-08 National Electrical Code *(This edition applies only to one-, two-, and three family dwellings)*
- 70—11 National Electrical Code *(including TIA 11-1) (This edition applies to all buildings other than one-, two-, and three-family dwellings)*
- 72—10 National Fire Alarm Code
- 80—10 Fire Doors and Other Opening Protectives
- 85—07 Boiler and Combustion System Hazards Code (Note: NFPA 8503 has been incorporated into NFPA 85)
- 92B—09 Smoke Management Systems in Malls, Atria and Large Spaces
- 99—05 Standard for Health Care Facilities
- 105—10 Standard for the Installation of Smoke Door Assemblies
- 110—10 Emergency and Standby Power Systems
- 111—10 Stored Electrical Energy Emergency and Standby Power Systems
- 120—10 Coal Preparation Plants
- 170—09 Standard for Fire Safety and Emergency Symbols
- 211—10 Chimneys, Fireplaces, Vents and Solid Fuelburning
- 252—08 Standard Methods of Fire Tests of Door Assemblies
- 253—06 Test for Critical Radiant Flux of Floor Covering Systems Using a Radiant Heat Energy Source
- 257—07 Standard for Fire Test for Window and Glass Block Assemblies
- 259—08 Test Method for Potential Heat of Building Materials
- 265—07 Method of Fire Tests for Evaluating Room Fire Growth Contribution of Textile Wall Coverings on Full Height Panels and Walls
- 268—07 Standard Test Method for Determining Ignitibility of Exterior Wall Assemblies Using a Radiant Heat Energy Source
- 285—06 Standard Method of Test for the Evaluation of Flammability Characteristics of Exterior Nonloadbearing Wall Assemblies Containing Combustible Components
- 286—06 Standard Method of Fire Test for Evaluating Contribution of Wall and Ceiling Interior Finish to Room Fire Growth
- 288—07 Standard Method of Fire Tests of Floor Fire Door Assemblies Installed Horizontally in Fire-resistance-rated Floor Systems
- 409—11 Aircraft Hangars
- 418—06 Standard for Heliports
- 484—09 Combustible Metals
- 654—06 Prevention of Fire & Dust Explosions from the Manufacturing, Processing and Handling of Combustible Particulate Solids
- 655—07 Prevention of Sulfur Fires and Explosions
- 664—07 Prevention of Fires and Explosions in Wood Processing and Woodworking Facilities
- 701—10 Standard Methods of Fire Tests for Flame Propagation of Textiles and Films
- 704—07 Standard System for the Identification of the Hazards of Materials for Emergency Response
- 1124—06 Manufacture, Transportation and Storage of Fireworks and Pyrotechnic Articles
- 2001—08 Clean Agent Fire Extinguishing Systems

PCI

Precast Prestressed Concrete Institute
175 W. Jackson Boulevard, Suite 500
Chicago, IL 60604-6938

- MNL 124—89 Design for Fire Resistance of Precast Prestressed Concrete
- MNL 128—01 Recommended Practice for Glass Fiber Reinforced Concrete Panels

PTI

Post-Tensioning Institute
8601 North Black Canyon Highway, Suite 103
Phoenix, AZ 85021

- PTI—*2008* Standard Requirements for Analysis of Shallow Concrete Foundations on Expansive Soils, Third Edition
- PTI—*2008* Standard Requirements for Design of Shallow Post-tensioned Concrete Foundation on Expansive Soils, Second Edition

RMI

Rack Manufacturers Institute
8720 Red Oak Boulevard, Suite 201
Charlotte, NC 28217

- ANSI/MH16.1—08 Specification for Design, Testing and Utilization of Industrial Steel Storage Racks

SDI

Steel Deck Institute,
P.O. Box 25
Fox River Grove, IL 60021

- ANSI/NC1.0—06 Standard for Noncomposite Steel Floor Deck
- ANSI/RD1.0—06 Standard for Steel Roof Deck

SJI

Steel Joist Institute,
1173B London Links Drive
Forest, VA 24551

- CJ-1.0—06 Standard Specification for Composite Steel Joists, CJ-series
- JG-1.1—05 Standard Specification for Joist Girders
- K-1.1—05 Standard Specification for Open Web Steel Joists, K-series
- LH/DLH-1.1—05 Standard Specification for Longspan Steel Joists, LH-series and Deep Longspan Steel Joists, DLH-series

SPRI

Single-Ply Roofing Institute,
411 Waverly Oaks Road, Suite 331B,
Waltham, MA 02452

- SPRI/ANSI/ES-1—03 Wind Design Standard for Edge Systems Used with Low Slope Roofing Systems
- RP-4—02 Wind Design Guide for Ballasted Single-ply Roofing Systems

TIA

Telecommunications Industry Association
2500 Wilson Boulevard
Arlington, VA 22201-3834

- TIA-222-G—*09* Structural Standards for Steel Antenna Towers and Antenna Supporting Structures including-Addendum 1, 222-G-1, Dated 2007

TMS

The Masonry Society,
3970 Broadway, Unit 201-D,
Boulder, CO 80304-1135

- 0216—*07* Standard Method for Determining Fire Resistance of Concrete and Masonry Construction Assemblies
- 0302—07 Standard Method for Determining the Sound Transmission Class Rating for Masonry Walls
- 402—08 Building Code Requirements for Masonry Structures
- 602—08 Specification for Masonry Structures

TPI

Truss Plate Institute,
218 N. Lee Street, Suite 312
Alexandria, VA 22314

- TPI 1—2007 National Design Standards for Metal-plate-connected Wood Truss Construction

UL

Underwriters Laboratories, Inc.
333 Pfingsten Road
Northbrook, IL 60062-2096

- 9—*09* Fire Tests of Window Assemblies
- 10A—*09* Tin Clad Fire Doors
- 10B—*08* Fire Tests of Door Assemblies
- 10C—*09* Positive Pressure Fire Tests of Door Assemblies
- 14B—*08* Sliding Hardware for Standard Horizontally-mounted Tin Clad Fire Doors
- 14C—*06* Swinging Hardware for Standard Tin Clad Fire Doors Mounted Singly and in Pairs

- 103—*10* Factory-built Chimneys, for Residential Type and Building Heating Appliances
- 127—*08* Factory-built Fireplaces
- 199E—04 Outline of Investigation for Fire Testing of Sprinklers and Water Spray Nozzles for Protection of Deep Fat Fryers
- 217—06 Single and Multiple Station Smoke Alarms 4101:1-35-01 37
- 263—03 Standard for Fire Test of Building Construction and Materials
- 268—*09* Smoke Detectors for Fire Protective Signaling Systems
- 300—05 Fire Testing of Fire Extinguishing Systems for Protection of Restaurant Cooking Areas
- 305—*97* Panic Hardware
- 325—02 Door, Drapery, Gate, Louver and Window Operations and Systems—with Revisions through February 2006
- 555—2006 Fire Dampers
- 555C—2006 Ceiling Dampers
- 555S—99 Smoke Dampers—with Revisions through July 2006
- 580—2006 Test for Uplift Resistance of Roof Assemblies
- 641—95 Type L Low-temperature Venting Systems
- 710B—04 Recirculating Systems—with Revisions through April 2006
- 723—*08* Standard for Test for Surface Burning Characteristics of Building Materials
- 790—04 Standard Test Methods for Fire Tests of Roof Coverings
- 793—*08* Standards for Automatically Operated Roof Vents for Smoke and Heat
- 864—03 Standards for Control Units and Accessories for Fire Alarm Systems—with Revisions through March 2006
- 924—06 Standard for Safety Emergency Lighting and Power Equipment
- 1040—96 Fire Test of Insulated Wall Construction—with Revisions through June 2001
- 1256—02 Fire Test of Roof Deck Construction—with Revisions through January 2007
- 1479—03 Fire Tests of Through-penetration Firestops—with Revisions through April 2007
- 1482—*10* Solid-fuel-type Room Heater
- 1715—97 Fire Test of Interior Finish Material—with Revisions through March 2004
- 1777—*07* Chimney Liners
- 1784—01 Air Leakage Tests of Door Assemblies—with Revisions through December 2004
- 1897—04 Uplift Tests for Roof Covering Systems
- 1975—06 Fire Test of Foamed Plastics Used for Decorative Purposes
- 1994—04 Standard for Luminous Egress Path Marking Systems—with Revisions through February 2005
- 2017—*08* Standards for General-purpose Signaling Devices and Systems
- 2079—04 Tests for Fire Resistance of Building Joint Systems—with Revisions through March 2006
- 2200—*98* Stationary Engine Generator Assemblies

ULC

Underwriters Laboratories of Canada,
7 Underwriters Road,
Toronto, Ontario, Canada M1R3B4

- CAN/ULC S102.2—*2010* Standard Method of Test for Surface Burning Characteristics of Flooring, Floor Coverings and Miscellaneous Materials and Assemblies—with 2000 Revisions

USC
United States Code,
c/o Superintendent of Documents
U.S. Government Printing Office,
Washington, DC 20402-9325

- 10 U.S.C. Sections 18233(A)(1) and 18237-1994
- 18 USC Part 1, Ch.40 Importation, Manufacture, Distribution and Storage of Explosive Materials

WDMA
Window and Door Manufacturers Association
1400 East Touhy Avenue #470
Des Plaines, IL 60018

- AAMA/WDMA/CSA 101/I.S.2/A440—08 Specifications for Windows, Doors and Unit Skylights

WRI
Wire Reinforcement Institute, Inc.
942 Main Street, Suite 300
Hartford, CT 06103

- WRI/CRSI—81 Design of Slab-on-ground Foundations—with 1996 Update

b. Ohio Plumbing Code

ANSI American National Standards Institute
25 West 43rd Street, Fourth Floor
New York, NY 10036

Standard Referenced	Title
A118.10—*10*	Specifications for Load Bearing, Bonded, Waterproof Membranes for Thin Set Ceramic Tile and Dimension Stone Installation
Z4.3—95 *(R2005)*	Minimum Requirements for Nonsewered Waste-Disposal Systems *(Standard is developed by the Portable Sanitation Association International-PSAI)*
Z21.22—99 (R2003)	Relief Valves for Hot Water Supply Systems with Addenda Z21.22a-2000 (R2003) and Z21.22b-2001 (R2003) *(Standard is developed by the Canadian Standards Association-CSA and is the same as CSA 4.4-M99)*

Z124.1.2—05	Plastic Bathtub *and Shower* Units *(Standard is developed by IAPMO)*
Z124.3—05	Plastic Lavatories *(Standard is developed by IAPMO)*
Z124.4—06	Plastic Water Closet Bowls and Tanks *(Standard is developed by IAPMO)*
Z124.6—07	Plastic Sinks *(Standard is developed by IAPMO)*
Z124.9—04	Plastic Urinal Fixtures. *(Standard is developed by IAPMO)*

AHRI Air-Conditioning, Heating, & Refrigeration Institute
4100 North Fairfax Drive, Suite 200
Arlington, VA 22203

Standard Referenced	Title
1010—02	Self-contained, Mechanically Refrigerated Drinking-Water Coolers

ASME American Society of Mechanical Engineers Three Park Avenue
New York, NY 10016-5990

Standard Referenced	Title
A112.1.2—2004	Air Gaps in Plumbing Systems
A112.1.3—2000 (R 2005)	Air Gap Fittings for Use with Plumbing Fixtures, Appliances and Appurtenances
A112.3.1—2007	Stainless Steel Drainage Systems for Sanitary, DWV, Storm and Vacuum Applications Above and Below Ground
A112.3.4—2000 (R 2004)	Macerating Toilet Systems and Related Components
A112.4.1—*2009*	Water Heater Relief Valve Drain Tubes
A112.4.3—1999 (R 2004)	Plastic Fittings for Connecting Water Closets to the Sanitary Drainage System
A112.6.1M—1997 (R2002)	Floor-affixed Supports for Off-the-floor Plumbing Fixtures for Public Use
A112.6.2—2000 (R2004)	Framing-affixed Supports for Off-the-floor Water Closets with Concealed Tanks
A112.6.3—2001 (R 2007)	2001 Floor and Trench Drains
A112.6.7—2001 (R 2007)	Enameled and Epoxy-coated Cast-iron and PVC Plastic Sanitary Floor Sinks
A112.14.1—2003	Backwater Valves
A112.14.3—2000	Grease Interceptors
A112.14.4—2001(R2007)	Grease Removal Devices
A112.18.1—2005	Plumbing Supply Fittings
CSA B125.1—2005/ A112.18.2—2005	Plumbing Waste Fittings
CSA B125.2—2005/ A112.18.3—2002	Performance Requirements for Backflow Protection Devices and Systems in Plumbing Fixture Fittings
A112.18.6—*2009*	Flexible Water Connectors.
A112.18.7—1999 (R2004)	Deck mounted Bath/Shower Transfer Valves with Integral Backflow Protection
A112.19.1M—*2008*	Enameled Cast Iron Plumbing Fixtures
A112.19.2—*2008*	Vitreous China Plumbing Fixtures and Hydraulic Requirements for Water Closets and Urinals.

A112.19.3M—*2008*	Stainless Steel Plumbing Fixtures (Designed for Residential Use
A112.19.4M—1994 (R 2004)	Porcelain Enameled Formed Steel Plumbing Fixtures.
A112.19.5—2005	Trim for Water-closet Bowls, Tanks and Urinals
A112.19.6—1995	Hydraulic Performance Requirements for Water Closets and Urinals
A112.19.7M—2006	HydromassageBathtub Appliances
A112.19.8M—2007	Suction Fittings for Use in Swimming Pools, Wading Pools, Spas, Hot Tubs
A112.19.9M—1991(R2002)	Nonvitreous Ceramic Plumbing Fixtures with 2002 Supplement
A112.19.12—2006	Wall Mounted and Pedestal Mounted, Adjustable, Elevating, Tilting and Pivoting Lavatory, Sink and Shampoo Bowl Carrier Systems and Drain Systems
A112.19.13—2001 (R2007)	ElectrohydraulicWater Closets
A112.19.15— 2005	Bathtub/Whirlpool Bathtubs with Pressure Sealed Doors A112.19.19—2006 Vitreous ChinaNonwaterUrinals
A112.21.2M—1983	Roof Drains
A112.36.2M—1991(R2002)	Cleanouts
B1.20.1—1983(R2006)	Pipe Threads, General Purpose (inch
B16.3—2006	Malleable Iron Threaded Fittings Classes 150 and 300
B16.4—2006	Gray Iron Threaded Fittings Classes 125 and 250
B16.9—*2007*	Factory-made Wrought Steel Buttwelding Fittings.
B16.11—*2009*	Forged Fittings, Socket-welding and Threaded.
B16.12—*2009*	Cast-iron Threaded Drainage Fittings
B16.15—2006	Cast Bronze Threaded Fittings
B16.18—2001(R 2005)	Cast Copper Alloy Solder Joint Pressure Fittings
B16.22—2001 (R2005)	Wrought Copper and Copper Alloy Solder Joint Pressure Fittings
B16.23—2002 (R 2006)	Cast Copper Alloy Solder Joint Drainage Fittings DWV
B16.26—2006	Cast Copper Alloy Fittings for Flared Copper Tubes.
B16.28—1994	Wrought Steel Buttwelding Short Radius Elbows and Returns
B16.29—*2007*	Wrought Copper and Wrought Copper Alloy Solder Joint Drainage Fittings (DWV)
BPVC Section IX—2010	*Welding and Brazing Qualifications.*

ASSE American Society of Sanitary Engineering
901 Canterbury Road, Suite A
Westlake, OH 44145

Standard Referenced	Title
1001—*08*	Performance Requirements for Atmospheric Type Vacuum Breakers
1002—*08*	Performance Requirements for Antisiphon Fill Valves (Ballcocks) for Gravity Water Closet Flush Tanks
1003—*09*	Performance Requirements for Water Pressure Reducing Valves.
1004—*08*	Performance Requirements for Backflow Prevention Requirements for Commercial Dishwashing Machines.

1005—99	Performance Requirements for Water Heater Drain Valves.
1006—*86*	Performance Requirements for Residential Use Dishwashers.
1007—*86*	Performance Requirements for Home Laundry Equipment
1008—*06*	Performance Requirements for Household Food Waste Disposer Units
1009—90	Performance Requirements for Commercial Food Waste Grinder Units
1010—04	Performance Requirements for Water Hammer Arresters
1011—04	Performance Requirements for Hose Connection Vacuum Breakers
1012—*09*	Performance Requirements for Backflow Preventers with Intermediate Atmospheric Vent.
1013—*09*	Performance Requirements for Reduced Pressure Principle Backflow Preventers and Reduced Pressure Fire Protection Principle Backflow Preventers
1015—*09*	Performance Requirements for Double Check Backflow Prevention Assemblies and Double Check Fire Protection Backflow Prevention Assemblies
1016—*05*	Performance Requirements for Individual Thermostatic, Pressure Balancing and Combination Control Valves for Individual Fixture Fittings
1017—*09*	Performance Requirements for Temperature Actuated Mixing Valves for Hot Water Distribution Systems.
1018—01	Performance Requirements for Trap Seal Primer Valves; Potable Water Supplied
1019—04	Performance Requirements for Vacuum Breaker Wall Hydrants, Freeze Resistant, Automatic Draining Type
1020—04	Performance Requirements for Pressure Vacuum Breaker Assembly
1022—03	Performance Requirements for Backflow Preventer for Beverage Dispensing Equipment
1024—04	Performance Requirements for Dual Check Valve Type Backflow Preventers (for Residential Supply Service or Individual Outlets
1035—*08*	Performance Requirements for Laboratory Faucet Backflow Preventers
1037—90	Performance Requirements for Pressurized Flushing Devices for Plumbing Fixtures
1044—01	Performance Requirements for Trap Seal Primer Devices Drainage Types and Electronic Design Types
1047—*09*	Performance Requirements for Reduced Pressure Detector Fire Protection BackflowPrevention Assemblies
1048—*09*	Performance Requirements for Double Check Detector Fire Protection BackflowPrevention Assemblies
1050—*09*	Performance Requirements for Stack Air Admittance Valves for Sanitary Drainage Systems.
1051—*09*	Performance Requirements for Individual and Branch Type Air Admittance Valves for Sanitary Drainage Systems-fixture and Branch Devices

1052—04	Performance Requirements for Hose Connection Backflow Preventers
1055—09	Performance Requirements for Chemical Dispensing Systems
1056—01	Performance Requirements for Spill Resistant Vacuum Breaker
1060—06	Performance Requirements for Outdoor Enclosures for Backflow Prevention Assemblies
1061—06	Performance Requirements for Removable and Nonremovable Push Fit Fittings
1062—06	Performance Requirements for Temperature Actuated, Flow Reduction Valves to Individual Fixture Fittings
1066—97	Performance Requirements for Individual Pressure Balancing In-line Valves for Individual Fixture Fittings
1069—05	Performance Requirements for Automatic Temperature Control Mixing Valves
1070—04	Performance Requirements for Water-temperature Limiting Devices
1072—07	Performance Requirements for Barrier Type Floor Drain Trap Seal Protection Devices
1079—05	Dielectric Pipe Unions.
5013—09	Performance Requirements for Testing Reduced Pressure Principle Backflow Prevention Assembly (RPA) and Reduced Pressure Fire Protection PrincipleBackflow Preventers(RFP)
5015—09	Performance Requirements for Testing Double Check Valve Backflow Prevention Assembly (DCVA)
5020—09	Performance Requirements for Testing Pressure Vacuum Breaker Assembly (PVBA)
5047—09	Performance Requirements for Testing Reduced Pressure Detector Fire Protection BackflowPrevention Assemblies (RPDA).
5048—09	Performance Requirements for Testing Double Check Valve Detector Assembly (DCDA).
5052—09	Performance Requirements for Testing Hose Connection Backflow Preventers
5056—09	Performance Requirements for Testing Spill Resistant Vacuum Breaker.

ASTM ASTM International
100 Barr Harbor Drive
West Conshohocken, PA 19428-2959

Standard Referenced	Title
A 53/A 53M—10	Specification for Pipe, Steel, Black and Hot-dipped, Zinc-coated Welded and Seamless
A 74—09	Specification for Cast-iron Soil Pipe and Fittings
A 312/A 312M—09	Specification for Seamless and Welded Austenitic Stainless Steel Pipes
A 733—03 (2009)e1	Specification for Welded and Seamless Carbon Steel and Austenitic Stainless Steel Pipe Nipples

A 778—01*(2009)e1*	Specification for Welded Unannealed Austenitic Stainless Steel Tubular Products
A 888—*09*	Specification for Hubless Cast-iron Soil Pipe and Fittings for Sanitary and Storm Drain, Waste, and Vent Piping Application
B 32—*08*	Specification for Solder Metal
B 42—*10*	Specification for Seamless Copper Pipe, Standard Sizes
B 43—*09*	Specification for Seamless Red Brass Pipe, Standard Sizes
B 75—*02*	Specification for Seamless Copper Tube
B 88—*09*	Specification for Seamless Copper Water Tube
B 152/B 152M—*09*	Specification for Copper Sheet, Strip Plate and Rolled Bar
B 251—*10*	Specification for General Requirements for Wrought Seamless Copper and Copper-alloy Tube
B 302—*07*	Specification for Threadless Copper Pipe, Standard Sizes
B 306—*09*	Specification for Copper Drainage Tube (DWV)
B 447—*07*	Specification for Welded Copper Tube
B 687—99(2005)e01	Specification for Brass, Copper and Chromium-plated Pipe Nipples
B 813—*10*	Specification for Liquid and Paste Fluxes for Soldering of Copper and Copper Alloy Tube
B 828—02	Practice for Making Capillary Joints by Soldering of Copper and Copper Alloy Tube and Fittings.
C 4—04 *(2009)*	Specification for Clay Drain Tile and Perforated Clay Drain Tile
C 14—07	Specification for Nonreinforced Concrete Sewer, Storm Drain and Culvert Pipe.
C 76—*10a*	Specification for Reinforced Concrete Culvert, Storm Drain and Sewer Pipe
C 296—*00 (2009)e1*	Specification for Asbestos-cement Pressure Pipe
C 425—04 *(2009)*	Specification for Compression Joints for Vitrified Clay Pipe and Fittings
C 428—05 (2006)	Specification for Asbestos-cement Nonpressure Sewer Pipe
C 443—05ae1	Specification for Joints for Concrete Pipe and Manholes, Using Rubber Gaskets
C 508—*00 (2009)e1*	Specification for Asbestos-cement Underdrain Pipe
C 564—*09a*	Specification for Rubber Gaskets for Cast-iron Soil Pipe and Fittings
C 700—*09*	Specification for Vitrified Clay Pipe, Extra Strength, Standard Strength, and Perforated.
C 1053—00(*2010*)	Specification for Borosilicate Glass Pipe and Fittings for Drain, Waste, and Vent (DWV) Applications
C 1173—*08*	Specification for Flexible Transition Couplings for Underground Piping System.
C 1277—*09a*	Specification for Shielded Coupling Joining Hubless Cast-iron Soil Pipe and Fittings
C 1440—*08*	Specification for Thermoplastic Elastomeric (TPE) Gasket Materials for Drain, Waste,and Vent (DWV), Sewer, Sanitary and Storm Plumbing Systems
C 1460—*08*	Specification for Shielded Transition Couplings for Use with Dissimilar DWV Pipe and Fittings Above Ground

C 1461—*08*	Specification for Mechanical Couplings Using Thermoplastic Elastomeric (TPE) Gaskets for Joining Drain, Waste and Vent (DWV) Sewer, Sanitary and Storm Plumbing Systems for Above and Below Ground Use
C 1540—*09a*	Specification for Heavy Duty Shielded Couplings Joining Hubless Cast-iron Soil Pipe and Fittings
C 1563—*08*	Standard Test Method for Gaskets for Use in Connection with Hub and Spigot Cast Iron Soil Pipe and Fittings for Sanitary Drain, Waste, Vent and Storm Piping Applications
D 1527—99(2005)	Specification for Acrylonitrile-Butadiene-Styrene (ABS) Plastic Pipe, Schedules 40 and 80
D 1785—06	Specification for Poly (Vinyl Chloride) (PVC) Plastic Pipe, Schedules 40, 80 and 120
D 1869—95(2005)e1	Specification for Rubber Rings for Asbestos-cement Pipe
D 2235—04	Specification for Solvent Cement for Acrylonitrile-Butadiene- Styrene (ABS) Plastic Pipe and Fittings
D 2239—03	Specification for Polyethylene (PE) Plastic Pipe (SIDR-PR) Based on Controlled Inside Diameter
D 2241—*09*	Specification for Poly (Vinyl Chloride) (PVC) Pressure-rated Pipe (SDR-Series)
D 2282—(2005)99e01	Specification for Acrylonitrile-Butadiene-Styrene (ABS) Plastic Pipe (SDR-PR)
D 2464—06	Specification for Threaded Poly (Vinyl Chloride) (PVC) Plastic Pipe Fittings, Schedule 80
D 2466—06	Specification for Poly (Vinyl Chloride) (PVC) Plastic Pipe Fittings, Schedule 40
D 2467—06	Specification for Poly (Vinyl Chloride) (PVC) Plastic Pipe Fittings, Schedule 80
D 2468—96a	Specification for Acrylonitrile-Butadiene-Styrene (ABS) Plastic Pipe Fittings, Schedule 40
D 2564—04 (2009) e01	Specification for Solvent Cements for Poly (Vinyl Chloride) (PVC) Plastic Piping Systems
D 2609—02 (2008)	Specification for Plastic Insert Fittings for Polyethylene (PE) Plastic Pipe.
D 2657—07	Practice for Heat Fusion-joining of Polyolefin Pipe and Fitting
D 2661—*08*	Specification for Acrylonitrile-Butadiene-Styrene (ABS) Schedule 40 Plastic Drain, Waste, and Vent Pipe and Fittings
D 2665—*09*	Specification for Poly (Vinyl Chloride) (PVC) Plastic Drain, Waste, and Vent Pipe and Fittings
D 2672—96a(*2009*)	Specification for Joints for IPS PVC Pipe Using Solvent Cement.
D 2683—*10*	Standard Specification for Socket-type Polyethylene fittings for Outside Diameter-controlled Polyethylene Pipe and Tubing
D 2729—*03*	Specification for Poly (Vinyl Chloride) (PVC) Sewer Pipe and Fittings
D 2737—03	Specification for Polyethylene (PE) Plastic Tubing

D 2751—05	Specification for Acrylonitrile-Butadiene-Styrene (ABS) Sewer Pipe and Fittings
D 2846/D 2846M—*09b*	Specification for Chlorinated Poly (Vinyl Chloride) (CPVC) Plastic Hot and Cold Water Distribution Systems
D 2855—96(*2010*)	Standard Practice for Making Solvent-cemented Joints with Poly (Vinyl Chloride) (PVC) Pipe and Fittings D 2949— 01ae01 Specification for 3.25-in Outside Diameter Poly (Vinyl Chloride) (PVC) Plastic Drain, Waste, and Vent Pipe and Fittings
D 3034—*08*	Specification for Type PSM Poly (Vinyl Chloride) (PVC) Sewer Pipe and Fittings
D 3035—*08*	Standard Specification for Polyethylene (PE) Plastic Pipe (DR-PR) Based on Controlled Outside Diameter
D 3139—98(2005)	Specification for Joints for Plastic Pressure Pipes Using Flexible Elastomeric Seals
D 3212—*07*	Specification for Joints for Drain and Sewer Plastic Pipes Using Flexible Elastomeric Seals
D 3261—*10a*	Standard Specification for Butt Heat Fusion Polyethylene (PE) Plastic fittings for Polyethylene (PE) Plastic Pipe and Tubing
D 3311—06a*09a*	Specification for Drain, Waste and Vent (DWV) Plastic Fittings Patterns
D 4068—*09*	Specification for Chlorinated Polyethlene (CPE) Sheeting for Concealed Water-containment Membrane
D 4551—96(*2008*)*e1*	Specification for Poly (Vinyl Chloride) (PVC) Plastic Flexible Concealed Water-containment Membrane
F 405—05	Specification for Corrugated Polyethylene (PE) Tubing and Fittings
F 409—02(*2008*)	Specification for Thermoplastic Accessible and Replaceable Plastic Tube and Tubular Fittings.
F 437—*09*	Specification for Threaded Chlorinated Poly (Vinyl Chloride) (CPVC) Plastic Pipe Fittings, Schedule 80
F 438—*09*	Specification for Socket-type Chlorinated Poly (Vinyl Chloride) (CPVC) Plastic Pipe Fittings, Schedule 40
F 439—*09*	Standard Specification for Chlorinated Poly (Vinyl Chloride) (CPVC) Plastic Pipe Fittings, Schedule 80
F 441/F 441M—*09*	Specification for Chlorinated Poly (Vinyl Chloride) (CPVC) Plastic Pipe, Schedules 40 and 80
F 442/F 442M—*09*	Specification for Chlorinated Poly (Vinyl Chloride) (CPVC) Plastic Pipe (SDR-PR)
F 477—*10*	Specification for Elastomeric Seals (Gaskets) for Joining Plastic Pipe
F 493—*10*	Specification for Solvent Cements for Chlorinated Poly (Vinyl Chloride) (CPVC) Plastic Pipe and Fittings
F 628—*08*	Specification for Acrylonitrile-Butadiene-Styrene (ABS) Schedule 40 Plastic Drain, Waste, and Vent Pipe with a Cellular Core
F 656—*10*	Specification for Primers for Use in Solvent Cement Joints of Poly (Vinyl Chloride) (PVC) Plastic Pipe and Fittings
F 714—*08*	Specification for Polyethylene (PE) Plastic Pipe (SDR-PR) Based on Outside Diameter

F 876—*10*	Specification for Cross-linked Polyethylene (PEX) Tubing
F 877—07	Specification for Cross-linked Polyethylene (PEX) Plastic Hot and Cold Water Distribution Systems
F 891—*10*	Specification for Coextruded Poly (Vinyl Chloride) (PVC) Plastic Pipe with a Cellular Core.
F 1055—98(2006)	Standard Specification for Electrofusion Type Polyethylene Fittings for Outside Diameter Controlled Polyethylene Pipe and Tubing
F 1281—07	Specification for Cross-linked Polyethylene/Aluminum/Cross-linked Polyethylene (PEX-AL-PEX) Pressure Pipe
F 1282—*10*	Specification for Polyethylene/Aluminum/Polyethylene (PE-AL-PE) Composite Pressure Pipe
F 1412—*09*	Specification for Polyolefin Pipe and Fittings for Corrosive Waste Drainage
F 1488—*09*	Specification for Coextruded Composite Pipe
F 1673—*10*	PolyvinylideneFluoride (PVDF) Corrosive Waste Drainage Systems
F 1807—07	Specification for Metal Insert Fittings Utilizing a Copper Crimp Ring for SDR9 Cross-linked Polyethylene (PEX) Tubing
F 1866—07	Specification for Poly (Vinyl Chloride) (PVC) Plastic Schedule 40 Drainage and DWV Fabricated Fittings.
F 1960—*10*	Specification for Cold Expansion Fittings with PEX Reinforcing Rings for use with Cross-linked Polyethylene (PEX) Tubing.
F 1974—*09*	Specification for Metal Insert Fittings for Polyethylene/Aluminum/Polyethylene and Cross-linked Polyethylene/Aluminum/Cross-linked Polyethylene Composite Pressure Pipe
F 1986—01(2006)	Specification for Multilayer Pipe, Type 2, Compression Fittings and Compression Joints for Hot and Cold Drinking Water Systems.
F 2080—*09*	Specifications for Cold-expansion Fittings with Metal Compression-sleeves for Cross-linked Polyethylene (PEX) Pipe
F 2098—*08*	Standard specification for Stainless Steel Clamps for Securing SDR9 Cross-linked Polyethylene (PEX) Tubing to Metal Insert Fittings
F 2159—*10*	Specification for Plastic Insert Fittings Utilizing a Copper Crimp Ring for SDR9 Cross-linked Polyethylene (PEX) Tubing
F 2262—*09*	Specification for Cross-linked Polyethylene/Aluminum/Cross-linked Polyethylene Tubing OD Controlled SDR9
F 2306/F 2306M—*08*	12" to 60" Annular Corrugated Profile-wall Polyethylene (PE) Pipe and Fittings for Gravity Flow Storm Sewer and Subsurface Drainage Applications
F 2389—*10*	Specification for Pressure-rated Polypropylene (PP) Piping Systems

F 2434—09	Standard Specification for Metal Insert Fittings Utilizing a Copper Crimp Ring for SDR9 Cross-linked Polyethylene (PEX) Tubing and SDR9 Cross-linked Polyethylene/ Aluminum/Cross-linked Polyethylene (PEXAL- PEX) Tubing.

AWS American Welding Society
550 N.W. LeJeune Road
Miami, FL 33126

Standard Referenced	Title
A5.8—04	Specifications for Filler Metals for Brazing and Braze Welding

AWWA American Water Works Association
6666 West Quincy Avenue
Denver, CO 80235

Standard Referenced	Title
C104/A21.4—08	Standard for Cement-mortar Lining for Ductile-iron Pipe and Fittings for Water
C110/A21.10—08	Standard for Ductile-iron and Gray-iron Fittings, 3 Inches through 48 Inches, for Water
C111/A21.11—06	Standard for Rubber-gasket Joints for Ductile-iron Pressure Pipe and Fittings
C115/A21.15—05	Standard for Flanged Ductile-iron Pipe with Ductile-iron or Gray-iron Threaded Flanges
C151/A21.51—09	Standard for Ductile-iron Pipe, Centrifugally Cast for Water C153/A21.53—06 Standard for Ductile-iron Compact Fittings for Water Service
C510—07	Double Check Valve Backflow Prevention Assembly
C511—07	Reduced-pressure Principle Backflow Prevention Assembly
C651—05	Disinfecting Water Mains
C652—02	Disinfection of Water-storage Facilities

CISPI Cast Iron Soil Pipe Institute
5959 Shallowford Road, Suite 419
Chattanooga, TN 37421

Standard Referenced	Title
301—09	Specification for Hubless Cast-iron Soil Pipe and Fittings for Sanitary and Storm Drain, Waste and Vent Piping Applications
310—09	Specification for Coupling for Use in Connection with Hubless Cast-iron Soil Pipe and Fittings for Sanitary and Storm Drain, Waste and Vent Piping Applications

CSA Canadian Standards Association
5060 Spectrum Way.
Mississauga, Ontario, Canada L4W 5N6

Standard Referenced	Title
B45.1—02 *(R2008)*	Ceramic Plumbing Fixtures.

B45.2—02 *(R2008)*	Enameled Cast-iron Plumbing Fixtures
B45.3—02 *(R2008)*	Porcelain Enameled Steel Plumbing Fixtures
B45.4—02 *(R2008)*	Stainless-steel Plumbing Fixtures
B45.5—02 *(R2008)*	Plastic Plumbing Fixtures
B45.9—99 *(R2008)*	Macerating Systems and Related Components
B64.1.2—*07*	Vacuum Breakers, Pressure Type (PVB
B64.2.1—*07*	Vacuum Breakers, Hose Connection Type (HCVB) with Manual Draining Feature
B64.2.1.1—*07*	Vacuum Breakers, Hose Connection Dual Check Type (HCDVB)
B64.4.1—*07*	Backflow Preventers, Reduced Pressure Principle Type for Fire Sprinklers (RPF)
B64.5—*07*	Backflow Preventers, Double Check Type (DCVA)
B64.5.1—*07*	Backflow Preventers, Double Check Type for Fire Systems (DCVAF)
B64.6—*07*	Backflow Preventers, Dual Check Valve Type (DuC)
B64.7—*07*	Vacuum Breakers, Laboratory Faucet Type (LFVB
B64.10/B64.10.1—*07*	Manual for the Selection and Installation of Backflow Prevention Devices/Manual for the Maintenance and Field Testing of Backflow Prevention Devices
B79—*08*	Floor, Area and Shower Drains, and Cleanouts for Residential Construction
B125—01	Plumbing Fittings
B125.3—2005	Plumbing Fittings
B137.1—*09*	Polyethylene Pipe, Tubing and Fittings for Cold Water Pressure Services
B137.2—*09*	PVC Injection-moulded Gasketed Fittings for Pressure Applications
B137.3—*09*	Rigid Poly (Vinyl Chloride) (PVC) Pipe for Pressure Applications
B137.5—*09*	Cross-linked Polyethylene (PEX) Tubing Systems for Pressure Applications—with Revisions through September 1992
B137.6—*09*	CPVC Pipe, Tubing and Fittings for Hot and Cold Water Distribution Systems— with Revisions through May 1986
B137.11—02	Polypropylene (PP-R) Pipe and Fittings for Pressure Applications
B181.1—*06*	ABS Drain, Waste and Vent Pipe and Pipe Fittings
B181.2—*06*	PVC Drain, Waste, and Vent Pipe and Pipe Fittings— with Revisions through December 1993
B182.1—*06*	Plastic Drain and Sewer Pipe and Pipe Fittings
B182.2—*06*	PVC Sewer Pipe and Fittings (PSM Type)
B182.4—*06*	Profile PVC Sewer Pipe and Fittings
B182.6—*06*	Profile Polyethylene Sewer Pipe and Fittings for Leak-proof Sewer Applications
B182.8—*06*	Profile Polyethylene Storm Sewer and Drainage Pipe and Fittings
CAN/CSA—A257.1M—*09*	Circular Concrete Culvert, Storm Drain, Sewer Pipe and Fittings

CAN/CSA—A257.2M—*09*	Reinforced Circular Concrete Culvert, Storm Drain, Sewer Pipe and Fittings
CAN/CSA—A257.3M—*09*	Joints for Circular Concrete Sewer and Culvert Pipe, Manhole Sections and Fittings Using Rubber Gaskets CAN/CSA-
B64.1.1—*07*	Vacuum Breakers, Atmospheric Type (AVB) CAN/CSA-B64.2—*07* Vacuum Breakers, Hose Connection Type (HCVB).
CAN/CSA—B64.2.2—*07*	Vacuum Breakers, Hose Connection Type (HCVB) with Automatic Draining Feature
CAN/CSA—B64.3—*07*	Backflow Preventers, Dual Check Valve Type with Atmospheric Port (DCAP)
CAN/CSA—B64.4—*07*	Backflow Preventers, Reduced Pressure Principle Type (RP)
CAN/CSA—B64.10—*07*	Manual for the Selection, Installation, Maintenance and Field Testing of Backflow Prevention Devices
CAN/CSA—B137.9—*09*	Polyethylene/Aluminum/Polyethylene Composite Pressure Pipe Systems
CAN/CSA—B137.10M—*09*	Cross-linked Polyethylene/Aluminum/Polyethylene Composite Pressure Pipe Systems
CAN/CSA—B181.3—*06*	Polyolefin Laboratory Drainage Systems
CAN/CSA—B182.4—*06*	Profile PVC Sewer Pipe and Fittings
CAN/CSA—B602—*10*	Mechanical Couplings for Drain, Waste and Vent Pipe and Sewer Pipe

ICC International Code Council, Inc.
500 New Jersey Ave, NW 6th Floor
Washington, DC 20001

Standard Referenced	Title
IFGC—09	International Fuel Gas Code *(including ICC Emergency Amendment changing IFGC Sections 406.7)*

ISEA International Safety Equipment Association
1901 N. Moore Street, Suite 808
Arlington, VA 22209

Standard Referenced	Title
Z358.1—*09*	Emergency Eyewash and Shower Equipment

NFPANational Fire Protection Association
1 Batterymarch Park
Quincy, MA 02169-7471

Standard Referenced	Title
70—*11*	National Electrical Code
99C—05	Gas and Vacuum Systems

NSFNSF International
789 Dixboro Road
Ann Arbor, MI 48105

Standard Referenced	Title
3—*2009*	Commercial Warewashing Equipment
14—*2010*	Plastic Piping System Components and Related Materials
18—*2009*	Manual Food and Beverage Dispensing Equipment
42—*2009*	Drinking Water Treatment Units—Aesthetic Effects
44—*2009*	Residential Cation Exchange Water Softeners
53—*2009e*	Drinking Water Treatment Units—Health Effects.
58—*2009*	Reverse Osmosis Drinking Water Treatment Systems
61—*2010a*	Drinking Water System Components—Health Effects
62—*2009*	Drinking Water Distillation Systems

PDI Plumbing and Drainage Institute
800 Turnpike Street, Suite 300
North Andover, MA 01845

Standard Referenced	Title
G101(*2010*)	Testing and Rating Procedure for Grease Interceptors with Appendix of Sizing and Installation Data

UL Underwriters Laboratories, Inc.
333 Pfingsten Road
Northbrook, IL 60062-2096

Standard Referenced	Title
UL 508—99	Industrial Control Equipment with Revision through July 2005

c. Ohio Mechanical Code

ACCA Air Conditioning Contractors of America
2800 Shirlington Road, Suite 300
Arlington, VA 22206

Standard reference number	Title
Manual D—95	Residential Duct Systems
183—2007	Peak Cooling and Heating Load Calculations in Buildings Except Low- Rise Residential Buildings

AHRI Air-Conditioning, Heating and Refrigeration Institute
4100 North Fairfax Drive, Suite 200
Arlington, VA 22203

Standard reference number	Title
700—*06*	Purity Specifications for Fluorocarbon and Other Refrigerants

ANSI American National Standards Institute
11 West 42nd Street
New York, NY 10036

Standard reference number	Title
Z21.8—1994 (R2002)	Installation of Domestic Gas Conversion Burners

ASHRAE American Society of Heating, Refrigerating and Air-Conditioning
Engineers, Inc.
1791 Tullie Circle, NE
Atlanta, GA 30329

Standard reference number	Title
Handbook—2009	ASHRAE Fundamentals Handbook—
15—2010	Safety Standard for Refrigeration Systems
34—2010	Designation and Safety Classification of Refrigerants
62.1—2010	Ventilation for Acceptable Indoor Air Quality
62.2. —2010	Ventilation for Acceptable Indoor Air Quality in Low-Rise Residential Buildings
170—2008	Ventilation of Health Care Facilities (with addendums a through h-2011)

ASME American Society of Mechanical Engineers
Three Park Avenue
New York, NY 10016-5990

Standard reference number	Title
B1.20.1—1983 (R2006)	Pipe Threads, General Purpose (Inch
B16.3—2006	Malleable Iron Threaded Fittings, Classes 150 & 300
B16.5—2009	Pipe Flanges and Flanged Fittings NPS 1/2 through NPS 24—.
B16.9—2007	Factory Made Wrought Steel Buttwelding Fittings
B16.11—2009	Forged Fittings, Socket-welding and Threaded
B16.15—2006	Cast Bronze Threaded Fittings
B16.18—2001 (Reaffirmed 2005)	Cast Copper Alloy Solder Joint Pressure Fittings
B16.22—2001 (Reaffirmed 2005)	Wrought Copper and Copper Alloy Solder Joint Pressure Fittings
B16.23—2002 (Reaffirmed 2006)	Cast Copper Alloy Solder Joint Drainage Fittings DWV
B16.24—2006	Cast Copper Alloy Pipe Flanges and Flanged Fittings: Class 150, 300, 400, 600, 900, 1500 and
B16.26—2006	Cast Copper Alloy Fittings for Flared Copper Tubes
B16.28—1994	Wrought Steel Buttwelding Short Radius Elbows and Returns
B16.29—2007	Wrought Copper and Wrought Copper Alloy Solder Joint Drainage Fittings-
B31.9—2010	Building Services Piping
BPVC—2010	Boiler & Pressure Vessel Code
BPVC Section IX—2010	Welding and Brazing Qualifications
CSD—1—2009	Controls and Safety Devices for Automatically Fired Boilers

ASSE American Society of Sanitary Engineering
901 Canterbury, Suite A
Westlake, OH 44145

Standard reference number	Title
1017—*09*	Temperature Actuated Mixing *Valves* for Hot Water Distribution Systems

ASTM ASTM International
100 Barr Harbor Drive
West Conshohocken, PA 19428

Standard reference number	Title
A 53/A 53M—*10*	Specification for Pipe, Steel, Black and Hot-dipped, Zinc-coated Welded and Seamless
A 106/A106M—*10*	Specification for Seamless Carbon Steel Pipe for High-Temperature Service
A 126—*04 (2009)*	Specification for Gray Iron Castings for Valves, Flanges and Pipe Fittings
A 254—*97 (2007)*	Specification for Copper Brazed Steel Tubing
A 420/A 420M—*10*	Specification for Piping Fittings of Wrought Carbon Steel and Alloy Steel for Low-Temperature Service
A 539—*99*	Specification for Electric-Resistance-Welded Coiled Steel Tubing for Gas and Fuel Oil Lines
B 32—*08*	Specification for Solder Metal
B 42—*10*	Specification for Seamless Copper Pipe, Standard Sizes
B 43—*09*	Specification for Seamless Red Brass Pipe, Standard
B 68—*02*	Specification for Seamless Copper Tube, Bright Annealed
B 75—*02*	Specification for Seamless Copper
B 88—*09*	Specification for Seamless Copper Water
B 135—*10*	Specification for Seamless Brass Tube
B 251—*10*	Specification for General Requirements for Wrought Seamless Copper and Copper-alloy Tube
B 280—*08*	Specification for Seamless Copper Tube for Air Conditioning and Refrigeration Field Service
B 302—*07*	Specification for Threadless Copper Pipe, Standard
B 813—*10*	Specification for Liquid and Paste Fluxes for Soldering of Copper and Copper Alloy Tube
C 315—*07*	Specification for Clay Flue Liners and Chimney Pots
C 411—*05*	Test Method for Hot-surface Performance of High-temperature Thermal Insulation
D 56—*05 (2010)*	Test Method for Flash Point by Tag Closed Tester
D 93—*10a*	Test Method for Flash Point of Pensky-Martens Closed Cup Tester
D 1527—*99(2005)*	Specification for Acrylonitrile-Butadiene-Styrene (ABS) Plastic Pipe, Schedules 40 and 80
D 1693—*08*	Test Method for Environmental Stress-Cracking of Ethylene Plastics

D 1785—06	Specification for Poly (Vinyl Chloride) (PVC) Plastic Pipe, Schedules 40, 80 and 120
D 2235—04	Specifications for Solvent Cement for Acrylonitrile-Butadiene-Styrene (ABS) Plastic Pipe and Fittings
D 2241—09	Specification for Poly (Vinyl Chloride) (PVC) Pressure-rated Pipe (SDR-Series
D 2282—99(2005)	Specification for Acrylonitrile-Butadiene-Styrene (ABS) Plastic Pipe (SDR-PR)
D 2412—10	Test Method for Determination of External Loading Characteristics of Plastic Pipe by Parallel-plate Loading
D 2447—03	Specification for Polyethylene (PE) Plastic Pipe, Schedules 40 and 80, Based on Outside Diameter
D 2466—06	Specification for Poly (Vinyl Chloride) (PVC) Plastic Pipe Fittings, Schedule 40
D 2467—06	Specification for Poly (Vinyl Chloride) (PVC) Plastic Pipe Fittings, Schedule 80
D 2468—96a	Specification for Acrylonitrile-Butadiene-Styrene (ABS) Plastic Pipe Fittings, Schedule 40
D 2513—09a	Specification for Thermoplastic Gas Pressure Pipe, Tubing, and
D 2564—04(2009)e01	Specification for Solvent Cements for Poly (Vinyl Chloride) (PVC) Plastic Piping Systems
D 2657—07	Standard Practice for Heat Fusion Joining of PolyolefinPipe and Fittings
D 2683—10	Specification for Socket-type Polyethylene Fittings for Outside Diameter-controlled Polyethylene Pipe and Tubing
D 2837—08	Test Method for Obtaining Hydrostatic Design Basis for Thermoplastic Pipe Materials or Pressure Design Basis for Thermoplastic Pipe Products
D 2846/D 2846M—09b	Specification for Chlorinated Poly (Vinyl Chloride) (CPVC) Plastic Hot and Cold Water Distribution Systems
D 2996—01(2007)e01	Specification for Filament-wound Fiberglass (Glass Fiber Reinforced Thermosetting Resin) Pipe
D 3035—08	Specification for Polyethylene (PE) Plastic Pipe (DR-PR) Based on Controlled Outside Diameter
D 3278—96(2004)e01	Test Methods for Flash Point of Liquids by Small Scale Closed-cup Apparatus
D 3261—10a	Standard Specification for Butt Heat Fusion Polyethylene (PE) Plastic Fittings for Polyethylene (PE) Plastic Pipe and
D 3309—96a(2002)	Specification for Polybutylene (PB) Plastic Hot and Cold Water Distribution Systems
D 3350—10	Specification for Polyethylene Plastics Pipe and Fittings Materials
E 84—10b	Test Method for Surface Burning Characteristics of Building Materials
E 119—10b	Test Method for Fire Tests of Building Construction and
E 136—09b	Test Method for Behavior of Materials in a Vertical Tube Furnace at 750 Degrees C
E 814—10	Test Method for Fire Tests of Through-penetration Fire
E 1509—04	Specification for Room Heaters, Pellet Fuel-burning

E 2231—09	Standard Practice For Specimen Preparation and Mounting of Pipe and Duct Insulation Materials to Assess Surface Burning Characteristics
E 2336—04 (2009)	Standard Test Methods for Fire Resistive Grease Duct Enclosure Systems
F 438—09	Specification for Socket Type Chlorinated Poly (Vinyl Chloride) (CPVC) Plastic Pipe Fittings, Schedule 40
F 439—09	Specification for Socket Type Chlorinated Poly (Vinyl Chloride) (CPVC) Plastic Pipe Fittings, Schedule 80
F 441/F 441M—09	Specification for Chlorinated Poly (Vinyl Chloride) (CPVC) Plastic Pipe, Schedules 40 and
F 442/F 442M—09	Specification for Chlorinated Poly (Vinyl Chloride) (CPVC) Plastic Pipe (SDR-PR).
F 493—10	Specification for Solvent Cements for Chlorinated Poly (Vinyl Chloride) (CPVC) Plastic Pipe and Fittings
F 876—10	Specification forCrosslinkedPolyethylene (PEX) Tubing
F 877—07	Specification for Crosslinked Polyethylene (PEX) Plastic Hot and Cold Water Distribution Systems.
F 1055—98(2006)	Specification for Electrofusion Type Polyethylene Fittings for Outside Diameter Controlled Polyethylene Pipe and
F 1281—07	Specification for Crosslinked Polyethylene/Aluminum/Crosslinked Polyethylene (PEX-AL-PEX) Pressure Pipe
F 1282—10	Standard Specification for Polyethylene/Aluminum/Polyethylene (PE- AL-PE) Composite Pressure Pipe
F 1476—07	Specification for Performance of Gasketed Mechanical Couplings for Use in Piping Applications
F 1924—05	Standard Specification for Plastic Mechanical Fittings for Use on Outside Diameter Controlled Polyethylene Gas Distribution Pipe and Tubing
F 1974—09	Standard Specification for Metal Insert Fittings for Polyethylene/ Aluminum/Polyethylene and Crosslinked Polyethylene/ Aluminum/Crosslinked Polyethylene Composite Pressure Pipe
F 2389—10	Specification for Pressure-Rated Polypropylene Piping Systems
F 2623—08	Standard Specification for Polyethylene of Raised Temperature (PE- RT) SDR 9 Tubing1

AWS American Welding Society
550 N.W. LeJeune Road P.O. Box 351040
Miami, FL 33135

Standard reference number	Title
A5.8—2004	Specifications for Filler Metals for Brazing and Braze Welding.

AWWA American Water Work Association
6666 West Quincy Avenue
Denver, CO 80235

Standard reference number	Title
C110/A21.10—08	Standard for Ductile Iron & Gray Iron Fittings, 2 inches Through 48 inches for Water

C115/A21.15—05	Standard for Flanged Ductile-iron Pipe with Ductile Iron or Grey-iron Threaded Flanges
C151/A21.51—09	Standard for Ductile-Iron Pipe, Centrifugally Cast for Water
C153/A21.53—06	Standard for Ductile-Iron Compact Fittings for Water Service

CSA Canadian Standards Association
5060 Spectrum Way Mississauga,
Ontario, Canada L4W 5N6

Standard reference number	Title
B137.9—M91 CAN/CSA	Polyethylene/Aluminum/Polyethylene (PE-AL-PE) Composite Pressure-Pipe Systems
B137.10—05	Cross-linked Polyethylene/Aluminum/Cross-linked Polyethylene Composite Pressure-Pipe Systems
ANSI CSA America	
FC1—04	Stationary Fuel Cell Power Systems

DOL Department of Labor Occupational Safety and Health Administration
c/o Superintendent of Documents
US Government Printing Office
Washington, DC 20402-9325

Standard reference number	Title
29 CFR Part 1910.1000	Air Contaminants (1974)
29 CFR Part 1910.1025	Toxic and Hazardous Substances

FS Federal Specifications*
General Services Administration
7th & D Streets Specification Section, Room 6039
Washington, DC 20407

Standard reference number	Title
WW-P-325B (1976)	Pipe, Bends, Traps, Caps and Plugs; Lead (for Industrial Pressure and Soil and Waste Applications

*Standards are available from the Supt. of Documents, U.S. Government Printing Office, Washington, DC 20402-9325.

ICC International Code Council, Inc.
500 New Jersey Ave, NW
6th FloorICC
Washington, DC 20001

Standard reference number	Title
IFGC—09	International Fuel Gas Code (including ICC Emergency Amendment changing IFGC Sections 406.7)

IIAR International Institute of Ammonia Refrigeration
1110 North Glebe Road

Arlington, VA 22201

Standard reference number	Title
2—99 (with Addendum A—2005)	Equipment, Design, and Installation of Ammonia Mechanical Refrigerating Systems

MSS Manufacturers Standardization Society of the Valve & Fittings Industry, Inc. 1
27 Park Street, N.E.
Vienna, VA 22180

Standard reference number	Title
SP—69—2003	Pipe Hangers and Supports—Selection and Application

NAIMA North American Insulation Manufacturers Association
44 Canal Center Plaza, Suite 310 Alexandria, VA 22314

Standard reference number	Title
AH116—02	Fibrous Glass Duct Construction Standards

NFPA National Fire Protection Association
1 Batterymarch Park
Quincy, MA 02169-7471

Standard reference number	Title
30A—08	Code for Motor Fuel-dispensing Facilities and Repair Garages
31—06	Installation of Oil-burning Equipment
37—10	Stationary Combustion Engines and Gas Turbines
58—11	Liquefied Petroleum Gas Code
69—08	Explosion Prevention Systems
70—11	National Electrical Code
72—10	National Fire Alarm and Signaling Code (including TIA 10-4 and TIA 10-5)
75—09	Protection of Information Technology Equipment
82—09	Incinerators and Waste and Linen Handling Systems and Equipment
85—07	Boiler and Combustion Systems Hazards Code
91—10	Exhaust Systems for Air Conveying of Vapors, Gases, and Noncombustible Particulate Solids
92B—09	Smoke Management Systems in Malls, Atria and Large Spaces
211—10	Chimneys, Fireplaces, Vents and Solid Fuel-burning Appliances
262—07	Standard Method of Test for Flame Travel and Smoke of Wires and Cables for Use in Air-handling Spaces
704—07	Identification of the Hazards of Materials for Emergency Response
853—10	Installation of Stationary Fuel Power Plants

SMACNA Sheet Metal & Air Conditioning Contractors National Assoc., Inc.
4201 Lafayette Center Drive

Chantilly, VA 20151-1209

Standard reference number	Title
SMACNA/ANSI—2005	HVAC Duct Construction Standards—Metal and Flexible (2005)
SMACNA—03	Fibrous Glass Duct Construction Standards

UL Underwriters Laboratories, Inc.
333 Pfingsten Road
Northbrook, IL 60062-2096

Standard reference number	Title
17—*08*	Vent or Chimney Connector Dampers for Oil-fired Appliances
103—*10*	Factory-built Chimneys, Residential Type and Building Heating Appliance
127—*08*	Factory-built Fireplaces
174—04	Household Electric Storage Tank Water Heaters—with Revisions through May 2006
181—05	Factory-made Air Ducts and Air Connectors—with Revisions through December 1998
181A—05	Closure Systems for Use with Rigid Air Ducts and Air Connectors— with Revisions through December 1998
181B—05	Closure Systems for Use with Flexible Air Ducts and Air Connectors— with Revisions through December 1998
207—01	Refrigerant-containing Components and Accessories, Nonelectrical— with Revisions through November 2004
263—03	Standard for Fire Test of Building Construction and Materials
268—*09*	Smoke Detectors for Fire Prevention Signaling Systems
268A—*08*	Smoke Detectors for Duct Applications
343—*08*	Pumps for Oil-Burning Appliances
391—*10*	Solid-fuel and Combination-fuel Central and Supplementary Furnaces
412—04	Refrigeration Unit Coolers—with Revisions through February 2007.
471—*10*	Commercial Refrigerators and Freezers
508—99	Industrial Control Equipment—with Revisions through July 2005
536—97	Flexible Metallic Hose—with Revisions through June 2003
555—06	Fire Dampers—with Revisions through January 2002.
555C—06	Ceiling Dampers
555S—99	Smoke Dampers—with Revisions through July 2006
586—*09*	High-efficiency, Particulate, Air Filter Units
641—95	Type L Low-temperature Venting Systems—with Revisions through August 2005
710—95	Exhaust Hoods for Commercial Cooking Equipment—with Revisions through February 2007.
710B—04	Recirculating Systems
723—*08*	Standard for Test for Surface Burning Characteristics of Building Materials
726—95	Oil-fired Boiler Assemblies—with Revisions through March 2006

727—06	Oil-fired Central Furnaces
729—03	Oil-fired Floor Furnaces—with Revisions through January 1999
730—03	Oil-fired Wall Furnaces—with Revisions through January 1999
731—95	Oil-fired Unit Heaters—with Revisions through February 2006
732—95	Oil-fired Storage Tank Water Heaters—with Revisions through February 2005
737—07	Fireplace Stoves
762—03	Outline of Investigation for Power Ventilators for Restaurant Exhaust Appliances
791—06	Residential Incinerators.
834—04	Heating, Water Supply and Power Boilers Electric—with Revisions through March 2006
858—05	Household Electric Ranges—with Revisions through April 2006
867—00	Electrostatic Air Cleaners—with Revisions through May 2004
875—09	Electric Dry Bath Heater
896—93	Oil-burning Stoves—with Revisions through May 2004
900—04	Air Filter Units
923—08	Microwave Cooking Appliances
959—01	Medium Heat Appliance Factory-built Chimneys—with Revisions through September 2006
1240—05	Electric Commercial Clothes
1261—01	Electric Water Heaters for Pools and Tubs—with Revisions through June 2004
1453—04	Electric Booster and Commercial Storage Tank Water Heaters—with Revisions through May 2006
1482—10	Solid-fuel Type Room Heaters
1777—07	Chimney Liners.
1812—09	Standard for Ducted Heat Recovery Ventilators
1815—09	Standard for Nonducted Heat Recovery Ventilators
1820—04	Fire Test of Pneumatic Tubing for Flame and Smoke Characteristics
1887—04	Fire Tests of Plastic Sprinkler Pipe for Visible Flame and Smoke Characteristics
1978—05	Grease Ducts
1995—05	Heating and Cooling Equipment.
2158—97	Electric Clothes Dryers—with Revisions through May 2004
2162—01	Outline of Investigation for Commercial Wood-fired Baking Ovens— Refractory Type
2200—98	Stationery Engine Generator Assemblies
2221—10	Tests of Fire Resistive Grease Duct Enclosure Assemblies

Glossary

Access—(a) Exit access—path or route to an exit; (b) Access for the disabled—facilities conforming to Chapter 11 Code and ADAAG (Accessible).

Alterations—Changing existing conditions or materials.

Appliances—Furnaces, or other equipment designed to utilize energy.

Approved—Acceptable by the enforcement official.

Assembly—(a) All materials, components, connections, etc., that are part of providing a fire resistance listing; (b) An occupancy involving large numbers of people, e.g., theatres, restaurants and athletic facilities.

Automatic—Fixture or unit operates without human intervention.

Building official—Enforcement officer of the jurisdiction having authority. Certified by the OBBS.

Certificate—Approved to enforce the OBC by the OBBS.
- Building Official
- Plans Examiner
- Building Inspector
- Auto. Sprinkler System Inspector
- Mechanical Inspector

City engineer—Elected or appointed official that controls site access to utilities and/or public streets.

Class—Class of interior finish flame spread when tested by ASTM E 84
- **A:** flame spread 0–25; smoke developed 0–450
- **B:** flame spread 26–75; smoke developed 0–450
- **C:** flame spread 76–200; smoke developed 0–450

Clear—The minimum actual dimension of an opening.

Compliance—Meeting the requirements of the Code.

Construction—Construction type.

Dampers—Device designed to close an opening—usually in ductwork.

Dead end—Path with only one option in exiting, also called "Common Path of Travel."

Door leaf—A unit that functions to open or close an opening.

Existing buildings—Building existing prior to the adoption of the code or a building having a valid building permit.

Exits—Aisles, corridors, paths, stairs, ramps, doors, etc., forming the access for occupants to leave a building or structure, also called "Means of Egress."

Fire marshal—Enforcement officer in the fire department.

Fire protection systems—Detectors, alarms, and fire suppression.

Fire-rated—Having a fire resistance rating; i.e., tested by ASTM E119, or similar tests.

Fire separation—An open unoccupied space of a certain distance.

Fire separation assembly—Assembly construction providing fire resistance.

Firestop—Closing an opening within concealed spaces in construction assemblies.

Fire suppressed—Having an automatic fire suppression system (e.g., *Sprinklers*).

Group A—Assembly Use Group, A-1, A-2, A-3, A-4, A-5.

Group B—Business Use Group.

Group E—Educational Use Group.

Group F—Factory & Industrial Use Group, F-1, F-2.

Group H—High Hazard Use Group, H-1, H-2, H-3, H-4, H-5.

Group I—Institutional Use Group, I-1, I-2, I-3, I-4.

Group M—Mercantile Use Group.

Group R—Residential Use Group, R-1. R-2, R-3, R-4.

Group S—Storage Use Group, S-1, S-2.

Group U—Utility and Miscellaneous Use Group.

Gypsum board—Drywall.

Habitable—Parts of residential dwellings for use by people, other than bathrooms, toilets, closets, corridors and utility rooms.

Hazard—Danger of fire, explosion, etc.

Impermeable—Resist the passage of water.

Interconnected—Connected units operate when any unit activates.

Kiosk—Sales space in the mall aisle, usually independent of adjacent tenant spaces.

Labeled—Identified as to meeting prescribed standard.

Lot line—Property line.

Nominal—Not the actual dimension.

Noncombustible—Construction Types I & II.

Occupancy—The purpose for which a building, or portion, is being used.

Occupiable—Designed for use by people; for work or fun (not the same as "habitable").

1-hour—Wall/Floor having a one-hour fire resistance when tested by ASTM E119.

Permit—Approval by the building department for construction.

Plenum—Space that is used for air movement.

Protected openings—having automatic closing devices to provide required fire resistance.

Protectives—Device that automatically closes an opening and provides the specified fire resistance.

Ratings—Fire resistance rating.

Repairs—Fixing existing conditions or materials.

Required—Mandatory.

Riser—Vertical portion of stair—measured from tread to tread.

Shafts—An opening between floors in a building.

Slip-resistant—An *undefined* term in the Code.

Smoke detectors—Automatic alarm device.

Sprinkled—Having fire suppression system installed.

Sprinklers—An automatic fire suppression system that delivers water to a fire.

Standpipes—The vertical system of supplying water for fire protection.

Story—Building level between successive floors or a floor and the roof (e.g., "story above/below grade").

Terminate—Point at which the vertical control of exhaust or a shaft stops.

Travel—The movement of people in the process of exiting.

Tread—Horizontal portion of stair—measured from nosing to nosing.

Type—Type I, II, III, IV & V differentiate construction characteristics by required fire resistance and combustibility.

Unoccupied—Not used by people.

Unprotected—Not having a fire resistance rating, or not having sprinklers.

TEACHER'S PLANNING GUIDE

Project-Based Inquiry Science™

ASTRONOMY

NSF

IT's ABOUT TIME®

HERFF JONES EDUCATION DIVISION

IT's ABOUT TIME®

HERFF JONES EDUCATION DIVISION

84 Business Park Drive, Armonk, NY 10504
Phone (914) 273-2233 Fax (914) 273-2227
www.its-about-time.com

Program Components

Student Edition	**Durable Equipment Kit**
Teacher's Planning Guide	**Consumable Equipment Kit**
Teacher's Resources Guide	

ISBN 978-1-58591-636-8
1 2 3 4 5 13 12 11 10 09

This project was supported, in part, by the **National Science Foundation**
under grant nos. 0137807, 0527341, and 0639978.
Opinions expressed are those of the authors and not necessarily
those of the National Science Foundation.

Janet L. Kolodner is a Regents' Professor in the School of Interactive Computing in the Georgia Institute of Technology's College of Computing. Since 1978, her research has focused on learning from experience, both in computers and in people. She pioneered the Artificial Intelligence method called *case-based reasoning*, providing a way for computers to solve new problems based on their past experiences. Her book, *Case-Based Reasoning*, synthesizes work across the case-based reasoning research community from its inception to 1993.

Since 1994, Dr. Kolodner has focused on the applications and implications of case-based reasoning for education. In her approach to science education, called Learning by Design™ (LBD), students learn science while pursuing design challenges. Dr. Kolodner has investigated how to create a culture of collaboration and rigorous science talk in classrooms, how to use a project challenge to promote focus on science content, and how students learn and develop when classrooms function as learning communities. Currently, Dr. Kolodner is investigating how to help young people come to think of themselves as scientific reasoners. Dr. Kolodner's research results have been widely published, including in *Cognitive Science, Design Studies,* and the *Journal of the Learning Sciences.*

Dr. Kolodner was founding Director of Georgia Tech's EduTech Institute, served as coordinator of Georgia Tech's Cognitive Science program for many years, and is founding Editor in Chief of the *Journal of the Learning Sciences.* She is a founder of the International Society for the Learning Sciences, and she served as its first Executive Officer. She is a fellow of the American Association of Artificial Intelligence.

Joseph S. Krajcik is a Professor of Science Education and Associate Dean for Research in the School of Education at the University of Michigan. He works with teachers in science classrooms to bring about sustained change by creating classroom environments in which students find solutions to important intellectual questions that subsume essential curriculum standards and use learning technologies as productivity tools. He seeks to discover what students learn in such environments, as well as to explore and find solutions to challenges that teachers face in enacting such complex instruction.

Dr. Krajcik has authored and co-authored over 100 manuscripts and makes frequent presentations at international, national, and regional conferences that focus on his research, as well as presentations that translate research findings into classroom practice. He is a fellow of the American Association for the Advancement of Science and served as president of the National Association for Research in Science Teaching. Dr. Krajcik co-directs the Center for Highly Interactive Classrooms, Curriculum and Computing in Education at the University of Michigan and is a co-principal investigator in the Center for Curriculum Materials in Science and The National Center for Learning and Teaching Nanoscale Science and Engineering. In 2002, Dr. Krajcik was honored to receive a Guest Professorship from Beijing Normal University in Beijing, China. In winter 2005, he was the Weston Visiting Professor of Science Education at the Weizmann Institute of Science in Rehovot, Israel.

Daniel C. Edelson is Vice President for Education and Children's Programs at the National Geographic Society. Previously, he was the director of the Geographic Data in Education (GEODE) Initiative at Northwestern University, where he led the development of Planetary Forecaster and Earth Systems and Processes. Since 1992, Dr. Edelson has directed a series of projects exploring the use of technology as a catalyst for reform in science education and has led the development of a number of software environments for education. These include My World GIS, a geographic information system for inquiry-based learning, and WorldWatcher, a data visualization and analysis system for gridded geographic data. Dr. Edelson is the author of the high school environmental science text, *Investigations in Environmental Science: A Case-Based Approach to the Study of Environmental Systems*. His research has been widely published, including in the *Journal of the Learning Sciences,* the *Journal of Research on Science Teaching, Science Educator*, and *Science Teacher*.

Brian J. Reiser is a Professor of Learning Sciences in the School of Education and Social Policy at Northwestern University. Professor Reiser served as chair of Northwestern's Learning Sciences Ph.D. program from 1993, shortly after its inception, until 2001. His research focuses on the design and enactment of learning environments that support students' inquiry in science, including both science curriculum materials and scaffolded software tools. His research investigates the design of learning environments that scaffold scientific practices, including investigation, argumentation, and explanation; design principles for technology-infused curricula that engage students in inquiry projects; and the teaching practices that support student inquiry. Professor Reiser also directed BGuILE (Biology Guided Inquiry Learning Environments) to develop software tools for supporting middle school and high school students in analyzing data and constructing explanations with biological data. Reiser is a co-principal investigator in the NSF Center for Curriculum Materials in Science. He served as a member of the NRC panel authoring the report Taking Science to School.

Mary L. Starr is a Research Specialist in Science Education in the School of Education at the University of Michigan. She collaborates with teachers and students in elementary and middle school science classrooms around the United States who are implementing *Project-Based Inquiry Science*. Before joining the PBIS team, Dr. Starr created professional learning experiences in science, math, and technology, designed to assist teachers in successfully changing their classroom practices to promote student learning from coherent inquiry experiences. She has developed instructional materials in several STEM areas, including nanoscale science education, has presented at national and regional teacher education and educational research meetings, and has served in a leadership role in the Michigan Science Education Leadership Association. Dr. Starr has authored articles and book chapters, and has worked to improve elementary science teacher preparation through teaching science courses for pre-service teachers and acting as a consultant in elementary science teacher preparation. As part of the PBIS team, Dr. Starr has played a lead role in making units cohere as a curriculum, in developing the framework for PBIS Teacher's Planning Guides, and in developing teacher professional development experiences and materials.

Project-Based Inquiry Science

Acknowledgements

Three research teams contributed to the development of *Project-Based Inquiry Science* (PBIS): a team at the Georgia Institute of Technology headed by Janet L. Kolodner, a team at Northwestern University headed by Daniel Edelson and Brian Reiser, and a team at the University of Michigan headed by Joseph Krajcik and Ron Marx. Each of the PBIS units was originally developed by one of these teams and then later revised and edited to be a part of the full three-year middle-school curriculum that became PBIS.

PBIS has its roots in two educational approaches, Project-Based Science and Learning by Design™. Project-Based Science suggests that students should learn science through engaging in the same kinds of inquiry practices scientists use, in the context of scientific problems relevant to their lives and using tools authentic to science. Project-Based Science was originally conceived in the hi-ce Center at the University of Michigan, with funding from the National Science Foundation. Learning by Design™ derives from Problem-Based Learning and suggests sequencing, social practices, and reflective activities for promoting learning. It engages students in design practices, including the use of iteration and deliberate reflection. LBD was conceived at the Georgia Institute of Technology, with funding from the National Science Foundation, DARPA, and the McDonnell Foundation.

The development of the integrated PBIS curriculum was supported by the National Science Foundation under grants no. 0137807, 0527341, and 0639978. Any opinions, findings and conclusions, or recommendations expressed in this material are those of the authors and do not necessarily reflect the views of the National Science Foundation.

PBIS Team

Principal Investigator
Janet L. Kolodner

Co-Principal Investigators
Daniel C. Edelson
Joseph S. Krajcik
Brian J. Reiser

NSF Program Officer
Gerhard Salinger

Curriculum Developers
Michael T. Ryan
Mary L. Starr

Teacher's Planning Guide Developers
Rebecca M. Schneider
Mary L. Starr

Literacy Specialist
LeeAnn M. Sutherland

NSF Program Reviewer
Arthur Eisenkraft

Project Coordinator
Juliana Lancaster

External Evaluators
The Learning Partnership
Steven M. McGee
Jennifer Witers

The Georgia Institute of Technology Team

Project Director:
Janet L. Kolodner

Development of PBIS units at the Georgia Institute of Technology was conducted in conjunction with the Learning by Design™ Research group (LBD), Janet L. Kolodner, PI.

Lead Developers, Physical Science:
David Crismond
Michael T. Ryan

Lead Developer, Earth Science:
Paul J. Camp

Assessment and Evaluation:
Barbara Fasse
Daniel Hickey
Jackie Gray
Laura Vandewiele
Jennifer Holbrook

Project Pioneers:
JoAnne Collins
David Crismond
Joanna Fox
Alice Gertzman
Mark Guzdial
Cindy Hmelo-Silver
Douglas Holton
Roland Hubscher
N. Hari Narayanan
Wendy Newstetter
Valery Petrushin
Kathy Politis
Sadhana Puntambekar
David Rector
Janice Young

The Northwestern University Team

Project Directors:
Daniel Edelson
Brian Reiser

Lead Developer, Biology:
David Kanter

Lead Developers, Earth Science:
Jennifer Mundt Leimberer
Darlene Slusher

Development of PBIS units at Northwestern was conducted in conjunction with:

The Center for Learning Technologies in Urban Schools (LeTUS) at Northwestern, and the Chicago Public Schools
Louis Gomez, PI;
Clifton Burgess, PI
for Chicago Public Schools.

The BioQ Collaborative
David Kanter, PI.

The Biology Guided Inquiry Learning Environments (BGuILE) Project
Brian Reiser, PI.

The Geographic Data in Education (GEODE) Initiative
Daniel Edelson, Director

The Center for Curriculum Materials in Science at Northwestern
Brian Reiser,
Daniel Edelson,
Bruce Sherin, PIs.

The University of Michigan Team

Project Directors:
Joseph Krajcik
Ron Marx

Literacy Specialist:
LeeAnn M. Sutherland

Project Coordinator:
Mary L. Starr

Development of PBIS units at the University of Michigan was conducted in conjunction with:

The Center for Learning Technologies in Urban Schools (LeTUS)
Ron Marx, Phyllis Blumenfeld,
Barry Fishman,
Joseph Krajcik,
Elliot Soloway, PIs.

The Detroit Public Schools
Juanita Clay-Chambers
Deborah Peek-Brown

The Center for Highly Interactive Computing in Education (hi-ce)
Ron Marx,
Phyllis Blumenfeld,
Barry Fishman,
Joseph Krajcik,
Elliot Soloway,
Elizabeth Moje,
LeeAnn Sutherland, PIs.

Field-Test Teachers

National Field Test
Tamica Andrew
Leslie Baker
Jeanne Bayer
Gretchen Bryant
Boris Consuegra
Daun D'Aversa
Candi DiMauro
Kristie L. Divinski
Donna M. Dowd
Jason Fiorito
Lara Fish
Christine Gleason
Christine Hallerman
Terri L. Hart-Parker
Jennifer Hunn
Rhonda K. Hunter
Jessica Jones
Dawn Kuppersmith
Anthony F. Lawrence
Ann Novak
Rise Orsini
Tracy E. Parham
Cheryl Sgro-Ellis
Debra Tenenbaum
Sarah B. Topper
Becky Watts
Debra A. Williams
Ingrid M. Woolfolk
Ping-Jade Yang

New York City Field Test
Several sequences of PBIS units have been field- tested in New York City under the leadership of Whitney Lukens, Staff Developer for Region 9, and Greg Borman, Science Instructional Specialist, New York City Department of Education

6th Grade
Norman Agard
Tazinmudin Ali
Heather Guthartz Aniba
Asher Arzonane
Asli Aydin
Shareese Blakely
John J. Blaylock
Joshua Blum
Tsedey Bogale
Filomena Borrero

Zachary Brachio
Thelma Brown
Alicia Browne-Jones
Scott Bullis
Maximo Cabral
Lionel Callender
Matthew Carpenter
Ana Maria Castro
Diane Castro
Anne Chan
Ligia Chiorean
Boris Consuegra
Careen Halton Cooper
Cinnamon Czarnecki
Kristin Decker
Nancy Dejean
Gina DiCicco
Donna Dowd
Lizanne Espina
Joan Ferrato
Matt Finnerty
Jacqueline Flicker
Helen Fludd
Leigh Summers Frey
Helene Friedman-Hager
Diana Gering
Matthew Giles
Lucy Gill
Steven Gladden
Greg Grambo
Carrie Grodin-Vehling
Stephan Joanides
Kathryn Kadei
Paraskevi Karangunis
Cynthia Kerns
Martine Lalanne
Erin Lalor
Jennifer Lerman
Sara Lugert
Whitney Lukens
Dana Martorella
Christine Mazurek
Janine McGeown
Chevelle McKeever
Kevin Meyer
Jennifer Miller
Nicholas Miller
Diana Neligan
Caitlin Van Ness
Marlyn Orque
Eloisa Gelo Ortiz
Gina Papadopoulos
Tim Perez
Albertha Petrochilos
Christopher Poli
Kristina Rodriguez

Nadiesta Sanchez
Annette Schavez
Hilary Sedgwitch
Elissa Seto
Laura Shectman
Audrey Shmuel
Katherine Silva
Ragini Singhal
C. Nicole Smith
Gitangali Sohit
Justin Stein
Thomas Tapia
Eilish Walsh-Lennon
Lisa Wong
Brian Yanek
Cesar Yarleque
David Zaretsky
Colleen Zarinsky

7th Grade
Mayra Amaro
Emmanuel Anastasiou
Cheryl Barnhill
Bryce Cahn
Ligia Chiorean
Ben Colella
Boris Consuegra
Careen Halton Cooper
Elizabeth Derse
Urmilla Dhanraj
Gina DiCicco
Lydia Doubleday
Lizanne Espina
Matt Finnerty
Steven Gladden
Stephanie Goldberg
Nicholas Graham
Robert Hunter
Charlene Joseph
Ketlynne Joseph
Kimberly Kavazanjian
Christine Kennedy
Bakwah Kotung
Lisa Kraker
Anthony Lett
Herb Lippe
Jennifer Lopez
Jill Mastromarino
Kerry McKie
Christie Morgado
Patrick O'Connor
Agnes Ochiagha
Tim Perez
Nadia Piltser
Chris Poli

Carmelo Ruiz
Kim Sanders
Leslie Schiavone
Ileana Solla
Jacqueline Taylor
Purvi Vora
Ester Wiltz
Carla Yuille
Marcy Sexauer Zacchea
Lidan Zhou

8th Grade
Emmanuel Anastasio
Jennifer Applebaum
Marsha Armstrong
Jenine Barunas
Vito Cipolla
Kathy Critharis
Patrecia Davis
Alison Earle
Lizanne Espina
Matt Finnerty
Ursula Fokine
Kirsis Genao
Steven Gladden
Stephanie Goldberg
Peter Gooding
Matthew Herschfeld
Mike Horowitz
Charlene Jenkins
Ruben Jimenez
Ketlynne Joseph
Kimberly Kavazanjian
Lisa Kraker
Dora Kravitz
Anthony Lett
Emilie Lubis
George McCarthy
David Mckinney
Michael McMahon
Paul Melhado
Jen Miller
Christie Morgado
Ms. Oporto
Maria Jenny Pineda
Anastasia Plaunova
Carmelo Ruiz
Riza Sanchez
Kim Sanders
Maureen Stefanides
Dave Thompson
Matthew Ulmann
Maria Verosa
Tony Yaskulski

Astronomy

Astronomy (PBIS) is based on *Astronomy,* a unit developed by the University of Michigan's Center for Highly Interactive Computing in Education (hi ce).

Astronomy

Lead Developers

Mary L. Starr

Contributors

Julia Plummer

Deano Smith

Astronomy **(Michigan version)**

Lead Developer

Julia Plummer

Contributors

Lisa Scott Holt

Steve Best

Joe Krajcik

Matthew P. Linke

The development of all versions of *Astronomy* was supported by the National Science Foundation under grant nos. 0137807, 0527341, and 0639978. Any opinions, findings, and conclusions or recommendations expressed in this material are those of the authors and do not necessarily reflect the views of the National Science Foundation.

Astronomy Teacher's Planning Guide

Learning Set 1

***Have Objects in the
Solar System Collided?***

Science Concepts: *Historical contributions
in astronomy, impact craters, telescopes,
characteristics of impact craters, satellite images,
astrogeology, erosion and weathering, age of
geological features (Earth and the Moon), meteors
and meteorites, components of the solar system,
asteroids, comets, asteroid belt, designing an
experiment, understanding models, independent
and dependent variables, experimental controls,
making predictions, communicating plans,
analyzing data, working with maps, using
visualization tools, using evidence to support claims,
developing explanations.*

1.0 Learning Set 1 Introduction

***Have Objects in the
Solar System Collided?***

1.1 Understand the Question

***Think About What Happens
When Objects Collide***

Learning Set 2

How Do Earth, the Moon, and the Sun Move Through Space?

Science Concepts: *Apparent motion, rotation and revolution, definition of a day, the Sun as the source of reflected light, phases of the Moon, orbital motion, Earth-Moon-Sun system, relative sizes of objects in the solar system, measurement on the celestial sphere, lunar eclipses and solar eclipses, total eclipses and partial eclipses, shadows (umbra and penumbra), characteristics of the Sun, solar atmosphere, fusion in stars, sunspots, gravity and motion, tides, formation of the Moon, understanding models, collecting and organizing data, building models, developing explanations, using evidence to support claims, using scientific knowledge, using visualization tools, simulations, scale models, scientific theories, making measurements.*

2.0 Learning Set Introduction

How Do Earth, the Moon, and the Sun Move Through Space?

2.1 Understand the Question

Think About How You Can Find Out About the Motions of Earth, the Moon, and the Sun

2.2 Model

Make a Model of the Apparent Motion of the Sun

2.3 Explore

Where Is the Moon Located, and How Does It Move?

2.4 Explore

How Do the Sizes of Earth and the Moon Compare, and How Far Apart Are They?

2.5 Explore

What Do Eclipses Tell You About Distances to the Sun and the Moon?

Learning Set 3
How Do Other Solar-System Objects Move Through Space?

Science Concepts: *Position of objects in the solar system, distances between solar system objects, scale models, calculating scale factors, designing models of the solar system, comparing characteristics of planets (inner and outer planets), revolution and definition of a year, astronomical unit, gravity and planetary motion, orbital characteristics, apparent motion of planets, heliocentric and geocentric models of the solar system, historical contributions in astronomy, formation of the solar system, using visualization tools, understanding models, building models, collaboration, building on the work of others, organizing and analyzing data, finding trends in data, using evidence to support claims.*

Welcome to Project-Based Inquiry Science!

Welcome to Project-Based Inquiry Science (PBIS): A Middle-School Science Curriculum!

This year, your students will be learning the way scientists learn, exploring interesting questions and challenges, reading about what other scientists have discovered, investigating, experimenting, gathering evidence, and forming explanations. They will learn to collaborate with others to find answers and to share their learning in a variety of ways. In the process, they will come to see science in a whole new, exciting way that will motivate them throughout their educational experiences and beyond.

What is PBIS?

In project-based inquiry learning, students investigate scientific content and learn science practices in the context of attempting to address challenges in or answer questions about the world around them. Early activities introducing students to a challenge help them to generate issues that need to be investigated, making inquiry a student-driven endeavor. Students investigate as scientists would, through observations, designing and running experiments, designing, building, and running models, reading written material, and so on, as appropriate. Throughout each project, students might make use of technology and computer tools that support their efforts in observation, experimentation, modeling, analysis, and reflection. Teachers support and guide the student inquiries by framing the guiding challenge or question, presenting crucial lessons, managing the sequencing of activities, and eliciting and steering discussion and collaboration among the students. At the completion of a project, students publicly exhibit what they have learned along with their solutions to the specific challenge. Personal reflection to help students learn from the experience is embedded in student activities, as are opportunities for assessment.

The curriculum will provide three years of piloted project-based inquiry materials for middle-school science. Individual curriculum units have been defined that cover the scope of the national content and process standards for the middle-school grades. Each Unit focuses on helping students acquire qualitative understanding of targeted science principles and move toward quantitative understanding, is infused with technology, and provides a foundation in reasoning skills, science content, and science process that will ready them for more advanced science. The curriculum as a whole introduces students to a wide range of investigative approaches in science (e.g., experimentation, modeling) and is designed to help them develop scientific reasoning skills that span those investigative approaches.

Technology can be used in project-based inquiry to make available to students some of the same kinds of tools and aids used by scientists in the field. These range from pencil-and-paper tools for organized data recording, collection, and management to software tools for analysis, simulation, modeling, and other tasks. Such infusion provides a platform for providing prompts, hints, examples, and other kinds of aids to students as they are engaging in scientific reasoning. The learning technologies and tools that are integrated into the curriculum offer essential scaffolding to students as they are developing their scientific reasoning skills, and are seamlessly infused into the overall completion of project activities and investigations.

Standards-Based Development

Development of each curriculum Unit begins by identifying the specific relevant national standards to be addressed. Each Unit has been designed to cover a specific portion of the national standards. This phase of development also includes an analysis of curriculum requirements across multiple states. Our intent is to deliver a product that will provide coverage of the content deemed essential on the widest practical scope and that will be easily adaptable to the needs of teachers across the country.

Once the appropriate standards have been identified, the development team works to define specific learning goals built from those standards, and takes into account conceptions and misunderstandings common among middle-school students. An orienting design challenge or driving question for investigation is chosen that motivates achieving those learning goals, and the team then sequences activities and the presentation of specific concepts so that students can construct an accurate understanding of the subject matter.

Inquiry-Based Design

The individual curriculum Units present two types of projects: engineering-design challenges and driving-question investigations. Design-challenge Units begin by presenting students with a scenario and problem and challenging them to design a device or plan that will solve the problem. Driving-question investigations begin by presenting students with a complex question with real-world implications. Students are challenged to develop answers to the questions. The scenario and problem in the design Units and the driving question in the investigation Units are carefully selected to lead the students into investigation of specific science concepts, and the solution processes are carefully structured to require use of specific scientific reasoning skills.

Pedagogical Rationale

Research shows that individual project-based learning units promote excitement and deep learning of the targeted concepts. However, achieving deep, flexible, transferable learning of cross-disciplinary content (e.g., the notion of a model, time scale, variable, experiment) and science practice requires a learning environment that consistently, persistently, and pervasively encourages the use of such content and practices over an extended period of time. By developing project-based inquiry materials that cover the spectrum of middle-school science content in a coherent framework, we provide this extended exposure to the type of learning environment most likely to produce competent scientific thinkers who are well grounded in their understanding of both basic science concepts and the standards and practices of science in general.

Evidence of Effectiveness

There is compelling evidence showing that a project-based inquiry approach meets this goal. Working at Georgia Tech, the University of Michigan, and Northwestern University, we have developed, piloted, and/or field-tested many individual project-based units. Our evaluation evidence shows that these materials engage students well and are manageable by teachers, and that students learn both content and process skills. In every summative evaluation, student performance on post-tests improved significantly from pretest performance (Krajcik, et al., 2000; Holbrook, et al., 2001; Gray et. al. 2001). For example, in the second year in a project-based classroom in Detroit, the average student at post-test scored at about the 95th percentile of the pre-test distribution. Further, we have repeatedly documented significant gains in content knowledge relative to other inquiry-based (but not project-based) instructional methods. In one set of results, performance by a project-based class

in Atlanta doubled on the content test while the matched comparison class (with an excellent teacher) experienced only a 20% gain (significance $p < .001$). Other comparisons have shown more modest differences, but project-based students consistently perform better than their comparisons. Most exciting about the Atlanta results is that results from performance assessments show that, within comparable student populations, project-based students score higher on all categories of problem-solving and analysis and are more sophisticated at science practice and managing a collaborative scientific investigation. Indeed, the performance of average-ability project-based students is often statistically indistinguishable from or better than performance of comparison honors students learning in an inquiry-oriented but not project-based classroom. The Chicago group also has documented significant change in process skills in project-based classrooms. Students become more effective in constructing and critiquing scientific arguments (Sandoval, 1998) and in constructing scientific explanations using discipline-specific knowledge, such as evolutionary explanations for animal behavior (Smith & Reiser, 1998).

Researchers at Northwestern have also investigated the changes in classroom practices that are elicited by project-based units. Analyses of the artifacts students produce indicate that students are engaging in ambitious learning practices, requiring weighing and synthesizing many results from complex analyses of data, and constructing scientific arguments that require synthesizing results from multiple complex analyses of data (Edelson et al, 1998; Reiser et al, 2001). Students are engaged in planning, performing, monitoring and revising their investigations, and reporting on their investigation processes as well as their results (Loh et al, 1998). In general, the classrooms engaging in project-based activities reveal substantial moves toward a scientific discourse community in which students focus on arguing from evidence, critiquing ideas, and conjecturing, rather than simply reporting on what they have read or been told (Tabak & Reiser, 1997).

Introducing PBIS

What Do Scientists Do?

1) Scientists...address big challenges and big questions.

Students will find many different kinds of *Big Challenges* and *Questions* in *PBIS* Units. Some ask them to think about why something is a certain way. Some ask them to think about what causes something to change. Some challenge them to design a solution to a problem. Most are about things that can and do happen in the real world.

Understand the Big Challenge or Question

As students get started with each Unit, they will do activities that help them understand the *Big Question* or *Challenge* for that Unit. They will think about what they already know that might help them, and they will identify some of the new things they will need to learn.

Project Board

The *Project Board* helps you and your students keep track of their learning. For each challenge or question, they will use a *Project Board* to keep track of what they know, what they need to learn, and what they are learning. As they learn and gather evidence, they will record that on the *Project Board*. After they have answered each small question or challenge, they will return to the *Project Board* to record how what they have learned helps them answer the *Big Question* or *Challenge*.

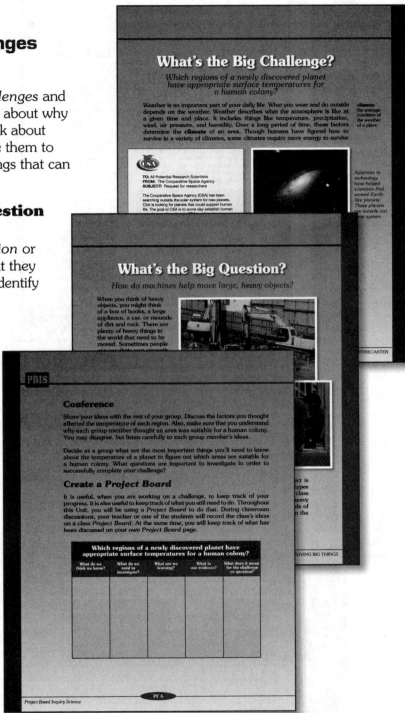

Learning Set 1

How Do Flowing Water and Land Interact in a Community?

The big question for this unit is *How does water quality affect the ecology of a community?* So far you have considered what you already know about what water quality is. Now you may be wondering where the water you use comes from. If you live in a city or town, the water you use may come from a river. You would want to know the quality of the water you are using. To do so, it is important to know how the water gets into the river. You also need to know what happens to the water as the river flows across the land.

You may have seen rivers or other water bodies near your home, your school, or in your city. Think about the river closest to where you live. Consider from where the water in the river comes. If you have traveled along the river, think about what the land around the river looks like. Try to figure out what human activities occur in the area. Speculate as to whether these activities affect the quality of water in the river.

To answer the big question, you need to break it down into smaller questions. In this *Learning Set,* you will investigate two smaller questions. As you will discover, these questions are very closely related and very hard to separate. The smaller questions are *How does water affect the land as it moves through the community?* and *How does land use affect water as it moves through a*

PBIS

Address the Big Challenge

How Do Scientists Work Together to Solve Problems?

You began this unit with the question, *how do scientists work together to solve problems?* You did several small challenges. As you worked on those challenges you learned about how scientists solve problems. You will now watch a video about real-life designers. You will see what the people in the video are doing that is like what you have been doing. Then you will think about all the different things you have been doing during this unit. Lastly, you will write about what you have learned about doing science and being a scientist.

Watch

IDEO Video

The video you will watch follows a group of designers at IDEO. IDEO is an innovation and design firm. In the video, they face the challenge of designing and building a new kind of shopping cart. These designers are doing many of the same things that you did. They also use other practices that you did not use. As you watch the video, record the interesting things you see.

After watching the video, answer the questions on the next page. You might want to look at them before you watch the video. Answering these questions should help you answer the big question of this unit: *How do scientists work together to solve problems?*

Learning Sets

Each Unit is composed of a group of *Learning Sets*, one for each of the smaller questions that needs to be answered to address the *Big Question* or *Challenge*. In each *Learning Set*, students will investigate and read to find answers to the *Learning Set's* question. They will also have a chance to share the results of their investigations with their classmates and work together to make sense of what they are learning. As students come to understand answers to the questions on the *Project Board*, you will record those answers and the evidence they collected. At the end of each *Learning Set*, they will apply their knowledge to the *Big Question* or *Challenge*.

Answer the Big Question/ Address the Big Challenge

At the end of each Unit, students will put everything they have learned together to tackle the *Big Question* or *Challenge*.

2) Scientists...address smaller questions and challenges.

What Students Do in a Learning Set

Understanding the Question or Challenge

At the start of each *Learning Set*, students will usually do activities that will help them understand the *Learning Set's* question or challenge and recognize what they already know that can help them answer the question or achieve the challenge. Usually, they will visit the *Project Board* after these activities and record on it the even smaller questions that they need to investigate to answer a *Learning Set's* question.

Investigate/Explore

There are many different kinds of investigations students might do to find answers to questions. In the *Learning Sets,* they might

- design and run experiments;
- design and run simulations;
- design and build models;
- examine large sets of data.

Don't worry if your students haven't done these things before. The text will provide them with lots of help in designing their investigations and in analyzing their data.

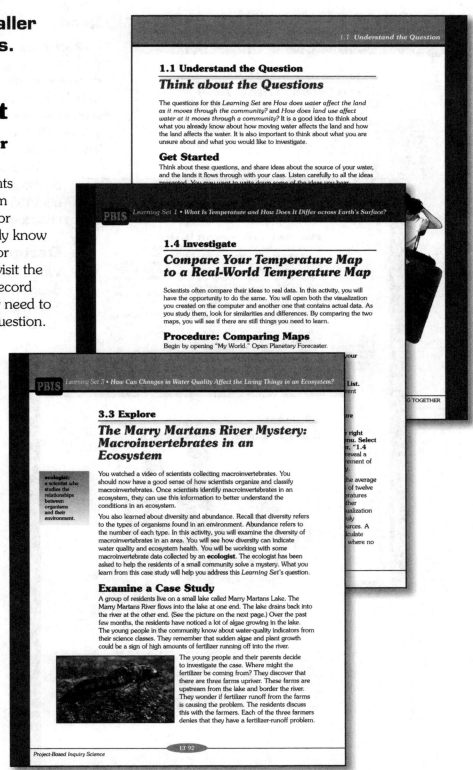

1.1 Understand the Question

Think about the Questions

The questions for this *Learning Set* are *How does water affect the land as it moves through the community?* and *How does land use affect water at it moves through a community?* It is a good idea to think about what you already know about how moving water affects the land and how the land affects the water. It is also important to think about what you are unsure about and what you would like to investigate.

Get Started

Think about these questions, and share ideas about the source of your water, and the lands it flows through with your class. Listen carefully to all the ideas presented. You may want to write down some of the ideas you hear.

Learning Set 1 • What Is Temperature and How Does It Differ across Earth's Surface?

1.4 Investigate

Compare Your Temperature Map to a Real-World Temperature Map

Scientists often compare their ideas to real data. In this activity, you will have the opportunity to do the same. You will open both the visualization you created on the computer and another one that contains actual data. As you study them, look for similarities and differences. By comparing the two maps, you will see if there are still things you need to learn.

Procedure: Comparing Maps

Begin by opening "My World." Open Planetary Forecaster.

Learning Set 3 • How Can Changes in Water Quality Affect the Living Things in an Ecosystem?

3.3 Explore

The Marry Martans River Mystery: Macroinvertebrates in an Ecosystem

ecologist: a scientist who studies the relationships between organisms and their environment.

You watched a video of scientists collecting macroinvertebrates. You should now have a good sense of how scientists organize and classify macroinvertebrates. Once scientists identify macroinvertebrates in an ecosystem, they can use this information to better understand the conditions in an ecosystem.

You also learned about diversity and abundance. Recall that diversity refers to the types of organisms found in an environment. Abundance refers to the number of each type. In this activity, you will examine the diversity of macroinvertebrates in an area. You will see how diversity can indicate water quality and ecosystem health. You will be working with some macroinvertebrate data collected by an **ecologist**. The ecologist has been asked to help the residents of a small community solve a mystery. What you learn from this case study will help you address this *Learning Set's* question.

Examine a Case Study

A group of residents live on a small lake called Marry Martans Lake. The Marry Martans River flows into the lake at one end. The lake drains back into the river at the other end. (See the picture on the next page.) Over the past few months, the residents have noticed a lot of algae growing in the lake. The young people in the community know about water-quality indicators from their science classes. They remember that sudden algae and plant growth could be a sign of high amounts of fertilizer running off into the river.

The young people and their parents decide to investigate the case. Where might the fertilizer be coming from? They discover that there are three farms upriver. These farms are upstream from the lake and border the river. They wonder if fertilizer runoff from the farms is causing the problem. The residents discuss this with the farmers. Each of the three farmers denies that they have a fertilizer-runoff problem.

Project-Based Inquiry Science

LT 92

Read

Like scientists, students will also read about the science they are investigating. They will read a little bit before they investigate, but most of the reading they do will be to help them understand what they have experienced or seen in an investigation. Each time they read, the text will include *Stop and Think* questions after the reading. These questions will help students gauge how well they understand what they have read. Usually, the class will discuss the answers to *Stop and Think* questions before going on so that everybody has a chance to make sense of the reading.

Design and Build

When the *Big Challenge* for a Unit asks them to design something, the challenge in a *Learning Set* might also ask them to design something and make it work. Often students will design a part of the thing they will design and build for the *Big Challenge*. When a *Learning Set* challenges students to design and build something, they will do several things:

- identify what questions they need to answer to be successful

- investigate to find answers to those questions

- use those answers to plan a good design solution

- build and test their design

Because designs don't always work the way one wants them to, students will usually do a design challenge more than once. Each time through, they will test their design. If their design doesn't work as well as they would like, they will determine why it is not working and identify other things they need to investigate to make it work better. Then, they will learn those things and try again.

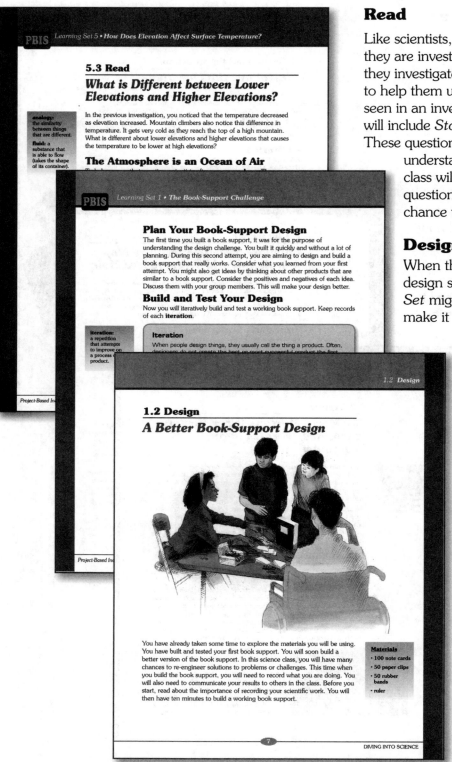

Explain and Recommend

A big part of what scientists do is explain, or try to make sense of why things happen the way they do. An explanation describes why something is the way it is or behaves the way it does. An explanation is a statement one makes built from claims (what you think you know), evidence (from an investigation) that supports the claim, and science knowledge. As they learn, scientists get better at explaining. You will see that students get better, too, as they work through the *Learning Sets*.

A recommendation is a special kind of claim—one where you advise somebody about what to do. Students will make recommendations and support them with evidence, science knowledge, and explanations.

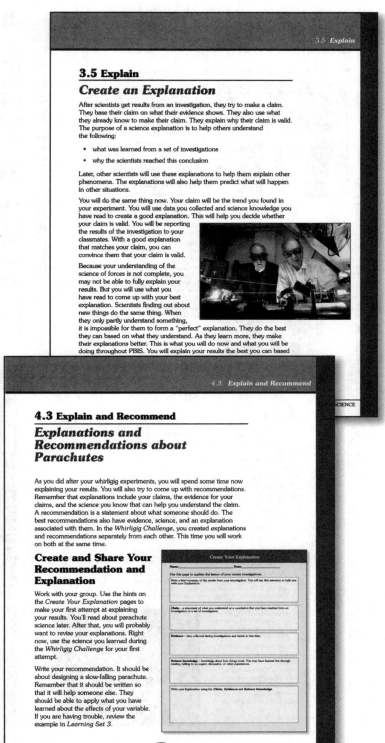

3.5 Explain
Create an Explanation

After scientists get results from an investigation, they try to make a claim. They base their claim on what their evidence shows. They also use what they already know to make their claim. They explain why their claim is valid. The purpose of a science explanation is to help others understand the following:

- what was learned from a set of investigations
- why the scientists reached this conclusion

Later, other scientists will use these explanations to help them explain other phenomena. The explanations will also help them predict what will happen in other situations.

You will do the same thing now. Your claim will be the trend you found in your experiment. You will use data you collected and science knowledge you have read to create a good explanation. This will help you decide whether your claim is valid. You will be reporting the results of the investigation to your classmates. With a good explanation that matches your claim, you can convince them that your claim is valid.

Because your understanding of the science of forces is not complete, you may not be able to fully explain your results. But you will use what you have read to come up with your best explanation. Scientists finding out about new things do the same thing. When they only partly understand something, it is impossible for them to form a "perfect" explanation. They do the best they can based on what they understand. As they learn more, they make their explanations better. This is what you will do now and what you will be doing throughout PBIS. You will explain your results the best you can based

4.3 Explain and Recommend
Explanations and Recommendations about Parachutes

As you did after your whirligig experiments, you will spend some time now explaining your results. You will also try to come up with recommendations. Remember that explanations include your claims, the evidence for your claims, and the science you know that can help you understand the claim. A recommendation is a statement about what someone should do. The best recommendations also have evidence, science, and an explanation associated with them. In the *Whirligig Challenge*, you created explanations and recommendations separately from each other. This time you will work on both at the same time.

Create and Share Your Recommendation and Explanation

Work with your group. Use the hints on the *Create Your Explanation* pages to make your first attempt at explaining your results. You'll read about parachute science later. After that, you will probably want to revise your explanations. Right now, use the science you learned during the *Whirligig Challenge* for your first attempt.

Write your recommendation. It should be about designing a slow-falling parachute. Remember that it should be written so that it will help someone else. They should be able to apply what you have learned about the effects of your variable. If you are having trouble, review the example in *Learning Set 3*.

DIVING IN TO SCIENCE

ASTRONOMY

3) Scientists...reflect in many different ways.

PBIS provides guidance to help students think about what they are doing and to recognize what they are learning. Doing this often as they are working will help students be successful student scientists.

Tools for Making Sense

Stop and Think

Stop and Think sections help students make sense of what they have been doing in the section they are working on. *Stop and Think* sections include a set of questions to help students understand what they have just read or done. Sometimes the questions will remind them of something they need to pay more attention to. Sometimes they will help students connect what they have just read to things they already know. When there is a *Stop and Think* in the text, students will work individually or with a partner to answer the questions, and then the whole class will discuss the answers.

Reflect

Reflect sections help students connect what they have just done with other things they have read or done earlier in the Unit (or in another Unit). When there is a *Reflect* in the text, students will work individually or with a partner or small group to answer the questions. Then, the whole class will discuss the answers. You may want to ask students to answer *Reflect* questions for homework.

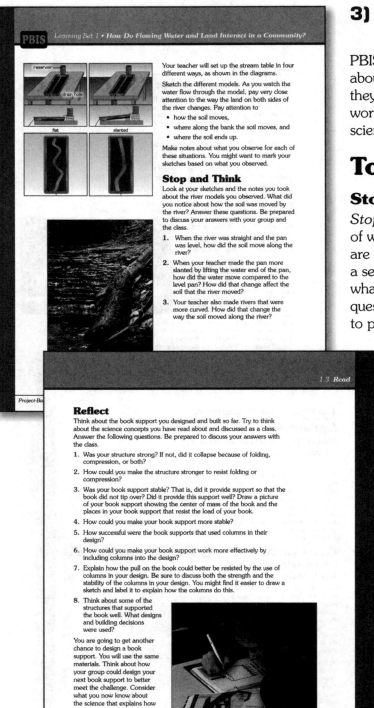

Analyze Your Data

Whenever students have to analyze data, the text will provide hints about how to do that and what to look for.

Mess About

"Messing about" is a term that comes from design. It means exploring the materials to be used for designing or building something or examining something that works like what is to be designed. Messing about helps students discover new ideas—and it can be a lot of fun. The text will usually give them ideas about things to notice as they are messing about.

What's the Point?

At the end of each *Learning Set*, students will find a summary, called *What's the Point?*, of the important information from the *Learning Set*. These summaries can help students remember how what they did and learned is connected to the *Big Question* or *Challenge* they are working on.

ASTRONOMY

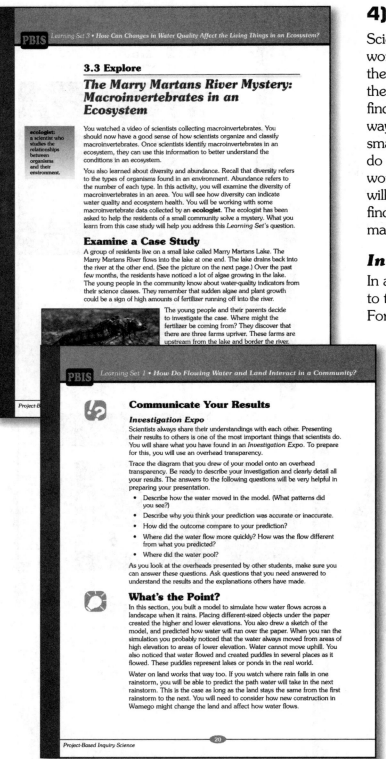

3.3 Explore

The Marry Martans River Mystery: Macroinvertebrates in an Ecosystem

ecologist: a scientist who studies the relationships between organisms and their environment.

You watched a video of scientists collecting macroinvertebrates. You should now have a good sense of how scientists organize and classify macroinvertebrates. Once scientists identify macroinvertebrates in an ecosystem, they can use this information to better understand the conditions in an ecosystem.

You also learned about diversity and abundance. Recall that diversity refers to the types of organisms found in an environment. Abundance refers to the number of each type. In this activity, you will examine the diversity of macroinvertebrates in an area. You will see how diversity can indicate water quality and ecosystem health. You will be working with some macroinvertebrate data collected by an **ecologist**. The ecologist has been asked to help the residents of a small community solve a mystery. What you learn from this case study will help you address this *Learning Set's* question.

Examine a Case Study

A group of residents live on a small lake called Marry Martans Lake. The Marry Martans River flows into the lake at one end. The lake drains back into the river at the other end. (See the picture on the next page.) Over the past few months, the residents have noticed a lot of algae growing in the lake. The young people in the community know about water-quality indicators from their science classes. They remember that sudden algae and plant growth could be a sign of high amounts of fertilizer running off into the river.

The young people and their parents decide to investigate the case. Where might the fertilizer be coming from? They discover that there are three farms upriver. These farms are upstream from the lake and border the river.

Communicate Your Results

Investigation Expo

Scientists always share their understandings with each other. Presenting their results to others is one of the most important things that scientists do. You will share what you have found in an *Investigation Expo*. To prepare for this, you will use an overhead transparency.

Trace the diagram that you drew of your model onto an overhead transparency. Be ready to describe your investigation and clearly detail all your results. The answers to the following questions will be very helpful in preparing your presentation.

- Describe how the water moved in the model. (What patterns did you see?)
- Describe why you think your prediction was accurate or inaccurate.
- How did the outcome compare to your prediction?
- Where did the water flow more quickly? How was the flow different from what you predicted?
- Where did the water pool?

As you look at the overheads presented by other students, make sure you can answer these questions. Ask questions that you need answered to understand the results and the explanations others have made.

What's the Point?

In this section, you built a model to simulate how water flows across a landscape when it rains. Placing different-sized objects under the paper created the higher and lower elevations. You also drew a sketch of the model, and predicted how water will run over the paper. When you ran the simulation you probably noticed that the water always moved from areas of high elevation to areas of lower elevation. Water cannot move uphill. You also noticed that water flowed and created puddles in several places as it flowed. These puddles represent lakes or ponds in the real world.

Water on land works that way too. If you watch where rain falls in one rainstorm, you will be able to predict the path water will take in the next rainstorm. This is the case as long as the land stays the same from the first rainstorm to the next. You will need to consider how new construction in Wamego might change the land and affect how water flows.

20

4) Scientists…collaborate.

Scientists never do all their work alone. They work with other scientists (collaborate) and share their knowledge. *PBIS* helps students by giving them lots of opportunities for sharing their findings, ideas, and discoveries with others (the way scientists do). Students will work together in small groups to investigate, design, explain, and do other science activities. Sometimes they will work in pairs to figure out things together. They will also have lots of opportunities to share their findings with the rest of their classmates and make sense together of what they are learning.

Investigation Expo

In an *Investigation Expo*, small groups report to the class about an investigation they've done. For each *Investigation Expo*, students will make a poster detailing what they were trying to learn from their investigation, what they did, their data, and their interpretation of the data. The text gives them hints about what to present and what to look for in other groups' presentations. *Investigation Expos* are always followed by discussions about the investigations and about how to do science well. You may want to ask students to write a lab report following an investigation.

Plan Briefing/Solution Briefing/ Idea Briefing

Briefings are presentations of work in progress. They give students a chance to get advice from their classmates that can help them move forward. During a *Plan Briefing*, students present their plans to the class. They might be plans for an experiment for solving a problem or achieving a challenge. During a *Solution Briefing*, students present their solutions in progress and ask the class to help them make their solutions better. During an *Idea Briefing*, students present their ideas, including their evidence in support of their plans, solutions, or ideas. Often, they will prepare posters to help them make their presentation. Briefings are almost always followed by discussions of their investigations and how they will move forward.

Solution Showcase

Solution Showcases usually happen near the end of a Unit. During a *Solution Showcase*, students show their classmates their finished products—either their answer to a question or solution to a challenge. Students will also tell the class why they think it is a good answer or solution, what evidence and science they used to get to their solution, and what they tried along the way before getting to their answers or solutions. Sometimes a *Solution Showcase* is followed by a competition. It is almost always followed by a discussion comparing and contrasting the different answers and solutions groups have come up with. You may want to ask students to write a report or paper following a *Solution Showcase*.

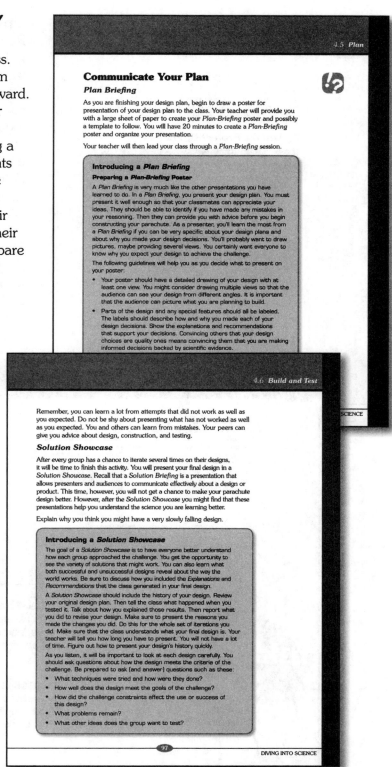

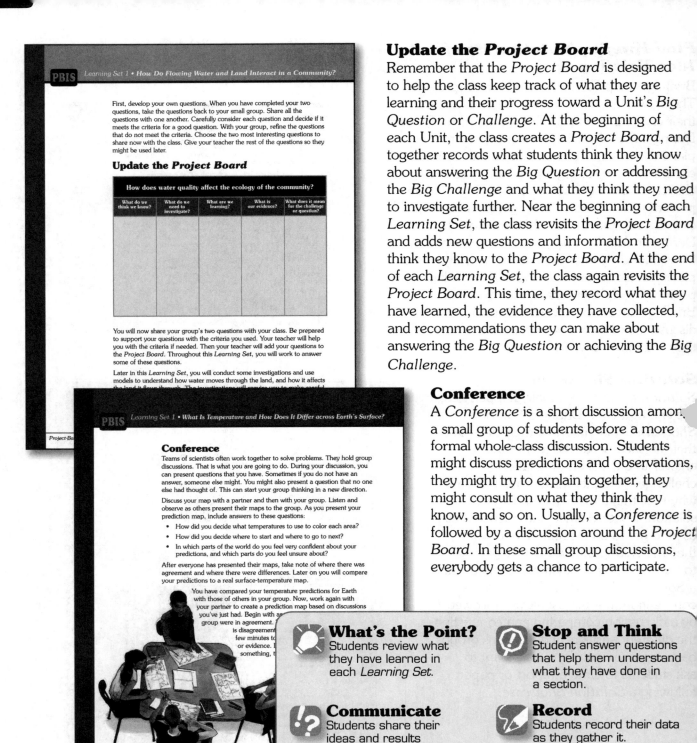

Update the *Project Board*

Remember that the *Project Board* is designed to help the class keep track of what they are learning and their progress toward a Unit's *Big Question* or *Challenge*. At the beginning of each Unit, the class creates a *Project Board*, and together records what students think they know about answering the *Big Question* or addressing the *Big Challenge* and what they think they need to investigate further. Near the beginning of each *Learning Set*, the class revisits the *Project Board* and adds new questions and information they think they know to the *Project Board*. At the end of each *Learning Set*, the class again revisits the *Project Board*. This time, they record what they have learned, the evidence they have collected, and recommendations they can make about answering the *Big Question* or achieving the *Big Challenge*.

Conference

A *Conference* is a short discussion among a small group of students before a more formal whole-class discussion. Students might discuss predictions and observations, they might try to explain together, they might consult on what they think they know, and so on. Usually, a *Conference* is followed by a discussion around the *Project Board*. In these small group discussions, everybody gets a chance to participate.

What's the Point?
Students review what they have learned in each *Learning Set*.

Stop and Think
Student answer questions that help them understand what they have done in a section.

Communicate
Students share their ideas and results with their classmates.

Record
Students record their data as they gather it.

NOTES

NOTES

UNIT OVERVIEW

Content

Astronomy is a physical science content unit. The *Big Question* for this Unit is *How Can You Know if Objects in Space Will Collide?* In the *Unit Introduction*, students read an account of a recent meteorite impact and observe collisions between objects in random and more orderly motion. Students set up a *Project Board* on which they will create a summary of what they know, what they need to investigate, what they are learning about any objects that may collide with Earth.

Learning Set 1 focuses on the effects of collisions. Students design experiments to investigate how the characteristics of an object and its motion affect the crater formed when it impacts a surface. Students explore the characteristics of craters on the Moon, use Earth-imaging software to search for and examine impact craters on Earth's surface, and compare and contrast lunar and Earth craters. Students read descriptions of the various bodies that comprise our solar system and an account of how the collision between Comet Shoemaker-Levy and the planet Jupiter was predicted. Students research an assigned solar-system body and consider the effects of a collision with 10-km diameter asteroid.

Next, students consider that in order to predict collisions with objects in space, the motions of those objects must be understood. In *Learning Set 2,* students read that early astronomers observed that objects observed in the sky have patterns of motion that are regular and predictable. Students focus on the regular and predictable motion of the Earth-Moon-Sun subsystem and the effects of those motions, such as phases of the moon, eclipses, and tides. Students develop a more concrete understanding of distances in the solar system and the relative sizes of solar system objects by creating a scale model of the Earth-Moon-Sun system and consider the theory that the Moon formed as the result of a collision between Earth and another large solar-system object.

In *Learning Set 3,* students move beyond the Earth-Moon-Sun system to investigate the sizes of other objects in the solar system, the distances between them, and how they move and interact. Students consider how building models of the solar system can help them better understand the relative scale and motion of the planets in the solar system. Students begin by researching different solar-system objects. They gather information that will serve as the basis for building scale models of the solar system and compare and contrast the characteristics of the inner and outer planets. The concept of scale is introduced in the context of determining an appropriate scale for a model of the solar system and choosing objects to represent the planets of the solar system. The class then creates a model of the solar system in which students physically represent planets and simulate orbital motion by walking around a central "Sun"

$55\frac{1}{2}$ *class periods*

A class period is considered to be one 40 to 50 minute class.

and analyze their simulation data to compare the planets' orbits, year length, and changing relative positions. Students read about the role of gravitational attraction in orbital motion and the historical development of the idea that the planets orbit the Sun in elliptical orbits. Students then use a different model of the solar system to simulate planets' orbital motions and determine their changing location against the background of stars in the sky as viewed from Earth. They then analyze data collected during the simulation to determine the role of perspective in the apparent retrograde motion of some planets when viewed from Earth, and the historical move from a geocentric to a heliocentric model of the solar system is described. Students read an account of the solar nebula theory of the formation of the solar system and how it accounts for the direction in which planets rotate and revolve, and their orbital plane. Students read about the characteristics of Near-Earth Objects and research parts of the solar system consisting of debris left over from its formation (Kuiper Belt, Trans-Neptunian Objects, Oort Cloud, and Centaur planets) and consider whether they are likely sources of an object that would collide with Earth. Students then consider the likelihood of a collision between solar system objects orbiting the Sun based on what they have learned about their motion.

In *Learning Set* 4 students expand their focus to consider objects outside the solar system that could collide with Earth. Students are reminded that Newton's laws of motion and gravity can be used to calculate the orbit of a newly discovered object and thereby determine its potential to collide with Earth. They read about the use of space probes, such as Voyager 1 and Voyager 2, to expand the scope of human observations of objects in the solar system and beyond and consider that what we know about the universe is based on our perception of the radiation emitted by stars and other objects in the universe. Students learn about factors that affect the apparent brightness of stars and how parallax is used to determine the distance to nearby stars. Students then focus on how information about the distances to stars and their positions relative to Earth can be used to construct a model of the Milky Way galaxy. The structure of the Milky Way galaxy is explored and the light year is introduced as a unit used to measure the vast distances between stars. Students read about the spectral analysis of starlight, the classification of stars into spectral classes, and how a Doppler shift in the light emitted by a star provides evidence of its motion relative to an observer on Earth. The development of the Hertzsprung-Russell diagram, how it contributed to our understanding of the structure and evolution of stars, the life cycles of different types of stars, and the potential danger to Earth posed by supernovae or black holes is described. Students examine the Shapley-Curtis debate about the size and structure of the universe and Hubble's use of Cepheid variables to establish that galaxies exist beyond the Milky Way galaxy. Students then examine images of 25 distant galaxies and develop a system to classify galaxies according to their structure. The *Learning Set* concludes with case studies of two space telescopes that are contributing to our knowledge and understanding of the universe: the Hubble Space Telescope and the Kepler Mission.

In *Answer the Big Question*, students assume the role of a science consultant to a movie producer and apply what they have learned throughout the Unit to write a report that includes a suggested collision between space objects that could be used as the basis for a popular movie, an explanation that will convince the movie producer that the collision is realistic, and a description of how the collision will look on-screen.

Investigations

In the *Unit Introduction*, students investigate collisions by comparing and contrasting the number of collisions between tennis balls in random and ordered motion. They also begin to understand the effects of collisions and what investigations they will need to do in order to answer the *Big Question* and then set up the *Project Board*.

In *Learning Set 1,* students mess about with collisions, simulating the impact between an object and the Moon's surface. They then design experiments to investigate how the characteristics of an object and its motion affect the crater formed when it impacts a surface. Students then analyze photographs of impact craters on the Moon and use Earth-imaging software to search for impact craters on Earth's surface and examine Earth's 25 largest meteor craters. Students then compare the appearance of meteor craters on Earth and impact craters on the Moon. Students analyze photographs of impact craters on Earth that have existed for different lengths of time. They then observe a fire syringe demonstration video that simulates the intense heating that occurs when a meteoroid compresses air in its path. Students then investigate solar system objects by performing Internet research.

In *Learning Set 2,* students investigate the regular, predictable motions of Earth and its Moon relative to the Sun and determine how the changing relative positions of Earth, the Moon, and the Sun account for the phases of the Moon, eclipses, and tides. Students analyze shadows cast by the Sun at different times of the day to plot the Sun's apparent path across the sky. Students then erect a gnomon on a globe representing Earth and, using a flashlight to represent the Sun, try to replicate the changes in the length and direction of the shadows they observed by either moving the globe, moving the flashlight, or moving both. Students investigate the Moon's apparent motion across the sky and the changes in its appearance by analyzing photographs of the Moon taken during the course of a day and over several weeks. They construct a model of the Earth-Moon-Sun system, simulate the Moon's revolution around Earth, and record the appearance of the Moon and the relative positions of the Earth, Moon, and Sun at the different phases of the Moon. Students then simulate the simultaneous rotation of a planet and revolution of a Moon for three different planets—Earth, X, and Y—and record their observations. Students construct a scale model of the Moon and Earth out of corresponding volumes of clay and investigate how the distance to an object affects how an observer perceives its size. They investigate the conditions that result in solar and lunar eclipses by simulating solar and lunar eclipses using a model of the Earth-Moon-Sun system.

In *Learning Set 3,* students move beyond the Earth-Moon-Sun system to investigate the sizes of other objects in the solar system, the distances between them, and how they move and interact. Students investigate other solar-system objects through research to obtain information that will serve as the basis for building solar-system models. They investigate the scale of the solar system and create a scale model showing the relative sizes and distances between the planets. The class investigates differences in the rate at which planets complete their orbit and the length of a year on planets at different distances from the Sun using a model representing planets and then simulate the orbital motion of the planets by walking along orbital paths around a central "Sun." Students then investigate how the planets' orbital motion causes their position to change relative to the fixed background of stars as viewed from Earth. They plot the changing positions of planets as they would appear to an observer on Earth on a *Planetary Orbit Simulation* chart, which is set up as a map of the solar system with major constellations plotted. In the *Back to the Big Question* section, students investigate parts of the solar system left over from its formation through research.

In *Learning Set 4,* students investigate objects outside the solar system that could collide with Earth. Students investigate factors that affect the apparent brightness of stars and determine that stars may look bright because they give off a lot of light, or because they are relatively close to Earth. Students also investigate how parallax is used to determine the distance to nearby stars. Students also investigate the structure of the Milky Way galaxy by analyzing an image of the Milky Way galaxy based on observations of the positions, distances, and motions of its stars, and consider the position of our solar system within the galaxy. Students observe a model that simulates the motion of stars in the Milky Way galaxy and experience the Doppler shift in a series of sound recordings made while a train is stationary, moving toward, and moving away from an observer. Students analyze images of 25 distant galaxies and develop a system to classify galaxies according to their structure and consider the possible effects of one galaxy colliding with another. They then investigate case studies of two space telescopes that are contributing to our knowledge and understanding of the universe: the Hubble Space Telescope and the Kepler Mission.

Nature of Science

Through repeated practice, students experience how scientists work together to refine their understanding and use what they know to answer important questions. To help students reflect on how their understanding grows through investigation just as scientists' understanding does, they set up a *Project Board* to keep a running record of what they know, what they need to investigate, their claims with the evidence they have to back these up, and how the information fits together to answer the *Big Question*. Throughout the Unit, students articulate changes in their conceptual understanding of science knowledge by completing *Create Your Explanation* pages. From the naked-eye observations of early astronomers, through the development of telescopes and spectroscopes to the deployment of space telescopes, students develop an appreciation for how technological advances extend the range and accuracy of human observations.

In *Learning Set 1*, students read about telescopic observations of the Moon ranging from Galileo's early discoveries to those made by Grove Karl Gilbert. In experiments similar to those run by Gilbert, they investigate factors affecting the craters formed when different types of objects impact a surface. They read that Eugene Shoemaker, a geologist, was the first scientist to recognize the possibility that craters on both Earth and on the Moon were caused by meteorite impacts. They also read about the observational work of Edmund Halley and Carolyn Shoemaker in tracking comets and the collision between Jupiter and a comet Carolyn Shoemaker, her husband Eugene, and David Levy had discovered a year earlier.

In *Learning Set 2*, students consider how technological advances enabled astronomers to improve upon the naked-eye observations of early astronomers. Using a variety of models, students follow the reasoning that led astronomers to their current understanding of the motions of the Earth-Moon-Sun system and the effects of those motions, such as phases of the moon, eclipses and tides.

In *Learning Set 3*, students trace the shift from the geocentric to the heliocentric model of the solar system. Students develop the understanding that scientific knowledge is subject to modification as new information challenges prevailing theories and new theories lead to looking at old observations in a new way by reading about the work of Ptolemy, Copernicus, Galileo, Brahe, Kepler, and Newton. Again, students make extensive use of models to simulate motions of solar-system objects, observe the effects of those motions, and consider alternate explanations for those observations.

In *Learning Set 4*, students develop the understanding that scientists collaborate and build upon the work of others by studying Annie Jump Cannon's painstaking work analyzing stellar spectra and categorizing stars into spectral classes provided the basis for Einar Hertzsprung and Henry Norris Russell's discovery of a relationship between the brightness of stars and the temperature of stars. They read how the pulsars discovered by Jocelyn Bell Burnell and Antony Hewish in 1967 were later proven to be neutron stars, and the work of Subrahmanyan Chandrasekhar on the structure of stars contributed to our current understanding of stellar evolution. To reinforce the concept that scientific knowledge is subject to modifications, students read an account of the famous 1920 debate between astronomers Harlow Shapley and Heber Curtis about whether nebulae were within the Milky Way galaxy or whether they were separate galaxies. They then read about how Edwin Hubble built on

Henrietta Swan Leavitt's work with Cepheid variable stars to prove that galaxies existed beyond the Milky Way, afterwards developing a classification system for galaxies. The work of these scientists also traces the steady expansion in humans' perception of the limits of the universe.

Artifacts

In the *Unit Introduction*, students keep a record of the collisions observed in a video and during the *Tennis Ball Demolition Derby*. Students set up the *Project Board* to help them keep track of what they know, what they need to investigate, their claims and the evidence they have to back these up, and how the information fits together to answer the *Big Question*. Throughout the Unit, students keep a written record of their responses to *Stop and Think* and *Reflect* questions.

In *Learning Set 1*, students keep a record of their observations of the craters formed when various objects impact a tub of flour covered with a colored powder. The *Impact Crater Planning Guide* page and *Impact Crater Experiment Results Guide* are a record of how students planned and organized their experiments, and the data collected to determine factors that affect the crater formed by a collision. Students create a graph of the data collected during their experiment. Students then create a class presentation to share the results and analysis of their investigation with other groups in an *Investigation Expo*. The *Solar System* pages contain a summary of information about solar-system objects that is used to construct models and predict the likelihood of a collision, and are used throughout the Unit. The *Big Question* page also is used throughout the Unit and is a record of information about evidence of past collisions and chances of future collisions that will be useful for their report at the end of the Unit.

In *Learning Set 2*, students keep a record of their observations of the Sun and shadows on a *Sundial Patterns* page. Students keep their sketches and written descriptions of what they did with the globe and the flashlight to simulate the pattern of shadow directions on a sundial during three investigations. The *Create Your Explanation* pages are a record of students' developing concept of the factors affecting the likelihood and effects of collisions and the structure and composition of the universe. Students keep records of the changes in the Moon's appearance and position in the sky over different periods of time. The *Phases of the Moon* page is a record of students' observations of the positions of Earth, the Sun, and the Moon at different phases. Students also develop a class presentation of their analyses of the phases that would be observed on Planets X, Y, and Earth. Students create clay models of Earth and the Moon and keep a written record of their calculations of distances between the Earth, Moon, and Sun. Students also keep sketches of the relative positions of the Earth, Moon, and Sun recorded during their simulations of solar and lunar eclipses.

In *Learning Set 3*, students create posters to share their research findings about solar-system objects with the class. Students keep a record of the calculations of scale and scale factors made when determining the appropriate scale for a model of the solar system. The *Solar-System Model* page contains a record of the actual and calculated scale values for the diameter and distances from the Sun to the planets in our solar system. Students also keep a record of the observations made when they simulated how several planets orbit the Sun. The *Planet Simulation* page and *Planetary Observations* page provide a record of students' investigation of the changes in planets' positions relative to one another and the background of stars when viewed from Earth. Students keep research findings and materials developed for their class presentation about a part of the solar system other than the eight planets and the asteroid belt.

In *Learning Set 4*, students keep a written record of their analysis of the photograph of light sources and their observations of the pupil of their eye after exposure to different periods of light and dark. The *Parallax View* page is a record of observations, data and data analysis computations made during students' investigations into how parallax is used to determine a star's distance from Earth. Students also should keep a record of their analysis of the table of the 25 brightest stars as seen from Earth and the 25 closest stars to Earth. Students keep a written record of observations made during the demonstrations of galactic motion and the Doppler shift. Students also keep a written record of the system they developed to classify galaxies and their class presentation of their classification of galaxies. They also keep notes made while viewing the NASA videos of the Hubble and Kepler Mission space telescopes and create a class presentation that describes their ideal space mission. Students then create a poster that gives the details of a collision between two objects in space

In *Answer the Big Question*, students write a report for a movie producer consisting of three parts: a proposed collision between objects in space for a movie script, an explanation of why the collision is realistic for use in a popular movie, and a description of what the collision will look like on screen.

Targeted Concepts, Skills, and Nature of Science	Section
Scientific knowledge is developed through observations, recording and analysis of data, and development of explanations based on evidence.	All sections
Scientists must keep clear, accurate, and descriptive records of what they do so they can share their work with others; consider what they did, why they did it, and what they want to do next.	All sections

Targeted Concepts, Skills, and Nature of Science	Section
Scientists often collaborate and share their findings. Sharing findings makes new information available and helps scientists refine their ideas and build on others' ideas. When another person's or group's idea is used, credit needs to be given.	All sections
Scientific questions are directed toward objects and events that can be described, explained, or predicted by scientific investigations.	Unit Intro
In a reliable investigation, only the manipulated (independent) variable and the responding (dependent) variable change. All other variables are held constant.	1.2
Observations and measurements are considered reliable if the results are repeatable by other scientists using the same procedures.	1.2
Scientists make claims (conclusions) based on evidence obtained (trends in data) from reliable investigations.	1.2, 1.5, 1.BBQ
Explanations are claims supported by evidence. Evidence can be experimental results, observational data, and any other accepted scientific knowledge.	1.5, 2.2, 2.3, 1-4.BBQ
Large numbers of chunks of rock revolve around the Sun. Some may meet Earth as it revolves around the Sun, plunge through Earth's atmosphere, glow and disintegrate due to friction and sometimes impact the ground.	Unit Intro
Impacts of solar-system bodies have created extensive cratering on the Moon and on other bodies in the solar system. Some craters can also be found on Earth, but most have been destroyed by the processes of plate tectonics, and/or the weathering, erosion, and deposition occurring at Earth's planetary surface.	1.2, 1.3, 1.4, 1.5
Meteoroids are small solar-system objects with the potential to collide with Earth. Most meteoroids that strike Earth's atmosphere rapidly burn up due to friction with the atmosphere resulting in a visible meteor. Those that survive and strike Earth as meteorites are fragmented and destroyed by the impact.	1.6

Targeted Concepts, Skills, and Nature of Science	Section
Comets leave behind grains of dust and ions. The dust and ions can be illuminated by the Sun as huge tails. If Earth passes through the trails of dust left behind, the particles rapidly burn up due to friction with the atmosphere, causing a meteor shower.	1.7
The Sun, the planets that revolve around it, and their moons, are the major bodies in the solar system. Other members that orbit the Sun include dwarf planets and small solar-system bodies, such as asteroids and comets.	Unit Intro, 1.7, 1.BBQ
The Moon orbits Earth, while Earth orbits the Sun. Except for the Sun, all objects in the solar system are seen by reflected light. The Moon's orbit around Earth, once in about 28 days, changes what part of the Moon is lighted by the Sun and how much of that part can be seen from Earth—the phases of the moon. The phases repeat in a cyclic pattern in about one month.	2.3
An object's apparent size depends on its distance from the observer.	2.4
An eclipse of the Moon occurs when the Moon enters Earth's shadow. An eclipse of the Sun occurs when the Moon is between Earth and the Sun, and the Moon's shadow falls on Earth.	2.5
Tides, or the cyclic rise and fall of ocean waters, are caused by the gravitational pulls of the Moon and (to a lesser extent) the Sun, as well as the rotation of Earth.	2.5
Enormous distances separate the objects in the solar system. Astronomical units and light years are measures of distances between the Sun, Earth, and the stars.	3.2
Natural phenomena often involve sizes, durations, and speeds that are extremely small or extremely large. These phenomena may be difficult to appreciate because they involve magnitudes far outside human experience.	3.2
A year is the time it takes a planet to complete one revolution around the Sun. Earth's revolution around the Sun defines the length of an Earth year as 365.25 days.	3.3
The path of a planet around the Sun is due to the gravitational attraction between the Sun and the planet.	3.3

10

Targeted Concepts, Skills, and Nature of Science	Section
The planets move around the Sun in elliptical orbits at predictable, but varying, speeds.	3.3
Different stars can be seen at different times of the year and planets change their positions against the background of stars over time.	3.4
Long ago, people thought all objects in the universe revolved around Earth (geocentric model) until scientists proved that Earth and the other planets revolve around the Sun (heliocentric model).	3.4
The apparent motions of the Sun, Moon, planets, and stars across the sky can be explained by Earth's rotation and revolution.	3.4
When viewed from Earth, stars remain in fixed positions relative to one another as they appear to move across the sky. Constellations are imaginary patterns of stars used by observers to track changes in the positions of objects viewed in the sky.	3.4
Around the planets orbit a great variety of moons. Flat rings of rock and ice debris orbit some planets, a large number of asteroids orbit the Sun between the orbits of Mars and Jupiter, and Earth is orbited by a moon and artificial satellites.	3.5, 3.BBQ
Our solar system coalesced out of a giant cloud of gas and debris about five billion years ago. The Sun formed when gas and debris heated up from the energy of falling together began releasing nuclear energy from the fusion of light elements into heavier ones in its extremely hot, dense core.	3.5
Stars that are relatively close to our solar system appear to shift slightly in their position relative to distant stars when viewed from different positions, an effect known as parallax. The parallax of a star can be used to calculate its distance from Earth.	4.2
Astronomical units and light years are measures of distances between the Sun, Earth, and the stars.	4.3
Other stars are like the Sun but are so far away that they look like points of light. Distances between stars are vast compared to distances within our solar system. Light from the Sun takes a few minutes to reach Earth, but light from the next nearest star takes a few years to arrive.	4.3

Targeted Concepts, Skills, and Nature of Science	Section
Our Sun is a medium-sized star within a spiral galaxy of stars known as the Milky Way.	4.3
The Doppler shift is the shift in wavelength of a spectrum line away from its normal wavelength caused by motion of the observer toward or away from the source. If the source is approaching the observer, there is a blueshift toward shorter wavelengths of light. If the source is moving away from the observer, there is a redshift towards longer wavelengths of light.	4.4
Different wavelengths of the electromagnetic spectrum such as light and radio waves are used to gain information about distances and properties of components of the universe.	4.5
Stars differ from each other in size, temperature, and age.	4.5
Stars form when gravity causes clouds of molecules to contract until nuclear fusion of light elements into heavier ones occurs. Fusion releases great amounts of energy over millions of years.	4.5
The Hertzsprung-Russell diagram shows the relationship between the luminosity and temperature of stars. The majority of stars lie on a diagonal band that extends from hot stars of high luminosity in the upper left corner to cool stars of low luminosity in the lower right corner. This band is called the main sequence.	4.5
Components of the universe include stars, galaxies, and nebulae.	4.6
Some distant galaxies are so far away that their light takes several billions of years to reach Earth.	4.6
The universe is vast and estimated to be over ten billion years old. The current theory is that the universe was created from an explosion called the Big Bang. A redshift (the Doppler shift) in the light from very distant galaxies provides evidence for this theory.	4.6
The planets of the solar system vary in size, composition, and surface features.	3.1, 3.2

Targeted Concepts, Skills, and Nature of Science	Section
The rotation of Earth on its axis every 24 hours produces the night-and-day cycle. To people on Earth, this turning of the planet makes it seem as though the Sun, Moon, planets, and stars are orbiting Earth once a day. This rotation also causes the Sun and Moon to appear to rise along the eastern horizon and to set along the western horizon. Earth's revolution around the Sun defines the length of the year as 365.25 days.	2.1, 2.2, 2.3
Humankind's need to explore continues to lead to the development of knowledge and understanding of the nature of the universe.	3.5, 4.7
Some stars appear brighter than others. Stars may look bright because they give off a lot of light, or because they are relatively close to Earth.	4.1, 4.2
Earth's Sun is the central and largest body in our solar system. The Sun is more than a million times greater in volume than Earth. Earth is the third planet from the Sun in a system that includes other planets and their moons, as well as smaller objects, such as asteroids and comets.	2.4, 3.1, 3.2, 3.BBQ
Most objects in the solar system have a regular and predictable motion. These motions explain such phenomena as a day, a year, phases of the Moon, eclipses, tides, meteor showers, and comets.	1.7, 1.BBQ, 2.1, 2.2, 2.3, 2.5, 2.BBQ
Humans perceive the universe by the radiation it emits. Technological advances have greatly extended the scope of human perception and led to the observations upon which our current theories of the universe are based.	4.1, 4.2, 4.7
A galaxy is a system of stars, cosmic dust, and gas held together by gravitation. Galaxies typically contain billions of stars, may have different shapes, and may be thousands of light-years in diameter; the universe contains billions of such galaxies.	4.3, 4.4, 4.6
Models are a representation of something in the world. Simulations use a model to imitate, or act out, real-life situations.	2.2, 2.3, 2.4, 2.5, 3.1, 3.2, 3.3, 4.2, 4.4

Unit Materials List

Quantities for 5 classes of 8 groups.		
Unit Durable Classroom Items	**Section**	**Quantity**
Rectangular tub	1.1, 1.2	1
Metric ruler, in./cm	1.1, 1.2, 2.4, 3.2, 3.4, 4.2	1
Meter stick	1.1, 1.2, 2.4	1
Foam ball, 5 cm	2.3	1
Ball, 6 in.	2.3, 2.5	1

Quantities based on groups of 4-6 students.		
Unit Durable Classroom Items	**Section**	**Quantity**
Flour, 5 lb	1.1, 1.2	2
Project Board, laminated	1.1, 1.3, 1.4, 1.5, 1.6, 1.7, 1.BBQ, 2.1, 2.2, 2.3, 2.BBQ, 3.1, 3.2, 3.3, 3.4, 3.5, 4.1, 4.4, 4.6, 4.BBQ	5
Project Board transparency	1.1, 1.3, 1.4, 1.5, 1.6, 1.7, 1.BBQ, 2.1, 2.2, 2.3, 2.BBQ, 3.1, 3.2, 3.3, 3.4, 3.5, 4.1, 4.4, 4.6, 4.BBQ	1
Push pins, pkg. of 100	1.4	1
Earth Science Content DVD	1.6	1
Modeling clay	2.2, 2.4	4
Flashlight	2.2, 2.5	1
Globe, tilt-mounted, 12 in.	2.2, 2.5	1
Wood splints, pkg. of 500	2.2, 2.3	1

Quantities based on groups of 4-6 students.		
Unit Durable Classroom Items	**Section**	**Quantity**
Toothpicks, pkg. of 100	2.4	1
Glass beaker, 250mL	4.4	1

Quantities for classes of 8 groups.		
Unit Consumable Classroom Items	**Section**	**Quantity**
Colored markers, set of 8 colors	1.2, 1.BBQ, 3.1	6
Restickable Easel Pad	1.2, 1.BBQ, 3.1	3
Unlined index cards, 3 in. x 5 in., pkg. of 100	1.4	1
D-cell alkaline battery	2.2, 2.5	4
Masking tape	3.3, 4.2	6
Planetary Orbit Simulation chart, 11 in. x 11 in.	3.4	3

NOTES

....

....

....

....

....

....

Unit Materials List

Additional Items Needed Not Supplied	Section	Quantity
Cocoa powder (for sprinkling)	1.1, 1.2	1 tsp per group
Objects for impact testing, such as erasers, wads of paper, coins, etc.	1.1, 1.2	1 set per group
Map of your region	1.3	1 per pair
Computer and monitor	1.4	2 per group
Earth-imaging software	1.4	2 per group
Access to the Internet, library, or any other information-gathering medium	1.BBQ, 3.1	1 per class
Pencil or pen	3.4	1 per group
Bright light source (to represent the Sun)	2.3	1 per group
Apple	3.2	1 per group
Calculator	3.2	1 per group
Peppercorn	3.2, 3.4	1 per group
Objects for solar-system model	3.2, 3.4	1 object per group
Access to open outdoor area	3.2	1 per class
Access to open area	3.3, 3.3	1 per class
Watch or clock with second hand	4.2	1 per class
Objects A,B,C placed on desks	4.2	1 set per class
Access to water	4.4	1 per class
Ground pepper flakes	4.4	1 per class
Projector	4.4	1 per class

What's the Big Question?

How Can You Know if Objects in Space Will Collide?

◀ *1 class period*

A class period is considered to be one 40 to 50 minute class.

Overview

The *Big Question* of Astronomy, *How Can You Know if Objects in Space Will Collide?*, is introduced in a reading about the makeup of the solar system and the many movies, television programs, and books about the threat of a collision between Earth and an object from space. A distinction is made between science fiction and science fact, and students consider how astronomers answer questions based on facts gathered by making observations and collecting data. Students then consider how they could answer the *Big Question* by gathering facts and performing experiments.

Students read an account of a recent meteorite impact and view a short video of collisions in action. Students meet in small groups to discuss what they observed in the video and share their ideas about factors that they think influence the outcome of a collision. The class then engages in an activity in which they observe the number of collisions that occur among tennis balls when they are moving randomly and when their motion is more organized. Students share their results with the class and consider how they relate to the *Big Question*.

Students then set up a *Project Board* on which they will create a summary of what they know, what they need to investigate, what they are learning about any objects in the solar system that may collide with Earth along with supporting evidence, and how what they are learning can help them address the *Big Question*.

NOTES

....

....

....

....

Targeted Concepts, Skills, and Nature of Science	Performance Expectations
Scientists often collaborate and share their findings. Sharing findings makes new information available and helps scientists refine their ideas and build on others' ideas. When another person's or group's idea is used, credit needs to be given.	Students share their ideas about factors that influence the outcome of collisions between objects after viewing the collision video. Students share the number of collisions that occur when their tennis ball is involved in random and in ordered motion. Students participate in a class discussion as they create their *Project Board,* which is an organizing record of their ideas and what they are learning.
Scientists must keep clear, accurate, and descriptive records of what they do so they can share their work with others; consider what they did, why they did it, and what they want to do next.	Students keep notes while reading and record their answers to questions posed in the student text. A record is also kept of ideas shared during conferences. Students record the number of collisions that occur between their tennis ball and others when involved in random motion and in ordered motion. Students create a *Project Board* on which they record their ideas and what they are learning.
Scientific questions are directed toward objects and events that can be described, explained, or predicted by scientific investigations.	Students formulate questions that can be answered through scientific investigations as they create the *Project Board.*
The solar system consists of the Sun and all of the planets, comets, asteroids, and other bodies that revolve around it.	Students are able to identify the objects that comprise the solar system.
Large numbers of chunks of rock revolve around the Sun. Some may meet Earth as it revolves around the Sun, plunge through Earth's atmosphere, glow and disintegrate due to friction and sometimes impact the ground.	Students are able to cite evidence that the Peekskill meteorite was a rock from space that collided with Earth.

Materials	
1 per student	Tennis ball
1 per class	*Collision* video
several per class	Trailers from movies in which Earth is threatened by a collision with an object from space

Activity Setup and Preparation

When obtaining tennis balls for each student, you might consider using tennis balls of several colors so that it is easier for students to track their tennis ball as it collides with others. Prepackaging the materials for groups speeds distribution and collection. Consider how and where to clear a large enough area in your classroom so that students can sit in a circle on the ground for the *Tennis Ball Demolition Derby.*

Homework Options

Reflection

- **Science Process:** Do you think the motion of the objects that make up our solar system is random or organized? Give reasons for why you think so. Do you think this makes it more or less likely that Earth will collide with an object from space?

Preparation for 1.1

- **Science Content:** You have read about the effects of the impact of the Peekskill meteorite. What do you think would have happened if the meteorite had been ten times larger? If it was moving faster?

NOTES

UNIT INTRODUCTION IMPLEMENTATION

What's the Big Question?

How Can You Know if Objects in Space Will Collide?

You have spent every day of your life on the planet called Earth. Without leaving Earth, you wake up, go to school, sleep, work, and play. Every day the Sun appears to move across the sky and then moves below the horizon as night approaches. You know that the Sun is very important to life on Earth. But Earth and the Sun are just two of the many important objects in our **solar system**. The solar system is like Earth's neighborhood. This neighborhood includes the Sun, eight planets and their moons, and all the other bodies that **revolve** around the Sun.

What other solar-system objects do you know about? What do **astronomers**, the scientists who study space and objects in space, know about the movements of these objects, and how do they predict these movements? How can they use their predictions to learn more?

Scientists learn about the solar system by making observations and collecting data. Astronomers, and other scientists, are gaining exciting new knowledge every day through the use of powerful telescopes and space probes speeding through the solar system.

Whenever scientists collect data, they are trying to answer questions. One question for astronomers today is how the objects in our solar system formed. In space, beyond our solar system, scientists have learned about stars. They have also observed places where stars and other planetary systems form.

Many movies, television shows, and books have featured the idea of objects from space colliding with Earth. In some of these stories, people and countries unite to stop a collision with Earth, and the world is saved. In others, the results of these collisions are disastrous and life on Earth is forever changed. All of these movies, television programs, and books are *science fiction,* or made-up stories that describe possible events resulting from advances in science or technology. Other stories are set in imaginary environments, such as alien planets or other solar systems.

solar system: a Sun and the planets, comets, asteroids, and other bodies that revolve around it.

revolve: to move in a curved path determined by gravity of another object.

astronomer: a scientist who studies space and objects in space.

AST 3

ASTRONOMY

What's the Big Question?

How Can You Know if Objects in Space Will Collide?

5 min

Students are introduced to the Big Question *of the Unit.*

○ Engage

Consider showing a movie trailer from a film in which Earth is threatened by a collision with an object from space. Ask students to recall any other movies, television programs, or books with a similar story line. Ask students whether Earth was saved or devastated in the story.

*A class period is considered to be one 40 to 50 minute class.

"What movies or television programs have you seen, or what books have you read that involved an object from space on a collision course with Earth? What happened in the story? Was disaster prevented or did the object collide with Earth?"

△ Guide

Introduce the *Big Question* by reading the introduction with students. Emphasize that our solar system consists of objects that orbit the Sun and that Earth is only one of many objects that do so. Ask students to share what they know about other objects they think orbit the Sun and make a class list of their ideas. At this point, students may only cite planets or their moons. Accept all answers, but point out that they will learn about the many different types of objects that make up the solar system as they address the *Big Question* in this Unit.

Ask students whether they think any of the stories they described earlier are true. Guide students to distinguish between science fiction and science fact by discussing the definition of a fact and how facts are established in science.

NOTES

....

....

....

....

....

....

....

Are collisions with objects from space a real threat? If so, can anything be done to prevent these collisions from happening? What objects have the potential to collide? To answer these questions, you must be able to separate science fact from science fiction. Facts are evidence that can be used to support or oppose a hypothesis or explanation. Fiction is invented in someone's imagination. The purpose of fiction is to entertain people. Scientists work only with facts.

In this Unit, you will gather facts and perform investigations to help you answer this *Big Question: How Can You Know if Objects in Space Will Collide?*

Welcome to Astronomy.
Enjoy your journey as a student scientist.

AST 4

Project-Based Inquiry Science

Ask students to share their answers to the questions:

- Are collisions with objects from space a real threat?

- Can anything be done to prevent these collisions from occurring?

- What objects have the potential to collide with Earth?

Students may not know the answers to these questions or may be unsure of their answers. Guide students to recognize that they will need to gather facts and evidence in order to answer such questions, and have confidence in those answers. Make sure students understand that the *Big Question* will serve as the framework for all of the investigations and readings in the Unit.

NOTES

_____

_____

_____

_____

_____

_____

_____

_____

_____

_____

_____

_____

_____

_____

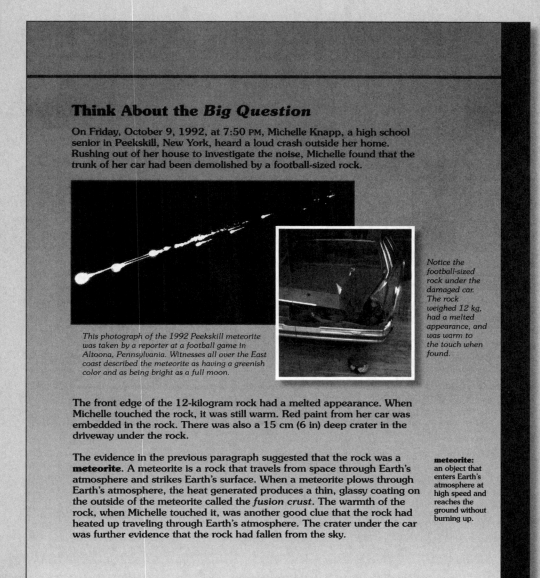

Think About the *Big Question*

On Friday, October 9, 1992, at 7:50 PM, Michelle Knapp, a high school senior in Peekskill, New York, heard a loud crash outside her home. Rushing out of her house to investigate the noise, Michelle found that the trunk of her car had been demolished by a football-sized rock.

This photograph of the 1992 Peekskill meteorite was taken by a reporter at a football game in Altoona, Pennsylvania. Witnesses all over the East coast described the meteorite as having a greenish color and as being bright as a full moon.

Notice the football-sized rock under the damaged car. The rock weighed 12 kg, had a melted appearance, and was warm to the touch when found.

The front edge of the 12-kilogram rock had a melted appearance. When Michelle touched the rock, it was still warm. Red paint from her car was embedded in the rock. There was also a 15 cm (6 in) deep crater in the driveway under the rock.

The evidence in the previous paragraph suggested that the rock was a **meteorite**. A meteorite is a rock that travels from space through Earth's atmosphere and strikes Earth's surface. When a meteorite plows through Earth's atmosphere, the heat generated produces a thin, glassy coating on the outside of the meteorite called the *fusion crust*. The warmth of the rock, when Michelle touched it, was another good clue that the rock had heated up traveling through Earth's atmosphere. The crater under the car was further evidence that the rock had fallen from the sky.

meteorite: an object that enters Earth's atmosphere at high speed and reaches the ground without burning up.

AST 5

Think About the *Big Question*

5 min

Students read an account of an actual meteorite impact and discuss their ideas.

△ Guide

Have students read the account of the Peekskill meteorite impact. Ask students to describe the evidence that supports the idea that the damage to Michelle Knapp's car was caused by a meteorite. Guide students to connect the effects of a meteorite traveling at high speed through the atmosphere with the direct (warmth, crater) and indirect evidence (nearby observations of streak, video of fireball) described in the account.

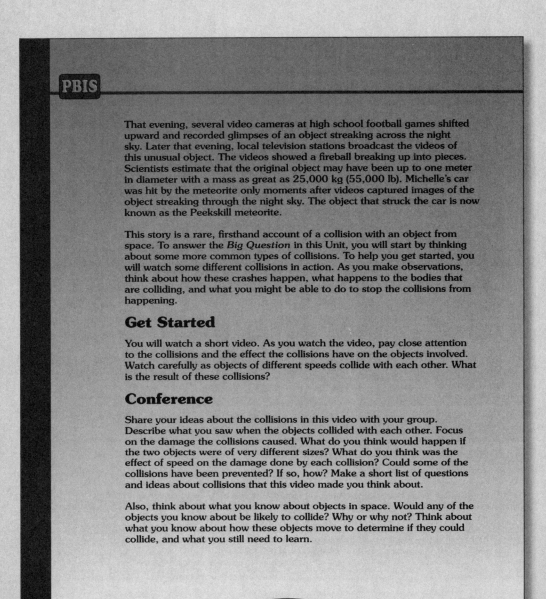

That evening, several video cameras at high school football games shifted upward and recorded glimpses of an object streaking across the night sky. Later that evening, local television stations broadcast the videos of this unusual object. The videos showed a fireball breaking up into pieces. Scientists estimate that the original object may have been up to one meter in diameter with a mass as great as 25,000 kg (55,000 lb). Michelle's car was hit by the meteorite only moments after videos captured images of the object streaking through the night sky. The object that struck the car is now known as the Peekskill meteorite.

This story is a rare, firsthand account of a collision with an object from space. To answer the *Big Question* in this Unit, you will start by thinking about some more common types of collisions. To help you get started, you will watch some different collisions in action. As you make observations, think about how these crashes happen, what happens to the bodies that are colliding, and what you might be able to do to stop the collisions from happening.

Get Started

You will watch a short video. As you watch the video, pay close attention to the collisions and the effect the collisions have on the objects involved. Watch carefully as objects of different speeds collide with each other. What is the result of these collisions?

Conference

Share your ideas about the collisions in this video with your group. Describe what you saw when the objects collided with each other. Focus on the damage the collisions caused. What do you think would happen if the two objects were of very different sizes? What do you think was the effect of speed on the damage done by each collision? Could some of the collisions have been prevented? If so, how? Make a short list of questions and ideas about collisions that this video made you think about.

Also, think about what you know about objects in space. Would any of the objects you know about be likely to collide? Why or why not? Think about what you know about how these objects move to determine if they could collide, and what you still need to learn.

AST 6

Project-Based Inquiry Science

Ask students if they think events like this are rare and to give evidence from the reading to support their answers. Ask students to think about the difference between an event being rare and a firsthand account of an event being rare. Guide students to understand that the majority of Earth's surface is not within sight of a human observer. Therefore, occurrences of the event may be less rare than firsthand experiences of the event.

"The passage you just read is described as a "rare-firsthand account."
What is meant by rare? If a *firsthand account* of an event is rare, why is
it not logical to assume that the event rarely occurs?**"**

Remind students that the challenge of the *Big Question* is to determine how
to know if a collision is going to occur. Point out that in order to predict
a collision, they will need to understand how and why collisions occur.
Therefore, they will begin to study collisions by actually observing some
colliding objects.

◯ Get Going

Before viewing the video, have students read the directions and ask them
to identify what it is that they will be looking for in the video. Make sure
students understand that they should be focusing on the characteristics of
the objects before they collide (size, direction of motion, speed, etc.) and
the effects of the collisions on the objects and their motion.

Show the video once and have students record their observations. Then
ask students to think about what they would like to observe more carefully
either because it occurred so quickly or because they didn't focus on it in
the first viewing. Then show the video a second time and have students
record their observations.

◯ Get Going

Have students read the instructions and the questions that will be the focus
of their small group discussion. Emphasize that they should take turns
sharing their observations and ideas with the other members of the group.

Ask students to work collaboratively in their groups to discuss the effects
of size, speed, and direction of motion of the two objects before and after
colliding, and the damage caused by the collision. Make clear that they
should keep a written record of their group's ideas and responses.

Ask students to consider what they know about the motion of objects in
space and what they need to know in order to predict the likelihood that
they will collide with Earth.

Get Started

10 min

*Students view a video
of collisions between
objects and consider the
effects of a collision on
the objects involved.*

Conference

10 min

*Students share their
ideas about the
collisions in the video
and how different
factors affect collisions.
Students then create
a list of ideas and
questions they have as
a result of viewing the
collisions in the video.*

Communicate: Share Your Ideas

5 min

Groups share their ideas about space and collisions with the class.

Communicate

Share Your Ideas

Share your questions and ideas about collisions with the class. Make a list of questions so that you will be able to remember them. Share your ideas and questions about objects from space that might collide. List those as well so you will remember them clearly.

Tennis Ball Demolition Derby

Cars in a demolition derby crash into each other, resulting in loud noises, dented metal, and jolts to the drivers. These collisions differ depending on how fast the cars are moving and how they strike one another. To help you answer some of your questions about collisions, you will explore the motion of tennis balls as they collide.

You will consider two types of motion: *random motion* and *ordered motion*. Each person in your class will roll a ball and you will make observations about the differences in the collisions when the motion is random and when it is somewhat organized. Each time you roll the balls, they will have a chance to collide. As you watch each type of motion, pay attention to how predictable the collisions are.

Materials
- tennis balls, 1 per student

Predict

Before doing the activity, read the entire procedure and predict which trial will have more collisions. Make predictions, too, about where collisions will occur and which trial might have more violent collisions.

Procedure

1. Each person in your class will get one ball. With your classmates, sit in a large circle. Without speaking or letting anyone know where you are going to roll the ball, choose a person in the circle, and prepare to roll the ball to them. When you hear the count, "Three, two, one, go!" all the balls should be rolled at the same time. Observe the movement of your ball and count the number of collisions your ball makes as it rolls along the floor. Write this number on a piece of paper and label it "Trial 1."

AST 7

ASTRONOMY

⬡ Get Going

Have groups take turns sharing their ideas with the class. They should discuss the ideas that their group agreed on and those that they disagreed on. Make a class list as students share their ideas.

⬡ Get Going

Have students read the introduction to the activity, then lead a brief discussion of the difference between random and ordered motion.

△ Guide

Have students read the entire procedure. Make sure students understand that in this investigation they will observe collisions between tennis balls in two different trials: one in which the tennis balls are moving randomly and one in which their motion is more organized.

Point out that in Trial 1, they will not know to whom each student will be rolling their ball, but in Trial 2 they will know each student's target. Ask students to consider how knowing the intended path of each ball could help them make their predictions. How might a diagram be of help?

Make clear to students that they should predict which trial will involve more collisions, where in the circle they think the greatest number of collisions will occur, and how violent they think the collisions will be. Have students record all of their predictions.

Review the steps of the procedure with the class, making sure that they understand how they will be creating random and ordered motions. Students should also understand that in both trials they are to observe the movement of their ball and the number of collisions it makes as it rolls along the floor. Clear a large area in the classroom and have students form a large circle, each student facing toward the center of the circle.

NOTES

....

....

....

....

....

Tennis Ball Demolition Derby

15 min

Students observe and then compare and contrast the number of collisions between tennis balls in random and ordered motion.

2. Then, repeat the same exercise, but this time you will roll a ball to one specific classmate, and *another* classmate will roll a ball to you. To start, each person will be given a number. You will count that number of places away from you, moving clockwise (left) around the circle. For example, if you were given the number *ten*, you would count ten places away from you, starting with the person on your left. You would roll the ball to the tenth person. Be sure the correct person knows he or she is receiving the ball from you. A different person will be rolling the ball to you. Check with that person, too. On the count of *three*, all the balls should be rolled at the same time. Observe the movement of your ball and count the collisions your ball makes as it rolls across the floor. Write this number on a piece of paper and label it "Trial 2."

!? Communicate

Share Your Results

Record on the board each student's count of the number of collisions in Trial 1 and Trial 2. As a class, compare the total number of collisions that occurred in Trial 1 with the total number in Trial 2. Also, look at the data to see if there are any trends. Discuss any differences in the timing or nature of the collisions during the two rolls.

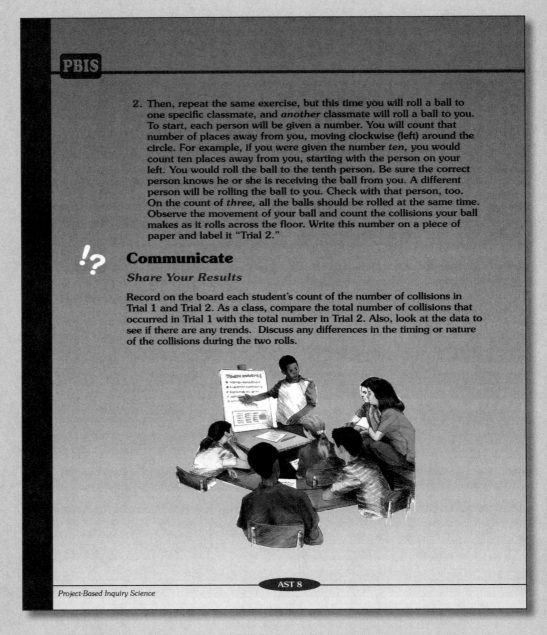

AST 8

After students are settled, distribute a tennis ball to each student and ask them to secretly choose another person in the circle. Tell students that at your signal, they should gently roll their ball to the person they have chosen. Make clear that they should count the number of times their ball collides with another as it rolls along the floor. They should also observe and record the locations and violence of the collisions.

Have students roll their ball and record the person toward which they rolled their ball as well as the number, location, and violence of collisions their ball experienced as "Trial 1." Next, assign the class a number. Then have students count clockwise from their position to find the person to whom they will roll their ball. The number should be a little less than half the number of students in the circle. For example, for a 30-person circle the number could be 12. Make sure that every student in the circle knows both their target and the person for whom they are the target.

Repeat the procedure used in the first trial for rolling the ball and counting collisions. Have students record the number, location, and violence of collisions their ball experienced as "Trial 2."

△ Guide

Point out why it is important for each group to share their information with the class. Because this is the first *Communicate* in this *Learning Set,* review the basic etiquette of group interaction. Emphasize the importance of not interrupting while another student is sharing, and of interacting respectfully during group discussions. Encourage students to ask nonjudgmental questions when they think something important has been left out or if they do not understand something.

As students share their results for the two trials, create a list of the class results and have students record this list in their science notebooks. Ask students to compare the total number of collisions in each trial and to examine the individual results of each trial for any data trends.

Lead a class discussion focusing on the nature of the motion in each of the two trials and how that might account for any differences in the number and nature of the observed collisions.

Communicate: Share Your Results

15 min

Students share their number of collisions in each of the two trials with the class and identify any data trends.

NOTES

....

....

....

....

....

Reflect

10 min

Students consider the implications of the results of their investigation of collisions.

Reflect

Use the results of your investigation to answer these questions with your group. Be prepared to share your answers with the class.

1. Did the results match your predictions? Why or why not?

2. Compare the collisions of the two trials in more detail. How were the collisions in the two trials similar to each other? How were they different? Were the collisions more violent in one trial? Where did most collisions occur in each trial? In each trial, how did early collisions affect later collisions?

3. What do you think would happen to the number of collisions if everyone had rolled two tennis balls each time?

4. What do you think would happen to the number of the collisions if the number of balls stayed the same but people sat in a circle that was three times bigger?

5. Is there any way to predict when specific collisions will occur in either trial? Why or why not?

6. How do you think the motion of the balls might compare to the way in which objects move and collide in the solar system?

7. Now that you know more about collisions, answer this question again: Are any of the objects you know about in space likely to collide? Why or why not?

Introducing the *Big Question*

The Big Question for this Unit is: How Can You Know if Objects in Space Will Collide? To answer this question you are going to have to understand how objects in the solar system move, how likely they are to collide with one another, and what happens when objects collide. You will also investigate objects outside the solar system to see if they could possibly collide with objects in our solar system. You will start by examining the evidence as Michelle and others did after the meteorite struck her car. Besides looking at past collisions, you will explore the motion of objects in space to investigate the likelihood of collisions in the future.

△ Guide and Assess

Have the class read the *Reflect* questions and record their answers. Encourage students to provide supporting evidence from the investigation for their answers. Help students develop an understanding of the importance of keeping accurate records by asking students to describe any difficulties they had in keeping track of the number and violence of the collisions in each trial and to consider how confident they are in the accuracy of what they recorded.

When students have completed the *Reflect* questions, hold a brief class discussion in which students share their answers. Assess students' responses to the *Reflect* questions by listening for the following information:

1. Students' answers will vary, but should cite both their prediction and their experimental results as supporting evidence.

2. Students' answers will vary, but should indicate that there were more collisions in Trial 1 and that they tended to be more violent and more widely scattered.

3. The number of collisions would increase.

4. The number of collisions would decrease.

5. It is difficult to predict specific collisions in Trial 1 because the initial path of each ball is unknown. In Trial 2, the initial path of each ball is known and can be drawn on a diagram of the circle. Once drawn, the paths can be analyzed to see where they intersect. However, unless the speed of each ball is also known, it is difficult to predict if the balls will arrive at the intersection point at the same time and collide.

6. In the solar system, all objects orbit the Sun. If their speed and orbital path can be determined, it can be plotted against the path of other solar-system objects to see if their paths intersect and if they will arrive at the intersection point at the same time and collide.

△ Guide

Read this section together with students or have them take turns reading aloud. Lead a brief class discussion focusing on the issues their end-of-Unit report must address. Encourage students to ask questions about the nature of the task they are to accomplish and clarify any aspects of the assignment about which they are unsure.

Introducing the *Big Question*

5 min

Students are given the details of a report they will make at the end of the Unit to answer the Big Question.

NOTES

....

....

....

Reflect

5 min

Students begin to consider what to add to the Project Board.

When you have completed this Unit, you will use what you have learned about how scientists know if two space objects will collide to develop an idea for a movie. To interest a movie producer in making a realistic movie about the possible collision of two space objects, you will need to put together all the information you gather in the *Learning Sets* as well as the results of all your investigations.

In your "pitch" to the movie producer, you will suggest space objects that might realistically collide, support your suggestion with an explanation of what makes the collision realistic, and a description of what such a collision might look like. You will also need to describe how such a collision would affect Earth, or other space object. The best idea will be one that is realistic, dramatic, and could affect Earth, or our Sun and Moon.

Reflect

Discuss the answers to these questions with your group. Sharing your answers with the class will prepare you to begin a *Project Board* for this Unit.

1. What do you already know that might be useful in answering the *Big Question*?

2. Examine the list of questions your class made earlier. Which of those questions need to be answered to answer the *Big Question*?

3. What other questions do you need to know answers to so that you can answer the *Big Question* and write your report?

Create a *Project Board*

When working on any challenge, it is useful to keep track of your progress. It is also helpful to keep track of what you still need to do. Throughout this Unit, you will use a *Project Board* for this purpose. During classroom discussions, one person in the class will record ideas and questions on a class *Project Board*. At the same time, you will keep track of what has been discussed on your own *Project Board* page.

AST 10

△ Guide

Ask students to discuss the *Big Question* with their groups. They should think about what they know about space and consider what they think may be the answer to the *Big Question*. Tell students to use the questions in the student text to guide their discussions. Listen as students discuss ideas with their groups as they will use these thought processes when they create the *Project Board*.

△ Guide

Lead a class discussion to develop smaller questions that could guide investigations that will help answer the *Big Question*. Guide the discussion in such a way that students identify questions about collisions. For example:

- What objects in the solar system could collide with Earth and what do you know about them?

- How do the characteristics of the objects that collide affect the outcome of the collision?

- What do you need to know about the characteristics and motion of the two objects in order to predict whether they will collide and what will happen if they do collide?

Create a *Project Board*

20 min

Students create a Project Board *and start to record their ideas.*

NOTES

Recall that a *Project Board* has space for answering five guiding questions:

- What do we think we know?
- What do we need to investigate?
- What are we learning?
- What is our evidence?
- What does it mean for the challenge or question?

How can you know if objects in space will collide?				
What do we think we know?	What do we need to investigate?	What are we learning?	What is our evidence?	What does it mean for the challenge or question?

To get started on this *Project Board,* you need to identify and record the important science question you will address for this Unit: *How can you know if objects in space will collide?* Record this question at the top of the *Project Board.*

In the first column of the *Project Board,* record what you think you know about any objects in the solar system that may collide. You discussed this among your groups during your earlier conference. Use the ideas your group came up with to make suggestions for the *Project Board.* Perhaps you have studied or read about some of these objects before. Even if it is a small fact or idea, talk about it. Discuss any factors that you think might be helpful in working toward the completion of your project.

⬡ Get Going

Tell the class that now that they have thought about the *Big Question* and have identified some of the smaller questions that need to be investigated in order to answer it, they are going to need a way to keep track of their progress.

Introduce students to the idea of a *Project Board* by having them read the selection in the text. Go over the five headings used in the *Project Board* and describe how the *Project Board* will be their ongoing record of their inquiry—what they are asking, what they are learning, the supporting evidence, and how it all contributes to answering the *Big Question*. Begin to add student ideas to the first two columns.

NOTES

....

....

....

....

....

....

....

....

....

....

....

....

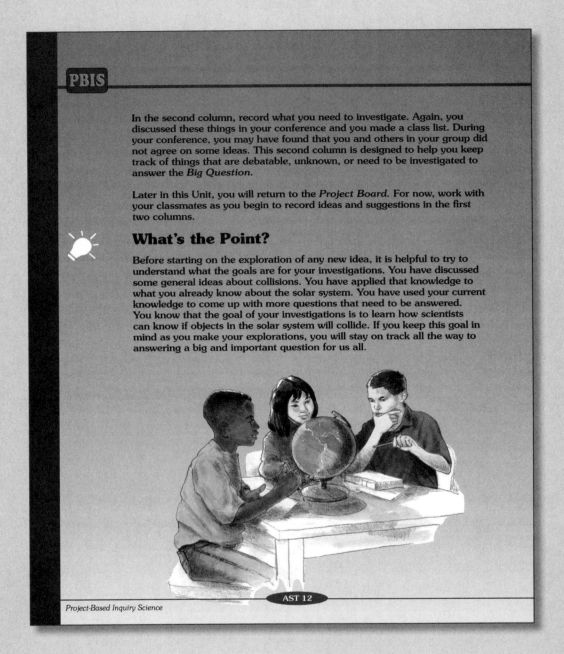

In the second column, record what you need to investigate. Again, you discussed these things in your conference and you made a class list. During your conference, you may have found that you and others in your group did not agree on some ideas. This second column is designed to help you keep track of things that are debatable, unknown, or need to be investigated to answer the *Big Question*.

Later in this Unit, you will return to the *Project Board*. For now, work with your classmates as you begin to record ideas and suggestions in the first two columns.

What's the Point?

Before starting on the exploration of any new idea, it is helpful to try to understand what the goals are for your investigations. You have discussed some general ideas about collisions. You have applied that knowledge to what you already know about the solar system. You have used your current knowledge to come up with more questions that need to be answered. You know that the goal of your investigations is to learn how scientists can know if objects in the solar system will collide. If you keep this goal in mind as you make your explorations, you will stay on track all the way to answering a big and important question for us all.

AST 12

△ Guide

Help students understand why it is important to articulate what they think they know before getting started. Specifying what they think they know will help them to recognize what they are learning later on.

Students may need help formulating questions when they are confused. An important part of managing discussions about this part of the *Project Board* is to provide that help. You have the opportunity here to model for your students how to ask good questions, pointing out what makes a good question. In this case, a good question is an answerable question that will help us to answer the *Big Question*.

Assessment Options

Targeted Concepts, Skills, and Nature of Science	How do I know if students got it?
Scientists often collaborate and share their findings. Sharing findings makes new information available and helps scientists refine their ideas and build on others' ideas. When another person's or group's idea is used, credit needs to be given.	**ASK:** After carrying out the *Tennis Ball Demolition Derby,* you reached certain conclusions about how random and ordered motion affected the number of collisions. How does everyone sharing their individual data with the class help increase your confidence in your conclusion? **LISTEN:** Students should answer by describing how the more evidence in support of a conclusion is available, the greater the confidence you can have in the conclusion. **ASK:** What are the advantages of having the class share the results of their investigations with others? **LISTEN:** Students' answers may include, but are not limited to: Sharing makes new information available to everyone in the class. It also provides each person with data about more trials than they could have obtained working on their own. Having data for more trials minimizes the possibility that chance or random errors were responsible for your experimental results, thereby increasing your confidence in the validity of the results.

Targeted Concepts, Skills, and Nature of Science	How do I know if students got it?
Scientists must keep clear, accurate, and descriptive records of what they do so they can share their work with others; consider what they did, why they did it, and what they want to do next.	**ASK:** How do you think the *Project Board* will help you answer the *Big Question*? **LISTEN:** Students should cite examples of how the *Project Board* serves as a vehicle for sharing ideas, keeping track of what they have learned, and seeing what they are doing in a larger context.
Scientific questions are directed toward objects and events that can be described, explained, or predicted by scientific investigations.	**ASK:** When we created the *Project Board*, we listed questions that needed to be addressed in order to answer the *Big Question*. Which of those questions can be answered by carrying out a scientific investigation? Give an example of an investigation that could answer one of those questions. **LISTEN:** Students' answers will vary, but should cite a question and a possible investigation that would answer the question. A typical student response might be: *Question: What effect does the mass of the objects in a collision have on the motion of the objects after the collision?* *Investigation: Set up an experiment in which you change the mass of one of the objects while keeping all other factors the same. Observe how the motion of each object changes after the collision.*

NOTES

....

Targeted Concepts, Skills, and Nature of Science	How do I know if students got it?
The solar system consists of the Sun and all of the planets, comets, asteroids, and other bodies that revolve around it.	**ASK:** What does the motion of all of the bodies in the solar system have in common? **LISTEN:** Students should answer that all bodies in the solar system revolve around the Sun. **ASK:** The Moon revolves around Earth. Would it be considered part of the solar system? Why or why not? **LISTEN:** Students should answer yes, because as it revolves around Earth, Earth revolves around the Sun. Therefore, the Moon also revolves around the Sun.
Large numbers of chunks of rock revolve around the Sun. Some may meet Earth as it revolves around the Sun, plunge through Earth's atmosphere, glow and disintegrate due to friction, and sometimes impact the ground.	**ASK:** What evidence supports the idea that the object that collided with Michelle Knapp's car in Peekskill, NY was a meteorite from space that had traveled through the atmosphere before striking the ground? **LISTEN:** Students should describe the crater under the car. It was still warm to the touch. Nearby video cameras recorded an object streaking across the night sky and a fireball breaking up into pieces at about the same time the car was hit.

NOTES

....

....

....

....

Teacher Reflection Questions

- Students often pose questions that are not answerable through scientific investigation. For example, broad, ill-defined questions such as, *Is Earth in danger if an object collides with it?* Ideally, they should identify a proposed relationship between an independent and dependent variable. For example, *If the mass of two colliding objects is increased while all other factors are kept constant, will their speed after the collision increase?* How did you help students develop the ability to generate questions that can be answered by scientific investigations?

- How much understanding of the objects that comprise the solar system and their motion was evident in class discussions? What ideas or concepts relating to the solar system will you have to address as you implement this Unit?

NOTES

LEARNING SET 1 INTRODUCTION

Learning Set 1

Have Objects in the Solar System Collided?

◀ *10 class periods*

A class period is considered to be one 40 to 50 minute class.

Students investigate craters as evidence of collisions between objects in the solar system. They design experiments to determine the connection between the characteristics of a crater and the characteristics of the body that collided with the surface to form it and then compare evidence of past collisions on Earth, the Moon, and other solar-system bodies.

Overview

The *Learning Set* opens with a brief historical overview of the idea that craters observed on the Moon's surface are the result of impacts of another smaller body. In *Section 1.1,* students mess about with collisions by simulating the impact between an object and the Moon's surface. While doing so, they observe the effects of a collision on both the object and the surface with which it collides. In *Section 1.2,* students design experiments to investigate how the characteristics of an object and its motion affect the crater formed when it impacts a surface. In *Section 1.3,* students explore the characteristics of craters on the Moon and in *Section 1.4* students use Earth-imaging software to search for impact craters on Earth's surface. Students then work in groups to examine satellite imagery of one of Earth's 25 largest meteor craters and compare its appearance with that of lunar impact craters. In *Section 1.5,* students create an explanation for the differences they observed between craters on Earth and on the Moon. After examining photographs of impact craters on Earth that have existed for different lengths of time and reading about the effects of weathering and erosion on structures exposed at Earth's surface, students revise their explanations. In *Section 1.6,* students read a description of what happens to a meteorite on its way to Earth's surface. They observe a demonstration video of the heating of air due to compression with a fire syringe. After reflecting on what they observed in the demonstration, students update the *Project Board.* In *Section 1.7,* students read descriptions of the various bodies that comprise our solar system and an account of how the collision between the comet, Shoemaker-Levy, and the planet Jupiter, was predicted. The *Learning Set* concludes with students researching an assigned solar-system body and considering what would happen if an asteroid collided with that body. Students begin work on a *Big Question* page that will serve as an organizer for information that will be useful for their report at the end of the Unit.

Targeted Concepts, Skills, and Nature of Science	Section
Scientists often collaborate and share their findings. Sharing findings makes new information available and helps scientists refine their ideas and build on others' ideas. When another person's or group's idea is used, credit needs to be given.	All sections
Scientists must keep clear, accurate, and descriptive records of what they do so they can share their work with others; consider what they did, why they did it, and what they want to do next.	All sections
Scientists make claims (conclusions) based on evidence obtained (trends in data) from reliable investigations.	1.2, 1.5, 1.BBQ
In a reliable investigation, only the manipulated (independent) variable and the responding (dependent) variable change. All other variables are held constant.	1.2
Observations and measurements are considered reliable if the results are repeatable by other scientists using the same procedures.	1.2
Explanations are claims supported by evidence. Evidence can be experimental results, observational data, and any other accepted scientific knowledge.	1.5
The Sun, the planets that revolve around it, and their moons are the major bodies in the solar system. Other members that orbit the Sun include dwarf planets and small solar-system bodies, such as asteroids and comets.	1.7, 1.BBQ
Most objects in the solar system have a regular and predictable motion. These motions explain such phenomena as a day, a year, phases of the Moon, eclipses, tides, meteor showers, and comets.	1.7, 1.BBQ
Meteoroids are small solar-system objects with the potential to collide with Earth. Most meteoroids that strike Earth's atmosphere rapidly burn up because of friction with the atmosphere resulting in a visible meteor. Those that survive and strike Earth as meteorites are fragmented and destroyed by the impact.	1.6

Targeted Concepts, Skills, and Nature of Science	Section
Impacts of solar-system bodies have created extensive cratering on the Moon and on other bodies in the solar system. Some craters also can be found on Earth, but most have been destroyed by the processes of plate tectonics, and/or the weathering, erosion, and deposition occurring at Earth's planetary surface.	1.2, 1.3, 1.4, 1.5
Comets leave behind grains of dust and ions. The dust and ions can be illuminated by the Sun as huge tails. If Earth passes through the trails of dust left behind, the particles rapidly burn up because of friction with the atmosphere, causing a meteor shower.	1.7

Activity Setup and Preparation

The Formation of our Solar System

Collisions have played a key role in both the formation and continued development of our solar system. The major objects that make up our solar system are Earth and seven other major planets that revolve around the Sun. More than 100 moons orbit the planets. Our solar system also includes numerous smaller objects that orbit the Sun, including dwarf planets, asteroids, meteoroids, and comets. However, more than 99 percent of the mass of the entire solar system is contained in the Sun.

Many scientists believe that the observational evidence best supports the nebular theory, which proposes that the solar system formed from a giant, rotating cloud of gas and dust, known as the *solar nebula*. Mutual gravitational attraction drew the dust and gas together; and as the nebula contracted, it spun faster and flattened into a disk. Most of the matter in the solar nebula was pulled toward the center and formed the Sun. The small remainder in the spinning disk formed the planets and other solar system objects.

According to theory, collisions and gravitational pressure at the center of the solar nebula became great enough to initiate the nuclear reactions that power the Sun. Distance from the Sun was a key factor in determining the planets' characteristics. Powerful emissions from the Sun *(solar wind)* swept away most of the nearby gases, leaving behind the solid, rocky terrestrial planets. As the solar wind weakened with distance, the more-distant planets had sufficient gravity to retain much of the gas that surrounded them and evolved into large, gaseous low-density planets. This explains why the inner terrestrial planets are solid and rocky while the outer planets are gas giants.

Turbulence in the dust and gas of the spinning disk caused it to fragment and sort itself into concentric rings based on the matter's mass and the speed at which it was revolving. Particles within the flattened disk collided and were held together by gravity forming larger particles, a process called *accretion*. Continued accretion slowly formed larger and larger bodies called *planetesimals*. Some of those planetesimals collided and combined to form the planets, while others formed moons, asteroids, and comets. The planets and asteroids all revolve around the Sun in the same direction and in roughly the same plane because they originally formed from this flattened disk.

Earth and the other terrestrial planets accreted by collisions. The larger and denser the planet, the stronger the gravitational pull exerted on an incoming object and the greater the energy of the impact. When an object collides with a planet, its energy of motion *(kinetic energy)* is converted to heat. The temperature reached depends on the rate of heat gain from impacts compared to the rate at which heat radiates away and is lost. Early in its formation, the rate of impacts on Earth generated enough heat to melt its silicate minerals and create a vast molten region extending inward from the surface. Eventually, Earth's gravity had attracted most of the bodies in space around it. With the surrounding area swept clean, the rate of impacts fell off; Earth cooled and formed a crust.

Because any hydrogen and other gases left from the solar nebula were quickly swept away by the solar wind, the primordial Earth had no atmosphere. Where did the gases of our present atmosphere originate? One likely source is outgassing, the release of water and trace gases contained in rocks. Another likely source of gases are comets. The outer solar system is cold enough that many volatile materials will condense or solidify, so comets are rich in ices of water, carbon dioxide, carbon monoxide, ammonia, and carbon compounds. At present, if you add up the comets' masses that orbit the Sun, it would exceed the mass of hundreds of Earths together. Computer-simulated models indicate that there were even more comets in the early solar system, and those comets commonly intersected Earth's orbit. A collision between a comet and Earth would have generated enough heat to melt the comet, releasing its icy gases. Hundreds of millions of years of collisions with comets would have added large amounts of gases to Earth's atmosphere. Almost no molecular oxygen has been found in comets, very little exists on Venus or Mars, and it was not present in Earth's early atmosphere. Only after the evolution of photosynthetic life did Earth develop an oxidizing atmosphere.

LEARNING SET 1 IMPLEMENTATION

Learning Set 1

Have Objects in the Solar System Collided?

The *Big Question* for this Unit is *How Can You Know if Objects in Space Will Collide?* To help you answer this question, you will break it down into smaller questions and answer those. In this *Learning Set,* you are going to answer the question, *Have objects in the solar system collided?* Scientists can only know about collisions if evidence of a collision is available. To answer the question for this *Learning Set,* you will use the same evidence scientists have used to decide if solar system objects have collided. That evidence will help you support a claim about whether collisions have occurred.

Do you see the "Man in the Moon" or the "Rabbit on the Moon"? Without a telescope or binoculars, you can only imagine what the bright spots and dark areas are.

The Moon is Earth's closest neighbor in the solar system. From early history, people have looked at the Moon and tried to explain the surface features they could see. Someone has probably pointed out the "Man in the Moon" to you. Some cultures have described the Moon's features as looking like a rabbit with a bright tail. If you look for the "Rabbit on the Moon,"

AST 13

ASTRONOMY

Learning Set 1

Have Objects in the Solar System Collided?

5 min

Students are introduced to the question they will answer in this Learning Set.

△ Guide

Begin by reminding students that the *Big Question* is *How can you know if objects from space will collide?* Then ask students if they know how often objects collide in space. Point out that knowing about collisions that occur between objects in space can help them think about how to predict whether objects in space will collide. Ask them how they would know if objects in space have collided.

*A class period is considered to be one 40 to 50 minute class.

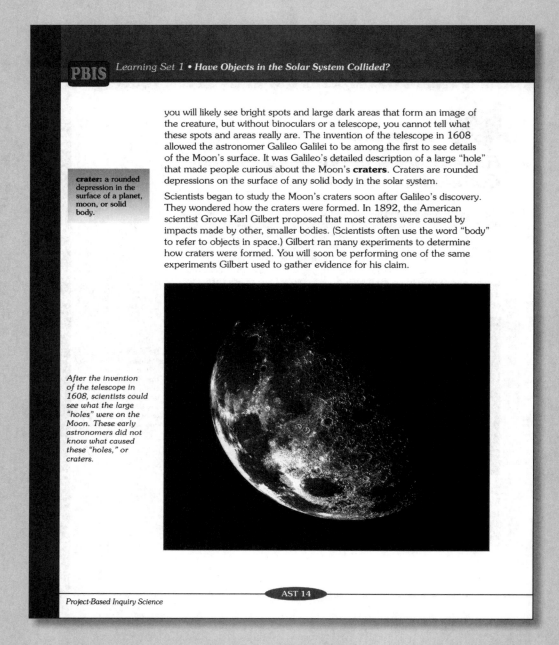

you will likely see bright spots and large dark areas that form an image of the creature, but without binoculars or a telescope, you cannot tell what these spots and areas really are. The invention of the telescope in 1608 allowed the astronomer Galileo Galilei to be among the first to see details of the Moon's surface. It was Galileo's detailed description of a large "hole" that made people curious about the Moon's **craters**. Craters are rounded depressions on the surface of any solid body in the solar system.

Scientists began to study the Moon's craters soon after Galileo's discovery. They wondered how the craters were formed. In 1892, the American scientist Grove Karl Gilbert proposed that most craters were caused by impacts made by other, smaller bodies. (Scientists often use the word "body" to refer to objects in space.) Gilbert ran many experiments to determine how craters were formed. You will soon be performing one of the same experiments Gilbert used to gather evidence for his claim.

crater: a rounded depression in the surface of a planet, moon, or solid body.

After the invention of the telescope in 1608, scientists could see what the large "holes" were on the Moon. These early astronomers did not know what caused these "holes," or craters.

AST 14

Tell students that in this *Learning Set* they will answer the question, *Have objects in the solar system collided?* Answering this question will help them answer the *Big Question* for the Unit. To answer it, they will examine examples of evidence of collisions between objects in the solar system.

Point out the picture of the Moon in student textbook. Discuss how the dark and light areas of the Moon have looked like many things to people, including the "Man in the Moon" and the "Rabbit on the Moon." Tell students that when Galileo began studying the Moon with a telescope, he was able to identify craters with walls that cast shadows on the Moon's surface. Much later, the American geologist, Grove Karl Gilbert, suggested that the craters were caused by collisions with smaller objects and ran experiments to determine how the craters were formed. Emphasize that students will perform one of the experiments Gilbert used. This will give them evidence that objects in the solar system have collided.

NOTES

NOTES

1.1 Understand the Question

Think About What Happens When Objects Collide

◀ *1 class period*

A class period is considered to be one 40 to 50 minute class.

Overview

Students consider what happens when objects collide by simulating the impact of an object and the Moon's surface. They drop various objects onto the surface of flour covered with a thin layer of colored powder in a plastic tub and observe the formation of impact craters. During their simulation, students use different objects and angles of impact, observing the effects of the collision on both the object and the surface with which it collides. Students share their observations with the class and discuss connections between the evidence left after a collision and the conditions of the collision. The section concludes with students updating their *Project Board*.

Targeted Concepts, Skills, and Nature of Science	Performance Expectations
Scientists often collaborate and share their findings. Sharing findings makes new information available and helps scientists refine their ideas and build on others' ideas. When another person's or group's idea is used, credit needs to be given.	Students share their observations and descriptions of the impacts of different objects with the surface of the material in the tub and the evidence left behind after the impact with the class. Students consider what they think they need to learn and what they need to investigate as they update the class *Project Board*.
Scientists must keep clear, accurate, and descriptive records of what they do so they can share their work with others; consider what they did, why they did it, and what they want to do next.	Students record their observations and descriptions of the effects of the impacts they simulated. Students participate in a class discussion updating the *Project Board*, an organizing record of their ideas and what they are learning.

Materials	
1 per group	Plastic tub filled with flour
	Colored powder for sprinkling
	Shaker-top containers
	Meter stick
	Set of objects to drop into the flour tub
	Plastic trash bag, cut along two sides, to cover work surface
2 per group	Ruler
1 per classroom	Trash can
1 per student	*Project Board* page
1 per class	Class *Project Board*

Activity Setup and Preparation

For each group, cut one plastic trash bag along two sides so that it opens flat. This can be placed beneath the tub to catch any material thrown out of the tub by impacts. These can be emptied into a trash can and reused after the activity.

Before class, fill the tubs with flour and place a sheet of wax paper over the surface of the flour. Tubs can then be stacked for ease of transport and distribution. Fill shaker-top containers with the cocoa powder for ease of distribution and sprinkling. Pre-package 4–6 objects of varying size, shape, and density for dropping onto the surface of the flour.

Note: It is not necessary to discard the flour after each class. The amount of cocoa powder sprinkled on the surface is generally small compared to the amount of flour in the tub. Stir the flour to evenly distribute the cocoa powder and the mixture will remain light enough in color to be reused.

Homework Options

Reflection

- **Science Process:** What is the long-term goal of this Unit? *(Students should answer that the long-term goal is to address the* Big Question: How can you tell if objects from space will collide with Earth?*)* What is the goal of this *Learning Set? (Students should understand that the goal of* Learning Set 1 *is to address the smaller question,* Have objects in the solar system collided?*)*

- **Science Content:** What type of event did you simulate in this activity? *(Students should describe how they simulated an impact between an object from space and one from the surface of the Moon.)*

- **Science Content:** What represented the surface of the Moon in the simulation? *(Students should identify that the tub of flour represented the Moon.)*

- **Science Content:** Sketch a diagram and describe the evidence of the impact's simulated activity. *(Students should draw and describe depressions in the surface and material scattered outside the rim of the depression.)*

- **Science Process:** How will the *Project Board* be helpful in reaching the long-term goal of answering the *Big Question? (Students should understand that the* Project Board *helps organize the smaller challenges, investigations, results, and conclusions gathered throughout the Unit. Putting all this information together on the* Project Board *organizes the information needed to reach the long-term goal of answering the* Big Question.*)*

Preparation for 1.2

- **Science Process:** Summarize the challenges you encountered when trying to describe and measure the evidence left behind after a collision. *(Students may answer that it was difficult to measure the width and depth of the depression without disturbing it. It also may have been difficult to describe the exact size, shape, and position of the bits of material thrown out of the depression by the impact.)*

- **Science Content:** Predict how the shape of an object will affect the shape of the crater formed when it impacts a surface. *(Students' answers may vary, but during the activity some may have observed that impacts by objects of varying shapes all produce rounded depressions.)*

NOTES

SECTION 1.1 IMPLEMENTATION

1.1 Understand the Question

Think About What Happens When Objects Collide

The question for this *Learning Set* is *Have objects in the solar system collided?* Before you can answer this question, you must first consider what happens when objects collide.

Get Started

You will simulate an impact between an object and the Moon's surface. You will use a plastic tub of flour and colored powder to represent the Moon. Use the ruler and meter stick to make measurements as you record your observations.

You will model what happens when different objects strike the Moon by observing what happens when different objects strike the flour in the tub. You may use any object that can safely be dropped into the plastic tub. Be imaginative about the types of objects you use. You may throw objects so that they strike the flour at an angle, but do not do so in a dangerous way.

Begin by making a chart like the one below. It should have three columns, one to describe the object being dropped or thrown into the tub, one to describe how it was dropped or thrown, and one to record what the flour looks like after the impact.

Materials
- plastic tub filled with flour
- colored powder for sprinkling
- ruler
- meter stick
- objects to drop into the flour

Object, including its size and shape	How the object was dropped or thrown	What the flour looks like after the impact

AST 15

ASTRONOMY

1.1 Understand the Question

Think About What Happens When Objects Collide

5 min

Students prepare for their collision simulations.

△ Guide

Begin by emphasizing that before students can determine that collisions have happened in the solar system, they need to understand what happens when objects collide. To develop an understanding of what happens when objects collide, they should observe what happens when some small objects collide with the surface of a tub of flour.

*A class period is considered to be one 40 to 50 minute class.

Get Started

20 min

Students set up and begin their simulations.

---

happens when objects collide.

Get Started

You will simulate an impact between an object and the Moon's surface. You will use a plastic tub of flour and colored powder to represent the Moon. Use the ruler and meter stick to make measurements as you record your observations.

You will model what happens when different objects strike the Moon by observing what happens when different objects strike the flour in the tub. You may use any object that can safely be dropped into the plastic tub. Be imaginative about the types of objects you use. You may throw objects so that they strike the flour at an angle, but do not do so in a dangerous way.

Begin by making a chart like the one below. It should have three columns, one to describe the object being dropped or thrown into the tub, one to describe how it was dropped or thrown, and one to record what the flour looks like after the impact.

Materials

• plastic tub filled with flour

• colored powder for sprinkling

• ruler

• meter stick

• objects to drop into the flour

Object, including its size and shape	How the object was dropped or thrown	What the flour looks like after the impact

△ Guide

Distribute materials and tell students that they should vary how they drop and throw different objects into the flour and observe what happens. They may use the objects you provide or they may use other objects, such as erasers, coins, or wads of paper. Monitor their choice of objects so that they do not use anything that might cause injury.

Emphasize that students must record their observations of what they do and what happens. Have them set up a chart like the one in the student text. Tell them they will share their observations with the class.

Be careful when you throw objects at an angle. Make sure you throw them only into the container holding the flour. Do not throw the objects harder than necessary for them to land in the tub.

Begin by sprinkling colored powder over the white flour. This will make it easy for you to track what happens to the flour when it is hit by an object. Take turns dropping objects on the flour. After each object is dropped or thrown at the flour, record what the object was, how it was dropped onto the flour, and the pattern made by the colored powder. Smooth out the flour and sprinkle more colored powder into the tub after each impact so that the tub has an even surface before each impact.

Record the shape of the surface in the tub after each collision and the pattern made by the colored powder. Each member of your group should take two turns dropping or throwing an object onto the flour.

Communicate

Share Your Observations

Discuss your observations as a class. Talk about what you found interesting and what questions the activity helped you think about. Consider the following questions in your discussion:

- How did the effects of the impact change as the conditions of the collision changed?

- Was the object affected by the impact?

- After the impact, what evidence was left that a collision occurred?

- What factors do you think affect the size and shape of the crater made by a collision?

- How do you think these collisions are similar to collisions on the Moon?

- What questions do you need to answer to know for sure which factors affect the size and shape of a crater caused by a collision?

- What questions do you need to answer before you can answer the bigger question, *Have objects in the solar system collided?*

◇ Evaluate

As groups investigate the impact objects make on the flour, make sure they stay on task and are not throwing their objects outside of the tubs of flour. Ask them what observations they have made and remind them, if necessary, to try different kinds of collisions with each object.

Communicate: Share Your Observations

15 min

Students share their observations with the class.

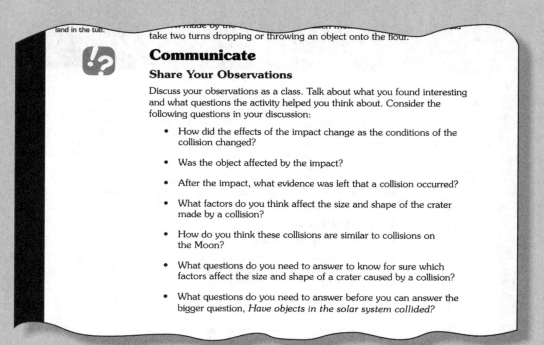

land in the tub.

take two turns dropping or throwing an object onto the flour.

Communicate

Share Your Observations

Discuss your observations as a class. Talk about what you found interesting and what questions the activity helped you think about. Consider the following questions in your discussion:

- How did the effects of the impact change as the conditions of the collision changed?

- Was the object affected by the impact?

- After the impact, what evidence was left that a collision occurred?

- What factors do you think affect the size and shape of the crater made by a collision?

- How do you think these collisions are similar to collisions on the Moon?

- What questions do you need to answer to know for sure which factors affect the size and shape of a crater caused by a collision?

- What questions do you need to answer before you can answer the bigger question, *Have objects in the solar system collided?*

△ Guide

When students have had time to observe how different objects collide with the flour, have them share their observations with the class. Tell them they should share what they found interesting and also to address each of the bulleted questions in the text.

As groups share their observations, encourage students to ask questions if anything is unclear or if they are not sure how to answer the *Communicate* questions. Emphasize that they should think about how groups' observations compare with their own.

NOTES

....

....

....

Update the *Project Board*

In the *What do we think we know?* column, record what you think you know about the effects of collisions. In the *What do we need to investigate?* column, record questions that will resolve any disagreements your class had about collisions. Also record any questions you need to investigate to know for sure which factors affect the size and shape of a crater caused by a collision. Then record questions you need to answer to help you understand whether objects in the solar system have collided.

How can you know if objects in space will collide?				
What do we think we know?	What do we need to investigate?	What are we learning?	What is our evidence?	What does it mean for the challenge or question?

Update the *Project Board*

10 min

Lead a class discussion to update the Project Board.

△ Guide

Ask students what questions they have about their observations and which of these questions will help them answer the *Big Question*. Record their questions on the *Project Board,* and have them record their questions on their own *Project Board* pages.

Assessment Options

Targeted Concepts, Skills, and Nature of Science	How do I know if students got it?
Scientists often collaborate and share their findings. Sharing findings makes new information available and helps scientists refine their ideas and build on others' ideas. When another person's or group's idea is used, credit needs to be given.	**ASK:** When you discussed your observations with the class, which factors seemed to have some effect on the depression formed by the impact of an object? **LISTEN:** Students should answer that the height from which the object was dropped, the speed and angle at which it collided with the surface, and the size and mass of the object were all factors that had an effect on the formation of the depression.
Scientists must keep clear, accurate, and descriptive records of what they do so they can share their work with others; consider what they did, why they did it, and what they want to do next.	**ASK:** Discuss how the *Project Board* will be helpful to our search for answers to the *Big Question?* **LISTEN:** Students should cite examples of how the *Project Board* serves as a vehicle for sharing ideas, keeping track of what they have learned, and seeing what they are doing in a larger context.

Teacher Reflection Questions

- How were you able to engage students in answering the question for this *Learning Set?*

- How were you able to keep students focused on the task when they investigated impacts with the flour? What might you try next time?

- What questions could you ask students when they share their observations with the class that would elicit more information and in greater detail?

- How were you able to keep students focused on the *Big Challenge* as you updated the *Project Board?*

- How did you implement the *Project Board* discussion to include students who feel inhibited about sharing their ideas?

1.2 Investigate

Model a Collision With the Moon

◀ *2 class periods*

A class period is considered to be one 40 to 50 minute class.

Overview

Students observe a photograph of an impact crater on the Moon and they are introduced to the terminology used to describe impact craters. A brief reading describes the elements of a well-designed experiment. Students are guided through the process of designing experiments to investigate how the characteristics of an object and its motion affect the crater formed when the object impacts a surface. Students identify a question that is subject to scientific investigation; formulate a hypothesis based on observations made while messing about; identify independent, dependent, and controlled variables; and design a procedure to test their hypothesis. After sharing their experimental design with the class and receiving constructive feedback, students revise their experiment. They then run their revised experiment, analyze their data, and share their results with the class. Students then reflect on what they have learned about impact craters and the objects that formed them from the results of the different experiments carried out by the class. They also update the *Project Board*.

Targeted Concepts, Skills, and Nature of Science	Performance Expectations
Scientists often collaborate and share their findings. Sharing findings makes new information available and helps scientists refine their ideas and build on others' ideas. When another person's or group's idea is used, credit needs to be given.	Students make a presentation to the class sharing their experiment's question, and hypothesis. They identify the independent, dependent, and controlled variables in their experiment, and the experimental procedures their group developed to test that hypothesis. The class offers constructive feedback.

NOTES

....

....

....

Targeted Concepts, Skills, and Nature of Science	Performance Expectations
Scientists must keep clear, accurate, and descriptive records of what they do so they can share their work with others; consider what they did, why they did it, and what they want to do next.	Students record the question they are investigating, their hypothesis, the details of their experimental design, data that were collected, and their data analysis. Students design a method of recording and organizing data so that it can be shared with the class after carrying out their experiment. Students experience that sharing accurate and complete data gathered by the entire class is helpful in identifying causes for differences in the characteristics of the craters formed by an impact.
Scientists make claims (conclusions) based on evidence obtained (trends in data) from reliable investigations.	Students analyze the results of their experiment and determine whether it supports their hypothesis.
In a reliable investigation, only the manipulated (independent) variable and the responding (dependent) variable change. All other variables are held constant.	Students should be able to give reasons for controlling variables other than the independent and dependent variables. Students should be able to cite specific examples of ways in which they are controlling variables in their experiment's procedure.
Observations and measurements are considered reliable if the results are repeatable by other scientists using the same procedures.	Students should be able to cite examples of how differences in measurement procedures will lead to differences in results. For example, differences in the point at which the object is dropped will result in differences in the crater formed by the impact.
Impacts of solar-system bodies have created extensive cratering on the Moon and on other bodies in the solar system. Some craters can be found on Earth, but most have been destroyed by the processes of plate tectonics and/or the weathering, erosion, and deposition occurring at Earth's planetary surface.	Students should be able to distinguish between impact craters and volcanic craters. Students should be able to identify similarities between craters formed by the impacts in their experiment and images of craters on the Moon shown in the student text.

Materials	
1 per group	Plastic tub filled with flour
	Colored powder for sprinkling
	Meter stick
	Set of 4 objects to drop into the flour (3 spheres—1 small, 1 large of the same material, 1 small of a different density, and 1 with an irregular shape)
	Poster board or newsprint
	Set of markers
	Plastic trash bag, cut along two sides, to cover work surface
1 per group (optional)	Modeling clay (from which students can fashion objects)
2 per group	Ruler
1 per student	*Impact Crater Experiment Planning Guide* page
	Impact Crater Experiment Results Guide page
	Project Board page
1 per class	Class *Project Board*

Activity Setup and Preparation

Decide beforehand how you will have students record their experimental design, data collected, and data analysis. The activity in this section uses the same setup as in the previous section. You may want to leave the classroom setup between class periods.

Homework Options

Reflection

- **Science Content:** Describe two ways in which craters can be formed. *(Students should describe how craters can form as a result of an impact or as a result of volcanic activity.)*

- **Science Content:** Compare and contrast your impact crater experiments with those performed by Grove Karl Gilbert. *(Students' answers should point out similarities and differences between those performed by the class and those performed by Gilbert. For example, Gilbert dropped clay balls into clay and sand and shot bullets at targets made of clay and sand. The class dropped a variety of objects onto flour covered by a colored powder.)*

- **Science Process:** Which variables were the most difficult to control when designing your experiment? *(Answers will vary, but students should cite variables such as the angle at which the object strikes the surface, the speed of the object when thrown at an angle, the flatness and "softness" of the surface, and the side of an irregular object that strikes the surface.)*

- **Science Process:** Analyze your measuring procedures and determine which were the most difficult to carry out in a consistently repeatable way and why. *(Answers will vary, but students should describe measuring the width of the crater because they must estimate the point at which to measure the greatest width, and measuring the angle at which the object strikes the surface because the event occurs so quickly.)*

Preparation for 1.3

- **Science Content:** Infer possible reasons for the differences in the size of the craters on the Moon shown in your text. *(Students should identify the size or speed of the object that impacted the Moon's surface to form the crater.)*

SECTION 1.2 IMPLEMENTATION

1.2 Investigate

Model a Collision With the Moon

impact crater: a crater formed when an object strikes a planet, moon, or solid body.

Scientists think that craters on the Moon were made by collisions with space objects. These kinds of craters are called **impact craters**. Impact craters are the direct result of a collision between an object and the surface of a planet, moon, or other solar-system body. But craters might happen for other reasons, too. Scientists can be sure a crater was caused by a collision with an object from space only if the size and shape of the crater is consistent with the kind of crater a collision would make.

Looking at a photograph of the Moon, you can see that the craters are many different sizes. The craters vary in diameter (width across) and depth. By looking at shadows, you can tell how high the walls of a crater are, and therefore, how deep the crater is. Galileo observed and commented on shadows and the heights of mountains on the Moon when he recorded his telescope observations of the Moon. In this section, you will investigate and identify the factors that affect the size and shape of an impact crater. In experiments similar to those run by Grove Karl Gilbert, you will make craters using different types of objects. This will allow you to identify any patterns in the resulting craters. Later, you will use what you learned to decide which of the craters on the Moon and on Earth are impact craters.

AST 18

Project-Based Inquiry Science

1.2 Investigate

Model a Collision With the Moon

5 min

Students are introduced to impact craters.

⭕ **Engage**

Begin by pointing out the photograph of the Moon in the student text. Ask students what differences they observe among the craters on the Moon's surface. Then ask if they have any ideas about the collisions that caused these craters, based on the differences they can observe. If the walls of one crater are higher than the walls of another crater, can anything be inferred about the collisions that caused the two craters? Tell students they will perform experiments similar to Grove Karl Gilbert's experiments by making craters with different objects and looking for patterns among those craters.

*A class period is considered to be one 40 to 50 minute class.

Parts of a Crater

5 min

Students prepare to design experiments by learning the vocabulary and concepts they will use.

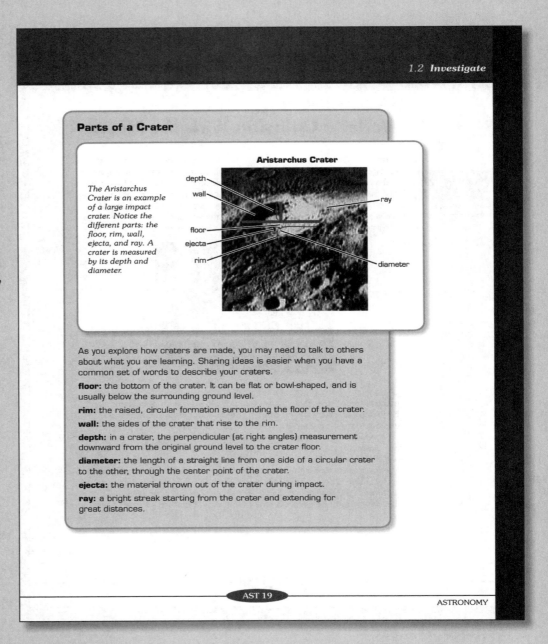

Parts of a Crater

Parts of a Crater

Aristarchus Crater

The Aristarchus Crater is an example of a large impact crater. Notice the different parts: the floor, rim, wall, ejecta, and ray. A crater is measured by its depth and diameter.

depth

wall

floor

ejecta

rim

ray

diameter

As you explore how craters are made, you may need to talk to others about what you are learning. Sharing ideas is easier when you have a common set of words to describe your craters.

floor: the bottom of the crater. It can be flat or bowl-shaped, and is usually below the surrounding ground level.

rim: the raised, circular formation surrounding the floor of the crater.

wall: the sides of the crater that rise to the rim.

depth: in a crater, the perpendicular (at right angles) measurement downward from the original ground level to the crater floor.

diameter: the length of a straight line from one side of a circular crater to the other, through the center point of the crater.

ejecta: the material thrown out of the crater during impact.

ray: a bright streak starting from the crater and extending for great distances.

AST 19

ASTRONOMY

△ Guide

Briefly go over the parts of the crater with the class. Let them know that it is important to understand each of these now, as they will use them later during their experiment planning and observations.

1.2

Be a Scientist

Designing an Experiment

When investigating an event in nature, scientists want to learn about the factors that influence it. In science, these factors are called **variables**. For example, two factors that might affect the formation of a crater are the size and speed of the object impacting the surface. The point of running experiments is to understand how some variable affects the event you are investigating.

An experiment is designed to test a **hypothesis**. A hypothesis is a prediction based on observations. It is what you think is the most likely answer to a question. In many cases, the hypothesis will be a statement about how one variable is related to other variables in the experiment.

As you design and run your experiment, there are several kinds of variables with which you will work.

- In an experiment, the experimenter controls the value of one variable. This is the one that is changed or varied in your experiment. This is called the **independent variable** (or **manipulated variable**).

- Most other factors must be kept the same (constant) during every trial. These are called **controlled variables**. By holding these variables constant, the experimenter can be sure that the results are affected only by the changes in the independent variable.

- Factors that might change when the manipulated variable is changed are called **dependent variables** (or **responding variables**). Their values are dependent on the value of the independent, or manipulated, variable. These are the variables you measure after each trial.

When scientists design an experiment, they think about the factors that might affect the results of the experiment. Then they identify the variable about which they want to find out more. They choose this variable as the independent (manipulated) variable. This is the one they vary to identify its effects. The other variables that could affect the outcome must be kept the same, or controlled, each time the procedure is carried out. If the experiment is designed well, then changes in the dependent variables can be assumed to result from changes made to the independent variable.

variable: a quantity whose value may change (vary) over the course of an experiment.

hypothesis: a prediction of what will happen to a dependent (responding) variable when a change is made to the independent (manipulated) variable while other variables are held constant. A hypothesis is not a guess; it is always based on what you know.

independent (manipulated) variable: a factor that is changed or manipulated in an experiment.

controlled variable: in an experiment, a variable that is kept constant (not changed).

dependent (responding) variable: a factor that is affected by changes in the independent (manipulated) variable.

Be a Scientist: Designing an Experiment

5 min

Students are introduced to the parts of an experiment and start to think about how they will use them.

⬡ Get Going

Discuss the concepts students will need to design an experiment. They will need to understand that *variables* are factors that can influence the outcome of an experiment. For instance, if students were performing experiments to determine which of two fertilizers led to the most rapid growth of plants, the soil the plants grew in, the sunlight they were exposed to, the amount of water they were exposed to, and the temperatures they were exposed to are all variables that would influence the outcome of their experiments.

The variable they change in an experiment is the *independent variable*. In the example of testing fertilizers, the type of fertilizer is the independent variable. In good experiments, all the other variables will be kept the same so only the change in the independent variable influences the results. The variables that are kept the same are called *controlled variables*. Finally, the variable that can change as a result of changes to the independent variable is the *dependent variable*. In the example of testing fertilizers, the dependent variable is plant growth.

NOTES

You have investigated how some different objects form craters and observed the craters formed by each object. The class made a list of the factors that you think might affect the size and shape of a crater, but you do not know for sure what the effect of each factor will be.

You will begin by developing a hypothesis about how one factor, such as the size or mass of an object, or the angle at which it hits, affects the size and shape of a crater. Then you will select objects for your experiment that will allow you to gather information to test your hypothesis. For this experiment, you will use the same plastic tub you used earlier. You will again sprinkle a thin layer of colored powder over the surface of the flour and throw or drop objects into the flour. The colored flour will help you see the ejecta and rays of the craters. After each trial, you will smooth out the flour and sprinkle more colored powder on the surface.

Design an Experiment

Each group in the class will be assigned a different factor to investigate and run an experiment to learn how that factor affects the shape and size of a crater. In your group, discuss and then design a good experiment to investigate the effects of your variable on a crater's shape and size. Remember to discuss and record the following aspects of your experiment's design.

Question

What question are you investigating or answering with this experiment? For example, you might be answering the question, *How does the mass of the object striking a surface affect the length, width, and depth of the crater that forms?*

AST 21

ASTRONOMY

Design an Experiment
15 min

Students design an experiment that tests one variable in crater formation.

△ Guide

Decide which factor of crater formation each group will investigate. Then let students know that they will again use the flour to observe how craters are formed. They should sprinkle colored powder over the surface of the flour to make it easier to observe patterns in the craters. They can sprinkle more colored powder on the surface after each trial. Assign factors to groups and let them begin.

○ Get Going

Have students meet in their groups to consider the factor they have been assigned. Distribute *Impact Crater Experiment Planning Guide* and *Impact Crater Experiment Results Guide* pages and tell students that the first step in designing their experiments is to ask a question. The student textbook gives an example question, *How does the mass of the object striking a surface affect the length, width, and depth of the crater that forms?* Their question should be about what effect one variable has on another. Then they should decide together on a question that answers how their factor affects the formation of a crater.

NOTES

Prediction

What do you think is the answer to the question? Start by writing a hypothesis. Your hypothesis is your prediction about how your independent (manipulated) variable and a dependent (responding) variable are related. Hypotheses are written as statements that can be tested, often using a format like this: "If I [*increase/decrease*] the [*independent variable*], then the [*dependent variable*] will [*increase/decrease/stay the same*]." You write a different hypothesis statement for each dependent variable that you think will be affected by a change in your independent variable.

If the question is about three dependent variables (for example, length, width, and depth), you would develop three hypothesis statements. You would state each hypothesis as, "If I drop a ball with less mass in the flour, the result will be a crater with [*greater/less/the same*] [*length/width/depth*]."

Variable Identification

- Which variable will you manipulate (change) in your experiment?

- What conditions and procedures will you keep the same (hold constant or control) in your experiment?

- What characteristics of each crater will you observe or measure?

- How many trials will you do for each value of your manipulated variable?

Procedure and Data

Write detailed instructions for how to conduct the experiment. Include the following:

- what object or objects you will drop or throw into the tub

- how you will drop or throw the object

- how you will measure the resulting crater

- how many trials you will perform

Make sure you can explain to the class why you think they will be able to trust your data.

AST 22

△ Guide

Tell students to use the question they chose to investigate to develop a hypothesis, or a prediction based on observations. Let them know that they can form a hypothesis by predicting how the independent variable affects the dependent variable of their investigative question.

◇ Evaluate

As students develop hypotheses, ask them about the questions they are asking and factors on which they are focusing. Make sure they are developing hypotheses that can be tested. Some factors students might think about are mass, size (volume), angle of impact, and speed.

△ Guide

Guide students to write a detailed procedure that will test one variable. Make certain that the students hold all other variables constant, and that their dependent variable is a measurable characteristic of a crater, such as diameter, depth, or height of walls.

NOTES

1.2 *Investigate*

Use an *Impact Crater Experiment Planning Guide* page and *Impact Crater Experiment Results Guide* to plan and organize your experiment. Use the hints on the planning page as a guide. Be sure to write enough in each section so that you will be able to present your experiment design to the class. The class will want to know that you have thought through all the parts of your plan.

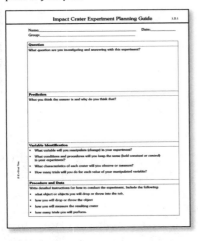

Communicate

Plan Briefing

As a group, present the plan for your experiment to the class. Discuss with the class ways to ensure that your experiment will successfully test your hypothesis and answer your question. Make sure your presentation answers the following questions:

- What question are you answering?

- What independent variable are you manipulating in your experiment?

△ Guide

Once students have developed questions and hypotheses, have them develop procedures to test their hypotheses. Their procedures should specify how they will run each trial, including how they will control all variables, how they will make measurements, and how they will record observations. Groups might have one member drop or throw objects into the flour, another to make measurements, and another to sketch observations. They will need to decide beforehand how to make sure the control variables do not change. If the angle of the object's descent is a control variable, students will have to decide how to keep this angle as close as possible to the same in each trial.

Communicate: *Plan Briefing*

15 min

Groups present their procedures to the class in a Plan Briefing.

Communicate

Plan Briefing

As a group, present the plan for your experiment to the class. Discuss with the class ways to ensure that your experiment will successfully test your hypothesis and answer your question. Make sure your presentation answers the following questions:

- What question are you answering?

- What independent variable are you manipulating in your experiment?

⬡ Get Going

After groups have had time to design their procedures, have them present their procedures to the class. Emphasize that groups should answer the bulleted questions in the student text during their presentations. They should tell the class what dependent variable they will be observing and how they will measure changes, what variables they will be controlling, how many trials they will run, and how they will make sure they make their measurements the same way in each trial.

NOTES

....

....

....

....

....

....

What are you investigating about that variable? How are you going to vary it to determine its effects? What objects will you use, and how will you drop or throw those objects into the sand?

- List all of the variables you will hold constant in your experiment.

- How many trials will you perform?

- What measurements will you be making in your experiment? Why are these the right ones? What steps will you take to ensure that all measurements are made in exactly the same way?

As you listen, decide whether each group's experiment can answer the question they want to answer. Do you think they are doing a good enough job controlling variables? Are they measuring the right things and using a good measurement method? If you think you can help them make their experiment better, raise your hand and offer your advice. Remember to be respectful.

Run Your Experiment

Revise your procedure based on advice from the class, and then show your procedure to the teacher. After your teacher approves your procedure, use that procedure to run your experiment and test your hypothesis. Record your data. Data include numerical results as well as sketches and written notes on observations you made during the different trials.

Analyze Your Data

Data analysis is an opportunity to put your data in a form that will help you and others understand it. It is not just a restating of the data. For this experiment, you might make a graph of the data. For example, for the question, *How does the mass of the object affect the depth of the crater?* you may draw a graph with mass on the horizontal axis (*y*-axis) and depth on the vertical axis (*x*-axis). Drawing a graph may help you to see any patterns in how the two variables are related.

In your group, think about these questions to help you analyze your data:

1. How will you describe the relationships between the independent variable and the dependent variables?

Project-Based Inquiry Science

◇ Evaluate

Make sure each group has developed a testable hypothesis with a dependent variable that can be isolated. Ensure that they have identified all the variables and made plans to control the variables that are not being tested. They should also have developed detailed plans for running each trial, making measurements and observations. Emphasize that it will be important to make detailed sketches of the craters. If any groups have not developed plans for controlling variables or making measurements, ask them questions to guide them to identify ways to improve their procedures and give them a chance to revise their procedures.

Run Your Experiment

10 min

Groups run their experiments.

be respectful.

Run Your Experiment

Revise your procedure based on advice from the class, and then show your procedure to the teacher. After your teacher approves your procedure, use that procedure to run your experiment and test your hypothesis. Record your data. Data include numerical results as well as sketches and written notes on observations you made during the different trials.

⬡ Get Going

Once groups have shared and finalized their procedures, have them run their experiments. Emphasize that they need to record their observations in the *Impact Crater Experiment Results Guide* page. Also emphasize that they will share their results with the class.

△ Guide and Assess

As groups run their experiments, monitor their progress and help them with any difficulties that arise. Take note of whether they are following their procedures and how they are controlling variables, making measurements, and recording their observations.

Analyze Your Data

15 min

Groups analyze their data and develop conclusions about the relationship of the independent and dependent variables.

notes on observations you made during the different trials.

Analyze Your Data

Data analysis is an opportunity to put your data in a form that will help you and others understand it. It is not just a restating of the data. For this experiment, you might make a graph of the data. For example, for the question, *How does the mass of the object affect the depth of the crater?* you may draw a graph with mass on the horizontal axis (*y*-axis) and depth on the vertical axis (*x*-axis). Drawing a graph may help you to see any patterns in how the two variables are related.

In your group, think about these questions to help you analyze your data:

1. How will you describe the relationships between the independent variable and the dependent variables?

△ Guide

Have students work with their groups to analyze the data they recorded. They can start by discussing the three questions in their text. They should also consider graphing their data. They can graph their observations with the independent variable on the horizontal axis (*y*-axis) and the dependent variable on the vertical axis (*x*-axis).

Emphasize that they will share their data analyses with the class. As they discuss their data, they should develop conclusions about the relationship between the independent and dependent variables. They should be ready to present their conclusions to the class and support their conclusions with evidence.

2. How will you work with data from multiple trials that were run for each value of the independent variable? Will you include each trial on your graph or will you average the data for the trials?

3. How can you use sketches of the craters to help you analyze the data?

For each hypothesis you wrote, develop a conclusion about the relationship between the independent variable and the dependent variable. Make sure you have evidence from your data to support each conclusion you make.

Then draw the right graphs or charts to help others to interpret your data the same way you did and come to the same conclusions. Your graphs or charts must include all of your data.

Studying Craters

Earlier you learned that an impact crater is formed by an object striking a larger body. However, there is another kind of crater that is also present on some bodies in the solar system. A volcanic crater is a bowl-shaped depression that forms around the opening of a volcano. Volcanoes are openings in the surface of a body through which hotter material can flow or burst through. Often, a series of eruptions of this material creates a cone-shaped hill with a crater at the top.

Grove Karl Gilbert was an American scientist who studied craters on the Moon and Earth at the end of the nineteenth century. At the time, all of the known craters on Earth were thought to have been formed by volcanoes.

An impact crater (above right) is formed when an object strikes a larger body. A volcanic crater (right) is a bowl-shaped depression that forms around the opening of a volcano.

AST 25

☐ Assess

As groups analyze their data, ask them what ideas they have discussed, if they can make a conclusion about the relationship of the independent and dependent variables, and if they can support their conclusions with evidence. Students should look for patterns in their data and base their conclusions on these patterns.

Studying Craters

<5 min

Students are introduced to another type of crater.

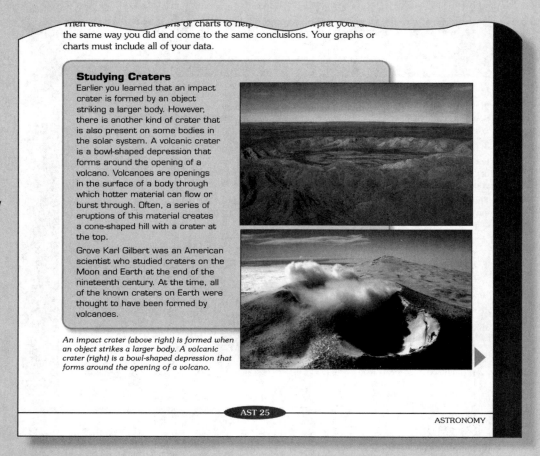

Then draw ...graphs or charts to help ... interpret your d... the same way you did and come to the same conclusions. Your graphs or charts must include all of your data.

Studying Craters

Earlier you learned that an impact crater is formed by an object striking a larger body. However, there is another kind of crater that is also present on some bodies in the solar system. A volcanic crater is a bowl-shaped depression that forms around the opening of a volcano. Volcanoes are openings in the surface of a body through which hotter material can flow or burst through. Often, a series of eruptions of this material creates a cone-shaped hill with a crater at the top.

Grove Karl Gilbert was an American scientist who studied craters on the Moon and Earth at the end of the nineteenth century. At the time, all of the known craters on Earth were thought to have been formed by volcanoes.

An impact crater (above right) is formed when an object strikes a larger body. A volcanic crater (right) is a bowl-shaped depression that forms around the opening of a volcano.

◯ Get Going

Tell students that craters on Earth are not only formed by collision impacts. Ask students if they know anything about volcanoes. Have them share their thoughts on the features of these structures. Then point out that volcanoes can form *volcanic craters*.

NOTES

....

....

....

Grove Karl Gilbert conducted a series of experiments to study the structure of impact craters. He dropped clay balls into clay and sand. He also shot bullets into targets made of clay and sand. Using conclusions he formed after these experiments, he hypothesized that the large dark areas on the Moon were more likely to be impact craters than volcanic craters.

Gilbert was the first to realize that Mare Imbrium on the Moon (left) resembled an impact crater more than a volcano.

Communicate Your Results

Investigation Expo

You will share the results and analysis of your investigation with other groups in an *Investigation Expo*. For your presentation, make a poster that includes the following information:

- the question you were answering in your investigation

- your hypothesis and why you made this hypothesis

- your independent variable and the values you gave it

- your dependent variables and how you measured each

- your procedure, including the variables you controlled

- your data, including measurements, notes, and sketches of the craters

- your data analysis

- your conclusion or conclusions

AST 26

Communicate Your Results: *Investigation Expo*

15 min

Groups share their results in an Investigation Expo.

△ Guide

Tell students they will share their observations and data analyses with the class in an *Investigation Expo*. Have them work with their groups to produce posters that show the information specified in the bulleted list in the student text.

Begin your presentation by stating your question, your hypothesis, your independent and dependent variables, and the reasons you chose those variables. Share with the class how you changed the independent variable and the results of each change. Use the sketches you made to show the effects of the change on the size, shape, or other features of the crater. As you describe the changes, use the language you have learned that describes each feature of a crater. Complete your presentation by sharing your conclusions.

As you listen, make sure you agree with the conclusions of each group. If you do not think that a group's data support their conclusion, raise your hand and explain why. If you have identified a different conclusion, tell the class what your conclusion is. After scientists give presentations, they have these kinds of discussions. Remember that the purpose of the discussion is to learn as much as you can about the effects of different factors on the size and shape of impact craters.

As each group makes its presentation, make a class list of the variables that were tested and the effects of each. When all the presentations are complete, discuss the variables each group tested to determine, as a class, which have the greatest effect on the size, shape, and other features of impact craters.

AST 27

ASTRONOMY

◯ Get Going

Have groups use their posters to present their results. Emphasize that they should explain their procedure, including their question, hypothesis, choice of variables to test, how they changed and controlled variables, and how they made measurements. They should share their sketches to show what they observed. Finally, they should share their conclusions and discuss how their evidence supports their conclusions.

△ Guide and Assess

As groups share their results, encourage students to ask questions about anything that is not clear or anything they think a group has not addressed. It may be necessary to model the kinds of questions you expect students to ask. Take note of how students are participating.

NOTES

Reflect

10 min

The class has a discussion considering what they know about craters from their experiments.

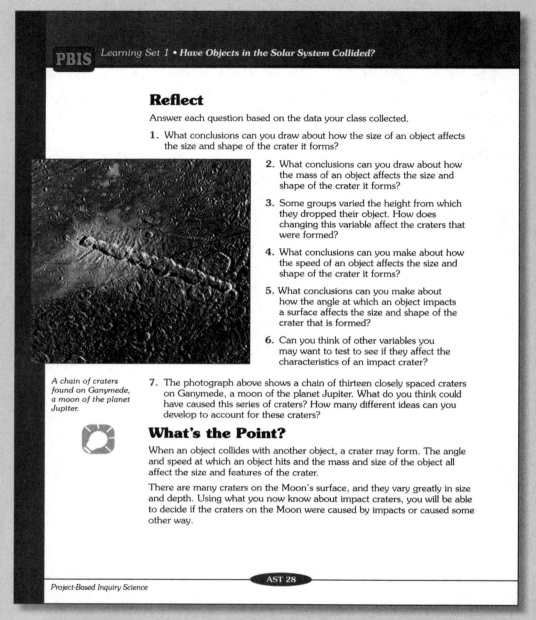

Reflect

Answer each question based on the data your class collected.

1. What conclusions can you draw about how the size of an object affects the size and shape of the crater it forms?

2. What conclusions can you draw about how the mass of an object affects the size and shape of the crater it forms?

3. Some groups varied the height from which they dropped their object. How does changing this variable affect the craters that were formed?

4. What conclusions can you make about how the speed of an object affects the size and shape of the crater it forms?

5. What conclusions can you make about how the angle at which an object impacts a surface affects the size and shape of the crater that is formed?

6. Can you think of other variables you may want to test to see if they affect the characteristics of an impact crater?

A chain of craters found on Ganymede, a moon of the planet Jupiter.

7. The photograph above shows a chain of thirteen closely spaced craters on Ganymede, a moon of the planet Jupiter. What do you think could have caused this series of craters? How many different ideas can you develop to account for these craters?

What's the Point?

When an object collides with another object, a crater may form. The angle and speed at which an object hits and the mass and size of the object all affect the size and features of the crater.

There are many craters on the Moon's surface, and they vary greatly in size and depth. Using what you now know about impact craters, you will be able to decide if the craters on the Moon were caused by impacts or caused some other way.

AST 28

Project-Based Inquiry Science

△ Guide

Lead a class discussion of the *Reflect* questions. Students should use all groups' conclusions from their data analyses to answer these questions. They should also use evidence from all groups' presentations to support their answers.

Questions 6 and 7 are meant to engage students in thinking about what they need to learn to explain different types of craters. They should think about all of the factors that might affect how a crater was formed and try to develop specific ideas for how the craters on Ganymede were formed.

1. Students' answers will vary, but their answers should be similar to the form, *The larger the size of the impact object, the larger the diameter of the crater. The size of the impact object does not affect the shape of the crater.*

2. Students' answers will vary, but should be similar to the form, *The larger the mass of the impact object, the larger the diameter of the crater. The mass of the impact object makes the crater deeper (or the walls higher).*

3. Students' answers will vary, but most will find that the higher the height of the impact object above the flour surface, the larger the diameter of the crater. They may also find that the crater is deeper (or has higher walls).

4. Students' answers will vary, but they should find results that are similar to varying the height (Question 3) since the speed of the impact object will increase as height increases.

5. Students' answers will vary, but most will find the craters that form in the bed of flour become more elliptical as the angle of impact decreases from the vertical (90°). They may also find that the amount of flour ejected increases as the angle of impact decreases.

6. Students' answers will depend upon how many variables the class successfully tested. It may happen that new variables will arise from the discussion or that it will be agreed that a variable should be retested.

7. Students' answers will vary. Some of their suggestions may be:

   - *The pattern of 13 craters on Ganymede was the result of a tight pattern of 13 meteorites striking Jupiter's moon simultaneously.*

   - *The pattern of 13 craters represents a gravitational anomaly underneath the surface that attracts meteors in that odd pattern.*

NOTES

....

....

....

Assessment Options

Targeted Concepts, Skills, and Nature of Science	How do I know if students got it?
Scientists often collaborate and share their findings. Sharing findings makes new information available and helps scientists refine their ideas and build on others' ideas. When another person's or group's idea is used, credit needs to be given.	**ASK:** How do you benefit from sharing your hypothesis, experiment, and procedures with others and listening to their feedback? **LISTEN:** Students should recognize that sharing gives all participants access to new information that may help them be more successful. Feedback from others is helpful because it makes them aware of problems that must be addressed. Being able to resolve problems before carrying out the procedure both increases the validity of the results and saves wasted time and effort.
Scientists must keep clear, accurate, and descriptive records of what they do so they can share their work with others; consider what they did, why they did it, and what they want to do next.	**ASK:** Outline the method you used to record and organize your data so that they could be easily analyzed and shared with others. **LISTEN:** Students should identify the specific strategies they used to organize their data, such as tables or charts, and how the data were organized for ease of analysis, such as sequencing or ordering results by the magnitude of a particular variable.

NOTES

....

....

....

....

....

Targeted Concepts, Skills, and Nature of Science	How do I know if students got it?
Scientists make claims (conclusions) based on evidence obtained (trends in data) from reliable investigations.	**ASK:** Illustrate how you used evidence to support your conclusions about your hypothesis. **LISTEN:** Students' answers will vary because groups investigated different independent variables. However, students should state specific examples of a trend in the dependent variable relative to the independent variable. For example, actual data that shows the depth of the crater increasing as the mass of the object increases. **ASK:** Express what you did to increase the reliability of your data. **LISTEN:** Students should state that they used the same procedure to collect all of their data and that they performed multiple trials to decrease the effects of chance and random errors.
In a reliable investigation, only the manipulated (independent) variable and the responding (dependent) variable change. All other variables are held constant.	**ASK:** Why is it important to control any variables that are not being tested? **LISTEN:** Students should describe that if more variables other than the one being tested are not held constant, one cannot know which of the variables that changed was responsible for causing any observed effect on the responding (dependent) variable.

NOTES

....

....

....

Targeted Concepts, Skills, and Nature of Science	How do I know if students got it?
Observations and measurements are considered reliable if the results are repeatable by other scientists using the same procedures.	**ASK:** Why was it important to describe the procedures, tools, and units to be used when making measurements as part of the overall procedure for measuring the size and shape of a crater? **LISTEN:** Students should cite specific examples of how differences in measurement procedures will result in differences in results. For example, differences in the point inside the crater at which depth is measured will result in differences in the depth of the crater. They should also indicate that specifying the units of measurement to be used facilitates comparison of results among groups.
Impacts of solar-system bodies have created extensive cratering on the Moon and on other bodies in the solar system. Some craters can also be found on Earth, but most have been destroyed by the processes of plate tectonics, and/or the weathering, erosion, and deposition occurring at Earth's planetary surface.	**ASK:** Compare and contrast a crater formed by an impact and one formed by a volcano. **LISTEN:** Students should describe how craters formed by volcanoes are typically found at the top of a cone-shaped mountain. The bottom of the crater is at a higher elevation than the surrounding land. Typically, while the rim of an impact crater rises above the elevation of the surrounding land, the bottom of the crater lies below the elevation of the surrounding land. **ASK:** Compare the craters formed in your experiment with the craters on the Moon shown in the student text. **LISTEN:** Students should describe how both craters were rounded depressions at a lower elevation than the surrounding land, surrounded by a raised rim, and showed evidence of material ejected outward in a ray-like pattern.

Teacher Reflection Questions

- What part of developing experimental questions and hypotheses was difficult for students? What part was easy? How can you better prepare them in the future?

- How were you able to help students understand the concepts of variables? What difficulties did they have in identifying variables? What would you do differently?

- What difficulties came up as students ran experiments with the flour? What can you do to prevent those difficulties in the future?

- When students were preparing their class presentations, how did you encourage them to rethink, reorganize, and refine their oral and written ideas?

- Which measurement or math skills did students find the most difficult? How might you help them to improve those skills?

- How could you tell that students understood the importance of supporting their conclusions with evidence? What opinions or overgeneralizations did your students include in their conclusions?

NOTES

....

....

....

....

....

....

....

....

NOTES

1.3 Explore

What Are the Characteristics of Craters on the Moon?

◀ **1 class period**

A class period is considered to be one 40 to 50 minute class.

Overview

Students explore the characteristics of craters on the Moon by examining photographs of several lunar craters. They compare the diameters of the lunar craters with distances on a local map to get a better sense of their scale. They analyze the characteristics of the craters shown in the photographs and compare them with those of the craters they made in their earlier experiments. They use their analyses of the photographs of lunar craters, the results of their experiments, and those carried out by other groups in the *Section 1.2* to create a description of the event that caused each of the lunar impact craters.

Targeted Concepts, Skills, and Nature of Science	Performance Expectations
Scientists often collaborate and share their findings. Sharing findings makes new information available and helps scientists refine their ideas and build on others' ideas. When another person's or group's idea is used, credit needs to be given.	Students draw upon the results of the experiments performed by their group and others in the class that were shared in the previous activity to construct a description of the event that caused each impact crater they analyzed.
Scientists must keep clear, accurate, and descriptive records of what they do so they can share their work with others; consider what they did, why they did it, and what they want to do next.	Students examine photographs of lunar craters and compare their characteristics with those of the craters formed during their earlier experiments. Students locate their position on a local map and identify places the map that are located at a distance from their position equal to that of the diameter of the craters shown in their text.

Targeted Concepts, Skills, and Nature of Science	Performance Expectations
Impacts of solar-system bodies have created extensive cratering on the Moon and on other bodies in the solar system. Some craters can also be found on Earth, but most have been destroyed by the processes of plate tectonics, and/or the weathering, erosion, and deposition occurring at Earth's planetary surface.	Students observe and record the characteristics of craters on the Moon.

Materials	
1 per group	Local map
	Ruler

Activity Setup and Preparation

The day before class, remind students to bring the results of their experiments from *Section 1.2* to class. If students have not already done so, have them create a written record of the variables and results of all of the experiments carried out by other groups.

Obtain a local map covering a radius of no less than 100 km (57 mi) around the school. The map should have a map scale and show enough detail that the school can be located on the map. If students are not yet familiar with the use of a map scale, you may want to conduct a briefly lesson on map scales.

Homework Options

Reflection

- **Science Process:** Summarize the procedure you used to identify a place located at the same distance from your school as the diameter of each crater on the Moon you analyzed. *(Students should describe how they would mark the position of the school on their map. Then use the map scale to mark off a distance equal to the crater's diameter. They should then draw a circle on the map around the school's location with a radius equal to the diameter of the crater. Students should understand that any place lying on the circle is located at a distance from the school equivalent to the diameter of the crater.)*

- **Science Content:** Connect your description of the event that formed each impact crater you analyzed with supporting data. *(Students should cite results of experiments performed by their group or other groups that indicate factors affecting the size, the depth, or surrounding features of a crater and connect that data to the characteristics of the craters they analyzed. For example, students may state that experimental results indicate that the greater the mass of an object, the larger the impact crater it will form; therefore, it is logical to infer that the event that formed the crater Daedalus involved a more massive object than the one that formed the crater Censorinus.)*

- **Science Content:** Point out the evidence that would lead you to infer that a crater was formed by an object that collided with the surface at a low angle? *(Students should describe a somewhat oval shape with ejecta piled up near one end.)*

Preparation for 1.4

- **Science Process:** If you wanted to determine whether Earth has been struck by an object from space, what evidence would you look for on Earth's surface? *(Students should suggest looking for impact craters that indicate Earth has been struck by an object from space.)*

- **Science Process:** What resources would be helpful to search for impact craters on Earth's surface? *(Students' answers will vary, but typically include: satellite images, aerial photographs, and geological maps.)*

- **Science Content:** Make a list of the characteristics you would look for if searching for an impact crater on Earth's surface. *(Students' answers will vary, but should include: nearly circular in outline, raised rim, concentric inner terraces, and evidence of ejecta.)*

NOTES

....

....

....

....

NOTES

SECTION 1.3 IMPLEMENTATION

1.3 Explore

What Are the Characteristics of Craters on the Moon?

You investigated how impact craters are formed and what affects their size and shape. You observed that the mass of an object affects the depth and diameter of a crater more than the shape. You may also have observed that most impact craters are round, even if they are created by irregularly shaped objects. The angle at which an object hits a surface can affect the appearance of the crater and ejecta. Objects hitting at a low angle can create a piling up of ejecta at one end of the crater. This can make the crater somewhat oval in shape.

An impact crater is like a collision record. In many cases, the object that caused the collision is destroyed or cannot be directly observed. However, the crater itself is a powerful tool for figuring out the motion and characteristics of the object that caused the collision. Using reasoning to reenact the conditions that led to a collision is an important tool in understanding what object could cause such a collision, predicting when collisions will occur, and predicting what will happen after a collision occurs.

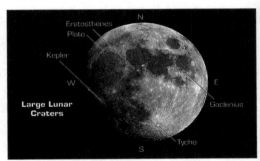

Lunar craters have been mapped since the invention of the telescope in 1608. As technology and space exploration have improved, these maps have become more accurate.

The Moon's surface is covered with craters. Scientists study these craters to learn about the history of the Moon and what happens when impacts occur. From Earth, the craters may look small, but many are hundreds of kilometers across. To help you understand the size of these craters, it is helpful to compare them to something with which you are more familiar on Earth.

AST 29

ASTRONOMY

1.3 Explore

What Are the Characteristics of Craters on the Moon?

10 min

Students consider what they have learned about impact craters to observe craters on Earth's Moon.

○ Engage

Point out the map of a lunar crater in the student text and ask the class if they have ideas about what might have caused the crater. Discuss how students' experiments showed that the size and shape of craters are affected by such factors as the mass of the colliding object and the angle at which it strikes. Using knowledge of how such factors affect the size and shape of craters, it is often possible to determine the characteristics and motion of the object that produced a crater.

*A class period is considered to be one 40 to 50 minute class.

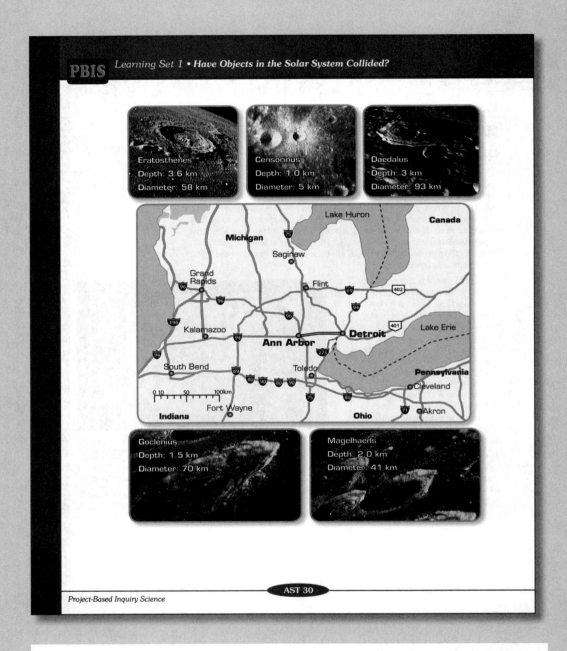

Eratosthenes
Depth: 3.6 km
Diameter: 58 km

Censorinus
Depth: 1.0 km
Diameter: 5 km

Daedalus
Depth: 3 km
Diameter: 93 km

Goclenius
Depth: 1.5 km
Diameter: 70 km

Magelhaens
Depth: 2.0 km
Diameter: 41 km

NOTES

....

....

....

Procedure

With your partner, observe the pictures of different lunar craters. The diameter of each one is given in kilometers. For the diameter of each crater, use a map to find a landmark on Earth that is the same distance from where you are right now. For example, the diameter of *Goclenius* is about 70 km. Look at the map on the previous page. If you were sitting in a school in Detroit, Michigan, the edge of this crater would end in Ann Arbor, Michigan, about 70 km away.

Reflect

1. After carefully observing each picture, compare these craters with those made in the experiments. Use characteristics of each crater, such as shape, ejecta, and size, to decide whether each is an impact crater or not. Which ones are impact craters? How do you know?

2. Compare the craters in the pictures. How are they the same? How are they different?

3. Most of the lunar craters you have observed are rather large. Think back to the experiment you did and apply what you learned to the formation of craters on the Moon. What can you infer about the size of the objects that collided with the Moon to make these craters?

4. Construct a description of the event that caused each impact crater you analyzed. Include your best guess for the size, speed, and angle of the object that collided with the Moon to form the crater.

> **Craters on the Moon**
> Based on the results of your experiment in the preceding section, you know that objects with more mass create craters with greater depth and diameter. By applying what you learned from the experiment, you can say that a crater such as *Daedalus* (depth: 3 km, diameter: 93 km) resulted from a collision with an object with much more mass than the object that created *Censorinus* (depth: 1 km, diameter: 5 km). However, it is also important to look at other variables, possibly tested by your classmates, that could also have an effect on the crater's size and shape.

AST 31

ASTRONOMY

Procedure

15 min

Students interpret the diameters of lunar craters in terms of Earth distances.

△ Guide

Have students meet with their groups and distribute the local maps. Tell them they will use these maps to interpret the size of the craters pictured in their texts in terms of landmarks on Earth. Then assign craters for each group to investigate, pointing out where they are in the student text.

Point out that the diameter of each crater is given. Have students find a landmark on Earth roughly the same distance from where they are as the diameter of each crater.

The student text gives the example of a classroom in Detroit. If students are having difficulty with the task, walk them through the example. Show them how if they were in Detroit and knew that the diameter of the crater Goclenius is 70 km, they could identify Ann Arbor, Michigan as a city about 70 km away.

Reflect

15 min

Students answer the Reflect *questions to further analyze their craters.*

Reflect

1. After carefully observing each picture, compare these craters with those made in the experiments. Use characteristics of each crater, such as shape, ejecta, and size, to decide whether each is an impact crater or not. Which ones are impact craters? How do you know?

2. Compare the craters in the pictures. How are they the same? How are they different?

3. Most of the lunar craters you have observed are rather large. Think back to the experiment you did and apply what you learned to the formation of craters on the Moon. What can you infer about the size of the objects that collided with the Moon to make these craters?

4. Construct a description of the event that caused each impact crater you analyzed. Include your best guess for the size, speed, and angle of the object that collided with the Moon to form the crater.

△ Guide

Have students work with their partners to answer the *Reflect* questions. Emphasize that they should think about how they can apply the conclusions they made in the last section about collisions and craters to answering these questions about the lunar craters they just observed.

After students have had time to answer the questions, lead a class discussion of their answers. Listen for students' understanding that craters with greater diameters and/or depths were probably caused by objects with greater mass. Also listen for an understanding that even the smallest of the craters in these pictures is on a much larger scale than the craters students produced in flour.

☐ Assess

1. Students should respond that all of the lunar craters are impact craters. Volcanic craters are located at the top of a mountain and their base is above the level of the surrounding surface.

2. Students should recognize that the craters are similar because they are circular in shape and have walls, floors, and rims. They are different in their size and the amount of ejected material.

3. Students should answer that, based on their data, the objects that struck the Moon to make such large craters must have been very large objects. Their diameters would be measured in kilometers.

4. Students' answers will vary, but should be similar to the form of: *The meteorite that struck the Moon causing the crater Censorius was traveling at low speed, was of rather small size (less than 1 km in diameter), and hit the Moon at a nearly vertical angle (90°).*

Craters on the Moon
Based on the results of your experiment in the preceding section, you know that objects with more mass create craters with greater depth and diameter. By applying what you learned from the experiment, you can say that a crater such as *Daedalus* (depth: 3 km, diameter: 93 km) resulted from a collision with an object with much more mass than the object that created *Censorinus* (depth: 1 km, diameter: 5 km). However, it is also important to look at other variables, possibly tested by your classmates, that could also have an effect on the crater's size and shape.

Craters on the Moon

5 min

Students answer the Reflect *questions to further analyze their craters.*

△ Guide

Tell students that they will be reading about the effect of variables on the craters made by meteoritic impact. Challenge them to determine which variables caused the effects they predicted in the *Reflect* questions. Help them to understand that one specific effect may be caused by more than one variable. For example, the size of the crater is influenced not only by the mass of the meteorite, but by its speed.

NOTES

_____

_____

_____

_____

_____

_____

_____

These lunar craters resulted from the impact of objects of various masses and speeds, hitting the surface at many different angles.

The angle at which an object strikes the surface affects the depth of the crater. An object that collides with the Moon at a small angle will not make a crater as deep as an object that crashes head on into the Moon. The angle will also affect the rays of the crater. More material will be thrown away from the impact in the same direction in which the object was moving, and less material will be thrown backward. Therefore, the relative length of the rays and the direction of the longest ray from a crater can help determine the direction and angle of the object's motion before the collision.

In your experiment, you may have found that objects crashing at a small angle form oval craters. All of the craters on the Moon are nearly circular. Objects that collide at high speed form circular craters, even if they strike at small angles. This happens because the surface of the larger object and the impacting object behave like liquids during high-speed collisions.

The speed of an object also affects other characteristics of a crater. Objects that are moving faster will form impact craters that are larger and deeper. The size of an object is not as important as its mass and speed in determining the size of the crater. In your experiment, if you gently dropped objects from a height of a few feet, the size of the crater closely matched the size of the object. When objects strike from a greater distance with greater speed, however, the size of the object is less important to the crater's size than is its distance and speed.

What's the Point?

Measurements of the diameter and depth of the craters can help you comprehend how big the craters are. Making a comparison to a common distance, such as the distance between two cities, can help you imagine the depth and width of a crater.

The most important factors for determining what the diameter of an impact crater on a solar-system body will be the mass and speed of the impacting object. These two factors, as well as the angle at which an object hits, determine the depth of the crater.

NOTES

....

....

....

Assessment Options

Targeted Concepts, Skills, and Nature of Science	How do I know if students got it?
Scientists often collaborate and share their findings. Sharing findings makes new information available and helps scientists refine their ideas and build on others' ideas. When another person's or group's idea is used, credit needs to be given.	**ASK:** When you created your description of the event that could have caused each impact crater, how were the results of the earlier experiments shared by other groups helpful to you? **LISTEN:** Students should describe how their group's experiment investigated the effects of only one factor. They should not describe how the results shared by other groups helped them identify other factors that could account for the differences in size, depth, and appearance of the craters they analyzed.
Scientists must keep clear, accurate, and descriptive records of what they do so they can share their work with others; consider what they did, why they did it, and what they want to do next.	**ASK:** The depth and diameter of each crater was given in the caption under its photograph. What other characteristics were you able to observe by careful examination of the photograph? **LISTEN:** Students should describe how they were able to determine the shape of the perimeter of the impact crater, concentric inner terraces, raised central mountains, and evidence of material ejected from the crater radiating around the outside of the rim. **ASK:** How did you determine that a place was the same distance from your school as the diameter of a particular crater? **LISTEN:** Students should describe how they used the map scale to mark off a distance equivalent to the crater diameter and comparing that to the distance between the school and that place.

NOTES

Targeted Concepts, Skills, and Nature of Science	How do I know if students got it?
Impacts of solar-system bodies have created extensive cratering on the Moon and on other bodies in the solar system. Some craters can also be found on Earth, but most have been destroyed by the processes of plate tectonics, and/or the weathering, erosion, and deposition occurring at Earth's planetary surface.	**ASK:** From the images of the Moon you examined, what percentage of the Moon's surface would you estimate is covered by impact craters? **LISTEN:** Student answers will vary, but should indicate that from what they observed in the photographs, most of the Moon's surface is covered by impact craters. **ASK:** What evidence did you observe that more than one impact event had occurred in the area shown in each photograph? What can you infer about these other impact events from the photographs? **LISTEN:** Students should answer that the presence of other craters indicates other collision impacts. Students should connect factors affecting the characteristics of an impact crater with differences between the named crater and others in the photograph. For example, the objects that collided with the Moon to form the smaller craters were probably smaller than those that made the larger craters.

Teacher Reflection Questions

- How did this activity provide students with the opportunity and time to work independently, in pairs, and in small groups?

- When students were examining the photographs of craters, what questions could you have asked to elicit greater detail in their descriptions?

- What additional assistance, support, and/or resources would have further enhanced this lesson?

- How did students apply their observations from their experiments to their analyses of the lunar craters depicted in their texts?

- How were you able to engage students in observing and analyzing the lunar craters depicted in their texts? What might you try next time?

1.4 Explore

Does Earth Have Craters Formed by Collisions With Space Objects?

◀ *2 class periods*

A class period is considered to be one 40 to 50 minute class.

Overview

Students use Earth-imaging software to search for impact craters on Earth's surface near their home or school. After experiencing little or no success, students use the Earth-imaging software to examine a crater in Arizona. They brainstorm locations on Earth where craters might be more visible and explore those locations for evidence of craters. After reading about the impact event that formed the Barringer Meteor Crater in Arizona, students work in pairs to examine satellite images of one of Earth's 25 largest meteor craters. Students compare the appearance of impact craters on Earth with the appearance of lunar impact craters. Each pair then marks the location of the crater they chose to explore on a world map and shares their observations with the class. After reflecting on differences between the number, distribution, and characteristics of Earth craters and lunar craters, students update the *Project Board*.

Targeted Concepts, Skills, and Nature of Science	Performance Expectations
Scientists often collaborate and share their findings. Sharing findings makes new information available and helps scientists refine their ideas and build on others' ideas. When another person's or group's idea is used, credit needs to be given.	Students share the location and characteristics of Earth's impact crater they investigated with the class. Students share the differences they observed between their assigned impact crater on Earth and the impact craters on the Moon that they examined earlier.
Scientists must keep clear, accurate, and descriptive records of what they do so they can share their work with others; consider what they did, why they did it, and what they want to do next.	Students record their observations and descriptions of their assigned Earth crater. Students participate in a class discussion and keep a record of the characteristics of the impact craters on Earth that were investigated by the class.

Targeted Concepts, Skills, and Nature of Science	Performance Expectations
Impacts of solar-system bodies have created extensive cratering on the Moon and on other bodies in the solar system. Some craters also can be found on Earth, but most have been destroyed by the processes of plate tectonics and/or the weathering, erosion, and deposition occurring at Earth's planetary surface.	Students observe that impact craters are fewer in number and more difficult to observe on Earth's surface than on the Moon's surface. Students consider possible reasons for the difference in the number and visibility of craters on Earth and on the Moon.

Materials	
1 per group	List of Earth's 25 largest impact craters Computer with Internet access Index card
1 per classroom	World map

Activity Setup and Preparation

Arrange beforehand for the class to have computer access with an Internet connection for this activity. Have the list of Earth's 25 largest impact craters by doing an Internet search before class.

Homework Options

Reflection

- **Science Content:** Earth is larger and has more mass than the Moon. Why would this make it more likely that an object in space would collide with Earth than with the Moon? *(Students should answer that Earth's larger size makes it a larger target and its greater mass results in stronger force of gravity attracting objects in space.)*

- **Science Content:** If it is more likely that an object would collide with Earth than with the Moon, how would that affect the number of impact craters you would expect to observe on Earth's surface compared to the Moon's surface? *(Students should answer that without erosion and tectonic plate effects, Earth would have more impact craters than are found on the surface of the Moon.)*

Preparation for 1.5

- **Science Content:** Other than size and mass, how does Earth differ from the Moon? *(Students should answer that Earth has an atmosphere, oceans, life, and is geologically active.)*

- **Science Process:** What new information about impact craters did you obtain by listening to presentations made by other students? *(Answers will vary, but may refer to some impact craters being hidden beneath surface layers of sediment, water, or ice.)*

NOTES

NOTES

SECTION 1.4 IMPLEMENTATION

1.4 Explore

Does Earth Have Craters Formed by Collisions With Space Objects?

When you look at pictures of the Moon, the entire surface seems covered with craters. If there have been collisions on Earth as well, why isn't Earth covered with craters? You may never have seen an impact crater on Earth, even if you have traveled all around the world. And, you do not know for sure if Earth has such craters. If Earth has even a few craters like those on the Moon, they should be easy to find using **satellite images**. You will use an Earth-imaging program to explore Earth's surface, looking for evidence of craters.

A crater is evidence of a past collision only when it is an impact crater, not a volcanic crater. You must determine what type of crater you are looking at before you can determine if it is evidence of a collision. As it turns out, all of the craters on the Moon are the result of impacts. But the same cannot be said about the craters on Earth.

You can use Earth-imaging software to inspect satellite images of Earth. The program will allow you to scroll east, west, north, and south, and also to zoom in and zoom out. The program will enable you to record the coordinates (latitude and longitude) of specific points on each image.

satellite image: an image taken by an artificial object placed in orbit around Earth.

Looking for Craters Near You

Procedure

1. Find a familiar landmark, such as your home or school. Use the navigation tools to explore the nearby area, searching for evidence of craters.

2. Record the location of any craters you find using longitude and latitude. Make a sketch of the crater and label it with the parts you find.

AST 33

ASTRONOMY

1.4 Explore

Does Earth Have Craters Formed by Collisions With Space Objects?

5 min

Students are introduced to the activity.

△ Guide

Begin by pointing out that in the images of the Moon examined by students, the surface seemed covered by craters. Ask students if they have ever seen a crater on Earth and if they think there are as many craters on Earth's surface as on the Moon. Tell students they will use satellite images to look for craters on Earth's surface.

*A class period is considered to be one 40 to 50 minute class.

Looking for Craters Near You

5 min

Students look for craters near their homes using Earth-imaging software.

Looking for Craters Near You

Procedure

1. Find a familiar landmark, such as your home or school. Use the navigation tools to explore the nearby area, searching for evidence of craters.

2. Record the location of any craters you find using longitude and latitude. Make a sketch of the crater and label it with the parts you find.

△ Guide

Have students open the Earth-imaging software and go over the steps in the student text. Make sure students know how to use the navigation tools in the software and let them locate a local landmark. If they find any craters, ask them what evidence they can find that the crater is from an impact. Emphasize that some craters on Earth are caused by geologic activity and may not be impact craters.

Be aware that students may have difficulty finding craters. Do not let them spend too much time looking for craters. If they cannot find any, ask them why they think they were unable to. Ask why they think craters might be less frequent on Earth's surface than on the surface of the Moon.

NOTES

Finding a Crater

Procedure

3. Enter *Meteor Crater in Arizona* into the search box of the program you are using. Wait until this area appears clearly on the map. This crater is also known as Barringer Meteorite Crater.

4. Explore the crater using the navigation tools. Scroll around the rim of the crater and record the different elevations, usually shown near the bottom of the screen. Scroll over the floor of the crater and record those elevations. Locate the rim, bowl, floor, and ejecta. Sketch the crater and label each crater part that you can observe.

> **The Barringer Meteorite Crater (Meteor Crater)**
>
> Meteor Crater is located in the middle of an Arizona desert. The crater is 1.3 km wide (0.8 mi) and 174 m deep (570 ft). This means that the crater is about as deep as a six-story building and as wide across as 14 football fields. Scientists agree that it was created by an impact from a meteorite that survived its trip through Earth's atmosphere.
>
>
> The meteorite that formed this crater struck Earth about 50,000 years ago, during the last Ice Age. The meteorite was only about 50 m (164 ft) across, about half a city block. Evidence from the crater indicates that the meteorite was made of the metals nickel and iron, and it had a mass greater than 100,000 tons. A 100,000-ton meteorite has the same mass as 15,000 large elephants or 400 Statues of Liberty.
>
> An impact that massive would have created a large crater and explosion. Scientists have calculated that the impact of the meteorite as it collided with Earth produced an explosion equal to over 20 million tons of

AST 34

Finding a Crater

5 min

Students observe the Barringer Meteorite Crater using Earth-imaging software.

△ Guide

Once students have finished searching for and observing craters near their homes, guide them to search Arizona for the Barringer Meteorite Crater. Have them enter *Meteor Crater in Arizona* in their software's search box. They may need to further specify that they are looking for a crater in Flagstaff, Arizona. Have them use the navigation tools to explore the features of the crater. They should record the different elevations around the rim and floor of the crater and note any ejecta.

The Barringer Meteorite Crater (Meteor Crater)

5 min

The class discusses Meteor Crater (or Barringer Meteorite Crater).

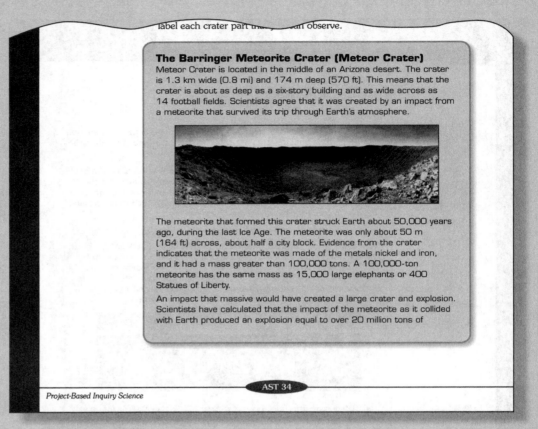

label each crater part they can observe.

The Barringer Meteorite Crater (Meteor Crater)

Meteor Crater is located in the middle of an Arizona desert. The crater is 1.3 km wide (0.8 mi) and 174 m deep (570 ft). This means that the crater is about as deep as a six-story building and as wide across as 14 football fields. Scientists agree that it was created by an impact from a meteorite that survived its trip through Earth's atmosphere.

The meteorite that formed this crater struck Earth about 50,000 years ago, during the last Ice Age. The meteorite was only about 50 m (164 ft) across, about half a city block. Evidence from the crater indicates that the meteorite was made of the metals nickel and iron, and it had a mass greater than 100,000 tons. A 100,000-ton meteorite has the same mass as 15,000 large elephants or 400 Statues of Liberty.

An impact that massive would have created a large crater and explosion. Scientists have calculated that the impact of the meteorite as it collided with Earth produced an explosion equal to over 20 million tons of

AST 34

Project-Based Inquiry Science

△ Guide

Once students have had a chance to explore Meteor Crater, use the student text to discuss what is known about the crater. Discuss how the crater was formed by a meteorite that struck Earth about 50,000 years ago. Despite the great size of the crater (1.3 km in diameter), the meteorite was only about 50 m across. Also, discuss the magnitude of the impact, which caused an explosion equal to over 20 million tons of explosives. As the class discusses, have them compare the facts in the student text to their recorded observations.

NOTES

....

....

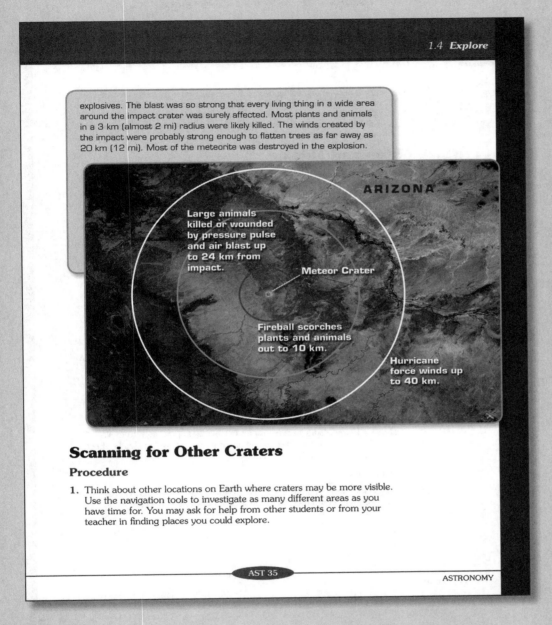

explosives. The blast was so strong that every living thing in a wide area around the impact crater was surely affected. Most plants and animals in a 3 km (almost 2 mi) radius were likely killed. The winds created by the impact were probably strong enough to flatten trees as far away as 20 km (12 mi). Most of the meteorite was destroyed in the explosion.

ARIZONA

Large animals killed or wounded by pressure pulse and air blast up to 24 km from impact.

Meteor Crater

Fireball scorches plants and animals out to 10 km.

Hurricane force winds up to 40 km.

Scanning for Other Craters

Procedure

1. Think about other locations on Earth where craters may be more visible. Use the navigation tools to investigate as many different areas as you have time for. You may ask for help from other students or from your teacher in finding places you could explore.

AST 35

ASTRONOMY

Scanning for Other Craters

5 min

Students use the Earth-imaging software to find more craters on Earth's surface.

○ Engage

Ask students where they think an impact crater would be likely to hit Earth and lead a discussion using their responses. They may suggest the Equator or the Polar regions. Since few meteorite craters are known, they might suggest that large, unpopulated regions such as eastern Russia and Mongolia would be likely places to look.

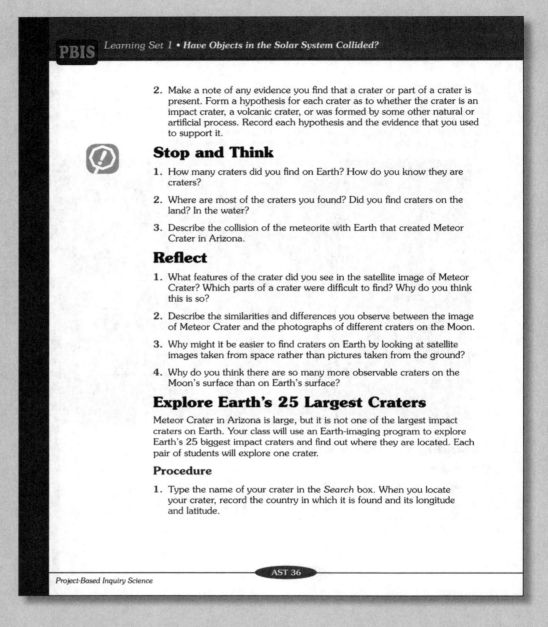

2. Make a note of any evidence you find that a crater or part of a crater is present. Form a hypothesis for each crater as to whether the crater is an impact crater, a volcanic crater, or was formed by some other natural or artificial process. Record each hypothesis and the evidence that you used to support it.

Stop and Think

1. How many craters did you find on Earth? How do you know they are craters?

2. Where are most of the craters you found? Did you find craters on the land? In the water?

3. Describe the collision of the meteorite with Earth that created Meteor Crater in Arizona.

Reflect

1. What features of the crater did you see in the satellite image of Meteor Crater? Which parts of a crater were difficult to find? Why do you think this is so?

2. Describe the similarities and differences you observe between the image of Meteor Crater and the photographs of different craters on the Moon.

3. Why might it be easier to find craters on Earth by looking at satellite images taken from space rather than pictures taken from the ground?

4. Why do you think there are so many more observable craters on the Moon's surface than on Earth's surface?

Explore Earth's 25 Largest Craters

Meteor Crater in Arizona is large, but it is not one of the largest impact craters on Earth. Your class will use an Earth-imaging program to explore Earth's 25 biggest impact craters and find out where they are located. Each pair of students will explore one crater.

Procedure

1. Type the name of your crater in the *Search* box. When you locate your crater, record the country in which it is found and its longitude and latitude.

AST 36

Project-Based Inquiry Science

Have students use the Earth-imaging software to look for those impact sites and others. Once they locate a crater, they should form a hypothesis and record the details of how they think that crater formed. Remind them to support their ideas with evidence.

△ Guide

Have students answer the *Stop and Think* questions in their groups and prepare to share with the class. Students should have observed that it was difficult to find craters on Earth. It was probably easiest to find craters in dry places.

1. Students' answers will vary, but they should indicate that it was difficult to find craters without more specific information. They should discuss how most craters are eroded and are often filled with water, causing them to look like lakes. They should identify that they are craters by their typical circular shape.

2. Students' answers will vary, but without specific instructions, it is unlikely any group of students will find more than one crater.

3. Students have read that about 50,000 years ago, a nickel-iron meteorite approximately 50 m in diameter hit Earth at about 13 km per second. This left a crater 1200 m in diameter and 170 m deep. They should describe this in their answers.

△ Guide

Have students discuss the *Reflect* questions with their groups and then lead a class discussion of their answers. Students should recognize that there are more craters on the surface of the Moon than on Earth's surface, and that the Moon's craters tend to have more defined features. They should begin to understand that environmental factors account for the differences between craters on Earth and craters on the Moon.

1. Students should have observed the rim, walls, floor, and rays from the Barrington Crater, but had difficulty observing the ejecta. They should deduce that the ejecta probably were reduced in size by erosion and covered with plant life, making them invisible.

2. Students should identify that the similarities between Moon craters and Meteor Crater are the shape and the characteristics of rim, walls, rays, and floor. However, the Moon craters are much better defined because of the lack of erosion.

3. Students' answers will vary, but most will argue that satellite images are better to use to find craters because they show the circular structure of the craters while ground photographs will not.

4. Students should answer that the Moon has no atmosphere, water, weather, or plant life, so the craters are unchanged for millions of years. The conditions on Earth work to "erase" the blemishes caused by meteorite strikes.

Explore Earth's 25 Largest Craters

10 min

Students use the Earth-imaging software to find and observe the most predominant impact craters on Earth.

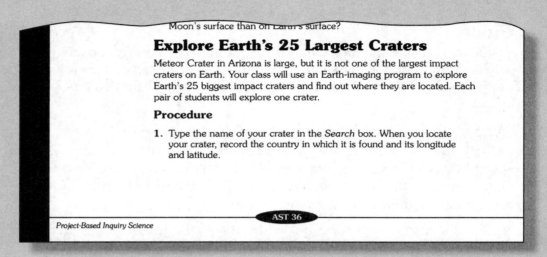

Moon's surface than on Earth's surface?

Explore Earth's 25 Largest Craters

Meteor Crater in Arizona is large, but it is not one of the largest impact craters on Earth. Your class will use an Earth-imaging program to explore Earth's 25 biggest impact craters and find out where they are located. Each pair of students will explore one crater.

Procedure

1. Type the name of your crater in the *Search* box. When you locate your crater, record the country in which it is found and its longitude and latitude.

Project-Based Inquiry Science

AST 36

△ Guide

Distribute index cards and assign each group one of the 25 largest craters to explore. Tell groups to type the name of their crater into the *Search* box in the Earth-imaging software and locate the crater.

Then, on an index card, have them make a detailed sketch of the crater, labeling all of the parts and features. They should list characteristics of the crater, including its size, age, and features. Remind them to indicate the scale of their sketch so it will be possible to compare the size of the craters depicted by the sketches.

NOTES

....

....

....

....

....

2. Make a sketch of your crater on an index card. Label all of the parts and features of the crater that you can observe. Include the **scale** on your drawing so that the sizes of different craters can be compared by using the sketches.

3. Describe any characteristics of the crater, such as the diameter, that you can determine from the satellite image.

4. Use the Internet to find other information about your crater, such as how old it is. Record any relevant or interesting information that you can find about the crater, such as how it was discovered or what is known about the object that formed the crater.

scale: the ratio of the size of a drawing of an object or place to the size of the actual object or place.

geologist: a person who is trained in and works in any of the geologic sciences.

geology (geologic): the study of the planet Earth: the materials of which it is made, the processes that act on these materials, the products formed, and the history of the planet and all its forms since its origin.

astrogeology: the study of the rocks, minerals, and surface features of moons and other planets, applying knowledge of Earth's geology.

Partners in Astronomy

Eugene Shoemaker, trained as a **geologist**, was the first scientist to recognize the possibility that craters on both Earth and on the Moon were caused by meteorite impacts. His 1952 visit to Meteor Crater in Arizona got him interested in the relationship between craters on Earth and on the Moon. He combined his interest in **geology** with astronomy, developing a new field of science known as **astrogeology**. This new area of science extends the study of geology into space.

Communicate

Share Your Findings

Post your index card and indicate your crater's location. As you listen to the description of each crater from the other groups, compare each one to the crater you investigated. Compare the location, diameter, and depth. Think about how the crater is different from yours. Think about how the mass and speed of the objects that caused the craters may compare.

Partners in Astronomy

5 min

Students read about Eugene Shoemaker and his interest in Meteor Crater.

◯ Get Going

Read the short passage with the class and introduce the terms *geology* and *astrogeology*. Ask students how what they know about the findings of geologists will be useful when trying to accomplish the goal of the Unit.

Communicate: Share Your Findings

15 min

Students share their findings on their terrestrial crater with the class.

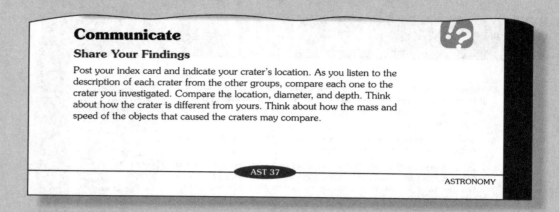

Communicate

Share Your Findings

Post your index card and indicate your crater's location. As you listen to the description of each crater from the other groups, compare each one to the crater you investigated. Compare the location, diameter, and depth. Think about how the crater is different from yours. Think about how the mass and speed of the objects that caused the craters may compare.

AST 37

ASTRONOMY

△ Guide

Have students attach their index cards to a world map over their crater's location. They should then share their findings with the class. As each group presents, students should think about how the group's crater is similar to or different from their crater. They should also think about how the objects that produced the craters might compare.

NOTES

Reflect

1. Describe any patterns you observe in the location of the craters.

2. How do Earth's craters compare to those found on the Moon?

3. Where else do you think craters might be located on Earth? Why would it be difficult to locate some of Earth's craters?

4. Why do you think craters on Earth's surface are more difficult to find than craters on the Moon?

Update the *Project Board*

You have observed craters on the Moon and explored craters on Earth. Now is a good time to update the *Project Board*. Add what you know about the impact of meteorites to the *What are we learning?* column. Be sure to include what you know about craters on the Moon, what you know about craters on Earth, and how those craters are similar and different from each other. Remember to add evidence for each of your entries in the *What are we learning?* column to the *What is our evidence?* column. Also, your observations most likely raised new questions. These questions, or other ideas about which you are unsure, should be added to the *What do we need to investigate?* column.

What's the Point?

Earth's craters are not as easy to locate as craters on the Moon. Lunar craters cover much of the Moon's surface and can easily be seen using a pair of binoculars or a telescope. New technology, such as satellite imaging, can help identify evidence of craters on Earth's surface. However, many fewer craters have been identified on Earth than on the Moon.

AST 38

Reflect

10 min

Students answer questions about craters on Earth and craters on the Moon using their knowledge from the section.

△ Guide and Assess

Lead a class discussion of the *Reflect* questions. Students should be developing confidence that there are fewer impact craters remaining on Earth's surface than on the surface of the Moon. Even when you look at Earth's surface from a distance, it is apparent that there are fewer craters.

1. Student answers will vary depending on the craters they observed.

2. Students should note that Earth has far fewer remaining craters to see than the Moon. Earth's craters are also less defined than the Moon's because of erosion.

3. Students should predict that the oceans would contain most of Earth's meteorites and these may or may not have left a crater. In any case, they would be almost impossible to find.

4. Students should understand that because of biological, geologic, tectonic, and weathering causes, craters on Earth are more difficult to see as time passes.

Update the Project Board

10 min

Lead a class discussion to update the Project Board.

Update the *Project Board*

You have observed craters on the Moon and explored craters on Earth. Now is a good time to update the *Project Board*. Add what you know about the impact of meteorites to the *What are we learning?* column. Be sure to include what you know about craters on the Moon, what you know about craters on Earth, and how those craters are similar and different from each other. Remember to add evidence for each of your entries in the *What are we learning?* column to the *What is our evidence?* column. Also, your observations most likely raised new questions. These questions, or other ideas about which you are unsure, should be added to the *What do we need to investigate?* column.

△ Guide

Ask students what information they can put in the *What are we learning?* column of the *Project Board*. They should have new science knowledge about meteorite impacts that they can put in this column. Record their ideas on the *Project Board* and have them record the ideas on their own *Project Board* pages. Then ask them what questions they have that they can put in the *What do we need to investigate?* column. Record their questions on the Project Board.

NOTES

Assessment Options

Targeted Concepts, Skills, and Nature of Science	How do I know if students got it?
Scientists often collaborate and share their findings. Sharing findings makes new information available and helps scientists refine their ideas and build on others' ideas. When another person's or group's idea is used, credit needs to be given.	**ASK:** What pattern to the distribution of impact craters on Earth's surface did you notice when the class plotted their impact craters on the world map? **LISTEN:** Students should have noticed that there seemed to be more impact craters nearer the Poles and fewer nearer the Equator.
Scientists must keep clear, accurate, and descriptive records of what they do so they can share their work with others; consider what they did, why they did it, and what they want to do next.	**ASK:** From the observations of other groups' crater explorations, describe the characteristics of Earth's impact craters. **LISTEN:** Students should describe how Earth's impact craters tend to be less distinct in their features, covered by vegetation, buried by sediments, or filled with water.
Impacts of solar-system bodies have created extensive cratering on the Moon and on other bodies in the solar system. Some craters can also be found on Earth, but most have been destroyed by the processes of plate tectonics, and/or the weathering, erosion and deposition occurring at Earth's planetary surface.	**ASK:** When you used the Earth-imaging software to scan Earth's surface, how successful were you in finding impact craters? If you used such a program to scan the Moon's surface, how successful do you think you would have been? **LISTEN:** Students' answers may vary, but most will indicate that their search for impact craters on Earth's surface was largely unsuccessful. Students' answers should indicate that they would be much more successful locating impact craters on the Moon.

Teacher Reflection Questions

- Was the instructional objective met in this section? How do you know that students learned what was intended?

- What challenges did you face having students work with the Earth-imaging software? How could you address those challenges when working with your classes in the future?

- How were you able to keep students focused on the task as they scanned for craters? What might you try next time?

- How do the activities and readings students just completed set the stage for the focus of the next section of this *Learning Set?*

NOTES

1.5 Explain

Why Are Craters More Difficult to Find on Earth Than on the Moon?

◀ *1 class period*

A class period is considered to be one 40 to 50 minute class.

Overview

Students examine photographs of impact craters on Earth that have existed for different lengths of time and read about the effects of weathering and erosion on structures exposed at Earth's surface. Students create an explanation for the differences they observed between craters on Earth and on the Moon and share their explanation with the class. Students revise their explanations based on what they have learned from the photographs they examined and what they have read, and discuss their revisions with the class. Students apply what they have learned by reflecting on how the current appearance of an impact crater on Earth's surface might change over time and considering how the crater left by an impact on water might differ from one that occurred on land. Students conclude the section by updating the *Project Board*.

Targeted Concepts, Skills, and Nature of Science	Performance Expectations
Scientists often collaborate and share their findings. Sharing findings makes new information available and helps scientists refine their ideas and build on others' ideas. When another person's or group's idea is used, credit needs to be given.	Students work in groups to create their explanation for why craters on Earth are different from craters on the Moon and share their explanations with the class. Students discuss the strengths and weaknesses of the explanations shared by others in the class and the class develops an explanation that best explains the differences between craters on the Moon and craters on Earth.

NOTES

....

....

Targeted Concepts, Skills, and Nature of Science	Performance Expectations
Scientists must keep clear, accurate, and descriptive records of what they do so they can share their work with others; consider what they did, why they did it, and what they want to do next.	Students use their previous records to assist them in creating their explanations. Students record their explanation for differences between craters on the Moon and craters on Earth, along with supporting evidence and science knowledge, on a *Create an Explanation* page. Students record the explanations shared by other groups in the class and the best explanation developed by the class. Students record what they have learned about differences between craters on Earth and on the Moon, the evidence supporting what they think they have learned, and what they think they still need to investigate on the *Project Board*.
Scientists make claims (conclusions) based on evidence obtained (trends in data) from reliable investigations.	Students develop a claim about why craters on Earth and on the Moon differ based on evidence obtained from their observations of Earth and Moon craters and their readings in this *Learning Set*.
Explanations are claims supported by evidence. Evidence can be experimental results, observational data, and any other accepted scientific knowledge.	Students develop an explanation for the differences between craters on Earth and on the Moon and support that explanation with evidence from their investigations and the science knowledge drawn from what they have read.
Impacts of solar-system bodies have created extensive cratering on the Moon and on other bodies in the solar system. Some craters can be found on Earth, but most have been destroyed by the processes of plate tectonics and/or the weathering, erosion and deposition occurring at Earth's planetary surface.	Students identify differences between craters on Earth and on the Moon, such as: number, exposure, distinctness of features, and observations that Earth craters may be filled with water or buried beneath sediments. Students identify reasons why craters on Earth differ from craters on the Moon, such as the lack of an atmosphere or hydrosphere on the Moon and thus, lack of agents of erosion; destruction of craters on Earth by plate tectonic processes, weathering and erosion and/or burial by deposition.

Materials	
1 per student	*Create Your Explanation* page
1 per class	Class *Project Board*

Homework Options

Reflection

- **Science Content:** What Earth systems are not present on the Moon? *(Students' answers should include, but are not limited to, atmosphere, hydrosphere, biosphere.)*

- **Science Content:** How does the Moon's lack of an atmosphere or hydrosphere explain why, compared to Earth, more craters are visible and why the features of Moon craters are more clearly visible? *(Students' answers will vary, but should refer to agents of erosion and the destructive processes of weathering and erosion.)*

- **Science Process:** Describe what was going through your mind when you completed the Claim and Evidence boxes on the Create Your Explanation page. *(This question should encourage students to engage in metacognition, i.e. the connections they were thinking about between their observations of craters on Earth and on the Moon and the science knowledge about craters that they had read about throughout the* Learning Set.*)*

- **Science Process:** What were some differences between your explanation and other groups' explanations? What claims do you think you could support with the evidence presented by other groups in the class? Would you need more information to support any of the claims presented by other groups in the class? *(These questions should encourage students to evaluate the explanations presented in class and to think about creating scientific explanations.)*

Preparation for 1.6

- **Science Content:** Earlier, you read a description of the impact of the Peekskill meteorite. What effect did Earth's atmosphere have on the incoming meteoroid? *(Students' answers should include heating due to friction with the air caused the meteoroid to glow and break apart into fragments.)*

NOTES

....

....

....

....

....

....

....

....

....

....

....

....

....

SECTION 1.5 IMPLEMENTATION

1.5 Explore

Why Are Craters More Difficult to Find on Earth Than on the Moon?

You have learned that craters are more common on the Moon than on Earth. You have also noticed that Earth's craters look quite different from the Moon's craters, and discussed some of the reasons why Earth's craters look so different. To understand the nature of collisions with these two bodies, you need to know why craters are more common on the Moon and why Earth's craters look so different from the Moon's craters.

Compare Lunar Craters to Craters on Earth

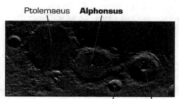

Ptolemaeus **Alphonsus**

Alpetragios Arzachel

The lunar crater Alphonsus is about 3.9 billion years old. It is still clearly visible on the Moon's surface. Notice that the rim, the evidence of ejecta, and the floor of the crater are all clear. Despite being far older than any crater found on Earth, its features are still intact and quite visible, with no evidence of change.

Earth's Meteor Crater in Arizona, which you observed in the last section, is 50,000 years old. Look at the photographs on the next page. These photographs show some craters on Earth that are older than Meteor Crater, ranging from 300,000 years old to about 212 million years old.

1.5 Explore

Why Are Craters More Difficult to Find on Earth Than on the Moon?

5 min

Students are introduced to the activity of the section.

○ Engage

Remind students of the evidence that there are more craters on the surface of the Moon than on Earth's surface. Ask them why they think there are more craters on the Moon than on Earth, and what evidence they can use to answer the question.

*A class period is considered to be one 40 to 50 minute class.

Compare Lunar Craters to Craters on Earth

5 min

Students observe lunar and terrestrial craters of different ages.

---

why Earth's ~~~~~ so different from the ~~~~~ ~~~~~.

Compare Lunar Craters to Craters on Earth

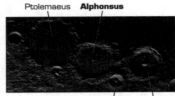

Ptolemaeus **Alphonsus**

Alpetragios   Arzachel

The lunar crater Alphonsus is about 3.9 billion years old. It is still clearly visible on the Moon's surface. Notice that the rim, the evidence of ejecta, and the floor of the crater are all clear. Despite being far older than any crater found on Earth, its features are still intact and quite visible, with no evidence of change.

Earth's Meteor Crater in Arizona, which you observed in the last section, is 50,000 years old. Look at the photographs on the next page. These photographs show some craters on Earth that are older than Meteor Crater, ranging from 300,000 years old to about 212 million years old.

AST 39

ASTRONOMY

△ Guide

Draw students' attention to the photograph of Alphonsus Crater. Point out that the features of this crater are clearly visible. Point out that Alphonsus Crater is 3.9 billion years old, making it older than any crater on Earth.

NOTES

....

....

....

....

....

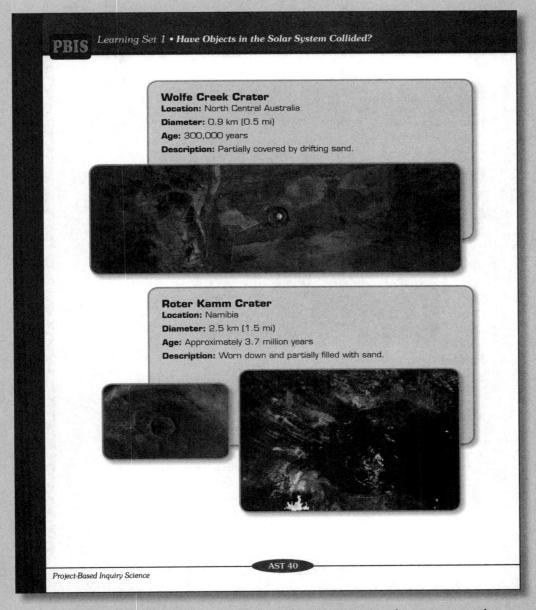

Wolfe Creek Crater
Location: North Central Australia
Diameter: 0.9 km (0.5 mi)
Age: 300,000 years
Description: Partially covered by drifting sand.

Roter Kamm Crater
Location: Namibia
Diameter: 2.5 km (1.5 mi)
Age: Approximately 3.7 million years
Description: Worn down and partially filled with sand.

AST 40

Project-Based Inquiry Science

Guide students to observe the pictures of craters on Earth. Point out that
these craters are older than Meteor Crater. Let students know that the age of
each is given and that they should observe the effect of age on the oldest
of them, Manicouagan Crater. Ask students how the oldest Earth crater
depicted compares to the most recent, and how that crater compares to
Alphonsus Crater (on the Moon). They should observe that the older craters
on Earth are much less distinct than the more recent craters and less distinct
than the crater on the Moon.

Reflect

10 min

Students answer questions comparing Moon craters to Earth craters and then share their answers with the class.

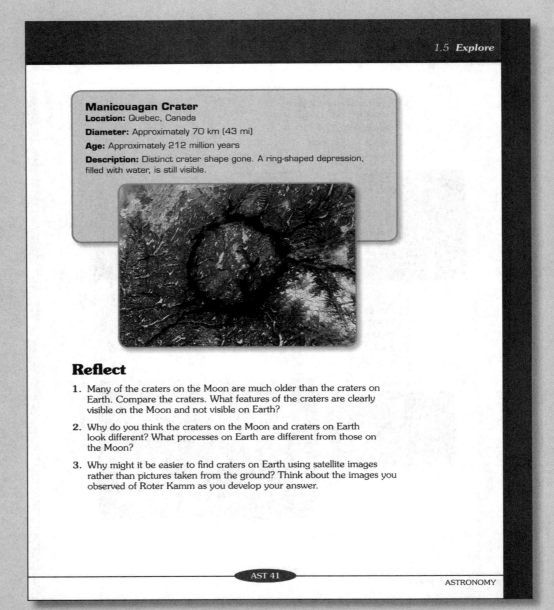

Manicouagan Crater
Location: Quebec, Canada

Diameter: Approximately 70 km (43 mi)

Age: Approximately 212 million years

Description: Distinct crater shape gone. A ring-shaped depression, filled with water, is still visible.

Reflect

1. Many of the craters on the Moon are much older than the craters on Earth. Compare the craters. What features of the craters are clearly visible on the Moon and not visible on Earth?

2. Why do you think the craters on the Moon and craters on Earth look different? What processes on Earth are different from those on the Moon?

3. Why might it be easier to find craters on Earth using satellite images rather than pictures taken from the ground? Think about the images you observed of Roter Kamm as you develop your answer.

AST 41

ASTRONOMY

△ Guide

Have students answer the *Reflect* questions in their groups. Students should use their observations of differences between craters on Earth and on the Moon to develop ideas about processes on Earth that could lead to those differences. Encourage them to think about what they know about how the Moon is different from the Earth. They should also think about why some of the older craters are more easily identified using satellite imagery than from the ground.

1. Students should observe that the craters on the Moon have much more defined characteristics like a rim, wall, floor, rays, and ejecta. The ejecta and rays of craters on Earth cannot be seen and the rims and walls are less distinct due to erosion.

2. Students should describe how there is little in the lunar world to disturb the craters once they form so they remain unchanged for millennia. On Earth, the processes of plant growth and weathering by wind and water cause a gradual decline in the vividness of the features.

3. Students should realize that it is easier to recognize craters on Earth by looking at satellite images, because one can see the characteristic circular shape from above.

NOTES

....

....

....

....

....

....

....

....

....

....

The Covering and Uncovering of Chicxulub Crater

5 min

The class discusses how erosion and weathering have affected Chicxulub and other terrestrial craters.

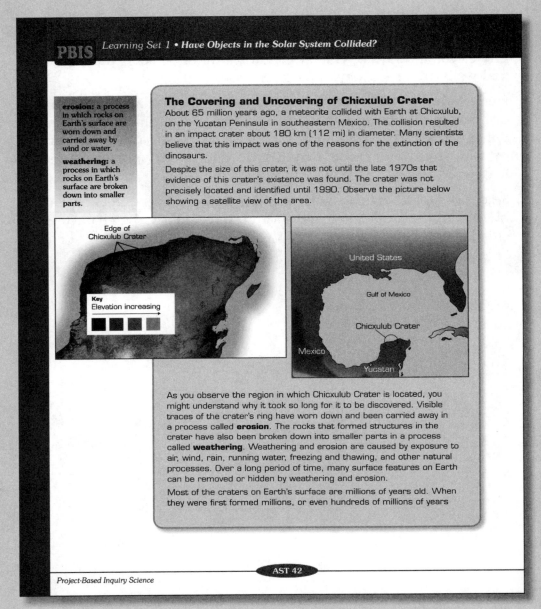

erosion: a process in which rocks on Earth's surface are worn down and carried away by wind or water.

weathering: a process in which rocks on Earth's surface are broken down into smaller parts.

The Covering and Uncovering of Chicxulub Crater

About 65 million years ago, a meteorite collided with Earth at Chicxulub, on the Yucatan Peninsula in southeastern Mexico. The collision resulted in an impact crater about 180 km (112 mi) in diameter. Many scientists believe that this impact was one of the reasons for the extinction of the dinosaurs.

Despite the size of this crater, it was not until the late 1970s that evidence of this crater's existence was found. The crater was not precisely located and identified until 1990. Observe the picture below showing a satellite view of the area.

Edge of Chicxulub Crater

Key
Elevation increasing

United States

Gulf of Mexico

Chicxulub Crater

Mexico

Yucatan

As you observe the region in which Chicxulub Crater is located, you might understand why it took so long for it to be discovered. Visible traces of the crater's ring have worn down and been carried away in a process called **erosion**. The rocks that formed structures in the crater have also been broken down into smaller parts in a process called **weathering**. Weathering and erosion are caused by exposure to air, wind, rain, running water, freezing and thawing, and other natural processes. Over a long period of time, many surface features on Earth can be removed or hidden by weathering and erosion.

Most of the craters on Earth's surface are millions of years old. When they were first formed millions, or even hundreds of millions of years

AST 42

△ Guide

Discuss the discovery of Chicxulub Crater. Point out that this is a very large and very old crater. Tell students it took a long time for people to discover the crater and ask them why they think it might have taken a long time. Then, tell students to look at the image of the crater in their text. They should notice that the features of the crater have been worn down. Let them know that the processes on Earth that cause this kind of change are *erosion* and *weathering*. Weathering breaks rocks down into smaller pieces, and erosion carries the pieces away. Both processes are caused by exposure to air, rain, freezing, thawing, and other weather events.

Ask students how the processes of erosion and weathering could explain the differences between craters on Earth and craters on the Moon. Point out that many of the causes of erosion are because of interactions in the atmosphere, such as wind and rain. The Moon has no atmosphere, so these causes are absent.

NOTES

ago, these craters may have looked like Meteor Crater or, perhaps, like some of the craters on the Moon. However, Earth's craters are constantly exposed to the processes of erosion and weathering.

Wind can blow particles away from the edges of craters or deposit new particles of rock and soil inside the crater, covering the floor and filling the bowl. Over many years, the shape and size of the crater change. Water is also a powerful agent of erosion. It washes away particles of rock from the sharp crater rims and deposits new materials inside the crater. At times, water may fill craters, making them look like circular lakes.

Many agents of erosion, such as wind and water from precipitation, are caused by interactions in the atmosphere, the mixture of gases surrounding Earth.

The Moon, unlike Earth, has no atmosphere, so there is no wind. The Moon also does not have flowing water, so the processes of weathering and erosion do not affect the Moon's surface features.

Not only does the Moon have no weather, the Moon's surface is much older than Earth's. Earth's surface changes much faster than the Moon's surface, in part because Earth's interior is still molten and in motion, while the Moon's interior is not. New surface is formed by volcanoes as Earth's molten interior seeps through cracks. Older parts of the surface are slowly pulled back down into Earth's interior at some regions of the ocean floor. This process slowly turns older rock back into molten material and can remove any trace of a crater. As a result, most of Earth's surface is no older than a few hundred million years. This means that most of the craters on Earth are millions of years old.

Impact craters on the Moon are often larger than those on Earth. Most of the Moon's large craters are billions of years old. At the time these large craters formed, there were probably similar craters on Earth. But Earth's surface is constantly renewed, and this process removes evidence of the large craters that may have existed on Earth billions of years ago.

The Chicxulub crater is still detectable, despite 65 million years of erosion and weathering, thanks to advances in science and technology. With a combination of satellite images, on-site inspections of geological structures, and testing done to samples from a site, scientists can locate and find evidence of impact craters on Earth.

AST 43

ASTRONOMY

Point out that in addition to erosion and weathering, Earth's surface changes because of geological processes. New surfaces are formed by volcanoes, and older parts of the surface are pulled into Earth's molten interior at certain places on the ocean floor. This means that most of Earth's surface is no older than a few hundred million years. The Moon's surface does not change as quickly, and many of the craters there are billions of years old—older than any structures on Earth's surface.

Stop and Think

1. What methods do scientists use to look for evidence of impact craters on Earth?

2. What did this reading tell you about why the impact craters on Earth look so different from the impact craters on the Moon?

3. What other factors do you think make the impact craters on Earth look different from those on the Moon? How do you think these factors might affect the creation of impact craters?

Explain

Use what you have just read, what you know about how impact craters are formed, and what you know about other differences between Earth and the Moon to develop an explanation of why Earth's impact craters look so different from the Moon's impact craters. Work with your group, and use a *Create Your Explanation* page to help you develop your explanation.

Begin by developing a claim. Your claim will be a statement about the similarities and differences between the impact craters on Earth and on the Moon.

Then record evidence that supports your claim. Your evidence might come from the experiments the class ran earlier in the Unit. It also might come from your observations of the satellite images, or it might come from the photographs you have been examining.

Science knowledge can come from what you have been reading. You also gained science knowledge when you used the Internet to look up information about Earth's impact craters in *Section 1.4*.

After recording your claim, evidence, and science knowledge, develop an explanation statement that pulls together your claim with your evidence and science knowledge. A good explanation will help somebody know what you think has been happening on Earth and on the Moon that makes the craters on the two bodies look so different from each other.

Create Your Explanation

Name: _____ Date: _____

Use this page to explain the lesson of your recent investigations.

Write a brief summary of the results from your investigation. You will use this summary to help you write your explanation.

Claim—a statement of what you understand or a conclusion that you have reached from an investigation or a set of investigations.

Evidence—data collected during investigations and trends in that data.

Science knowledge—knowledge about how things work. You may have learned this through reading, talking to an expert, discussion, or other experiences.

Write your explanation using your **Claim, Evidence** and **Science knowledge** from above.

Stop and Think

10 min

Students answer questions about the reading.

△ **Guide and Assess**

Discuss student answers with the class.

1. Students should respond that scientists today use satellite images, on-site inspections, and sample testing to locate and find evidence of impact craters on Earth.

2. Students should explain that impact craters on Earth are subject to erosion and weathering, which changes their appearance over time.

3. Students' answers will vary. They may suggest that the atmosphere itself has an early effect on crater formation. As the meteorite goes through the atmosphere at very high speed, the object becomes smaller, even exploding in some cases. Meteorites that hit the oceans, of course, will leave no impact crater.

Explain

10 min

Students create explanations of the differences between terrestrial and lunar craters.

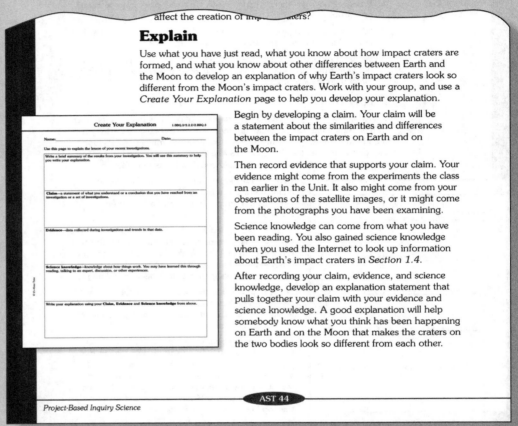

Explain

Use what you have just read, what you know about how impact craters are formed, and what you know about other differences between Earth and the Moon to develop an explanation of why Earth's impact craters look so different from the Moon's impact craters. Work with your group, and use a *Create Your Explanation* page to help you develop your explanation.

Begin by developing a claim. Your claim will be a statement about the similarities and differences between the impact craters on Earth and on the Moon.

Then record evidence that supports your claim. Your evidence might come from the experiments the class ran earlier in the Unit. It also might come from your observations of the satellite images, or it might come from the photographs you have been examining.

Science knowledge can come from what you have been reading. You also gained science knowledge when you used the Internet to look up information about Earth's impact craters in *Section 1.4*.

After recording your claim, evidence, and science knowledge, develop an explanation statement that pulls together your claim with your evidence and science knowledge. A good explanation will help somebody know what you think has been happening on Earth and on the Moon that makes the craters on the two bodies look so different from each other.

AST 44

Project-Based Inquiry Science

○ Engage

Point out that students have evidence that there are more craters on the surface of the Moon than on Earth's surface. Ask them why they think there are more craters on the Moon than on Earth, and what evidence they can use to answer the question. Tell them they will now create explanations of the difference between terrestrial and lunar craters.

△ Guide

Distribute *Create Your Explanation* pages and tell students they should use everything they have learned about how craters form and differences between Earth and the Moon to come up with an explanation of the differences between craters on the Moon and craters on Earth. Remind students that scientific explanations connect claims to evidence and science knowledge. In this case, their claims should be about the differences between craters on Earth and craters on the Moon, and their evidence should come from their experiments, photographs, and satellite imagery.

◯ Get Going

Have students work with their groups to create explanations using *Create Your Explanation* pages. Let them know that they will share their explanations with the class.

As students work on their explanations, monitor their progress and help them with any difficulties they encounter. Ask them what evidence they are using and how their evidence supports their claims. If their evidence does not support their claims, ask them if there is other evidence they can use or if they need to revise their claims.

NOTES

Communicate: Share Your Explanation

15 min

Students share their explanations with the class and the class develops a claim everybody agrees on.

Communicate

Share Your Explanation

When everyone is finished, share your explanation with the class. When it is your group's turn, begin by presenting your claim. Then present your evidence and science knowledge. After that, present your explanation statement.

As each group shares their explanation, listen carefully for how each explanation is similar to yours or different from yours. Record any differences you notice and any disagreements you have so you will remember them after all of the explanations have been presented.

After all of the explanations have been presented, discuss their strengths and weaknesses. As a class, select or develop a claim and explanation that everyone thinks best explains the difference in craters on Earth and on the Moon.

Reflect

To answer the questions below, use the explanation the class has developed. Be prepared to share your answers with the class.

1. What changes would you expect to observe in Meteor Crater if you could come back and look at it a million years from now?

2. Which of the craters examined by your class would Meteor Crater be most like in a million years?

3. Another difference between Earth and the Moon is that Earth has water on its surface. How do you think the structure of a crater would change if a meteorite struck water instead of striking land?

4. Why do you think there are fewer impact craters on Earth than on the Moon?

5. Why do you think impact craters on the Moon are larger than impact craters on Earth?

AST 45

△ Guide

Have groups share their explanations with the class. As each group shares its explanation, students should record the explanation and ask questions if anything is unclear. They should evaluate the strengths and weaknesses of the explanation, and the class should use the best points of each group's explanations to discuss these strengths and weaknesses. Working together, they should develop a new explanation they think best explains the differences they observed between craters on Earth and on the Moon.

△ Guide and Assess

Have students answer the *Reflect* questions with their groups. Let them know that they will share their answers with the class.

When leading a discussion of the answers, listen for evidence that students understand how erosion and weathering affect craters over long periods of time and how the presence of water and an atmosphere can affect crater formation.

1. Students should realize that if they returned in a million years and looked for Meteor Crater, it would be more difficult to find. Erosion and weathering would remove more of its defining character.

2. Students should predict that Meteor Crater will be most like the Wolfe Creek Crater in a million years, unless the climate changes radically. However, it will be subject to wind and erosion more than the effects of water.

3. Students may hypothesize that if a meteor struck an ocean, there would be no crater. If it struck a very large lake, the crater would be smaller and quickly fill with water.

4. Students may suggest that there are fewer impact craters on Earth for two major reasons:

   • 70 percent of the Earth is covered by oceans, so there is no trace of a meteorite

   • weathering and erosion remove evidence of impact craters

5. Students may guess that the larger impact craters on Earth have been obliterated by the eons of weathering.

Reflect

10 min

Students consider further explorations of Meteor Crater, the Moon's craters, and Earth's craters.

NOTES

....

....

....

....

....

What's the Point?

Over time, erosion and weathering by wind, water, and other natural processes, create large changes in the craters formed on Earth. The Moon has no wind or flowing water, so erosion and weathering do not affect craters on the Moon as they do on Earth. The Moon's surface is also much older than Earth's, so the craters on the Moon are much older than craters on Earth. The Moon's craters are also larger than Earth's impact craters. Billions of years ago, when large craters formed on the Moon, similar craters formed on Earth. As Earth's surface is renewed, evidence of the older craters is completely erased.

The first footprints on the Moon, made by Apollo 11 astronauts Neil Armstrong and Buzz Aldrin, will be there for a million years. There is no erosion or weathering by wind or water to affect them.

NOTES

....

....

....

Assessment Options

Targeted Concepts, Skills, and Nature of Science	How do I know if students got it?
Scientists often collaborate and share their findings. Sharing findings makes new information available and helps scientists refine their ideas and build on others' ideas. When another person's or group's idea is used, credit needs to be given.	**ASK:** How did the explanations shared by the class help you to revise your explanation? **LISTEN:** Students should describe how the explanations shared by other groups made new information available and helped them refine their ideas and build on others' ideas.
Scientists must keep clear, accurate, and descriptive records of what they do so they can share their work with others; consider what they did, why they did it, and what they want to do next.	**ASK:** How did you use your observations to create an explanation? **LISTEN:** Students should have used their observations as evidence to support their claims.
Scientists make claims (conclusions) based on evidence obtained (trends in data) from reliable investigations.	**ASK:** What observations or other sources of scientific information did you find most helpful when you created your explanation? **LISTEN:** Students should identify the observations of satellite images of Earth and Moon craters, and their readings in the text that help them develop their explanations.
Explanations are claims supported by evidence. Evidence can be experimental results, observational data, and any other accepted scientific knowledge.	**ASK:** How did you support the claim you made in your explanation? **LISTEN:** Students should cite specific evidence from their observations and science knowledge obtained from their readings to support their claims.

Targeted Concepts, Skills, and Nature of Science	How do I know if students got it?
Impacts of solar-system bodies have created extensive cratering on the Moon and on other bodies in the solar system. Some craters can also be found on Earth, but most have been destroyed by the processes of plate tectonics, and/or the weathering, erosion and deposition occurring at Earth's planetary surface.	**ASK:** What are some processes that occur on Earth, but not the Moon, that account for the differences you observed between craters on Earth and on the Moon? **LISTEN:** Students should identify weathering, erosion, deposition, and plate tectonic processes.

Teacher Reflection Questions

- Which examples of Earth and Moon craters did you find most effective for helping students grasp the difference between craters on Earth and on the Moon? What made those examples so effective?

- How did you help students recognize that their claims about why Earth and Moon craters differ needed to be supported with evidence?

- How does identifying possible reasons for differences between Earth and Moon craters prepare students for the next section of this *Learning Set?*

SECTION 1.6 INTRODUCTION

1.6 Explore

What Happens When a Meteorite Hits Earth?

◀ 1 class period

A class period is considered to be one 40 to 50 minute class.

Overview

This section opens with a reading that traces the path of a meteoroid as it is attracted by Earth's gravity, plunges through the atmosphere as a glowing meteor, and possibly survives to strike Earth's surface as a meteorite. A fire syringe demonstration is then performed to simulate the intense heating that occurs when a meteoroid compresses air in its path. After reflecting on connections between the fire syringe simulation and the effects of Earth's atmosphere on a meteoroid, students again update the *Project Board*.

Targeted Concepts, Skills, and Nature of Science	Performance Expectations
Scientists often collaborate and share their findings. Sharing findings makes new information available and helps scientists refine their ideas and build on others' ideas. When another person's or group's idea is used, credit needs to be given.	Together as a class, students identify information that should be added to the *What are we learning?* and *What do we need to investigate?* columns of the *Project Board*.
Scientists must keep clear, accurate, and descriptive records of what they do so they can share their work with others; consider what they did, why they did it, and what they want to do next.	Students use the notes they made while reading and their observations of the fire syringe demonstration to answer the *Reflect* questions.
Meteoroids are small solar-system objects with the potential to collide with Earth. Most meteoroids that strike Earth's atmosphere rapidly burn up due to friction with the atmosphere resulting in a visible meteor. Those that survive and strike Earth as meteorites are fragmented and destroyed by the impact.	Students describe the effects of the atmosphere on a meteoroid as it travels toward Earth's surface. Students distinguish between a meteoroid, a meteor and a meteorite.

Materials	
1 per class	*Fire Syringe* video Class *Project Board*

Homework Options

Reflection

- **Science Content:** What is the difference between a meteoroid, a meteor, and a meteorite? *(Students should identify that a meteoroid is an object with the potential to collide with Earth; a meteor is a meteoroid that has been heated to glowing by friction with the air as it travels through Earth's atmosphere, and a meteorite is any part of a meteoroid that survives passage through the atmosphere and impacts Earth's surface.)*

- **Science Content:** If the plunger on the fire syringe had been pushed down more slowly, do you think the paper would still have ignited? Why or Why not? *(Students' answers will vary, and should be supported by specific reasons. They may answer that the paper would not ignite, because if the plunger is depressed slowly, there is more time for the heat that is created to be lost to its surroundings.)*

- **Science Process:** Why is it important to record observations as soon as they are made during a demonstration? *(Students' answers should explain that if observations are not immediately recorded, it is possible to forget details of what was observed.)*

- **Science Process:** Why would it be helpful to read the *Reflect* questions before observing the fire syringe demonstration? *(Students should answer that reading the questions beforehand would prepare the observer for details to which they may not otherwise have noticed.)*

Preparation for 1.7

- **Science Content:** All of the bodies in our solar system revolve around the Sun. What would you need to know about a solar-system body if you wanted to predict whether it was likely to collide with Earth? How would this help you predict the likelihood of a collision? *(Students should indicate that they would need to know the path around the Sun and rate of motion of both the object and Earth. They should describe how they can then plot their projected paths, determine whether they will intersect, and whether both will arrive at the intersection at the same time.)*

SECTION 1.6 IMPLEMENTATION

◀ *1 class period* *

1.6 Explore

What Happens When a Meteorite Hits Earth?

From Meteoroid to Meteor to Meteorite

The solar system is full of debris. Besides planets, moons, and the Sun, our solar system contains many smaller bodies that you will learn about in the next section. A **meteoroid** is any one of these bodies that travels through the solar system with the potential to collide with Earth.

Most objects in the solar system travel through space very quickly. For example, Earth revolves around the Sun at a speed of about 30 kilometers per second. Other objects, such as meteoroids, travel at similar speeds, or even faster. You can imagine that if two objects moving at these speeds collide, the impact will be quite violent.

The first thing that happens to a meteoroid as it approaches Earth is that it falls under the influence of Earth's gravity. Earth's gravity pulls objects toward Earth's center. As a meteoroid approaches Earth, gravity will alter its path, causing the meteoroid to bend toward Earth's surface. Most meteoroids can pass by Earth with their motion deflected slightly by gravity, but without ever having a collision. Other meteoroids strike Earth's atmosphere.

When a meteoroid comes within 50 kilometers of Earth's surface, it is well within Earth's atmosphere. The meteoroid collides with air particles in Earth's atmosphere. However, the meteoroid is moving so quickly that it pushes together the air particles in front of it. This compressed air heats up and vaporizes layers of the meteoroid. The heat is so intense that it changes the top layers of the solid meteoroid into gas. The meteoroid heats up to the point that it begins to glow, and the hot gases escaping from the meteoroid also create a bright stream of light. The object is now clearly visible from Earth's surface, and it is now called a **meteor**. The flashes of light are often called shooting stars or falling stars, but these are not stars at all.

> **meteoroid:** a small-solar system body that has the potential to become a meteor.
>
> **meteor:** an object that enters Earth's atmosphere with such speed that it glows.

Meteor showers are events during which many meteors appear in the same part of the sky during the same night.

AST 47

ASTRONOMY

1.6 Explore

What Happens When a Meteorite Hits Earth?

From Meteoroid to Meteor to Meteorite

10 min

The class reads about and discusses what happens when a meteorite hits Earth.

○ Engage

Ask the class if they have ever heard a forecast for a meteor shower and then gone to view it. Students probably are familiar with this term, although they may not know what it is. If any students have seen one before, ask them to describe what they saw. Then ask that student if they know what the shooting objects were made of.

*A class period is considered to be one 40 to 50 minute class.

Most meteors completely break apart and burn up in Earth's atmosphere before they have time to collide with Earth's surface. The original meteoroid may have been too small, or it may have entered the atmosphere at a small angle, or it may have been made of materials that break apart or vaporize easily. Only a few meteors survive the trip and strike Earth. These objects are the ones called meteorites.

Earth's atmosphere slows down a meteorite, but after passing through Earth's atmosphere, meteorites are still often traveling at great speeds when they impact Earth's surface. The crater formed is much larger than the meteorite. Remember, the object that formed the 1.3-km Meteor Crater was only 50 m wide.

In many cases, a meteorite is destroyed by its impact. Scientists are forced to look for fragments of the meteorite or other indicators of the original object. One thing scientists look for are small spheres of meteoritic iron among the ejecta around the rim of a crater. Many meteoroids contain significant quantities of iron, so this metal shows up in the fragments of meteorites.

Stop and Think

1. Why are impacts between meteorites and Earth so violent?

2. If Earth's gravity were stronger, what effect would you expect this to have on meteoroids passing by Earth? On meteorites that strike Earth?

3. How does Earth's atmosphere affect the motion of a meteoroid?

4. Why do some meteoroids that are traveling toward Earth never hit Earth's surface?

5. Why do meteors glow?

Observe

Meteors travel through the atmosphere so fast that they glow. In the video, you will see a fire syringe used to simulate a meteor traveling through the sky. The plunger will act like the meteoroid, compressing air in its path. As the plunger is pushed down quickly, more pressure will build up in the cylinder. This will create intense heat at the bottom of a cylinder.

AST 48

⚠ Guide

Discuss what happens when one of the smaller objects in the solar system collides with Earth. When one of these objects is in space, it is called a *meteoroid*. If a meteoroid enters the atmosphere, it collides with and compresses air particles, generating heat and light. These objects are often visible from Earth's surface and are called *meteors* (the streaks of light are often called *shooting stars*).

Most of these objects are so small that they do not reach Earth's surface. They break up, burn up, or vaporize. The few that do reach Earth's surface are called *meteorites*. They often are destroyed on impact, in which case scientists look for fragments or other evidence of the original object. Meteorites often hit Earth at great speeds, creating craters much larger than the meteorite.

△ Guide and Assess

Discuss the *Stop and Think* questions in class.

1. Students should know that collisions of meteorites and Earth are violent because of the masses involved in the collision and the great speed with which they collide.

2. Students should suggest that if Earth's gravity were stronger, more meteoroids would be pulled into Earth's orbit and become meteors and meteorites. The impact velocity of the meteorites would be greater if the Earth's gravity were stronger.

3. Students should remember that Earth's atmosphere acts to slow down a meteorite.

4. Students should explain that some meteoroids never hit Earth, because they may have completely burned up before hitting the ground. Others are largely ice and may be dispersed or even explode before striking Earth.

5. Students should recall that meteors glow because their interaction with the atmosphere creates great heat.

△ Guide

Tell students they will now observe a video that simulates how a meteor entering the atmosphere generates heat. Before starting the video, guide them to understand what they should observe. Tell them the plunger represents a meteor. A piece of paper will be placed in the bottom of the syringe. Emphasize that they should closely watch the paper during the demonstration. Let them know that as the plunger is pressed down, it will compress the air in the tube in the same way a meteor compresses air. This will generate heat.

Stop and Think

10 min

Students answer questions about the reading.

Observe

10 min

Students watch a video demonstration using a fire syringe to show how compressing air creates intense heat.

Reflect

1. What did you observe happen to the tissue paper inside the cylinder?

2. Do you think the gas is the source of the glow in the syringe, or the tissue paper? Why? What does this tell you about the reason(s) a meteor glows?

3. If a meteor burns up before it reaches the ground, is there any evidence that a collision took place? Why or why not?

Update the *Project Board*

Record what you now know about what happens when meteoroids hit Earth and the Moon in the *What are we learning?* column of the *Project Board*. Be sure to include what you know about how and why impact craters on Earth and on the Moon are different from each other. As always, make sure you include supporting evidence for anything added to this column in the *What is our evidence?* column. Your evidence may come from what you have read, your experiments, and the demonstration.

You now have a lot of experience thinking about what happens when meteoroids strike Earth or the Moon. You may be wondering about where these objects come from and what different types of objects exist, and whether these different objects can strike Earth or the Moon. Can these solar system objects strike other planets? Add these questions and any others you have to the *Project Board* in the *What do we need to investigate?* column.

What's the Point?

Earth's atmosphere makes it difficult for meteoroids to get all the way to Earth without burning up. Air particles in the atmosphere are compressed by the object. This creates enough heat to vaporize an object before it reaches Earth's surface. The Moon has no atmosphere. Therefore, meteoroids meet no resistance as they speed toward the Moon, so they do not vaporize. Only the larger and faster-moving objects are able to pass through Earth's atmosphere and become meteorites by striking the surface. For this reason, more meteoroids hit the Moon than Earth, even though Earth is so much larger than the Moon.

AST 49

ASTRONOMY

Reflect
10 min

Students think about their observations of the fire syringe and answer questions to build on their understanding of meteors.

△ Guide

Give students some time to answer the questions, then lead a discussion of their answers. Students should demonstrate an understanding that a meteor entering Earth's atmosphere compresses air molecules, which generates intense heat, just as the compressed air in the fire syringe generated intense heat. This heat will often destroy a meteorite before it reaches Earth's surface.

1. Students should describe how the tissue paper was ignited by the heat.

2. Students should answer that the tissue paper was the source of the glow in the syringe, demonstrating that it is the meteor that glows, not the atmospheric gases.

3. Students should understand that if a meteor burns up before reaching the ground, there would be no crater evidence of a collision. The only evidence would be visual—the sight of a shooting star.

△ Guide

Ask students what they have learned about what happens when meteoroids hit Earth and the Moon that they should record on the *Project Board*. Record their answers in the *What are we learning?* column and have them record their answers on their own *Project Board* pages. Ask them what evidence supports these ideas, and record their responses in the *What is our evidence?* column.

Ask students what they can record in the *What do we need to investigate?* column. They should now have questions about where meteoroids come from and what different kinds of meteoroids there are. They may also have questions about what other kinds of collisions occur in the solar system.

Update the Project Board

15 min

Students participate in class discussion to update the Project Board.

Assessment Options

Targeted Concepts, Skills, and Nature of Science	How do I know if students got it?
Scientists often collaborate and share their findings. Sharing findings makes new information available and helps scientists refine their ideas and build on others' ideas. When another person's or group's idea is used, credit needs to be given.	**ASK:** When the class updated the *What are we learning?* column of the *Project Board,* what supporting evidence that other students provided helped you better understand what happens when a meteorite hits Earth? **LISTEN:** Students should cite information provided by other students that helped them refine their ideas.

Targeted Concepts, Skills, and Nature of Science	How do I know if students got it?
Scientists must keep clear, accurate, and descriptive records of what they do so they can share their work with others; consider what they did, why they did it, and what they want to do next.	**ASK:** How did you use the records you kept of the fire syringe demonstration? **LISTEN:** Students should have used their records to provide supporting evidence for their answers to the *Reflect* questions and for information added to the *Project Board*.
Meteoroids are small solar-system objects with the potential to collide with Earth. Most meteoroids that strike Earth's atmosphere rapidly burn up due to friction with the atmosphere resulting in a visible meteor. Most of those that survive and strike Earth as meteorites are fragmented and destroyed by the impact.	**ASK:** If Earth's atmosphere was thicker and extended farther above its surface, how might that affect the number of meteorites that strike Earth's surface? **LISTEN:** Students should predict that fewer meteorites would strike Earth's surface because the increase in friction and distance over which friction would act on the meteorite would make it more likely that it would burn up before reaching the surface.

Teacher Reflection Questions

- What difficulties did students have with the concept of heating due to compression (adiabatic heating)?

- How did you help students connect their observations of the fire syringe demonstration with what they read about what happens to a meteoroid when it enters Earth's atmosphere?

- How were you able to connect the concepts in this section with the *Big Question?*

1.7 Read

What Other Evidence Exists of Past Collisions in Our Solar System?

◀ *1 class period*

A class period is considered to be one 40 to 50 minute class.

Overview

Students read descriptions of the different kinds of bodies making up our solar system that could potentially collide with Earth. They read about how the collision between the Shoemaker-Levy comet and the planet Jupiter was scientifically predicted. They examine images of the collision showing the effects on both the comet and the planet. Students then consider a series of *Stop and Think* questions in which they consider what they have learned about impacts from what they have read and observed. The *Solar System* page is introduced as an organizer that students will use throughout the Unit to summarize what they are learning about our solar system and how the parts of the system interact through gravity, collisions, and radiation. After recording information about solar system bodies on the *Solar System* page, students discuss what they have recorded with the class and then revise or add to what they have written based on information shared by others. The class then collaborates to update the *Project Board* with new information about the solar system that is relevant to the questions on the *Project Board*.

Targeted Concepts, Skills, and Nature of Science	Performance Expectations
Scientists often collaborate and share their findings. Sharing findings makes new information available and helps scientists refine their ideas and build on others' ideas. When another person's or group's idea is used, credit needs to be given.	Students share with the class the information about solar-system objects they recorded on their *Solar System* page. The class engages in a discussion and collaborates to update the *Project Board*.

147

Targeted Concepts, Skills, and Nature of Science	Performance Expectations
Scientists must keep clear, accurate, and descriptive records of what they do so they can share their work with others; consider what they did, why they did it, and what they want to do next.	Students record information about the various solar system objects described in the reading on the *Solar System* page.
The Sun, the planets that revolve around it and their moons, are the major bodies in the solar system. Other members that orbit the Sun include dwarf planets and small solar-system bodies such as asteroids and comets.	Students identify and describe the characteristics of the major and minor bodies that make up our solar system.
Most objects in the solar system have a regular and predictable motion. These motions explain such phenomena as a day, a year, phases of the Moon, eclipses, tides, meteor showers, and comets.	Students describe the orbits of the major and minor bodies that make up our solar system.
Comets leave behind grains of dust and ions. The dust and ions can be illuminated by the Sun as a huge tail called a coma. If Earth passes through the trails of dust left behind, the particles rapidly burn up due to friction with the atmosphere, causing a meteor shower.	Students describe the composition and motion of comets. Students describe how and why comets develop a coma as they approach the Sun.

Materials	
1 per student	*Solar System* page
1 per class	Class *Project Board*
1 per class (optional)	High-resolution images of the collision of the Shoemaker-Levy comet and Jupiter for projection

Project-Based Inquiry Science

Activity Setup and Preparation

You may want to show students images of the collision of the Shoemaker-Levy comet and Jupiter. Before class, do an Internet search for these images.

Homework Options

Reflection

- **Science Content:** What is the difference between the composition of an asteroid and a comet? *(Students should describe how asteroids mainly are composed of rock, while comets mainly are composed of ice and dust.)*

- **Science Content:** What tools does an astronomer use to identify and determine the motion of comets and other solar system objects? *(Students should name telescopes and digital or photographic images of objects in space.)*

- **Science Process:** Describe the reasons why it is important to record information on the Solar System page and the *Project Board? (Students should point out the need for information gathered throughout the Unit when they write and present their report at the end of the Unit.)*

- **Science Process:** How could you use images of a solar-system object made over time to determine its path and rate of motion? *(Students should describe how changes in a solar-system object's position could be plotted to determine the object's path and measurements the time it took to cover the distance from one position to another could be used to calculate its rate of motion.)*

Preparation for 1.BBQ

- **Science Process:** What evidence would you look for on other planets or solar-system bodies to determine whether they have collided with other objects? *(Students should suggest looking for impact craters on the surfaces of solar-system bodies and other planets that indicate a collision.)*

- **Science Process:** Astronomers have obtained close-up images of most of the major bodies in our solar system. How do you think those images were obtained? *(Students should describe astronomers using telescopes and by sending out space probes equipped with image-sensing instruments to obtain space images.)*

NOTES

SECTION 1.7 IMPLEMENTATION

1.7 Read

What Other Evidence Exists of Past Collisions in our Solar System?

So far, you have learned about evidence of collisions on Earth and the Moon, and you have learned some things about what happens when these collisions occur. You can learn even more about potential collisions between solar-system objects by looking at collisions in other parts of the solar system. The solar system contains many different types of objects, some of which could be dangerous to Earth, and some of which are not. Other solar-system bodies also contain evidence of past collisions. In this section, you will get an introduction to the solar system and learn about one collision that scientists were actually able to observe from Earth.

dwarf planet: a round solar-system body that is smaller than a planet.

asteroid belt: a region of the solar system between Mars and Jupiter in which most asteroids are located.

Planets and Planet-like Objects

To understand the collisions that caused the impact craters on Earth and the Moon, you need to know more about the types of objects that are in the solar system. You already know that the solar system includes the Sun, eight planets, and their moons.

The eight planets, in order from closest to the Sun to farthest away, are Mercury, Venus, Earth, Mars, Jupiter, Saturn, Uranus, and Neptune.

The solar system also includes **dwarf planets**. Dwarf planets are planet-like objects that are not large enough to be considered planets. The smallest planet, Mercury, is about 2,440 km (1516 mi) in diameter, so all dwarf planets are smaller than Mercury. Dwarf planets are round, like planets. However, planets travel in nearly circular paths around the Sun, with no other objects traveling in the same circle. Dwarf planets may travel in oval orbits, or they may travel in a circular path around the Sun, like planets.

As of 2009, five dwarf planets were known: Ceres, Pluto, Eris, Makemake, and Haumea. Ceres, the smallest dwarf planet, is located in the **asteroid belt** between Mars and Jupiter. Pluto was classified as a planet between 1930, the year of its discovery, and 2006. It is now considered a dwarf

AST 50

Project-Based Inquiry Science

△ Guide

Begin by telling students they will be able to understand much more about potential collisions with Earth by learning more about other parts of the solar system. Emphasize that some of the different kinds of objects in the solar system could be dangerous to Earth, but many others are not. In this section, they will learn more about the solar system by learning about a collision that scientists were able to observe.

1.7 Read

What Other Evidence Exists of Past Collisions in Our Solar System?

5 min

Students read more about the solar system.

*A class period is considered to be one 40 to 50 minute class.

Planets and Planet-like Objects

5 min

Students are introduced to the planets and dwarf planets of our solar system.

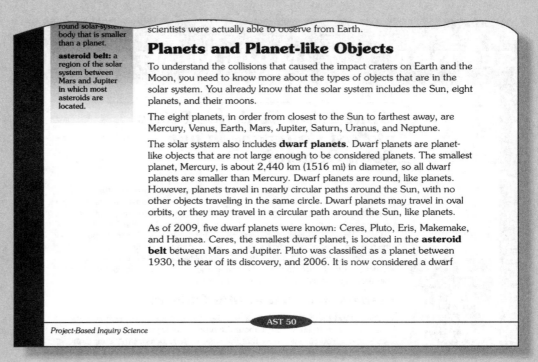

round solar-system body that is smaller than a planet.

asteroid belt: a region of the solar system between Mars and Jupiter in which most asteroids are located.

scientists were actually able to observe from Earth.

Planets and Planet-like Objects

To understand the collisions that caused the impact craters on Earth and the Moon, you need to know more about the types of objects that are in the solar system. You already know that the solar system includes the Sun, eight planets, and their moons.

The eight planets, in order from closest to the Sun to farthest away, are Mercury, Venus, Earth, Mars, Jupiter, Saturn, Uranus, and Neptune.

The solar system also includes **dwarf planets**. Dwarf planets are planet-like objects that are not large enough to be considered planets. The smallest planet, Mercury, is about 2,440 km (1516 mi) in diameter, so all dwarf planets are smaller than Mercury. Dwarf planets are round, like planets. However, planets travel in nearly circular paths around the Sun, with no other objects traveling in the same circle. Dwarf planets may travel in oval orbits, or they may travel in a circular path around the Sun, like planets.

As of 2009, five dwarf planets were known: Ceres, Pluto, Eris, Makemake, and Haumea. Ceres, the smallest dwarf planet, is located in the **asteroid belt** between Mars and Jupiter. Pluto was classified as a planet between 1930, the year of its discovery, and 2006. It is now considered a dwarf

AST 50

Project-Based Inquiry Science

△ Guide

Point out the picture of the solar system in the student text and discuss the major objects of the solar system. Show students that the solar system contains eight planets—Mercury, Venus, Earth, Mars, Jupiter, Saturn, Uranus, and Neptune—their moons, and the Sun.

NOTES

planet because of its size and oval path around the Sun. Eris, Makemake, and Haumea are all located much farther away than Neptune from the Sun and have oval paths around the Sun. They were not even identified until 2004 and 2005, so perhaps many more dwarf planets are still awaiting investigation.

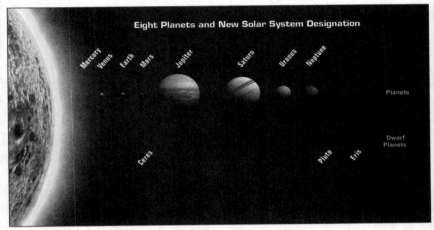

Eight Planets and New Solar System Designation

Mercury · Venus · Earth · Mars · Jupiter · Saturn · Uranus · Neptune

Planets

Dwarf Planets

Ceres · Pluto · Eris

In addition to the eight planets, scientists have created the category of dwarf planets. Pictured in this artist's illustration are the three largest dwarf planets: Ceres, Pluto, and Eris.

Small Solar-System Bodies

Besides planets and dwarf planets, other smaller objects also revolve around the Sun. Objects in the solar system that revolve around the Sun but are not large enough to be called dwarf planets are called *small solar-system bodies*.

Bodies in the solar system are classified by the International Astronomical Union (IAU), a group of astronomers recognized as the worldwide authority in astronomy. One of the duties of IAU is to establish names for all of the objects scientists discover. Another duty is to give standard meanings to

AST 51

Point out to students that the solar system also contains planet-like objects called *dwarf planets*. Dwarf planets are smaller than the smallest planet, Mercury, and they sometimes have a different type of orbit from planets. Describe to students how planets have nearly circular orbits and dwarf planets may have oval-shaped orbits. Five dwarf planets are known: Ceres, Pluto, Eris, Makemake, and Haumea. Ceres is located in the asteroid belt; and the other dwarf planets are farther from the Sun than Neptune. Emphasize that Eris, Makemake, and Haumea were all discovered recently, so it is possible that there are many more dwarf planets beyond Neptune.

Small Solar-System Bodies

5 min

Students are introduced to the concept of small solar-system bodies.

Small Solar-System Bodies

Besides planets and dwarf planets, other smaller objects also revolve around the Sun. Objects in the solar system that revolve around the Sun but are not large enough to be called dwarf planets are called *small solar-system bodies*.

Bodies in the solar system are classified by the International Astronomical Union (IAU), a group of astronomers recognized as the worldwide authority in astronomy. One of the duties of IAU is to establish names for all of the objects scientists discover. Another duty is to give standard meanings to

AST 51

△ Guide

Have a class discussion about small solar-system bodies (SSSB), describing them as objects in the solar system that are too small to be called planets. Point out to students that asteroids are irregularly shaped rocks and are considered SSSB's. They orbit the Sun in a region called the *asteroid belt*, located between Mars and Jupiter. There are also some asteroids in other parts of the solar system.

NOTES

PBIS *Learning Set 1 • Have Objects in the Solar System Collided?*

asteroid: a rocky or metallic solar-system body that revolves around the Sun, between 10 m (33 ft) and about 500 km (310 mi) in diameter.

comet: a small, icy solar-system body that revolves around the Sun and forms a tail as it gets closer to the Sun.

coma: the cloud of gas and dust that forms around a comet as parts of the comet vaporize.

words to allow easier communication between astronomers. Some of the other objects that you need to know about to answer the *Big Question* are **asteroids** and **comets**.

Asteroids are irregularly shaped rocks that revolve around the Sun but are too small to be considered planets or dwarf planets. Over one million asteroids revolve around the Sun in a group located between Mars and Jupiter. This region is called the asteroid belt. However, a few asteroids can also be found in other parts of the solar system. An object is generally not considered an asteroid unless it is larger than 10 m (32 ft) across. The largest asteroids are 500 km (311 mi) across.

Comets are another important type of small solar-system body. Comets are small icy objects, usually less than 10 km (6 mi) across. They are made up of mostly ice and dust. Although comets are about the same size as some asteroids, they are less massive, because they are made of ice instead of rock and iron. Comets are often referred to as "dirty snowballs," because dust and ice are their main ingredients.

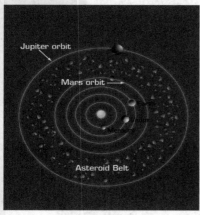

This illustration of the asteroid belt shows the location of one million asteroids.

Most of the time, comets are found far out in the solar system. Sometimes, they move in closer to the Sun. As they approach the Sun, some of the surface ice starts to melt and vaporize, producing a large cloud called a **coma**. Comas can reach up to 2.4 million km (1.5 million mi) in diameter! Light and charged particles flowing from the Sun push the gas and dust around the comet into a long, curved tail.

The gas and dust that form the comet's tail are left behind as the comet continues in its orbit. Later, Earth's motion in the solar system might take it through this same debris trail. The debris collides with Earth's atmosphere, but it burns up long before any of it reaches the ground. Because Earth collides with many such particles at the same time, the result is sometimes a spectacular display of meteors called a meteor shower.

Project-Based Inquiry Science

Discuss with the class how comets are another kind of SSSB. They are comprised of ice and dust, and even though they are about the same size as asteroids, they are less massive. Emphasize that when comets are far from the Sun—as they usually are—they are solid. When they approach the Sun, some of the surface ice melts and vaporizes, producing a cloud called a *coma*. Light and particles from the Sun push the cloud of gas and dust into a tail.

Earth can also pass directly through the tail of a comet. The result is a more spectacular meteor shower, but as long as the body of the comet misses Earth, no damage will occur.

Halley's Comet, the famous comet named after English astronomer Edmund Halley, can be viewed from Earth every 76 years. Halley's Comet, like many others, has a predictable pattern of movement. It made its last close approach to the Sun on February 9, 1986, and it will next streak by the Sun on July 28, 2061.

Carolyn Shoemaker: Comet hunter.

All comets are named after the person or people who discovered them. Carolyn Shoemaker is the most accomplished comet hunter alive. She has found more than 800 asteroids and 32 comets. Carolyn Shoemaker, like all comet hunters, is successful because she patiently observes changes in the sky, using a telescope and numerous slides taken of space objects.

Comets consist mainly of ice and dust. The comet's large cloud, called the coma, is surface ice that starts to melt and vaporize as the comet approaches the Sun.

AST 53

ASTRONOMY

NOTES

....

....

....

Watching a Collision in the Solar System

In the summer of 1994, pieces of a large comet crashed into Jupiter. Pictures of this remarkable event appeared throughout the media.

About a year before the collision, in March 1993, Carolyn Shoemaker, her husband Eugene, and David Levy had discovered that comet. Using a telescope, the three spotted the comet and watched as it passed Jupiter. The comet had passed very close to Jupiter, and the gravity of Jupiter was strong enough to break it into 21 large pieces. This made the comet appear as a string of pearls.

Comet Shoemaker-Levy 9 collided with Jupiter in many pieces.

The scientists shared their findings with others. Scientists were able to predict that the next time the comet came close to Jupiter, it would actually collide with Jupiter. They were right. Beginning in July 1994, the world watched as piece after piece of the comet, named Shoemaker-Levy 9, smashed into Jupiter's atmosphere.

Jupiter's surface is not rocky like that of Earth. Jupiter's surface is composed of liquid hydrogen and helium under intense pressure. So, the result of a collision with Jupiter is much different from one on Earth.

When the first fragment of Shoemaker-Levy 9 hit Jupiter, its impact released as much energy as 225,000 million tons of dynamite and produced a plume of gas and debris that rose 1000 km (621 mi) above the planet's cloud layers. The impact completely destroyed the fragment, leaving small particles, similar to dust. Each impact of the broken comet pieces also formed a dark spot on Jupiter. These large spots were made of debris from the comet. Several impact sites were about half the diameter of Earth.

As the remaining fragments of the comet hit Jupiter, more dark spots appeared from the impacts. Some fragments did not leave any marks on Jupiter, perhaps because of their small size. Although they remained visible for several weeks after the collision, the dark spots eventually disappeared.

AST 54

Watching a Collision in the Solar System

5 min

Students read about and discuss the collision of Shoemaker-Levy 9 with Jupiter.

△ Guide

Discuss the collision of Shoemaker-Levy 9 with Jupiter. Emphasize that the astronomers, Carolyn and Eugene Shoemaker, with David Levy, discovered the comet using a telescope and predicted how and when it would collide with Jupiter. Because they accurately predicted when the collision would take place, they were able to observe it. Despite the dramatic effects of the collision, including a 1000-km plume of gas and debris and dark spots where fragments of the comet hit Jupiter, all evidence of the collision eventually disappeared. Point out that Shoemaker-Levy 9 broke into pieces before it collided with Jupiter and, therefore, it produced a series, or chain, of collisions.

Stop and Think

10 min

Students answer questions about the reading.

Today there is no evidence of the Shoemaker-Levy 9 comet colliding with Jupiter in 1994.

Stop and Think

1. When Shoemaker-Levy 9 hit Jupiter, the impacts caused many changes. Describe the impacts and the changes.

2. The impact of the comet and Jupiter was the first to be predicted by scientists. Why do you think impacts with Jupiter may not have been observed or recorded before? What do you think happened to the evidence of the collisions?

3. How was the impact with Jupiter different from impacts that have occurred on Earth or the Moon?

4. At the end of *Section 1.2*, you were shown a photo of a string of craters on one of the moons of Jupiter. How does what you learned about the Shoemaker-Levy 9 comet change your understanding of how those craters formed?

Reflect

Throughout this Unit, you will read more about the solar system. You just read about some of the objects in the solar system. However, the solar system is more than a collection of objects. It is a system that is constantly in motion, with its different parts interacting through collisions, gravity, and radiation.

By the end of this Unit, you will be able to write a thorough description of how the solar system works. You will be able to explain how it was formed, where the different parts come from, and how they interact with one another.

You will now begin to record what you are learning about the solar system. Later, you will use this information to develop your explanations. Use the questions that follow to help you record your knowledge on a *Solar System* page.

AST 55

ASTRONOMY

△ Guide

Have students answer the *Stop and Think* questions on their own. You also can assign these for homework. Students' answers should demonstrate an understanding that collisions on Jupiter may not leave evidence, unlike collisions on the Moon. They also should infer that other comets may break apart before collision the way Shoemaker-Levy 9 did. This could cause a chain of craters like the one they observed on one of Jupiter's moons.

1. Students should recall that Shoemaker-Levy 9 broke into 21 large fragments. When the first of these struck the surface of Jupiter, a plume of gas and debris caused a plume that rose 1000 km above the visible surface. Dark spots appeared on the surface of Jupiter, which eventually disappeared. Since Jupiter is a gas planet, there were no impact craters.

2. Students may suggest that new technology and more sensitive equipment made it possible to observe and record collisions with Jupiter in the past. Evidence of the collisions probably disappeared because of mixing of the gaseous layers.

3. Students should describe how Earth and the Moon are solid planets, and any collisions would cause visible damage. Jupiter is a gas planet and most collisions would be absorbed by the gaseous layers.

4. Students may suggest that the chain of craters on Ganymede were the result of the breaking up of a comet before it struck Ganymede. This may cause a series of closely spaced impact craters.

△ Guide

Distribute *Solar System* pages and have students record what they have learned about the solar system. They should record the characteristics and motion of the types of solar-system objects they have learned about. Emphasize that only later, will they be able to complete some rows; for now they should focus on the rows they know.

Reflect

5 min

Students record what they are learning their Solar System *pages.*

NOTES

....

....

....

....

....

....

Solar System		1.7.1/2.BIQ.2

Name: _____ Date: _____

Solar System Object	What characteristics does this object have?	How does this object move?
The Sun		
The Moon		
Inner Planets (Mercury, Venus, Earth, Mars)		
Outer planets (Jupiter, Saturn, Uranus, Neptune)		
Dwarf planets		
Asteroids, comets, meteoroids		
Other small solar-system bodies		

1. Use what you have learned in this section and anything you have learned previously to start filling out a *Solar System* page. For each type of object in the solar system that you have read about in this Unit, list its characteristics, and then describe its motion. Do not worry if there are rows or columns on the page that you do not understand. You can skip those and return to them later in the Unit.

2. After you have finished working on your *Solar System* page, get together with your group to discuss your page. Use your discussion to add to or revise what you have written. Notice any disagreements you have with other group members.

3. With your group, identify what else you need to learn about the solar system to be able to answer the *Big Question*.

Update the *Project Board*

Add what you now know about the solar system to the *What have we learned?* column of the *Project Board*. Don't forget to add evidence to the *What is our evidence?* column. You have generated questions about the solar system. Add those to the *What do we need to investigate?* column of the *Project Board*. Make sure your personal *Project Board* matches the class Project Board.

What's the Point?

The solar system consists of eight planets and their moons, as well as a number of dwarf planets and other small solar-system bodies. These bodies include asteroids, comets, and meteoroids. All of the bodies in the solar system can be involved in collisions. In one spectacular collision in 1994, scientists watched a comet as it broke apart and then collided with the planet Jupiter.

AST 56

1. Students should describe the characteristics of each object they have studied in this Unit. They should list its characteristics and then its motion.

2. Students should consult with their group and revise, if necessary, any inaccurate statements.

3. Student answers will vary but should focus on knowledge about the solar system.

▲ Guide

Ask students what new information they can record in the *What are we learning?* column of the *Project Board* and what evidence they have. Record their answers on the *Project Board*. Ask them if they have any ideas for things they need to investigate, and record their ideas in the *What do we need to investigate?* column.

Update the Project Board

10 min

Lead a discussion to update the Project Board.

Assessment Options

Targeted Concepts, Skills, and Nature of Science	How do I know if students got it?
Scientists often collaborate and share their findings. Sharing findings makes new information available and helps scientists refine their ideas and build on others' ideas. When another person's or group's idea is used, credit needs to be given.	**ASK:** How does sharing the information on your *Solar System* page with the class help you? **LISTEN:** Students should have used the class discussion to identify mistakes and inaccuracies in their record.
Scientists must keep clear, accurate, and descriptive records of what they do so they can share their work with others; consider what they did, why they did it, and what they want to do next.	**ASK:** Why is it important that the information recorded on the *Solar System* page be accurate? **LISTEN:** Students should realize that if the information is not accurate, the claims and supporting evidence used to develop the report at the end of the Unit will not be valid.
The Sun, the planets that revolve around it and their moons, are the major bodies in the solar system. Other members that orbit the Sun include dwarf planets and small solar-system bodies such as asteroids and comets.	**ASK:** Which of the objects you have read about so far would be considered small solar-system bodies? **LISTEN:** Students should identify meteoroids, asteroids and comets as small solar-system bodies.

Targeted Concepts, Skills, and Nature of Science	How do I know if students got it?
Most objects in the solar system have a regular and predictable motion. These motions explain such phenomena as a day, a year, phases of the Moon, eclipses, tides, meteor showers, and comets.	**ASK:** What is the shape of the orbit of most planets in our solar system? **LISTEN:** Students should answer that most planet orbit in a nearly circular oval. **ASK:** How do the orbits of small solar-system bodies compare with those of planets? **LISTEN:** Students should describe the orbits of small solar-system bodies as less circular; more oval shaped than the orbits of planets. **ASK:** Why is it possible to predict that Halley's Comet will next be visible on July 28, 2061? **LISTEN:** Students should answer that the motion of Halley's Comet is regular and predictable, orbiting the Sun in an oval path that carries it close to Earth every 76 years.
Comets leave behind grains of dust and ions. The dust and ions can be illuminated by the Sun as a huge tail called a coma. If Earth passes through the trails of dust left behind, the particles rapidly burn up due to friction with the atmosphere, causing a meteor shower.	**ASK:** What is the composition of the "tail" or coma of a comet? What causes these particles to be released by the comet and pushes them out in a long, curved tail? **LISTEN:** Students should describe particles of gas and dust released by the melting comet as it approaches the Sun; light and charged particles flowing outward from the Sun push the cloud of particles released by melting into a tail-like shape.

Teacher Reflection Questions

- How were you able to engage students in sharing their *Solar System* page and asking each other questions about the information they recorded? What might you do differently next time?

- How can you encourage students to actively take notes as they read scientific information? What graphic organizers could you suggest they use to organize their notes?

- How can the *Solar System* page be used as an assessment tool?

NOTES

NOTES

Back to the Big Question

How Can You Know if Objects in Space Will Collide?

◄ **1 class period**

A class period is considered to be one 40 to 50 minute class.

Overview

The *Learning Set* concludes with students returning to the *Big Question* to consider their progress toward addressing it. Students do research to obtain information about an assigned solar-system object, consider what would happen if it collided with Earth, and think about whether it is likely to collide with Earth in the next 30 years. Students create a poster to share their research findings with the class during an *Investigation Expo*. Students then reflect on issues and investigations that still need to be addressed in order to answer the *Big Question* and begin work on a *Big Question* page that will serve as an organizer for information that will be useful for their report at the end of the Unit. Students work in pairs to construct their first explanation of how to tell if space objects will collide and what will happen if they collide. After sharing their explanation with other pairs, students revise their explanation based on feedback from their peers. Students then work in groups to select the explanation they think best tells whether their object will collide with Earth and present it to the class. After reflecting on the reliability and completeness of the explanations shared by the class, students update the *Project Board* with information about different solar system objects.

Targeted Concepts, Skills, and Nature of Science	Performance Expectations
Scientists often collaborate and share their findings. Sharing findings makes new information available and helps scientists refine their ideas and build on others' ideas. When another person's or group's idea is used, credit needs to be given.	Students collaborate in small groups to research a solar-system object and present their findings to the class during an *Investigation Expo*.
	Students collaborate in pairs to create explanations of how you can tell if space objects will collide and what will happen if they collide with other.
	Student share their explanations with other pairs and groups share their best explanations with the class.

Targeted Concepts, Skills, and Nature of Science	Performance Expectations
Scientists must keep clear, accurate, and descriptive records of what they do so they can share their work with others; consider what they did, why they did it, and what they want to do next.	Students create a poster summarizing their research findings about their solar-system object. Students record their claims about how you can tell if space objects will collide and what will happen if they collide along with supporting evidence and science knowledge on a *Create Your Explanation* page. Students keep a written record of their answers to the *Reflect* questions.
Scientists make claims (conclusions) based on evidence obtained (trends in data) from reliable investigations.	Students make claims about how you can tell if space objects will collide and what will happen if they collide and cite supporting evidence and science knowledge that supports their claims. Groups discuss and reach a consensus about the likelihood that the object they researched will collide with another solar-system body.
The Sun, the planets that revolve around it and their moons, are the major bodies in the solar system. Other members that orbit the Sun include dwarf planets and small solar-system bodies, such as asteroids and comets.	Students can identify and describe major and minor solar-system bodies.
Most objects in the solar system have a regular and predictable motion. These motions explain such phenomena as a day, a year, phases of the Moon, eclipses, tides, meteor showers, and comets.	Students can describe the motion of most objects in the solar system as regular and predictable.

Materials

1 per student	*Big Question* page *Create Your Explanation* page
1 per class	Access to information resources to research Class *Project Board*

Homework Options

Reflection

- **Practice/Review:** How do you think what you have learned will help you predict whether an object from space will collide with Earth? *(Students should recognize that they are now better able to identify objects in space that, like Earth, are part of our solar system and the effects of a collision with an object from space.)*

- **Science Process:** What are the benefits of keeping a record of what you learn about objects in the solar system on the *Solar System* page? *(Students should realize that it organizes the information to record their data so that relationships between the various parts of the system can be more easily seen. It also summarizes information that will be needed to develop the report at the end of the Unit.)*

Preparation for Learning Set 2

- **Science Process:** In this *Learning Set,* you learned about the objects that make up our solar system and the effects of collisions. To successfully predict whether an object will collide with Earth, what do you need to know about both Earth and the other objects in our solar system? *(Students should identify their location, the path along which they are moving, and their rate of motion.)*

NOTES

....

....

....

....

....

....

....

NOTES

BACK TO THE BIG QUESTION IMPLEMENTATION

 Learning Set 1

Back to the Big Question

How can you know if objects in space will collide?

The study of craters has provided scientists with a lot of information about when objects have collided and the sizes of the objects. Astrogeologists are one group of scientists who study different solar-system objects. By continuing to study these objects, scientists have an understanding of collisions that occurred in the past. They are also beginning to understand the changes that could happen on Earth as a result of collisions, what caused the collisions, and how often they occur.

The *Big Question* for the Unit is *How can you know if objects in space will collide?* Understanding the evidence of collisions can help you begin to answer this question. You will conclude this Unit by writing a report that answers the question. This *Learning Set* discussed the question, *Have objects in the solar system collided?* So far, you have looked at evidence of collisions on Earth, the Moon, and Jupiter. You have also been introduced to some of the objects in the solar system that might collide with one another. Now you will focus on one specific object and predict what would happen if it collided with Earth.

Explore

Each group will use the Internet and other resources to gather information about one of the four solar-system objects described on the next page. You will be assigned an object your group will study. As you gather the information, you should remember that you are responsible for teaching other groups about your solar-system object. Based on what you find, you will answer two questions: *What would happen if this object collided with Earth?* and *Is it likely that this object will collide with Earth in the next 30 years?*

AST 57

ASTRONOMY

Learning Set 1

Back to the Big Question

5 min

Students read about how astrogeologists study solar-system objects and consider how they will use their findings to answer the Big Question.

△ Guide

Remind students that the *Big Question* for the Unit is *How can you know if objects in space will collide?* and that the first step to answer the *Big Question* is to answer the *Learning Set* question, *Have objects in the solar system collided?* Point out that students now know a lot about how to tell if an object has collided with Earth or the Moon or even, to a lesser degree, Jupiter, but they have not explored the effects of collisions on other solar-system objects.

*A class period is considered to be one 40 to 50 minute class.

Explore

5 min

Student are assigned solar-system bodies to research.

Explore

Each group will use the Internet and other resources to gather information about one of the four solar-system objects described on the next page. You will be assigned an object your group will study. As you gather the information, you should remember that you are responsible for teaching other groups about your solar-system object. Based on what you find, you will answer two questions: *What would happen if this object collided with Earth?* and *Is it likely that this object will collide with Earth in the next 30 years?*

△ Guide

Tell students that they will learn more about what happens when objects collide with other solar-system bodies by researching solar-system bodies and comparing them to Earth and the Moon. Each group will research a different solar-system body. The class will use each group's findings for the rest of the Unit while students learn more about predicting the motion of solar-system objects.

NOTES

....
....
....
....
....
....
....
....
....

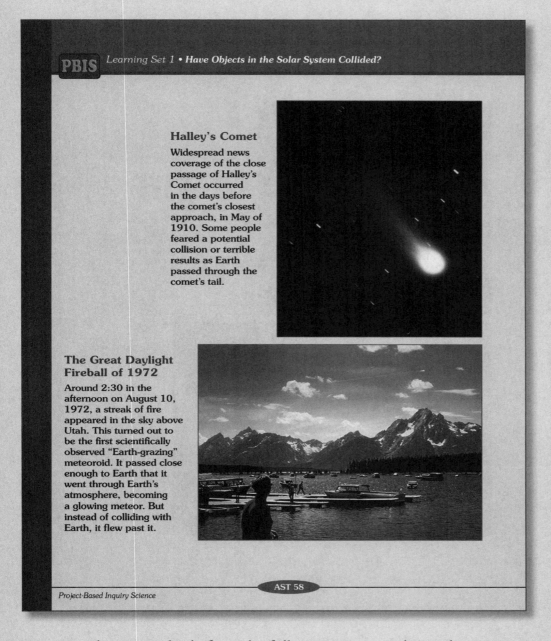

Halley's Comet

Widespread news coverage of the close passage of Halley's Comet occurred in the days before the comet's closest approach, in May of 1910. Some people feared a potential collision or terrible results as Earth passed through the comet's tail.

The Great Daylight Fireball of 1972

Around 2:30 in the afternoon on August 10, 1972, a streak of fire appeared in the sky above Utah. This turned out to be the first scientifically observed "Earth-grazing" meteoroid. It passed close enough to Earth that it went through Earth's atmosphere, becoming a glowing meteor. But instead of colliding with Earth, it flew past it.

AST 58

Project-Based Inquiry Science

Assign a solar-system body from the following pages in the student text to each group, and tell students what resources they can use for their research. The solar-system bodies to research include Halley's Comet, the Great Daylight Fireball of 1972, Asteroid 1999 AN10, and Asteroid 433 Eros. Read through the descriptions with the class before groups begin to research.

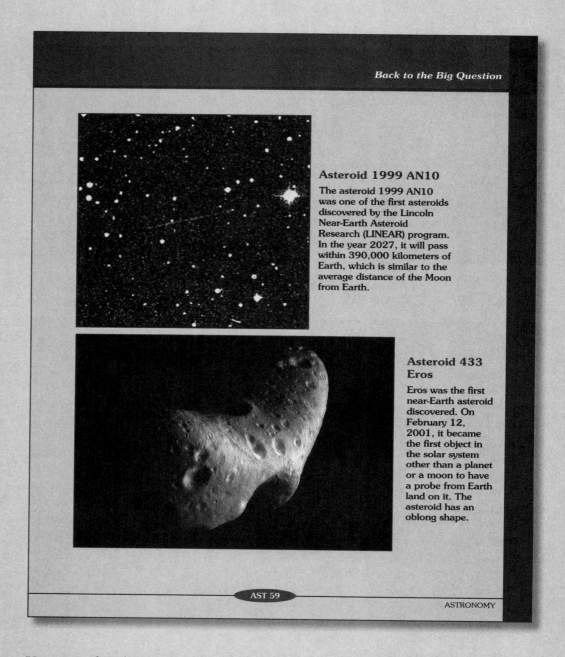

Asteroid 1999 AN10

The asteroid 1999 AN10 was one of the first asteroids discovered by the Lincoln Near-Earth Asteroid Research (LINEAR) program. In the year 2027, it will pass within 390,000 kilometers of Earth, which is similar to the average distance of the Moon from Earth.

Asteroid 433 Eros

Eros was the first near-Earth asteroid discovered. On February 12, 2001, it became the first object in the solar system other than a planet or a moon to have a probe from Earth land on it. The asteroid has an oblong shape.

AST 59

ASTRONOMY

You may decide to take the class to a computer lab or library. You could also assign the research for homework. Emphasize that the two questions students need to answer with their research are: *What would happen if a small asteroid hit our object?* and *Could this body collide with Earth or another solar system body?*

Procedure

1. Using available resources, gather the following information about the solar-system object assigned to your group.

   - size
   - mass
   - composition
   - distance from the Sun (give a range if this distance varies)
   - how and when the object was discovered
   - any other interesting information

2. Determine among your group members what you think would happen if your solar-system object were to collide with Earth. List your ideas and the supporting evidence. Your evidence is the information you have gathered about your solar-system object and the evidence from past collisions that you have studied in this *Learning Set*.

3. Determine among your group members whether you think your object is likely to collide with Earth in the next 30 years. List your ideas and the supporting evidence.

4. Prepare a poster to share with the class. Be sure to include a picture of your solar-system object, the information you gathered, and your answers to the two questions. Make sure you include the evidence used for your answers. Be prepared to explain how your group reached your conclusions and why.

Communicate

Investigation Expo

When you have finished your information gathering and discussions and prepared your poster, you will share what you learned with the class in an *Investigation Expo*. In this *Expo*, each group will take turns presenting their information and conclusions to the class. So that others will be able to learn from your work and use your information, you must clearly present the information on your poster.

Procedure
5 min

Students start to research their solar-system bodies.

△ Guide

Go over the procedure with the class. They will need to gather the information listed in Step 1. Then they will need to discuss what they think would happen if an asteroid were to collide with their solar-system body, and record their ideas and supporting evidence. Finally, they should determine whether they think their solar-system body will collide with another solar-system body, and record their ideas and supporting evidence.

◯ Get Going

Have students research their solar-system bodies, either in class or at home, and then have them meet with their groups to discuss what would happen if an asteroid collided with their solar-system body and whether they think their solar system body will collide with another solar-system body. Emphasize that they will share their ideas with the class.

△ Guide and Assess

As groups are discussing their ideas and evidence, monitor their progress and help them as necessary. Ask them what ideas they have discussed and what evidence supports their ideas. Ask them if the evidence could support alternative ideas.

Communicate: Investigation Expo

15 min

Students share their research and ideas with the class.

evidence used for your answers. Be prepared to explain how your group reached your conclusions and why.

Communicate

Investigation Expo

When you have finished your information gathering and discussions and prepared your poster, you will share what you learned with the class in an *Investigation Expo*. In this *Expo*, each group will take turns presenting their information and conclusions to the class. So that others will be able to learn from your work and use your information, you must clearly present the information on your poster.

Project-Based Inquiry Science

AST 60

◯ Get Going

Have each group prepare a poster that includes a picture of their solar-system body, their answers to the two questions, and evidence to support their answers. Then have groups present their research using the posters in an *Investigation Expo*.

As each group presents, students should listen carefully and ask questions to clarify the groups' conclusions. Point out the questions students might ask that are listed in students' text.

NOTES

....

....

While you are listening to the presentations of other groups, be ready to ask questions so that you can better understand the groups' conclusions. Some questions you might want to ask include these:

- What type of solar-system object is your object: a comet, an asteroid, or something else?

- What evidence of past collisions with similar objects helped you predict what might happen if your object collided with Earth?

- What was the most important evidence used to reach your conclusion about the likelihood of a collision?

Reflect

Now that you have listened to all the presentations in your class, you need to start thinking about preparing your report that answers the *Big Question: How can you know if objects in space will collide?* The first step in writing a good report is organizing all of the information you have. Right now, you don't have enough information to write a complete report, but you can still get started with organizing it.

Use the *Big Question* page to list what you have learned so far about the objects in the solar system. Use the first column to record the objects or types of objects that you think your report should include. It will help if you can group objects together. For example, instead of listing different comets separately, you can list comets as a type of object, and make notes on individual comets in the last three columns as needed.

Use the last three columns to record information that would be useful for your report. The *Evidence of Past Collisions* column should list any evidence that these objects have collided with other space objects in the past. The *Chance of Future Collisions* column should list any evidence that these objects could collide with other space objects in the future. The *What Would Happen?* column should list your ideas on what would happen if a collision occurred and what could be done to prevent such a collision.

Big Question

How Can You Know if Objects in Space Will Collide?

Type of Object	Evidence of Past Collisions	Chance of Future Collisions	What Would Happen?

Reflect

5 min

Students record what they know about the solar system on their Big Question *pages.*

△ Guide

Let students know that they do not yet have enough information to write a report, but they can start organizing the information they do have. Distribute *Big Question* pages and tell students what goes in each column. Then have students record as much information as they can on their *Big Question* pages.

Explain

10 min

Students develop an explanation for two space objects.

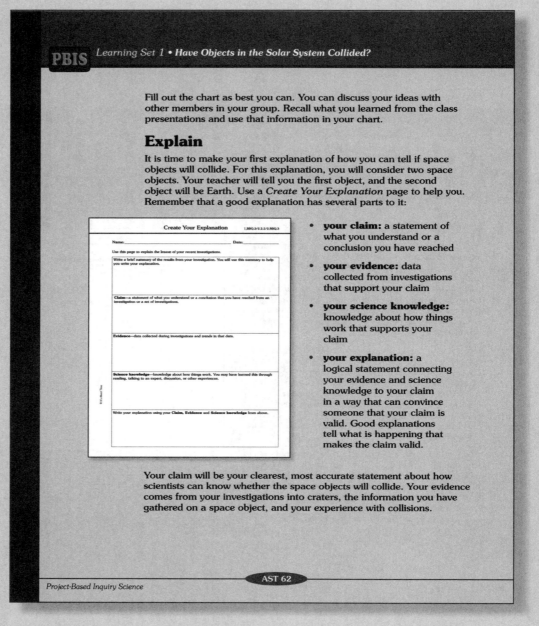

Fill out the chart as best you can. You can discuss your ideas with other members in your group. Recall what you learned from the class presentations and use that information in your chart.

Explain

It is time to make your first explanation of how you can tell if space objects will collide. For this explanation, you will consider two space objects. Your teacher will tell you the first object, and the second object will be Earth. Use a *Create Your Explanation* page to help you. Remember that a good explanation has several parts to it:

- **your claim:** a statement of what you understand or a conclusion you have reached

- **your evidence:** data collected from investigations that support your claim

- **your science knowledge:** knowledge about how things work that supports your claim

- **your explanation:** a logical statement connecting your evidence and science knowledge to your claim in a way that can convince someone that your claim is valid. Good explanations tell what is happening that makes the claim valid.

Your claim will be your clearest, most accurate statement about how scientists can know whether the space objects will collide. Your evidence comes from your investigations into craters, the information you have gathered on a space object, and your experience with collisions.

△ Guide

Let students know that there will be two parts to consider in their explanations. Tell students which space object they will focus on and that they will also focus on Earth. They should determine a way to tell if their space object will collide with Earth. Distribute the *Create Your Explanation* pages, and let students begin working in their groups. Remind them of the parts of the claim, and guide them to check that they have all those parts when their group arrives at an explanation.

Your science knowledge comes from your reading. Use what you have learned so far to make the best explanation you can right now. It may be easier to express your explanation by attaching phrases to sketches than to simply use words. Feel free to combine sketches and words in your explanation. You will have a chance later in the Unit to revise your explanation.

Communicate

Share Your Explanation

Share your group's explanation with the rest of the class. As you are listening to the explanations of other groups, look for anything they have to say about determining whether two space objects will collide that you did not include in your explanation.

AST 63

ASTRONOMY

Communicate: Share Your Explanation

10 min

Groups share their explanations with the rest of the class.

⬡ Get Going

Have groups take turns sharing their explanations with the class. As students listen to presentations, they should assess whether that group addresses all parts of a good explanation.

Reflect

5 min

Students think about the claims of other groups.

Reflect

With your group, answer the following questions.

1. How trustworthy and complete do you think your explanation is?

2. What else do you need to investigate and learn to improve your explanation of how scientists can know if two space objects will collide?

Update the *Project Board*

It is now time to update the *Project Board* with information about different solar-system objects. Think about what is most important about each solar-system object you learned about. Consider the similarities and differences among these objects and include this information in the *What are we learning?* column. Support your learning with evidence from your research or reading. Record this evidence in the *What is our evidence?* column.

Although you are learning about many different objects in the solar system, there may still be some things you think you know but are not quite sure about. You should record these ideas in the *What do we think we know?* column. In the *Investigation Expo*, you listened to presentations about what would happen if some of these objects hit Earth. The information in those presentations will be useful for your report. Add this information to the *What does this mean for the challenge or question?* column.

You may also have realized that you need to learn more about the objects in the solar system to determine if collisions will occur. For example, you need to understand how objects in the solar system move in relation to one another. You also need to understand how gravity works. Add these and any other questions to the *What do we need to learn?* column of the *Project Board*.

⬡ Get Going

Have students meet with their groups to discuss the explanations that were shared. Tell them to use the questions in the student text to guide their evaluation discussions.

◬ Guide

Tell students that they should now record what they have learned about the solar system on the *Project Board*. Ask each group what they think is most important about the solar-system object they learned about. Record their ideas in the *What are we learning?* column. Ask them what the similarities and differences are among the solar-system bodies studied by the class, and record students' answers in the *What are we learning?* column. Ask them what evidence they can put in the *What is our evidence?* column, and record their answers on the *Project Board*.

Then ask students if they have any ideas about things they should investigate. Record their answers in the *What do we need to investigate?* column of the *Project Board*.

Update the *Project Board*

15 min

The class has a discussion to update the Project Board.

Assessment Options

Targeted Concepts, Skills, and Nature of Science	How do I know if students got it?
Scientists often collaborate and share their findings. Sharing findings makes new information available and helps scientists refine their ideas and build on others' ideas. When another person's or group's idea is used, credit needs to be given.	**ASK:** How did everyone in the class benefit by sharing information about the solar-system object they researched? **LISTEN:** Students should recognize that by sharing their research findings, the class had access to information about more objects in the solar system than they had obtained through their own research.

NOTES

....

....

....

Targeted Concepts, Skills, and Nature of Science	How do I know if students got it?
Scientists must keep clear, accurate, and descriptive records of what they do so they can share their work with others; consider what they did, why they did it, and what they want to do next.	**ASK:** What resources did you use to research your solar-system body so that you could create the poster for the *Investigation Expo?* **LISTEN:** Students should identify specific resources they used, such as books, magazines, and Internet Web sites. **ASK:** What information about solar-system objects did you record on the *Big Question* page? **LISTEN:** Students should cite information about the object or type of object, evidence of past collisions, chance of future collisions, and what would happen if a collision occurred.
Scientists make claims (conclusions) based on evidence obtained (trends in data) from reliable investigations.	**ASK:** How did the research shared by other groups help you support your claims about whether the object you researched could collide with Earth? **LISTEN:** Students should recognize that research done by other groups about objects similar to the one their group researched provided additional evidence to support their claims. **ASK:** What information was most useful as evidence to support your claims? **LISTEN:** Students should recognize that information about the location of the object and its path around the Sun was most useful when predicting whether it would collide with Earth; evidence of past collisions on the body was most useful for supporting claims about what would happen if an object collided with the body.

Targeted Concepts, Skills, and Nature of Science	How do I know if students got it?
The Sun, the planets that revolve around it and their moons, are the major bodies in the solar system. Other members that orbit the Sun include dwarf planets and small solar-system bodies, such as asteroids and comets.	**ASK:** What are some of the ways in which the planets in our solar system differ? **LISTEN:** Students should recognize that the planets differ in size, composition, and distance from the Sun. **ASK:** What new information about planets, dwarf planets, and small solar-system bodies did you obtain from the *Investigation Expo?* **LISTEN:** Students should cite specific information such as size, mass, composition, distance from the Sun and evidence of past collisions.
Most objects in the solar system have a regular and predictable motion. These motions explain such phenomena as a day, a year, phases of the Moon, eclipses, tides, meteor showers, and comets.	**ASK:** After all of the groups had shared their research with the class, what revisions did you make to your *Solar System* page? **LISTEN:** Students should describe how they revised the information they had recorded based on the information presented during the *Investigation Expo.* **ASK:** What motions of Earth would you consider regular and predictable? **LISTEN:** Students should consider its revolution around the Sun and its rotation.

Teacher Reflection Questions

- During this *Learning Set,* how did you guide the readings? What would you improve upon when you guide students through a reading in the next *Learning Set?*

- How did you get students to contribute to the discussion of what to add to the *Project Board?* What are some other techniques you could try?

- What questions or techniques did you find most successful in helping students connect what they have been learning to the *Big Question?*

NOTES

LEARNING SET 2 INTRODUCTION

Learning Set 2

How Do Earth, the Moon, and the Sun Move Through Space?

◀ 11½ class periods

A class period is considered to be one 40 to 50 minute class.

Students investigate the regular, predictable motions of Earth and its Moon relative to the Sun and determine how the changing relative positions of Earth, the Moon, and the Sun account for the phases of the Moon, eclipses and tides.

Overview

Learning Set 2 opens with students considering that in order to predict collisions between solar-system objects, the motions of those objects must be understood. Students read that early astronomers observed that objects in the sky have patterns of motion that are regular and predictable. In *Section 2.1*, students observe through a series of images that the Sun's position in the sky changes throughout the day. Students analyze shadows cast by the Sun at different times of day to plot the Sun's apparent path across the sky. They also consider how the Sun's regular and predictable motion can be used to measure time. In *Section 2.2*, students create a model of the Earth-Sun system and simulate motions of the system that could result in the changes in shadow length and direction observed in *Section 2.1*. Students then create an explanation for the observed changes in the position of the Sun in the sky throughout the day. In *Section 2.3*, students observe that the Moon's position in the sky and appearance change over time in a regular and predictable way. Students read that the Moon is visible only by the reflected sunlight and that at the different phases of the Moon, different portions of its illuminated half are facing Earth. Students then model the relative positions of Earth, the Moon, and Sun at each phase, and the simultaneous motions of Earth and the Moon. In *Section 2.4*, students develop a more concrete understanding of distances in the solar system and the relative sizes of solar-system objects by creating a scale model of the Earth-Moon-Sun system. In *Section 2.5*, students use the model of the Earth-Moon-Sun system created earlier to simulate lunar and solar eclipses, noting the phase of the Moon at which each occurs. The section concludes with a reading focusing on how tides are caused by the combined effects on Earth of the gravity of the Sun and Moon.

ASTRONOMY

In the *Back to the Big Question* section, students consider the theory that the Moon formed as the result of a collision between Earth and another large solar-system object.

Targeted Concepts, Skills, and Nature of Science	Section
Scientists often collaborate and share their findings. Sharing findings makes new information available and helps scientists refine their ideas and build on others' ideas. When another person's or group's idea is used, credit needs to be given.	All sections
Scientists must keep clear, accurate, and descriptive records of what they do so they can share their work with others; consider what they did, why they did it, and what they want to do next.	All sections
Scientific knowledge is developed through observations, recording and analysis of data, and development of explanations based on evidence.	All sections
Models are a representation of something in the world. Simulations use a model to imitate, or act out, real-life situations.	2.2, 2.3, 2.4, 2.5
Explanations are claims supported by evidence. Evidence can be experimental results, observational data, and any other accepted scientific knowledge.	2.2, 2.3, 2.BBQ
Earth's Sun is the central and largest body in our solar system. The Sun is more than a million times greater in volume than Earth. Earth is the third planet from the Sun in a system that includes other planets and their moons, as well as smaller objects, such as asteroids and comets.	2.4
Most objects in the solar system have a regular and predictable motion. These motions explain such phenomena as a day, a year, phases of the Moon, eclipses, tides, meteor showers, and comets.	2.1, 2.2, 2.3, 2.5, 2.BBQ
The rotation of the earth on its axis every 24 hours produces the night-and-day cycle. To people on Earth, this turning of the planet makes it seem as though the Sun, Moon, planets, and stars are orbiting the earth once a day. This rotation also causes the Sun and Moon to appear to rise along the eastern horizon and to set along the western horizon. Earth's revolution around the Sun defines the length of the year as 365.25 days.	2.1, 2.2, 2.3
An object's apparent size depends on its distance from the observer.	2.4

Targeted Concepts, Skills, and Nature of Science	Section
The Moon orbits Earth while Earth orbits the Sun. Except for the Sun, all objects in the solar system are seen by reflected light. The Moon's orbit around Earth once in about 28 days changes the part of the Moon lighted by the Sun and how much of that part can be seen from Earth—the phases of the Moon. The phases repeat in a cyclic pattern in about one month.	2.3
An eclipse of the Moon occurs when the Moon enters Earth's shadow. An eclipse of the Sun occurs when the Moon is between Earth and the Sun, and the Moon's shadow falls on the Earth.	2.5
Tides, or the cyclic rise and fall of ocean waters, are caused by the gravitational pulls of the Moon and (to a lesser extent) the Sun, as well as the rotation of Earth.	2.5

Understanding for Teachers

Apparent Daily Motion

Celestial objects are objects seen in the sky that are not within Earth's atmosphere. Stars, the Sun, the Moon, planets, and comets are all examples of celestial objects. Aurora, clouds, rainbows, meteors, and other phenomena seen in the sky that are part of, or within, Earth's atmosphere are *not* considered celestial objects.

All celestial objects appear to move across the sky from east to west along a path that is an arc, or part of a circle. All celestial objects move along their circular paths at a constant rate of 15°/h, or one complete circle every day (24h/day × 15°/h = 360°/day). This is called *apparent daily motion*. In the Northern Hemisphere, the circles formed by completing the arcs along which celestial objects move are all centered very near the star Polaris. The apparent circular motion of celestial objects causes them to come into view from below the eastern horizon and to sink from view beneath the western horizon (rise in the east and set in the west).

This motion is referred to as *apparent motion* because the motion of an object is always judged with respect to some other object or point. The idea of absolute motion or rest is misleading because there are several possible reasons why an object may *appear* to be moving to an observer: the observer is standing still and the object is moving; the object is standing still and the observer is moving; or both object and observer are moving but at different speeds, in different directions, or both.

Early astronomers observed daily and yearly cyclic patterns in the changing positions of celestial objects. Because the distribution of stars is random, early astronomers invented constellations—imaginary patterns of stars—to help them keep track of the changing positions of celestial objects. Understanding these patterns of motion was very useful. Such changes could be used to determine time, and to find one's position on Earth, because the position of celestial objects changes with both time and location.

The Celestial Sphere

Early observers of the sky reasoned that when they looked at the sky they were standing still because their senses gave them no signs that they were moving. Therefore, they interpreted the motion of celestial objects to mean that the celestial objects were moving. They visualized all celestial objects as revolving around a motionless Earth.

One effect of apparent daily motion is that the sky appears to move as if it were a single object. Imagine a bus driving toward you with *School Bus* painted in big letters on its side. The word *School* does not get any closer to the word *Bus*, because the bus is moving in that direction. The letters and words stay in a fixed pattern because they are part of the same object—the bus. In much the same way, the stars stay in fixed positions relative to one another as they move across the sky. It is not surprising then, that early astronomers imagined that the sky was a single object—a huge dome. Since the "dome" of the sky was in motion, and new parts would come into view as others dropped out of sight, they imagined that it extended beyond the horizon. As they followed through on this model, they realized that if the dome were extended far enough it would form a hollow ball, or sphere, surrounding the Earth. They imagined a huge "sky ball," or *celestial sphere,* slowly spinning around the motionless Earth. The celestial sphere model was used because it explained many observations. It explained why the stars remained in fixed positions relative to one another and all moved in the same direction at the same speed—they were part of one object. It explained why objects would appear, arc across the sky, disappear, and then reappear the next day: the sphere rotated around Earth at its center.

Projecting Earth's Equator and Poles onto the sky forms a useful coordinate system for locating objects on the celestial sphere. Earth's Equator, North Pole, and South Pole would correspond to a *Celestial Equator* and *North* and *South Celestial Poles* on the celestial sphere. Celestial objects can be located in the sky by their position in relation to these celestial reference points. The star *Polaris* is located very close to the North Celestial Pole. This makes it a convenient reference point for determining the north-south positions of celestial objects in the Northern Hemisphere. The Sun is a convenient reference point for determining the east-west position of objects on the celestial sphere. Objects to the west of the Sun on the celestial sphere will rise before the Sun and set before the Sun. Objects to the east of the Sun trail behind it rising after the Sun and setting after the Sun.

The Sun's Apparent Path

Due to Earth's rotation, the Sun moves along an imaginary path through the sky as part of the celestial sphere every day. However, the apparent position of the Sun with respect to the background stars also changes as Earth orbits the Sun. When the Earth has made one complete revolution in its orbit, the Sun will return to its starting point against the background stars. In other words, the Sun traces out a closed path on the celestial sphere once a year. The apparent path of the Sun through the stars on the celestial sphere over the course of the year is called the *ecliptic*. Since the Earth's axis of rotation is tilted 23.5° to the plane of its orbit, the ecliptic is tilted 23.5° with respect to the Celestial Equator. The Sun, the Moon, and the planets are always found near the ecliptic because all of these solar system objects lie nearly in the same plane.

The Sun's daily apparent path through the sky changes with the seasons because the Sun's position relative to an observer changes as Earth orbits the Sun. The points of sunrise and sunset vary, as does the altitude of the Sun at noon.

In December, the North Pole of Earth's axis of rotation is tilted at its farthest angle away from the Sun. Therefore, to an observer in the United States the position of sunrise is to the south of east and the position of sunset is south of west. The noon Sun is at its lowest altitude of the year and the length of the Sun's path is shortest, so the daylight period is shortest.

In June, the North Pole of Earth's axis of rotation is tilted at its farthest angle toward the Sun. Therefore, the Sun rises north of east, sets north of west, and rises to a higher altitude. The Sun's path is at its longest, so the daylight period is longest.

In March and September, the North Pole of Earth's axis of rotation is tilted neither toward nor away from the Sun. Therefore, the Sun rises due east and sets due west. The Sun's altitude at noon is mid-way between its highest and lowest points. The length of the Sun's path results in exactly equal periods of daylight and darkness.

From December to June, the Sun's path gets longer each day and the altitude of the Sun at noon increases. On June 21, the altitude of the Sun at noon stops increasing. Therefore, this date is called the *summer solstice* (from Latin, meaning *Sun stop*). From June to December, the Sun's path gets shorter each day and the altitude of the Sun at noon decreases. On December 21, the altitude of the Sun at noon stops decreasing. Therefore, this date is called the *winter solstice*. March 21 and September 21, when the daylight and darkness periods are equal, are called respectively the *spring* and *autumnal equinox* (from Latin, meaning *equal night*). This cyclic pattern of change repeats annually.

The Sun's apparent path also varies with latitude. The diagram below shows what two observers at different latitudes would see on a given day as Earth rotated. As you can see, the observer near the Equator would see the sun at a higher altitude at noon than the observer in New York State on the same day.

The altitude of the noon sun at any location can be determined quite easily if you know the latitude of that location and the latitude at which the Sun is directly overhead on that day. To find the altitude of the Sun at noon, find the difference between the latitude of the location and the latitude at which the sun is directly overhead. Then subtract this number of degrees from 90°.

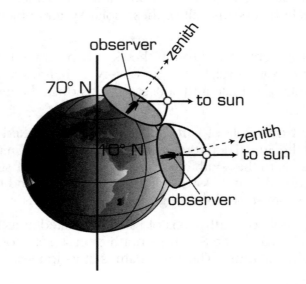

Earth's Motions

Rotation is a motion in which every part of an object is moving in a circular path around a central line called the *axis of rotation*. Earth's axis of rotation is a line that passes through the North Pole, the center of Earth, and the South Pole. It is almost directly aligned with the star Polaris and is tilted at an angle of 23.5° from a perpendicular to the plane passing through the centers of Earth and the Sun. Earth rotates at a rate of 15°/h, or one complete rotation every 24 hours.

Revolution is the motion of one object around another object along a path called an orbit. The revolving object is called a *satellite* and the object around which a satellite revolves is called its *primary*. Thus, Earth is a satellite of the Sun. The plane of Earth's orbit is called the *ecliptic* because eclipses occur when Earth, the Moon, and Sun align in this plane. As Earth rotates, it revolves around the Sun once every 365.25 days.

Earth's axis of rotation is tilted 23.5° from a perpendicular to the plane of its orbit. Spinning like a top, Earth's axis remains fixed in space as it moves around the Sun. As a result, the Northern Hemisphere is tilted toward the Sun in June and away from the Sun in December.

As Earth revolves around the Sun, the side facing the Sun experiences day, and the side facing away from the Sun experiences night. Stars are only visible at night, therefore, the portion of the universe with stars visible at night to an observer on Earth varies cyclically as Earth revolves around the Sun.

Moon's Motions

As Earth revolves around the Sun, the Moon revolves around Earth in an elliptical orbit with a period of 27.32 days. The Moon's orbit is tilted at an angle of about 5° from the plane of Earth's orbit around the Sun. The Moon moves rapidly in its orbit, covering 13° every day. As a result, each day its position against the backdrop of stars changes by 13°, or about 26 times its apparent diameter. The Moon also rotates on its axis once every 27.32 days. Thus, the same side of the Moon always faces Earth.

Although the Moon makes one revolution in 27.32 days, it takes 29.5 days for the Moon to go through a complete cycle of phases. Why the extra two days? Imagine the Moon is between Earth and the Sun at the new Moon phase. At the same time that the Moon revolves around Earth, Earth is revolving around the Sun at a rate of about 1°/day. By the time the Moon has completed one revolution, Earth has moved 27° in its orbit. Moving at about 13°/day, it takes the Moon about two days to catch up to Earth and align with it and the Sun in a new Moon phase, or about 29.5 days in total from new Moon to new Moon.

Phases

The Moon can be seen only by sunlight that reflects from its surface. Because the Moon is a sphere, at any given time, only half of the Moon is illuminated by sunlight. An observer on Earth is only able to see the portion of the Moon that is illuminated by the Sun. As the Moon moves around Earth, different portions of the Moon's illuminated side face Earth and the Moon passes through a cycle of phases.

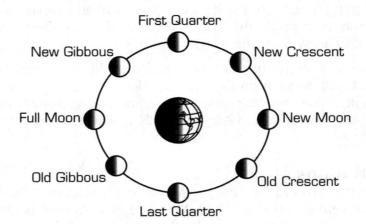

Eclipses

Earth and the Moon are both illuminated by the Sun and cast shadows in space. When the Moon passes directly between Earth and the Sun, it blocks the Sun, casting a shadow on Earth, and a *solar eclipse* occurs. As you can see above, the umbra of the shadows cast by Earth and the Moon are extremely long and narrow. The small, circular shadow the Moon casts on Earth is never more than 269 km in diameter.

Together, the small size of the Moon's shadow and the 5° tilt of the Moon's orbit make it easy for the shadow to miss Earth at full and new moons. Thus, total solar eclipses are rare. In order for a total solar eclipse to occur, the plane of the Moon's orbit must intersect the shadows being cast by Earth and the Moon.

The Moon's orbit is elliptical; therefore, its distance from Earth varies. If the Moon aligns with the Sun when it is at its farthest away from Earth, the Moon's umbra does not reach Earth's surface and a total solar eclipse does not occur. Instead, a type of partial eclipse called an *annular eclipse* occurs. In an annular eclipse, the Moon is too far from Earth to completely block an observer's view of the Sun. The outer edges of the Sun are still visible as a ring, or *annulus,* of light.

When the Moon moves through Earth's shadow at its full stage, a lunar eclipse occurs. If the Moon moves into Earth's umbra, a total lunar eclipse occurs. When the Moon passes through Earth's umbra it does not completely disappear from view. Although sunlight does not reach the Moon directly, some long waves of red light are bent far enough as they pass through Earth's atmosphere to reach the Moon and the Moon glows with a dull red color during a total lunar eclipse.

If the Moon moves into Earth's penumbra, a partial lunar eclipse is seen. During a partial lunar eclipse, the Moon is only partially dimmed because Earth only blocks part of the Sun's light.

Tides

The mutual attraction of gravity between Earth and your body pulls you toward Earth's center with a force. This force is commonly known as your weight. However, even though the Moon is farther away from you than Earth's center and has less mass than Earth, it still exerts a measurable force on you and everything else on Earth.

Attracted by the Moon's gravity, water in the oceans flows into a bulge of water on the side of Earth facing the moon. A bulge of water also forms on Earth's far side because the Moon pulls on Earth's center more strongly than on Earth's far side. This pulls Earth away from the oceans on the far side and water flows into this space creating a bulge. Water flowing into these bulges from the area between the bulges creates regions of shallow water between the deeper water in the bulges.

The position of the tidal bulges remains fixed in line with the Moon as Earth rotates on its axis. As a location is carried into a tidal bulge by the rotating Earth, the water deepens and the tide rises on the beach. As the location rotates out of the tidal bulge, the water becomes shallower and the tide falls. Since there are two bulges on opposite sides of Earth, the tide rises and falls twice a day.

The Sun also exerts a gravitational pull on Earth's waters and produces tidal bulges in Earth's oceans. At new moon and full moon, the Sun's tidal bulges align with the Moon's tidal bulges and add together. The result is very high and very low tides. These are called *spring tides,* not because they happen during the spring season, but because the water "springs" up so high. During the first and third quarter moons, the Sun's tidal bulges and Moon's tidal bulges are at right angles to each other. The tidal bulges nearly cancel each other out and "neap tides" occur in which there is very little difference between high and low tides.

ASTRONOMY

NOTES

LEARNING SET 2 IMPLEMENTATION

Learning Set 2

How Do Earth, the Moon, and the Sun Move Through Space?

Using a telescope, you can see most of the big objects in our solar system from right where you are on Earth. The one big solar-system object you cannot see in the sky is Earth itself. Only the few people who have traveled in space have seen Earth from a different viewpoint. So, how can you find out about where objects in the solar system are located? And what is Earth's place in the solar system?

In *Learning Set 1,* you learned about some solar-system objects that have collided with other solar-system bodies, including Earth. You can tell from the size of the craters formed that the impacting objects must have been moving at great speeds. But remember that Earth is also moving through the solar system. So, to accurately predict whether an object in space will collide with another object, you need to know where the object is, how it is moving, where the other object is, and how that object is moving.

People on Earth have always looked up at the sky and wondered about what they saw. The two most noticeable objects are the Sun and the Moon. From your place here on Earth, you have observed the Moon, our closest neighbor. Over a certain period of time, you may have noticed how the Moon's appearance changes from day to day. You may have observed patterns in these changes and questioned why they occur. Ancient astronomers did the same thing. Over time, they realized that the movements of the Sun and the Moon are predictable.

In this *Learning Set,* you will do something similar to what ancient astronomers did. You will observe patterns in the movements of the Moon and Sun. Then, based on what you observe, you will do your best to determine how the Sun, Moon, and Earth move through space. This will prepare you to learn about movements of other objects in the solar system. You will need to know all of this to answer the *Big Question.*

The Moon is often visible during daylight hours.

AST 65

ASTRONOMY

Learning Set 1

How Do Earth, the Moon, and the Sun Move Through Space?

5 min

Students are introduced to the Learning Set *question.*

△ Guide

Begin by pointing out that students have learned a lot about the composition of the solar system. This is necessary for them to predict whether objects in the solar system might collide. Emphasize that they also need to understand how Earth is moving to predict whether something might collide with it. Point out that answering the question of the *Learning Set* will help them to answer the *Big Question: How can you know if objects in space will collide?*

*A class period is considered to be one 40 to 50 minute class.

Let students know they will use observations of the Sun and Moon to answer the *Learning Set* question. They will use the same observations that ancient astronomers used to make predictions about Earth and its cycles. Emphasize that ancient astronomers were able to predict annual floods and tell when to plant crops without using telescopes or advanced mathematics.

NOTES

SECTION 2.1 INTRODUCTION

2.1 Understand the Question

Think About How You Can Find Out About the Motions of Earth, the Moon, and the Sun

◄ $1\frac{1}{4}$ *class periods*

A class period is considered to be one 40 to 50 minute class.

Overview

Students assume the role of early astronomers who relied on observations and thinking skills to figure out how objects in the solar system move in relation to one another. Working in small groups, students examine images of the shadow cast by a sundial showing changes throughout the day. Students record their observations on a *Sundial Patterns* page and reflect on any patterns they detect. They analyze their data and consider the relationship between the size of a shadow, the direction of that shadow, and the location of the light source that create the shadow. After reading about sundials as timekeeping instruments, students reflect on the limitations of sundials. Using what they have learned about sundials as a starting point, students brainstorm ways in which the movement of objects in the solar system could be determined by observations made from Earth's surface. Students then discuss their ideas and update the *What do we think we know?* and *What do we need to investigate?* columns of the *Project Board*.

Targeted Concepts, Skills, and Nature of Science	Performance Expectations
Scientists often collaborate and share their findings. Sharing findings makes new information available and helps scientists refine their ideas and build on others' ideas. When another person's or group's idea is used, credit needs to be given.	Students engage in a brainstorming session in which they share ideas about how observations made from Earth can be used to determine the motions of objects in the solar system.

NOTES

....

....

Targeted Concepts, Skills, and Nature of Science	Performance Expectations
Scientists must keep clear, accurate, and descriptive records of what they do so they can share their work with others; consider what they did, why they did it, and what they want to do next.	Students record the length and direction of shadows cast by a sundial at different times of the day on their *Sundial Patterns* pages. Students create a list of ideas about how the movements of objects in the solar system could be determined by Earth-based observations.
Most objects in the solar system have a regular and predictable motion. These motions explain such phenomena as a day, a year, phases of the Moon, eclipses, tides, meteor showers, and comets.	Students observe that the length and direction of a shadow cast by a sundial changes in a regular and predictable pattern and relate the observed changes in the shadow to regular and predictable changes in the Sun's position in the sky.
The rotation of the earth on its axis every 24 hours produces the night-and-day cycle. To people on Earth, this turning of the planet makes it seem as though the Sun, Moon, planets, and stars are orbiting Earth once a day. This rotation also causes the Sun and Moon to appear to rise along the eastern horizon and to set along the western horizon. Earth's revolution around the Sun defines the length of the year as 365.25 days.	Students describe the apparent motion of the Sun as it moves across the sky. Students recognize that the Sun's apparent motion is due to Earth's rotation on its axis.

Materials

1 per student	*Sundial Patterns* page *Project Board* page
1 per class	Class *Project Board*

NOTES

....

....

Homework Options

Reflection

- **Science Content:** A student observes the shadow cast by a sundial and a short time later observes that the shadow has gotten longer. Were the two observations made before or after midday? Why? *(Students should infer that the two observations were made after midday. Shadows increase in length when the Sun's position in the sky gets lower. The Sun rises and moves higher in the sky until midday; after midday, the Sun moves lower and lower in the sky until it sets.)*

- **Science Content:** A student in New York is out in the schoolyard on a sunny day and notes that it is exactly 12 noon. In what general direction does the student's shadow point? *(Students should indicate that the shadow should point north.)*

- **Science Process:** How could you determine whether the Sun's apparent path through the sky varies during the year? *(Students should suggest observing the length and direction of the shadows cast throughout the day at different times throughout the year.)*

Preparation for 2.2

- **Science Process:** Suppose you set up a sundial on a sheet of paper on your desk and your teacher drew the outline of a shadow on the paper. How could you determine where to hold a flashlight so that when it is turned on the shadow cast by the sundial would fall within the outline drawn by your teacher? *(Students should suggest aligning the flashlight with an imaginary line extending from the tip of the shadow outline to the tip of the gnomon of the sundial.)*

NOTES

....

....

....

....

NOTES

SECTION 2.1 IMPLEMENTATION

◀ $1\frac{1}{4}$ *class periods**

2.1 Understand the Question

Think About How You Can Find Out About the Motions of Earth, the Moon, and the Sun

You know that the Sun rises in the east and sets in the west. This movement is predictable and has been observed for hundreds of thousands of years. You have probably learned that the spinning of Earth causes this *apparent movement* of the Sun across the sky. *Apparent movement* refers to what the movement of objects in space looks like to an observer on Earth. However, because Earth is also moving, the apparent movement you observe is not necessarily the same as the actual movement of those objects. People have not always known that Earth is spinning. Until 1850, nobody could prove that Earth rotates. Then the French scientist Jean Foucault designed an experiment with a large pendulum swinging in a circle of pegs. The pendulum shifted slowly and knocked down pegs throughout the day. Because of the way he had set up the experiment, only a rotating movement of Earth could have caused the pendulum to knock down the pegs. That was the first time a scientist had provided evidence that Earth is rotating.

Although Foucault's pendulum seemed to swing back and forth in one line, because of the rotating movement of Earth, it changed position and, throughout the day, it knocked down many pegs.

AST 66

Project-Based Inquiry Science

2.1 Understand the Question

Think About How You Can Find Out About the Motions of Earth, the Moon, and the Sun

5 min

Students are introduced to the concept of apparent movement.

△ **Guide**

Let students know that in this section they will use basic observations of shadows to investigate the motion of Earth. Like early scientists, they will make inferences about the motions of Earth, the Sun, and the Moon based on these basic observations.

*A class period is considered to be one 40 to 50 minute class.

ASTRONOMY

Get Started

5 min

Students learn how to use the Sundial Patterns *page to record observations of a sundial's shadow for the following activity.*

You learned in *Learning Set 1* that Earth revolves around the Sun. It is easy to confuse the term rotation with the term *revolution*. Rotation refers to spinning. Revolution refers to moving around another object. It may help to remember that an object can spin in place, like a rotating top. If an object is revolving, it cannot stay in place as it moves around another object. And of course, an object can rotate and revolve at the same time, as Earth does.

Knowing where objects are located in the solar system requires knowing how they are moving. That was hard for astronomers to determine. For the next few days, you are going to imagine that you know absolutely nothing about the movement of Earth. You are going to observe the apparent motion of the Sun across the sky, experiencing what it was like for early scientists who relied on observations to figure out how Earth and other objects in the sky move in relation to one another. You will be using shadows to observe the apparent motion of the Sun across the sky. Then you will use your observations to try to explain why the length and direction of a shadow changes throughout the day.

sundial: a device that measures time using shadows cast by an object that blocks the Sun's light.

You will do this by examining the shadows made by a **sundial**. A sundial is a device that measures time using the shadows the Sun makes. The simplest type of sundial is a stick in the ground with a flat surface around it on all sides. As far back as 3500 B.C.E., people realized that one could measure how time passed by looking at the shadows of a sundial.

Get Started

You will be observing images that show how a sundial's shadow changes over the course of a day. You will observe how the position of the Sun in the sky relates to the shadows. You will then consider how changes in the shadows relate to the apparent motion of the Sun. You will organize your observations on a *Sundial Patterns* page.

Your *Sundial Patterns* page has two parts. The bottom space is for recording the length and direction of each shadow you observe. The upper space is for recording the position of the Sun in the sky that corresponds to each shadow.

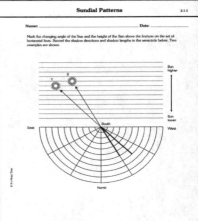

AST 67

ASTRONOMY

△ Guide

Let students know they will now observe images showing the shadows cast by a simple sundial at regular intervals throughout the day. Emphasize that students should carefully observe the differences between the shadows at different times, and they should consider how the position of the Sun in the sky relates to the direction and length of the shadow. This will help them make inferences about the motions of Earth and the Sun.

⬡ Get Going

Distribute *Sundial Patterns* pages and explain how to record observations on them. On the lower half of the *Sundial Patterns* page is a diagram on which students can record the direction and length of each observed shadow of the sundial. Emphasize that they should number their observations. Also point out that the cardinal directions are marked on the diagram. On the upper half of the *Sundial Patterns* page is a set of horizontal lines. Here they should record the position of the Sun that causes the shadow observed. They should number the positions of the Sun so it is clear which position corresponds to which shadow observation, as shown by the observations for Images #1 and #2 (already completed).

NOTES

Procedure: The Apparent Motion of the Sun

10 min

Students observe the sundial shadows images with their groups.

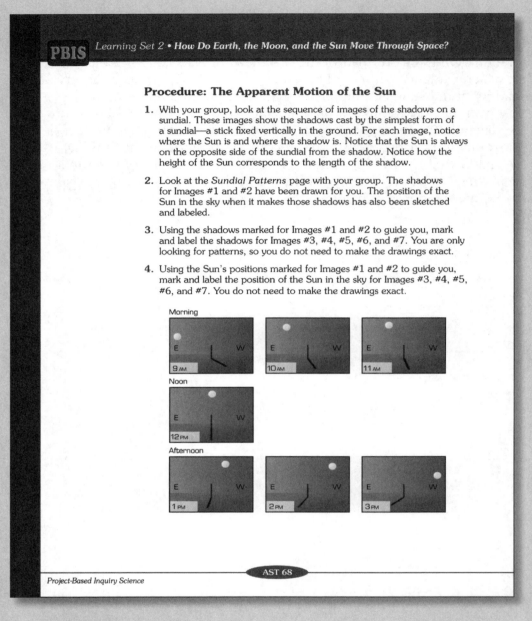

Procedure: The Apparent Motion of the Sun

1. With your group, look at the sequence of images of the shadows on a sundial. These images show the shadows cast by the simplest form of a sundial—a stick fixed vertically in the ground. For each image, notice where the Sun is and where the shadow is. Notice that the Sun is always on the opposite side of the sundial from the shadow. Notice how the height of the Sun corresponds to the length of the shadow.

2. Look at the *Sundial Patterns* page with your group. The shadows for Images #1 and #2 have been drawn for you. The position of the Sun in the sky when it makes those shadows has also been sketched and labeled.

3. Using the shadows marked for Images #1 and #2 to guide you, mark and label the shadows for Images #3, #4, #5, #6, and #7. You are only looking for patterns, so you do not need to make the drawings exact.

4. Using the Sun's positions marked for Images #1 and #2 to guide you, mark and label the position of the Sun in the sky for Images #3, #4, #5, #6, and #7. You do not need to make the drawings exact.

Morning

| 9 AM | 10 AM | 11 AM |

Noon

| 12 PM |

Afternoon

| 1 PM | 2 PM | 3 PM |

AST 68

Project-Based Inquiry Science

△ Guide

Briefly go over the procedure with the class. Then have students work with their groups to observe the images of the sundial shadows at different times of day and record their answers on their *Sundial Patterns* pages.

Analyze Your Data

1. Describe any patterns you can observe in the shadows throughout the day.

2. Describe any patterns you can observe in the position of the Sun throughout the day.

3. Why do you think the length of the shadow changes throughout the day?

4. How do the sundial shadows record the apparent movement of the Sun across the sky?

5. What do you know about shadows that helped you answer these questions?

Reflect

1. What do you think the sundial shadows would look like if images were produced for two days in a row?

2. What would you tell people about the apparent motion of the Sun across the sky? How would you support what you tell them with your observations?

How a Sundial Works

Sundials are tools developed by ancient civilizations for measuring time. A sundial uses positions of the Sun throughout the day to measure time. As Earth rotates, the position of the Sun appears to change. As the position of the Sun changes throughout the day, so does the position of the shadows it makes.

Shadows occur because light travels in a straight line. If an object blocks the path of some rays of sunlight, the area on the ground directly behind the object appears darker because less light reaches it. The darker area is the object's shadow. A stick casts the shortest shadow on the ground when the Sun is at its highest point in the sky. You can see in the diagram on the next page that when the Sun is lower in the sky, the shadow is longer because the stick blocks more of the ground from receiving direct sunlight. Light from the Sun casts the longest shadows at sunrise and sunset, when the Sun is lowest in the sky.

AST 69

ASTRONOMY

⚠ Guide and Assess

Have students meet with their groups to discuss their observations and answer the questions in the student text. Emphasize that they will share their results with the class.

As groups discuss their observations and the questions, monitor their progress and help them with any difficulties they may have. Check to make sure they understand how to make a diagram of the Sun's apparent position. They should notice that the shadows appear longest in the early morning and the late evening, and shortest in the middle of the day. They

Analyze Your Data

5 min

Groups analyze their sundial patterns data by answering the Analyze Your Data *questions.*

should also note that the shadows point west in the morning and east in the evening. Students also may notice that the shadows are symmetrical about the north-south axis.

1. Students should report that the shadows are very long in the morning and get progressively shorter until midday. After midday, the shadows get longer each hour until sunset, when they are longest. The shadows also begin pointing west in the morning and move progressively eastward until midday, when they point north. After midday, the shadows move eastward hourly and point farthest east at sunset.

2. Students should describe the positions of the Sun during the day as beginning low in the east in the early morning and moving progressively higher and westward. At midday, the Sun is nearly overhead. After midday, it moves westward and lower in the sky until sunset, when it is lowest (on the horizon) and most westward.

3. Students should explain that the length of the shadow changes during the day because of the changing position of the Sun. As the Sun gets higher in the sky, the shadow gets shorter.

4. Students should reply that the sundial shadows provide a continuous record of the Sun's position, because a straight line from the tip of the shadow through the tip of the gnomon leads directly to the Sun.

5. Students' answers will vary, but some will state that they know their shadow is longest early in the morning and late in the afternoon. At midday, there is hardly any shadow at all. Also, they should know that shadows are directly opposite the Sun from the object making the shadow.

Reflect

5 min

Students think further about the sundial shadows and apparent motion of the Sun.

Reflect

1. What do you think the sundial shadows would look like if images were produced for two days in a row?

2. What would you tell people about the apparent motion of the Sun across the sky? How would you support what you tell them with your observations?

△ Guide

Lead a class discussion of the *Reflect* questions. This discussion should help students interpret their observations in terms of the Sun's apparent motion and connect them to their everyday experience. They know the Sun rises every morning and sets every evening in much the same way, so it is reasonable to suspect that they would observe the same pattern in their sundial shadows every day.

1. Students should respond that sundial images recorded two days in a row would be nearly identical since the positions of the Sun and Earth are nearly identical.

2. Students might say that the Sun apparently moves from east to west each day. It rises in the east, moves higher in the sky until midday, and then sets in the west. The shadows recorded from the sundial are evidence of this apparent movement.

How a Sundial Works

Sundials are tools developed by ancient civilizations for measuring time. A sundial uses positions of the Sun throughout the day to measure time. As Earth rotates, the position of the Sun appears to change. As the position of the Sun changes throughout the day, so does the position of the shadows it makes.

Shadows occur because light travels in a straight line. If an object blocks the path of some rays of sunlight, the area on the ground directly behind the object appears darker because less light reaches it. The darker area is the object's shadow. A stick casts the shortest shadow on the ground when the Sun is at its highest point in the sky. You can see in the diagram on the next page that when the Sun is lower in the sky, the shadow is longer because the stick blocks more of the ground from receiving direct sunlight. Light from the Sun casts the longest shadows at sunrise and sunset, when the Sun is lowest in the sky.

How a Sundial Works

5 min

Students read about the history of sundials and their properties.

△ **Guide**

Before students answer the *Reflect* questions, discuss how sundials work. Tell students that sundials were developed to measure time using the position of the Sun. Light from the Sun travels in a straight line, so a shadow occurs where the gnomon blocks the light rays. This area appears darker than the surrounding area.

NOTES

_____

_____

_____

_____

_____

_____

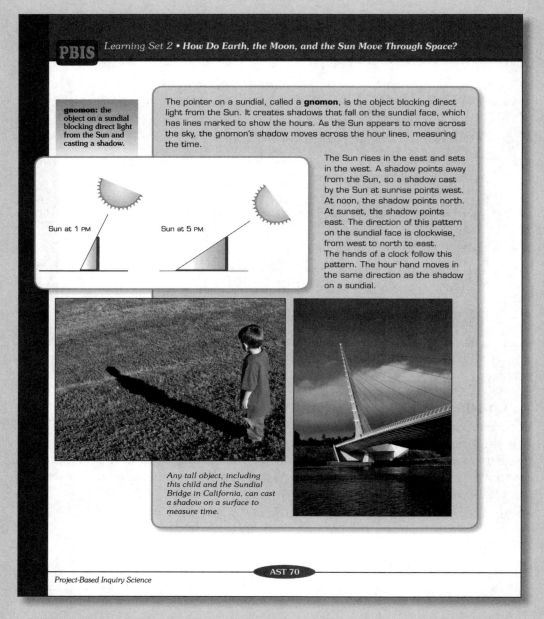

gnomon: the object on a sundial blocking direct light from the Sun and casting a shadow.

The pointer on a sundial, called a **gnomon**, is the object blocking direct light from the Sun. It creates shadows that fall on the sundial face, which has lines marked to show the hours. As the Sun appears to move across the sky, the gnomon's shadow moves across the hour lines, measuring the time.

Sun at 1 PM

Sun at 5 PM

The Sun rises in the east and sets in the west. A shadow points away from the Sun, so a shadow cast by the Sun at sunrise points west. At noon, the shadow points north. At sunset, the shadow points east. The direction of this pattern on the sundial face is clockwise, from west to north to east. The hands of a clock follow this pattern. The hour hand moves in the same direction as the shadow on a sundial.

Any tall object, including this child and the Sundial Bridge in California, can cast a shadow on a surface to measure time.

AST 70

Project-Based Inquiry Science

Point out the diagram showing how the position of the Sun relates to the length of the shadow in the student text. Ask students if they can see from the diagram why the shadow points west in the morning and east in the evening, and if they can explain why the shadow is longer when the Sun is lower.

Reflect

1. How could you use a vertical stick to create a sundial? What do you think you would need to know to tell the correct time using the shadow of the stick?

2. Why do you think sundials are not used as time-keeping instruments today?

3. Where would the Sun have to be for a vertical stick to cast no visible shadow on a sunny day?

4. How would you explain to someone why the Sun seems to move throughout the day when observed from Earth?

5. What else do you need to know to give a more complete explanation about where the Sun is and why it seems to move across the sky?

6. Think about how the Sun's apparent movement makes it seem as if the Sun goes around Earth. Yet you know that the Sun is at the center of the solar system and that Earth revolves about the Sun. What does that tell you about what else you need to know to determine the location and movement of objects in the solar system?

Update the *Project Board*

In the *What do we think we know?* column of the *Project Board*, record what you think you know about how to identify the location and motion of objects as seen from Earth. In the *What are we learning?* column of the *Project Board*, record the questions the class has generated. Update your own *Project Board* during the class discussion.

What's the Point?

You have observed that the Sun's position in the sky changes throughout the day. Shadows cast by an object that blocks sunlight change from long in the morning to short at midday to long in the afternoon. The direction of this pattern of shadows is from west to north to east. Since a shadow points in the direction opposite the Sun's position, you know that the direction of the Sun's apparent path across the sky is from east to west. Sundials are used to measure time using the position of a gnomon's shadow as it crosses hour lines on the face of the sundial.

Reflect

10 min

The class has a discussion of the Reflect *questions.*

△ Guide and Evaluate

Lead a class discussion of the *Reflect* questions. Use the questions to ensure that students understand what sundials do and how the apparent motion of the Sun can be tracked using a sundial.

1. Students may reply that a sundial can be made by placing one end of a stick into the ground so that it is exactly vertical in reference to the ground. They would need to know the east, north, and west directions exactly to mark them on the ground.

2. Students should understand that sundials are not used today for two reasons: they are not portable and they are not accurate enough.

3. Students should describe how the Sun would have to be directly overhead for there to be no shadow cast by a vertical stick. This would only happen on the Equator at midday.

4. Students should understand that the Sun appears to move from east to west because Earth is rotating on its axis from east to west. This is counter-clockwise as viewed from the North Pole.

5. Students' answers will vary. They may suggest that to know why the Sun is never directly overhead in the Northern Hemisphere one needs to know about the Equator and the measurement of latitude.

6. Students may know that they will need to know, for each object, the distance from the Sun, the direction of rotation, and the period of revolution.

Update the Project Board

15 min

The class has a discussion to update the Project Board.

movement of objects in the solar system?

Update the *Project Board*

In the *What do we think we know?* column of the *Project Board*, record what you think you know about how to identify the location and motion of objects as seen from Earth. In the *What are we learning?* column of the *Project Board*, record the questions the class has generated. Update your own *Project Board* during the class discussion.

△ **Guide**

Have students meet with their groups to discuss how they can determine the movement of objects in the solar system based only on observations from Earth. Emphasize that they should use their experience in making observations of the Sun's motions using a sundial as an example of how the movements of objects in the solar system can be inferred from observations on Earth. Tell them they will share their ideas with the class.

As groups discuss their ideas, monitor their progress and ask them about their ideas. It is more important that they generate ideas than identify specific methods or questions.

When groups have had time to brainstorm, have them share their ideas with the class. Record their ideas in the *What do we think we know?* and the *What do we need to investigate?* columns of the *Project Board*. Also have students record the class's ideas on their own *Project Board* pages.

You know Earth is actually revolving around the Sun, so it might be difficult for you to figure out how the Sun could look like it is moving. It was also difficult for scientists to figure that out. Even after scientists knew Earth was revolving around the Sun, it was hundreds of years before they proved that Earth rotates. Yet understanding Earth's movements and the movements of other space objects are essential for predicting whether an object in space will collide with Earth. In the rest of the *Learning Set*, you will be answering your questions about the locations and movements of the Sun, Moon, and Earth. Then, in later *Learning Sets,* you will know how to determine the location and movement of other space objects.

In this composite picture of our solar system are the eight planets and four of Jupiter's largest moons, taken as if from Earth's moon.

NOTES

....

....

....

Assessment Options

Targeted Concepts, Skills, and Nature of Science	How do I know if students got it?
Scientists often collaborate and share their findings. Sharing findings makes new information available and helps scientists refine their ideas and build on others' ideas. When another person's or group's idea is used, credit needs to be given.	**ASK:** Which ideas brainstormed by your group do you think have the greatest likelihood of success? The least likelihood of success? **LISTEN:** Students' answers will vary, but should cite specific ideas that their group listed during the brainstorming session and the reason why they think it would or would not be successful.
Scientists must keep clear, accurate, and descriptive records of what they do so they can share their work with others; consider what they did, why they did it, and what they want to do next.	**ASK:** What trends did you observe in the data you collected? How does this relate to trends in the Sun's position in the sky? **LISTEN:** Students should observe trends in which the length of the shadows decreased from sunrise to midday and the direction of the shadows changed from west to north; from midday to sunset the length of the shadows increased and the direction of the shadows changed from north to east. Shadows decrease in length as the Sun's position in the sky becomes higher; shadows increase in length as the Sun's position in the sky becomes lower. The direction in which a shadow points is directly opposite the direction in which the Sun is located in the sky.

NOTES

....

....

Targeted Concepts, Skills, and Nature of Science	How do I know if students got it?
Most objects in the solar system have a regular and predictable motion. These motions explain such phenomena as a day, a year, phases of the Moon, eclipses, tides, meteor showers, and comets.	**ASK:** What was predictable about the changes in the length and direction of the shadows you observed? **LISTEN:** Students should describe how in the morning, the shadows decreased in length over time and changed direction from pointing west to pointing toward north. After midday, the shadows increased in length and changed direction from pointing north to pointing toward the east. **ASK:** How is midday related to the shadow made by the gnomon? **LISTEN:** Students should describe how at midday, the shadow cast by the gnomon is shortest for the day and points in a northern direction.
The rotation of the earth on its axis every 24 hours produces the night-and-day cycle. To people on Earth, this turning of the planet makes it seem as though the Sun, Moon, planets, and stars are orbiting the earth once a day. This rotation also causes the Sun and Moon to appear to rise along the eastern horizon and to set along the western horizon. Earth's revolution around the Sun defines the length of the year as 365.25 days.	**ASK:** How could you determine the Sun's apparent path across the sky throughout the day? **LISTEN:** Students should answer that for each observation, plot the Sun's position in the sky by extending a line from the tip of the shadow through the tip of the gnomon into the sky. Then connect the points marking the Sun's position at different times of the day to create a line representing its path through the sky. **ASK:** Describe the Sun's apparent path through the sky. **LISTEN:** Students' descriptions should include how the Sun appears to move from east to west across the sky, rising along the eastern horizon, moving higher in the sky until reaching its highest point around midday and then moves lower in the sky before setting along the western horizon.

Teacher Reflection Questions

- How could you help students connect the length and direction of a shadow cast by a sundial with the Sun's position in the sky?

- How did you prepare students to participate in the brainstorming session?

- When students discussed the shadows they observed, what conceptions about light were revealed that you will need to address in future lessons?

NOTES

2.2 Model

Make a Model of the Apparent Motion of the Sun

◀ $1\frac{1}{4}$ *class periods*

A class period is considered to be one 40 to 50 minute class.

Overview

Students use a simple model to simulate motions that could result in the shadow observations made in *Section 2.1*. Students erect a gnomon on a globe representing Earth and use a flashlight to represent the Sun. They then try to replicate the changes in the length and direction of the shadows observed earlier by either moving the globe or moving the flashlight. After successfully producing changes in shadows that correspond to those observed earlier, students read a scientific description of how the Earth's rotation causes the Sun to appear to rise along the eastern horizon, move across the sky, and set along the western horizon. Students create explanations of which Earth/Sun motions cause you to see the Sun move across the sky every day. After sharing their explanations and supporting evidence with the class, the class considers how differences in explanations could be resolved and collaborates to reach consensus on one explanation. Students then update the *What are we learning?*, *What is our evidence?*, and *What do we need to investigate?* columns of the *Project Board*.

Targeted Concepts, Skills, and Nature of Science	Performance Expectations
Scientists often collaborate and share their findings. Sharing findings makes new information available and helps scientists refine their ideas and build on others' ideas. When another person's or group's idea is used, credit needs to be given.	Students share their explanation for how Earth motions in relation to the Sun cause the observed changes in shadow length and direction and discuss the strengths and weaknesses of different explanations.
Scientists must keep clear, accurate, and descriptive records of what they do so they can share their work with others; consider what they did, why they did it, and what they want to do next.	Students record the changes in shadow length and direction observed in their model that were associated with motions of the globe or flashlight. Students record their claim and supporting evidence on the *Create Your Explanation* page.

Targeted Concepts, Skills, and Nature of Science	Performance Expectations
Models are a representation of something in the world. Simulations use a model to imitate, or act out, real-life situations.	Students create a model of the Earth-Sun system.
Scientists make claims (conclusions) based on evidence obtained (trends in data) from reliable investigations.	Students develop a claim about cause of the changes in shadows observed in *Learning Set 1* based on evidence obtained using their Earth-Sun model.
Explanations are claims supported by evidence. Evidence can be experimental results, observational data, and any other accepted scientific knowledge.	Students create explanations about how Earth moves in relation to the Sun to cause the changes in shadow length and direction observed in *Learning Set 1*.
The rotation of the earth on its axis every 24 hours produces the night-and-day cycle. To people on Earth, this turning of the planet makes it seem as though the Sun, Moon, planets, and stars are orbiting the earth once a day. This rotation also causes the Sun and Moon to appear to rise along the eastern horizon and to set along the western horizon. Earth's revolution around the Sun defines the length of the year as 365.25 days.	Students describe how Earth's rotation causes the Sun to appear to rise along the eastern horizon, move across the sky, and set along the western horizon.

Materials

1 per group	Earth globe mounted on an axis Flashlight Small stick Modeling clay
1 per student	*Create Your Explanation* page *Project Board* page
1 per class	Class *Project Board*

Activity Setup and Preparation

Prepackage the materials for each group for ease of distribution and collection. Check that all of the flashlights are working and have fresh batteries available.

Homework Options

Reflection

- **Science Content:** Formulate two possible relative motions of Earth and the Sun that could account for the changes in the sundial shadows you observed in *Section 2.1.* (*Students should name Earth's rotation while the Sun remains stationary, or revolution of the Sun around a stationary Earth.*)

- **Science Content:** If using more light sources would cause more shadows to form, why do baseball stadiums use many light sources to illuminate the field for a night game? (*Students should understand that the light from a source shining in one direction will illuminate the shadow caused by a light source shining in the opposite direction.*)

- **Science Process:** Decide which kind of evidence would best support the explanation that the observed changes in the shadows were caused by Earth's motion rather than the Sun's motion? (*Students should answer that it is proof that Earth rotates on its axis.*)

- **Science Process:** Why do you think people found it so difficult to believe that Earth rotated? (*Students' answers will vary, but should include examples such as: we do not perceive Earth's rotation.*)

Preparation for 2.3

- **Science Content:** The flags of many countries include images of the Moon with a crescent shape. From your experience, what other shapes have you seen when you observed the Moon? (*Students' answers will vary, but should include a complete circle, a half circle and other variations in shape.*)

- **Science Process:** What could you do to determine if the Moon also appears to move across the sky? (*Students should suggest observing its position in the sky over time to determine whether its position changes.*)

NOTES

SECTION 2.2 IMPLEMENTATION

2.2 Model

Make a Model of the Apparent Motion of the Sun

You observed shadows to record the apparent motion of the Sun across the sky during the day. However, it was hard to know what the pattern of the shadows made by the sundial illustrated about the Sun's actual motion or the location of the Sun and Earth in the solar system. In this section, you will use simple materials to make a model to help you understand the Sun's movement across the sky and the location of the Sun in relation to Earth.

In the model, you will use a flashlight to represent the Sun. You will use a globe to represent Earth. The globe spins on an **axis**, which is a line through the globe that doesn't move as the globe spins. You will manipulate the globe and flashlight until your model can make the same shadows that you observed in the images.

axis: a line through the center of a body, around which the body rotates, or spins; Earth's imaginary axis passes through the North Pole and the South Pole.

Investigation 1: Make a Model that Shows Changes in the Shadow's Direction

Procedure

1. Find the area where you live on the globe. Use the clay to securely attach the pencil to that location. The pencil should be pointed directly away from the center of the globe.

Materials
- short pencil
- clay
- flashlight
- Earth globe mounted on an axis

AST 73

ASTRONOMY

2.2 Model

Make a Model of the Apparent Motion of the Sun

5 min

Students are introduced to the investigations they will run to determine which motions of the Sun cause certain shadow patterns.

△ Guide

Let students know that they will use a model to replicate the data they gathered in the last section to better understand the Sun's movement across the sky. They will use a globe to represent Earth and a flashlight to represent the Sun. Using the globe and the flashlight, they will replicate the changes in the shadows they observed on the sundial.

*A class period is considered to be one 40 to 50 minute class.

Investigation 1: Make a Model that Shows Changes in the Shadow's Direction

5 min

Students investigate the effects of the direction of sunlight on shadow patterns on Earth.

observed in the images.

Investigation 1: Make a Model that Shows Changes in the Shadow's Direction

Procedure

1. Find the area where you live on the globe. Use the clay to securely attach the pencil to that location. The pencil should be pointed directly away from the center of the globe.

Materials
- short pencil
- clay
- flashlight
- Earth globe mounted on an axis

⬡ Get Going

Distribute materials and go over the procedures for the three investigations with the class.

△ Guide

Tell students that the purpose of *Investigation 1* is to determine what motions of the Sun could cause the changes they observed in the shadow's direction. To do this, they will attach a small stick to the globe on the location where they live, and use a flashlight to replicate the changes in the shadow's direction they observed. They will then record descriptions of what they did to the globe and flashlight to replicate the changes they observed in the direction of the shadow.

NOTES

....

....

....

....

....

....

....

2. Use the flashlight to represent the Sun and the pencil attached to the globe to represent the gnomon of a sundial. Move the flashlight and/or the globe so that the changes in the *direction* the shadow is pointing are the same as they were on the sundial. Do not worry yet about making sure the shadows are the right length.

(Hint: To find directions, first find north. You know where the North Pole is on the globe. That should help you.)

3. Record a description of the way the direction of the shadows changed. Then record a description of what you did to the globe and the flashlight to simulate the pattern of shadow directions on a sundial. Write several sentences and sketch what you did.

Investigation 2: Make a Model to Show Changes in the Shadow's Length

Procedure

1. Use the same setup. The pencil should be attached to the globe at your location on Earth. It should point straight up from the center of the globe. The flashlight will be your Sun.

2. Move the flashlight and/or the globe so that the changes in the *length* of the shadow are the same as you observed for the sundial. Do not worry about whether the direction of the shadows is also accurate.

3. Record a description of how the length of the shadows changed. Then record a description of what you did to the globe and the flashlight to simulate the pattern of shadow lengths on a sundial. Write several sentences and sketch what you did.

Investigation 3: Make a Model to Show Changes in Both the Shadow's Length and Direction

Procedure

1. Use the same setup. The pencil should be attached to the globe at your location on Earth. It should point straight up from the center of the globe. The flashlight will be your Sun.

Investigation 2: Make a Model to Show Changes in the Shadow's Length

5 min

Students investigate how the differences in the Sun's motion effects the length of the shadow.

Tell students that the purpose of *Investigation 2* is to determine which motions of the Sun could cause the changes they observed in the shadow's length. To do this, they will use the same setup with the globe and flashlight as in *Investigation 1,* but this time they will use the flashlight to replicate the changes they observed in the shadow's length. They will record descriptions of what they did to the globe and flashlight to replicate the changes they observed in the length of the shadow.

Investigation 3: Make a Model to Show Changes in Both the Shadow's Length and Direction

5 min

Students test the effects of the two factors together.

Investigation 3: Make a Model to Show Changes in Both the Shadow's Length and Direction

Procedure

1. Use the same setup. The pencil should be attached to the globe at your location on Earth. It should point straight up from the center of the globe. The flashlight will be your Sun.

Tell students that in *Investigation 3* they will determine what motions of the Sun could cause both the changes they observed in the shadow's direction and the changes in its length. They will use the same setup, but they will replicate both changes of the shadow.

NOTES

....
....
....
....
....
....
....
....
....
....
....

2. This time, move the flashlight and/or globe so that the changes in both the direction and length of the shadows are the same as they were on the sundial.

3. Record a description of the way the direction and length of the shadows changed. Then record a description of what you did to the globe and/or the flashlight to simulate the pattern of shadows on a sundial. Write several sentences and sketch what you did.

Reflect

1. Which motion or motions did you use to replicate the shadow pattern: spinning the globe, moving the flashlight, or both?

2. Answer this question if your answer to the first question was "both." Do you think spinning the globe and moving the flashlight are both necessary to replicate the shadow pattern? Why or why not?

3. Answer this question if your answer to the first question was only spinning the globe or only moving the flashlight but not both. Do you think you could produce the same pattern in the shadows by switching which object moves? Why or why not?

4. With your group, develop a claim about which movements of Earth and/or the Sun cause you to see the Sun move across the sky every day.

AST 75

ASTRONOMY

△ Guide

As groups run their investigations, monitor their progress and help them with any difficulties that arise. Some groups may rotate the globe, and some may move their flashlight. Either way is fine; they should soon see that rotating the globe and moving the flashlight around the globe have the same effect. Emphasize that they should keep careful records of what they do and of their results.

Reflect

5 min

Groups answer the questions about their shadow observations.

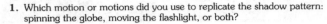

Reflect

1. Which motion or motions did you use to replicate the shadow pattern: spinning the globe, moving the flashlight, or both?

2. Answer this question if your answer to the first question was "both." Do you think spinning the globe and moving the flashlight are both necessary to replicate the shadow pattern? Why or why not?

3. Answer this question if your answer to the first question was only spinning the globe or only moving the flashlight but not both. Do you think you could produce the same pattern in the shadows by switching which object moves? Why or why not?

4. With your group, develop a claim about which movements of Earth and/or the Sun cause you to see the Sun move across the sky every day.

△ Guide and Assess

Have students work with their groups to answer the *Reflect* questions. As they discuss the questions with their groups, ask them what ideas they have discussed and how they can support their ideas. If they think that only rotating the globe or only moving the flashlight would replicate the shadow pattern, ask them what reasons they can provide to support this position. If they think that both replicate the shadow pattern, ask them how this can be.

1. Students should describe which motions they used for each shadow pattern based on their notes taken during the investigations.

2. Students' answers will vary. They should realize that either motion will replicate the shadow pattern and that both motions are not necessary.

3. Students' answers will vary. Students should eventually realize that either motion will work.

4. Students' answers will vary.

NOTES

....

....

....

....

....

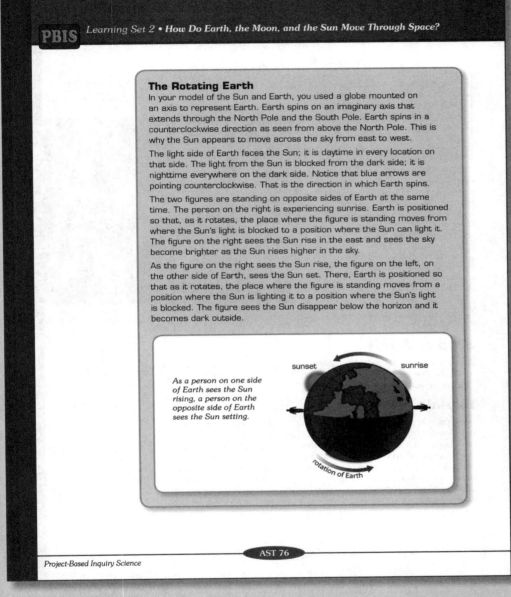

The Rotating Earth

In your model of the Sun and Earth, you used a globe mounted on an axis to represent Earth. Earth spins on an imaginary axis that extends through the North Pole and the South Pole. Earth spins in a counterclockwise direction as seen from above the North Pole. This is why the Sun appears to move across the sky from east to west.

The light side of Earth faces the Sun; it is daytime in every location on that side. The light from the Sun is blocked from the dark side; it is nighttime everywhere on the dark side. Notice that blue arrows are pointing counterclockwise. That is the direction in which Earth spins.

The two figures are standing on opposite sides of Earth at the same time. The person on the right is experiencing sunrise. Earth is positioned so that, as it rotates, the place where the figure is standing moves from where the Sun's light is blocked to a position where the Sun can light it. The figure on the right sees the Sun rise in the east and sees the sky become brighter as the Sun rises higher in the sky.

As the figure on the right sees the Sun rise, the figure on the left, on the other side of Earth, sees the Sun set. There, Earth is positioned so that as it rotates, the place where the figure is standing moves from a position where the Sun is lighting it to a position where the Sun's light is blocked. The figure sees the Sun disappear below the horizon and it becomes dark outside.

As a person on one side of Earth sees the Sun rising, a person on the opposite side of Earth sees the Sun setting.

sunset   sunrise

rotation of Earth

The Rotating Earth

5 min

Students discuss how Earth's rotation causes the Sun to appear to move from east to west.

△ Guide

Discuss the rotation of Earth. Just like the globes students used to represent Earth, Earth rotates on an axis. Earth's axis is an imaginary line that extends through the North Pole to the South Pole.

Tell students that if they were to watch Earth spin from above the North Pole, they would see it spin in a counterclockwise direction. Emphasize that this is why the Sun appears to move from east to west. Point out the diagrams in the textbook and explain that, to the person in the diagram, the Sun initially appears to be to the east and then it appears to be to the west.

Imagine that you are the figure on the right. It is sunrise, and you see the Sun rising in the east. If you stood in that position until sunset, what would you see? It would appear to you that the Sun is moving across the sky from east to west. When the Sun sets, you will not be able to see it anymore. After sunset, the Sun's light is blocked by the light side of Earth.

Each day, you can watch the Sun rise (if it isn't cloudy or raining). After many hours of light, the Sun sets. After many hours of darkness, the Sun comes up again. During this time, from sunrise to sunrise, Earth completes one rotation on its axis. It takes about 24 hours for Earth to complete one rotation. The time it takes for one rotation is called a **day**.

day: the amount of time it takes a body to spin once on its axis.

Sunsets can produce spectacular displays of color.

Stop and Think

Revise your claim about which movements of Earth and/or the Sun cause us to see the Sun move across the sky every day. You can probably make your claim more complete and accurate now.

Explain

You probably understand more now about the movement of Earth and why you see the Sun move across the sky from east to west every day. You have already made a claim about the movement of Earth and/or the Sun. With your group, you will now develop an explanation statement of which movements of Earth and/or the Sun cause you to see the Sun move across the sky every day. Use a *Create an Explanation* page to help you develop your explanation statement. Remember that a good explanation has four features:

AST 77

ASTRONOMY

Point out that the time it takes Earth to complete a rotation is one day. One day after the person in the diagram is moved into the light region (sunrise) of Earth from the dark, he or she will be moved into the light region (sunrise) from the dark again.

△ Guide

Monitor the students' progress toward understanding the rotation of Earth and how this influences our perception of the motion of the Sun. Help them understand that what one thinks one sees is not always accurate.

NOTES

△ Guide

Let students know that they will now create an explanation of how Earth moves in relation to the Sun to produce the changes they observed in the position of the shadow.

NOTES

Stop and Think

5 min

Students revise their claim about the movements of Earth and the Sun.

Explain

10 min

Groups create explanations of how the motion of Earth in relation to the Sun causes the shadow patterns they observed.

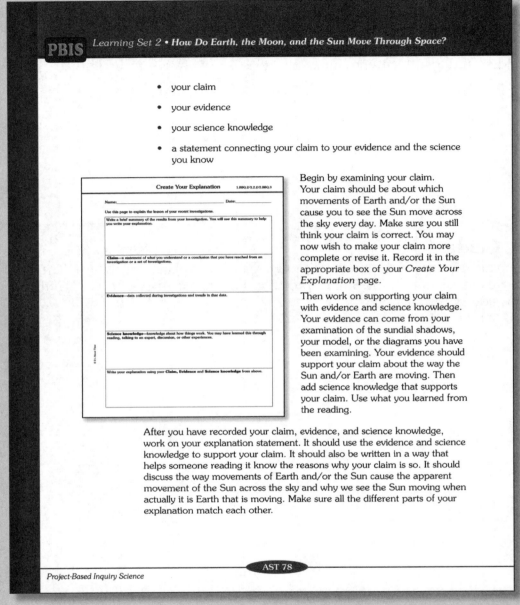

- your claim

- your evidence

- your science knowledge

- a statement connecting your claim to your evidence and the science you know

Create Your Explanation 1.BIQ.2/2.2.2/2.BIQ.3

Name:_____ Date:_____

Use this page to explain the lesson of your recent investigations.

Write a brief summary of the results from your investigation. You will use this summary to help you write your explanation.

Claim—a statement of what you understand or a conclusion that you have reached from an investigation or a set of investigations.

Evidence—data collected during investigations and trends in that data.

Science knowledge—knowledge about how things work. You may have learned this through reading, talking to an expert, discussion, or other experiences.

Write your explanation using your **Claim, Evidence** and **Science knowledge** from above.

Begin by examining your claim. Your claim should be about which movements of Earth and/or the Sun cause you to see the Sun move across the sky every day. Make sure you still think your claim is correct. You may now wish to make your claim more complete or revise it. Record it in the appropriate box of your *Create Your Explanation* page.

Then work on supporting your claim with evidence and science knowledge. Your evidence can come from your examination of the sundial shadows, your model, or the diagrams you have been examining. Your evidence should support your claim about the way the Sun and/or Earth are moving. Then add science knowledge that supports your claim. Use what you learned from the reading.

After you have recorded your claim, evidence, and science knowledge, work on your explanation statement. It should use the evidence and science knowledge to support your claim. It should also be written in a way that helps someone reading it know the reasons why your claim is so. It should discuss the way movements of Earth and/or the Sun cause the apparent movement of the Sun across the sky and why we see the Sun moving when actually it is Earth that is moving. Make sure all the different parts of your explanation match each other.

AST 78

Distribute *Create Your Explanation* pages and briefly review the parts of a good explanation with the class. A good explanation connects a claim to evidence using reason. In this case, the claim is about how the motion of Earth in relation to the Sun causes the shadow patterns that students observed. Their evidence will come from their investigations.

◇ Evaluate

As groups develop their explanations, ask them what reasons they are using to connect their evidence to their claims. Make sure their evidence includes only observations and does not include interpretations or opinions.

Communicate

Share Your Explanation

Your class will now meet to share and discuss each group explanation. Working together, the class will then select and develop an explanation that best explains how Earth moves in relation to the Sun. This explanation will be supported by evidence from your investigations and other knowledge that you and your classmates can contribute.

Different people in the class may have different explanations. The class should decide together on one explanation. Alternate explanations should be recognized, and reasons why that explanation was not chosen should be given. The explanation you choose can include questions that need to be answered. You may also have ideas for other tests that can be performed to prove whether this explanation is right or wrong.

Update the *Project Board*

Now that you have completed an explanation about the apparent motion of the Sun based on your observations and models, it is a good time to update the *Project Board*. You will focus on the two columns *What are we learning?* and *What is our evidence?* When you record what you are learning in the third column, you may be confirming some of the things you think you know from the first column. Or, you may be answering some of the questions you recorded in the *What do we need to investigate?* column.

What's the Point?

Because Earth is spinning, each day the Sun first appears, or rises, in the east. The Sun then seems to travel west, rising higher in the sky and reaching its highest point at midday. After midday, the Sun appears to continue traveling west and to get lower in the sky, until it disappears, or sets, in the west. However, it is not the Sun that is moving. Instead, it is Earth's rotation that makes the Sun appear to move across the sky.

AST 79

ASTRONOMY

Communicate: Share Your Explanation

15 min

Groups share their explanations with the class.

△ Guide

Have groups share their explanations with the class. As each group shares its explanation, students should record the explanation and ask questions if anything is unclear. They should evaluate the strengths and weaknesses of the explanation, and the class should discuss these strengths and weaknesses. Emphasize that students should express their disagreements respectfully.

Working together, the class should select one group's explanation or develop a new explanation they think best explains how the motion of Earth in relation to the Sun causes the shadow patterns they observed. The class should also state why each of the alternative explanations was not chosen.

Update the *Project Board*

performed ~~to prove whether this explanation is right or wrong.~~

Now that you have completed an explanation about the apparent motion of the Sun based on your observations and models, it is a good time to update the *Project Board*. You will focus on the two columns *What are we learning?* and *What is our evidence?* When you record what you are learning in the third column, you may be confirming some of the things you think you know from the first column. Or, you may be answering some of the questions you recorded in the *What do we need to investigate?* column.

△ Guide

Ask students what they have learned that they can record in the *Project Board*. Record their ideas in the *What are we learning?* column, and have them record their ideas on their own *Project Board* pages. Ask them what evidence they have for their ideas, and record their responses in the *What is our evidence?* column. This may include data from their investigations or science knowledge from the readings.

Assessment Options

Targeted Concepts, Skills, and Nature of Science	How do I know if students got it?
Scientists often collaborate and share their findings. Sharing findings makes new information available and helps scientists refine their ideas and build on others' ideas. When another person's or group's idea is used, credit needs to be given.	**ASK:** What were two different explanations for the observed changes in the sundial shadows shared by groups? **LISTEN:** Students' answers will vary, but should include motion of the Sun (flashlight) and Earth's (globe) rotation.

NOTES

....

....

Targeted Concepts, Skills, and Nature of Science	How do I know if students got it?
Scientists must keep clear, accurate, and descriptive records of what they do so they can share their work with others; consider what they did, why they did it, and what they want to do next.	**ASK:** What records did you keep to provide evidence to support your explanation? **LISTEN:** Students should cite their record of changes in the length and direction of the shadows and relative positions and direction of motion of the flashlight and the globe. **ASK:** What supporting evidence did you provide for your explanation? **LISTEN:** Students' responses should cite data about the changes in the direction and length of shadows associated with motions of the flashlight or globe. They should also cite information from readings about the scientific explanation for the Sun's apparent motion through the sky and the day-night cycle.
Models are a representation of something in the world. Simulations use a model to imitate, or act out, real-life situations.	**ASK:** Correlate the objects used in your model with the Sun, Earth, and the sundial's gnomon. **LISTEN:** Students should describe how the flashlight represented the Sun, the globe represented Earth, and the pencil, or stick, represented the sundial's gnomon.

NOTES

....

....

....

Targeted Concepts, Skills, and Nature of Science	How do I know if students got it?
Scientists make claims (conclusions) based on evidence obtained (trends in data) from reliable investigations.	**ASK:** What did you claim was the cause of the changes observed in the sundial shadows? What was your evidence for this claim? **LISTEN:** Students should claim that the changes were visible because of changes in the position of the Sun while Earth remained stationary; that the sundial changed position because Earth rotated and the Sun remained stationary, or both. Students should cite the ability to replicate the pattern of changes observed in the sundial shadows with either or both motions.
Explanations are claims supported by evidence. Evidence can be experimental results, observational data, and any other accepted scientific knowledge.	**ASK:** How did you obtain the experimental results needed to support your explanation? **LISTEN:** Students should describe how the replicated their results by simulating the motion of Earth or the Sun using the globe and flashlight model.
The rotation of the earth on its axis every 24 hours produces the night-and-day cycle. To people on Earth, this turning of the planet makes it seem as though the Sun, Moon, planets, and stars are orbiting the earth once a day. This rotation also causes the Sun and Moon to appear to rise along the eastern horizon and to set along the western horizon. Earth's revolution around the Sun defines the length of the year as 365.25 days.	**ASK:** When you simulated Earth's rotation with your model, in what direction did you have to rotate the globe to replicate the changes in the sundial shadows observed earlier? If Earth rotated in this direction, in what direction would the Sun appear to move? **LISTEN:** Students should describe how the globe had to be rotated from west to east. This would cause the Sun to appear to move from east to west.

Teacher Reflection Questions

- What challenges did students face in recording the observations they made while simulating Earth and Sun motions using the model? What type of format could you suggest they record their observations?

- How much difficulty did students have with the idea that two completely different motions could result in the same set of observations? What examples from everyday life could you cite that would help your students better understand this idea?

- Interdisciplinary/cross-curricular teaching can increase students' motivation for learning and their level of engagement. In contrast to learning skills in isolation, when students participate in interdisciplinary experiences they see the value of what they are learning and become more actively engaged. (Resnick, 1989) What interdisciplinary/cross-curricular learning experiences centering on early astronomy could you plan with your class' social studies teacher?

NOTES

....

....

....

....

....

....

....

....

NOTES

2.3 Explore

Where Is the Moon Located, and How Does It Move?

◀ 3 class periods

A class period is considered to be one 40 to 50 minute class.

Overview

Students explore the Moon's apparent motion across the sky and the changes in its appearance. They examine a series of images showing the motions of the Sun and Moon as seen from Earth during the course of a single day and record their observations. Students analyze their data, compare and contrast the apparent paths of the Sun and Moon, and consider where and when the Moon is visible to an observer on Earth. Next, students examine a series of images and record the changes in the Moon's appearance that occur over the course of two weeks. Students analyze their data, comparing and contrasting the changes in the Moon's appearance and position during one day and during two weeks. They read why the Moon, and any other solar-system object except the Sun, is only visible by reflected light and why its appearance when viewed from Earth changes cyclically. Students construct a model of the Earth-Moon-Sun system and simulate the Moon's revolution around Earth. Students record the appearance of the Moon and the relative positions of the Earth, Moon, and Sun at the different phases of the Moon on a *Phases of the Moon* page. They simulate the simultaneous rotation of a planet and revolution of a Moon for three different planets—Earth, Planet X, and Planet Y—and record their observations. Groups share their observations with the class, and the class discusses the relative positions of a planet and moon in relation to a sun for any given phase of a moon. After reading about the motions of the Earth-Moon-Sun system students revise their earlier explanations to include the motion and phases of the Moon observed from Earth. The class then updates the *Project Board,* focusing on the *What are we learning?, What is our evidence?* and *What do we need to investigate?* columns.

Targeted Concepts, Skills, and Nature of Science	Performance Expectations
Scientists often collaborate and share their findings. Sharing findings makes new information available and helps scientists refine their ideas and build on others' ideas. When another person's or group's idea is used, credit needs to be given.	Students share their observations of the relative motions of Earth, Planet X, and Planet Y, and their respective moons and the class discusses how differences in rate of rotation or revolution affect the phases of a moon observed from a planet.
Scientists must keep clear, accurate, and descriptive records of what they do so they can share their work with others; consider what they did, why they did it, and what they want to do next.	Students record the changes in the appearance of the Moon and the relative positions of Earth, the Moon, and Sun throughout the lunar cycle on a *Phases of the Moon* page. Students record revisions to their earlier explanations on their *Create Your Explanation* page.
Models are a representation of something in the world. Simulations use a model to imitate, or act out, real-life situations.	Students create a model of the Earth-Moon-Sun system and simulate motions of Earth and the Moon.
Explanations are claims supported by evidence. Evidence can be experimental results, observational data, and any other accepted scientific knowledge.	Students revise their explanations of the motions that cause the Sun to appear to move across the sky to include the Moon's apparent motion and the changing appearance of the Moon throughout the lunar cycle.
Most objects in the solar system have a regular and predictable motion. These motions explain such phenomena as a day, a year, phases of the Moon, eclipses, tides, meteor showers, and comets.	Students are able to explain the phases of the Moon in terms of the Moon's regular and predictable revolution around Earth.
The rotation of the earth on its axis every 24 hours produces the night-and-day cycle. To people on Earth, this turning of the planet makes it seem as though the Sun, Moon, planets, and stars are orbiting the earth once a day. This rotation also causes the Sun and Moon to appear to rise along the eastern horizon and to set along the western horizon. Earth's revolution around the Sun defines the length of the year as 365.25 days.	Students model and describe how Earth's rotation results in the Moon's apparent daily motion across the sky. Students identify Earth's period of rotation as the basis for the day and the lunar cycle as the basis for the month.

Targeted Concepts, Skills, and Nature of Science	Performance Expectations
The Moon orbits Earth while Earth orbits the Sun. Except for the Sun, all objects in the solar system are seen by reflected light. The Moon's orbit around Earth once in about 28 days changes what part of the Moon is lighted by the Sun and how much of that part can be seen from Earth—the phases of the moon. The phases repeat in a cyclic pattern in about one month.	Students identify the relative positions of Earth, the Moon, and Sun at each of the phases of the Moon. Students describe why only the illuminated portion of the Moon is visible from Earth.

Materials	
1 per student	*Phases of the Moon* page White plastic foam ball Long, thin dowel, or chopstick *Create Your Explanation* page
1 per class	Bright light source (i.e. overhead projector or floodlight)

Activity Setup and Preparation

You may want to prepackage foam balls and dowels for each group to facilitate distribution and collection of materials after the activity. Consider premounting the foam balls on the dowels and securing them with glue. These can then be used for all of your classes.

Before students run the activity, turn off the lights in the classroom, turn on the bright light source, and determine the best position for the light source in your classroom so that all students will be able to carry out the investigation.

Homework Options

Reflection

- **Science Content:** Compare and contrast the Moon's period of rotation with the length of the lunar cycle. *(Students should answer that the Moon's period of rotation is 27 days and the length of a lunar cycle is 29.5 days.)*

- **Science Content:** A student models the positions of Earth, the Moon and the Sun during the full moon phase. Predict how the phase observed would be affected if at this point the student only rotates the Moon. *(Students should describe how the phase observed would be unaffected. Rotating the Moon would not affect the portion of the illuminated half of the Moon visible to an observer on Earth. However, it would affect the region of the Moon's surface that was illuminated so that, for example, different craters might be visible.)*

- **Science Process:** Design a way to measure the length of the lunar cycle. *(Students should describe observing the Moon daily and counting the number of days between successive appearances of the same phase.)*

Preparation for 2.4

- **Science Process:** Predict how the apparent size of an object would change as it moves farther from an observer. *(Students' answer should describe how the farther away an object is located from an observer, the smaller its apparent size.)*

- **Science Process:** Devise a method that you could use to measure the apparent size of a distant object. *(Students' methods should include comparing the apparent size to a standard measuring scale held at a specific distance from the eye of an observer or measuring its angular diameter.)*

- **Science Process:** If you could see both the full Moon and the Sun side by side in the sky, how do you think their apparent sizes would compare? How could you find out how they compare? *(Student answers will vary. They may suggest doing research to find measurements that have been made by astronomers of the apparent diameter of the Sun and the Moon.)*

Project-Based Inquiry Science

SECTION 2.3 IMPLEMENTATION

2.3 Explore

Where Is the Moon Located, and How Does It Move?

The different shapes of the Moon are familiar sights in the night sky, but not everyone knows why the Moon appears to move across the sky and to change shape during each month.

The second brightest object in Earth's sky, much closer to Earth than the Sun, is the Moon. The Moon is probably the most observed object in our solar system. Most people can tell you features of the Moon or, perhaps, some old stories about what makes up the Moon. However, not everyone knows how the Moon moves across the sky and why it changes its appearance the way it does. In this section you will investigate the Moon's apparent motion across the sky and work to figure out its location in relation to Earth and the way it actually moves.

Investigation 1: The Moon's Path in One Day

You will investigate the Moon's apparent motion across the sky in a single day and then compare this motion to the apparent motion of the Sun. You saw that the Sun's apparent movement across the sky is caused by Earth's motion. As you explore the Moon's location and movement, keep that in mind. Perhaps the Moon's movement is also related to Earth's motion.

Procedure

1. With your group, examine Image #1, which shows the Moon's position every two hours as seen from Earth on a day in June.

2. Then examine Image #2, which shows the Sun's position every two hours as seen on the same day from the same location on Earth.

AST 80

2.3 Explore

Where Is the Moon Located, and How Does It Move?

5 min

Students begin to consider the Moon and its role in our solar system.

△ Guide

Begin by telling students that by using what they understand of the apparent motion of the Sun, they will investigate why the Moon seems to move across the sky and change its appearance.

*A class period is considered to be one 40 to 50 minute class.

Investigation 1: The Moon's Path in One Day

15 min

during each m... ...o Earth and the way it ac... ...ves.

Investigation 1: The Moon's Path in One Day

You will investigate the Moon's apparent motion across the sky in a single day and then compare this motion to the apparent motion of the Sun. You saw that the Sun's apparent movement across the sky is caused by Earth's motion. As you explore the Moon's location and movement, keep that in mind. Perhaps the Moon's movement is also related to Earth's motion.

Procedure

1. With your group, examine Image #1, which shows the Moon's position every two hours as seen from Earth on a day in June.

2. Then examine Image #2, which shows the Sun's position every two hours as seen on the same day from the same location on Earth.

△ Guide

Have students meet with their groups. Allow students some time to examine *Image #1* and *Image #2*. Then tell them to copy the *Comparing the Apparent Motions of the Moon and Sun* chart from the student text.

NOTES

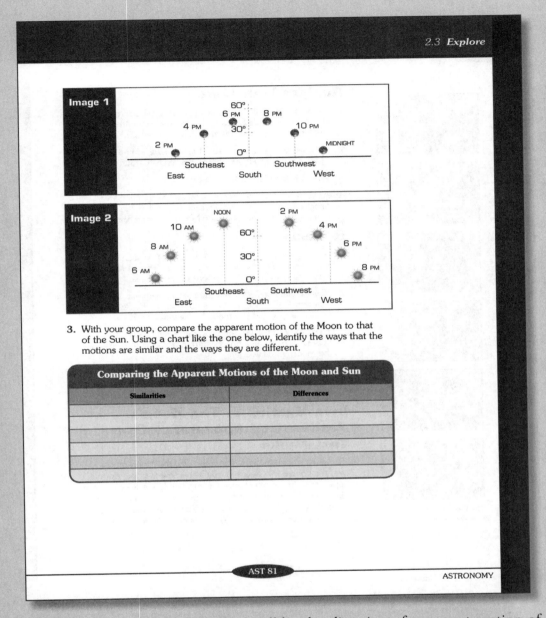

3. With your group, compare the apparent motion of the Moon to that of the Sun. Using a chart like the one below, identify the ways that the motions are similar and the ways they are different.

Comparing the Apparent Motions of the Moon and Sun	
Similarities	**Differences**

The similarities that students find will be the direction of apparent motion of the two bodies and that they both rise to a peak in an arc-like fashion, rising in the east and setting in the west. The major difference is that the hour of the day for rising, peaking, and setting is different by four hours. The Moon's motion is the earlier one.

Analyze Your Data

5 min

Students answer questions about the movement of the Moon.

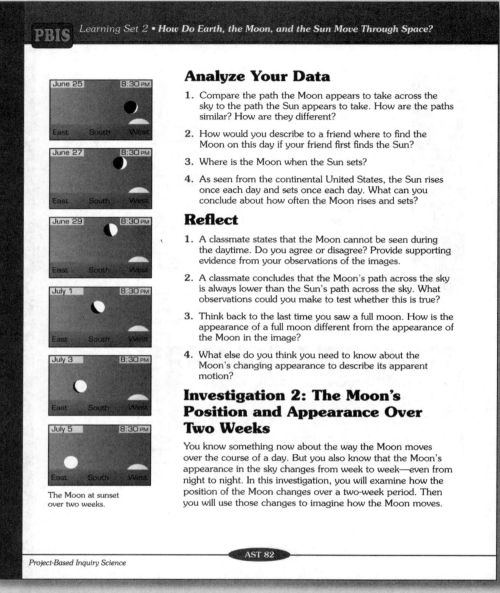

The Moon at sunset over two weeks.

Analyze Your Data

1. Compare the path the Moon appears to take across the sky to the path the Sun appears to take. How are the paths similar? How are they different?

2. How would you describe to a friend where to find the Moon on this day if your friend first finds the Sun?

3. Where is the Moon when the Sun sets?

4. As seen from the continental United States, the Sun rises once each day and sets once each day. What can you conclude about how often the Moon rises and sets?

Reflect

1. A classmate states that the Moon cannot be seen during the daytime. Do you agree or disagree? Provide supporting evidence from your observations of the images.

2. A classmate concludes that the Moon's path across the sky is always lower than the Sun's path across the sky. What observations could you make to test whether this is true?

3. Think back to the last time you saw a full moon. How is the appearance of a full moon different from the appearance of the Moon in the image?

4. What else do you think you need to know about the Moon's changing appearance to describe its apparent motion?

Investigation 2: The Moon's Position and Appearance Over Two Weeks

You know something now about the way the Moon moves over the course of a day. But you also know that the Moon's appearance in the sky changes from week to week—even from night to night. In this investigation, you will examine how the position of the Moon changes over a two-week period. Then you will use those changes to imagine how the Moon moves.

AST 82

△ Guide

Once students have had a chance to make observations of the images, lead a class discussion of the *Analyze Your Data* questions. Students should use observations from the images to compare the paths and positions of the Moon and the Sun. If students disagree about what they observed or are unable to answer the questions, have them look at the images again, emphasizing that they should record their observations carefully. Students should be able to describe the arc of the Moon's path as being farther south and shorter than the arc of the Sun's path. They also should observe that the Moon appears to be about the same distance from the Sun throughout the day.

1. Students should observe that the paths of the Sun and Moon across the sky are similar in direction and speed, but differ in height (the Sun is higher). Also, the Moon is four hours ahead of the Sun.

2. If the friend finds the Sun prior to 2 PM, the Moon will not be visible. However, students should see that at 2 PM both the Sun and Moon are visible. The Moon will be rising on the eastern horizon and the Sun will be past midday.

3. When the Sun sets at 8 PM, students should see that the Moon will be about 1 PM in the sky, just past midday.

4. Students should realize that the Moon also rises and sets once each day.

△ Guide

Have students answer the *Reflect* questions with their groups. As they work on these questions, monitor their progress. Ask them what ideas they discussed and what disagreements they had. These *Reflect* questions should help them identify what they need to determine in their investigation.

1. Students should disagree, citing that they have experienced seeing the Moon during the day. Their data will reinforce this belief because it shows the Moon during the daylight hours of the Sun.

2. Students should reply that they need to take observations and data for a year to determine if the Moon's path is always lower than the Sun's path. They also might realize that they would need to qualify the claim with data about the latitude.

3. Students' answers will vary depending on their previous experience with the Moon.

4. Students' answers will vary.

Reflect
10 min

Students answer questions about the Moon's appearance from Earth.

Investigation 2: The Moon's Position and Appearance Over Two Weeks

10 min

Groups use the images in the student text to observe the Moon's position and appearance over two weeks.

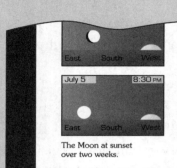

The Moon at sunset over two weeks.

motion:

Investigation 2: The Moon's Position and Appearance Over Two Weeks

You know something now about the way the Moon moves over the course of a day. But you also know that the Moon's appearance in the sky changes from week to week—even from night to night. In this investigation, you will examine how the position of the Moon changes over a two-week period. Then you will use those changes to imagine how the Moon moves.

△ Guide

Point out to students that because they have observed how the position and appearance of the Moon changes over the course of a day, they will observe how the Moon's position and appearance changes over the course of two weeks. With their groups, they will observe a series of images showing the Moon at sunset every two days over a two-week period. They will record observations about the position and shape of the Moon.

NOTES

....

....

....

....

....

....

....

Procedure

1. With your group, look at the sequences of images of the Moon on the previous page. These images show the position of the Moon at sunset every two days for a period of two weeks.

2. Discuss the changes in the Moon's position and appearance with your group. Record your observations in a chart like the one below.

The Moon's Appearance Over Two Weeks			
Date and time	How high is the Moon?	Direction to look for the Moon	Apparent shape of the Moon

Analyze Your Data

1. Describe the changes in the apparent shape of the Moon over two weeks.

2. When does the Moon appear to be closest to the Sun at sunset? When does the Moon appear to be farthest from the Sun at sunset?

3. When does the Moon appear lowest in the sky at sunset? When does the Moon appear highest at sunset?

4. Suppose you and a friend together observe the Moon at sunset tonight. How would you describe to your friend where to find the Moon tomorrow night at sunset?

Reflect

1. How is the changing position of the Moon over two weeks similar to the changes you observed in the images you used, for the investigation (the Moon's motion during one day)? How is the changing position of the Moon over two weeks different from the changes that occur in one day?

2. In which direction is the Moon's position at sunset shifting, east to west or west to east? What do you think is the reason for the shift being in this direction?

AST 83

◯ Get Going

Have students meet with their groups and discuss what they observe in the pictures. Have them copy *The Moon's Appearance Over Two Weeks* chart from their text and then record their observations.

Analyze Your Data

10 min

Students answer questions based on Investigation 2.

Analyze Your Data

1. Describe the changes in the apparent shape of the Moon over two weeks.

2. When does the Moon appear to be closest to the Sun at sunset? When does the Moon appear to be farthest from the Sun at sunset?

3. When does the Moon appear lowest in the sky at sunset? When does the Moon appear highest at sunset?

4. Suppose you and a friend together observe the Moon at sunset tonight. How would you describe to your friend where to find the Moon tomorrow night at sunset?

△ Guide

When groups have had time to record their observations, lead a class discussion of the *Analyze Your Data* questions. Students should be able to describe how the apparent position and shape of the Moon change based on their observations. They also should be able to find the days when the Moon appears closest to the Sun and lowest in the sky. If there is any disagreement about the answers to these questions, have students look at the images again and resolve the disagreement by checking their observations. Students' ideas about where the Moon would be tomorrow night at sunset should reflect an understanding that the Moon's position at sunset is more eastward with respect to the Sun each day in the cycle.

1. Students should describe the changes in the Moon's apparent shape as:

   On June 25, the Moon is a very thin crescent, just past the new moon stage. On June 27, the crescent has grown larger as the Moon moves away from the Sun. The Moon continues to grow (wax) through June 29, July 1 and July 3, and it moves further and further away from the Sun. It achieves full moon status on July 5 as it is just rising as the Sun sets.

2. Students should report that the Moon is closest to the Sun at sunset on June 25. They should also report that the Moon is farthest from the Sun at sunset on July 5.

3. Students should observe that the Moon appears lowest in the sky as sunset on July 5 and that it appears highest at sunset on June 29.

4. Students should calculate that they can inform their friend that the Moon will be to the left of its position on the night before, about 10° to 15°.

Reflect

1. How is the changing position of the Moon over two weeks similar to the changes you observed in the images you used, for the investigation (the Moon's motion during one day)? How is the changing position of the Moon over two weeks different from the changes that occur in one day?

2. In which direction is the Moon's position at sunset shifting, east to west or west to east? What do you think is the reason for the shift being in this direction?

△ Guide

Lead a class discussion of the *Reflect* questions. Students should recognize that over a the course of a day, the position of the Moon changes with the position of the Sun, so that the distance between the two bodies appears to stay about the same; whereas over a two-week period, the position of the Moon changes relative to the Sun, so that the distance between the two bodies appears to change. They should be able to see that the change of the Moon's position relative to the Sun's position is from west to east, though they may have different ideas about why.

1. Students should explain that the images of the Moon's position during one day are similar to the images of the Moon's position over two weeks, because both show an arc-like pattern that is regularly spaced. The two sets of images are different in that the movement is from east to west in the one-day data, while it is from west to east in the two-week data.

2. Students should understand that the Moon's position at sunset in the two-week images is from west to east. This is because the Moon is revolving around Earth from west to east.

NOTES

....

....

....

....

Moonlight

5 min

Students read how the light of the Moon is reflected light.

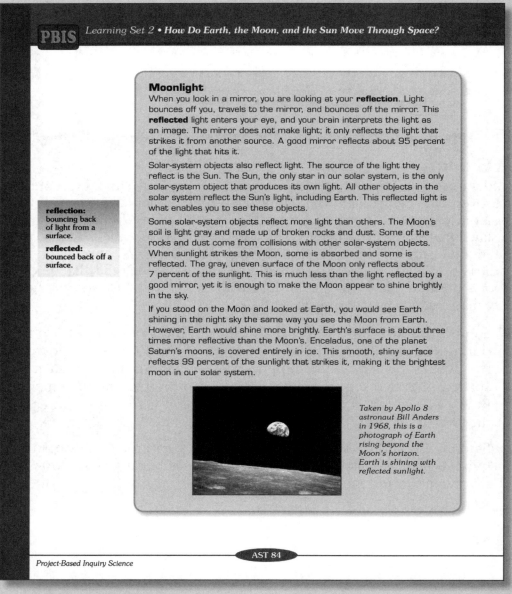

Moonlight

When you look in a mirror, you are looking at your **reflection**. Light bounces off you, travels to the mirror, and bounces off the mirror. This **reflected** light enters your eye, and your brain interprets the light as an image. The mirror does not make light; it only reflects the light that strikes it from another source. A good mirror reflects about 95 percent of the light that hits it.

Solar-system objects also reflect light. The source of the light they reflect is the Sun. The Sun, the only star in our solar system, is the only solar-system object that produces its own light. All other objects in the solar system reflect the Sun's light, including Earth. This reflected light is what enables you to see these objects.

Some solar-system objects reflect more light than others. The Moon's soil is light gray and made up of broken rocks and dust. Some of the rocks and dust come from collisions with other solar-system objects. When sunlight strikes the Moon, some is absorbed and some is reflected. The gray, uneven surface of the Moon only reflects about 7 percent of the sunlight. This is much less than the light reflected by a good mirror, yet it is enough to make the Moon appear to shine brightly in the sky.

If you stood on the Moon and looked at Earth, you would see Earth shining in the night sky the same way you see the Moon from Earth. However, Earth would shine more brightly. Earth's surface is about three times more reflective than the Moon's. Enceladus, one of the planet Saturn's moons, is covered entirely in ice. This smooth, shiny surface reflects 99 percent of the sunlight that strikes it, making it the brightest moon in our solar system.

reflection: bouncing back of light from a surface.

reflected: bounced back off a surface.

Taken by Apollo 8 astronaut Bill Anders in 1968, this is a photograph of Earth rising beyond the Moon's horizon. Earth is shining with reflected sunlight.

AST 84

Project-Based Inquiry Science

△ Guide

Discuss how the light we see from the Moon and the planets is reflected from the Sun. The student text uses the example of light reflected on a mirror. The light is not generated by the mirror; instead, it bounces off the mirror. Similarly, the Moon and the planets do not generate light. The Sun generates light, and the light of the Sun is reflected off the other solar-system objects. Point out that some solar-system objects reflect more light than others. Earth reflects about three times as much light as the Moon does, while one of Jupiter's moons, Enceladus, reflects much more than either—about 99 percent.

Reflect

1. On the right is a composite image of Earth and the Moon taken from space. Only part of Earth is illuminated. How could Earth shining with reflected sunlight account for Earth not looking like a sphere in the photograph?

2. Where do you think the Sun is located in this picture—to the left, to the right, above, or below Earth and the Moon? How do you know?

phase of the Moon: the illuminated part of the Moon visible from Earth at a given time.

Phases of the Moon

Observing the Moon over several months, you would see the same pattern of different lunar shapes repeated month after month, just as ancient astronomers observed thousands of years ago. Looking closely, you can see that what is changing is actually the portion of the Moon that is illuminated. The different illuminated portions of the Moon as seen from Earth are called the **phases of the Moon**.

The phases of the Moon are part of a cycle that takes a little less than a month to complete. The cycle begins with none of the Moon visible. This phase is called the *new moon*. During the next two weeks, you can observe a little more of the Moon being illuminated each day. These are the phases you investigated in the six images of the Moon at sunset.

Reflect

5 min

Students answer questions using their knowledge of reflected light.

△ Guide

Lead a class discussion of the *Reflect* questions. Students may begin to connect the idea that the light of the Moon and Earth is reflected light related to the changing shape of the Moon that they observed. To help them answer the first question, you may need to remind them that there is one source of light in the solar system—the Sun. You might also point out that in the picture, the Moon and Earth are illuminated on the same side. This is because both the Moon and Earth are illuminated by the Sun, so the side of each body that faces the Sun is illuminated. Using this fact, they can identify the direction of the Sun.

1. Students should suggest that the Earth is not fully illuminated as a sphere because of the perspective taken by the photograph. From the perspective of the Sun, the Earth would be a fully illuminated sphere.

2. Students should answer that the Sun is located to the left of the Earth because the right side of the Earth is in shadow.

Phases of the Moon

5 min

Students are introduced to the phases of the Moon.

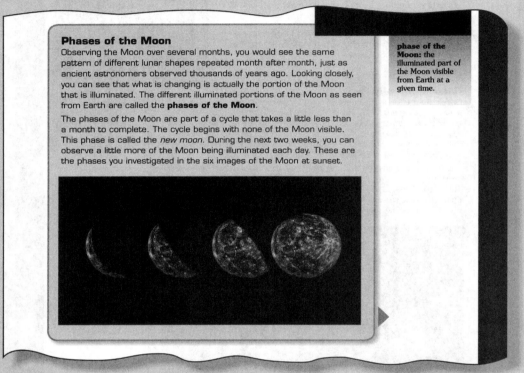

Phases of the Moon

Observing the Moon over several months, you would see the same pattern of different lunar shapes repeated month after month, just as ancient astronomers observed thousands of years ago. Looking closely, you can see that what is changing is actually the portion of the Moon that is illuminated. The different illuminated portions of the Moon as seen from Earth are called the **phases of the Moon**.

The phases of the Moon are part of a cycle that takes a little less than a month to complete. The cycle begins with none of the Moon visible. This phase is called the *new moon*. During the next two weeks, you can observe a little more of the Moon being illuminated each day. These are the phases you investigated in the six images of the Moon at sunset.

phase of the Moon: the illuminated part of the Moon visible from Earth at a given time.

△ Guide

Tell students that what they just observed about the illuminated portions of the Moon and Earth facing the Sun can help them understand why the apparent shape of the Moon changes. When the Moon seems to change shape, what actually changes is the illuminated portion of the Moon visible from Earth.

The different shapes of this visible portion are known as the *phases of the Moon*. The Moon passes through all of the phases in a cycle, or the *lunar cycle,* which takes a little less than a month. The cycle begins with the new moon, when none of the illuminated portion of the Moon is visible, and over the next two weeks, progressively more of the illuminated portion becomes visible. At the end of two weeks, all of the illuminated portion is visible, a phase called the *full moon.* After the full moon, less of the illuminated portion is visible each day until the Moon again reaches the new moon phase.

PBIS   *Learning Set 2 • How Do Earth, the Moon, and the Sun Move Through Space?*

One week after new moon, the right half of the Moon is illuminated. This phase is called the *first quarter moon*. After two weeks, the visible Moon looks like a complete circle. It is called a *full moon*. During the two weeks after the full moon, you can observe that less and less of the Moon is illuminated each day. One week after the full moon, the left half of the Moon is illuminated. This phase is called the *last quarter moon*. The cycle begins again two weeks after the full moon, when once more none of the Moon is visible and the Moon is back in the new moon phase.

Stop and Think

1. How much of the Moon is illuminated at any particular time?

2. At the first quarter moon, how much of the illuminated part of the Moon can you see?

3. At the full moon, how much of the illuminated part of the Moon can you see?

4. Why do you think that you see more of the illuminated part of the Moon at full moon than at the first quarter moon?

Make a Model of the Motions of the Earth-Moon-Sun System

Knowing that the Moon reflects light from the Sun, and does not produce its own light, provides a clue as to why the Moon changes in appearance. However, you may not yet understand enough about the interactions among Earth, the Sun, and the Moon to be able to fully explain the Moon's changes in appearance. To help you develop that understanding, you will explore how motions of Earth, the Sun, and the Moon result in the changing appearance of the Moon as seen from Earth.

Before you start the activity, think back to the model you made of the Sun and Earth. You used a flashlight to represent the Sun. You used your Sun to make shadows of a pencil on a globe representing Earth. In that model, two types of motion were possible: Earth could spin on its axis or the flashlight

AST 86

Tell students that understanding how the positions and motions of the Sun, the Moon, and Earth relate to one another will help them understand why the appearance of the Moon changes. They will use a model to explore this.

Stop and Think

10 min

Students answer questions related to the Phases of the Moon *reading.*

Stop and Think

1. How much of the Moon is illuminated at any particular time?
2. At the first quarter moon, how much of the illuminated part of the Moon can you see?
3. At the full moon, how much of the illuminated part of the Moon can you see?
4. Why do you think that you see more of the illuminated part of the Moon at full moon than at the first quarter moon?

△ Guide and Assess

Assist the students in consolidating their understanding of the reading. After giving the students a few minutes to answer the questions alone, lead a class discussion of the answers.

1. Students may not know it, but 50 percent of the Moon is illuminated all of the time, except when there is an eclipse of the Moon.

2. Students should reply that at first quarter moon, they can only see half of the illuminated part of the Moon.

3. Students should respond that at full moon, they can see all of the illuminated part of the Moon.

4. Students should respond that they can see more of the illuminated part of the Moon at full moon because of their perspective.

Make a Model of the Motions of the Earth-Moon-Sun System

<5 min

Students are introduced to the investigation using models to explore the motions of the Earth-Moon-Sun system.

Make a Model of the Motions of the Earth-Moon-Sun System

Knowing that the Moon reflects light from the Sun, and does not produce its own light, provides a clue as to why the Moon changes in appearance. However, you may not yet understand enough about the interactions among Earth, the Sun, and the Moon to be able to fully explain the Moon's changes in appearance. To help you develop that understanding, you will explore how motions of Earth, the Sun, and the Moon result in the changing appearance of the Moon as seen from Earth.

Before you start the activity, think back to the model you made of the Sun and Earth. You used a flashlight to represent the Sun. You used your Sun to make shadows of a pencil on a globe representing Earth. In that model, two types of motion were possible: Earth could spin on its axis or the flashlight

△ Guide

Distribute materials and tell students they will run two investigations modeling Earth, the Moon, and the Sun to determine what causes the phases of the Moon. Tell them that for both investigations, you will use a bright light to simulate the Sun. The foam balls will simulate the Moon. Then go over the procedure for *Investigation 3*.

(the Sun) could move around Earth. You found that the rotation, or spin, of Earth could explain why the Sun appears to move across the sky.

This time you will be observing a different type of movement—the movement of one solar-system object around another one. The path that one solar-system object takes in moving around another object is called an **orbit**. You may also say that one object orbits the other object.

For this next model, three objects are involved, one each to represent Earth, the Sun, and the Moon. Your task is to determine what combination of objects rotating and objects orbiting one another accounts for changes in the Moon's phases and our view of the phases. You will start by looking only at the Moon's motion and then add in Earth's motion.

Investigation 3:
Simulate the Motion of the Moon

Procedure

1. Mount the plastic foam ball on the chopstick or wooden dowel. The ball will represent the Moon.

2. You will set up a light source to represent the Sun. In this demonstration, the Sun will not move.

3. In this model, your head will represent Earth. Your eyes are like the eyes of an observer on Earth's surface.

4. Each group member will have a chance to hold the model Moon and observe the phase of the model Moon. When it is your turn, stand with your back to the model Sun. Hold the model Moon in front of you at arm's length, a little higher than your head. Holding it like this will allow observers standing behind you to see. You should be able to see that one half of the ball is illuminated. The entire illuminated half is facing you.

5. While the first group member holds the model Moon, discuss as a group which phase of the Moon you are observing. After you reach agreement, sketch the phase in the correct row of the table on your *Phases of the Moon* page.

orbit: the path that a solar-system object takes in revolving around another solar-system object.

Materials
- plastic foam ball to represent the Moon
- chopstick or long, thin wooden dowel
- bright light source to represent the Sun
- *Phases of the Moon* page

AST 87

ASTRONOMY

Investigation 3: Simulate the Motion of the Moon

10 min

Students explore how the motion of the Moon effects light shining on Earth.

△ Guide

Tell students they will mount the foam balls on chopsticks or dowels and hold them out at arm's length, slightly above their heads. In this position, the student holding the foam ball will imagine that his or her head occupies the position of Earth, and he or she sees what an observer on Earth would see. At first, they will hold the foam ball so the illuminated side faces them. The other members of the group will record the relative positions of the Sun, the Moon, and Earth on their *Phases of the Moon* pages. Each member

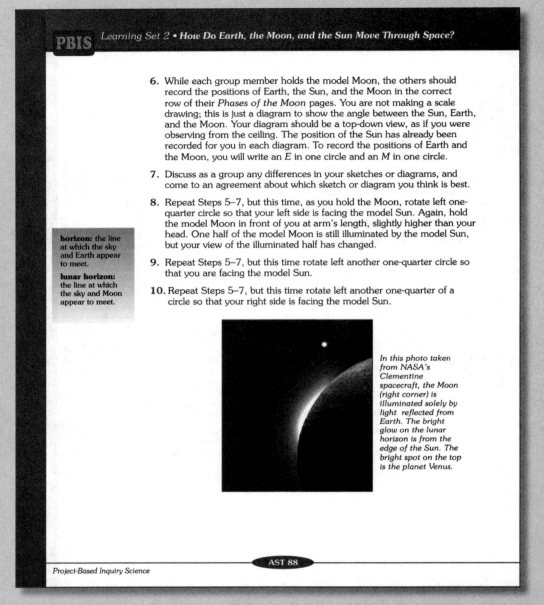

6. While each group member holds the model Moon, the others should record the positions of Earth, the Sun, and the Moon in the correct row of their *Phases of the Moon* pages. You are not making a scale drawing; this is just a diagram to show the angle between the Sun, Earth, and the Moon. Your diagram should be a top-down view, as if you were observing from the ceiling. The position of the Sun has already been recorded for you in each diagram. To record the positions of Earth and the Moon, you will write an *E* in one circle and an *M* in one circle.

7. Discuss as a group any differences in your sketches or diagrams, and come to an agreement about which sketch or diagram you think is best.

8. Repeat Steps 5–7, but this time, as you hold the Moon, rotate left one-quarter circle so that your left side is facing the model Sun. Again, hold the model Moon in front of you at arm's length, slightly higher than your head. One half of the model Moon is still illuminated by the model Sun, but your view of the illuminated half has changed.

9. Repeat Steps 5–7, but this time rotate left another one-quarter circle so that you are facing the model Sun.

10. Repeat Steps 5–7, but this time rotate left another one-quarter of a circle so that your right side is facing the model Sun.

horizon: the line at which the sky and Earth appear to meet.

lunar horizon: the line at which the sky and Moon appear to meet.

In this photo taken from NASA's Clementine spacecraft, the Moon (right corner) is illuminated solely by light reflected from Earth. The bright glow on the lunar horizon is from the edge of the Sun. The bright spot on the top is the planet Venus.

AST 88

Project-Based Inquiry Science

will take turns holding the foam ball. Then they repeat their observations with the ball held at arm's length three times, rotating one-quarter circle to the left each time. Each time, they will see a different portion of the illuminated half of the foam ball.

Turn on the bright light representing the Sun and have groups run their investigations. As groups work, monitor their progress and help them with any difficulties that arise. Make sure they record observations for each phase of the Moon.

Investigation 4: Simulate the Motions of the Moon and Earth

You will now try to simulate how the Moon and Earth move at the same time.

Procedure

1. Start by modeling Planet X and its moon. Planet X, like Earth, rotates on its axis once per day. The moon of Planet X also takes one day to make one complete orbit. To model this, hold the model moon in front of you at arm's length, slightly above the top of your head. Rotate slowly in place. Record your observations of the phases of the moon. Describe how one complete rotation of the planet compares with one complete orbit of the moon.

2. Let each group member take a turn repeating Step 1. Watch as each group member simulates Planet X's motion.

3. Now you will simulate Planet Y and its moon. Planet Y, like Earth, rotates on its axis once per day. However, the moon of Planet Y takes four days to orbit Planet Y. This simulation will require two group members. One member of your group will be Planet Y. Another will hold the plastic foam ball to represent Planet Y's moon. Planet Y should spin once in 10 seconds, and the model moon should take 40 seconds to complete an orbit. Practice this, and decide as a group that you are simulating the movement of Planet Y and its moon correctly. When you are satisfied that you are simulating the motion of the spinning planet and orbiting moon correctly, the student representing Planet Y should observe the moon's phases and record observations of the phases.

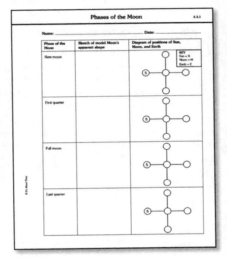

Investigation 4: Simulate the Motions of the Moon and Earth

10 min

△ Guide

Tell students they will now model how the Moon and Earth move together. Go over the procedure for this investigation. They will begin by modeling a planet and its moon that are similar to Earth and the Moon. This Planet X rotates on its axis once a day, but its moon completes an orbit in one day—a shorter period than Earth's moon. To model this, a student will hold a foam ball at arm's length, slightly above his or her head, and turn in a full circle while observing the light on the foam ball as he or she turns.

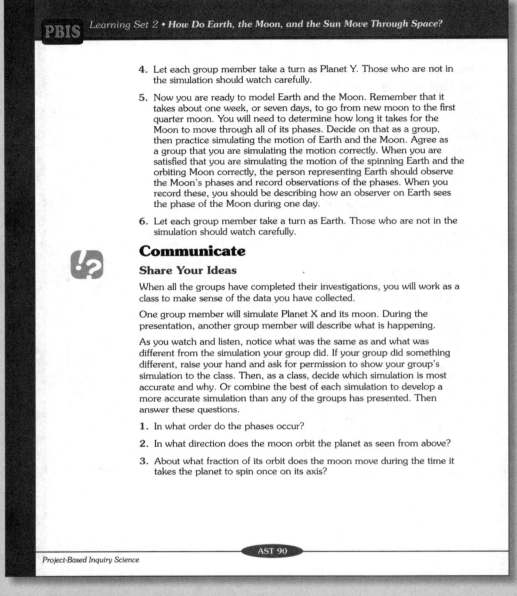

4. Let each group member take a turn as Planet Y. Those who are not in the simulation should watch carefully.

5. Now you are ready to model Earth and the Moon. Remember that it takes about one week, or seven days, to go from new moon to the first quarter moon. You will need to determine how long it takes for the Moon to move through all of its phases. Decide on that as a group, then practice simulating the motion of Earth and the Moon. Agree as a group that you are simulating the motion correctly. When you are satisfied that you are simulating the motion of the spinning Earth and the orbiting Moon correctly, the person representing Earth should observe the Moon's phases and record observations of the phases. When you record these, you should be describing how an observer on Earth sees the phase of the Moon during one day.

6. Let each group member take a turn as Earth. Those who are not in the simulation should watch carefully.

Communicate

Share Your Ideas

When all the groups have completed their investigations, you will work as a class to make sense of the data you have collected.

One group member will simulate Planet X and its moon. During the presentation, another group member will describe what is happening.

As you watch and listen, notice what was the same as and what was different from the simulation your group did. If your group did something different, raise your hand and ask for permission to show your group's simulation to the class. Then, as a class, decide which simulation is most accurate and why. Or combine the best of each simulation to develop a more accurate simulation than any of the groups has presented. Then answer these questions.

1. In what order do the phases occur?

2. In what direction does the moon orbit the planet as seen from above?

3. About what fraction of its orbit does the moon move during the time it takes the planet to spin once on its axis?

Then they will model Planet Y, which rotates once a day but has a moon that completes an orbit in four days. This will require two students. One student will rotate in a full circle, modeling the motion of the planet, while the other student, carrying the foam ball, completes a circle around the rotating student. They will need to coordinate their motions so the student in the center rotates four times while the student on the outside completes one orbit. This may take a few tries. When they have successfully modeled this, they should record their observations.

Finally, students will model Earth and the Moon. To do this, they will again need one student to stand in the center and rotate and another student to orbit the rotating student. This time, students will need to consider that it takes about seven days for the Moon to go from new moon to quarter moon. That means the student in the center will have to rotate seven times while the orbiting student moves through the first quarter of the orbit. By the time the orbiting student completes an orbit, the student in the center will have rotated 27 times. This may take a few tries. Emphasize that the closer students get to a constant rate of motion, the more meaningful their observations will be. When they have successfully modeled Earth and the Moon, they should record their observations.

Consider asking advanced students to observe how the time at which the Moon rises each day changes throughout the lunar cycle. This could be accomplished by marking the point at which the Moon first enters the field of vision of the rotating student in each rotation with a piece of masking tape on the floor. Students should observe that the Moon rises slightly later each day. (The Moon, in fact, rises about 50 minutes later each day, on average.)

△ Guide

Have groups share the results of *Investigation 4* with the class. To do this, they will demonstrate their models of Planet X and its moon, Planet Y and its moon, and Earth and the Moon. As two students from the group demonstrate these models, another group member will describe what is happening.

As each group presents their results, have students listen for answers to the questions listed.

Communicate: Share Your Ideas

15 min

Groups share the results of their investigations with the class.

NOTES

....

....

....

....

....

Reflect

10 min

Students answer the questions, considering what they observed in Investigations 3 and 4.

If you have trouble answering any of these questions, ask questions to the class. If you disagree with the answers, respectfully offer your thoughts and ideas for improvement.

Repeat this sequence for Planet Y and its moon, and for Earth and the Moon.

Reflect

1. Remember that the shape of the Moon is a sphere. At the full moon, how much of the Moon's surface is illuminated? How much of the Moon's surface is illuminated at the new moon?

2. Imagine that a person in Florida and a person in California observe the Moon on the same night. Do both people see the same phase of the Moon? Why or why not?

3. Simply by looking at the Sun and the Moon in the sky, there is no way to tell how far apart they are. However, you had to make some assumptions about how far apart the three objects were. What assumptions did you use in your model?

4. If the Sun orbited Earth to cause day and night, what problems might this pose for your model of the phases of the Moon?

Motions of the Earth-Moon-Sun System and Phases of the Moon

As you may have noticed, the Moon's changes in appearance can be explained by the Moon's orbit around Earth. The Moon is visible because sunlight is reflected from its surface. Half of the Moon is always illuminated, but only at the full moon is the entire illuminated portion of the Moon facing Earth.

Phases of the Moon depend on how Earth, the Moon, and the Sun are positioned relative to one another. As the Moon orbits Earth, the angles among the Sun, Earth, and the Moon change. At the new moon, the Moon is located between Earth and the Sun, and the side of the Moon that is illuminated faces away from Earth. You do not see the Moon because the side you are looking at is dark. At the full moon, the Moon is on the side of Earth opposite the Sun. The illuminated side of the Moon is facing toward Earth, so the entire illuminated side of the Moon is visible.

△ Guide

Have students discuss the *Reflect* questions with their groups. Let them know they will discuss their answers with the class. When groups have had time to discuss the questions, lead a class discussion of their responses. This discussion should help students reach the conclusion that about half of the Moon is always illuminated, but its appearance depends on your perspective. The discussion also should help students recognize that, without knowing the exact causes of the phases of the Moon, there are many arrangements of Earth, the Moon, and the Sun you might think were possible. For instance, you might make the Sun closer to Earth than the Moon, or you might make the Sun orbit Earth.

1. Students should realize that 50 percent of the Moon's surface is illuminated at both full moon and new moon phases.

2. Students' answers may vary, but most should realize that a person in Florida and a person in California will see the same phase of the Moon on the same night. This is a result of the Moon, Earth, and Sun all having the same relative positions.

3. Students should remember that they assumed that the Sun was much farther away than the Moon.

4. Students may suggest that, if the Sun orbited Earth, the phases of the Moon would change quite rapidly and would not be the same as actually viewed.

△ Guide

Discuss how changes in the Moon's position lead to changes in its appearance, as discussed in the student text. This passage should largely confirm students' observations. Half of the Moon is always illuminated, but only at the full moon is the entire half facing Earth. When the Moon is between the Sun and Earth, the illuminated side faces away from Earth, so you do not see the Moon from Earth. This is the new moon.

Because it takes the Moon the same time to rotate around its axis as it takes it to orbit Earth (27 days), the same side of the Moon always faces Earth. For that reason, you always see the same craters on the Moon's surface.

Motions of the Earth-Moon-Sun System and Phases of the Moon

5 min

Students read about what causes the phases of the Moon.

NOTES

....

....

....

....

....

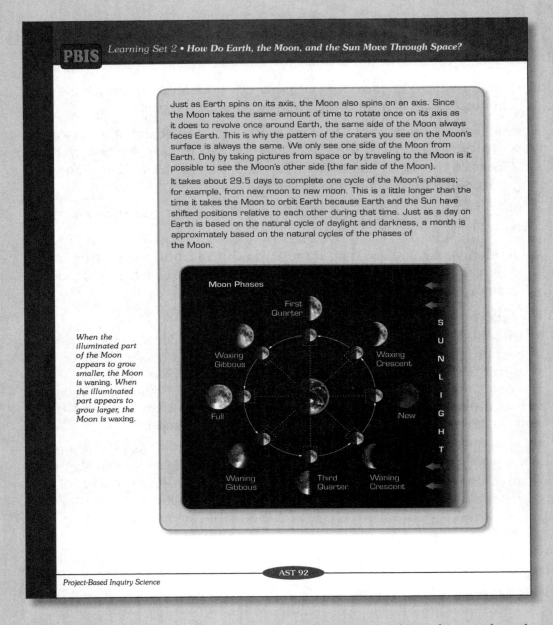

Just as Earth spins on its axis, the Moon also spins on an axis. Since the Moon takes the same amount of time to rotate once on its axis as it does to revolve once around Earth, the same side of the Moon always faces Earth. This is why the pattern of the craters you see on the Moon's surface is always the same. We only see one side of the Moon from Earth. Only by taking pictures from space or by traveling to the Moon is it possible to see the Moon's other side (the far side of the Moon).

It takes about 29.5 days to complete one cycle of the Moon's phases; for example, from new moon to new moon. This is a little longer than the time it takes the Moon to orbit Earth because Earth and the Sun have shifted positions relative to each other during that time. Just as a day on Earth is based on the natural cycle of daylight and darkness, a month is approximately based on the natural cycles of the phases of the Moon.

When the illuminated part of the Moon appears to grow smaller, the Moon is waning. When the illuminated part appears to grow larger, the Moon is waxing.

Moon Phases

First Quarter

Waxing Gibbous

Waxing Crescent

SUNLIGHT

Full

New

Waning Gibbous

Third Quarter

Waning Crescent

AST 92

Project-Based Inquiry Science

Tell students that a lunar cycle takes 29.5 days to complete—longer than the Moon's orbit. This is because Earth's position relative to the Sun changes during a lunar cycle, so it takes longer for the cycle to reach a new moon. This 29.5-day period is the natural basis for the calendar period of a month.

Revise Your Explanation

Earlier you wrote a claim and explanation statement about the apparent motion of the Sun in the sky. First, you will revise that explanation to include new information so that the apparent motion of the Sun is accounted for on your *Create Your Explanation* page. Next, you will develop a second statement that explains the apparent motion of the Moon during one month. Your claim will be the Moon's apparent motion and your explanation statement will include why people see it that way. This explanation should also account for the changing phases of the Moon. Record your explanation on another *Create Your Explanation* page.

Communicate

Share Your Explanation

Your class will now meet to share and discuss your explanations. Working together, the class will select and develop an explanation that best explains the apparent motion of the Sun and of the Moon. This explanation will be supported by evidence from your investigations and other knowledge that you and your classmates can contribute.

Reflect

1. How would you go about trying to prove that Earth is closer to the Moon than to the Sun?

2. Suppose a new space object is found: Asteroid Q2010. Astronomers study it for weeks and see that it is moving slowly in a straight line. The motions of Earth, the Moon, and the Sun are predictable. What does this indicate to you about the likelihood of determining whether Asteroid Q2010 will collide with Earth, the Moon, or the Sun?

3. Now suppose that another asteroid is identified, Asteroid Z2010, but astronomers do not yet know which way it is moving. What does this tell you about the likelihood of determining whether Asteroid Q2010 will collide with Asteroid Z2010?

Revise Your Explanation

10 min

Students revise their explanations of the apparent motion of the Sun and add an explanation of the apparent motion of the Moon.

△ Guide

Have students work with their groups to revise their explanations for the apparent motion of the Sun to also explain the apparent motion of the Moon. Their explanations should also explain the phases of the Moon. Emphasize that they need to use evidence and science knowledge to support their claims. They can use evidence from their investigations and science knowledge from their texts.

As groups revise their explanations, monitor their progress. Ask groups what evidence they are using to support their claims.

Communicate: Share Your Explanation

10 min

Students share their explanations with the class.

Communicate

Share Your Explanation

Your class will now meet to share and discuss your explanations. Working together, the class will select and develop an explanation that best explains the apparent motion of the Sun and of the Moon. This explanation will be supported by evidence from your investigations and other knowledge that you and your classmates can contribute.

△ Guide

Have groups present their explanations with the class. After discussion, the class will select the best explanation for the motion of the Sun and the Moon.

Reflect

5 min

Students answer questions in the Reflect section.

Reflect

1. How would you go about trying to prove that Earth is closer to the Moon than to the Sun?

2. Suppose a new space object is found: Asteroid Q2010. Astronomers study it for weeks and see that it is moving slowly in a straight line. The motions of Earth, the Moon, and the Sun are predictable. What does this indicate to you about the likelihood of determining whether Asteroid Q2010 will collide with Earth, the Moon, or the Sun?

3. Now suppose that another asteroid is identified, Asteroid Z2010, but astronomers do not yet know which way it is moving. What does this tell you about the likelihood of determining whether Asteroid Q2010 will collide with Asteroid Z2010?

△ Guide

Have students discuss the *Reflect* questions with their groups. Let them know they will discuss their answers with the class. When groups have had time to discuss the questions, lead a class discussion of their responses.

1. Students' answers will vary. Some will suggest sending a rocket to the Moon and the Sun at the same speed. The rocket that gets to its target first will show which is closer. A few might suggest using radar to determine the distance. Still others might suggest waiting for an eclipse.

2. Students should recognize that, since the motions of all four bodies are predictable, it would be easy to determine if Asteroid Q2010 will collide with the Earth, the Moon, or the Sun.

3. Students should respond that if the pathway of Asteroid Z2010 is unknown, then it cannot be determined if it will strike Earth, the Moon, or the Sun.

Update the *Project Board*

Now that you have explained the apparent motion of both the Sun and the Moon, it is a good time to update the *Project Board*. Add what you know about Earth's rotation, the Moon's apparent motion, and the Moon's phases to the *What are we learning?* column. Make sure to add evidence to the *What is our evidence?* column. In the *What do we think we know?* column, include anything you think affects the likelihood of objects colliding. If you still have questions about the location and motion of objects in the solar system, record them in the *What do we need to investigate?* column.

How can you know if objects in space will collide?				
What do we think we know?	What do we need to investigate?	What are we learning?	What is our evidence?	What does it mean for the challenge or question?

What's the Point?

The rotation of Earth causes the daily apparent motion of the Moon across the sky. Earth spins on its axis once per day. This is why the Moon, like the Sun, rises once each day and sets once each day. Like the Sun, the Moon rises in the east, moves across the sky, and then sets in the west.

The phases of the Moon are determined by the angle between Earth, the Sun, and the Moon. As the Moon moves in its path around Earth, one-half of the Moon (the side facing the Sun) is always illuminated. Because different amounts of the illuminated side face Earth, the Moon appears in different phases.

Project-Based Inquiry Science

△ Guide

When students have finished revising their explanations, ask what they have learned that can be added to the *Project Board*. Record their answers in the *What are we learning?* column, and have students record them on their own *Project Board* pages. Then ask students what evidence they have, and record their answers in the *What is our evidence?* column. Students' claims and evidence from their explanations should also go on their own *Project Board*.

Update the Project Board

15 min

The class has a discussion to update the Project Board.

Assessment Options

Targeted Concepts, Skills, and Nature of Science	How do I know if students got it?
Scientists often collaborate and share their findings. Sharing findings makes new information available and helps scientists refine their ideas and build on others' ideas. When another person's or group's idea is used, credit needs to be given.	**ASK:** How does the rate at which a moon revolves around a planet affect the sequence of the phases that would be observed from the planet's surface? **LISTEN:** Students should describe how the sequence in which the phases would be seen would remain unchanged, but the time between phases would be affected.
Scientists must keep clear, accurate, and descriptive records of what they do so they can share their work with others; consider what they did, why they did it, and what they want to do next.	**ASK:** How does the appearance of the phases between the new moon and next full moon compare with the phases between the full moon and next new moon? **LISTEN:** Students should describe how the phases look similar, but during the first half of the lunar cycle (new moon-full moon) the illuminated portion of the Moon appears to the right while during the second half of the lunar cycle the illuminated portion appears to the left.
Models are a representation of something in the world. Simulations use a model to imitate, or act out, real-life situations.	**ASK:** In your model, what represented Earth? An observer on Earth? The Moon? The Sun? **LISTEN:** Students should identify how the student's head represented Earth, the student's eyes represented an observer, the foam ball represented the Moon, and the bright light source represented the Sun.

NOTES

....

Targeted Concepts, Skills, and Nature of Science	How do I know if students got it?
Explanations are claims supported by evidence. Evidence can be experimental results, observational data, and any other accepted scientific knowledge.	**ASK:** What sources of evidence did you draw upon to provide supporting evidence for your explanation? **LISTEN:** Students answers will vary, but typically refer to the *Phases of the Moon* page and the *Motions of the Earth-Moon-Sun System* and *Phases of the Moon* text box.
Most objects in the solar system have a regular and predictable motion. These motions explain such phenomena as a day, a year, phases of the Moon, eclipses, tides, meteor showers, and comets.	**ASK:** How is the Moon's motion regular and predictable? **LISTEN:** Students should describe how the Moon revolves around Earth and rotates at a constant rate. Rotation and revolution are cyclic changes in position. Once the period of a cycle is known, the future position of an object in cyclic motion can be predicted.
The rotation of the earth on its axis every 24 hours produces the night-and-day cycle. To people on Earth, this turning of the planet makes it seem as though the Sun, Moon, planets, and stars are orbiting the earth once a day. This rotation also causes the Sun and Moon to appear to rise along the eastern horizon and to set along the western horizon. Earth's revolution around the Sun defines the length of the year as 365.25 days.	**ASK:** What motion of the Earth-Moon-Sun system is the basis for the day? The month? **LISTEN:** Students should identify Earth's period of rotation as the basis for the day and the lunar cycle of the Moon's revolution around Earth is the basis for the month. **ASK:** In what direction does the Moon appear to move across the nighttime sky on any given date? **LISTEN:** Students should answer that the Moon appears to move from east to west. **ASK:** If Earth rotates 360° in one day, how many degrees will Earth rotate in one hour? By how many degrees will the position of the Moon or Sun appear to change in one hour? **LISTEN:** In both cases, students' answer should be 15°.

Targeted Concepts, Skills, and Nature of Science	How do I know if students got it?
The Moon orbits Earth while Earth orbits the Sun. Except for the Sun, all objects in the solar system are seen by reflected light. The Moon's orbit around Earth once in about 28 days changes what part of the Moon is lighted by the Sun and how much of that part can be seen from Earth—the phases of the moon. The phases repeat in a cyclic pattern in about one month.	**ASK:** If the Moon's position in relation to Earth and the Sun corresponds to 12:00 on a clock at the new moon phase, what time on the clock would correspond to the full moon phase? The last quarter phase? **LISTEN:** Students should answer that the full moon will be at 6:00 and the last quarter will be at 9:00.

Teacher Reflection Questions

- Which strategies used in the *Learning Set* do you think were most successful in making abstract ideas more concrete for your students?

- What difficulties did students have with revising their explanations? How did you address these? What ideas do you have for the future?

- The written *Reflect* questions can be used as a formative assessment to help you monitor student progress. Students' questions and their answers can help you identify what students are learning and what ideas they hold that need further clarification. Were the assessment techniques used in this section appropriate to the type and quantity of information presented? Did students complete the assessment under conditions promoting the best possible performance?

2.4 Explore

How Do the Sizes of Earth and the Moon Compare, and How Far Apart Are They?

◄ *2 class periods*

A class period is considered to be one 40 to 50 minute class.

Overview

Students consider that the distance to an object affects how an observer perceives its size. Therefore, the apparent size of an object when viewed from Earth may not indicate its actual size or distance from an observer. Students are given a globe to represent Earth and asked to predict the ratio of the Moon's diameter to Earth's diameter. They are then provided with the actual Moon/Earth *volume* ratio obtained by other means and construct a scale model out of corresponding volumes of clay. Students measure and record the diameters of the Moon and Earth in their scale model, calculate the model's Moon/Earth diameter ratio and compare it with their predicted ratio. After reflecting on why their predictions may not have been accurate, students consider the Earth/Sun diameter ratio and predict the volume of a model Sun if made to the same scale. Students then collaborate in small groups to predict the scale model distance between the Moon and Earth. After sharing their prediction and their rationale for that prediction with the class, they learn that the Earth-Moon distance corresponds to approximately 30 Earth diameters. Students measure the diameter of their model Earth, place the model Moon at the correct distance from their model Earth, and compare that distance with their earlier prediction. Students reflect on why their predictions may have been inaccurate and consider what the scale model distance to the Sun would have to be to correctly represent its distance from Earth. The section concludes with a reading about the celestial sphere model of the sky and the issues faced by astronomers when estimating the relative sizes and distances to objects viewed in the sky.

Targeted Concepts, Skills, and Nature of Science	Performance Expectations
Scientists often collaborate and share their findings. Sharing findings makes new information available and helps scientists refine their ideas and build on others' ideas. When another person's or group's idea is used, credit needs to be given.	Students share with the class their predictions of the relative diameters of and distances between the Moon and Earth and discuss the reasons for their predictions.
Scientists must keep clear, accurate, and descriptive records of what they do so they can share their work with others; consider what they did, why they did it, and what they want to do next.	Students record their predictions, measurements, and calculations of the scale model diameters of the Moon and Earth and the distances between them.
Models are a representation of something in the world. Simulations use a model to imitate, or act out, real-life situations.	Students create a scale model of Earth and the Moon and complete the calculations necessary to add the Sun to the Model.
Earth's Sun is the central and largest body in our solar system. The Sun is more than a million times greater in volume than Earth. Earth is the third planet from the Sun in a system that includes other planets and their moons, as well as smaller objects, such as asteroids and comets.	Students calculate the scale model volume of the Sun and its distance from Earth.

Materials	
1 per group	Clay Metric ruler
5 per group	Toothpicks (round)
1 per group (optional)	Calculator

NOTES

....

....

Activity Setup and Preparation

Prepackage materials for each group to facilitate distribution and collection at the end of the activity. Modeling clay is usually packaged in rectangular blocks. Calculate the volume of a block of clay and provide each group with approximately 100 cm³ of clay.

NOTE: To facilitate dividing the clay into 50 equal volumes, you may want to consider having students roll the clay into a cylinder with a uniform diameter and then measuring off appropriate lengths of clay.

Homework Options

Reflection

- **Science Content:** The scale of a model can be expressed as the ratio of the size of the actual object to the size of the model object. The Moon's actual diameter is 3476 km, or 347,600,000 cm. Calculate the scale of your model Moon. *(Students' answers will vary, but if they used 100 cm³ of clay and followed the instructions in the text, the volume of their scale model Moon would be about 2 cm³. This volume of clay would form a sphere with a diameter of roughly 1.5 cm.*

$$V_{sphere} = \frac{4}{3}\pi r^3$$

$$\frac{2 \text{ cm}^3}{\frac{4}{3}} = r^3$$

$$r = 0.77 \text{cm}$$
$$D = 1.54 \text{cm}$$

   Thus, the scale of their model is 347,600,000 cm:1.54 cm, or roughly 226 million to 1.)

- **Science Content:** In this activity, you learned that the Moon is located 30 Earth diameters from Earth. The diameter of the planet Mars is about twice the diameter of the Moon, but it is located about 6000 Earth diameters from Earth. How would the size of the planet Mars compare with the size of the Moon when viewed from Earth? *(Students should answer that Mars would appear to have a much smaller diameter than the Moon—about 1/100th the diameter of the Moon.)*

- **Science Process:** When building your model, the instructions in the text directed you to break the clay into 50 equal parts. Describe how your group accomplished this task. How could you have changed your procedure so that the clay was divided into equal parts more accurately? *(Students' answers will vary. This question is designed to have students evaluate their procedure and recognize the usefulness of measuring instruments.)*

Preparation for 2.5

- **Science Content:** Draw a diagram of what you think the Sun looks like from Earth during a total solar eclipse. *(Students' answers will vary, but will give the teacher a sense of their prior experiences with eclipses.)*

- **Science Process:** To "eclipse" means to cover, or hide from view. Stand about 1 m (about 3 ft) away from a mirror and look at your face in the mirror through one eye. How far from your eyes must you hold the palm of your hand so that it completely blocks the image of your face in the mirror? How far from your face must you hold your thumb so that it completely blocks the image of your face in the mirror? *(Students' answers will vary, but should indicate that in order to block the image of their face, they must hold their thumb closer to their eyes than their palm.)*

NOTES

....

....

....

....

....

....

....

SECTION 2.4 IMPLEMENTATION

2.4 Explore

How Do the Sizes of Earth and the Moon Compare, and How Far Apart Are They?

When you are going on a trip, you may be watching for a famous landmark; for example, a statue or a lighthouse. When you spot the landmark in the distance, it may look tiny. As you get closer to your destination, the structure appears to get larger and larger. You don't realize its great size until you are finally right next to it, and then you might realize how small you are compared to it.

To determine whether objects are likely to collide with Earth, the Moon, or the Sun, it is important to know how big they are. Both the Sun and the Moon appear to be about the same size in the sky. Does that mean they *are* the same size? Just from looking at the sky, there is no way to determine their actual size or how far apart they are. But if you can determine the distance to each object, then you can tell how large each object must be for it to appear the way it does in the sky.

Predict

A globe is often used to represent Earth. If this were the size of Earth, how big do you think the Moon would be, using the same scale? Maybe you think the Moon would be the size of a softball, about one quarter the size of Earth. Or, maybe you think the Moon is more like a marble, about one hundredth the size of Earth. Or, perhaps you think the right size is somewhere in between.

This photograph of Earth and the Moon was taken from Mars, which is 192 million km (115 million mi) away. The brightness of the Moon has been enhanced to make it more visible.

AST 95

ASTRONOMY

2.4 Explore

How Do the Sizes of Earth and the Moon Compare, and How Far Apart Are They?

5 min

Students start to consider their perception of size.

△ Guide

Begin by asking students how they might determine how large the Moon is in comparison with Earth. Emphasize that the size of distant objects can be very hard to judge. The student text uses the example of landmarks viewed from far away.

Tell students it will be important to determine how large objects in the solar system are to determine whether they are likely to collide. Students will now determine how large the Moon is.

*A class period is considered to be one 40 to 50 minute class.

Predict

5 min

Students predict the relative size of the Moon.

you can tell ~~~~ge each object must be for it to appear the way it does in the sky.

Predict

A globe is often used to represent Earth. If this were the size of Earth, how big do you think the Moon would be, using the same scale? Maybe you think the Moon would be the size of a softball, about one quarter the size of Earth. Or, maybe you think the Moon is more like a marble, about one hundredth the size of Earth. Or, perhaps you think the right size is somewhere in between.

This photograph of Earth and the Moon was taken from Mars, which is 192 million km (115 million mi) away. The brightness of the Moon has been enhanced to make it more visible.

△ Guide

Tell students they will begin by predicting how the size of the Moon compares with the size of Earth. They will make the comparison on a smaller, more familiar scale using a globe to represent Earth. Thinking of the globe representing Earth's size, they will choose another object they think would show the relative size of the Moon. They might choose another globe, a softball, or a marble.

NOTES

How Do the Sizes of Earth and the Moon Compare, and How Far Apart Are They?

2.4

Decide what spherical object you think would be most like the size of the Moon. Share your ideas with your group and discuss what knowledge you used to choose your object. You may change the object you have chosen based on your discussion.

Once your group has settled on an object that would represent the Moon, use available resources to determine the diameter of the object you have chosen. Then measure the diameter of the globe you have used in the previous activities. After that, divide the diameter of the globe by the diameter of the sphere that represents the Moon. This will give you a prediction of the relative sizes of Earth and the Moon.

Build a Scale Model of Earth and the Moon

You will now build and analyze a scale model of the Earth-Moon system. You will use clay to model Earth and the Moon. As you work through the procedure, keep in mind your prediction about the sizes of these two solar-system bodies. Think about how accurately you predicted the relative size of each object.

Materials
- clay
- toothpicks
- ruler
- meter stick

Procedure

1. Break the clay into 50 equal parts. Roll them into balls using your hands so that you can easily compare their sizes. Do not worry if some are slightly bigger than others; the pieces do not have to be exactly the same size.

2. Take one of the 50 little balls and set it aside. Use the other 49 pieces and combine them to create a larger ball. The smaller ball, which is $\frac{1}{50}$ of the original amount of clay, represents the size of the Moon. The larger ball, which is $\frac{49}{50}$ of the original amount of clay, represents the size of Earth.

3. Use your ruler to measure the diameter of each ball. Record your measurements, then find the ratio of the diameter of Earth to the diameter of the Moon by dividing the two numbers.

AST 96

Have students meet with their groups and choose a spherical object they think is most like the size of the Moon. Then have them determine the diameter of the object. They may measure the diameter or look it up. Also have them measure the diameter of the globe they have been using. Once they have both diameters, they should divide the diameter of the globe by the diameter of the other sphere and record the ratio. This is their prediction for the ratio of Earth's diameter to the Moon's diameter.

Build a Scale Model of Earth and the Moon

10 min

Students use clay to model Earth and the Moon.

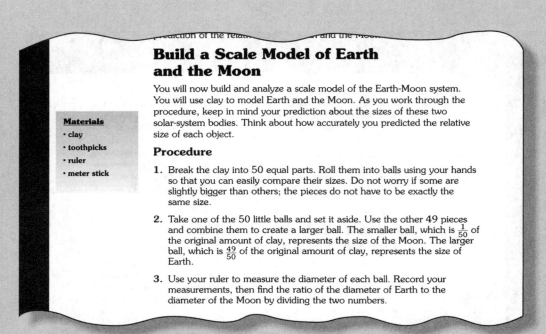

Build a Scale Model of Earth and the Moon

You will now build and analyze a scale model of the Earth-Moon system. You will use clay to model Earth and the Moon. As you work through the procedure, keep in mind your prediction about the sizes of these two solar-system bodies. Think about how accurately you predicted the relative size of each object.

Materials
- clay
- toothpicks
- ruler
- meter stick

Procedure

1. Break the clay into 50 equal parts. Roll them into balls using your hands so that you can easily compare their sizes. Do not worry if some are slightly bigger than others; the pieces do not have to be exactly the same size.

2. Take one of the 50 little balls and set it aside. Use the other 49 pieces and combine them to create a larger ball. The smaller ball, which is $\frac{1}{50}$ of the original amount of clay, represents the size of the Moon. The larger ball, which is $\frac{49}{50}$ of the original amount of clay, represents the size of Earth.

3. Use your ruler to measure the diameter of each ball. Record your measurements, then find the ratio of the diameter of Earth to the diameter of the Moon by dividing the two numbers.

△ Guide

Distribute materials and let students know they will now build a scale model of the Earth-Moon system, which they will use to determine how the size of the Moon compares to the size of Earth. Emphasize that they should think about how accurate their predictions were as they build their models.

◯ Get Going

Quickly go over the procedure with the class. They will break the clay into 50 equal parts. Then they will roll 49 of the pieces into a large sphere and the remaining piece they will roll into a small sphere. The large sphere represents Earth. The small sphere represents the Moon. They will use their ruler to measure the diameter of each sphere and then divide the larger diameter by the smaller and record the ratio.

Have groups build their models. As they work, monitor their progress and help them with any difficulties that arise.

NOTES

....

....

....

Reflect

1. Compare the ratio from your clay model to the ratio you calculated in your prediction. How did the results of this activity compare to the prediction you made about the relative size of the Moon compared to Earth?

2. Most people think the Moon is much larger than it actually is, compared to Earth. What surprised you about the relative size of the Moon compared to Earth?

3. The diameter of the Sun is about 110 times the diameter of Earth. How big would the Sun be in your model, if it were made to the same scale?

Predict

You have created two scale objects showing that the volume of Earth is 49 times greater than the volume of the Moon. Now you will complete your model by determining how far apart your Earth model and Moon model should be.

Start by predicting how far apart the model Earth and model Moon should be in your scale model. Select one set of clay balls made by a member of your group. Work with your group to come to an agreement on how far apart Earth and the Moon should be. Measure and record that distance. Discuss with your group if you think that distance is too small or too large. Adjust the distance if you wish, repeating the measurement if necessary. Be prepared to share your prediction, and the reasons for it, with the class.

Communicate

Share Your Ideas

When each group has finished making their predictions, share them with the class. As each group shares their prediction, make a record of it along with a note about the reasons for their prediction. You may want to make a poster for the classroom with all of the predictions on it. This way you can compare and discuss each group's ideas.

AST 97

Reflect

5 min

Students answer questions about their Earth-Moon models.

△ Guide

Students will work in their groups to answer the questions in the *Reflect* section and then you will lead a discussion using their answers.

1. Students' answers will depend upon their prediction.

2. Students' answers will depend upon their prediction.

3. Students can calculate that, if the diameter of their clay-ball Earth is 5.7 cm, then the model Sun would have a diameter of 6.27 cm, or 6.3 m.

Predict

5 min

Students predict the distance between Earth and the Moon.

Predict

You have created two scale objects showing that the volume of Earth is 49 times greater than the volume of the Moon. Now you will complete your model by determining how far apart your Earth model and Moon model should be.

Start by predicting how far apart the model Earth and model Moon should be in your scale model. Select one set of clay balls made by a member of your group. Work with your group to come to an agreement on how far apart Earth and the Moon should be. Measure and record that distance. Discuss with your group if you think that distance is too small or too large. Adjust the distance if you wish, repeating the measurement if necessary. Be prepared to share your prediction, and the reasons for it, with the class.

△ Guide

Tell students that now that they have modeled the relative sizes of Earth and the Moon, they will model the distance between them relative to their sizes. They will begin by predicting how far the piece of clay modeling the Moon should be from the piece of clay modeling Earth to represent the distance between Earth and the Moon.

Have students work with their groups to decide how far apart the piece of clay modeling Earth and the piece of clay modeling the Moon should be. For each possible distance students discuss, they should discuss the reasons they might choose that distance. Once everyone in a group agrees that the distance in their model is correct, they should measure and record the distance. Emphasize that they will share their predictions.

Communicate: Share Your Ideas

10 min

Groups share their ideas with the class.

Communicate

Share Your Ideas

When each group has finished making their predictions, share them with the class. As each group shares their prediction, make a record of it along with a note about the reasons for their prediction. You may want to make a poster for the classroom with all of the predictions on it. This way you can compare and discuss each group's ideas.

△ Guide

When groups have finished making and recording their predictions, have them share their ideas with the class. They should share their prediction along with their reasons for the prediction. As each group shares their prediction, the rest of the class should record the prediction along with the reasons the group gives for it.

Model the Distance Between Earth and the Moon

You have predicted the distance between Earth and the Moon. Now you will use the model to find the actual scale distance.

Procedure

1. Measure the diameter of your Earth model using a toothpick. Push the toothpick through the clay model of Earth. Try to push the toothpick in so that it passes through the middle of the sphere and a little bit of it is coming out of both sides. Mark the toothpick on each side of the sphere where it touches the sphere.

2. Remove the toothpick and measure between the two marks. This will tell you the diameter of your Earth. Record this measurement to the nearest tenth of a centimeter.

3. To find the actual distance between Earth and the Moon, multiply this distance by 30. Use a meter stick to measure the correct distance from your clay Earth. Place your Moon model at the correct distance from your Earth model.

Reflect

1. How did the correct distance from Earth to the Moon in the scale model compare to the distance you predicted? List reasons why the evidence you used helped your prediction be accurate or led to your prediction being inaccurate.

2. Think about how large the Moon appears in the sky. How does the model help you explain why the Moon is the size that it is?

3. The diameter of the Sun is about 400 times the diameter of the Moon. Yet the Sun and the Moon appear to be about the same size in the sky. How much farther away do you think the Sun must be from Earth than the Moon? Give evidence to support your answer.

4. Use your answer from Question 3 to determine how far away from Earth you would place the Sun in your scale model.

Model the Distance Between Earth and the Moon

5 min

Students model the distance between Earth and the Moon.

△ Guide

Have students begin by measuring the diameter of their Earth model by sticking a toothpick through it, marking where it protrudes from the model, and then measuring the distance between the two marks. Have them record this measurement to the nearest tenth of a centimeter. They should then multiply this measurement by 30 to get the distance between Earth and the Moon. Have them place their Moon model this distance from their Earth model.

Reflect

15 min

Students think about their Earth-Moon models and answer questions with their groups.

Reflect

1. How did the correct distance from Earth to the Moon in the scale model compare to the distance you predicted? List reasons why the evidence you used helped your prediction be accurate or led to your prediction being inaccurate.

2. Think about how large the Moon appears in the sky. How does the model help you explain why the Moon is the size that it is?

3. The diameter of the Sun is about 400 times the diameter of the Moon. Yet the Sun and the Moon appear to be about the same size in the sky. How much farther away do you think the Sun must be from Earth than the Moon? Give evidence to support your answer.

4. Use your answer from Question 3 to determine how far away from Earth you would place the Sun in your scale model.

△ Guide

Have students work with their groups to answer the *Reflect* questions. Then lead a brief class discussion of their responses. Groups should have come up with about the same distance. They should infer that a reduction in the apparent size of an object by 400 times indicates an increase of 400 times the distance. They may be able to use observations from the classroom as evidence of this. If a student stands 10 ft away, her apparent size is half of what it is if she stands 5 ft away. (Holding a ruler a fixed distance from your eyes, you can compare the apparent size of objects.)

1. Students' answers will depend upon their prediction and the evidence they used to make their prediction.

2. Students' answers will vary, but most will say that the great distance between the two bodies makes the Moon appear much smaller than it really is.

3. Students' answers will vary, but some will reason that the Sun must be about 400 times as far away as the Moon. Their evidence might be that their thumb covers only half as much when held twice as far from their eye.

4. Students can calculate that if the scale-model Moon is 1.71 m (5.6 ft) from Earth, the Sun must be 400 times as far, or about 684 m (2244 ft) from Earth. This is not quite 0.5 mi.

NOTES

....

....

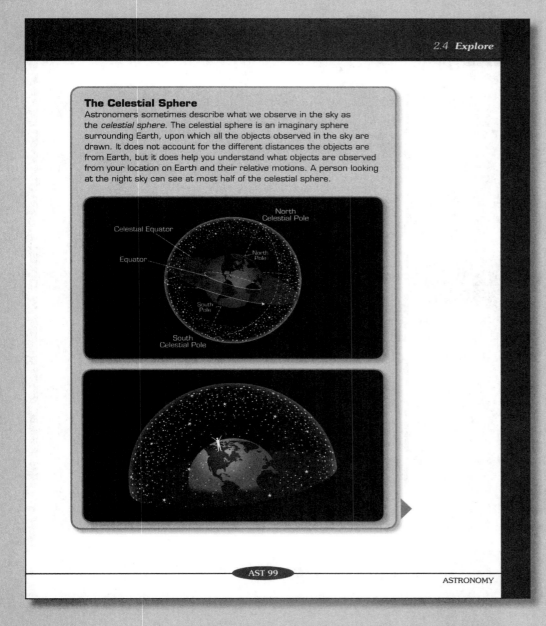

The Celestial Sphere

Astronomers sometimes describe what we observe in the sky as the *celestial sphere*. The celestial sphere is an imaginary sphere surrounding Earth, upon which all the objects observed in the sky are drawn. It does not account for the different distances the objects are from Earth, but it does help you understand what objects are observed from your location on Earth and their relative motions. A person looking at the night sky can see at most half of the celestial sphere.

AST 99

ASTRONOMY

The Celestial Sphere

5 min

Students are introduced to the celestial sphere.

△ Guide

Introduce the concept of the celestial sphere. Guide students to understand that the celestial sphere is an imaginary sphere surrounding Earth, and all the objects we observe in the sky can be imagined to lie on the celestial sphere. The celestial sphere is useful for navigating the sky seen from Earth's surface. Only half of the celestial sphere is visible to a given observer at a time.

Because the stars in the sky do not appear to move with respect to each other, they can be used as a fixed background.

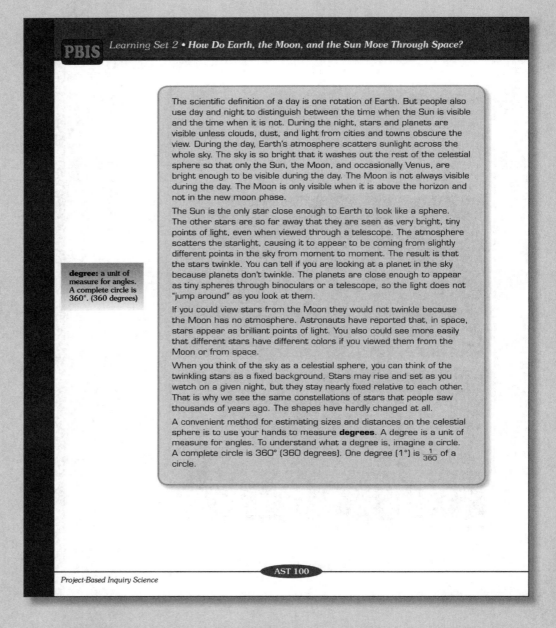

The scientific definition of a day is one rotation of Earth. But people also use day and night to distinguish between the time when the Sun is visible and the time when it is not. During the night, stars and planets are visible unless clouds, dust, and light from cities and towns obscure the view. During the day, Earth's atmosphere scatters sunlight across the whole sky. The sky is so bright that it washes out the rest of the celestial sphere so that only the Sun, the Moon, and occasionally Venus, are bright enough to be visible during the day. The Moon is not always visible during the day. The Moon is only visible when it is above the horizon and not in the new moon phase.

The Sun is the only star close enough to Earth to look like a sphere. The other stars are so far away that they are seen as very bright, tiny points of light, even when viewed through a telescope. The atmosphere scatters the starlight, causing it to appear to be coming from slightly different points in the sky from moment to moment. The result is that the stars twinkle. You can tell if you are looking at a planet in the sky because planets don't twinkle. The planets are close enough to appear as tiny spheres through binoculars or a telescope, so the light does not "jump around" as you look at them.

degree: a unit of measure for angles. A complete circle is 360°. (360 degrees)

If you could view stars from the Moon they would not twinkle because the Moon has no atmosphere. Astronauts have reported that, in space, stars appear as brilliant points of light. You also could see more easily that different stars have different colors if you viewed them from the Moon or from space.

When you think of the sky as a celestial sphere, you can think of the twinkling stars as a fixed background. Stars may rise and set as you watch on a given night, but they stay nearly fixed relative to each other. That is why we see the same constellations of stars that people saw thousands of years ago. The shapes have hardly changed at all.

A convenient method for estimating sizes and distances on the celestial sphere is to use your hands to measure **degrees**. A degree is a unit of measure for angles. To understand what a degree is, imagine a circle. A complete circle is 360° (360 degrees). One degree (1°) is $\frac{1}{360}$ of a circle.

AST 100

Project-Based Inquiry Science

Discuss how distances on the celestial sphere can be measured in degrees. Because the celestial sphere is imaginary, these are not real distances. They are angles, with the observer at the vertex of each angle and the rays of each angle passing through objects on the celestial sphere. Just as with a geometric circle, a complete rotation around the celestial sphere has 360°.

The width of your fist, held at arm's length, covers about 10° of the sky. Your thumb, also held at arm's length, covers about 2°, and your pinky finger covers about 1°. You can practice estimating with hand measurements by starting with something familiar. Hold your fist out in front of you at arm's length, pointing to the horizon. Place your other fist, also at arm's length, on top of your first fist. Alternate fists until you have gone nine fists up from the horizon, which would equal 90°. The last fist you make should be pointing straight up. This is because one quarter of a circle is equal to 90° (360° divided by 4).

Try measuring a familiar object in the night sky, such as the Big Dipper. The Big Dipper should be about twice the width of a fist held at arm's length, or 20°. Once you are comfortable with the technique, use it to estimate the width of the Moon. Think about how the Moon's size might compare with the size of the Sun. At sunset, without looking directly at the Sun, you can safely estimate the width of the Sun by blocking its light.

Never look at the Sun. It is very dangerous to look directly at the Sun.

Tell students they can use their hands to measure distances on the celestial sphere in degrees. The width of a fist held at arm's length covers about 10° of the sky. A thumb measures about 2° and a pinky finger measures about 1°. Students can use this method to measure the Big Dipper or the Moon.

What's the Point?

The diameter of the Sun is about 110 times the diameter of Earth, and Earth is a little less than four times the diameter of the Moon. The distance between Earth and the Moon is about 30 times Earth's diameter. The distance from Earth to the Sun is about 400 times the distance from Earth to the Moon. From our perspective, Earth seems very large. However, it is very small compared to the size of the Sun. When you consider the distance from Earth to the Sun, you will realize how much larger the Sun is than it appears when observed from Earth.

The celestial sphere is the appearance of the sky from Earth. The stars can be considered points fixed relative to one another on the celestial sphere. Viewed against this background, the Sun and the Moon appear to be the same size, about one half a degree in diameter. Yet, the size of the Sun and the Moon are very different from each other, and they are very different distances from Earth.

With advanced space exploration technology on Earth and in satellites, astronomers can further their understanding of distant objects in space.

AST 102

NOTES

....

How Do the Sizes of Earth and the Moon Compare, and How Far Apart Are They?

2.4

Assessment Options

Targeted Concepts, Skills, and Nature of Science	How do I know if students got it?
Scientists often collaborate and share their findings. Sharing findings makes new information available and helps scientists refine their ideas and build on others' ideas. When another person's or group's idea is used, credit needs to be given.	**ASK:** Which group did you think gave the strongest supporting evidence and most logical reasoning for their prediction? Did any of the supporting evidence or reasoning shared by other groups cause you to reconsider your own ideas? Why or why not? **LISTEN:** Students' answers will vary. The purpose of this question is to elicit self-evaluation and evaluation of the ideas shared by other groups.
Scientists must keep clear, accurate, and descriptive records of what they do so they can share their work with others; consider what they did, why they did it, and what they want to do next.	**ASK:** How did you organize the observations, measurements, and calculations to make it easier for you to share your work with others? **LISTEN:** Students' answers should describe their use of tables, charts, and diagrams.
Models are a representation of something in the world. Simulations use a model to imitate, or act out, real-life situations.	**ASK:** Why would it be difficult to create a scale model of the Sun using clay? **LISTEN:** Students should recognize that the Sun is 400 times the diameter of Earth and a ball of clay representing the Sun to scale would impossible to make. **ASK:** How can you determine a model's scale? **LISTEN:** Students should describe how they determine scale by determining the ratio between actual distance and distance in the model.

Targeted Concepts, Skills, and Nature of Science	How do I know if students got it?
Earth's Sun is the central and largest body in our solar system. The Sun is more than a million times greater in volume than Earth. Earth is the third planet from the Sun in a system that includes other planets and their moons, as well as smaller objects, such as asteroids and comets.	**ASK:** The equation for calculating the volume of a sphere is: $$V_{sphere} = \frac{4}{3} \pi r^3$$ How much greater than Earth's volume is the Sun's volume? **LISTEN:** Students should state that the Sun's volume is about 800,000 times greater than Earth's volume.

Teacher Reflection Questions

- What classroom management issues did you face in carrying out this investigation? How could you improve these when doing this investigation with other classes?

- How does creating a model of the Earth-Moon-Sun system set the stage for the focus of the next section of this *Learning Set?*

- What naïve or preconceived science concepts about the Moon and Earth have come up in class discussions? Where during the Unit might you challenge some of these conceptions?

NOTES

....

....

....

....

2.5 Explore

What Do Eclipses Tell You About Distances to the Sun and the Moon?

◀ **1 class period**

A class period is considered to be one 40 to 50 minute class.

Overview

The section opens with a reading that introduces the concept of an eclipse and describes the conditions that result in solar and lunar eclipses. Students then simulate a solar eclipse using a model of the Earth-Moon-Sun system. After considering the size of the Moon's shadow on Earth and the relative positions of the Earth, Moon, and Sun during a solar eclipse, students read a detailed description of the Sun. Students use their model of the Earth-Moon-Sun system to simulate a lunar eclipse and consider the time of day and phase of the Moon during which lunar eclipses occur. A series of *Reflect* questions guide students to compare and contrast solar and lunar eclipses. Students then read about the causes of tides and their relationship to the relative positions and motions of the Earth, Moon and Sun.

Targeted Concepts, Skills, and Nature of Science	Performance Expectations
Scientists often collaborate and share their findings. Sharing findings makes new information available and helps scientists refine their ideas and build on others' ideas. When another person's or group's idea is used, credit needs to be given.	Students share and discuss their answers to the *Stop and Think* and *Reflect* questions and evaluate their answers based on information shared by others.
Scientists must keep clear, accurate, and descriptive records of what they do so they can share their work with others; consider what they did, why they did it, and what they want to do next.	Students record the relative positions of the Earth, Moon and Sun in their models that resulted in successful simulations of solar and lunar eclipses. Students record detailed notes during their readings and their answers to the *Stop and Think* and *Reflect* questions.

Targeted Concepts, Skills, and Nature of Science	Performance Expectations
Most objects in the solar system have a regular and predictable motion. These motions explain such phenomena as a day, a year, phases of the Moon, eclipses, tides, meteor showers, and comets.	Students simulate the motions of the Earth-Moon-Sun system and predict the relative positions of Earth, the Moon, and Sun during solar and lunar eclipses.
An eclipse of the Moon occurs when the Moon enters Earth's shadow. An eclipse of the Sun occurs when the Moon is between Earth and the Sun, and the Moon's shadow falls on Earth.	Students simulate solar and lunar eclipses and identify the shadows cast by one object on another during each type of eclipse.
Tides, or the cyclic rise and fall of ocean waters, are caused by the gravitational pulls of the Moon and (to a lesser extent) the Sun, as well as the rotation of Earth.	Students define tides and describe how they are caused by the gravitational attraction of the Moon and Sun on a rotating Earth.

Materials	
1 per class	Strong light source
1 per group	Globe, mounted on axis that can rotate
1 per student	White plastic foam ball Thin wooden dowel

Activity Setup and Preparation

The setup for this activity is the same as in *Section 2.4*. Using the same process as last time, decide where to best position the light source in the classroom for students to use. Also decide beforehand how to distribute materials.

NOTES

....

....

....

Homework Options

Reflection

- **Science Content:** Why do you think total lunar eclipses generally last longer than total solar eclipses to an observer on Earth? *(Students should answer that Earth's shadow is larger than the Moon's shadow, therefore it takes longer for the Moon to pass through Earth's shadow during a total lunar eclipse than it takes the Moon's shadow to pass over an observer during a total solar eclipse.)*

- **Science Content:** Why do we not see a total lunar eclipse every time the Moon is at the full moon phase? *(Students should answer that because the Moon's orbit is tilted relative to the Earth's orbit around the Sun.)*

- **Science Process:** What would you need to know to calculate how long a total solar eclipse will be visible to an observer on Earth that passes directly through the center of the Moon's shadow on Earth? *(Students should identify that they would need to know the diameter of the Moon's shadow and the speed at which Earth's surface is rotating at the observer's location.)*

- **Science Process:** A student wants to build a mechanical model of the Earth-Moon-Sun system that uses gears to move the objects in the model. Based on what you have read, what motions must the gears produce in the model and what must the rates of those motions be in order to accurately represent the Earth-Moon-Sun system? *(Students should describe how the model Earth must rotate on its axis as it revolves around the model Sun The model Moon must rotate on its axis as it revolves around the revolving and rotating Earth. The model Earth must rotate 365.25 times during every revolution around the Sun. The Moon must rotate on its axis once every 27 Earth rotations and revolve around the revolving and rotating Earth so that it aligns with the Earth and Sun every 29.5 Earth rotations.)*

Preparation for 2.BBQ

- **Science Content:** Why is it unlikely that Earth, the Moon, or Sun will collide with one another? *(Students should respond that this collision would be unlikely because they move in nearly circular orbits around one another.)*

NOTES

....

....

....

....

....

....

....

....

....

....

....

....

....

....

....

....

SECTION 2.5 IMPLEMENTATION

2.5 Explore

What Do Eclipses Tell You About Distances to the Sun and the Moon?

In the year 585 B.C.E., in what is now Iran, two armies had been at war with each other for five years. One day, as they were engaged in battle, suddenly "the day was turned into night." The armies saw it as a sign to stop fighting immediately. Although the Sun soon reappeared, a treaty was signed, and the war was over.

This event, reported by the Greek historian Herodotus, may very well have been an **eclipse**. Eclipse means to cut off or block a view. An eclipse occurs when an object in space partially or totally blocks the light by which we see another object in space. Two types of eclipses are **solar eclipses** and **lunar eclipses**. In a solar eclipse, the Moon blocks our view of the Sun. In a lunar eclipse, the Moon moves into Earth's shadow, so the Moon is no longer seen by reflected sunlight.

In the last section, you discovered that the Sun and the Moon appear to be about the same size in the sky. This is an interesting coincidence, because it means that both objects can have a **total eclipse**. A total eclipse happens when one space object totally blocks the light by which we see another object in space. Sometimes an eclipse is partial. In a **partial eclipse**, only part of a space object disappears from view.

During a total solar eclipse, the Moon passes between the Sun and Earth, so Earth becomes dark. At any single location on Earth, total solar eclipses occur rarely, about once every 370 years.

eclipse: the blocking of light from one object in space by another object in space, as seen from a particular location.

solar eclipse: when the Moon passes between the Sun and Earth, so that light from the Sun is partially or totally blocked.

lunar eclipse: when the Moon passes through Earth's shadow so that some or all of the Moon can only be seen by reflected light from Earth.

total eclipse: the complete blocking of light from one object in space by another object in space, as seen from a particular location.

partial eclipse: the blocking of a portion of light from one object in space by another object in space, as seen from a particular location.

AST 103

ASTRONOMY

2.5 Explore

What Do Eclipses Tell You About Distances to the Sun and the Moon?

5 min

Students are introduced to the concept of eclipses.

△ Guide

Begin by introducing the concepts of lunar and solar eclipses using the historical example of solar eclipse in the student text. During a battle between the Lydians and the Medes, the Sun disappeared and "the day was turned into night." Ask students if they can explain what probably happened to the Sun. Tell students that this was an example of a solar eclipse, when another object in the solar system, the Moon, blocked the Sun. Another type of eclipse is a lunar eclipse, in which Earth's shadow darkens the Moon, making it invisible.

*A class period is considered to be one 40 to 50 minute class.

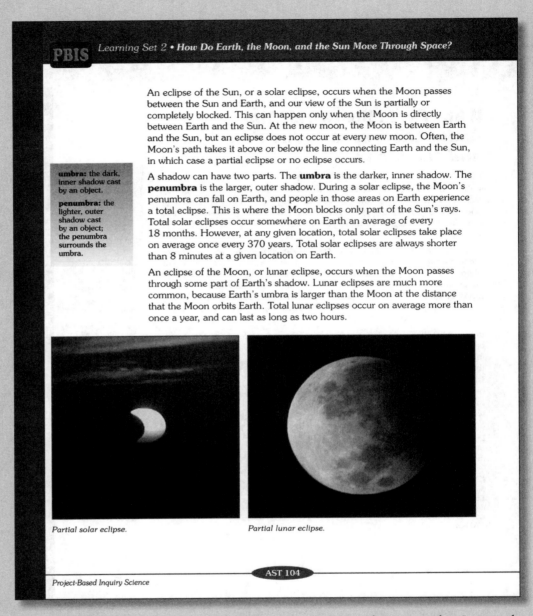

An eclipse of the Sun, or a solar eclipse, occurs when the Moon passes between the Sun and Earth, and our view of the Sun is partially or completely blocked. This can happen only when the Moon is directly between Earth and the Sun. At the new moon, the Moon is between Earth and the Sun, but an eclipse does not occur at every new moon. Often, the Moon's path takes it above or below the line connecting Earth and the Sun, in which case a partial eclipse or no eclipse occurs.

umbra: the dark, inner shadow cast by an object.

penumbra: the lighter, outer shadow cast by an object; the penumbra surrounds the umbra.

A shadow can have two parts. The **umbra** is the darker, inner shadow. The **penumbra** is the larger, outer shadow. During a solar eclipse, the Moon's penumbra can fall on Earth, and people in those areas on Earth experience a total eclipse. This is where the Moon blocks only part of the Sun's rays. Total solar eclipses occur somewhere on Earth an average of every 18 months. However, at any given location, total solar eclipses take place on average once every 370 years. Total solar eclipses are always shorter than 8 minutes at a given location on Earth.

An eclipse of the Moon, or lunar eclipse, occurs when the Moon passes through some part of Earth's shadow. Lunar eclipses are much more common, because Earth's umbra is larger than the Moon at the distance that the Moon orbits Earth. Total lunar eclipses occur on average more than once a year, and can last as long as two hours.

Partial solar eclipse.

Partial lunar eclipse.

AST 104

An eclipse of the Sun occurs when the Moon passes between the Sun and Earth, blocking the Sun from the view of some people on Earth. This occurs only when the Moon passes directly between the Sun and Earth. Even though the Moon is roughly between the Sun and Earth at a new moon, this does not usually cause an eclipse.

To people in the Moon's umbra, or the darkest part of its shadow, none of the Sun will be visible. To people in the Moon's penumbra, or the outskirts of its shadow, part of the Sun will be visible. An eclipse of the Sun occurs when the Moon passes through Earth's shadow. Emphasize that lunar eclipses are much more common than solar eclipses.

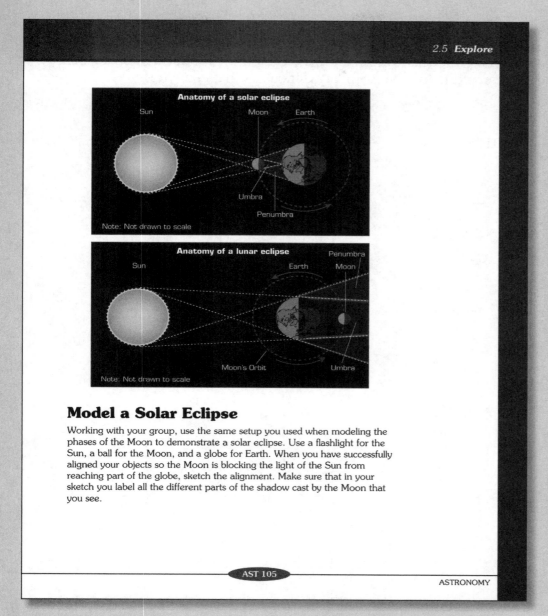

Anatomy of a solar eclipse

Sun   Moon   Earth

Umbra

Penumbra

Note: Not drawn to scale

Anatomy of a lunar eclipse   Penumbra

Sun   Earth   Moon

Moon's Orbit   Umbra

Note: Not drawn to scale

Model a Solar Eclipse

Working with your group, use the same setup you used when modeling the phases of the Moon to demonstrate a solar eclipse. Use a flashlight for the Sun, a ball for the Moon, and a globe for Earth. When you have successfully aligned your objects so the Moon is blocking the light of the Sun from reaching part of the globe, sketch the alignment. Make sure that in your sketch you label all the different parts of the shadow cast by the Moon that you see.

AST 105

ASTRONOMY

Model a Solar Eclipse

10 min

Students model a solar eclipse.

△ Guide

Distribute materials and tell students they will now model a solar eclipse using the same setup from their investigations in *Section 2.4*. They should align the flashlight, foam ball, and globe so the foam ball casts a shadow on the globe. Then they should make a sketch showing the alignment of the objects and the shadow and label the parts of the shadow in their sketch.

Then have groups model an eclipse. Emphasize that when they have successfully modeled an eclipse, they should sketch the alignment and label the parts of the shadow. As groups work on their models, monitor their progress and help them with any difficulties that come up.

NOTES

_____

_____

_____

_____

_____

_____

_____

_____

_____

_____

_____

_____

_____

_____

Stop and Think

Use your sketch to answer the following questions:

1. How much of Earth do you think can be covered by the shadow of the Moon? Why do you think this?

2. During what phase of the Moon can a solar eclipse occur? How much of the Moon is visible during a solar eclipse?

fusion reaction: a change in which one or more low-mass elements produces a higher-mass element, with a release of enormous amounts of energy.

corona: outer portion of the Sun's atmosphere, consisting of superheated gases.

The Sun

Like all stars, the Sun is a hot ball composed mostly of hydrogen and helium. Its temperature is about 5700°C at its surface. This seems pretty hot, until you learn that at the center of the Sun, the temperature is nearly 14,000,000°C! This is hot enough to smash together two hydrogen atoms to form a helium atom. This is called a **fusion reaction**, and it releases the energy that life on Earth needs to survive.

The Sun also has an atmosphere, part of which is called the **corona**. The corona is composed of superheated gases. Normally, the surface of the Sun is so bright that the dimmer corona usually cannot be seen from Earth. But during a total solar eclipse, the corona is visible as a band of hot gas that surrounds the darkened disk of the Sun.

Looking at the Sun, even through most filters, can severely damage your eyes and even cause blindness. Scientists use other means to observe the Sun's disk, such as using special filters and mirrors to observe a projection of the Sun on a screen. If you observe such an image over a period of time, you will discover that the Sun's appearance changes from day to day. Like the Moon, the Sun's appearance can change, but the Sun's changes are more difficult to observe.

AST 106

Project-Based Inquiry Science

Stop and Think

5 min

Students answer the questions about their model eclipses.

△ Guide

Have students work with their groups to answer the *Stop and Think* questions. Then lead a brief class discussion of their responses. Students should think about the relative sizes of the Moon and Earth and the distances between the Sun, the Moon, and Earth. Because the Moon is much smaller than Earth and is much closer to Earth than to the Sun, its shadow cannot cover a large portion of Earth. Students should use what they learned from the Moon-phases model to answer the second question. Because the Moon must be between the Sun and Earth, this can happen only during the new moon.

1. Students' answers will vary, but most will realize that being smaller than Earth, the Moon can only cover a small portion of the Earth with its shadow.

2. Students should recognize that a solar eclipse can only occur at the new moon phase and that none of the Moon is visible, because there is no reflected light from the Sun. The Moon is visible from reflected Earth-light.

The Sun

5 min

Students read about the composition of the Sun.

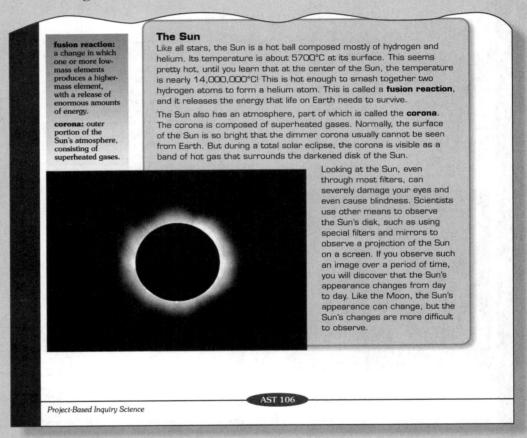

fusion reaction: a change in which one or more low-mass elements produces a higher-mass element, with a release of enormous amounts of energy.

corona: outer portion of the Sun's atmosphere, consisting of superheated gases.

The Sun

Like all stars, the Sun is a hot ball composed mostly of hydrogen and helium. Its temperature is about 5700°C at its surface. This seems pretty hot, until you learn that at the center of the Sun, the temperature is nearly 14,000,000°C! This is hot enough to smash together two hydrogen atoms to form a helium atom. This is called a **fusion reaction**, and it releases the energy that life on Earth needs to survive.

The Sun also has an atmosphere, part of which is called the **corona**. The corona is composed of superheated gases. Normally, the surface of the Sun is so bright that the dimmer corona usually cannot be seen from Earth. But during a total solar eclipse, the corona is visible as a band of hot gas that surrounds the darkened disk of the Sun.

Looking at the Sun, even through most filters, can severely damage your eyes and even cause blindness. Scientists use other means to observe the Sun's disk, such as using special filters and mirrors to observe a projection of the Sun on a screen. If you observe such an image over a period of time, you will discover that the Sun's appearance changes from day to day. Like the Moon, the Sun's appearance can change, but the Sun's changes are more difficult to observe.

AST 106

Project-Based Inquiry Science

△ Guide

Briefly discuss the composition of the Sun. Like other stars, the Sun is composed mostly of hydrogen and helium. Energy is released by fusion reactions in the center of the Sun. The temperature at the center is nearly 14,000,000 °C, while at the surface, the temperature is about 5700 °C.

The Sun's atmosphere includes a band of hot gases, called the *corona,* that can be seen around the edges of the darkened disk during a total solar eclipse.

The Sun's image contains dark spots called sunspots. These spots are still very bright; they look dark only in comparison to the rest of the Sun. Sunspots rotate around the Sun, which shows that the Sun also rotates on an axis, much like Earth and the Moon.

An active sunspot viewed sideways.

Model a Lunar Eclipse

Work with your group, and use the setup from the phases of the Moon activity to model a lunar eclipse. When you have successfully aligned the Sun, Earth, and the Moon to form a total lunar eclipse, make a drawing. Make sure you label the umbra and penumbra in your drawing.

AST 107

ASTRONOMY

Tell students that the Sun's appearance constantly changes. Unfortunately, because it is dangerous to look at the Sun, these changes are difficult to observe. By using special equipment, including filters and mirrors, scientists are able to observe these changes. The surface of the Sun is marked by sunspots that rotate around the Sun, showing that the Sun rotates on an axis, just like Earth and the Moon. Emphasize that you should not look at the Sun because it can damage your eyes.

Model a Lunar Eclipse

5 min

Students use their models to make a lunar eclipse.

Model a Lunar Eclipse

Work with your group, and use the setup from the phases of the Moon activity to model a lunar eclipse. When you have successfully aligned the Sun, Earth, and the Moon to form a total lunar eclipse, make a drawing. Make sure you label the umbra and penumbra in your drawing.

△ Guide

Distribute materials, if necessary, and have students model a lunar eclipse with a flashlight, foam ball, and globe. Have them sketch the alignment and the shadow when they have successfully modeled the eclipse, labeling the umbra and penumbra in their sketch.

NOTES

Stop and Think

Use your drawing to answer the following questions:

1. During what phase of the Moon can a lunar eclipse occur? What part of the Moon, if any, can be seen during a lunar eclipse?

2. Can a lunar eclipse occur at night? Why or why not?

3. From where on Earth might a lunar eclipse be visible?

Reflect

1. What would someone on the Moon see when facing Earth during a total solar eclipse on Earth? Why?

2. What would happen to the number and length of lunar and solar eclipses if the Moon were twice the diameter that it actually is?

3. Some people have trouble remembering the correct term for the two types of eclipses. What is a good way to remember the difference that you can teach to a friend?

4. Why do people rarely see a total solar eclipse, while many people have seen a total lunar eclipse?

What's the Point?

During the new moon, a solar eclipse may occur. If the Moon passes directly between the Sun and Earth, the shadow of the Moon falls on Earth and our view of the Sun is partially or completely blocked. A lunar eclipse may occur only at the full moon. Earth's shadow falls on the Moon.

Just a narrow sliver of the full moon is visible during this lunar eclipse.

Stop and Think

5 min

Students answer questions about eclipses.

△ Guide

When groups have modeled lunar eclipses, have them answer the *Stop and Think* questions. Then lead a brief class discussion of their responses. Students should use what they learned from their models of Moon phases to determine in which phase a lunar eclipse can occur. Because the Moon must be on the side of Earth opposite the Sun, a lunar eclipse must occur during the full moon.

1. Students should recognize that a lunar eclipse can only occur at full moon when the Sun is opposite the Moon. The Moon cannot be seen during a lunar eclipse.

2. Students should respond that a lunar eclipse can only occur at night and only at full moon. This is because the Sun and the Moon must be on opposite sides of the Earth.

3. Students should reply that a lunar eclipse can only be seen on the night side of the Earth.

Reflect

10 min

The class answers questions, gaining further understanding into eclipses.

Reflect

1. What would someone on the Moon see when facing Earth during a total solar eclipse on Earth? Why?

2. What would happen to the number and length of lunar and solar eclipses if the Moon were twice the diameter that it actually is?

3. Some people have trouble remembering the correct term for the two types of eclipses. What is a good way to remember the difference that you can teach to a friend?

4. Why do people rarely see a total solar eclipse, while many people have seen a total lunar eclipse?

△ Guide and Assess

Lead a class discussion of the *Reflect* questions. Look for signs that students understand how the relative positions and sizes of Earth, the Sun, and the Moon determine how eclipses are experienced on Earth.

1. Students should understand that a solar eclipse is a shadow cast on Earth's surface that does not cover the entire surface. Therefore, an observer on the Moon would see a disk-shaped shadow on part of Earth's surface.

2. Students also should understand that if the Moon were twice its actual diameter, the frequency and length of both lunar and solar eclipses would change. Partial lunar eclipses would occur more frequently, because Earth would more frequently pass in front of some portion of the enlarged Moon. But total lunar eclipses would occur less frequently. Solar eclipses would occur more frequently, because the Moon would occupy a greater portion of the daytime sky.

3. Students' answers will vary.

4. Students may remember that there are many more lunar eclipses than solar eclipses. Also, Earth is much larger than the Moon and so it is more likely that the entire disk of the Moon is covered.

More to Learn

How Are Tides Caused by Gravity of the Sun and the Moon?

Earth and the other planets are kept in orbit around the Sun by the Sun's gravity. Any two objects pull on each other because of the force of gravity. The more massive an object is, the greater the force of gravity pulls on another object. The Sun is much more massive than Earth, so Earth is prevented from moving off into space and is instead pulled into orbit around the Sun. In the same way, the Moon is pulled into orbit around Earth because Earth is much more massive than the Moon.

However, the Moon's gravity does have an effect on Earth. If you live near the ocean, or if you have visited the seashore, you know that the line where the water reaches the shore changes dramatically throughout the day. **Tides** are the rise and fall of water in the oceans. There can be two high tides and two low tides in a 24-hour period, with the highest and lowest levels occurring about every 6 hours.

Tides are caused by the gravitational attraction between Earth and the Moon. The Moon's gravity distorts the sea level so that the sea is slightly higher on the side of Earth closer to the Moon and also on the side farther from the Moon. As Earth spins on its axis, the part of Earth that faces the Moon changes. When a location is oriented so that it faces toward the Moon, or opposite the Moon, the bulge of water is at its highest point, and there is a **high tide**. Between the two bulges are low areas, because water has been pulled away to form the bulge. A location in one of these low areas has a **low tide**.

At any given location on Earth, there can be two high tides and two low tides in a 24-hour period. However, because the Moon takes 24 hours and 50 minutes to return to the same position above a given location, high tides and low tides occur about 50 minutes later each day. For example, if high tide at a location is at 10:00 AM one day, it will be at 10:50 AM the next day.

tide: the rise and fall of the surface level of a body of water due to the Moon's and the Sun's gravitational pull.

high tide: the time, for a certain location, when the tide is at its highest point.

low tide: the time, for a certain location, when the tide is at its lowest point.

More to Learn: *How Are Tides Caused by Gravity of the Sun and the Moon?*

5 min

Students learn about tides.

△ Guide

Either assign the *More to Learn* for homework, or briefly discuss tides in class. Discuss how the same gravitational pull that is responsible for holding objects in orbit is responsible for tides. All objects have a gravitational pull, and the larger the object, the larger the pull. Earth orbits the Sun because the Sun has a larger gravitational pull, and the Moon orbits Earth because Earth has a larger gravitational pull.

High tide on left, low tide on right. Each occurs twice in a 24-hour period.

The Sun also has an influence on tides. Even though the Sun is farther away, it has much more mass than the Moon. If the Sun and the Moon are pulling in the same direction on Earth, when the three bodies are in a line, then the tides are stronger. If the Sun is pulling on Earth at a right angle from the Moon, then the tides are weaker.

Earth

Moon

Gravitational attraction

However, the Moon's gravitational pull is great enough to cause tides in the ocean. At the part of Earth facing the Moon, there is a bulge in the water. The highest point in this bulge is high tide. There is also a bulge on the opposite side of Earth. Between these two bulges, the water is at a lower point, known as low tide.

The Sun also influences the tides, and the bulges are highest when the Sun, the Moon, and Earth are in a line. They are lowest when the Sun is at a right angle from the Moon.

Assessment Options

Targeted Concepts, Skills, and Nature of Science	How do I know if students got it?
Scientists often collaborate and share their findings. Sharing findings makes new information available and helps scientists refine their ideas and build on others' ideas. When another person's or group's idea is used, credit needs to be given.	**ASK:** Which answers shared by others in your class were the same and which were different from your own? What evidence shared by others convinced you to change an answer you had given? **LISTEN:** Students' answers will vary. The purpose of this question is to engage students in an evaluating answers based on supporting evidence.
Scientists must keep clear, accurate, and descriptive records of what they do so they can share their work with others; consider what they did, why they did it, and what they want to do next.	**ASK:** What do you think is the most effective way to record information about the eclipses you simulated using your model of the Earth-Moon-Sun system? **LISTEN:** Students' answers will vary. Students should recognize that in this case, diagrams are an effective way to record information.
Most objects in the solar system have a regular and predictable motion. These motions explain such phenomena as a day, a year, phases of the Moon, eclipses, tides, meteor showers, and comets.	**ASK:** During which phases of the moon can lunar and solar eclipses occur? **LISTEN:** Students should answer that solar eclipses can occur during the new moon phase and lunar eclipses can occur during the full moon phase.

NOTES

....

....

Targeted Concepts, Skills, and Nature of Science	How do I know if students got it?
An eclipse of the Moon occurs when the Moon enters Earth's shadow. An eclipse of the Sun occurs when the Moon is between the Earth and Sun, and the Moon's shadow falls on Earth.	**ASK:** How do the shadows of Earth and the Moon compare? **LISTEN:** Students should describe how Earth's shadow is larger and extends farther into space than the Moon's shadow. **ASK:** Why is it not possible for a solar eclipse to be visible everywhere on Earth? **LISTEN:** Students should answer that a solar eclipse is only visible if an observer is on the side of Earth facing the Sun at the time of the eclipse and the Moon's shadow is much smaller than Earth, and a solar eclipse is only visible within that small shadow.
Tides, or the cyclic rise and fall of ocean waters, are caused by the gravitational pulls of the Moon and (to a lesser extent) the Sun, as well as the rotation of Earth.	**ASK::** Identify the two objects whose gravitational pull causes tides on Earth. **LISTEN:** Students should identify the Sun and the Moon. **ASK:** The Sun is much more massive than the Moon. Why does the gravitational pull of the Moon have a greater effect on Earth's tides than the gravitational pull of the Sun? **LISTEN::** Students should understand that gravitational pull is directly related to mass, but it is inversely proportional to the square of the distance between two objects. Therefore, gravity decreases quickly with distance. The Sun's gravitational pull on Earth is weaker than the Moon's, because the Sun is much farther from Earth than the Moon.

Teacher Reflection Questions

- In this section, students were introduced to new information in several readings. What formative assessments did you use with the students to identify what they have learned?

- How much understanding of the distinction between an umbral eclipse and a penumbral eclipse was evident in class discussions? How could you make this distinction clearer to students?

- In what ways did interspersing the reading selections in this section amid the activities make for a more effective approach toward learning?

NOTES

....

....

....

....

....

....

....

....

....

....

....

NOTES

Back to the Big Question

How Can You Know if Objects in Space Will Collide?

◀ *1 class period*

A class period is considered to be one 40 to 50 minute class.

Overview

The section opens with a brief summary of the interactions and motions of the Earth-Moon-Sun system that were the focus of this *Learning Set*. Students update the information on the *Solar System* page begun earlier in the *Learning Set*. The class views a video describing the impact theory of the Moon's formation. Then students meet in small groups and, guided by a series of *Reflect* questions, discuss the ideas and evidence presented in the video. Each group then shares their answers to the *Reflect* questions and the class evaluates their answers. After reaching consensus on the best answers, the class records these answers on a poster. Students apply what they have learned about gravity and Earth's motions to revise their explanation of whether the object they researched at the end of *Learning Set 1* will collide with Earth. Students then collaborate with others who researched the same object to reach a consensus on an explanation for whether that object will collide with Earth. After groups have shared their explanations with the class, the class updates the *Project Board*.

Targeted Concepts, Skills, and Nature of Science	Performance Expectations
Scientists often collaborate and share their findings. Sharing findings makes new information available and helps scientists refine their ideas and build on others' ideas. When another person's or group's idea is used, credit needs to be given.	Students share and discuss their answers to *Reflect* questions with the class, and the class collaborates to reach consensus on the best answers to the questions.
	Students collaborate with others who researched the same solar system object at the end of *Learning Set 1* to reach consensus on an explanation of whether that object will collide with Earth.

Targeted Concepts, Skills, and Nature of Science	Performance Expectations
Scientists must keep clear, accurate, and descriptive records of what they do so they can share their work with others; consider what they did, why they did it, and what they want to do next.	Students record their answers to the *Reflect* questions about the video describing the impact theory of the Moon's formation. Students record information about the Earth-Moon-Sun system on their *Solar System* page and on the *Project Board*.
Explanations are claims supported by evidence. Evidence can be experimental results, observational data, and any other accepted scientific knowledge	Students can identify the evidence supporting the claim that the Moon formed as a result of a collision between Earth and an object from space. Students revise their earlier explanation of whether the solar system object they researched at the end of *Learning Set 1* will collide with Earth.
Most objects in the solar system have a regular and predictable motion. These motions explain such phenomena as a day, a year, phases of the Moon, eclipses, tides, meteor showers, and comets.	Students recognize that the motions of the Earth-Moon-Sun system make it unlikely that these objects will collide with one another.

Materials

1 per student	*Create Your Explanation* page
1 per class	*Moon Theory* video Class *Project Board*

NOTES

....

....

....

....

Homework Options

Practice and Review

- **Science Content:** Construct a labeled diagram showing the orbits of Earth around the Sun and the Moon around Earth. *(Students' answers will vary, but should show Earth's orbit as a near circle around the Sun and the Moon's orbit as a near circle around Earth. Earth, Moon, Sun and the orbits should be labeled.)*

- **Science Content:** Why must the Moon revolve more than 360° around Earth between one new moon phase and the next? *(In the time it takes the Moon to make one revolution around Earth, Earth has revolved around the Sun and is in a different position in its orbit. Therefore, the Moon must revolve farther around Earth to align with Earth and the Sun.)*

- **Science Content:** Draw a labeled diagram showing the position of the high tides on Earth at the new moon and first quarter moon phases. *(Students' diagrams should show high tides aligned with the Moon at each phase.)*

- **Science Process:** How is the *Project Board* helpful to our search for answers to the *Big Question? (Students should cite examples of how the* Project Board *serves as a vehicle for sharing ideas, keeping track of what they have learned, and seeing what they are doing in a larger context.)*

- **Science Process:** Look back at the notes and diagrams you made during this *Learning Set.* If someone else looked at your notes and diagrams, how closely would their understanding of what you read and their mental image of what you observed match what you actually read and observed? *(Students should be able to identify details missing in their notes and diagrams and recognize ways in which their recording of observations could be improved.)*

NOTES

....

....

....

NOTES

BACK TO THE BIG QUESTION IMPLEMENTATION

Learning Set 2

Back to the Big Question

How can you know if objects in space will collide?

In this *Learning Set,* you explored how Earth, the Moon, and the Sun interact. You learned that the Moon orbits Earth and Earth orbits the Sun. These orbits are predictable, so the location of each object in the solar system can be known to a high degree of accuracy. At the same time, each object is spinning on its axis. Because the rate that each object is spinning is also known, the way each object is oriented in space is also known to a high degree of accuracy.

By understanding the interactions and motions of the Earth-Moon-Sun system, you have an important building block in place for understanding the entire solar system. Return to your *Solar System* page and add the information you have learned about the characteristics and motions of the Moon, the Sun, and Earth.

Because Earth, the Moon, and the Sun move in predictable paths that do not intersect, they are not likely to collide with one another. However, the Moon may have had a central role in the largest collision in Earth's history.

A **theory** is a model or set of ideas used to explain how or why an event happens or happened. One question astronomers often ask is, *How did the Moon form?* Some astronomers believe that Earth and the Moon formed at the same time, when the entire solar system formed. In this theory, Earth and the Moon slowly collected debris that littered their orbit around the Sun. However, the theory accepted by most astronomers today is that the Moon's formation was more violent and dramatic.

> **theory:** a model or set of ideas used to explain why things occur or have occurred; a theory is based on comprehensive experimental evidence but is subject to change should new evidence be presented that contradicts the theory.

Solar System   1.7.1/2.BBQ.2

Name: ....   Date: ....

Solar System Object	What characteristics does this object have?	How does this object move?
The Sun		
The Moon		
Inner Planets (Mercury, Venus, Earth, Mars)		
Outer planets (Jupiter, Saturn, Uranus, Neptune)		
Dwarf planets		
Asteroids, comets, meteoroids		
Other small solar-system bodies		

AST 111

ASTRONOMY

Learning Set 2

Back to the Big Question

10 min

Students update their Solar System *pages and watch an animation explaining a theory of the Moon's origin.*

△ Guide

Have students record new information they have learned about objects in the solar system on their *Solar System* pages. They should record what they have learned about the characteristics and motions of the Moon, the Sun, and Earth.

*A class period is considered to be one 40 to 50 minute class.

When students have had time to update their *Solar System* pages, discuss the origins of the Moon. Tell students that scientists have theories to answer the question, *How did the Moon form?* Tell them they will now watch an animation to explain the theory that is currently most widely accepted. Emphasize that according to this theory, Earth was formed at the same time as the rest of the planets, but the Moon was formed later.

NOTES

You will see an animation that illustrates this theory. In this theory, Earth formed at the same time as the rest of the planets, and at first there was no Moon. Then, after the event described in the animation, the Moon formed. Watch the animation carefully. Write down any questions you have about what you saw.

Reflect

In your group, discuss the questions you had about the animation. Record any ideas you have that might answer the questions. Also record ways you could find out whether your ideas are correct. Use this opportunity to update your *Big Question* page. Add what you have learned about collisions from watching the animation.

Reflect

As a group, answer the following questions. When you are finished, choose one person from your group to read your answer aloud to the class. A different person should read the answer to each question.

Big Question	1.BBQ.1/2.BBQ.2

Name: _____ Date: _____

How Can You Know if Objects in Space Will Collide?

Type of Object	Evidence of Past Collisions	Chance of Future Collisions	What Would Happen?

1. Describe the theory of the Moon's formation that is shown in the animation. How did scientists use computer models to test the theory?

2. In the theory presented in the animation, in what ways would material that makes up the Moon be the same as material that makes up Earth? In what ways might the material inside Earth and the Moon be different?

3. If the event that happened in the animation happened today, how would it affect life on Earth?

4. How did this animation change your understanding of collisions?

5. How is this theory a useful explanation for the formation of the Moon? Is there another possible theory for the formation of the Moon?

Reflect
5 min

Students discuss their questions and ideas about the animation with their groups.

△ Guide

Have students meet with their group and discuss questions they had about the animation. Have them record any ideas they have about possible answers to their questions and ways they could investigate those questions. They should record any questions that will help them answer the *Big Question: How can you know if objects in space will collide?* on their *Big Question* pages.

Reflect

5 min

Groups answer the Reflect *questions.*

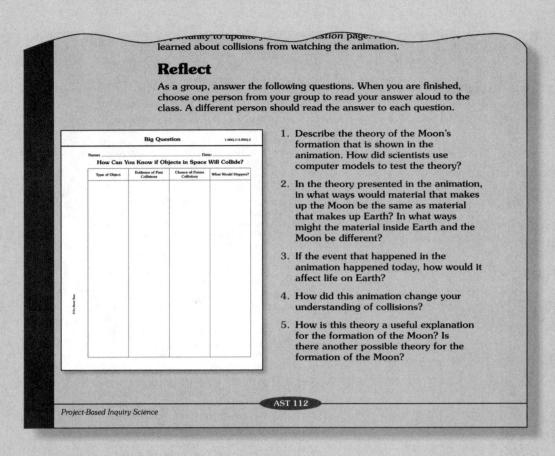

...rtunity to update... ...estion page. ... learned about collisions from watching the animation.

Reflect

As a group, answer the following questions. When you are finished, choose one person from your group to read your answer aloud to the class. A different person should read the answer to each question.

Big Question   1.BIIQ.1/2.BIIQ.2

Name: _____   Date: _____

How Can You Know if Objects in Space Will Collide?

Type of Object	Evidence of Past Collisions	Chance of Future Collisions	What Would Happen?

1. Describe the theory of the Moon's formation that is shown in the animation. How did scientists use computer models to test the theory?

2. In the theory presented in the animation, in what ways would material that makes up the Moon be the same as material that makes up Earth? In what ways might the material inside Earth and the Moon be different?

3. If the event that happened in the animation happened today, how would it affect life on Earth?

4. How did this animation change your understanding of collisions?

5. How is this theory a useful explanation for the formation of the Moon? Is there another possible theory for the formation of the Moon?

AST 112

Project-Based Inquiry Science

△ Guide and Assess

Have students work with their groups to answer the *Reflect* questions. Emphasize that they will share their answers with the class.

As groups work, monitor their progress and ask them what ideas they have discussed. Listen for evidence that students are evaluating the theory and its implications for the *Big Question*.

1. Students should accurately describe the animation regarding the Moon's formation.

2. Students may suggest that the material that makes up the Moon would be the same material that makes up the surface layers of Earth. The materials that make up the interior of Earth may not be found on the Moon since these were not a major part of the dislodged material.

3. Students should realize that such a collision today would destroy most life.

4. Student answers will vary. Some may suggest that the Moon is an asteroid that was captured by Earth. Others may suggest that the Moon formed at the same time as Earth.

5. Student answers will vary. Students may answer with something similar to the following: *The theory presented in the animation is a useful theory because it explains that the Moon formed from material originally found on Earth. This theory is supported by analysis of the composition of moon rocks. Yes, there are other possible theories for the formation of the Moon, such as, it could have formed at the same time as Earth from gas and dust particles. Other possibilities include the capture of the Moon by Earth's gravitational field.*

NOTES

Communicate: Share Your Answers

15 min

Groups share their answers with the class.

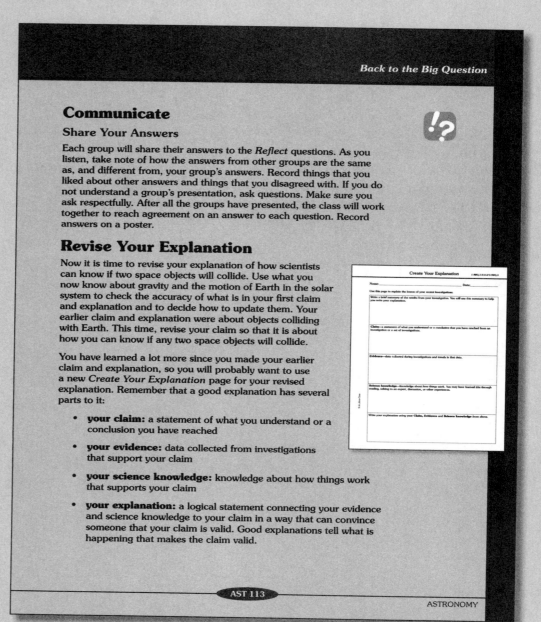

Communicate

Share Your Answers

Each group will share their answers to the *Reflect* questions. As you listen, take note of how the answers from other groups are the same as, and different from, your group's answers. Record things that you liked about other answers and things that you disagreed with. If you do not understand a group's presentation, ask questions. Make sure you ask respectfully. After all the groups have presented, the class will work together to reach agreement on an answer to each question. Record answers on a poster.

Revise Your Explanation

Now it is time to revise your explanation of how scientists can know if two space objects will collide. Use what you now know about gravity and the motion of Earth in the solar system to check the accuracy of what is in your first claim and explanation and to decide how to update them. Your earlier claim and explanation were about objects colliding with Earth. This time, revise your claim so that it is about how you can know if any two space objects will collide.

You have learned a lot more since you made your earlier claim and explanation, so you will probably want to use a new *Create Your Explanation* page for your revised explanation. Remember that a good explanation has several parts to it:

- **your claim:** a statement of what you understand or a conclusion you have reached

- **your evidence:** data collected from investigations that support your claim

- **your science knowledge:** knowledge about how things work that supports your claim

- **your explanation:** a logical statement connecting your evidence and science knowledge to your claim in a way that can convince someone that your claim is valid. Good explanations tell what is happening that makes the claim valid.

AST 113

ASTRONOMY

△ Guide

Have groups share their answers to the *Reflect* questions with the class. As groups present, students should respectfully offer any comments they have or ask questions about anything that is unclear. They should also record what they agreed with and what they disagreed with.

After all groups have shared their answers, lead a class discussion to agree on answers to the questions. Either record the answers on a poster or have a student record them on a poster, and display the poster on the wall.

△ Guide

Have students meet in their groups to update their claims based on their new knowledge of and understanding of gravity and the motion on Earth. Distribute *Create Your Explanation* pages to students and point out that they should use the bulleted points in the student text to remind them of the components of a good explanation.

Revise Your Explanation
10 min

Students revise their explanation about whether scientists can know if two space objects can collide.

NOTES

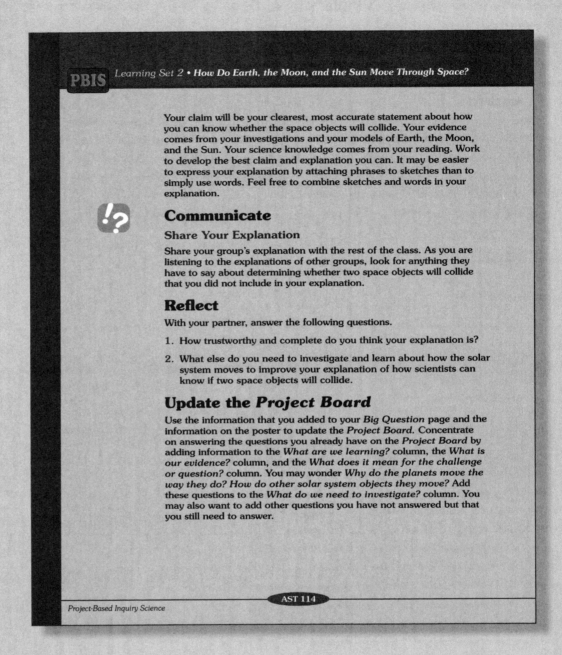

Your claim will be your clearest, most accurate statement about how you can know whether the space objects will collide. Your evidence comes from your investigations and your models of Earth, the Moon, and the Sun. Your science knowledge comes from your reading. Work to develop the best claim and explanation you can. It may be easier to express your explanation by attaching phrases to sketches than to simply use words. Feel free to combine sketches and words in your explanation.

Communicate

Share Your Explanation

Share your group's explanation with the rest of the class. As you are listening to the explanations of other groups, look for anything they have to say about determining whether two space objects will collide that you did not include in your explanation.

Reflect

With your partner, answer the following questions.

1. How trustworthy and complete do you think your explanation is?

2. What else do you need to investigate and learn about how the solar system moves to improve your explanation of how scientists can know if two space objects will collide.

Update the *Project Board*

Use the information that you added to your *Big Question* page and the information on the poster to update the *Project Board*. Concentrate on answering the questions you already have on the *Project Board* by adding information to the *What are we learning?* column, the *What is our evidence?* column, and the *What does it mean for the challenge or question?* column. You may wonder *Why do the planets move the way they do? How do other solar system objects they move?* Add these questions to the *What do we need to investigate?* column. You may also want to add other questions you have not answered but that you still need to answer.

Emphasize to students that there should be a final claim that they agree on to share with the class. To the best of their ability, they should make this claim their clearest and most accurate statement yet.

○ Get Going

Have each group take turns sharing their explanations. Encourage students to ask questions if they are unsure of any parts of the explanations the students share. Remind the class that as a group presents their claim, they should be listening for and identify the parts of the claims.

> NOTES
> ....
>
> ....

△ Guide

Allow pairs of students to answer the questions and then lead a brief discussion of the student answers.

1. Student answers will vary.

2. Student answers will vary.

> NOTES
> ....
>
> ....

△ Guide

Once the class has agreed on answers to the *Reflect* questions, draw students' attention to the *Project Board*. Ask them what information they recorded on their *Big Question* pages, and record this information in the *What are we learning?* column, along with evidence in the *What is our evidence?* column. Have students record this information on their *Project Board* pages. Also record information from the poster the class just created on the *Project Board*, and have students record it on their own *Project Board* pages. Then ask students what they can put in the *What does it mean for the challenge or question?* column for each of the ideas they just recorded. Record their responses on the *Project Board*. Finally, ask students what questions they still need to answer, and record their responses in the *What do we need to investigate?* column.

Communicate: Share Your Explanation

10 min

Students share their explanations with the class.

Reflect

5 min

Students work with a partner to answer the Reflect *questions.*

Update the Project Board

15 min

The class has a discussion to update the Project Board.

Assessment Options

Targeted Concepts, Skills, and Nature of Science	How do I know if students got it?
Scientists often collaborate and share their findings. Sharing findings makes new information available and helps scientists refine their ideas and build on others' ideas. When another person's or group's idea is used, credit needs to be given.	**ASK:** What evidence presented in the video did you not recall until the class discussed the *Reflect* questions? **LISTEN:** Students' answers will vary. This question is meant to underscore the importance of sharing information. **ASK:** When you met with other students that had researched the same solar-system object, what did the group do that helped you reach agreement on an explanation? What could the group have done better? **LISTEN:** Students' answers will vary. These questions are intended to engage students in an evaluation of their group process.
Scientists must keep clear, accurate, and descriptive records of what they do so they can share their work with others; consider what they did, why they did it, and what they want to do next.	**ASK:** You were instructed to write down questions you had about what you saw in the video. What else could you have done during the video that would have helped you answer the *Reflect* questions? **LISTEN:** Students should recognize that they could have kept more detailed notes during the video.

NOTES

_____

_____

_____

_____

_____

Targeted Concepts, Skills, and Nature of Science	How do I know if students got it?
Explanations are claims supported by evidence. Evidence can be experimental results, observational data, and any other accepted scientific knowledge	**ASK:** What evidence described in the video did you find most convincing? Why? **LISTEN:** Students' answers will vary, but should cite specific examples of evidence that is was based on experimental results or observational data. For example, data about relating the Moon's composition to Earth's obtained from samples collected on the Moon. **ASK:** When you met with other students that had researched the same solar-system object at the end of *Learning Set 1*, what new evidence and science knowledge did the group decide to include in your explanation of whether the object would collide with Earth? **LISTEN:** Students' answers will vary, but should compare their earlier explanation with their revised explanation and identify changes in evidence and science knowledge cited to support their claim.
Most objects in the solar system have a regular and predictable motion. These motions explain such phenomena as a day, a year, phases of the Moon, eclipses, tides, meteor showers, and comets.	**ASK:** If one object orbits another in a nearly circular path, why is it unlikely that the two objects will collide? **LISTEN:** Students should understand that in order to collide, the distance between the objects must be zero and an object in a near circular orbit is always at almost the same distance from the object it orbits.

Teacher Reflection Questions

- In this section, students viewed a video about the impact theory of the Moon. What aspects were most interesting to students? Which ones were sources of some confusion?

- How were you able to connect the information about the impact theory of the Moon's formation to the investigations carried out in *Learning Set 1?*

NOTES

LEARNING SET 3 INTRODUCTION

Learning Set 3

◀ **11 class periods**

A class period is considered to be one 40 to 50 minute class.

How Do Other Solar-System Objects Move Through Space?

Students now move beyond the Earth-Moon-Sun system to investigate the sizes of other objects in the solar system, the distances between them, and how they move and interact.

Overview

The introduction to *Learning Set 3* guides students to recognize that in order to predict if objects in space will collide; they will need to consider the motion of objects in the solar system other than just Earth and the Moon. Students consider how building models of the solar system can help them better understand the relative scale and motion of the planets in the solar system. In *Section 3.1,* groups research different solar-system objects and gather information that will serve as the basis for building scale models of the solar system. Groups share their information with the class, and the class records the data about all of the solar-system objects on their *Solar System* page. Students then compare and contrast the characteristics of the inner and outer planets. In *Section 3.2,* the concept of scale is introduced and students determine an appropriate scale for a model of the solar system. Students then create a model of the solar system in two stages. First, students use the chosen scale to identify commonplace objects that correctly represent the relative sizes of the Sun and the planets. Then students use the scale to place the model Sun and planets at distances from one another that correspond to their actual distances from one another. In *Section 3.3,* the class creates a model of the solar system in which students physically represent planets and simulate orbital motion by walking around a central "Sun." During the simulation, students observe and record the relative positions of the planets at given time intervals. Students then analyze their data and compare the planets' orbits, year length, and changing relative positions. After reading about the role of gravitational attraction in orbital motion and the historical development of the idea that the planets orbit the Sun in elliptical orbits, students update the *Project Board.* In *Section 3.4,* students use a model of the solar system to simulate planets' orbital motions and determine their changing location against the background of stars in the sky as viewed from Earth. The model is a solar system "map" showing the planets' orbital paths and the constellations in the background of stars surrounding the solar system. Planetary motion is simulated by plotting each planet's monthly change in position along its orbit. Students record the changing location of each planet against the background of stars in the sky as viewed from Earth. They then analyze data collected during the simulation to determine the role of perspective in the apparent retrograde motion of some planets when viewed from Earth. Students then consider the historical move from a geocentric to a heliocentric model of the solar system. In *Section 3.5,* students read an account of the solar nebula theory of the formation of the solar system and the asteroid belt and how the theory accounts for the direction in which planets rotate and revolve, and their orbital plane. Students then consider how the orbital motion of planets and their moons makes it unlikely that they will collide with Earth. The section concludes with a reading about the characteristics of Near-Earth objects and why they are more likely to collide with Earth than planets or moons. The *Learning Set* concludes with a *Back to the Big Question* in which groups are assigned to research a part of the solar system other than the eight planets, their moons, and the asteroid belt (Kuiper Belt, Trans-Neptunian Objects, Oort Cloud and Centaur planets) and consider whether they are likely sources of an object that would collide with Earth. In *Back to the Big Question,* students consider the likelihood of a collision between solar-system objects orbiting the Sun based on what they have learned about their orbits. Students revise their earlier predictions about a collision between a 10 km asteroid and the solar-system object they researched earlier to include what could cause an asteroid's orbit to change so that a collision could occur.

Targeted Concepts, Skills, and Nature of Science	Section
Scientists often collaborate and share their findings. Sharing findings makes new information available and helps scientists refine their ideas and build on others' ideas. When another person's or group's idea is used, credit needs to be given.	All sections
Scientists must keep clear, accurate, and descriptive records of what they do so they can share their work with others; consider what they did, why they did it, and what they want to do next.	All sections
Models are a representation of something in the world. Simulations use a model to imitate, or act out, real-life situations.	3.1, 3.2, 3.3

Project-Based Inquiry Science

Targeted Concepts, Skills, and Nature of Science	Section
Earth's Sun is the central and largest body in our solar system. The Sun is more than a million times greater in volume than Earth. Earth is the third planet from the Sun in a system that includes other planets and their moons, as well as smaller objects, such as asteroids and comets – some with orbits that lie beyond the planets.	3.1, 3.2, 3.BBQ
The planets of the solar system vary in size, composition, and surface features.	3.1, 3.2
Enormous distances separate the objects in the solar system. Astronomical units and light years are measures of distances between the Sun, Earth, and the stars.	3.2
Natural phenomena often involve sizes, durations, and speeds that are extremely small or extremely large. These phenomena may be difficult to appreciate because they involve magnitudes far outside human experience.	3.2
The planets move around the Sun in elliptical orbits at predictable but varying speeds.	3.3
The path of a planet around the Sun is due to the gravitational attraction between the Sun and the planet.	3.3
A year is the time it takes a planet to complete one revolution around the Sun. Earth's revolution around the Sun defines the length of an Earth year as 365.25 days.	3.3
Long ago people thought all objects in the universe revolved around Earth (geocentric model) until scientists proved that Earth and the other planets revolve around the Sun (heliocentric model).	3.4
The apparent motions of the Sun, Moon, planets, and stars across the sky can be explained by Earth's rotation and revolution.	3.4
When viewed from Earth, stars remain in fixed positions relative to one another as they appear to move across the sky. Constellations are imaginary patterns of stars used by observers to track changes in the positions of objects viewed in the sky.	3.4

ASTRONOMY

Targeted Concepts, Skills, and Nature of Science	Section
Different stars can be seen at different times of the year and planets change their positions against the background of stars over time.	3.4
Our solar system coalesced out of a giant cloud of gas and debris about five billion years ago. The Sun formed when gas and debris heated up from the energy of falling together began releasing nuclear energy from the fusion of light elements into heavier ones in its extremely hot, dense core.	3.5
Around the planets orbit a great variety of moons. Flat rings of rock and ice debris orbit some planets, a large number of asteroids orbit the Sun between the orbits of Mars and Jupiter, and Earth is orbited by a moon and artificial satellites.	3.5, 3.BBQ
Humankind's need to explore continues to lead to the development of knowledge and understanding of the nature of the Universe.	3.5

Understanding for Teachers

From a Geocentric to a Heliocentric Model

Aristotle

To terrestrial observers, it appears that Earth stands still and everything else moves around it. In trying to imagine how the universe works, people in ancient times logically started with those apparent truths. The ancient Greek thinkers, particularly Aristotle, set a pattern that was to last for about 2000 years: a large, stationary Earth at the center of the universe, and—the Sun, the Moon, and stars were arranged around Earth in a perfect sphere, with all these bodies orbiting along perfect circles at constant speeds.

There were some problems with the geocentric model. Early astronomers also observed a few "wandering stars"—the planets—that changed position with respect to the background of stars in the sky. Furthermore, the planets appeared not to move around Earth in perfect circles but rather to change speed and sometimes even go into reverse, following odd looping paths.

Ptolemy

The Egyptian astronomer, Ptolemy, refined this model by adding more circles which spun on the main circles. His elegant mathematical model of circular motions enabled astronomers to predict the positions of objects viewed in the sky fairly accurately and accounted for the apparently irregular motions of planets. Ptolemy's view was that each planet was fixed to a large sphere that was, in turn, fixed to a larger sphere. The smaller sphere and its attached planet spun around the larger sphere at the same time that the larger sphere spun around Earth. As a result, there could be times when, to an observer on Earth, the planet appeared to be moving backward. Ptolemy called the motions of the smaller spheres *epicycles* and the motions of the larger spheres *deferents*. With Ptolemy's ingenious modifications, the geocentric model was able to successfully explain most naked eye observations of the universe. However, as the centuries passed, the discrepancies between the positions of objects predicted by Ptolemy's model and what was actually observed became so large they could not be ignored. Over time, Arabian and later European astronomers made corrections to the model, recalculating constants and even adding new epicycles. By the 1500s, the model was often off by as much as 2°—four times the angular diameter of the Moon!

Copernicus

By the beginning of the 1500s, the Julian calendar was off by about 11 days. Both the Hebrew calendar, based on the Moon, and the Julian calendar, based on the Sun, had to be used to calculate the phase of the Moon that determined the date of Easter, a major church holiday. A secretary of Pope Sixtus IV asked Nicolaus Copernicus, a Polish priest-mathematician, to work on the problem of calendar reform. Copernicus recognized that any calendar reform would have to resolve the relationship between the Sun and the Moon. After much study of the problem, Copernicus proposed an elegant mathematical solution in which the center of the universe was a point near the Sun, and Earth orbited the Sun once a year and spun on its axis once a day. Realizing that an orbiting and spinning Earth was thought to be inconsistent with some biblical passages, he distributed a brief outline of his ideas, but his full argument in favor of the model was not published until his death in 1543. But Copernicus' model still used perfect circular motions and was nearly as complicated as the old Earth-centered model. In addition, his model seemed at odds with common-sense perceptions that Earth did not move, and that everything appeared to move around the Earth. It also required a universe that was far larger than had been imagined, and that Earth was not the center of the universe, but just a commonplace object orbiting the Sun. Most scholars saw little advantage to the model and too many ideas associated with the traditional Earth-centered model that would have to be given up.

Tycho Brahe and Johannes Kepler

As measuring instruments improved and astronomical measurements became more precise, scientists found that neither the heliocentric nor the geocentric system worked if all bodies had to have uniform circular motion. Shortly after Copernicus died, a Danish nobleman named Tycho Brahe became interested in astronomy. He convinced the King of Denmark to fund a world-class observatory with many ingenious devices for measuring the motions of celestial objects. Without the aid of the telescope, (which had not yet been invented) he made what are still considered some of the most precise naked-eye observations and measurements ever recorded. After the King of Denmark died, Brahe obtained a position as court astronomer to the Holy Roman Emperor in Prague and took all of his data from the observatory in Denmark. The emperor commissioned him to publish a revision of astronomical tables based on the Ptolemaic model and Brahe hired several young mathematicians to help him with the task.

One of Brahe's assistants was Johannes Kepler. Shortly thereafter, Brahe died unexpectedly. Before he died, he had recommended Kepler as his successor. After taking over as court astronomer, Kepler spent six years trying to work out the orbit of Mars. After years of studying Brahe's observational data (six years alone trying to work out the orbit of Mars), Kepler made three important discoveries about the motions of planets as they revolve around the Sun:

- Each planet revolves around the Sun in an elliptical orbit with the Sun at one focus of the ellipse.

- The planets do not move at a constant velocity in their orbits. Each planet sweeps out equal areas of its elliptical orbit in equal periods of time.

- There is a mathematical relationship between the time it takes a planet to complete one revolution around the Sun and its average distance from the Sun. A planet's period of revolution squared is proportional to its distance from the Sun cubed. ($T^2 \alpha R^3$)

An ellipse is a closed curve, the locus of points such that the sum of the distances from any point on the ellipse to two other fixed points (each called a focus of the ellipse) is constant. An ellipse has a major axis and a minor axis; lines running through the center of the ellipse connecting the two points farthest apart and the two points closest together on the ellipse. The foci of an ellipse always lie along the major axis, and are equidistant from the center of the ellipse.

The closer together the foci, the more near to circular the ellipse will be. The farther apart the foci, the less circular the ellipse, i.e., the more flattened or elongated its shape. The degree to which an ellipse deviates from being circular is called its *eccentricity*.

Eccentricity is expressed as the ratio between the distance between the foci and the length of the major axis.

$$e = \frac{d}{l}$$

Where e = eccentricity; d = distance between foci; and l = length of major axis.

In a perfect circle, the distance between the foci is zero, that is, the two points merge into a single point – the center of the circle. The eccentricity of a perfect circle would be 0,

$$\frac{0}{\text{length of major axis}} = 0$$

In a straight line, the foci are located at the ends of the line. Therefore the distance between the foci and the length of the major axis are both the same as and the length of the line and eccentricity is 1,

$$\frac{\text{length of line}}{\text{length of line}} = 1$$

Because the orbit of each planet is an ellipse with the Sun located at one of the foci, the distance from each planet to the Sun varies during its orbit. For example, Earth's distance varies from 147×10^6 km on January 3 when it is closest to the Sun (perihelion) to 152×10^6 km on July 6 when it is farthest from the Sun (aphelion). The difference between these distances, 5×10^6 km is very small compared to the length of the major axis, 299×10^6 km. Therefore, the eccentricity of Earth's orbit is very small, 0.0167 ($\frac{5}{299} = 0.0167$). This indicates that Earth's orbit is very nearly a perfect circle. Many diagrams show Earth's orbit in a perspective view that greatly exaggerates its eccentricity. If viewed from directly overhead, it would appear very nearly a circle.

The elliptical shape of a planet's orbit alters its velocity. The time it takes the planet to move from any one point to the next point in its orbit are equal. However, the distances from one point to the next are not equal. The planet is moving fastest when it is closest to the Sun and slowest when it is farthest from the Sun.

Kepler did not know why this was the case, he only determined that the variation in velocity occurred. We now know that this cyclic change in the velocity of planets as they orbit the Sun is because gravitational force between a planet and the Sun changes as the distance between them changes. As the planet approaches the Sun, distance decreases, gravitational force increases, and since it is acting in the same direction in which the planet is moving, the planet's orbital velocity increases. As the planet moves away from the Sun, distance increase, gravitational force decreases, and since it is now acting opposite to the direction in which the planet is moving, the planet's orbital velocity decreases.

The time it takes a planet to complete one revolution around the Sun is called its period of revolution, or orbital period. By Kepler's time, it was already known that period of revolution increased with distance from the Sun. However, Kepler's careful analysis of Brahe's observational data showed that there is a mathematical relationship between distance and period of revolution: period of revolution squared is proportional to distance from the Sun cubed.

$$T^2 \alpha R^3$$

Galileo and Newton

Shortly after Kepler published his work, Galileo observed the sky with a telescope and made several discoveries that further undermined the Ptolemaic model. His discovery of craters on the Moon and spots on the Sun challenged the old view that the heavens were perfect and unchanging. He saw moons circling Jupiter, challenging the view that everything revolved around Earth. He saw Venus going through a full set of phases, which was not possible according to the Ptolemaic model. Galileo also studied motion and argued that if Earth is in motion, so are all of the objects on it. An observer on Earth would not perceive its motion because the observer would be moving at the same speed as the Earth. An object that is dropped moves sideways at the same speed as Earth and falls on a spot directly beneath its point of release.

In the same year that Galileo died, the great mathematician and physicist Isaac Newton was born in England. Newton brought together the discoveries of Copernicus, Kepler, and Galileo. Newton built on the work of Galileo, refining and repeating his investigations of falling bodies using balls and ramps, and developed three laws of motion (inertia, the relationship between force, mass and acceleration, and the forces involved with interacting objects). Newton also recognized the connection between the changes in motion Galileo observed in balls rolling down and up ramps and the changes Kepler identified in the motion of planets as they moved closer and farther away from the Sun. The idea that falling objects were attracted to the Earth was not new. However, Newton realized that the Moon would circle Earth only if some force pulled the Moon towards Earth's center. Newton's great insight was to recognize that the force that keeps the Moon in orbit around Earth is the same force that causes an object near Earth to fall to the ground – gravity. And that the same force could keep planets in orbit around the Sun. Newton's genius was in recognizing that this force of attraction, or gravity, existed throughout the universe; that all objects are attracted to one another with a force that depends on their mass and the distance from one another. Newton expressed this relationship in a simple mathematical relationship:

$$F = \frac{Gm_1m_2}{d^2}$$

How does gravity keep an object moving in a curved orbit? Imagine a cannonball shot from a cannon aimed horizontally. If there were no gravity, inertia would cause the cannonball to move horizontally in a straight line until acted upon by an unbalanced force. However, with gravity pulling the ball toward Earth's center, its path curves downward and eventually it strikes Earth's surface. If a more powerful charge is used, more force is exerted on the ball and it will travel farther horizontally before it strikes Earth's surface. If the force exerted on the cannonball was powerful enough, the ball would travel far enough horizontally that as its path curved downward because of gravity, Earth's surface would curve away because of its spherical shape, and the cannonball would never strike Earth's surface. Instead, gravity would cause the cannonball to fall downward at the same rate that Earth surface curves away from it and it would fall endlessly in a circular path around the Earth – it would be in orbit.

In the same way, Newton proposed that it is a combination of inertia and gravity that keeps planets moving in their curved paths around the Sun. The combination of a planet's forward motion and its motion toward the Sun due to gravity causes the planet to orbit the Sun. With Newton's explanation of the causes of motion, the heliocentric model became more widely accepted and began to displace the geocentric model of the universe. However, it is one thing to propose that Earth moves; it is quite another thing to actually prove it. The arguments in favor of rotation and revolution may make sense, but making sense is not scientific proof. It wasn't until 1851 that the French physicist Jean Foucault provided proof of Earth's rotation.

Foucault used an ingeniously simple method to prove Earth's rotation. Gravity pulls a pendulum toward Earth's center; it does not exert a lateral force on the pendulum to change the plane in which it swings. Therefore, in the absence of any lateral forces, a pendulum should continue to swing freely in a fixed plane. Foucault reasoned that the more massive the pendulum, the greater the force that would be needed to push it out of its plane of motion, making it unlikely that small breezes would change its direction of motion. He also recognized that as the length of a pendulum increases, its period increases and it would swing for many hours before coming to rest. Foucault argued that if Earth were motionless, such a pendulum would swing in a plane that would not change over time. However, if Earth rotated, it would change position relative to the swinging pendulum. The result would be a pendulum whose plane of swing would appear to rotate relative to the ground in a direction opposite Earth's rotation. Foucault's idea is easiest to understand if you visualize a pendulum swinging over a turntable. If the turntable is motionless, the pendulum's path relative to the turntable doesn't change. If it rotates beneath the pendulum, the pendulum's path changes relative to the turntable.

In 1851, Foucault suspended a freely swinging pendulum from the inside of the dome of the Pantheon building in Paris. The high dome allowed the use of a 60-meter long pendulum. Foucault fastened a heavy weight to the pendulum, fastened it to one side of the room with a thin cord and sealed all of the entrances to eliminate possible drafts that could exert a lateral force on the pendulum. He then burned the cord to set the pendulum swinging freely in a fixed plane. Through the windows, observers were able to watch the pendulum rotate slowly in a direction opposite Earth's rotation, thus proving that Earth rotates.

NOTES

LEARNING SET 3 IMPLEMENTATION

Learning Set 3

How Do Other Solar-System Objects Move Through Space?

You have compared the sizes of Earth and the Moon, determined the distance between them, and explored how the motions of the Sun, Earth, and the Moon interact. However, if you want to make a prediction about which solar-system objects might collide with each other, you need to know about the rest of the objects in the solar system, how close they are to one another, and how they move. You probably already know something about the planets, but to answer the *Big Question*, you will need to know how far the planets are from each other and their relative sizes. You will also need to know why solar-system objects move the way they do. That will help you figure out how planets can affect the paths of space objects.

Pictured is an artist's illustration of the eight planets in the solar system, and the Moon. Scientists and students can make models of the solar system in many different ways.

AST 115

ASTRONOMY

Learning Set 3

How Do Other Solar-System Objects Move Through Space?

5 min

Students consider how size may influence their answer to the Big Question.

△ Guide

Begin by pointing out that students need to know about other objects in the solar system to predict whether objects could collide with each other. Just as students investigated the sizes of Earth, the Moon, and the Sun, and the distances and interactions between them, they will need to investigate the sizes of other objects in the solar system, the distances between them, and how they interact.

*A class period is considered to be one 40 to 50 minute class.

orrery: a mechanical model of our solar system used to show the relative positions and movements of the planets.

scale model: a representation of an object that is related to the actual dimensions of the object by a fixed ratio.

One way to develop an understanding of the solar system is to build a model. Scientists use models to help them understand the solar system, and you will do the same thing. Like scientists, you may find that the process of building the model will give you a better understanding of the relationships and relative sizes of the planets.

Scientists and artists have been building models of our solar system for over two thousand years. Because our solar system is very complex, scientists have developed many different types of models. Each type allows them to explore different characteristics of the solar system.

One type of model scientists use to understand our solar system is called an **orrery**. An orrery is a model that shows the relative positions and motions

of the planets. The first modern orrery was built in 1704. Like all models, an orrery represents our solar system well in some ways, but not in every way. While the orrery shows the motion of solar-system objects and how they may line up, it does not accurately show the sizes or distances between the objects. An orrery is a good tool for understanding how solar-system objects move, but for a better understanding of the chances of solar-system objects colliding, a model needs to show how big the objects are and the distances between them.

This orrery uses a crank handle and gears to move planets and the Moon in their orbits. The objects can spin and revolve.

Another type of model is a **scale model**. A scale model is a representation of an object related to the object's actual dimensions. You cannot go on a field trip to the planets, so the best way to understand how far the planets are from each other and how big they are is to build scale models. You will do that in this *Learning Set*. First you will build a scale model that shows the relative sizes and distances of the planets. Then you will use models to help you visualize the motions of the planets. You will also read about the orbits of planets and other solar-system objects and find out why objects travel in those orbits.

Tell students that models can be an effective way to investigate objects that are too large to investigate directly. Discuss how scientists have been using models of the solar system for over 2000 years. Introduce the *orrery* as a kind of model used to show the relative positions of objects in the solar system. Tell students that orreries do not accurately represent the scale of objects in the solar system. Since students want to determine whether objects might collide with each other, they need a model that accurately represents scale. Tell them that in this *Learning Set,* they will build scale models of the solar system.

3.1 Understand the Question

Think About Making a Model of the Solar System

◀ *2 class periods*

A class period is considered to be one 40 to 50 minute class.

Overview

Students consider the challenges to understanding the size of the solar system posed by its large scale and consider how building models of the solar system can help them better understand the relative sizes of the planets and their motions. Each group is assigned to research and become experts on a different solar-system body. Groups prepare posters to share what they have learned about their assigned solar system body and what they think would happen to that object if it collided with a 10-km wide asteroid. Students record information shared by all of the groups on their *Solar System* page, which will provide data needed for investigations throughout the *Learning Set*. After reflecting on the information shared by all of the groups and looking for patterns in the solar-system data, students discuss their ideas, update the *What are we learning?* and *What is our evidence?* columns of the *Project Board* and consider *What do we need to investigate?* in order to predict collisions between solar-system objects.

Targeted Concepts, Skills, and Nature of Science	Performance Expectations
Scientists often collaborate and share their findings. Sharing findings makes new information available and helps scientists refine their ideas and build on others' ideas. When another person's or group's idea is used, credit needs to be given.	Students engage in research into a specific solar-system object and then share their research findings with the class.
Scientists must keep clear, accurate, and descriptive records of what they do so they can share their work with others; consider what they did, why they did it, and what they want to do next.	Students record information about all of the solar-system objects researched by the class on a *Solar System* page. Students create a poster to share their research findings and their ideas about the effects of an asteroid collision with the class in an *Investigation Expo.*

Targeted Concepts, Skills, and Nature of Science	Performance Expectations
Models are a representation of something in the world. Simulations use a model to imitate, or act out, real-life situations.	Students describe how their research findings will help them build a model of the solar system.
The planets of the solar system vary in size, composition, and surface features and move around the Sun in elliptical orbits at predictable but varying speeds.	Students compare and contrast the characteristics of the planets in the solar system with those of Earth and the Moon.

Materials	
several per student	Research resources
1 per class	Class *Project Board*
1 per class (optional)	Orrery, or other solar-system model

Activity Setup and Preparation

Make arrangements for students to have access to resources, such as the Internet, the library, or books, magazines and other print materials for researching solar-system objects.

Homework Options

Reflection

- **Science Content:** Examine the information shared by all of the groups in your class. Which planet in the solar system is closest in size to the Earth? Which is closest in size to Earth's Moon? *(Students should cite that Venus' diameter is 12,103.6 km and Earth's diameter is 12,756 km in their answers. They should also cite that the Moon's diameter is 3475 km and Mercury's diameter is 4878 km.)*

- **Science Process:** Compare and contrast the usefulness of the resources you used to research your solar-system object. How can you tell if a resource is a reliable source of information? *(Answers will vary. However, students should cite specific types of information resources such as books, journals, magazines, internet sites, and so on. Students should consider scientific books and publications, institutes of higher learning and government agencies as more reliable than informal sources.)*

Preparation for 3.2

- **Science Content:** Compare Earth's diameter with that of Jupiter. Compare Jupiter's diameter with the Sun's diameter. *(Students should answer that Jupiter's diameter is about 11 times larger than Earth's diameter. The Sun's diameter is 10 times larger than Jupiter's diameter.)*

- **Science Process:** What are two ways to express the relative sizes of two objects? *(Students should answer that they can express relative size as a ratio:*

$$\frac{\text{size of object 1}}{\text{size of object 2}}$$

Or as a factor: a number by which the size of object 1 is multiplied to equal the size of object 2.)

NOTES

....

....

....

....

....

....

....

NOTES

SECTION 3.1 IMPLEMENTATION

3.1 Understand the Question

Think About Making a Model of the Solar System

The *Big Question* for this Unit is *How can you know if objects in space will collide?* You know collisions occur because you have seen evidence of impacts. You also know the relationships among Earth, the Moon, and Sun. To make accurate predictions, it is necessary to know more about the other objects in the solar system and their motions.

One of the hardest things to understand about the solar system is how huge it is. You can start by visualizing its size this way. Think about getting from New York to Los Angeles. The driving distance from New York to Los Angeles is 4784 km (2973 mi). It would take about two days of driving day and night to get from one city to the other. That may seem like a great distance. However, it is only a small part of the distance it takes to go all the way around Earth. The distance around Earth at the Equator is called Earth's *circumference.* The circumference of Earth is more than eight times greater than the distance from New York to Los Angeles. If you could drive nonstop around the globe, it would take about 17 days. Other solar-system objects are larger than Earth, and the distances between solar-system objects are even greater. Earth is about 150 million kilometers from the Sun. This is 3733 times Earth's circumference. If you could drive to the Sun in a car, it would take you about 284 years to get there! Other planets are even farther from the Sun.

The circumference of Earth, measured around the Equator, is 40,075 km (24,901 mi). That is more than eight times greater than the distance from New York to Los Angeles.

AST 117

ASTRONOMY

3.1 Understand the Question

Think About Making a Model of the Solar System

5 min

Students consider what they still need to know to start answering the Big Question.

△ Guide

Begin by reminding students that the *Big Question* for the Unit is *How can you know if objects in space will collide?* Tell them that in order to answer this question, they will need to know more about other objects in the solar system.

*A class period is considered to be one 40 to 50 minute class.

One particularly important part of determining the likelihood of collisions is learning about the distances between objects and the sizes of those objects. This is difficult, because the sizes of objects in the solar system and the distances between them are on a larger scale than distances that are familiar from everyday life. The student text uses the example of driving from New York to Los Angeles. This is much farther than most people travel on a regular basis, about 4784 km (2973 miles), but it is less than an eighth of Earth's circumference.

Tell them that in order to investigate solar-system bodies and develop an understanding of their relative sizes and distances from each other, they will build a model of the solar system.

NOTES

One way to better understand these sizes and distances is to make a scale model of the solar system. In this *Learning Set*, you will build a scale model of the Sun and the eight planets in the solar system. However, before you can begin building your model, you need to learn more about each of the objects that will be in your model.

Get Started

Each group in your class is going to become an expert on a different object in the solar system. Your model will have nine objects in it—the Sun and eight planets—so data for all nine objects are necessary to complete the model. Your teacher will tell you which object your group will investigate. Your solar-system object will either be the Sun or one of the seven planets other than Earth. As you gather information, remember that you will be responsible for teaching other groups about your solar-system object.

Procedure

1. Using available resources, gather the following information about the solar-system object assigned to your group. If your assigned object is the Sun, then some of the information does not apply.

   • size

   • mass

   • length of day (time to make one full revolution on its axis)

   • length of year (time to make one full orbit around the Sun)

   • composition

   • atmosphere

   • average distance from the Sun

   • similarities between your solar-system object and Earth or the Moon

   • differences between your solar-system object and Earth or the Moon

   • evidence of collisions between your solar-system object and other solar-system objects

AST 118

Project-Based Inquiry Science

Get Started

5 min

Groups are assigned solar-system bodies to investigate.

△ Guide

Let students know they will work with their groups to become experts on one solar-system body. They will then collaborate with the class to build a model of the solar system. Emphasize that the work of the class depends on the work of each group, and each group will be responsible for informing the class about their solar-system body.

Assign each group a solar-system body, making sure that each solar-system body is assigned to at least one group.

Briefly go over the procedure with the class. Groups will need to gather the information listed in Step 1 on their solar-system body. Note that the group that is assigned to the Sun will not need to find information on length of day, length of year, or average distance from the Sun.

Once they have gathered the information, they will make a prediction about what they think would happen if an asteroid that is about 10 km in diameter were to collide with their solar-system body. They will record their ideas and their supporting evidence. Then they will use posters to share with the class their information and their ideas about a collision with a 10-km asteroid.

NOTES

- any other interesting information

2. After collecting your information, make a prediction among your group members about what you think would happen if an asteroid that is about 10 km (6 mi) across were to collide with your solar-system object. List your ideas and the supporting evidence. Your evidence may include what you have learned so far in this Unit.

3. Prepare a poster to share what you have learned with the class. Include a picture or sketch of your solar-system object, the information you gathered, and your answer to the question, *What would happen if a 10-km asteroid were to hit the solar-system object?* Make sure you include the evidence you used to answer this question. Be prepared to describe how your group reached this conclusion and why.

An artist imagines a collision of a huge asteroid with a planet such as Earth.

Communicate

Investigation Expo

When you have finished your investigation and prepared your poster, you will share what you learned with the class in an *Investigation Expo*. So that others will be able to learn from your work and use the information you present, you must clearly present what you know about your space object. Use your poster to guide your presentation. First, present the characteristics of your space object. Then present what you think would happen if a 10-km asteroid hit your space object. Support your answer with evidence.

△ Guide and Assess

As groups work, monitor their progress and help them with any difficulties that arise. Ask questions to engage them in interpreting the information they are gathering.

TEACHER TALK

"How does the size of your solar-system body compare to the size of Earth? Is a year on their solar-system body longer or shorter than a year on Earth?"

When students have had time to gather information, have them develop predictions for what they think would happen if a 10-km asteroid collided with their solar-system object. Emphasize that they should use evidence from their investigations in this Unit as well as the information they just gathered about the object.

Have groups prepare posters showing a picture of their solar-system body, the information they gathered about the solar-system body, and their predictions about what would happen if a 10-km asteroid were to collide with it. They should also include any evidence they have to support their conclusions.

Communicate: Investigation Expo

20 min

Groups share their findings in an Investigation Expo.

Communicate

Investigation Expo

When you have finished your investigation and prepared your poster, you will share what you learned with the class in an *Investigation Expo*. So that others will be able to learn from your work and use the information you present, you must clearly present what you know about your space object. Use your poster to guide your presentation. First, present the characteristics of your space object. Then present what you think would happen if a 10-km asteroid hit your space object. Support your answer with evidence.

△ Guide

Let students know that they will now share their research with the class in an *Investigation Expo*. They should use their posters to communicate their research, their predictions, and the evidence supporting their predictions.

NOTES

....

....

....

....

....

As you listen to the presentations of other groups, make sure you understand what they are telling you about the characteristics of the space object they are reporting on. Ask questions if there is something you do not understand or if you think their information is incomplete. Also, be sure you agree with each group's answer to what would happen if a 10-km asteroid hit their space object. If you do not agree with their conclusion or you think their evidence did not fully support their answer, raise your hand and ask about their conclusions. Remember to be respectful. Here are some questions you might want to ask:

- How is your solar-system object similar to Earth or Earth's moon?

- How is your solar-system object different from Earth or Earth's moon?

- Describe any evidence that your object has ever been hit by another space object. What do you think happened?

- What was the most important evidence used to reach your conclusions?

Reflect

After listening to all of the presentations, you probably have a much better understanding of the planets that make up the solar system. Use what you have just heard to answer these questions.

1. What patterns do you see in the sizes of the planets?

2. What patterns do you see in the length of time it takes a planet to orbit the Sun?

Mercury, Venus, Earth, and Mars

Have groups present. Emphasize that as each group presents, students should listen for evidence of past collisions and information that supports the group's conclusions. Point out the bulleted questions in their text and tell them they can use these as examples of questions they can ask the group.

Reflect

15 min

The class considers the findings of all the groups and answers questions about the solar system.

Reflect

After listening to all of the presentations, you probably have a much better understanding of the planets that make up the solar system. Use what you have just heard to answer these questions.

1. What patterns do you see in the sizes of the planets?

2. What patterns do you see in the length of time it takes a planet to orbit the Sun?

△ Guide

Lead a class discussion of the *Reflect* questions. Students may recognize patterns in the class observations. However, it is enough at this point for students to begin looking for patterns. They will have more opportunities to observe how the orbital periods of solar-system objects compare and how their distances from the Sun compare.

Have students record the information they learned from the class presentations in their *Solar System* pages. Ask them to think about why the *Solar System* page divides the planets into inner and outer planets. Are there differences between inner and outer planets?

1. Students should notice that the inner planets are smaller and solid bodies; the outer planets are very large and consist of gas.

2. Students should note that the inner planets are closer and orbit the Sun in shorter periods of time than the outer planets.

3. Students may summarize the grouping of planets as follows:

   Mercury, Venus, Earth, and Mars are inner planets, smaller in size, and solid in makeup. Collisions between these would be disastrous. They may also note that Venus and Earth have atmospheres.

   Jupiter, Saturn, Uranus, and Neptune are outer planets, larger in size, gaseous in makeup, and collisions would be absorbed.

NOTES

....

....

....

3. Mercury, Venus, Earth, and Mars are different from Jupiter, Saturn, Uranus, and Neptune in several ways. Compare these two groups of planets. What similarities and differences do you find in the composition, atmosphere, and potential effect of collisions?

4. Your *Solar System* page divides the planets into two groups, the inner planets and the outer planets. Does this grouping make sense to you? What do you think the terms *inner planet* and *outer planet* refer to? What are other ways you could group the planets?

5. What else do you need to know to make a scale model of the solar system?

Update the *Project Board*

You have learned a lot about the Sun and the planets from the class presentations. Add to the *What do we think we know?* column the things you now know about how planets move around the Sun. Add to the *What do we need to investigate?* column any questions that you think need to be answered in order to accurately construct a scale model of the solar system or to predict collisions between solar-system objects.

What's the Point?

In this *Learning Set,* your goal is to gain a complete understanding of all of the components of the solar system. You have learned many facts about the planets from the presentations. In the rest of the *Learning Set* you will use this knowledge to make models that you can study to learn more about objects in the solar system and their motions.

Jupiter, Saturn, Uranus, and Neptune

AST 121

4. Students may reply that the grouping does make sense to them. Inner planets refer to those closer to the Sun; outer planets refer to those farther from the Sun. Students may suggest that the planets could be grouped by size, composition, apparent brightness, number of moons, average temperature, color, etc.

5. Student answers will vary.

Update the Project Board

15 min

The class has a discussion to update the Project Board.

solar system

Update the *Project Board*

You have learned a lot about the Sun and the planets from the class presentations. Add to the *What do we think we know?* column the things you now know about how planets move around the Sun. Add to the *What do we need to investigate?* column any questions that you think need to be answered in order to accurately construct a scale model of the solar system or to predict collisions between solar-system objects.

△ Guide

When students have updated their *Solar System* pages, ask them what information they can add to the *What are we learning?* column of the *Project Board*. Record their answers on the *Project Board* and have students record them on their own *Project Board* pages. Also ask students what evidence they have to support these ideas, and record their answers in the *What is our evidence?* column.

Then ask students what they still need to investigate to be able to predict whether solar-system objects in space might collide. Record their responses in the *What do we need to investigate?* column of the *Project Board*.

Assessment Options

Targeted Concepts, Skills, and Nature of Science	How do I know if students got it?
Scientists often collaborate and share their findings. Sharing findings makes new information available and helps scientists refine their ideas and build on others' ideas. When another person's or group's idea is used, credit needs to be given.	**ASK:** How did dividing up the task of researching solar-system objects and then sharing research findings benefit everyone in the class? **LISTEN:** Answers will vary, but may include that it made more efficient use of everyone's time and effort because research on one object was not repeated by multiple groups. By sharing research findings every person obtained information that they did not have to work to obtain.

Targeted Concepts, Skills, and Nature of Science	How do I know if students got it?
Scientists must keep clear, accurate, and descriptive records of what they do so they can share their work with others; consider what they did, why they did it, and what they want to do next.	**ASK:** Why is it important to record all of the research findings shared by other groups on your *Solar System* page? **LISTEN:** Students should understand that all of the information will be useful when building a model of the solar system. **ASK:** What information recorded in previous *Learning Sets* helped you predict the effects of an asteroid collision with your object? **LISTEN:** Students should cite the data about the sizes of impact craters and the objects that formed them recorded in *Learning Set 1*.
Models are a representation of something in the world. Simulations use a model to imitate, or act out, real-life situations.	**ASK:** Which research findings shared by the class do you think will be most helpful in building a model of the solar system? **LISTEN:** Students should identify size, average distance from the Sun, and the length of a year, because it will determine how large to make the model planets, how far apart they should be placed, and how fast they should move in their orbits to accurately represent the solar system.
The planets of the solar system vary in size, composition, and surface features and move around the Sun in elliptical orbits at predictable but varying speeds.	**ASK:** Which two outer planets are closest in size? Which two inner planets? **LISTEN:** Students should answer that the outer planets Neptune and Uranus are closest in size; the inner planets Earth and Venus are closest in size. **ASK:** Which two adjacent planets are farthest apart? **LISTEN:** Students should answer that Uranus and Neptune are separated by more than 10 AU.

Teacher Reflection Questions

- What difficulties did students have in understanding the concepts related to planets' orbits? What can you do in the future to help them with these difficulties?

- How were you able to keep students focused on gathering information on their solar-system body? What might you try next time?

- How did you ensure that all of the groups in your class had equal access to resources?

- What strategies could you use to encourage students to rethink, reorganize, and refine their oral and written ideas?

- What factors negatively or positively affected the success of the activity?

NOTES

3.2 Develop a Model

Choose Objects for a Model of the Solar System

◀ *3 class periods*

A class period is
considered to be one
40 to 50 minute class.

Overview

The section opens with a reading about the concept of scale and how it is
used to create a scale model. Students calculate the scale of the solar system
if Earth is represented by an apple. Students then use that scale to calculate
the diameter of a model Sun and determine that if the Earth is apple-sized,
the Sun would not fit in the classroom. Students repeat their calculations
using a peppercorn to represent Earth. They find that at that scale, the size
of a model Sun is more manageable. Each expert group (from *Section 3.1*)
uses the Earth-as-a-peppercorn scale to calculate the corresponding size of
their assigned planet and chooses an appropriate object to represent that
planet. Groups share their data with the class and it is recorded on a *Solar
System Model* page. Groups then use the Earth-as-a-peppercorn scale to
calculate the scale model distance between their planet and the Sun. Groups
share their data with the class and students complete their *Solar System
Model* pages. In an appropriate location, the class constructs a model of the
solar system. The model Sun is placed on the ground and, beginning with
Mercury, each expert group identifies the distance from the model Sun at
which their model planet should be placed. After the model solar system
is complete, students observe the relationships between the sizes of the
planets and their distances from one another in the model. Students then
reflect on the vast scale of the solar system and read about the Astronomical
Unit used by astronomers to measure long distances. The section concludes
with the class updating the *What are we learning?* and *What is our
evidence?* columns of the *Project Board.*

Targeted Concepts, Skills, and Nature of Science	Performance Expectations
Scientists often collaborate and share their findings. Sharing findings makes new information available and helps scientists refine their ideas and build on others' ideas. When another person's or group's idea is used, credit needs to be given.	Students calculate the diameter of a model planet and its distance from a model Sun using an Earth-as-a-peppercorn scale and share their results with the class.
Scientists must keep clear, accurate, and descriptive records of what they do so they can share their work with others; consider what they did, why they did it, and what they want to do next.	Students record the actual and calculated scale model diameters of the Sun and the planets, and the actual and scale model distances between the Sun and the planets on their *Solar-System Model* pages. The class completes a *Solar-System Model* page that summarizes data from all groups.
Models are a representation of something in the world. Simulations use a model to imitate, or act out, real-life situations.	Students create a model of the solar system using the same scale for planet diameter and distance from the Sun.
The planets of the solar system vary in size, composition, and surface features.	Students observe the relative sizes of the Sun and planets and the distances separating them using a scale model of the solar system.
Enormous distances separate the objects in the solar system. Astronomical units and light years are measures of distances between the Sun, Earth, and the stars	Students observe the large distances separating the objects in the solar system compared to their sizes. Students define an astronomical unit.
Natural phenomena often involve sizes, durations, and speeds that are extremely small or extremely large. These phenomena may be difficult to appreciate because they involve magnitudes far outside human experience.	Students demonstrate an appreciation of the enormous scale of the solar system.

Materials	
1 per student	*Solar-System Model* page Calculator
1 per class	Set of objects to represent the Sun and the planets Class *Project Board* Class *Solar System Model* page

Activity Setup and Preparation

Obtain a set of objects that can be used to represent the Sun and planets to scale with Earth represented as a peppercorn.

For example:

- Sun: any ball, diameter 22 cm
- Mercury: a pinhead, diameter 1 mm
- Venus: a peppercorn, diameter 2 mm
- Earth: a peppercorn
- Mars: a pinhead
- Jupiter: a chestnut or a pecan, diameter 23 mm
- Saturn: a hazelnut or an acorn, diameter 18 mm
- Uranus: a peanut or coffee bean, diameter 8mm
- Neptune: a peanut or coffee bean

Consider obtaining a tape reel for measuring the distances between planets in the solar system model.

Homework Options

Reflection

- **Science Content:** How did the size of the Sun compare when viewed from Earth and when viewed from Jupiter in your solar system model? If you were on the planet Jupiter, do you think the Sun would appear brighter or dimmer than it appears on Earth? *(Students should answer that the Sun appears much smaller when viewed from Jupiter than when viewed from Earth. Compared to its appearance when viewed from Earth, the Sun would appear much dimmer when viewed from Jupiter.)*

- **Science Content:** How do you think the amount of solar energy that strikes Earth compares with the total amount of energy that streams out of the Sun? *(Students should describe how Earth intercepts a very tiny fraction of the Sun's energy.)*

- **Science Process:** How could you calculate the number of model Earths that would fit inside the model Sun? *(Students should describe how they calculate the volume of Earth and the Sun using the formula, $Volume = \frac{4}{3}\pi r^3$, and then divide the Sun's volume by Earth's volume.)*

- **Science Process:** Suppose you wanted to place a model human in your solar system model. How could the size of a model human be calculated? What object could you use to represent a human? *(Students should use the Earth-as-a-peppercorn scale to calculate the scale size corresponding to the actual height of a typical human, which is about 1.7 m. Students will have difficulty identifying an object that could be used to represent a human, because at the Earth as a peppercorn scale, a human would be incredibly small— about 2.6×10^{-8} cm in height, about twice the size of an atom.)*

Preparation for 3.3

- **Science Content:** Which of the following objects do you think best represents the shape of Earth's orbit around the Sun: a basketball, a football, an egg, or a pear? *(Student answers will vary. This question is designed to uncover any misconceptions about the shape of Earth's orbit that need to be addressed in the next section. A basketball is the correct shape.)*

- **Science Process:** Assuming the Sun's size does not change, how could you tell if Earth's distance from the Sun changes as it orbits the Sun? *(Students should describe doing this by measuring the apparent size of the Sun when viewed from Earth. If the Sun's size does not change and its distance from Earth does not change, its apparent size will not change. However, a change in apparent size would be evidence that the distance between Earth and the Sun changed.)*

SECTION 3.2 IMPLEMENTATION

3.2 Develop a Model

Choose Objects for a Model of the Solar System

Now that you know a little about the Sun and each of the planets in the solar system, you can begin to plan a scale model of the solar system. A scale model is a representation of an object or system that is larger, or smaller, than the actual size. This allows you to more easily study objects that are too small, too large, too far away, or too dangerous to study up close. The solar system is extremely large, so a scale model is a useful tool for studying its characteristics.

scale: the ratio of the distance between two points on a representation (such as a map or profile) and the actual distance between those two points.

scale factor: a ratio used to convert the actual sizes of an object to sizes in a model of that object.

You already know something about scale models. A map is a type of scale model because it is a different size than the area it represents. A well-drawn map allows you to compare distances from one place to another. A map also has a small bar on it that shows you how distances on the map compare to the actual distance on Earth's surface. This bar is called a **scale**, and the scale has a **scale factor**. A scale factor is a number used to convert from actual sizes to sizes that are used on the map. The scale might be stated in words. For example, the scale on the map might state a scale factor like this: 1 cm (0.4 in.) is equal to 10 km (6 mi). When the map was made, measurements of Earth's surface features were converted to map measurements using the scale factor. Each measurement was scaled down so that 1 centimeter on the map is equal to 10 kilometers on Earth. The map is much smaller than the actual area, but the map represents the area accurately because it is drawn to scale.

In this sample map, 2.1 cm equals 12 km, and 3.5 cm equals 12 miles.

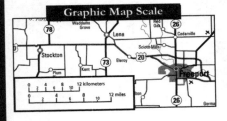

You will begin planning your solar-system model by thinking about a scale that could be used for the model. You know that the sizes of the planets vary. Some planets are smaller than Earth, and some are much larger. The distances between planets are much greater than the sizes of the planets. Determining the scale of a model can be difficult and requires you to think about how the model will be used.

AST 122

Project-Based Inquiry Science

3.2 Develop a Model

Choose Objects for a Model of the Solar System

5 min

Students start using their knowledge of solar-system objects to begin building model solar systems.

△ Guide

Begin by telling students that now that they have gathered information about solar-system objects, they will build a model of the solar system. Tell them that they will make scale models. A *scale model* is a model that is larger or smaller than the actual object or collection of objects.

The student text uses map scale as an example of scale models. The sizes of actual objects can be found by multiplying their sizes on the map by a scale factor. Point out that to make such a map, the scale factor to be used needs to be chosen to determine how large to represent objects.

*A class period is considered to be one 40 to 50 minute class.

ASTRONOMY

Tell students that they will choose a scale for their model. To choose a scale, they should consider how large they want the objects in their model to be. They do not want the objects in their model to be larger than the room, but they also want their objects large enough to be visible.

NOTES

For now, think only about the size of each of the solar-system objects—the Sun and the eight planets. Your job is to figure out what scale factor to use so that all of the objects in your model are able to fit in the classroom. For now, do not worry about how you will get objects through the door. Later, you will determine the distances between solar-system objects using the same scale.

Calculating Scale Factors: Can you Use an Apple to Represent Earth?

The first step in planning a scale model is to determine the scale factors you will use. One way to start is by choosing a model object that you could use to represent one object in the model. Then use calculations to see if the scale factor for this object will work for the other objects in your model. You will begin by calculating whether you can use an apple to represent Earth.

To determine whether an apple is a good size for Earth, you will first need to calculate the scale factor for using an apple to represent Earth. The procedure below shows you how to do that calculation, as well as how to calculate the diameter of a model Sun using the same scale factor. Follow the procedure, using a calculator to do the calculations on your own. Make sure your calculations match those in the procedure.

Apple diameter = 4 inches or 10 centimeters

Will this apple be the right size to represent Earth?

AST 123

ASTRONOMY

Calculating Scale Factors: Can You Use an Apple to Represent Earth?

5 min

Students calculate the scale factor for their model.

⬡ Get Going

Ask students to define the term *model*. Discuss any models they may have made in the past. Ask students to describe the process of representing those objects and the importance of scale in their models.

Procedure

1. **Determine the size of the model Earth.** The photograph shows an average-sized apple with a ruler next to it. The diameter of the apple in the picture is about 10 cm (4 in.).

Materials
• calculator

2. **Compare the measurement of the model Earth with the actual Earth to get the scale factor.**

Actual diameter of Earth: 12,756 km

Diameter of the model Earth: 10 cm

To find the ratio of the diameter of Earth to the diameter of the apple, you divide. This ratio, rounded to the nearest whole number, is the scale factor for the model.

$$\frac{12,756 \text{ km}}{10 \text{ cm}} = \frac{1275.6 \text{ km}}{\text{cm}} \approx \frac{1276 \text{ km}}{\text{cm}}$$

This means that 1 centimeter in the model represents an actual distance of 1276 kilometers. The scale factor can be written as follows:

Scale: 1 cm = 1276 km

3. **Use the scale factor to find the diameter of the Sun in your model.** You can determine how big the other objects in your model would be using this scale. You begin with the actual size of the object you will model. The Sun's diameter is 1,392,000 km.

Actual diameter of the Sun: 1,392,000 km

If an apple is used to represent Earth, then every object in the model will have the same scale factor you calculated for the apple. To calculate the diameter of the model Sun in centimeters, divide the actual diameter of the Sun in kilometers by the scale factor.

$$1,392,000 \text{ km} \quad \div \quad \frac{1276 \text{ km}}{\text{cm}} \quad = \quad 1091 \text{ cm}$$

(diameter of the Sun)   (scale factor)

Diameter of the model Sun: 1091 cm

4. **Evaluate how large the model Sun would be.** To know if an object will fit in the classroom, you need to understand how big it really is. If an apple were used to model Earth, then the model Sun would have a diameter of 1091 centimeters. But how big is 1091 centimeters? If you convert 1091 cm into meters, you find that it is almost 11 m (36 ft).

AST 124

△ Guide

Distribute calculators and tell students that they will begin by calculating what the size of the largest object in the solar system (the Sun) would be if they used an apple to represent Earth. Tell them the diameter of an apple is about 10 cm.

To determine the diameter of any solar-system object at this scale, students will first need to find the scale factor of the model, which they can use to find the size of any solar-system object in the model. To do this, they should divide the actual diameter of Earth (12,756 km) by the diameter of the model Earth. This gives them the scale.

They should find that 1 cm = 1276 km.

Using this scale, they can multiply the actual size (km) of any object in the solar system by $\frac{1 \text{ cm}}{1276 \text{ km}}$ to find the size of the object in the model.

Tell students they will next use the scale factor to determine the size of the Sun in the model. To do this, they should multiply the actual diameter of the Sun (1,392,000 km) by $\frac{1 \text{ cm}}{1276 \text{ km}}$. The diameter of the model Sun is about 1090 cm.

Once students understand that the diameter of the Sun would be about 1090 cm, have them convert centimeters to feet. They should find that their model Sun would be almost 36 ft. Ask them if that would be too large to fit in the classroom. They should realize that the apple model of the Earth will not work.

NOTES

....

....

....

....

....

....

....

....

....

Analyze Your Data

If you use an apple as your model Earth, will the other objects in your model solar system fit in your classroom? Answer these questions to decide.

1. The diameter of the Sun in this model would be 11 m. What is about 11 m (36 ft) from where you are right now? It may help to think of the length of football field, which is 101 m (120 yd).

2. Think about how large your classroom is. Usually, the ceiling height in a classroom is about 2.75 m (9 ft). Will a ball that is 11 meters in diameter fit into your classroom?

3. In order for every object in the solar system to be small enough to fit into the classroom, does Earth have to be smaller or larger than the size of an apple? What other objects do you think you could you use to represent Earth?

4. What procedure will you follow to determine if the object you choose will be a good model for Earth? Which space objects would you have to calculate the sizes of to decide that? Why?

Materials
• calculator

Can You Use a Peppercorn to Represent Earth?

When Earth is represented in your model by an apple, the model Sun is too big to fit into a classroom. A peppercorn is much smaller than an apple and might be a better object to represent Earth. A peppercorn is tiny compared to the apple, with a diameter of only 0.2 cm. To determine if a peppercorn is a good size for your model Earth, you must repeat the same calculations you did for the apple. Follow the procedure below, using a calculator to make your own calculations. Make sure your calculations match those in the procedure.

Procedure

1. **Determine the size of the model Earth.** The photograph on right shows average-sized peppercorns. Measure the diameter of one peppercorn. You should find that it is about 0.2 cm.

Could one of these peppercorns be your model Earth?

△ Guide

Lead a brief discussion of the *Analyze Your Data* questions. Students should understand that a sphere with a diameter of 11 m would be much too large to fit in most rooms, including the classroom. The ceiling of the classroom is probably only about 2.5 m high. A fourth-story window might be 11 m off the ground. Make sure students understand that their model needs to use a smaller object than an apple to represent Earth.

Analyze Your Data

5 min

Students have a class discussion and answer the Analyze Your Data *questions.*

1. Student answers will vary, but they should realize that this size is too large to fit into the classroom.

2. Students should understand that this model of the Sun will not fit into the classroom.

3. Students should realize that Earth cannot be represented by an apple. They must suggest something much smaller, such as a seed.

4. Students should respond that they need to calculate two factors to make certain that the model solar system will fit into their classroom. The first calculation will be the scale size of each object, including the planets and Sun. The second calculation is the distance of each planet from the Sun.

△ **Guide**

Tell students they will use a peppercorn to represent Earth. A peppercorn has a diameter of about 2 mm.

Can You Use a Peppercorn to Represent Earth?

5 min

Students find the scale of their model using a peppercorn to represent Earth.

NOTES

_____

_____

_____

_____

_____

_____

_____

_____

_____

2. **Compare the measurement of the model Earth with the actual Earth to get the scale factor.**

> Actual diameter of Earth: 12,756 km

> Diameter of the model Earth: 0.2 cm

To find the scale factor, divide the actual diameter of Earth by the diameter of your model Earth.

$$12{,}756 \text{ km} \div 0.2 \text{ km} \approx \frac{63{,}780 \text{ km}}{\text{cm}}$$

This means that 1 centimeter in the model represents an actual distance of 63,780 kilometers. That is the scale factor for this model.

> Scale: 1 cm = 63,780 km

3. **Use the scale factor to find the diameter of the Sun in your model.** You begin with the actual size of the object you will model.

> Actual diameter of the Sun: 1,392,000 km

If a peppercorn is used to represent Earth, then every object in the model will have to use the same scale factor you calculated for the peppercorn. To calculate the diameter of the model Sun in centimeters, divide the actual diameter of the Sun in kilometers by the scale factor.

$$1{,}392{,}000 \text{ km} \quad \div \quad \frac{63{,}780 \text{ km}}{\text{cm}} \quad \approx \quad 22 \text{ cm}$$
$$\text{(diameter of the Sun)} \qquad \text{(scale factor)}$$

> Diameter of the model Sun: 22 cm

This model Sun is much smaller than the one you had when using an apple to represent Earth.

Stop and Think

1. How big is 22 centimeters? There are 2.54 centimeters in an inch. Figure out how big 22 centimeters is. Then list three spherical objects that are about that big.

2. What object might you use to represent the Sun if it needs to be about 22 centimeters in diameter?

Ask students what the diameter of the Sun is when Earth's diameter is 2 mm. They will again need to find the scale by dividing the diameter of the peppercorn by the actual diameter of Earth, and then they will need to use the new scale factor to find the diameter of the model Sun. They should find it to be about 20.3 cm. Emphasize that at this scale, the Sun and all of the other solar-system objects will have manageable sizes.

1. Students should calculate that 22 cm is about 9 inches.
2. Students should find that a soccer ball is about 22 cm in diameter.

NOTES

....

....

....

....

....

....

....

....

....

....

....

....

....

Stop and Think

5 min

Students answer the questions found in the Stop and Think *section.*

ASTRONOMY

Choose Model Objects to Represent the Sun and Planets

15 min

Students calculate the diameters of the objects that will represent their solar-system object and the distance of the object from the Sun in the model. Then they choose the best object to represent their solar-system object.

Choose Model Objects to Represent the Sun and Planets

Your class will construct a model of the solar system using a peppercorn as a model Earth. You have already calculated the scale factor for Earth in this model. Now you will choose objects to represent the other objects in the solar system. Each must be chosen using the scale factor you chose for Earth. In the last section, each group became an expert on the characteristics of a planet or the Sun. Now you will work with your group to find an object of the correct size to represent your solar-system object in the class model of the solar system.

Procedure

1. Record the scale factor at the top of your *Solar-System Model* page.

2. In the table, find the row for your solar-system object. In this row, record the actual diameter of your solar-system object in the *Diameter* column.

3. Use the scale factor to calculate the diameter of your model object in centimeters. Record this measurement in the *Diameter of the model object* column.

4. Find a round object that is about that size. If possible, choose an object that is available in your classroom. Record the name of your object in the *Model object that is the correct size* column.

5. Now, use the scale factor to calculate the distance your object is from the Sun. First, record the average actual distance your object is from the Sun in the *Average distance from the Sun* column. Then calculate the distance your model object should be from the model Sun. Use the formula

$$\frac{\text{Actual distance from Sun}}{\text{Scale factor}} = \text{Distance from model Sun}$$

Solar System Model   3.2.1

Name: _____   Date: _____

Scale 1 cm = _____ km

Solar-system object	Diameter (km)	Diameter of the model object (cm)	Model object that is the correct size	Average distance from the Sun (km)	Distance from the model Sun (cm)	Paces from the model Sun
Sun						
Mercury						
Venus						
Earth						
Mars						
Jupiter						
Saturn						
Uranus						
Neptune						

AST 127

ASTRONOMY

⬡ Get Going

Show students a collection of objects they will use to model their solar-system object. Tell them they will need to find the diameter their object needs to accurately represent the relative size of their solar-system object. Then they will select an object with that diameter from the collection.

Have students use the new scale to calculate the diameter of the object they will use to represent their solar-system body. Have them record the scale at the top of their *Solar-System Model* page and have them record the actual diameter, the scale diameter, the actual distance from the Sun, and the scale distance from the Sun of their object.

◇ Evaluate

As students calculate scale diameters and distances, monitor their progress and make sure they are performing their calculations correctly. You can use the completed *Solar-System Model* page below to evaluate their work.

Solar-System Model

3.2.1

Name: _____ Date: _____

Scale 1 cm = _63422_ km

Solar-system body	Diameter (km)	Diameter of the model object (cm)	Model object that is the correct size	Average distance from the Sun (km)	Distance in the model
Sun	1,287,475 km	20.3 cm	standard bowling ball	na	na
Mercury	4,828 km	.1 cm	head of a pin	57,936,384 km	914 cm
Venus	12,070 km	.2 cm	peppercorn	107,826,048 km	1,700 cm
Earth	12,875 km	.2 cm	peppercorn	149,668,992 km	2,360 cm
Mars	6,437 km	.1 cm	head of a pin	228,526,848 km	3,603 cm
Jupiter	144,841 km	2.3 cm	chestnut	778,922,496 km	12,282 cm
Saturn	120,701 km	1.9 cm	filbert	1,427,488,128 km	22,508 cm
Uranus	51,499 km	.8 cm	peanut	2,869,460,352 km	45,244 cm
Neptune	48,280 km	.8 cm	peanut	4,496,507,136 km	70,898 cm

Then have students choose an object with the correct diameter to represent their solar-system object.

ASTRONOMY

Communicate: Share Your Data

15 min

Groups share their data with the class.

Communicate

Share Your Data

When it is your group's turn to present, share your data with the class, and record your data on a large class *Solar-System Model* page so that everyone can see it. Each member of the class should also complete their own *Solar-System Model* page. Everyone in the class will need to have their own set of data for the next activity.

Analyze Your Data

1. Which is the smallest solar-system object? How much smaller is it than Earth?

2. Which is the largest solar-system object? How much larger is it than Earth?

3. What surprised you about the sizes of the everyday objects you are using to represent the Sun and planets?

4. Look carefully at the column that shows the average distance from the Sun. Use what you know about the sizes of objects you are familiar with to visualize how far the planets will be from each other in a scale model of the orbits. How far do you think it will be from the model Sun to the model Mercury (the first planet from the Sun)? How far do you think your group's model solar-system object will be from the model Sun? How do you think you can represent these distances?

5. Now assume that you will be walking the distance between model objects using large paces. Assume that one pace is 1 meter. Divide the model distance (in cm) between your planet and the Sun by 100. This will tell you about how many paces it would take to walk from the model Sun to your model planet.

6. Record the number of paces from the model Sun to your model planet in the last column of the class *Solar-System Model* page.

△ Guide

Tell students that before they build their model of the solar system, they need to share their data with the class so that everyone knows what the structure of the solar system model will be.

Record the groups' data on a class *Solar-System Model* page. You can use a transparency with an overhead or a poster. Project or hang the page where students can see it. As groups share, have students record the data on their *Solar-System Model* pages.

☐ Assess

1. Students should respond that the smallest solar-system object is Mercury. It has about one half the diameter of Earth.

2. Students should note that the largest solar-system object is the Sun, which has a diameter which is 100 times the diameter of Earth.

3. Student answers will vary.

4. Students should respond that Mercury is about 9 m from the Sun in this model solar system. Student answers will vary depending on their solar-system object. They may suggest that a football field will be needed to represent the distances in this model solar system.

5. Student answers will vary, but they will divide the cm by 100 to obtain the distance of their object in meters.

6. Student answers will vary depending on their model object.

**Analyze
Your Data**

15 min

*Students analyze their
data in groups.*

NOTES

....

....

....

....

....

....

....

....

Reflect

1. Record the distance in paces from the Sun to each planet on your *Solar-System Model* page.

2. Calculate the distance in paces from your planet to the two closest planets. Be prepared to share your data with the class.

3. What, if anything, surprises you about the distances from the Sun to the planets or from your planet to the two closest planets?

Walk Your Model

How Much Space Do You Need?

You will have to take a long walk to model the distances from the Sun to the planets. Take your *Solar-System Model* page with you for the walk, and take your group's model solar-system object. Your teacher will take the model Earth. Your class will begin the walk together. You will stop when you have paced off the correct model distance for each planet. You will either place the model objects on the ground at those places or the group assigned to that planet will stand at their planet's distance from the Sun and watch the others walk to the next planet's orbit.

Materials
- model solar-system objects
- completed *Solar-System Model* page

Procedure

1. First, go to the place your teacher tells you is the location of the model Sun. Place the object that represents the Sun on the ground. The teacher may instead ask the Sun group to remain in the Sun's place.

2. Your teacher will now walk away from the Sun and call out distances in meters. Walk with the teacher. When you reach the correct model distance for your planet, call out to the class "[my planet] is here!" Then put your model planet on the ground or stand at the place for your planet as the other groups move on. For example, the first group to reach its planet's orbit will be the Mercury group. The Mercury group should say "Mercury is here!" and then put their model Mercury on the ground or remain in Mercury's place.

3. At each place you stop, look back at the other objects or groups. Notice how far away you are getting from the Sun and the other planets.

⬡ Get Going

Give students a few minutes to answer the *Reflect* questions. These questions should help students interpret their data and the scale that they are using.

1. Students will divide each distance in cm by 100 to obtain the distance in meters.

2. Student answers will vary.

3. Student answers will vary. They may be surprised that it was possible to find the planets at all, given the size and distances involved.

△ Guide

Take students to the location you have selected for their solar-system model. Have them bring the objects they selected to represent their solar-system objects.

At the location, have the group that was assigned the Sun set their object on the ground. Then tell the group assigned Mercury that they are going to determine where they should set down the object representing Mercury. To do this, they will use the number of paces they calculated. Emphasize that other groups will need to do their calculation for their solar-system objects. Also point out that a "pace" should consist of an average step with one foot followed by an average step with the other foot. This will be slightly more than a yard, approximately a meter. (The correct distance for Mercury will be about 9 paces, or 18 steps.)

When the Mercury group has put down their object, have students look back at the ball representing the Sun. Then have the Venus group measure out the distance to Venus in paces. (Note that they can simply subtract the paces that the Mercury group measured out from Venus's distance from the Sun.) Again have students look back at the Sun and Mercury. Students should begin to develop a sense of the great amount of space between solar-system objects relative to their size.

You can use the table below to help students determine the distances between solar-system objects and to check their work.

Walk Your Model: How Much Space Do You Need?

30 min

Students walk their model.

Number of Paces Between Solar-System Bodies

Mercury to Venus	Venus to Earth	Earth to Mars	Mars to Jupiter	Jupiter to Saturn	Saturn to Uranus	Uranus to Neptune
8	7	12	87	102	227	257

NOTES

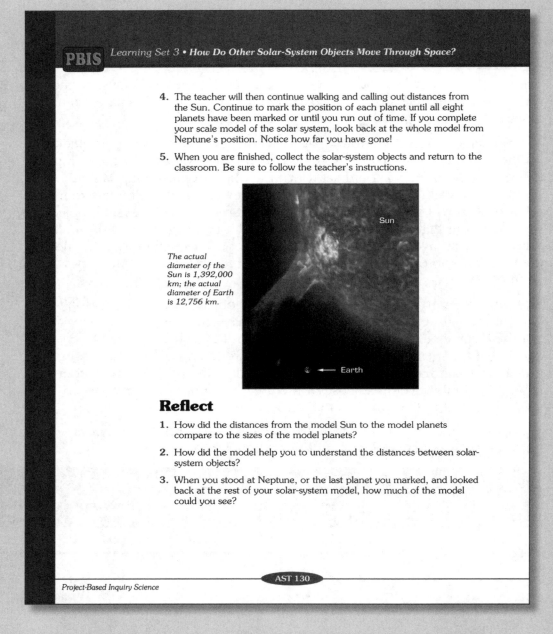

4. The teacher will then continue walking and calling out distances from the Sun. Continue to mark the position of each planet until all eight planets have been marked or until you run out of time. If you complete your scale model of the solar system, look back at the whole model from Neptune's position. Notice how far you have gone!

5. When you are finished, collect the solar-system objects and return to the classroom. Be sure to follow the teacher's instructions.

The actual diameter of the Sun is 1,392,000 km; the actual diameter of Earth is 12,756 km.

Sun

◄— Earth

Reflect

1. How did the distances from the model Sun to the model planets compare to the sizes of the model planets?

2. How did the model help you to understand the distances between solar-system objects?

3. When you stood at Neptune, or the last planet you marked, and looked back at the rest of your solar-system model, how much of the model could you see?

By the time students reach Mars, they should be able to see that the Sun appears to be far away. When they reach Jupiter, it will be difficult or impossible to see the objects they have already set down. This is the objective of the activity, and it may not be necessary to go beyond Jupiter. If you do not have enough space to measure out the distances to Saturn, Uranus, and Neptune, or if you feel that students get the point and do not need to see the remaining distances, you can take them back after Jupiter. If you take them back after Jupiter, point out that the distances between the objects in the outer solar system are even greater than the distances between the object in the inner solar system. The distance from Mars to Jupiter was 87 paces. The distance from Jupiter to Saturn is slightly greater, and the distances from Saturn to Uranus and from Uranus to Neptune are more than twice the distance from Mars to Jupiter.

△ Guide and Assess

Lead a brief discussion of the *Reflect* questions. These questions should help students interpret their observations. Look for evidence that they understand how small solar-system objects are in relation to the great distances between them. Note that if the class did not reach Neptune when they built their model, they should think about how the model appeared from the farthest planet they reached.

1. Students should respond that the distances were much greater than the sizes of the model planets.

2. Student answers will vary, but should reflect the impressive vastness of space.

3. Students should describe a solar system in which they could only see the Sun.

Reflect

5 min

Students apply their observations of the model solar system to their understanding of its actual measurements.

NOTES

4. Suppose you wanted to make a new model with the goal of fitting the orbits of every planet within your classroom. What do you think the sizes of the planets and the Sun in such a model would be?

5. Do you think that planets in our solar system can collide with each other? Why or why not? What would you need to know to know to determine whether your answer to this question is correct?

Measuring Long Distances

As you saw from building your model, the distances from the Sun to the farthest planets are very large. For example, Neptune is nearly 4.5 billion kilometers from the Sun. Because those distances are so large, instead of expressing them in kilometers, astronomers have defined a different unit that they use to describe distances in the solar system. Remember that the average distance from Earth to the Sun is about 150 million kilometers (93 million miles). Astronomers define this distance as 1 **astronomical unit (AU)**. They then use this unit to express other distances in space. When they measure in astronomical units, they are comparing all other distances to the distance between the Sun and Earth. For example, the distance from Mars to the Sun is about 1.5 AU, or about 1.5 times the distance from Earth to the Sun. And Neptune is about 30 AU from the Sun. That means it is 30 times farther from the Sun than Earth is. The number 30 is easier to grasp than 4.5 billion!

astronomical unit (AU): a measure of distance based on Earth's orbit. One AU is equal to the average distance of Earth from the Sun, about 150 million kilometers.

Update the *Project Board*

You have just experienced the relative sizes of the Sun and planets in the solar system and their relative distances from each other and from the Sun. You might have been amazed at the vast distance that the solar system occupies. The scale of the solar system has important consequences for your prediction of whether objects will collide with Earth. Fill in the *What are we learning?* and *What is our evidence?* columns of the *Project Board* with the insights you have gained from making a solar-system model. Then add new questions you have generated to the *What do we need to investigate?* column.

4. Student answers will vary, but an accurate estimate would be that the solar system would be reduced by about 100 times. The Sun would be the size of a peppercorn and the largest planets would be grains of sand.

5. Students should understand that the planets in the solar system are not likely to collide, because they are in stable, predictable orbits and they are very far apart.

⚠ Guide

Briefly introduce Astronomical Unit (AU) as what scientists use to measure great distances. Scientists define 1 AU as the distance from Earth to the Sun. Neptune is about 30 AU from the Sun. Point out that this means Neptune is about 30 times as far away from the Sun as Earth is.

⚠ Guide

Ask students what new information they can record in the *What are we learning?* column of the *Project Board*. Record their answers on the class *Project Board* and have students record them on their own *Project Board* pages. Also record their evidence in the *What is our evidence?* column. They should include conclusions they reached about the scale of the solar system.

Measuring Long Distances

5 min

Students are introduced to Astronomical Units.

Update the Project Board

15 min

The class has a discussion to update the Project Board.

NOTES

What's the Point?

A scale model can be constructed using a scale factor. The scale factor is a ratio that relates actual distances to distances in the model. You can find a scale factor using one object in a model. In a model of the solar system, you first find the scale factor for one object, such as Earth. You then use the scale factor to find the size of each model object. The scale factor also is used to calculate the distance between model objects. In a solar-system model, it helps to find the model size of the largest object, the Sun, to make sure the model will not be too large.

No model can perfectly represent all features. Your model represented the sizes of the objects and the distances between the objects accurately. However, this meant the model planets had to be far from the model Sun. This made it difficult to visualize the entire model at once.

The actual distances to planets are large numbers when measured in kilometers. Astronomers use a unit called the astronomical unit (AU) to measure distances in the solar system. The astronomical unit is defined as the average distance from Earth to the Sun, which is about 150 million kilometers.

To study and develop models in astronomy, scientists need to quantify distances that are unimaginable. The approximate distance of 150 million kilometers between Earth and the Sun is 1 astronomical unit.

AST 132

Assessment Options

Targeted Concepts, Skills, and Nature of Science	How do I know if students got it?
Scientists often collaborate and share their findings. Sharing findings makes new information available and helps scientists refine their ideas and build on others' ideas. When another person's or group's idea is used, credit needs to be given.	**ASK:** How did sharing results with the class decrease the amount of work you had to do to complete the *Solar-System Model* page? **LISTEN:** Students should answer that instead of having to calculate sizes and distances for all of the planets, their group had to do the calculations for one planet.
Scientists must keep clear, accurate, and descriptive records of what they do so they can share their work with others; consider what they did, why they did it, and what they want to do next.	**ASK:** What records made in previous sections provided data that you were able to use when completing the *Solar-System Model* page in this section? **LISTEN:** Students should have used their *Solar System Data* page from the previous section. **ASK:** How did you determine the diameter of your model planet? **LISTEN:** Students should describe using the Earth-as-a-peppercorn scale to calculate the scale model size of their group's planet.
Models are a representation of something in the world. Simulations use a model to imitate, or act out, real-life situations.	**ASK:** In the class solar system model, what represented each of the planets in the solar system? **LISTEN:** Students should identify the objects representing each planet from their *Solar-System Model* page.
The planets of the solar system vary in size, composition, and surface features.	**ASK:** How did the sizes of the inner planets compare with the sizes of the outer planets? How did the spacing of the inner and outer planets compare? **LISTEN:** Students should describe how the inner planets are much smaller than the outer planets. The inner planets are more closely spaced than the outer planets.

Targeted Concepts, Skills, and Nature of Science	How do I know if students got it?
Enormous distances separate the objects in the solar system. Astronomical units and light years are measures of distances between the Sun, Earth, and the stars	**ASK:** Why do astronomers use Astronomical Units to measure distances in the solar system? **LISTEN:** Students should understand that the distances are so vast that when using smaller units, such as kilometers, the values of the distances are very large. Using larger units of measure, makes it easier to compare and contrast distances in the solar system. **ASK:** What is an Astronomical Unit? **LISTEN:** Students should answer that an Astronomical Unit is equivalent to the average distance between Earth and the Sun.
Natural phenomena often involve sizes, durations, and speeds that are extremely small or extremely large. These phenomena may be difficult to appreciate because they involve magnitudes far outside human experience.	**ASK:** When the class constructed the model of the solar system, when did you begin to realize the vastness of the solar system compared to the objects it contains? **LISTEN:** Student answers will vary, but should refer to observations that led them to consider the small size of the objects in the solar system compared to the distances that separate them.

Teacher Reflection Questions

- At what point in placing the model planets at their scale distances from the Sun did students first show evidence of recognizing the small sizes of the planets compared to their distance from the Sun?

- What probing questions could you ask to reinforce this developing conception of the vast scale of the solar system?

- Why is this idea important for teaching?

- What specifically might have been changed to improve the delivery of the activity?

SECTION 3.3 INTRODUCTION

3.3 Explore

How Can You Predict the Locations of the Planets?

◀ *2 class periods*

A class period is considered to be one 40 to 50 minute class.

Overview

Having investigated the relative sizes of the planets and the distances between them in the last section, students now focus on the planets' orbital motions. The concept of a period is introduced and students create a not-to-scale model of the solar system in which students represent planets and simulate the orbital motion of the planets by walking along orbital paths around a central Sun. Students observe the differences in the rate at which planets complete their orbit and compare and contrast the length of a period on planets at different distances from the Sun. Students read about the role of gravity in the orbital motion of the planets and consider the relationship between orbital period and distance from the Sun. Students then read about the elliptical shape of the planets' orbits, the characteristics of an ellipse, and how ellipses can be constructed. Eccentricity is introduced as a measure of the elongation of an ellipse and students consider the eccentricity of the orbits of the planets in the solar system. Students then update the *Project Board* focusing on the *What do we think we know?* and *What do we need to investigate?* columns.

Targeted Concepts, Skills, and Nature of Science	Performance Expectations
Scientists often collaborate and share their findings. Sharing findings makes new information available and helps scientists refine their ideas and build on others' ideas. When another person's or group's idea is used, credit needs to be given.	The class discusses the changes in the relative positions of the planets as students simulate orbital motion in their solar system model.

Targeted Concepts, Skills, and Nature of Science	Performance Expectations
Scientists must keep clear, accurate, and descriptive records of what they do so they can share their work with others; consider what they did, why they did it, and what they want to do next.	Students keep a record of how the relative positions of the planets changed during the orbital motion simulation and of their analysis of how that motion affects observations made from the perspective of different planets.
Models are a representation of something in the world. Simulations use a model to imitate, or act out, real-life situations.	Students create a model of the solar system and simulate the orbital motions of some of the planets.
The planets move around the Sun in elliptical orbits at predictable but varying speeds.	Students construct an ellipse and describe how eccentricity indicates the degree to which an ellipse is elongated. Students identify the relationship between orbital period and distance from the Sun.
A year is the time it takes a planet to complete one revolution around the Sun. Earth's revolution around the Sun defines the length of an Earth year as 365.25 days.	Students define a year and identify the relationship between distance from the Sun and year length.
The path of a planet around the Sun is due to the gravitational attraction between the Sun and the planet.	Students define gravity and describe how it keeps planets in orbit around the Sun.

Materials	
1 per class	Class *Project Board* Tape

Activity Setup and Preparation

Before class, identify an area that is large enough to accommodate the orbits of the planets that students will simulate. If the radius of Mercury's orbit is 50 cm, Venus would be at about 1 m, Earth at 1.5 m, Mars at 2 m, and Jupiter at about 6 m. The schoolyard, gym, or cafeteria will generally provide sufficient space. Mark the position of the Sun and draw the orbital paths of the five planets nearest the Sun as near circles on the ground. This can be done using chalk attached to a string.

Homework Options

Reflection

- **Science Content:** How many Mercury years occur during one Earth year? *(Students should identify between 2 and 3.)* How many Earth years occur during one Mars year? *(Students should identify almost two.)*

- **Science Process:** When you ran the simulation, how could you tell that a planet had completed one year? *(Students should describe that by observing when the model planet had completed one orbit and returned to its starting position, indicated that the planet had completed one year.)*

- **Science Process:** During the simulation, Jupiter never completed its orbit. How could you estimate the number of Earth years it would take Jupiter to complete its orbit? *(Students should describe how to estimate the fraction of its orbit Jupiter covered in one Earth year. Then divide that fraction into 1 to determine the number of Earth years it would take to complete one orbit.)*

Preparation for 3.4

- **Science Content:** As Earth orbits the Sun, the side of Earth facing the Sun experiences daylight and the side facing away from the Sun experiences darkness. Why do you think different stars are visible in the night sky in June and in January? *(Students should understand that an observer on Earth only sees stars at night. As Earth moves in its orbit from June to January, its position relative to the Sun changes, meaning its nighttime side faces different parts of the surrounding universe, and different stars will be visible.)*

- **Science Process:** Early astronomers believed that Earth was stationary, located at the center of the universe, and that everything in the universe revolved around Earth. What would provide the best evidence that this idea is incorrect? *(Students should answer that because the idea requires Earth to be stationary, scientific proof that the Earth moves would be the best evidence that the idea is incorrect.)*

NOTES

....

....

....

....

....

....

....

....

....

....

....

....

....

SECTION 3.3 IMPLEMENTATION

3.3 Explore

How Can You Predict the Locations of the Planets?

In the model your class just made, you walked off the distances to each of the planets starting from the Sun. The distances in the model probably were greater than you thought they would be.

Your final model was laid out in a straight line. Think about the amount of space you would need if you wanted to show how the planets actually orbit the Sun!

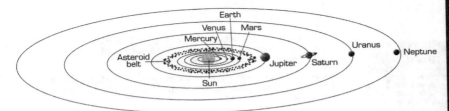

Can the planets collide with each other? You can only know the answer to this question if you know how the planets move in relation to each other. You know that the planets orbit the Sun, but you may not know exactly how close they get to each other or what their orbits look like. To find out whether the planets can collide with each other, you need to know these things.

In *Learning Set 2,* you learned that Earth orbits the Sun. The other planets also orbit the Sun. Each planet orbits the Sun in a path that is nearly circular. In this *Learning Set,* you will simulate the orbits of the planets. You will have a chance to see how the planets move around the Sun in relation to one another.

AST 133

ASTRONOMY

3.3 Explore

How Can You Predict the Locations of the Planets?

5 min

Students start thinking about adding orbit patterns to their solar system models.

*A class period is considered to be one 40 to 50 minute class.

△ Guide

Begin by reminding students how the solar-system objects were spaced in the models they built. Ask them how their model would be different if they had to show the way the planets orbit the Sun. They should recognize that they would need a lot more space. They would need to measure out the number of paces to their solar-system object on every side of the Sun. Tell them they will now investigate the orbits of Earth and a few other planets.

Students start to consider revising their model.

Build a Moving Model of the Solar System

A moving model, or simulation, of the solar system will show you the orbits of various planets compared to each other. However, to make a simulation in which you can see the relative motion of the planets, you will have to make some adjustments to the model you have been using. The model will not be to scale for size or distance. Also, it will be easier to visualize if the number of solar-system objects is limited to six—the Sun, Mercury, Venus, Earth, Mars, and Jupiter. Six students in the class will represent the Sun and planets. The rest of the class should watch carefully and offer advice as the six students set themselves up. Then the class should watch as the Sun and planets carry out the simulation.

Set Up the Model

period (of an orbiting object): the time it takes an object to complete one revolution around another space object.

1. Begin by positioning a person representing the Sun in the middle of the space you are using for your model. Use a large enough space to allow five students to move in circular orbits about the Sun.

2. Arrange five students in a straight line out from the Sun, at about equal distance from each other. Remember that you are not using an accurate distance scale for this model.

3. In this simulation, Earth is the planet in the middle. Earth will take one minute to go around the Sun. The student who is representing Earth should practice walking one quarter of the way around the Sun in 15 seconds. Another student should act as a clock and count off seconds.

4. The time it takes a planet to move around the Sun is called its **period**. Mercury and Venus will move faster than Earth, while Mars and Jupiter will move more slowly than Earth. Using the numbers on the table as a guide, calculate how much time each model planet will take to travel one quarter of its orbit around the Sun. Enter these values in the last row of the table.

5. Each person representing a planet should practice walking his or her orbit at the correct speed. Someone will need to count off seconds. To learn how fast to walk, practice walking one quarter of the orbit in the time calculated in the last row of the table.

△ Guide

Tell students that they will now build a moving model of the solar system. They will focus on how solar-system objects move and will not involve distances, so their model will not be to scale. Also, to make it easier to understand what is happening, they will model only six solar-system objects: the Sun, Mercury, Venus, Earth, Mars, and Jupiter.

△ Guide

Tell students that six students will model the motions of solar-system objects, each representing one of the six solar-system objects in the model. The student representing the Sun will stand at the center, and the other five students will walk in circles of different diameters around the Sun to show the orbits of the planets. The rest of the class will watch the simulation. Emphasize that students who are watching the simulation should pay attention to how many orbits the different planets complete during a minute (representing a year), and that they should pay attention to the relative positions of the planets throughout each of Earth's orbits.

Choose six students to run the simulation. Position one of the students at the center of the space representing the solar system. Use tape to mark a line along which all of the planets will start. The line should start at the Sun and run to the edge of the space representing the solar system. Have the five students representing planets stand along this line, spaced at equal distances.

Set Up the Model
10 min

Students prepare to run the simulations.

NOTES

	Mercury	Venus	Earth	Mars	Jupiter
Orbital period (in Earth years)	0.24 years	0.62 years	1 year	1.88 years	11.86 years
Orbital period in model (1 Earth year = 1 minute)	14 seconds	37 seconds	60 seconds	109 seconds	712 seconds
One-quarter of orbital period in model			15 seconds		

Simulate the Movement of the Planets

1. All model planets should start in a straight line. Someone should act as a clock.

2. Begin the simulation. The clock should count out seconds. Each student should be careful to walk at the correct speed around the Sun. Model planets should try to observe the motion of the other planets as they walk.

3. Every minute, when Earth is back to the beginning of its orbit, pause the simulation. All the model planets should stop. Check where the other planets are. Use tape to mark the spot on the floor where each planet is after every Earth year. Label each piece of tape with the planet's name and the number of the Earth year at which the position was marked.

4. Repeat for 10 Earth years.

Analyze Your Data

After running the simulation, work together to analyze the data from the simulation. These questions will help you analyze the data. The first two questions are specific to a particular planet and require information from the person representing that planet. Other questions are for the rest of the class to answer.

1. How did the motion of the other planets appear from Mercury?

2. How did the motion of the other planets appear from Jupiter?

3. Mercury and Venus have orbital periods that are shorter than Earth's. How must they move, compared to Earth, to simulate the orbits correctly?

AST 135

ASTRONOMY

Simulate the Motion of the Planets

10 min

◯ Get Going

Tell students to slowly walk around the Sun in circles. The student simulating Earth should try to complete an orbit in about a minute. Someone should act as a clock. Students simulating the other planets should try to complete their orbits in the times listed in the table in the student text. Students standing nearer the Sun should walk faster than those standing away from the Sun. Because the circumferences of the orbits are greater the farther the planets are from the Sun, the difference in how fast students simulating different planets will not have to be great to get the right orbital periods, with the exception of Jupiter, which will have to move significantly slower than the other planets. Emphasize that the students simulating planets should pay close attention to the positions of the other planets as they walk around the Sun, by asking *How do the other planets appear throughout their orbit?*

When the student simulating Earth returns to the start line, stop the group and use tape to mark each of the planets' positions. Record the planet and the number of the orbit—for instance, "Mercury 1"—on each piece of tape. Then have students resume walking around the Sun. Stop them every minute and mark their positions. For each planet, you should have a series of markers on the floor by the end of the simulation—for instance, "Jupiter 1," "Jupiter 2," "Jupiter 3," "Jupiter 4," ..., "Jupiter 10."

△ Guide

Have the class examine the annual Earth-positions of the planets in the simulation as marked on the floor. Ask them what patterns they observe and how the orbits of the planets compare.

Lead a class discussion of the questions.

1. The student who simulated Mercury should respond that the motions of the other planets appeared to be slower.

2. The student who simulated Jupiter should respond that the motions of the other planets appeared fast.

3. Students will respond that Mercury and Venus should have shorter orbital periods and move somewhat faster.

Analyze Your Data

20 min

The class discusses the simulations.

NOTES

....

....

....

....

....

4. Jupiter is farther from the Sun than Earth. Jupiter's speed is slower than Earth's speed. How many times does Earth orbit the Sun in the time it takes Jupiter to orbit the Sun?

gravity: the force of attraction between two objects due to their mass; the greater the mass in each object, the stronger the attraction; the more distance between the objects, the weaker the attraction.

universe: everything that exists, including all objects in space.

Why Do Planets Orbit the Sun?

When you drop a ball, it falls to Earth. You can predict that the ball will fall every time. On Earth this is what you have learned to expect. The ball falls because the ball and Earth are attracted to each other. This attraction is called **gravity**, and it happens between every object in the **universe**, not just balls or other falling objects and Earth.

Two factors determine the strength of the force of gravity that two objects exert on each other. If the mass of either object increases, the attraction between the objects increases. But as the distance between two objects increases, the attraction between them decreases.

The Sun and all the planets are attracted to each other. As you know, the Sun has much more mass than any planet. Therefore, the Sun pulls on each planet more strongly than the planets pull on each other.

If the Sun is pulling all of the planets toward it, why do the planets remain in their orbits? What keeps the planets from falling into the Sun? Any object in motion has a tendency to resist any change in its motion. An object will keep moving in a straight line unless something causes it to change its motion. This means that a planet would continue to move in a straight line off into space unless a force acted on it to change its motion. In the solar system there is a force acting on the planet. The gravitational attraction between the planet and the Sun pulls the planet toward the Sun. As a result of gravity, planets move around the Sun instead of continuing off into space in a straight line.

Think about spinning a ball on a string above your head. As you spin the ball, it is being pulled toward you by the string. You are applying a force to hold the string. This force is directed toward you. The force on the string is similar to the force of gravity pulling a planet toward the Sun. If you let go of the string, the ball will fly off in a straight line. The force of the string that pulls the ball toward you is the force that changes the straight-line motion of the ball. When that force is removed, the ball is free to travel in a straight line.

AST 136

Project-Based Inquiry Science

4. Students should be able to answer this by looking at the tape markings on the floor. The answer should be about 11.

△ Guide

Briefly discuss how gravity keeps the planets in orbit around the Sun and keeps moons in orbit around their planets. Tell them that all objects exert a gravitational pull on each other. The more massive an object is, the greater the gravitational pull it exerts on other objects. The Sun, as the most massive body in the solar system, exerts the greatest gravitational pull on other objects of any solar-system body.

Discuss that the effect of the Sun's gravity on other solar-system objects is like the effect of a string when you swing a ball overhead. If you let go of the string, the ball would move in a straight line (until Earth's gravity pulled it down). The string prevents the ball from flying away from your hand. Similarly, if it wasn't for the Sun's gravitational pull, the other solar-system objects would move in a straight line, flying away from the solar system.

Why Do Planets Orbit the Sun?

10 min

The class discusses why planets orbit the Sun.

NOTES

Gravity is also the force responsible for the orbits of moons around the planets. For example, the Moon orbits Earth because of the gravitational attraction between Earth and the Moon. But why does the Moon orbit Earth when Earth has so much less mass than the Sun? Remember that distance also affects the strength of gravity's force of attraction. The Moon is much closer to Earth than to the Sun, so the gravitational pull from Earth is strong enough to pull the Moon into orbit around Earth.

Because the attractions among the planets are small compared to the Sun's gravity, the orbits of the planets stay the same for very long periods of time. However, a gravitational tug from a large planet such as Jupiter can significantly change the orbit of an asteroid or a comet. For this reason, the orbits of small objects can change over time, and they must be tracked closely to be able to predict where they will be at any given time.

Imagine spinning a ball on a string above your head. The ball is being pulled toward you the way gravity pulls a planet toward the Sun.

Reflect

1. On Earth, a **year** is equal to 365.25 days, or about 12 months. This is how long it takes Earth to orbit the Sun. Scientists define a year as the time it takes a planet to orbit the Sun. This means that the length of a year is different for every planet. What do you notice about the orbital periods, or years, of the planets between the Sun and Earth compared to those beyond Earth?

2. Eris is a dwarf planet farther away from the Sun than Neptune. Its average distance is about 100 AU from the Sun. Using what you have learned from the simulation, how do you think the orbital period of Eris would compare to those of Earth and Jupiter?

year: the time it takes for a solar-system object to make one complete revolution around the Sun.

AST 137

ASTRONOMY

The orbits of the moons around their planets are also due to gravity. For instance, the Moon orbits Earth because Earth's gravity prevents it from flying off into space.

Emphasize that the orbits of planets are fairly stable, because the gravitational pull of the Sun is much stronger than the gravitational pull of any other objects in the solar system. But the smaller objects, such as asteroids or comets, can change orbits over time due to the gravitational influence of the larger planets.

△ Guide

Have students work with their groups to answer the questions. As they work, monitor their progress and ask them what ideas they have discussed.

Lead a class discussion of their responses. Look for evidence students understand that the orbital period of a planet is related to its distance from the Sun. The farther a planet is from the Sun, the longer its orbital period is.

1. Students should recognize that the orbital periods of planets beyond the Earth are much longer than Earth's orbital period.

2. Students should answer that the orbital period of Eris is longer than that of Earth or Jupiter.

Reflect

15 min

Groups answer the questions and then have class discussion.

NOTES

....

....

....

....

....

....

....

....

....

....

....

....

3. What do you think would happen to Jupiter's orbit if Jupiter were to replace Earth at a distance of 1 AU from the Sun?

4. Jupiter orbits the Sun at a distance of about 5 AU, and Saturn orbits the Sun at a distance of about 10 AU. Compare the likelihood of the following objects colliding with either Jupiter or Saturn:

   a) a meteoroid with a circular orbit at a distance of 7 AU from the Sun

   b) a meteoroid with an elliptical orbit that varies from 4 AU to 15 AU from the Sun

elliptical orbit: an orbit in the shape of a flattened circle (ellipse).

ellipse: a shape that is a squashed or flattened circle. The sum of the distances from a point on the ellipse to each of the two foci is the same for every point on the ellipse.

eccentricity: a measurement used to describe the shape of an ellipse.

focus (plural, foci): one of two fixed points that determine the shape of an ellipse.

The Shape of Planetary Orbits

In your simulation, you moved in nearly circular orbits around the Sun. And what you just read about gravity tells you that the orbits of planets could be circular, just like when you spin a ball above your head on a string. However, no perfectly circular solar-system orbits have been discovered.

If the orbits of planets are not in the shape of a circle, what shape are they? Each planet moves around the Sun in an **elliptical orbit**. An elliptical orbit is in the shape of an **ellipse**. You can think of an ellipse as a "squashed" or flattened circle. The degree to which an ellipse appears flattened is described by a number called its **eccentricity**. The eccentricity of an ellipse is a number between 0 and 1 that tells how different the shape of an ellipse is from a circle. The closer the shape is to a circle, the lower the eccentricity. The eccentricity of a circle is 0. It is not flattened at all. Eccentricities that are close to 1 describe ellipses that are very stretched out. Earth's orbit has an eccentricity of 0.0167, which is very close to 0. Some solar-system objects, such as comets, can have elongated orbits with eccentricities close to 1.

If a planet's orbit were a perfect circle, the Sun would sit right in the center of the circle. Every point on the orbit would be the same distance from the Sun. Instead of a center, ellipses have two **foci**. (Note that foci is the plural form of **focus**.) For any point on an elliptical orbit, the sum of the distances from the point to the two foci is always the same. You can draw an ellipse using two pushpins, a loop of string, and a pencil as shown. The farther apart you make the two foci, the more stretched out the ellipse is.

AST 138

3. Students may suggest that, due to gravity, Jupiter would fall into the Sun if it were at 1 AU.

4. a) Student should respond that it is unlikely that an asteroid with a constant circular orbital distance (and period) would collide with either Jupiter or Saturn.

   b) Students should respond that it is more likely that an asteroid with a variable elliptical orbit which varies for 4 AU to 15 AU will collide with either Jupiter or Saturn.

△ Guide

Students may have difficulty with the concepts of eccentricity and foci. Help them to understand that the comparisons are to a circle which has no eccentricity and only one focal point.

The Shape of Planetary Orbits

5 min

Students read about the orbits of the planets.

NOTES

All of the objects going around the Sun have elliptical orbits. In each case, the Sun is located at one focus of the orbit. For example, think about Earth's orbit. Because the orbit is nearly circular, the foci are very close together. At the closest point to the Sun in its orbit, Earth is 147 million kilometers from the Sun. At the farthest point in its orbit, Earth is 152 million kilometers from the Sun. A difference of 5 million kilometers may seem like a lot, but it is a small fraction of the total distance between Earth and the Sun. You might think it would be warmer on Earth when it is closer to the Sun, but in fact Earth is farthest from the Sun in July, when it is summer in the Northern hemisphere.

The orbits of the planets are nearly circular, but objects like comets and asteroids can have flattened orbits. This means that the foci are farther apart. For these orbits, the distance between the object and the Sun changes a great deal throughout the orbit.

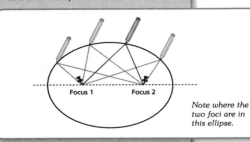

Note where the two foci are in this ellipse.

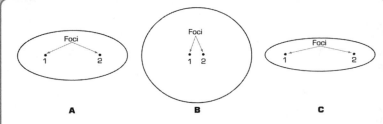

The more flattened the ellipse, the greater its eccentricity. Earth's orbit is almost circular, so the foci are very close together. Which of the ellipses pictured is the most eccentric? Which one is the least?

AST 139

ASTRONOMY

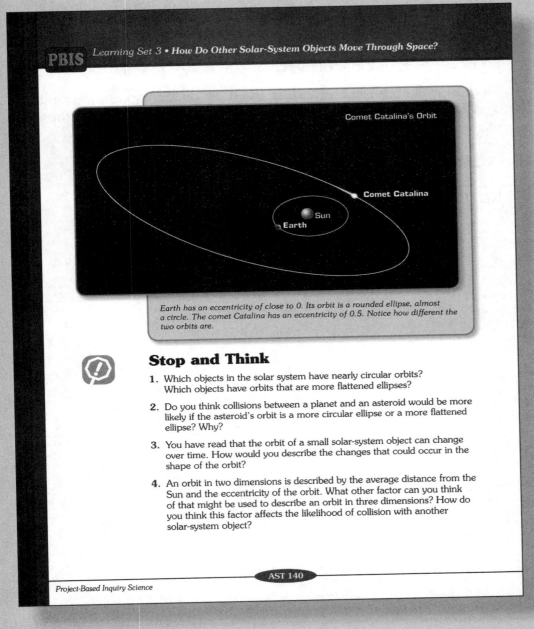

PBIS

Comet Catalina's Orbit

Comet Catalina

Sun

Earth

Earth has an eccentricity of close to 0. Its orbit is a rounded ellipse, almost a circle. The comet Catalina has an eccentricity of 0.5. Notice how different the two orbits are.

Stop and Think

Stop and Think

10 min

Students answer questions, applying their understanding of ellipses.

1. Which objects in the solar system have nearly circular orbits? Which objects have orbits that are more flattened ellipses?

2. Do you think collisions between a planet and an asteroid would be more likely if the asteroid's orbit is a more circular ellipse or a more flattened ellipse? Why?

3. You have read that the orbit of a small solar-system object can change over time. How would you describe the changes that could occur in the shape of the orbit?

4. An orbit in two dimensions is described by the average distance from the Sun and the eccentricity of the orbit. What other factor can you think of that might be used to describe an orbit in three dimensions? How do you think this factor affects the likelihood of collision with another solar-system object?

AST 140

Project-Based Inquiry Science

△ Guide and Assess

Give the students some time to answer the *Stop and Think* questions in their groups. Then lead a brief discussion of the answers.

1. Students should answer that all of the planets have nearly circular orbits with eccentricities near 0. Mercury has somewhat more eccentricity.

2. Student answers will vary, but most will think that asteroids with a more flattened ellipse and greater eccentricity would be more likely to collide with a planet.

3. Student answers will vary. Some students will suggest that asteroids in flattened ellipses could come under the strong gravitational influence of a larger planet and fly out of their regular orbit, making them a hazard to other planets.

4. Students may realize that adding the third dimension could bring the gravitational influences of other planets into play. Therefore, how close they come to other large planets may be a factor.

NOTES

Update the *Project Board*

So far in this *Learning Set* you have considered the sizes of several solar-system objects and the distance of these objects from the Sun. You learned about the shape of orbits and simulated how several planets orbit the Sun. This is all important information that will be needed to answer the *Big Question* for the Unit and should now be added to the *Project Board*.

Record your ideas about the motions of solar-system objects in the *What are we learning?* and *What is our evidence?* columns. Record any questions you still have or things you need to investigate further to predict when collisions between space objects may occur under *What do we need to investigate?* You will learn more about objects in the solar system and answer many of your questions during the rest of the *Learning Set*.

What's the Point?

Solar-system objects that orbit the Sun move in elliptical orbits. The shape of these orbits may be close to a perfect circle or may be more flattened in shape. Scientists describe the shape of elliptical orbits by measuring their eccentricities. An ellipse with an eccentricity close to 0 is nearly circular, and an ellipse with an eccentricity close to 1 is elongated.

Planets close to the Sun take less time to orbit the Sun than Earth, while the planets farther from the Sun take more time to orbit the Sun. The time it takes each object to make one full trip around the Sun is a year. This means a year for Venus is shorter than an Earth year, while a year for Mars is longer than an Earth year.

Two factors account for planets and other solar-system objects remaining in their orbits. One factor is the tendency of an object in motion to remain in motion in a straight line unless acted on by another force. Gravity is the second factor that accounts for solar-system objects remaining in their orbits. Gravitational attraction between the Sun and each solar-system object bends the object's path into an elliptical orbit.

Update the Project Board

10 min

Students have class discussion to update the Project Board.

△ Guide

Ask students what ideas they have about the motions of solar-system objects. Record their answers in the *What do we think we know?* column of the *Project Board*, and have students record them in their own *Project Board* pages. Then ask them what questions they still have and what they need to investigate to predict whether objects in space can collide. Record their responses in the *What do we need to investigate?* column of the *Project Board*.

Assessment Options

Targeted Concepts, Skills, and Nature of Science	How do I know if students got it?
Scientists often collaborate and share their findings. Sharing findings makes new information available and helps scientists refine their ideas and build on others' ideas. When another person's or group's idea is used, credit needs to be given.	**ASK:** How did the class collaborate to successfully run the simulation? **LISTEN:** Students should describe how some students had to move along the orbital paths, others kept track of how many "years" had elapsed on each planet, others had to mark positions at different times, and when the simulation was stopped, students had to describe the locations of the planets from their perspective, and so on. **ASK:** When the class discussed the changes in the relative positions of the planets, why was it helpful for the students representing the planets to describe what they saw? **LISTEN:** Students should answer that as observers, most of the class was looking at the model from the outside. The descriptions shared by the student "planets" helped the class understand how the model appeared from a different perspective.
Scientists must keep clear, accurate, and descriptive records of what they do so they can share their work with others; consider what they did, why they did it, and what they want to do next.	**ASK:** How could the class keep a record of the changing positions of the planets during the simulation? **LISTEN:** Students should describe by marking the positions of the planets at regular intervals, such as every Earth month.
Models are a representation of something in the world. Simulations use a model to imitate, or act out, real-life situations.	**ASK:** Compare and contrast the solar system model you created with the actual solar system. **LISTEN:** Student answers will vary, but may include: the planets' sizes, the distances between them and their rate of motion were not to scale; the shapes of the planets' orbits were not ellipses.

Targeted Concepts, Skills, and Nature of Science	How do I know if students got it?
The planets move around the Sun in elliptical orbits at predictable but varying speeds.	**ASK:** Summarize the equipment needed and the procedure you would follow to construct an ellipse. **LISTEN:** Students may suggest using push pins, a loop of string, and a pencil. They should place the two push pins at a distance apart corresponding to the distance between the foci of the ellipse. Place the loop of string around the pins. Place the pencil in the loop and, keeping the string taut, move it around the pins to draw the ellipse. **ASK:** Express the relationship between distance from the Sun and the time it took a planet to complete one orbit. **LISTEN:** Students should answer that the greater a planet's distance from the Sun, the longer it took to complete its orbit.
A year is the time it takes a planet to complete one revolution around the Sun. Earth's revolution around the Sun defines the length of an Earth year as 365.25 days.	**ASK:** How many times does Earth rotate on its axis during a year? **LISTEN:** Students should answer 365.25 times **ASK:** When the class ran the simulation, Mercury completed about four orbits during the time that Earth completed one orbit. How could you estimate the length of a year on Mercury in Earth days? **LISTEN:** Answers should include that if Mercury completes four orbits to Earth's one orbit, the length of a Mercury year is one quarter the length of an Earth year. Divide the number of days in an Earth year by four to determine the number of days in a Mercury year.

Targeted Concepts, Skills, and Nature of Science	How do I know if students got it?
The path of a planet around the Sun is due to the gravitational attraction between the Sun and the planet.	**ASK:** If gravity suddenly disappeared, how would the motion of the planets change? **LISTEN:** Students should answer that the planets would move in straight lines in the direction they were traveling at the instant gravity disappeared. **ASK:** What two factors determine the strength of the force of gravity? **LISTEN:** Students should identify the masses of the two objects and the distance between their centers.

Teacher Reflection Questions

- To what extent did your questioning during the simulation of orbital motion foster critical and creative thinking?

- What was the most effective reading assignment in this section? Why did you think this one was more effective than others?

- Which examples used in the readings could you have easily demonstrated for the class? How would that have enhanced their understanding of the concept addressed in the reading?

- What types of students do you need to spend more time serving?

- What additional assistance, support, and/or resources would have further enhanced this section of the *Learning Set?*

- Students will soon use a model to analyze how the actual motions of the planets lead to their apparent motions against the background of the constellations. How can you prepare them to think about the actual motions of the planets and the apparent motions of the planets?

SECTION 3.4 INTRODUCTION

3.4 Explore

What Do Moving Planets Look Like From Earth?

◀ **2 class periods**

A class period is considered to be one 40 to 50 minute class.

Overview

Students investigate how the planets' orbital motion causes their position to change relative to the fixed background of stars. They read about why the stars remain in fixed relative positions, constellations, and the origin of the word *planet*. Students then set up a solar system model consisting of a "map" representing the orbital paths of Earth, the five planets visible to the unaided eye from Earth, circles representing the monthly position of the planets. The perimeter of the model shows twelve major constellations in the background stars surrounding the solar system. By plotting the monthly change in the positions of the planets in their orbits relative to Earth, students simulate planets' orbital motion and record their changing location against the constellations in the background stars when viewed from Earth. Students analyze data collected during the simulation to determine patterns of change and the role of perspective in the apparent retrograde motion of some planets when viewed from Earth. Students then read an account of the historical move from a geocentric to a heliocentric model of the structure of the solar system.

Targeted Concepts, Skills, and Nature of Science	Performance Expectations
Scientists often collaborate and share their findings. Sharing findings makes new information available and helps scientists refine their ideas and build on others' ideas. When another person's or group's idea is used, credit needs to be given.	Students collaborate in small groups to identify patterns in the data collected during the simulation of planets' orbital motion.
Scientists must keep clear, accurate, and descriptive records of what they do so they can share their work with others; consider what they did, why they did it, and what they want to do next.	Students record the number of Earth months it takes each planet to orbit the Sun and the monthly changes in the positions of the planets against the constellations of the background stars as viewed from Earth.

Targeted Concepts, Skills, and Nature of Science	Performance Expectations
Models are a representation of something in the world. Simulations use a model to imitate, or act out, real-life situations.	Students use the *Planetary Orbit Simulation* chart to simulate the changing relative positions of planets due to orbital motion.
Long ago people thought all objects in the universe revolved around Earth (geocentric model) until scientists proved that Earth and the other planets revolve around the Sun (heliocentric model).	Students compare and contrast the geocentric and heliocentric models of the structure of the solar system. Students cite evidence that supports the heliocentric model over the geocentric model.
The apparent motions of the Sun, Moon, planets, and stars across the sky can be explained by Earth's rotation and revolution.	Students describe how Earth's rotation and revolution account for apparent daily and annual motions of planets and stars.
When viewed from Earth, stars remain in fixed positions relative to one another as they appear to move across the sky. Constellations are imaginary patterns of stars used by observers to track changes in the positions of objects viewed in the sky.	Students use the positions of constellations in the fixed background of stars to track changes in the positions of planets as viewed from Earth.
Different stars can be seen at different times of the year and planets change their positions against the background of stars over time.	Students use the *Planetary Orbit Simulation* chart to identify the constellations in the fixed background of stars that will be visible from Earth at different times of the year. Students identify patterns and anomalies, such as retrograde motion, in the data they collected about the changes in the positions of the planets against the background of stars as viewed from Earth.

Materials	
1 per group	*Planet Simulation* page *Planetary Observations* page Ruler or straight edge *Planetary Orbit Simulation* chart
1 per student	Pencil

Activity Setup and Preparation

Running the procedure before class will familiarize you with the layout of the *Planetary Orbit Simulation* chart and the data collection method so that you are better able to address students' questions.

Homework Options

Reflection

- **Science Content:** If you looked out at the stars on a clear night in March, which constellations would not be visible? Why? *(Students should refer to their* Planetary Observations *page and identify the constellation behind the Sun in March and/or its adjacent constellations.)*

- **Science Content:** According to the model, how many Earth months does it take for Mars to complete one revolution around the Sun? *(Students should describe how Mars completes one revolution in 23 Earth months, or a little less than two Earth years.)*

- **Science Process:** What did you do to identify any patterns or trends in the movements of the planets on the *Planet Simulation* page as viewed from Earth? *(Students' answers should indicate that they analyzed the sequence of the constellations with which the planets aligned.)*

Preparation for 3.5

- **Science Content:** What evidence have you learned that supports the idea that there are objects in the solar system that are much smaller than the planets? *(Students should cite impact craters on Earth and meteorites are evidence that smaller objects exist in the solar system.)*

- **Science Process:** What would you have to know to be able to predict whether an object in orbit around the Sun would strike Earth? *(Students should answer that by tracking the object's motion one could determine its orbital path. Once the object's orbital path is known, it could be compared with Earth's known orbital path to determine if the orbits cross. If the orbits cross, the object could impact Earth.)*

NOTES

3.4 Explore

What Do Moving Planets Look Like From Earth?

In *Learning Set 2*, you saw how difficult it was to determine the real motion of objects in the solar system simply by observing what was seen in the sky. However, in *Learning Set 2*, you only had to deal with two objects in the sky, the Sun and the Moon. Now imagine how difficult the problem becomes when you consider all of the planets.

You also learned that the stars rise and set each night, but that they stay fixed in relation to one another. Long ago, observers named patterns they see in the stars. These patterns are called *constellations*.

Oct 12 Oct 7 Oct 3 Sept 27 Sept 19 Sept 14 Sept 8   Sept 1 Aug 28 Aug 23 Aug 21

Early astronomers noticed the movement of planets across the sky. In this composite image, Mars is seen moving to the left over the course of about two months.

Early astronomers used the fixed background of stars to track the motions of the Sun, the Moon, and the planets. They noticed that a few bright star-like objects moved slowly in different paths across the sky and seemed to "wander" among the stars. At times, these objects even seemed to reverse their direction against the background. The word "planet" comes from a Greek word meaning "wanderer." The Greeks gave these objects this name because the planets did not remain fixed like the stars.

AST 142

Project-Based Inquiry Science

3.4 Explore

What Do Moving Planets Look Like From Earth?

5 min

Students are introduced to constellations.

△ Guide

Begin by discussing how there are patterns in the stars that change very little over time. These patterns are called *constellations*. Tell students that early astronomers were able to track the apparent motion of the Sun, the Moon, and the planets against the backdrop of these patterns.

*A class period is considered to be one 40 to 50 minute class.

In the last section, you ran a simulation of five planets orbiting the Sun. This model showed the motion of the planets as though you were observing from outside the solar system. The model worked well to compare the rates at which each planet orbits the Sun. However, the model did not represent the relative positions of the planets as you see them from Earth. Now, you will see what the moving planets look like from Earth and, like the ancient astronomers, you will learn to predict their movements.

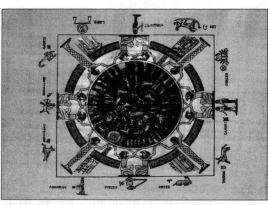

The ancient Egyptians based their calendars on observations of the stars. Around the outside edge of the Egyptian calendar pictured are 12 star constellations, each representing a period of about 30 days

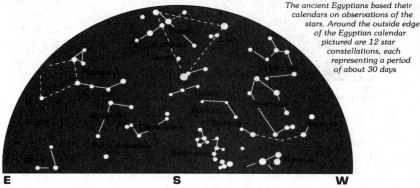

Stars stay fixed in relation to one another. The patterns that they form have been observed by people since ancient times. They named some of these patterns "constellations."

AST 143

ASTRONOMY

Tell students that early astronomers were interested in tracking the apparent motion of the planets because, unlike the stars, the planets appeared to wander. Tell them that the word *planet* comes from a Greek word for wanderer. In addition to moving across the sky, the planets seemed to reverse direction at times. Tell students they will now use a model to investigate how the orbits of the planets cause their apparent motion, as seen from Earth.

Stop and Think

1. How did the motions of the planets look when viewed from outside of the solar system? How do you think your view of the motions of the planets would change if you viewed them from Earth?

2. Describe how early astronomers might have used a background of stars to identify planets.

Chinese astronomers are believed to have been the first to map the position of the stars, as seen in this map from 4 B.C.E.

Simulating Motions of the Planets

Knowing the positions of the planets, and being able to predict where they will be in the future, would be important to anyone trying to predict

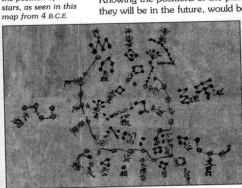

if, and when, objects in the solar system might collide. In this activity, you will use the model on the *Planetary Orbit Simulation* chart, which shows the orbits of five planets. This model also includes the Sun and 12 constellations. These constellations can be thought of as landmarks in the sky, against which you can compare the movements of the planets. Using this representation, you will work with a model of the planets as they are seen from Earth. You will record your observations on the *Planetary Orbit Observations* page.

Materials
- ruler
- pencil
- *Planetary Orbit Observations* page
- *Planetary Orbit Simulation* chart

Procedure

1. Examine the model on the *Planetary Orbit Simulation* chart. Find the orbits of Mercury, Venus, Earth, Mars, and Jupiter. Review the model with your group.

   a) Locate the Sun.

   b) Locate the 12 constellations.

   c) Locate the numbered positions of the five planets.

AST 144

Project-Based Inquiry Science

Stop and Think

5 min

Students answer the Stop and Think *questions.*

△ Guide

Have students answer the *Stop and Think* questions before they simulate the motions of the planets. As students work, monitor their progress, and ask them what kind of ideas they have discussed about using the constellations to identify planets.

1. Student answers will vary. They should answer that no one has been outside the solar system, so it is difficult to imagine.

2. Students should reply that early astronomers saw that the stars did not change their positions during the lifetimes of the astronomers and were considered "fixed" in position. These stars could be used to mark the changes of position of planets which had regular movements.

Simulating Motions of the Planets

5 min

Students are introduced to the activity.

Chinese astronomers are believed to have been the first to map the position of the stars, as seen in this map from 4 B.C.E.

...ice how to identify planets.

Simulating Motions of the Planets

Knowing the positions of the planets, and being able to predict where they will be in the future, would be important to anyone trying to predict

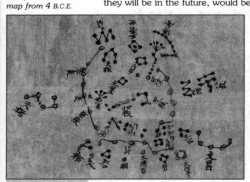

if, and when, objects in the solar system might collide. In this activity, you will use the model on the *Planetary Orbit Simulation* chart, which shows the orbits of five planets. This model also includes the Sun and 12 constellations. These constellations can be thought of as landmarks in the sky, against which you can compare the movements of the planets. Using this representation, you will work with a model of the planets as they are seen from Earth. You will record your observations on the *Planetary Orbit Observations* page.

Materials
• ruler
• pencil
• *Planetary Orbit Observations* page
• *Planetary Orbit Simulation* chart

Procedure

1. Examine the model on the *Planetary Orbit Simulation* chart. Find the orbits of Mercury, Venus, Earth, Mars, and Jupiter. Review the model with your group.

a) Locate the Sun.

b) Locate the 12 constellations.

c) Locate the numbered positions of the five planets.

AST 144

Project-Based Inquiry Science

△ Guide

Distribute the *Planetary Orbit Simulation* charts and *Planetary Orbit Observations* pages. Point out that the orbits of five planets—Mercury, Venus, Earth, Mars, and Jupiter—are shown on the *Planetary Orbit Simulation* chart in the student text, along with the Sun at the center and the constellations at the border. Emphasize that as students run their simulations, they will use the constellations as landmarks by which they can compare the motions of the planets.

2. Find position 1 for each planet. This represents where each planet is in the month of January in a particular year.

3. Determine which constellation is seen behind Mercury when observed from Earth in January. To do this, line up Earth in position 1 with Mercury in position 1, continuing the line to the constellations in the outer circle. This is the constellation that would appear behind Mercury as seen from Earth in January. Record the name of the constellation in the January row of the table on the *Planetary Orbit Observations* page.

4. Using the same procedure as you used in Step 3, record the constellations behind Venus, Mars, Jupiter, and the Sun as seen from Earth in January. For the Sun, you will not need to find a position number because the Sun does not change its position.

5. After one month, each planet will be in position 2. Using the same procedure you used in Step 3, observe which constellation is behind each planet and the Sun in February. This time, however, make your observations using position 2 for each planet. Record the names of the constellations in the February row of the table on the *Planetary Orbit Observations* page.

6. Continue making observations for the Sun and each planet one month at a time. After position 3, you will need to add in position numbers for each planet. For Mercury, position 4 will be the same as position 1, position 5 will be the same as position 2, and so on. Record the background constellations on the *Planetary Orbit Observations* page.

AST 145

ASTRONOMY

△ **Guide**

Go over the procedure with the class. They will put markers on the *Planetary Orbit Simulation* chart to represent the planets and move them around the orbits marked on the board. They will move each planet one space for each month. In order to make it easier for students to analyze the relationships of the pieces on the chart, have them start with Mercury and Earth only. After they complete one year (one Earth orbit), they can add Venus and rerun the simulation. Then they can add Mars, and, finally, Jupiter. Note that they will need to start the year over each time, so they can see how the position of each of the other planets relates to the position of Earth in January.

Planetary Orbit Simulation

AST 146

Project-Based Inquiry Science

As students run the simulation, they should record their observations in their *Planetary Orbit Observations* pages. They should note what constellation is behind the Sun from Earth's perspective each month. Point out that this constellation, the other five constellations in that half of the celestial sphere, and any planets in front of these constellations from Earth's perspective will not be visible to an observer on Earth. This is because the stars and planets are not visible during the day, and an observer on Earth will be turned away from this side of the sky at night. That is, Earth will be between the observer and this side of the celestial sphere at night, blocking the observer's view.

Students should also note which constellation appears behind each planet. In the first year they simulate, they should note the constellations behind Mercury.

△ Guide and Assess

Then have groups run the simulations. As they work, monitor their progress and assist them with any difficulties that come up.

NOTES

Analyze Your Data

20 min

Students answer the Analyze Your Data *questions.*

Analyze Your Data

1. Describe any patterns or trends you were able to identify in the movements of the five planets as seen from Earth.

2. How did the position of Mercury in each month compare with the position of the Sun? How did the position of Venus in each month compare with the position of the Sun?

3. By studying the *Planetary Orbit Simulation* page and your data, describe when and where in the night sky you should look if you want to find Mercury or Venus. (Caution: Do not attempt to observe these planets without first discussing safety issues with your teacher.)

4. How does the Sun progress through the constellations throughout the year? In which direction around the circle does the Sun's background constellation move, clockwise or counterclockwise? In which direction do the background constellations for Mercury and Venus move?

5. What, if any, is the relationship between the locations of Mars and Jupiter and the position of the Sun?

6. What did you notice about the pattern of background constellations for Mars and Jupiter?

Determining the Structure of the Solar System

The simulation you just used made it very clear that the motion of the planets as seen from Earth is confusing. However, you have already learned that the planets move in nearly circular orbits around the Sun. Ancient astronomers had to figure this out for themselves. Astronomers have been able to accurately predict the position of the planets in the sky for over two thousand years. But, the correct model for the solar system was not agreed upon until the 1600s.

A good model of the solar system must account for many observations. One of the most difficult observations to represent in a solar-system model is **retrograde motion**. In general, the planets move across the sky from west to east against the background of fixed stars. During retrograde motion, planets such as Mars and Jupiter appear to reverse direction and travel east to west. You observed the retrograde motion of Mars and Jupiter on the *Planetary Orbit Simulation* page.

retrograde motion: motion of an outer planet in which the planet appears to reverse direction as seen from Earth.

AST 147

ASTRONOMY

△ Guide and Assess

Have students answer the *Analyze Your Data* questions with their groups. As they discuss the questions, ask them what ideas they have discussed. When students have answered the *Analyze Your Data* questions, lead a class discussion of their responses.

Students should recognize that Mercury and Venus are always near the Sun on the celestial sphere. For this reason, Mercury is very hard to observe, and both Mercury and Venus are near the horizon when they are visible.

Students should also note that Mars appears to move backwards at times—a phenomenon known as *retrograde motion.*

1. Students may notice that the Sun moves about one constellation counter-clockwise each month and covers all of the constellations in one Earth year. They may also notice that Mercury and Mars appear to go backwards (clockwise, retrograde) at times. Jupiter spends about one Earth year in each constellation. In general, all of the solar-system objects move clockwise through the constellations.

2. Students should respond that both Mercury and Venus are always within two constellations of the Sun. This means that they will appear near the Sun and be difficult to see.

3. Students may suggest that people should look for Mercury or Venus very near the western horizon after sunset or very near the eastern horizon before sunrise.

4. Students should understand that the Sun progresses through the constellations in a counter-clockwise manner. The background constellations appear to move clockwise if the Sun is considered to be stationary. The constellations also generally move clockwise with regard to the motions of Mercury and Venus.

5. Students should answer that there is little relationship between the locations of Mars and Jupiter and the position of the Sun. They do appear to slowly move in the same direction as the Sun.

6. Students should answer that the pattern of background constellations changes very slowly for Mars and Jupiter.

NOTES

....

....

....

....

....

....

Determining the Structure of the Solar System

15 min

Students discuss the geocentric and heliocentric models of the solar system.

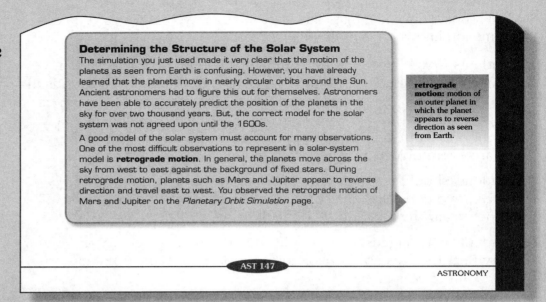

Determining the Structure of the Solar System

The simulation you just used made it very clear that the motion of the planets as seen from Earth is confusing. However, you have already learned that the planets move in nearly circular orbits around the Sun. Ancient astronomers had to figure this out for themselves. Astronomers have been able to accurately predict the position of the planets in the sky for over two thousand years. But, the correct model for the solar system was not agreed upon until the 1600s.

A good model of the solar system must account for many observations. One of the most difficult observations to represent in a solar-system model is **retrograde motion**. In general, the planets move across the sky from west to east against the background of fixed stars. During retrograde motion, planets such as Mars and Jupiter appear to reverse direction and travel east to west. You observed the retrograde motion of Mars and Jupiter on the *Planetary Orbit Simulation* page.

retrograde motion: motion of an outer planet in which the planet appears to reverse direction as seen from Earth.

AST 147

ASTRONOMY

△ Guide

Discuss how the apparent motions of the planets against the backdrop of the constellations, which students observed in their simulation, are hard to interpret if you do not already know how the planets orbit the Sun. Tell students that early astronomers generally assumed that Earth was the center of the observed universe, and that the Sun and the other planets orbited Earth. Aristarchus, a Greek astronomer, developed an early heliocentric model in 280 B.C.E., but it was not widely accepted. Ptolemy developed a geocentric model 400 years later that became widely accepted until the 16th century.

NOTES

....

....

....

....

....

....

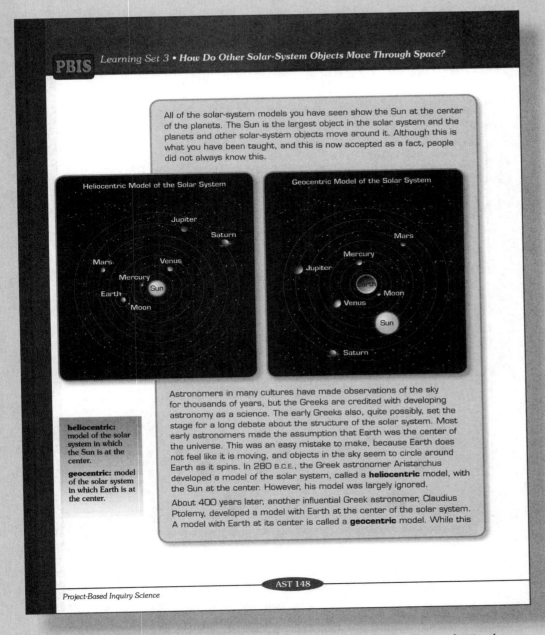

All of the solar-system models you have seen show the Sun at the center of the planets. The Sun is the largest object in the solar system and the planets and other solar-system objects move around it. Although this is what you have been taught, and this is now accepted as a fact, people did not always know this.

Heliocentric Model of the Solar System

Jupiter
Saturn
Mars
Venus
Mercury
Sun
Earth
Moon

Geocentric Model of the Solar System

Mars
Mercury
Jupiter
Earth
Moon
Venus
Sun
Saturn

heliocentric: model of the solar system in which the Sun is at the center.

geocentric: model of the solar system in which Earth is at the center.

Astronomers in many cultures have made observations of the sky for thousands of years, but the Greeks are credited with developing astronomy as a science. The early Greeks also, quite possibly, set the stage for a long debate about the structure of the solar system. Most early astronomers made the assumption that Earth was the center of the universe. This was an easy mistake to make, because Earth does not feel like it is moving, and objects in the sky seem to circle around Earth as it spins. In 280 B.C.E., the Greek astronomer Aristarchus developed a model of the solar system, called a **heliocentric** model, with the Sun at the center. However, his model was largely ignored.

About 400 years later, another influential Greek astronomer, Claudius Ptolemy, developed a model with Earth at the center of the solar system. A model with Earth at its center is called a **geocentric** model. While this

AST 148

Tell students that in the late 15th century, an astronomer named Nicolaus Copernicus proposed that a heliocentric model of the solar system could be much simpler than the Ptolemaic model. In 1609, another famous astronomer, Galileo, began using a telescope to make observations that supported the heliocentric model. The student text provides examples of Venus's phases, which are not compatible with a geocentric model. Also incongruous with the Ptolemaic way of thinking was Galileo's observation that several moons orbited Jupiter rather than orbiting Earth.

geocentric model allowed Ptolemy to accurately predict the positions of the planets, it relied on some complex details to predict retrograde motion of a planet like Mars. Ptolemy's model also included some slight imperfections in the calculations. Despite these imperfections, Ptolemy's model remained widely accepted until the 1500s because it could be used to accurately predict positions of the planets in the sky. In 1473, the Polish astronomer Nicolaus Copernicus worked to improve on Ptolemy's geocentric model. He found that a much simpler model is possible when the Sun is the center of the solar system. His heliocentric model could explain retrograde motion by showing the relative motion of the faster-moving Earth as it passes a slower-moving outer planet. But the heliocentric model of Copernicus also had imperfections and in fact it was no better than Ptolemy's model in predicting the motions of the planets. Yet the Copernicus model got scientists thinking about the solar system in a different way.

The debate about the two models continued for more than a century. Finally, in 1609, Galileo started using the newly invented telescope to make observations. His data supported the heliocentric model. First of all, Galileo discovered four objects that orbited Jupiter. These were later named the Galilean moons of Jupiter. This proved that it was possible for solar-system objects to orbit objects other than Earth. Later, Galileo showed that Venus had phases similar to the Moon's phases. In the geocentric model, the Sun is never between Venus and Earth, so you would never see a "full Venus" phase. Galileo's data showed that Venus does have all the same phases that the Moon does, including the "full Venus" phase.

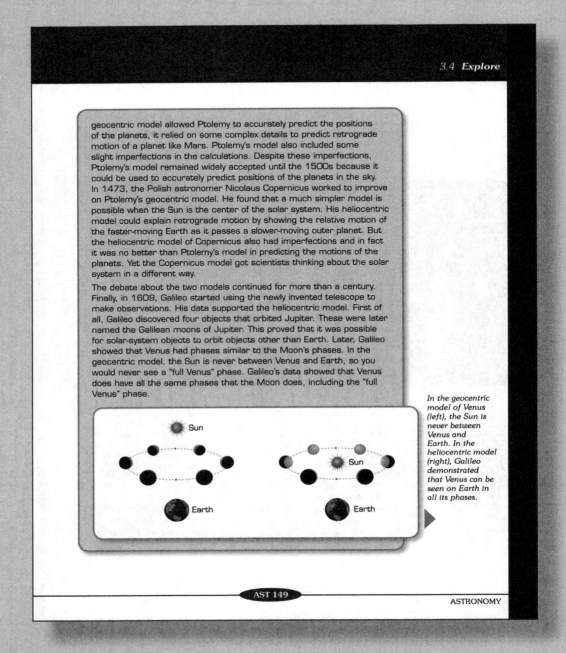

In the geocentric model of Venus (left), the Sun is never between Venus and Earth. In the heliocentric model (right), Galileo demonstrated that Venus can be seen on Earth in all its phases.

At about the same time, Johannes Kepler developed three laws of planetary motion, which showed that the planets had elliptical orbits and how a heliocentric model could predict the motions of the planets more accurately than the Ptolemaic model.

Largely for religious reasons, it was many years before Galileo's observations were accepted. At the time, people preferred a universe with Earth at its center. But finally, scientific thinking triumphed, and the heliocentric model of the solar system was accepted.

It took nearly 2000 years for people to move from first recognizing the difference between stars and planets to showing that Earth orbits the Sun. At about the same time that the heliocentric model was finally accepted, astronomers also figured out the elliptical nature of the orbits. It was the assumption Copernicus made that the orbits of the planets were circular that caused the imperfections in his model.

In the 16th century, Danish astronomer Tycho Brahe made even more accurate observations. He insisted that nightly observations be made at his observatory. He wrote his observations and data analyses in several books. From these exact observations, Brahe's assistant, Johannes Kepler, a German astronomer and mathematician, studied and analyzed the heliocentric model of Copernicus.

By 1609, Kepler had developed three laws of planetary motion. In these laws, Kepler described how the planets move and how the orbits of the planets can be predicted. Kepler's laws proved that planets do not orbit the Sun in perfect circles. Instead, the shape of each orbit is an ellipse. In 1687, Newton published his *law of universal gravitation*. He used math to prove Kepler's laws. Astronomers could now confidently use the heliocentric model to accurately predict the positions of the planets and other objects in the solar system.

Johannes Kepler (right), an assistant to astronomer Tycho Brahe, built his theories on knowledge he gained from Brahe's work. Sir Isaac Newton then used Kepler's laws to formulate his own laws. Scientists can always learn from the work of others.

Stop and Think

5 min

Students answer the Stop and Think *questions.*

Stop and Think

1. Models often form the basis of a scientific theory. One thing that all scientific theories must do is make accurate predictions. Scientists will accept a theory until a better theory comes along. Why do you think it took so long for the heliocentric model to be accepted?

2. Why was the heliocentric model accepted? In what ways was the heliocentric model better than the geocentric model?

3. What role did accurate observations play in the acceptance of the heliocentric model?

4. How do you think scientists use Newton's law of universal gravitation when trying to predict whether two solar-system objects will collide?

What's the Point?

Ancient astronomers recognized that some objects in the sky moved against the fixed background of the stars. These objects were called planets. Ptolemy's geocentric model, with Earth at the center, was widely accepted until the 1500s because it could accurately predict positions of the planets. A heliocentric model, with the Sun at the center of the solar system, was not widely accepted until the 1600s. A heliocentric model with elliptical orbits allows astronomers to accurately predict the positions of planets.

Planets closer to the Sun than Earth (Mercury and Venus) always appear in the sky near the Sun's location. That is why Mercury and Venus are only visible within a few hours of sunrise or sunset. Planets farther from the Sun can rise and set at any time.

The planets generally move in a counterclockwise direction in the sky, from west to east. However, during retrograde motion the outer planets, such as Mars and Jupiter, appear to reverse direction and move clockwise (east to west) for periods of time.

AST 151

ASTRONOMY

△ Guide and Assess

Circulate the classroom to help students find the answers to the questions. Then lead a brief discussion of the correct answers.

1. Students should understand that the Ptolemeic model worked very well and accurately made most predictions. It was also more natural to view Earth as the center of the universe since the celestial sphere does move cyclically and one cannot feel the Earth moving.

2. Students should understand that the heliocentric model was accepted because it was simpler than the geocentric model and could make even better predictions. The phases of Venus could be accounted for with a heliocentric model but not a geocentric model.

3. Students should reply that accurate observations of the phases of the planet Venus were very important in the acceptance of the heliocentric model.

4. Students may suggest that scientists use Newton's law of universal gravitation to predict whether one solar-system object will fall into the gravitational field of another, thus causing a collision.

Assessment Options

Targeted Concepts, Skills, and Nature of Science	How do I know if students got it?
Scientists often collaborate and share their findings. Sharing findings makes new information available and helps scientists refine their ideas and build on others' ideas. When another person's or group's idea is used, credit needs to be given.	**ASK:** How could your group have worked better to identify patterns or trends in the data you collected? **LISTEN:** Student answers will vary. The purpose of this question is to engage students in evaluation of their group process skills.
Scientists must keep clear, accurate, and descriptive records of what they do so they can share their work with others; consider what they did, why they did it, and what they want to do next.	**ASK:** How did your group determine the length of time it took for each planet to orbit the Sun? **LISTEN:** Students should describe by counting the number of circles that make up each orbit. They should identify that each successive mark corresponds to one month. **ASK:** Which planets' changes in position as viewed from Earth did not continuously follow the sequence in which the constellations appear around the perimeter of the *Planetary Orbit Simulation* chart? **LISTEN:** Students should name all of the planets.

Targeted Concepts, Skills, and Nature of Science	How do I know if students got it?
Models are a representation of something in the world. Simulations use a model to imitate, or act out, real-life situations.	**ASK:** What were you simulating by moving the markers from one spot to the next on the model board? **LISTEN:** Students should know they were simulating the motion of the planets along their orbital paths.
Long ago people thought all objects in the universe revolved around Earth (geocentric model) until scientists proved that Earth and the other planets revolve around the Sun (heliocentric model).	**ASK:** How does the geocentric model account for the observation that the Sun, stars, and planets move across the sky from east to west? How does the heliocentric model account for this observation? **LISTEN:** Students should answer that in a geocentric model, objects move in circles around the Earth. In a heliocentric model, Earth rotates on its axis.
The apparent motions of the Sun, Moon, planets, and stars across the sky can be explained by Earth's rotation and revolution.	**ASK:** How does Earth's rotation account for the apparent daily motions of the Sun and stars? **LISTEN:** As Earth rotates from west to east, these objects appear to move from east to west. **ASK:** How does Earth's revolution account for the observation that the constellations of the fixed background of stars changes cyclically during the course of a year? **LISTEN:** Students should answer that stars are only visible from the side of Earth facing away from the Sun. As Earth orbits the Sun, the side facing away from the Sun faces different parts of the surrounding universe. Therefore, different stars and constellations will be visible at different points in its orbit.

Targeted Concepts, Skills, and Nature of Science	How do I know if students got it?
When viewed from Earth, stars remain in fixed positions relative to one another as they appear to move across the sky. Constellations are imaginary patterns of stars used by observers to track changes in the positions of objects viewed in the sky.	**ASK:** Suppose you made a sketch of the constellation Taurus. How do you think your sketch would compare with a sketch made by Tycho Brahe? Ptolemy? **LISTEN:** Students should recognize that the sketches would look the same, because the positions of the stars relative to one another as viewed from Earth appears fixed. Even the nearest star is so far from Earth that the distance from one end of Earth's orbit to the other is an incredibly tiny fraction of its distance from Earth. Therefore, Earth's change in position relative to the stars is virtually imperceptible to an observer on Earth and the positions of the stars appear fixed.
Different stars can be seen at different times of the year and planets change their positions against the background of stars over time.	**ASK:** Use the *Planetary Orbit Simulation* chart to answer this question: Imagine you are on Mercury during the month of July on Earth, how would the constellations seen in the sky at night on Mercury compare with those seen from Earth? **LISTEN:** Students should answer that from Mercury the constellations Scorpio, Libra, Virgo, Leo and Cancer would be seen. From Earth, Taurus, Aries, Pisces, Aquarius, and Capricorn would be seen. **ASK:** Why would Venus not be visible at night to an observer on Earth when both planets are in Position 1? **LISTEN:** Students should answer that it would not be visible because night occurs on the side of Earth facing away from the Sun and Venus is on the side of Earth facing toward the Sun.

Teacher Reflection Questions

- How well do you feel that students understood the geocentric and heliocentric models that were presented in this section? What evidence do you have?

- To what extent are your assessment techniques fair and appropriate for evaluating progress and for making instructional decisions?

- What factors negatively or positively affected the success of the activity?

NOTES

SECTION 3.5 INTRODUCTION

3.5 Explore

Where in the Solar System Are Smaller Objects Found?

◀ **1 class period**

A class period is considered to be one 40 to 50 minute class.

Overview

Having determined that the orbits of the planets do not intersect and therefore are unlikely to collide with Earth, students consider other objects in the solar system that orbit the Sun. The section opens with a reading about theories of the formation of the solar system and how the solar nebula theory accounts for the direction in which planets rotate and revolve, their orbital plane, and the existence of smaller objects, such as asteroids. Students consider how the orbital motion of planets and their moons makes it unlikely that they will collide with Earth and read about the characteristics of Near-Earth Objects (NEO's) and why they are more likely to collide with Earth than planets or moons.

Targeted Concepts, Skills, and Nature of Science	Performance Expectations
Scientists often collaborate and share their findings. Sharing findings makes new information available and helps scientists refine their ideas and build on others' ideas. When another person's or group's idea is used, credit needs to be given.	Students share their responses to the *Stop and Think* questions and collaborate to update the *Project Board*.
Scientists must keep clear, accurate, and descriptive records of what they do so they can share their work with others; consider what they did, why they did it, and what they want to do next.	Students make notes of important ideas as they read. Students participate in a class discussion updating their *Project Board*, which is an organizing record of their ideas and what they are learning.

Targeted Concepts, Skills, and Nature of Science	Performance Expectations
Our solar system coalesced out of a giant cloud of gas and debris about five billion years ago. The Sun formed when gas and debris heated up from the energy of falling together began releasing nuclear energy from the fusion of light elements into heavier ones in its extremely hot, dense core.	Students describe the events that led to the formation of the solar system according to the solar nebula theory.
Around the planets orbit a great variety of moons. Flat rings of rock and ice debris orbit some planets, and Earth is orbited by a moon and artificial satellites.	Students identify small solar-system objects and describe events that could change their orbit so that it crosses Earth's orbit.
Humankind's need to explore continues to lead to the development of knowledge and understanding of the nature of the Universe.	Students describe how the space exploration will provide astronomers with information about the solar system.

Materials	
1 per class	Class *Project Board*

Homework Options

Reflection

- **Science Content:** What caused the cloud of dust and gas from which the solar system formed to collapse in on itself? *(Students should identify mutual gravitational attraction as the cause of the cloud.)*

- **Science Content:** How does the solar nebula theory account for the observation that all of the planets orbit the Sun in the same direction and in roughly the same plane? *(Students should describe how the cloud of dust and gas from which the solar system collapsed in on itself began to spin. The planets formed from the material in the spinning disk surrounding the Sun. Therefore, they all lie in the plane of that disk and all move in the direction in which the disk was spinning.)*

- **Science Process:** How could you organize the notes you take while reading so that they can serve as a more effective resource? *(Students' answers will vary. Students should suggest the use of graphic organizers, such as two-column notes, ISP chart [information/sources/page], concept maps, word webs, problem-solution charts and so on.)*

Preparation for 3 BBQ

- **Science Content:** Make a list of all of the different objects in the solar system that have been identified so far in this Unit. Do you think there are any other objects in the solar system? Why? *(Student answers will vary. Answers may include, but are not limited to, the Sun, the planets, moons, asteroids, NEO's, meteoroids, dust, and gas. Students answers should indicate that it is likely that there are other objects in the solar system.)*

NOTES

....

....

....

....

....

....

....

....

....

....

....

ASTRONOMY

NOTES

3.5 Explore

Where in the Solar System Are Smaller Objects Found?

In *Learning Set 1,* you read about some of the other objects in the solar system. You learned about dwarf planets and smaller solar system objects such as asteroids, comets, and meteoroids. Now that you have developed a model of the sizes and distances of the planets in the solar system, you can use that model as a map to help you understand where the other solar-system objects are found. You must know where those solar system objects can be found to know if solar-system objects will collide.

The universe most likely started as a large collection of gas and dust, as this artist's rendering illustrates.

Answering the question of where the other solar-system objects are located is easier if you understand how the solar system was formed. The solar system has not existed forever. The universe is about 14 billion years old, but the solar system formed less than 5 billion years ago.

AST 152

Project-Based Inquiry Science

3.5 Explore

Where in the Solar System Are Smaller Objects Found?

15 min

Students review what they have learned throughout the Unit, preparing them for the upcoming activity.

⬡ **Get Going**

Remind students of earlier discussions of small solar-system objects. Tell them that now they can use their model of the solar system and their knowledge of sizes and distances to more fully understand these objects.

*A class period is considered to be one 40 to 50 minute class.

Formation of the Solar System

5 min

The class reads how the solar system formed.

Formation of the Solar System

Scientists have several theories about how the solar system formed. There are small differences in the theories, but they are all the same in many ways. All of the current theories say that the universe started as a large collection of gas and dust in space. This gas and dust was in a cloud much greater in size than the orbit of Neptune. The gas and dust started to spin and collapse in on itself. As parts of the cloud spun faster and faster around the center, and different pieces collided with each other, the cloud became a flattened disk with a bulge at the center. The center of the bulge became very hot, and as soon as it was hot enough for fusion to occur, the Sun was officially born.

According to current theories, most of the mass in the cloud collapsed inward to form the Sun. But the parts that remained outside the bulge in the disk continued to collide and combine with each other. Eventually, eight little balls formed within the disk, sweeping up everything in their path. These eight balls eventually became the eight planets.

According to scientists, the parts of the mass that did not become part of the Sun continued to collide and combine with one another. As in this illustration, the remaining eight balls became the eight planets in our solar system.

AST 153

ASTRONOMY

△ Guide

Tell students that the solar system is not as old as the universe. The universe is about 14 billion years old, but the solar system is only about 5 billion years old. Scientists have several theories of how the solar system formed, and they continue to collect data that can help them determine which theory is correct.

PBIS

This theory of the solar system's formation accounts for two important facts about the way the planets orbit the Sun. The planets all travel in the same direction around the Sun, counterclockwise, as seen from above. The planets orbit in the same direction around the Sun because the original disk was spinning in that direction. Also, all of the planets lie within the same *orbital plane* because they all formed within the flattened disk of matter surrounding the new Sun. You can think of the orbital plane of the solar system as a tabletop. The planets all orbit the Sun as if they were marbles rolling on the tabletop. Most solar-system objects have orbits that are tilted a little bit. This means that part of the orbit is above the orbital plane and part is below the orbital plane. Some objects have orbits that are tilted much more, but these orbits most likely were the result of collisions or near misses.

Remember the story of the Moon's formation that you read about in *Learning Set 2*. In this scenario, the Moon came into being after Earth had already formed. Because a collision probably brought about the Moon's formation, the Moon does not quite lie in the orbital plane of the planets. In fact, the Moon's orbit is tilted 5° away from the orbital plane.

An artist imagines the asteroid belt.

According to these theories, even after the planets formed, there was still material left over from the formation of the solar system. The early history of the solar system was filled with collisions, the records of which still exist on the Moon and other objects in the solar system. Other bits of leftover material formed the other smaller objects in the solar system. For example, some rocky, iron-rich material collected in between the orbits of Mars and Jupiter. This collection of over one million rocky objects, each over a kilometer in diameter, is now called the *asteroid belt*.

AST 154

Project-Based Inquiry Science

Tell students that all of these theories agree that the solar system began as a cloud of gas and dust in space. This cloud was much wider than the current solar system. The cloud began to spin and contract, and it gradually became a flattened disk with a bulge at the center. The bulge eventually became hot enough for fusion to occur, leading to the development of the Sun. The parts of the cloud that did not collapse into the Sun formed the planets and smaller solar-system objects.

Most asteroids are found in the asteroid belt. However, asteroids can be found throughout the solar system. Some of these other asteroids may have formed in the asteroid belt and then their orbits changed because they passed too close to Jupiter.

A million asteroids in one area seems like a lot. It may seem that collisions would occur all the time, at least within the asteroid belt. Have you ever watched a science fiction film with a "chase scene" through the asteroids? There are no doubt collisions among the asteroids as they tumble through space, which makes for exciting special effects. However, one thing to remember is that there is a lot of space in space! The area between the orbits of Mars and Jupiter is over two quintillion square kilometers (2,000,000,000,000,000,000 km²) in size. If you assume that there are a million asteroids in the asteroid belt, and they all lie in the orbital plane, then there is only one asteroid per two trillion square kilometers (2,000,000,000,000 km²) of the orbital plane. This means that in an area that is four times the area of Earth's surface, you would only find one rock about a kilometer in diameter.

Astronomers have investigated whether the asteroid belt could be debris left over from destruction of a planet between Mars and Jupiter. Scientists now think, though, that there is not enough debris in the asteroid belt to account for the destruction of such a planet.

Astronomers learn about the solar system through the use of telescopes in space, such as the Hubble, and on Earth. This telescope is part of NASA's Catalina Sky Survey in Arizona.

AST 155

ASTRONOMY

Tell students that this model of the formation of the solar system is in accordance with the observation that all of the planets orbit the Sun in the same direction. They also orbit in the same orbital plane. This is because they all formed from the same spinning disk.

You know there is evidence on the Moon's surface of many impacts that occurred in the past. You also know that the Moon may have formed in a collision that occurred after the planets formed. Scientists think that the early solar system had much more debris than there is now. There may have been several periods of intense bombardment in the early solar system. During these periods, collisions would have occurred much more frequently than they do now. One way of thinking about this is that collisions are less likely now because most of the objects that would collide have already done so.

In science, a theory is the best explanation that scientists have at any given time. The best explanation is one that has lots of data to support it. To learn more about the formation of the solar system and about how objects in the solar system move, scientists collect data using telescopes and space probes. They also use computer models and simulations to help them test their theories. Scientists build computer models to match their theories, and they use them to simulate what happens in the universe over billions of years.

If a model is good, then the simulation will show solar-system objects moving in space the way we see them move today. The data astronomers collect from observing the sky and the data collected from computer simulations should match. If a theory about the formation of the solar system is accurate, the computer simulation should predict where astronomers would find other solar-system objects that have never been sighted before. When astronomers find solar-system objects they have not seen before, they gain evidence to support their theories. In science, the best theory is the one that explains available data and makes the best predictions.

Stop and Think

1. Describe the events that led to the formation of the solar system.

2. Why do the planets all move in the same direction around the Sun?

3. The asteroid belt contains over a million objects 1 kilometer or more in diameter and countless smaller objects. Why is it still correct to describe the asteroid belt as a relatively empty place?

Project-Based Inquiry Science

Discuss how most asteroids are found in the asteroid belt. The asteroid belt is a band of over a million rocky bodies between Mars and Jupiter. Even though most asteroids are found in the asteroid belt, they can be found anywhere in the solar system. It is also important to note that there is a lot of empty space in the asteroid belt. There is only one asteroid per 2 trillion km^2 of the orbital plane.

Stop and Think

5 min

Students have a class discussion of the Stop and Think *questions.*

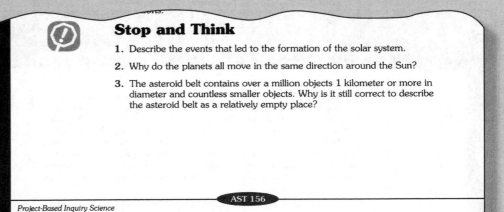

Stop and Think

1. Describe the events that led to the formation of the solar system.

2. Why do the planets all move in the same direction around the Sun?

3. The asteroid belt contains over a million objects 1 kilometer or more in diameter and countless smaller objects. Why is it still correct to describe the asteroid belt as a relatively empty place?

AST 156

Project-Based Inquiry Science

△ Guide and Assess

Lead a brief class discussion of the *Stop and Think* questions. Listen for evidence that students understand the theory of the formation of the solar system presented in the text.

1. Students should describe the formation of the solar system as an event 5 billion years ago when a large mass of gas and dust began to collect, condense, and rotate. This formed a huge disk of spinning matter somewhat thicker in the center. This center became the Sun which began to generate heat and light through nuclear fusion. Planets, asteroids, and other bodies formed in the same manner at some distance from the center.

2. Students should understand that the planets all revolve about the Sun in the same direction because they all formed from the original spinning mass of gas and dust.

3. Students will know that space is mostly empty space. Each asteroid has an average of 2 trillion km² in the orbital plane.

NOTES

....

....

....

....

3.5 Explore

Near-Earth Objects

Knowing about the formation of the solar system may give you some clues about where other smaller objects in the solar system might be found and how they move. Smaller objects that orbit around larger objects are called **satellites**. Many of the objects in the solar system lie in well-defined orbits that do not cross Earth's orbit, so they are unlikely to collide with Earth. Other objects are moons of other planets. These moons will never stray far from the planet they orbit. Gravity from the planet they orbit will keep them far from the orbits of other planets.

Some of the smaller solar-system objects, such as comets, have flattened elliptical orbits. When they are far from the Sun, beyond the orbit of Neptune, comets travel slowly. Some take thousands of years to orbit once around the Sun. But because their orbits are very elliptical, their path is more likely to cross the path of a planet, similar to the way the Shoemaker-Levy 9 comet crossed paths with Jupiter.

Another factor in determining whether an object will collide with a solar-system object is whether the object's orbit is *inclined*. Some dwarf planets, such as Pluto, have orbits that are inclined at a great angle from the orbital plane of the solar system. This means that they are much less likely to cross the path of another planet because they do not spend much time in the orbital plane.

Any asteroids and comets that cross the orbit of Earth are tracked by the governments of the world. These objects are classified as **Near-Earth Objects (NEOs)**. Once an NEO is detected, it is reported and monitored. In the United States, NASA catalogs all NEOs that have the potential to be catastrophic if they collided with Earth. Scientists monitor the orbits of NEOs and investigate questions such as how many there are, their origins, and their threat to Earth.

satellite: a smaller object that is in orbit around a larger object.

Near-Earth Objects (NEOs): asteroids and comets that cross the orbit of Earth.

Stop and Think

1. Does a space object have to have an Earth-crossing orbit in order to collide with Earth? Why or why not?

2. Do you think the number of objects listed as Near-Earth Objects is always increasing, or could the list become shorter?

AST 157

ASTRONOMY

Near-Earth Objects

5 min

The students discuss Near-Earth Objects.

△ Guide

Discuss how the planets and their moons are unlikely to collide with Earth because they have well-defined orbits that do not cross Earth's orbit. Point out that there are, however, smaller solar-system objects with very elliptical orbits that are more likely to cross Earth's orbit. Shoemaker-Levy 9, the comet that collided with Jupiter, was an example of a smaller solar-system body with a highly elliptical orbit.

Tell students that any asteroids and comets that cross the orbit of Earth are tracked by governments. They are classified as *Near-Earth Objects* (NEO's). In the United States, NASA tracks all NEO's that have the potential for catastrophic collisions with Earth.

Stop and Think

5 min

Students answer the questions in the Stop and Think *section.*

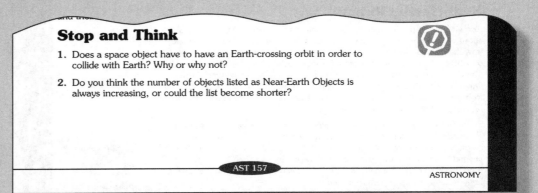

Stop and Think

1. Does a space object have to have an Earth-crossing orbit in order to collide with Earth? Why or why not?

2. Do you think the number of objects listed as Near-Earth Objects is always increasing, or could the list become shorter?

AST 157

ASTRONOMY

△ Guide and Assess

Lead a brief class discussion of the *Stop and Think* questions. Listen for evidence that students understand the factors involved in the probability of a NEO colliding with Earth.

1. Students should understand that an object must have an Earth-crossing orbit in order to collide with Earth because that is where Earth is.

2. Students should suggest that the number of NEOs is probably decreasing as collisions occur. There is a small chance that new objects from outer space could be trapped by the gravitational forces of the solar system.

NOTES

....

....

....

....

....

Reflect

1. Look back to the kinds of objects listed on your *Solar System* page. Which of these objects do you think are most likely to have a collision with another solar-system object?

2. Which solar-system objects do you think are very unlikely to collide with Earth? Why?

3. Which solar-system objects do you think would be most likely to collide with Earth? Why?

Update the *Project Board*

You have read a little about the formation of the solar system and the location of small solar-system objects. Your *Project Board* may have questions like *Where did all of these solar-system objects come from?* and *How did the solar system form?* You can now start to answer these questions in the *What we are learning?* and *What is our evidence?* columns.

Your reading may have raised more questions. For example, you might wonder *Where do comets come from?* If there are still things you are unsure about, or things that, if answered, would increase your confidence about what you think you know, record them in the *What do we need to investigate?* column.

What's the Point?

The solar system formed from a cloud of gas and dust a little less than 5 billion years ago. The Sun formed in the middle, and the planets formed from the leftover gas and dust that had collected in a disk around the Sun. Material that did not go into the formation of planets made up the asteroids, comets, and other objects that travel around the solar system. Near-Earth Objects (NEOs) are those objects that cross Earth's orbit.

Reflect

10 min

Students answer the Reflect *questions.*

△ Guide and Assess

After allowing students a few minutes to answer the *Reflect* questions in their group, lead a brief discussion of each question to make certain that students can apply what they have learned.

1. Student answers will vary, but some will suggest that the asteroids are most likely to collide with another object because there are so many. Others will suggest that the Sun or the more massive planets are most likely to invite collisions because of their strong gravitational forces.

2. Students should think that the other planets are most unlikely to collide with Earth, because they have well-established orbits which do not cross the Earth's path.

3. Most students will believe that an asteroid is most likely to collide with Earth because there are so many. Others will suggest that an unknown comet is more likely.

Update the Project Board

15 min

The class has a discussion to update the Project Board.

Update the *Project Board*

You have read a little about the formation of the solar system and the location of small solar-system objects. Your *Project Board* may have questions like *Where did all of these solar-system objects come from?* and *How did the solar system form?* You can now start to answer these questions in the *What we are learning?* and *What is our evidence?* columns.

Your reading may have raised more questions. For example, you might wonder *Where do comets come from?* If there are still things you are unsure about, or things that, if answered, would increase your confidence about what you think you know, record them in the *What do we need to investigate?* column.

△ Guide

Ask students what new information they can record in the *What are we learning?* column of the *Project Board*. Record their answers on the class *Project Board*, and have them record their answers on their own *Project Board* pages. Then ask them what their evidence is, and record their responses on the *Project Board*.

Assessment Options

Targeted Concepts, Skills, and Nature of Science	How do I know if students got it?
Scientists often collaborate and share their findings. Sharing findings makes new information available and helps scientists refine their ideas and build on others' ideas. When another person's or group's idea is used, credit needs to be given.	**ASK:** Why is it a good idea for the members of your group to share the notes they made while reading? **LISTEN:** Answers may include that some students in the group may have identified important ideas or information that others had overlooked.

Targeted Concepts, Skills, and Nature of Science	How do I know if students got it?
Scientists must keep clear, accurate, and descriptive records of what they do so they can share their work with others; consider what they did, why they did it, and what they want to do next.	**ASK:** Why is it important to take notes while reading? **LISTEN:** Students may answer that if notes are not kept, there is no record of what was learned during the reading. Notes help the reader summarize information, organize it in such a way that relationships are easier to identify, and thereby help make complex material easier to understand.
Our solar system coalesced out of a giant cloud of gas and debris about five billion years ago. The Sun formed when gas and debris heated up from the energy of falling together began releasing nuclear energy from the fusion of light elements into heavier ones in its extremely hot, dense core.	**ASK:** At what point did the material that collapsed in on itself become the Sun? **LISTEN:** Students should identify when the temperature was hot enough to trigger nuclear fusion reactions. **ASK:** In what part of the solar nebula did the planets form? **LISTEN:** Students should identify the spinning disk that surrounded the central bulge.
Around the planets orbit a great variety of moons. Flat rings of rock and ice debris orbit some planets, and Earth is orbited by a moon and artificial satellites.	**ASK:** Where in the solar system is the asteroid belt located? **LISTEN:** Students should identify its location between the orbits of Jupiter and Mars. **ASK:** Why do scientists now believe that the asteroid belt was not formed by a giant collision that destroyed a planet? **LISTEN:** Answers should include that it is because there is not enough debris in the asteroid belt to account for a planet-sized object.

Targeted Concepts, Skills, and Nature of Science	How do I know if students got it?
Humankind's need to explore continues to lead to the development of knowledge and understanding of the nature of the Universe.	**ASK:** What information do scientists hope to obtain from the future space explorations? **LISTEN:** Students should identify the age and composition of Mars; whether Mars has the materials needed to support life, evidence of past life on Mars, evidence of geological activity on Mars, and so on.

Teacher Reflection Questions

- How did you encourage students to take notes during the reading and what organizers did you suggest?

- What additional resources and experiences could you have provided to heighten students' interest in the reading material?

- How could you have structured the reading so that there was a better balance of students working individually, in small groups, and as a class?

NOTES

Back to the Big Question

How Can You Know if Objects in Space Will Collide?

◀ *1 class period*

A class period is considered to be one 40 to 50 minute class.

Overview

The section begins with students updating their *Solar System* page with information gained throughout the *Learning Set* about the structure and motion of the solar system. Students review their earlier predictions about the effects of a collision with a 10-km asteroid and make any changes based on what they have now learned. Groups research a part of the solar system other than the eight planets, their moons, and the asteroid belt (Kuiper Belt, Trans-Neptunian Objects, Oort Cloud and Centaur planets) and consider whether they are likely objects to collide. Students then develop a presentation, sharing their research findings with the class. Students evaluate one another's presentations, provide constructive feedback, and a class discussion of the research findings ensues. The class identifies the most important findings and students add them to their *Big Question* page. Students return to their earlier explanation of whether any two objects will collide. Collaborating in groups, they apply what they now know to revise and expand their explanations to include possible collisions other objects in the solar system. After sharing their revised explanations with the class, the class updates the *Project Board*.

Targeted Concepts, Skills, and Nature of Science	Performance Expectations
Scientists often collaborate and share their findings. Sharing findings makes new information available and helps scientists refine their ideas and build on others' ideas. When another person's or group's idea is used, credit needs to be given.	Student share their research findings by giving a class presentation.
	Students evaluate the research findings shared with the class and collaborate with the class to identify the most important findings.
	Students collaborate in groups to revise and expand their earlier explanations of whether two objects will collide.

Targeted Concepts, Skills, and Nature of Science	Performance Expectations
Scientists must keep clear, accurate, and descriptive records of what they do so they can share their work with others; consider what they did, why they did it, and what they want to do next.	Students record information about the structure and motion of the solar system on their *Solar System* page. Students record their research findings about their assigned parts of the solar system on the *Big Question* page and organize it in such a way that they can be effectively presented to the class. Students summarize the research findings of all of the groups in the class on their *Big Question* page.
Explanations are claims supported by evidence. Evidence can be experimental results, observational data, and any other accepted scientific knowledge.	Students revise their explanations of the *Big Question*.
Earth's Sun is the central and largest body in our solar system. The Sun is more than a million times greater in volume than Earth. Earth is the third planet from the Sun in a system that includes other planets and their moons, as well as smaller objects, such as asteroids and comets – some with orbits that lie beyond the planets.	Students identify objects revolving around the Sun whose orbits lie beyond that of the planets.
Around the planets orbit a great variety of moons. Flat rings of rock and ice debris orbit some planets, a large number of asteroids orbit the Sun between the orbits of Mars and Jupiter, and Earth is orbited by a moon and artificial satellites.	Students identify regions of the solar system that lie beyond the orbits of the planets and the types of objects found in those regions.

Materials

1 per student	*Create Your Explanation* page Researching resources
1 per class	Class *Project Board*

Activity Setup and Preparation

Make arrangements for students to have access to resources for researching solar-system objects, such as internet access, the library, or have books, magazines and other print materials available in the classroom.

Homework Options

Reflection

- **Science Content:** What are some differences between the Kuiper Belt and the Oort Cloud? *(Students should answer The Kuiper Belt is a disk-shaped region of icy debris located about 4.5 to 7.5 billion km from the Sun, the Oort Cloud is an immense spherical cloud surrounding our Solar System at a distance of 18-30 trillion km from the Sun.)*

- **Science Content:** Compare and contrast the motion of planets around the Sun with uniform circular motion. *(Answers should include that in uniform circular motion, planets would remain at a constant distance from the Sun and move at a constant speed in their orbits. The planets orbit the Sun in elliptical paths, therefore their distance to the Sun varies throughout their orbit, and their orbital speed changes as well, increasing as they approach the Sun and decreasing as they move away from the Sun.)*

- **Science Content:** Describe the origin of solar-system objects, such as asteroids and comets, and the variables that would affect their entry into and motion through and within our solar system. *(Students should describe how asteroids and comets formed from material that remained in the spinning disk of dust and gas surrounding the central bulge that formed the Sun. Random collisions and changes in the gravitational forces in the solar system due to changes in the distances between solar-system objects can cause changes in their orbits. Changes in the orbits of asteroids or comets can cause them to cross the orbits of the planets.)*

- **Science Process:** What are some of the methods, procedures, and instruments used by scientists to explore the solar system? *(Student answers will vary, and may include but are not limited to observations of the sky made with telescopes, spectroscopes, and other instruments that sense electromagnetic radiation, space probes, analysis of objects from space that reach Earth's surface, and measuring instruments for determining location in the sky, such as astrolabes and sextants.)*

- **Science Process:** How could you figure out how long it takes light from the Sun to reach Earth? *(Students should suggest doing research to determine the speed of light, then substitute it and Earth's distance from the Sun in the speed equation, $Speed = \frac{distance}{time}$ and solve for time.)*

NOTES

....

....

....

....

....

....

....

....

....

....

....

....

....

....

....

Learning Set 3

Back to the Big Question

How can you know if objects in space will collide?

In this *Learning Set,* in you learned a lot about the structure and motion of the solar system. Use what you have learned to update your *Solar System* page. You learned about the positions of objects in the solar system. You also learned about motions of objects in the solar system. You constructed several different models of the solar system. You can add the ideas you got from these explorations to your *Solar System* page.

Now that you have a better understanding of the solar system, it may be easier for you to understand what objects might collide in space. Use what you have learned in *Learning Set 3* to add to your *Big Question* page. After the next *Learning Set,* you will use the information on this page to construct your report.

At the beginning of this *Learning Set* you became an expert on the Sun or one of the planets in the solar system. You developed a description of what would happen if a 10-kilometer asteroid collided with your object. Your idea of what would happen might have changed as you proceeded through the rest of the *Learning Set.* A good way to prepare for your report on collisions is to revise this description based on what you just learned. You might also be able to add details to your description. For example, you can now describe what could cause the orbit of a 10-kilometer asteroid to change, leading to a collision with your object.

Conference

To complete your understanding of the solar system, and the ways scientists determine if two objects in space will collide, you need to find out more about what happened to the debris left after the formation of the solar system.

AST 159

ASTRONOMY

Learning Set 3

Back to the Big Question

5 min

Students record what they have learned in the Learning Set.

△ **Guide**

Begin by having students update their *Solar System* pages and their *Big Question* pages. Emphasize that they will use the information to answer the *Big Question: How can you know if objects in space will collide?* Also have groups use the new information they have learned to quickly revise their descriptions of what would happen if a 10-km asteroid collided with their object.

*A class period is considered to be one 40 to 50 minute class.

Conference

10 min

Conference

To complete your understanding of the solar system, and the ways scientists determine if two objects in space will collide, you need to find out more about what happened to the debris left after the formation of the solar system.

AST 159

ASTRONOMY

△ Guide

Introduce the four terms in the textbook—Kuiper Belt, Trans-Neptunian Objects, Oort Cloud, Centaur planets—that relate to new parts of the solar system. Tell students that they will investigate these terms. You should explain that the Trans-Neptunian Objects include the Kuiper Belt, the Oort cloud, and the "scattered disk." The "scattered disk" could be the fourth group as it contains a larger object, Eris.

Assign groups to one of these four types of objects and have them research their objects

NOTES

....

....

....

....

....

....

....

Each of the following terms relates to a part of the solar system other than the eight planets and the asteroid belt.

- Kuiper Belt

- Trans-Neptunian Objects

- Oort Cloud

- Centaur planets

Your group will be assigned one of these terms to study and explore. Using available resources, determine the characteristics and the origins of the objects described by your term. Determine if any of these objects have ever been classified as Near-Earth Objects. Then determine the likelihood that such an object will ever collide with other space objects. Use this information to prepare a presentation for the class.

Your presentation should include the size and location of your objects, how they were discovered, how long they take to orbit the Sun, whether a large planet could alter their orbit, and which other orbits cross theirs.

Communicate

Share Your Data

Listen to each group as they give their presentation. If different groups are covering the same material, see if the information gathered by each group is in agreement. Try to resolve any differences in the findings of the groups.

As you listen to each presentation, if you disagree with, or do not understand, a group's presentation, ask questions. Make sure you ask respectfully. Some good questions to ask include:

- What are the objects made of and how big are they?

- How were the objects discovered?

- How long do they take to orbit the Sun?

- Is it likely for the objects to have their orbits altered by Jupiter or another large planet?

- Which orbits of other space objects cross the orbit of their space object?

AST 160

⬡ Get Going

Assign each group to one of the terms and have each group research their term using whatever resources are available—the library or a computer lab, for instance. Tell them that they will need to determine whether any of these objects have been classified as a Near-Earth Object. They will also need to determine the characteristics and origins of these objects. Emphasize that they will present their findings to the class.

Communicate: Share Your Data

Groups present their findings.

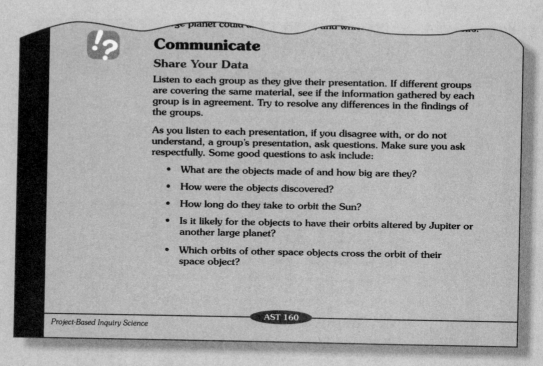

Communicate

Share Your Data

Listen to each group as they give their presentation. If different groups are covering the same material, see if the information gathered by each group is in agreement. Try to resolve any differences in the findings of the groups.

As you listen to each presentation, if you disagree with, or do not understand, a group's presentation, ask questions. Make sure you ask respectfully. Some good questions to ask include:

- What are the objects made of and how big are they?
- How were the objects discovered?
- How long do they take to orbit the Sun?
- Is it likely for the objects to have their orbits altered by Jupiter or another large planet?
- Which orbits of other space objects cross the orbit of their space object?

Project-Based Inquiry Science   AST 160

⚠ Guide

When groups have had a chance to research their type of object, have them present what they learned to the class. Emphasize that as each group presents, students should ask questions if anything is unclear, and they should make sure that groups' information is consistent. For instance, if two groups were assigned the same type of object, their information should be in agreement.

NOTES

....

....

....

....

....

After listening to all of the presentations, add the most important findings to your *Big Question* page. Some of the information you heard may make it into your report on the likelihood of an object from space colliding with Earth.

Revise Your Explanation

In this *Learning Set,* you learned about the structure of the solar system beyond Earth, the Moon, and the Sun. Now it is time to use this knowledge to revise your claim and explanation from the end of *Learning Set 2.* Use what you have recorded on your *Solar System* and *Big Question* pages to help you revise your claim and explanation. Edit your old *Create Your Explanation* page to make a revised explanation, or use a new one. Remember that a good explanation has several parts to it.

- **your claim:** a statement of what you understand or a conclusion you have reached

- **your evidence:** data collected from investigations that support your claim

- **your science knowledge:** knowledge about how things work that supports your claim

- **your explanation:** a logical statement connecting your evidence and science knowledge to your claim in a way that can convince someone that your claim is valid. Good explanations tell what is happening that makes the claim valid.

Your claim will be your clearest, most accurate statement about how to determine whether space objects will collide. Your evidence comes from your models of the solar system and from the information you have gathered on planets and other objects in the solar system. Your science knowledge comes from your reading. Work with your group to develop the best explanation you can. It may be easier to express your explanation by attaching phrases to sketches than to simply use words. Feel free to combine sketches and words in your explanation.

AST 161

ASTRONOMY

Revise Your Explanation

5 min

Students return to their claims and update them based on their new science knowledge.

△ Guide

Guide students in groups to revise their explanations and then present their revisions to the class. Review the parts of a good explanation with them.

Communicate: Share Your Explanation

10 min

Groups share their revised explanation with the class.

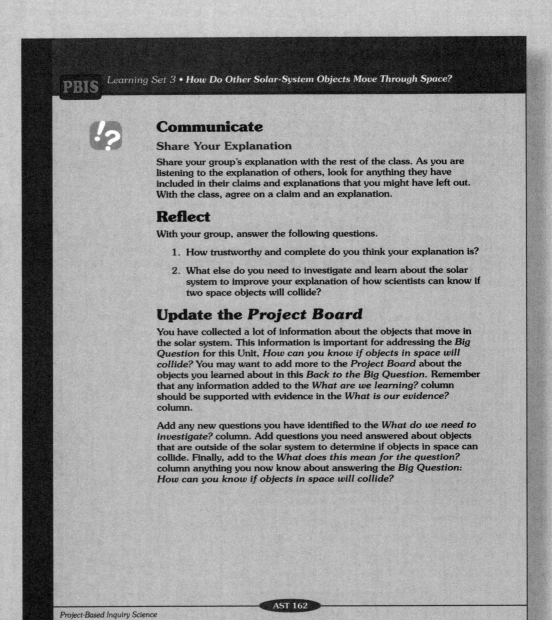

Communicate

Share Your Explanation

Share your group's explanation with the rest of the class. As you are listening to the explanation of others, look for anything they have included in their claims and explanations that you might have left out. With the class, agree on a claim and an explanation.

Reflect

With your group, answer the following questions.

1. How trustworthy and complete do you think your explanation is?

2. What else do you need to investigate and learn about the solar system to improve your explanation of how scientists can know if two space objects will collide?

Update the *Project Board*

You have collected a lot of information about the objects that move in the solar system. This information is important for addressing the *Big Question* for this Unit, *How can you know if objects in space will collide?* You may want to add more to the *Project Board* about the objects you learned about in this *Back to the Big Question*. Remember that any information added to the *What are we learning?* column should be supported with evidence in the *What is our evidence?* column.

Add any new questions you have identified to the *What do we need to investigate?* column. Add questions you need answered about objects that are outside of the solar system to determine if objects in space can collide. Finally, add to the *What does this mean for the question?* column anything you now know about answering the *Big Question: How can you know if objects in space will collide?*

AST 162

Project-Based Inquiry Science

◯ Get Going

Have students take turns sharing their groups explanations with the class. Encourage students to ask questions if they do not understand any part of the presented explanations.

Allow students in groups time to answer the Reflect questions and then lead a brief discussion of the answers.

1. Student answers will vary be they should support their opinions with reasons.

2. Student answers will vary.

△ Guide

Ask students what new ideas they have about the motions of solar-system bodies and how these ideas might affect their explanation about collisions in the solar system. Record their answers in the *What do we think we know?* column of the *Project Board*, and have students record them in their own *Project Board* pages.

NOTES

Assessment Options

Targeted Concepts, Skills, and Nature of Science	How do I know if students got it?
Scientists often collaborate and share their findings. Sharing findings makes new information available and helps scientists refine their ideas and build on others' ideas. When another person's or group's idea is used, credit needs to be given.	**ASK:** Based on the research findings shared by the class, which region(s) of the solar system are thought to exist but have not yet been directly observed? Why not? **LISTEN:** Students should identify the Oort cloud. The objects that make up the Oort cloud are so small and so distant from the Sun that their reflected light is too dim to detect with Earth-based telescopes.
Scientists must keep clear, accurate, and descriptive records of what they do so they can share their work with others; consider what they did, why they did it, and what they want to do next.	**ASK:** Look back at your research notes and diagrams and consider your mental image of the part of the solar system you researched. If someone else looked at your notes and diagrams, how closely would their mental image of that part of the solar system compare with yours? **LISTEN:** Students should be able to identify details missing in their notes and diagrams and recognize ways in which their recording of research findings could be improved.
Explanations are claims supported by evidence. Evidence can be experimental results, observational data, and any other accepted scientific knowledge.	**ASK:** Rank the supporting evidence for your revised explanations according to how strongly it supports your new or revised claims. **LISTEN:** Student answers will vary. This question is designed to engage students in evaluating the validity of their supporting evidence.

Targeted Concepts, Skills, and Nature of Science	How do I know if students got it?
Earth's Sun is the central and largest body in our solar system. The Sun is more than a million times greater in volume than Earth. Earth is the third planet from the Sun in a system that includes other planets and their moons, as well as smaller objects, such as asteroids and comets—some with orbits that lie beyond the planets.	**ASK:** A third-grader asks your opinion of a poster of the solar system made as a science project. The poster shows only the Sun and nine planets. All of the planets and the Sun are shown as same-sized circles. The planets are shown orbiting the Sun in egg-shaped orbits that overlap. What would you suggest that the third-grader change about the poster? **LISTEN:** Student answers will vary but should include ideas such as: point out that Pluto is no longer considered a planet, show the eight planets as having different sizes, show the planets orbiting the Sun in near circular orbits, show that smaller objects than the planets also orbit the Sun, show that the solar system does not end at the orbit of the outermost planet, and so on.
Around the planets orbit a great variety of moons. Flat rings of rock and ice debris orbit some planets, a large number of asteroids orbit the Sun between the orbits of Mars and Jupiter, and Earth is orbited by a moon and artificial satellites.	**ASK:** Which regions of the solar system are considered likely sources of comets? Why? **LISTEN:** Students should identify the Kuiper Belt and the Oort Cloud, because they are thought to consist of a large number of icy, comet-size objects.

Teacher Reflection Questions

- In this section, students were introduced to new information. What formative assessments did you use with the students to identify what they have learned?

- Scientists never do all their work alone. In PBIS, students are given many types of opportunities to share ideas, research findings, and other types of information. What are some of the different strategies used in *Learning Set 3* to engage students in collaboration and sharing?

- Social interactions are powerful learning tools. Students who create positive bonds with peers build a strong self image and confidence necessary for success. What activities in this *Learning Set* fostered social interactions that created positive bonds between students?

NOTES

LEARNING SET 4 INTRODUCTION

Learning Set 4

How Do Objects Outside Our Solar System Move Through Space?

◀ **13 class periods**

A class period is considered to be one 40 to 50 minute class.

Students move beyond the solar system to consider possible sources of objects that could collide with Earth.

Overview

Students expand their focus to consider objects outside the solar system that could collide with Earth. They are reminded that Newton's laws of motion and gravity can be used to calculate the orbit of a newly discovered object and thereby determine its potential to collide with another object. They read about the use of space probes, such as *Voyager 1* and *2,* to expand the scope of human observations of objects in the solar system and beyond. *Section 4.1* guides students to understand that most of what we know about the universe is based on our perception of the radiation emitted by stars and other objects in the universe. Students develop an appreciation for the challenges faced by astronomers by examining images of light sources and images made at different times and by considering how information can be inferred from those images. In *Section 4.2,* students investigate factors that affect the apparent brightness of stars and determine that stars may look bright because they give off a lot of light, or because they are relatively close to Earth. Students also investigate how parallax is used to determine the distance to nearby stars. *Section 4.3* opens with a description of the Milky Way galaxy. Students consider how information about the distances to stars and their positions relative to Earth could be used to construct a model of the Milky Way galaxy. Students are guided to recognize that distances between stars are vast compared to distances within our solar system and the light-year is introduced as a unit used to measure distances to stars. In *Section 4.4,* students investigate the structure of the Milky Way galaxy. They observe a demonstration of motion that results in a spiral-arm shape and simulate the sampling techniques used by astronomers to compare the population of stars in different regions of the galaxy. Students then read about the spectral analysis of starlight and how a Doppler shift in the light emitted by a star provides evidence of its motion relative to an observer on Earth. Students examine an image of the Milky Way galaxy based on observations of the positions, distances and motions of its stars and consider the position of our solar system within the galaxy. In *Section 4.5*, students read about Annie Jump Cannon's analysis of stellar spectra and classification of stars into spectral classes. They read a description of the development of the Hertzsprung-Russell diagram and how it contributed to our understanding of the structure and evolution of stars. Students also read about the life cycles of different types of stars and consider the potential danger to Earth posed by supernovas and black holes. *Section 4.6* opens with a description of the Shapley-Curtis debate about the size and structure of the universe, and Hubble's use of data from the Andromeda nebula to establish that galaxies exist beyond the Milky Way galaxy. Students then examine images of four distant galaxies and develop a system to classify galaxies according to their structure. After reading about Hubble's system for classifying galaxies, students consider the possible dangers of one galaxy colliding with another. In *Section 4.7*, students examine case studies of two space telescopes that are contributing to our knowledge and understanding of the universe: the Hubble Space Telescope and the Kepler Mission. Through readings and by viewing NASA video footage, students are made aware of the discoveries that can be made with these technologically advanced instruments. The *Learning Set* concludes with students returning to the *Big Question* and writing a report for a movie producer suggesting a collision between space objects that could be used as the basis for a popular movie. Students collaborate in small groups to reach consensus on a collision to suggest for the movie and to revise their earlier explanations of the likelihood of a collision in space so that it will convince the movie producer that the collision idea is realistic. Students present their ideas and revised explanations to the class and reflect on how their explanation compares with those presented by other groups.

Targeted Concepts, Skills, and Nature of Science	Section
Scientists often collaborate and share their findings. Sharing findings makes new information available and helps scientists refine their ideas and build on others' ideas. When another person's or group's idea is used, credit needs to be given.	All sections
Scientists must keep clear, accurate, and descriptive records of what they do so they can share their work with others; consider what they did, why they did it, and what they want to do next.	All sections
Models are a representation of something in the world. Simulations use a model to imitate, or act out, real-life situations.	4.2, 4.4

Targeted Concepts, Skills, and Nature of Science	Section
The universe is vast and estimated to be over ten billion years old. The current theory is that the universe was created from an explosion called the Big Bang. A redshift (the Doppler effect) in the light from very distant galaxies provides evidence for this theory.	4.6
Components of the universe include stars, galaxies, and nebulae.	4.6
Humans perceive the universe by the radiation it emits. Technological advances have greatly extended the scope of human perception and led to the observations upon which our current theories of the universe are based.	4.1, 4.2, 4.7
The Doppler shift is the shift in wavelength of a spectrum line away from its normal wavelength caused by motion of the observer toward or away from the source. If the source is approaching the observer there is a blueshift towards shorter wavelengths of light. If the source is moving away from the observer, there is a redshift towards longer wavelengths of light.	4.3
Other stars are like the Sun but are so far away that they look like points of light. Distances between stars are vast compared to distances within our solar system. Light from the Sun takes a few minutes to reach Earth, but light from the next nearest star takes a few years to arrive.	4.3
Some stars appear brighter than others. Stars may look bright because they give off a lot of light, or because they are relatively close to Earth.	4.1, 4.2
Stars that are relatively close to our solar system appear to shift slightly in their position relative to distant stars when viewed from different positions, an effect known as parallax. The parallax of a star can be used to calculate its distance from Earth.	4.2
Astronomical Units and light-years are measures of distances between the Sun, Earth, and the stars.	4.3
Stars form when gravity causes clouds of molecules to contract until nuclear fusion of light elements into heavier ones occurs. Fusion releases great amounts of energy over millions of years.	4.5
Stars differ from each other in size, temperature, and age.	4.5

Targeted Concepts, Skills, and Nature of Science	Section
The Hertzsprung-Russell diagram shows the relationship between the luminosity and temperature of stars. The majority of stars lie on a diagonal band that extends from hot stars of high luminosity in the upper left corner to cool stars of low luminosity in the lower right corner. This band is called the main sequence.	4.5
A galaxy is a system of stars, cosmic dust and gas held together by gravitation. Galaxies typically contain billions of stars, may have different shapes, and may be thousands of light-years in diameter; the universe contains billions of such galaxies.	4.3, 4.4, 4.6
Our Sun is a medium-sized star within a spiral galaxy of stars known as the Milky Way.	4.3
Some distant galaxies are so far away that their light takes several billions of years to reach earth.	4.6
Different wavelengths of the electromagnetic spectrum such as light and radio waves are used to gain information about distances and properties of components of the universe.	4.5
Humankind's need to explore continues to lead to the development of knowledge and understanding of the nature of the Universe.	4.7

Activity Setup and Preparation

Electromagnetic Radiation

Stars emit an entire spectrum of electromagnetic radiation from high energy gamma rays through x-rays, visible light, and low energy radio waves. The major source of the radiation is the changing state of electrons when they move from an "excited" state back to a "ground" state. When this happens, electromagnetic radiation is emitted. Radiation of this type is characterized by wavelength, frequency, and amplitude. Frequency (hertz, v) and wavelength (meters, λ) have an inverse relationship which is expressed in the equation $c = v$, where c is the speed of light. As the name implies, there is an electric component and a magnetic component to this energy.

An electromagnetic field does not require a medium to carry it and it will travel through empty space. All electromagnetic radiation travels at 300,000 km/s (about 186,000 mi/s) in a vacuum. This velocity is called the *speed of light*.

The electromagnetic spectrum is a continuum in which electromagnetic waves are classified by their wavelength ranging from short waves, such as x-rays, to long waves, such as radio waves. The wavelength, or distance between "ripples," of visible light waves falls between 10^{-6} and 10^{-7} meters.

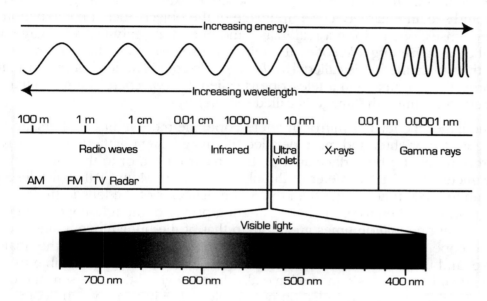

A moving wave contains energy. It can exert forces on matter with which it interacts. The energy carried outward from a source particle by electromagnetic waves is called *electromagnetic radiation*.

Humans perceive the universe by the electromagnetic radiation it emits. When humans "see" a star or any other object, it is because the lens of the eye has focused visible light emanating from that object to form an image on the retina. The retina is lined with specialized nerve cells that respond to light and send information to the brain, where it is interpreted. Nerve cells in the retina respond to two characteristics of light—intensity and wavelength. The brain interprets intensity as brightness and wavelength as color.

Astronomical Instruments

Telescopes

The human eye contains a lens that forms images. Many of the instruments used by astronomers are simply improvements on this model. A lens is a curved piece of glass that bends, or refracts light. A convex lens bends light in such a way that the light waves entering one side of the lens all intersect at one point, or converge, on the other side of the lens. The same outcome can be obtained with a curved mirror. Instead of the light converging because it is bent as it passes through a lens, the light is reflected off the surface of a curved mirror in such a way that it converges.

Whether it gives off its own light, or reflects light from another source, every point on an object sends out light in all directions. As a lens or curved mirror causes the light coming from each point on an object to converge, a real image of the object is formed. Suppose a lens is used to form a real image and then a magnifying glass is used to examine the image. The eye would see an enlarged, close-up image of the object. Such a combination of two lenses, one to form a real image and one to magnify the real image, is called a *refracting telescope*. If a mirror is used to create the real image that is then magnified, it is called a *reflecting telescope*. The lens or mirror that forms the real image in a telescope is called the *objective*. The magnifier used to examine the image is called the *eyepiece*.

The larger the lens or mirror in a telescope, the more light it gathers, and the larger, brighter and more detailed the image. Light-gathering power is proportional to the surface area of the lens or mirror, or to the square of its diameter. The 5-m diameter of the objective of the Mount Palomar telescope is about 1000 times larger than the 5-mm diameter of the lens in the human eye. Therefore, the light-gathering power of the telescope is 1000^2, or about one million times greater than that of the human eye. Using the telescope, humans can perceive objects too dim to be seen with the unaided eye, and under magnification can see details in the image not visible to the unaided eye. Instruments have also been devised that use sensors to detect electromagnetic radiation not visible to the human eye and convert it into images the eye can see. These technological advances have greatly increased the observational evidence about the universe.

Spectroscopes

Isaac Newton demonstrated that white light is actually a combination of all colors. He passed light through a triangular piece of glass, or *prism,* and found that the prism spread the light out into a rainbow of colors, or *spectrum.* A prism spreads white light out into its separate colors because the angle at which a light wave is refracted depends on its wavelength. With a short wavelength, blue light is refracted the most, and with a long wavelength, red light is refracted the least. The spreading out of light into its component colors is called *dispersion.*

In a prism spectroscope, light from a star is passed through a slit placed at the focus of a lens. The light waves emerge from the lens and then pass through a prism that disperses it into a spectrum. The spectrum then enters a telescope, which focuses the light into a real image of the slit that is examined with a magnifier. If the light source emits light of all wavelengths, the slit images blend together forming a continuous spectrum. If any wavelengths of light are absent, there is only a dark image of the slit where that color should be and these appear as black lines crossing the continuous spectrum. If the telescope in a spectroscope is replaced with an electronic device that measures the brightness of light, the device is called a *spectrophotometer.* If a spectroscope is equipped with a camera that allows a star's spectrum to be photographed, it is called a *spectrograph.* Photographs of spectra could then be saved, analyzed, and categorized.

Stellar Magnitude

Stars may appear bright because they give off more light, or because they are closer to Earth. The farther away a source of light is located, the dimmer it appears to an observer. Therefore, astronomers distinguish between a star's apparent brightness and its luminosity, or the actual amount of light a star emits into space each second. The Sun is the nearest and best-known star, therefore the luminosity of other stars is often stated in terms of the Sun's luminosity, which is 3.85×10^{28} watts.

The observed brightness of a source falls off as the square of the distance from the source decreases. Thus, if two stars had exactly the same luminosity, but one was twice as far away as the other, the distant star would look $\left(\frac{1}{2}\right)^2$, or only $\frac{1}{4}$ as bright as the closer one because only one-fourth of the light would reach your eye.

In the second century B.C.E., the astronomer Hipparchus classified stars into six brightness classes, or magnitudes — from stars of the first magnitude, which were the very brightest in the sky, to stars of the sixth magnitude, were just visible to the human eye. The number assigned to a star's brightness on this scale is called its *apparent magnitude* because it describes how bright a star appears to an observer on Earth.

The modern magnitude scale defines a first magnitude star as exactly 100 times brighter than a sixth magnitude star. This is consistent with how human eyes respond to changes in brightness. What humans perceive as a linear increase of one magnitude in brightness, is precisely measured as a geometric increase in brightness of 2.5 times. Thus, a difference of five magnitudes corresponds to a brightness difference of 100 times $(2.5 \times 2.5 \times 2.5 \times 2.5 \times 2.5 = 100)$. Stars that are 2.5 times brighter than first magnitude are zero-magnitude stars. The very brightest stars actually have negative magnitudes. For example, Sirius has magnitude 1.5 and the Sun has magnitude 27.

To overcome this problem, astronomers devised a scale in which stars are assigned a brightness based upon how bright they would appear if they were all placed at the same distance from Earth. The absolute magnitude of a star is the magnitude it would have if it were moved from its actual distance to a distance of 10 parsecs from the Earth. A parsec is about 3.26 light-years, or about 3.08×10^{13} km.

Analyzing Spectra

Unless an object is at absolute zero, its particles are in constant motion and will emit electromagnetic waves. An object's temperature is related to the average speed of the particles of matter of which it is composed (average, because some of the particles are moving faster and some are moving slower). The speed at which a particle of matter moves determines the wavelength of the electromagnetic waves it emits. The faster it is moving, the shorter the wavelength of the waves it emits. Thus, some of the particles in a star emit short wavelength radiation while others emit long wavelength radiation. The result is that a star will give off radiation that is a mix of many different wavelengths – a continuous spectrum. However, the hotter the star, the faster the average speed of its particles, and the greater the number of waves with short wavelengths it emits. Astronomers can determine the temperature of a star by analyzing the wavelengths of the electromagnetic radiation it emits.

The Sun radiates most intensely in the yellow range. However, the peak wavelength emitted by a star is not the only wavelength it is emitting. Stars emit a mix of wavelengths, so we perceive their light as white tinted the color of the peak wavelength, or as pastel shades of color. Thus, the Sun appears white with a decidedly yellow hue. The star Betelgeuse radiates most intensely in the red range. Since red light has a longer wavelength than yellow light, Betelgeuse has a lower temperature than the Sun.

Joseph von Fraunhofer first used a spectroscope to examine light from the Sun in 1814. He saw "an almost countless number of strong and weak vertical lines, which are, however, darker than the rest of the color image; some appeared to be almost perfectly black" and mapped almost 600 of the black lines (20,000 are recognized today). When he examined the spectra of the Moon, Mars, and Venus and found that they matched the Sun's exactly, he reasoned that these objects were reflecting light from the Sun, not emitting their own light. However, when he examined the light from Sirius and other bright stars, he found that the pattern of black lines in each star's spectrum was different, and the spectra of all of the stars differed from that of the Sun.

When a spectroscope is used to examine light from chemicals burned in the lab, only a few colors are present in it and each color forms a distinct image of the slit called a *spectral line*. After extensive research, it became clear when burned as a gas, each element produced a unique pattern of bright spectral lines, or *emission spectrum*. Thus, emission spectra can be used to identify elements.

Around 1860, Gustav Kirchoff performed a series of experiments using spectroscopes. He knew that a glowing hot solid, liquid, or gas emits a continuous spectrum. He also knew that the glowing gas of an element forms a spectrum of bright lines. So Kirchoff decided to combine the two. He found that when a hot, glowing gas is placed in front of a hotter source of a continuous spectrum, the gas absorbs light at the same wavelengths that it would emit if viewed alone, producing a spectrum with dark lines, called an *absorption spectrum.* In other words, the pattern of dark lines is identical to the pattern of colored emission lines that would be produced by the elements in the gas. Kirchoff then applied these discoveries to the Sun's spectrum. He concluded that light from the hot interior of the Sun passes through cooler gases in its outer atmosphere. Thus, the dark lines in the solar spectrum were the fingerprints of elements in the Sun, and by extension, the same is true of all stars. In this way, astronomers are able to determine the composition of stars by analyzing their spectral lines.

In the 1870s, a New York physician and amateur astronomer named Henry Draper used photographic plates to record the spectra of stars for later study. When he died, his widow gave the plates to the Harvard College Observatory and funded a program to photograph the spectra of many thousands of stars. Based upon similarity of spectral lines, the project director, Edward C. Pickering, devised a scheme for classifying stars with an alphabetical sequence of letters—A, B, C, D, etc. Between 1918 and 1924 the Henry Draper Catalogue of stellar spectra was published in which nearly 400,000 stellar spectra were classified by Annie Jump Cannon of the Harvard Observatory. Based upon her work, some of Pickering's classes were combined or dropped, and the sequence was reordered O, A, B, F, G, K, M.

The relationship between the temperatures of stars and their luminosities and was discovered independently by two astronomers: Ejnar Hertzsprung of Denmark, and Henry N. Russell of the United States. The H-R Diagram (or Hertzsprung-Russell diagram), is a plot of the luminosity versus surface temperature of stars.

NOTES

LEARNING SET 4 IMPLEMENTATION

Learning Set 4

How Do Objects Outside Our Solar System Move Through Space?

Astronomers use Newton's laws of motion and gravity to predict accurately the motion of many solar-system objects. As soon as a new solar-system object is identified, its location and speed are measured from Earth at several points in its orbit. From this data, the entire orbit can be calculated. Once the orbit is known, astronomers can compare it to the known orbits of the planets and other solar-system objects to predict whether the newly identified object is on a collision course.

space probe: a remotely controlled spacecraft with data collection equipment used to gather data about objects in space.

However, accurately determining the orbits of objects in our solar system can be difficult. Because the images we see through telescopes are distorted by Earth's atmosphere, scientists also use other technologies to explore what is happening in space. They can launch a **space probe** from Earth that will send back photographs and other information. Scientists have also launched telescopes into space. A telescope in space can "see" dimmer objects and also provide sharper images than a telescope used on Earth.

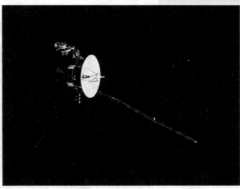

An artist's version of the space probe, Voyager 1 in flight.

The photographs and other data collected by space probes and telescopes have helped scientists study stars and discover space objects and even whole solar systems outside of our solar system. This data have also allowed scientists to investigate the origin of the universe. All of this information has helped scientists develop a detailed picture of our place in the universe.

AST 163

ASTRONOMY

Learning Set 4

How Do Objects Outside Our Solar System Move Through Space?

5 min

Students are introduced to the Learning Set question.

△ Guide

Begin by telling students that they now know about the orbits of the outer planets. Emphasize that once the orbits of solar-system objects are known, scientists can calculate the probability that they will collide with other solar-system bodies. Then tell them there are also objects outside the solar system. Tell them they will now investigate whether any of these objects can collide with objects in our solar system.

Describe how scientists use space probes and telescopes on Earth and in space to obtain images of stars and other space objects outside the solar

*A class period is considered to be one 40 to 50 minute class.

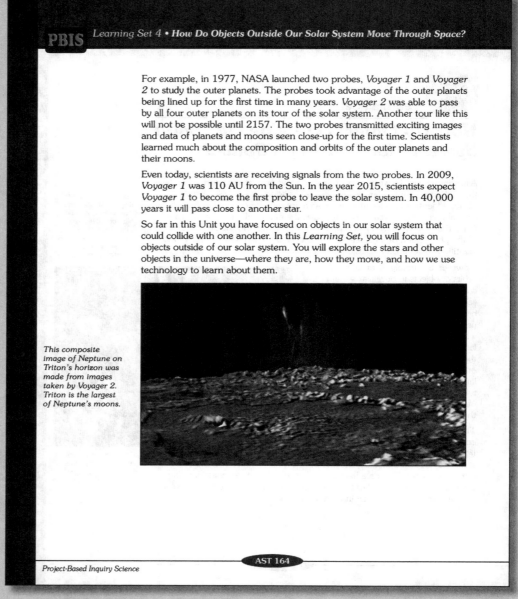

For example, in 1977, NASA launched two probes, *Voyager 1* and *Voyager 2* to study the outer planets. The probes took advantage of the outer planets being lined up for the first time in many years. *Voyager 2* was able to pass by all four outer planets on its tour of the solar system. Another tour like this will not be possible until 2157. The two probes transmitted exciting images and data of planets and moons seen close-up for the first time. Scientists learned much about the composition and orbits of the outer planets and their moons.

Even today, scientists are receiving signals from the two probes. In 2009, *Voyager 1* was 110 AU from the Sun. In the year 2015, scientists expect *Voyager 1* to become the first probe to leave the solar system. In 40,000 years it will pass close to another star.

So far in this Unit you have focused on objects in our solar system that could collide with one another. In this *Learning Set,* you will focus on objects outside of our solar system. You will explore the stars and other objects in the universe—where they are, how they move, and how we use technology to learn about them.

This composite image of Neptune on Triton's horizon was made from images taken by Voyager 2. Triton is the largest of Neptune's moons.

system. One shortcoming of telescopes on Earth is that the images you see through the telescopes are distorted by Earth's atmosphere. Scientists send probes (remote-controlled spacecraft) into space to send back photographs and other information. They can also send telescopes into space to send back photographs. These images help scientists discover and study stars and space objects.

Discuss the examples of *Voyager 1* and *Voyager 2,* two probes that were launched to study the outer planets. These probes transmitted images of the outer planets and their moons as they passed by them. *Voyager 1* is expected to leave the solar system in 2015.

SECTION 4.1 INTRODUCTION

4.1 Understand the Question

Think About How Objects Outside Our Solar System Move Through Space

◀ *1 class period*

A class period is considered to be one 40 to 50 minute class.

Overview

Students consider what can be inferred by studying the light from stars. To develop an appreciation of the challenges astronomers face in stars, students are given photographic images of lights and are challenged to make observations and draw inferences about the size, brightness, and distance to the lights. Students share their ideas and supporting evidence with the class and the class reflects on and discusses how the light from stars can be analyzed to provide information about the sizes, distances, motions and compositions of stars. The section concludes with students updating the *What do we think we know?* and *What do we need to investigate?* columns of the *Project Board*.

Targeted Concepts, Skills, and Nature of Science	Performance Expectations
Scientists often collaborate and share their findings. Sharing findings makes new information available and helps scientists refine their ideas and build on others' ideas. When another person's or group's idea is used, credit needs to be given.	Students share their individual ideas with their group and their group's ideas with the class as they consider what conclusions can be drawn about the lights in a photographic image.
Scientists must keep clear, accurate and descriptive records of what they do so they can share their work with others; consider what they did, why they did it, and what they want to do next.	Students keep a written record of their observations and inferences about the photographic image of lights. Students keep a written record of their answers to the *Reflect* and *Stop and Think* questions.

Targeted Concepts, Skills, and Nature of Science	Performance Expectations
Humans perceive the universe by the radiation it emits. Technological advances have greatly extended the scope of human perception and led to the observations upon which our current theories of the universe are based.	Students identify light as the primary source of information about stars. Students demonstrate an appreciation for the challenges astronomers face in determining the nature of stars from the light they emit.
Some stars appear brighter than others. Stars may look bright because they give off a lot of light, or because they are relatively close to Earth.	Students identify distance and actual brightness as two factors affecting the appearance of a star to an observer on Earth.

NOTES

....

....

....

....

....

....

....

....

....

....

....

....

Homework Options

Reflection

- **Science Content:** Only the light that enters the eye through a small opening called the pupil is perceived by humans. Suppose you kept looking at a 100-W light bulb as you moved farther and farther away from it. The light bulb keeps emitting the same amount of light. How does the brightness of the bulb when you are close to it compare with its brightness when you are 100 m away? How does the way in which you perceive light account for what you observe? *(Students should describe how the light bulb will appear brighter when closer to it than it does 100 m away. The light appears dimmer when you are farther away, because as the light travels away from the bulb, it spreads out and less of the light emitted by the light bulb enters your eye.)*

- **Science Process:** What evidence could you look for that would indicate the distance to a light source? *(Student answers will vary, but may include brightness, and blocking of the light source by closer objects.)*

Preparation for 4.2

- **Science Content:** How could you position a 300-W light bulb and a 100-W light bulb so that both would appear to have the same brightness to an observer? *(Students should describe how they would place the 300-W light bulb at a greater distance from the observer than where the 100-W light bulb would be placed from the observer.)*

- **Science Process:** Why would you not be able to determine the average height of males in a country's population by measuring the height of males in an elementary school? *(Students should understand that the sample does not accurately represent the group from which it was drawn.)*

NOTES

....

....

....

NOTES

SECTION 4.1 IMPLEMENTATION

4.1 Understand the Question

Think About How Objects Outside Our Solar System Move Through Space

When you look at the night sky, you can see thousands of stars. They all appear as dazzling, twinkling points of light. Some stars are very bright, and some are so dim you can barely see them. Are the brighter stars closer, or are they giving off more light? And are the stars really fixed, or do they move through space? These are questions astronomers have been asking for hundreds of years.

It would seem that there is little that you can learn from gazing at a point of light and comparing it to other points of light. But astronomers have been able to study the light in many ways. They also have learned much by studying Earth's closest star, the Sun. One thing they have learned through these studies is that Newton's laws of motion and gravity apply to the stars. In *Learning Set 2* and *Learning Set 3,* you read about how astronomers were able to infer the structure of the solar system from what they saw in the sky. Now you will learn how scientists have built up a three-dimensional moving model of the universe from what they see in the sky as well.

Get Started

Scientists use photographic images to study objects in the night sky. They make some assumptions about what types of objects would have produced the images. They also compare different objects within an image or different images of the same part of the sky taken at different times. You will practice using these same methods in two investigations.

Each group will be assigned one photograph. Study your image. Compare the different lights in the image. Notice how the lights are similar to or different from one another. Then work as a group to answer the questions.

AST 165

ASTRONOMY

4.1 Understand the Question

Think About How Objects Outside Our Solar System Move Through Space

5 min

Students discuss how observations of the night sky can be used to learn about stars.

△ Guide

Begin by pointing out what students know about the stars beyond the outer reaches of the solar system. Students know how the stars appear in the night sky. Some appear very bright, and some appear very dim. They seem to be points of light, and they seem stationary. Point out that there is a lot more to learn in order to understand these observations. Ask students how they might determine whether the stars that appear very bright are nearer than other stars or whether they simply emit more light. How might

*A class period is considered to be one 40 to 50 minute class.

they determine whether the stars are really stationary? Tell them these are questions astronomers have been working with for centuries, and students will address them in this *Learning Set*.

Get Started

Get Started

Scientists use photographic images to study objects in the night sky. They make some assumptions about what types of objects would have produced the images. They also compare different objects within an image or different images of the same part of the sky taken at different times. You will practice using these same methods in two investigations.

Each group will be assigned one photograph. Study your image. Compare the different lights in the image. Notice how the lights are similar to or different from one another. Then work as a group to answer the questions.

Get Started

10 min

Groups answer the questions using the photographs of lights.

△ Guide

Point out that astronomers work with observations from the night sky, using photographic images to study objects, to answer questions about where stars are and how they might move through space. Tell students that understanding what they see in photographs can be challenging. Tell them they will begin to learn about the challenges of understanding observations of the night sky and solutions to those challenges by practicing making observations of lights from photographs. They will note what assumptions they make about the lights in the images, and they will compare different objects within the images to come to an understanding of how the objects are related.

NOTES

....

....

....

....

....

....

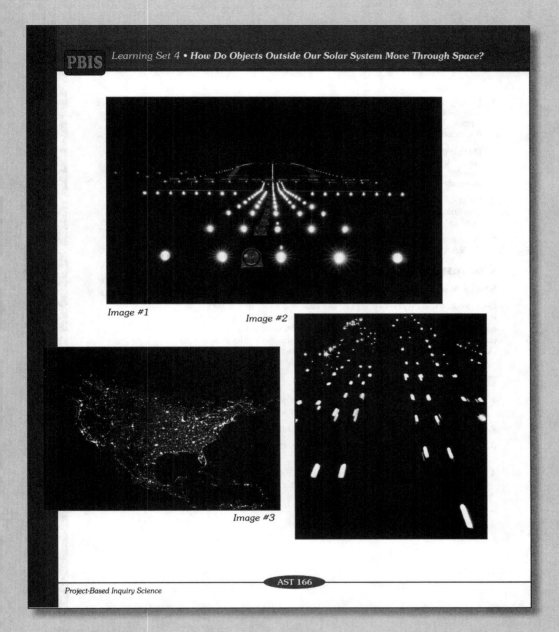

Image #1

Image #2

Image #3

AST 166

Project-Based Inquiry Science

⬡ Get Going

Assign images to groups. Each group should look at one of the three photographs. Have them study the photographs and answer the questions in their text, based on their observations. Emphasize that they should think about the challenges involved in determining the distances and relationships of light sources in photographs, and about ways scientists might be able to address those challenges.

1. Do you think all of the lights in your photograph are the same distance away from the camera, or are some of the lights closer and some farther? What evidence suggests the distance of each light from the camera?

2. Do you think all the lights would be the same brightness if they were viewed from a distance of 100 meters, or do you think some lights are brighter and some are not as bright? What evidence did you use to decide?

3. What do you think your image is? What evidence supports your conclusion? What additional information besides the image itself do you need to be sure about what it is?

4. What assumptions have you made about the objects that are producing the lights in your image?

Communicate

Share Your Conclusions

Each group should show its image to the class and share its answers to the four questions. As you listen to others, pay attention to the information each group was able to gather from its image. Try to determine if the group could have come to other conclusions based on the same information. Notice how much information from the image each group uses to draw its conclusions and how much knowledge they apply from other sources.

Reflect

1. In each image, how much of the information gathered was in the image itself, and how much was inferred from other sources of information?

2. What factors do you think determine the brightness of a star in the sky?

3. Do you think all stars are the same size? Why do you think some are brighter than others?

4. Do you think there might be stars that are moving toward our solar system? How do you think the light from a star would change if the star were getting closer to us?

AST 167

ASTRONOMY

△ Guide and Assess

As groups discuss their photographs and the questions, monitor their progress. Ask them what they have been able to determine about the lights in their photographs, how they were able to determine it, and what difficulties they have had. Students should recognize that some things may be difficult or impossible to determine from the photographs. They should give reasons why they believe some lights are more distant than others or that some lights are brighter than others. For instance, they may recognize that the runway lights seem to form lines that appear to run toward a horizon, suggesting that the lights closest together are farthest away; and in the satellite view of Earth, they may recognize that some of the lights seem to be larger than others, which could suggest that they are closer than the others. It should be noted that none of this is conclusive evidence.

1. Students analyzing Image #1 may answer that the lights appear to be at different distances. Some seem closer, and some seem farther away. The evidence is the apparent size of the lights. The larger size indicates they are closer. Other evidence is the distance apart for lights of same size. As they grow smaller, they appear to be closer together.

   Students analyzing Image #2 may answer that the lights appear to be at different distances. Their evidence is identical to students with Image #1.

   Students analyzing Image #3 may conclude that their lights are all about the same distance away. This is a night photograph of the United States.

2. Students analyzing Images #1 and #2 may conclude that if all the lights were at a 100 m distance, they would have the same brightness. Students analyzing Image #3 would probably say that the lights from cities would be of different brightness at 100 m.

3. Students with Image #1 should reason that their photograph has caught the runway lights of an airport at night. Students with Image #2 should conclude that their photograph shows the headlights of cars at night. Students with Image #3 should see that their photograph is of the United States at night from space.

4. Student answers will vary, but will probably say that their major assumption is based on the distance between the camera and the lights being photographed. If they were all taken from 2 cm away, very different conclusions would be reached.

△ Guide

Have groups share their conclusions about their photographs. They should show their photograph to the class and share their answers to the analysis questions. As each group presents, the rest of the class should evaluate whether their conclusions are accurately supported by their evidence. They should make comments if they think a group's conclusions are not supported by evidence, and they should ask questions to clarify if necessary.

Communicate: Share Your Conclusions

15 min

Groups share their conclusions with the class.

Reflect

10 min

Students have a class discussion of the Reflect *questions.*

Reflect

1. In each image, how much of the information gathered was in the image itself, and how much was inferred from other sources of information?

2. What factors do you think determine the brightness of a star in the sky?

3. Do you think all stars are the same size? Why do you think some are brighter than others?

4. Do you think there might be stars that are moving toward our solar system? How do you think the light from a star would change if the star were getting closer to us?

△ Guide

Lead a class discussion of the *Reflect* questions. Students should recognize that they need to use inferences and prior knowledge to interpret what they see in the images. Based on this, they should understand that interpreting images of the night sky requires a lot of investigation. You should also try to help students identify the distance of an object and its actual brightness as two factors determining its apparent brightness. Students may not have enough information to form any definite ideas about Questions 3 and 4, but the questions should engage them in thinking about how they can use observations of the light from stars to make inferences.

1. Students should recognize that it was the pattern of the lights which helped identify the source of the light in each photograph.

2. Students should suggest that the apparent brightness of a star may be due to actual brightness, distance away from Earth, or size of the star.

3. Students will probably know that all stars are not the same size. They should understand that distance and size are two factors affecting the apparent brightness.

4. Students should understand that a star would appear brighter as it got closer to Earth.

NOTES

....

....

5. Think about all the prior knowledge you needed to analyze the images in the investigation. Then think about what knowledge you need to understand images of stars in the sky. What do you think you need to investigate to know more about the location and movement of space objects outside of our solar system?

6. What do you think you need to investigate to decide whether any of those space objects might enter our solar system and collide with solar-system objects?

Update the *Project Board*

In the *What do we think we know?* column, record what you know about stars and other space objects outside of our solar system. Also record knowledge you used to interpret the photographs. In the *What do we need to investigate?* column, record questions you have about stars and space objects outside of our solar system. Also record any ideas you have about investigations that will help you better understand the distances between stars and the motion of stars other than the Sun.

How can you know if objects in space will collide?				
What do we think we know?	What do we need to investigate?	What are we learning?	What is our evidence?	What does it mean for the challenge or question?

What's the Point?

From your class discussions, you have probably realized that even a simple photograph can be interpreted in more than one way. This suggests that if you want to draw conclusions from the data in a photograph, it would be a good idea to confirm your conclusions with additional information that is not in the photograph. Think about this in the next section as you explore brightness of stars and distances to the stars.

5. Student answers will vary, but they may say they need to know the distance of stars from Earth, or the direction that stars are going.

6. Student answers will vary, but they may say they need to know the size, speed, or direction of travel for the space objects.

Update the Project Board

10 min

Students engage in a discussion to update the Project Board.

Update the *Project Board*

In the *What do we think we know?* column, record what you know about stars and other space objects outside of our solar system. Also record knowledge you used to interpret the photographs. In the *What do we need to investigate?* column, record questions you have about stars and space objects outside of our solar system. Also record any ideas you have about investigations that will help you better understand the distances between stars and the motion of stars other than the Sun.

How can you know if objects in space will collide?				
What do we think we know?	What do we need to investigate?	What are we learning?	What is our evidence?	What does it mean for the challenge or question?

△ Guide

Lead a discussion of what students think they know about the stars. Record students' ideas in the *What do we think we know?* column of the *Project Board,* and have them record them on their *Project Board* pages. This should include knowledge they used to interpret the photographs. Ask them what they need to find out about the stars and record their answers in the *What do we need to investigate?* column.

Assessment Options

Targeted Concepts, Skills, and Nature of Science	How do I know if students got it?
Scientists often collaborate and share their findings. Sharing findings makes new information available and helps scientists refine their ideas and build on others' ideas. When another person's or group's idea is used, credit needs to be given.	**ASK:** How were you able to distinguish between observations and inferences in the information shared by other groups? **LISTEN:** Students should understand the inferences are conclusions based on observations. Information shared by other groups should be evaluated based on the supporting evidence. If the evidence is something that can be directly observed in the image, it is not an inference. If the evidence is based on other sources of information, it is an inference.

Targeted Concepts, Skills, and Nature of Science	How do I know if students got it?
Scientists must keep clear, accurate and descriptive records of what they do so they can share their work with others; consider what they did, why they did it, and what they want to do next.	**ASK:** What characteristics of the lights in the photograph you analyzed would be considered direct observations? **LISTEN:** Students' answers will vary, but may include color, size, relative position, and relative intensity.
Humans perceive the universe by the radiation it emits. Technological advances have greatly extended the scope of human perception and led to the observations upon which our current theories of the universe are based.	**ASK:** How are human beings aware of the existence of stars? **LISTEN:** Students should answer that they are aware of the stars by the light emitted by the stars. **ASK:** What characteristics of stars are most readily apparent to human observers on Earth? **LISTEN:** Students should identify brightness and color. **ASK:** How could you tell the difference between light coming from an incandescent and a fluorescent light bulb? **LISTEN:** Student answers typically indicate that they think they could tell the light from different types of light bulbs apart based on brightness and color.
Some stars appear brighter than others. Stars may look bright because they give off a lot of light, or because they are relatively close to Earth.	**ASK:** How might it be possible for a very bright object to appear dim to an observer? **LISTEN:** Students should answer that a bright object could appear dim if it is located far from the observer.

Teacher Reflection Questions

- In this section, students observed images of light sources. Students need to realize that the actual brightness and distance both affect how bright a light source appears to an observer. What issues did students encounter when they were developing these understandings?

- How much understanding of the distinction between observations and inferences was evident in class discussions? How could you make this distinction clearer to students?

- How did the activities in this section contribute toward students' understanding the challenges faced by astronomers when studying stars?

NOTES

SECTION 4.2 INTRODUCTION

4.2 Explore

How Can You Know How Bright a Star Is and How Far Away It Is?

◄ *2 class periods*

A class period is considered to be one 40 to 50 minute class.

Overview

Section 4.2 opens with a brief discussion of how the distance between an observer and a light source affects how bright it appears to the observer. Students then explore another factor that affects the perceived brightness of a light source: changes in the diameter of the pupil of the human eye. Students consider the connection between pupil size and the aperture of devices, such as binoculars, which greatly increase the number of stars that can be perceived by the human eye. After reading about the magnitude scale used to describe the brightness of a star and the distinction between apparent and absolute magnitude, students develop an understanding of how astronomers measure the distances to nearby stars by measuring distances in the classroom based on parallax. Students carry out two measurement procedures, one in which the parallax observations are made from positions 5 cm apart and one made from positions 50 cm apart. They analyze their data and determine the distance to objects based on their parallax. After sharing their results with the class, students discuss factors that affect the accuracy of their measurements and possible sources of error, and reflect on the limitations of the parallax method for determining distances. Students then read about the connections between how they used parallax to measure distances in the classroom and the parallax method used by astronomers to determine the distances to stars.

Targeted Concepts, Skills, and Nature of Science	Performance Expectations
Scientists often collaborate and share their findings. Sharing findings makes new information available and helps scientists refine their ideas and build on others' ideas. When another person's or group's idea is used, credit needs to be given.	Students collaborate in small groups to measure distances in the classroom based on parallax, using two different procedures for making observations, and share their results with the class. The class discusses the accuracy of the distance calculations that were made using the two procedures and possible sources of error.

Targeted Concepts, Skills, and Nature of Science	Performance Expectations
Scientists must keep clear, accurate and descriptive records of what they do so they can share their work with others; consider what they did, why they did it, and what they want to do next.	Students keep a written record of their responses to the *Reflect* and *Stop and Think* questions. Students record their parallax observations and distance calculations on a *Parallax* page. The class keeps a record of the distance calculations based on parallax made by all groups.
Models are a representation of something in the world. Simulations use a model to imitate, or act out, real-life situations.	Students create a model of the universe consisting of an observer on Earth, nearby stars, and background stars. They then use it to simulate the determination of the distance to nearby stars using parallax.
Humans perceive the universe by the radiation it emits. Technological advances have greatly extended the scope of human perception and led to the observations upon which our current theories of the universe are based.	Students recognize that binoculars extend the scope of human perception.
Some stars appear brighter than others. Stars may look bright because they give off a lot of light, or because they are relatively close to Earth. Apparent magnitude is a measure of a star's brightness relative to other stars as seen by an observer on Earth. Absolute brightness is a measure of a star's brightness relative to other stars when all of the stars are viewed from the same distance.	Students distinguish between apparent brightness and absolute brightness. Students identify distance and the amount of light emitted by an object as factors that affect its brightness to an observer on Earth.
Stars that are relatively close to our solar system appear to shift slightly in their position relative to distant stars when viewed from different positions, an effect known as parallax. The parallax of a star can be used to calculate its distance from Earth.	Students calculate the distance to an object based on its parallax.

Materials	
1 per student	*Parallax View* page
1 per group	Ruler Objects A, B, C, and D Calculator
1 per class	Masking tape (for marking observation points)

Activity Setup and Preparation

Before class, set up the observation stations and objects for the parallax experiments. The ideal setup for these experiments requires a long classroom, gymnasium, or hallway. The observation area will be a long, skinny rectangle. Near one of the short sides of the rectangle, set up the observation stations. The observation stations for *Investigation 1* should have a single X marked with masking tape on a desktop. The stations for *Investigation 2* should have two X's marked with masking tape on a desktop that are 50 cm apart. Students will have to take turns making observations, so fit as many observation stations as possible within the space available. On a long table, or on four separate desks, set up four objects between the observation stations and the facing wall. From the perspective of the observation stations, the objects should not overlap but they should be relatively close together. One object should be about 2 m away, one should be 3 m away, one should be 4 m away, and one should be 5 m away. The objects would ideally be labeled or discernible in some way, but not be too large. The distances do not need to be exact. The wall facing the observation stations should have some kind of patterned background that students can use to estimate distances on the wall (this is the field of distant stars that students are using to make their distance calculations). A brick or cement wall works, as does any kind of art or design.

If this is not feasible in your classroom, set up the observation stations near the center of the room facing outward toward the classroom walls. Stations do not need to have the same background, but the far wall should be completely behind the objects from students' perspective (i.e. the corner of the room should not be within their line of sight behind the objects). The distances between the four objects can be decreased so that they fit between the observation stations and the wall.

Measure the actual distance between each observation station and the wall; measure the distance from the observation station to each of the four objects. Set up a chart for recording the distances calculated by each group to use during the parallax activity.

Homework Options

Reflection

- **Science Content:** What is the relationship between the distance of an object from an observer and its parallax? *(Students should identify that as distance from the observer increases, parallax decreases.)*

- **Science Content:** Refer to the lists of the 25 brightest and 25 closest stars. Which star do you think would show the greatest parallax to an observer on Earth, Deneb or Sirius A? Why? *(Students should identify that Sirius A would show the greatest parallax, because it is closer to Earth than Deneb.)*

- **Science Process:** In the procedure to determine distance to an object based on parallax, you measured parallax as the distance by which the object appeared to change position. You were able to do this because there was something on the wall of known size that gave you a sense of scale. Astronomers do not have objects in the background of known size that can be used to establish scale, therefore they do not measure parallax as a distance. What is another way in which the parallax of an object could be measured? *(Students should answer that the parallax can be measured as an angle; the angular difference in the position of the object relative to the fixed background of stars when viewed along two different lines of sight.)*

- **Science Process:** Research the definition of the term *parsec*. *(Student answers should state that a parsec is the distance from Earth at which a star would have a parallax angle of 1 second of arc [1/3600 of an angle of 1°]. One parsec represents a distance of just over 19 trillion miles [~31 trillion kilometers]).*

Preparation for 4.3

- **Science Content:** The solar system consists of the Sun and the objects that orbit the Sun. What must an object have for the entire solar system to orbit that object? *(Student answers will vary, but should indicate that the object needs a very large mass to exert enough gravitational attraction to hold the entire solar system in orbit.)*

- **Science Process:** An astronomical unit (AU) is equivalent to the mean distance between Earth and the Sun. Why is this unit not very useful when measuring distances to stars? *(Students should understand that the distance to stars is very great compared to the astronomical unit.)*

4.2 Explore

How Can You Know How Bright a Star Is and How Far Away It Is?

At the beginning of *Section 4.1*, you thought about a question astronomers have investigated for many years: *Are the brighter stars closer, or are they giving off more light?* You will now have the chance to explore factors that affect the brightness of stars. You will also find out how astronomers determine distances to the closest stars.

When you compare two lights in a photograph, as you did in the last section, the brightness of each light depends on at least two factors. One factor is how much light is given off by the light source. For example, a streetlight gives off more light than a 25-watt light bulb, so you would expect a streetlight to look brighter than a 25-watt light bulb.

Suppose, however, that you stand 1 meter from a 25-watt light bulb and 100 meters from a streetlight. Now the 25-watt light bulb will appear brighter than the streetlight. The distance to a light source is a second factor that affects the brightness of light that enters your eyes. The farther away you are from a light source, the less bright it will appear to your eyes.

The streetlight in the photograph on left looks very bright. How bright would it look from a block away? What about 10 blocks away? Or 100 blocks away?

AST 169

ASTRONOMY

4.2 Explore

How Can You Know How Bright a Star Is and How Far Away It Is?

5 min

Students are introduced to the activity.

△ **Guide**

Tell students they will now explore the factors that affect the observed brightness of stars, and they will begin to answer the question *Are the brighter stars closer, or are they giving off more light?* Point out that the question identifies at least two factors that can affect the observed brightness of stars in photographs — how much light a star gives off and how distant the star is.

**A class period is considered to be one 40 to 50 minute class.*

To help students understand how these factors can affect the observed brightness of stars or other light sources, discuss the examples given in their text. Some common human-made light sources give off more light than others. A streetlight gives off more light than a 25-W bulb, so you would expect the streetlight to look brighter in a photograph. However, if the 25-W bulb is much nearer than the streetlight, it will appear to be brighter. The two factors that affect how bright the streetlight and 25-W bulb appear to be are the amount of light each gives off and how far away each is.

NOTES

What Other Factor Affects How Bright an Object Appears?

Now you will work with a partner to discover another factor that affects how bright an object appears to be. You and your partner will record observations made in Steps 2–5, using a table like the one below.

	Left eye	Right eye
Appearance of each eye after five minutes in the dark		
Differences in what each eye sees after one eye is covered for one minute	Covered—	Uncovered—
Appearance of each eye at the end of the activity		

Materials
• watch or clock with second hand

Procedure

1. Work "in the dark" for five minutes, with the room lights off. If there are shades in the room, they will be pulled down to keep the room dark. During this time, you should not look at any bright sources of light, such as a computer screen. Follow instructions about what work do during these five minutes.

2. After the five minutes have passed, have your partner look at your eyes and record observations in the first row of your table. At the same time, you will observe your partner's eyes and record observations in his or her table.

3. Cover your left eye with your hand for one minute. Your teacher will turn on the ceiling lights and also keep track of the time. During this minute, look up at the ceiling lights of your classroom with your right eye (keeping your left eye covered).

4. After one minute has passed, look at one wall of the classroom, first with your left eye open and your right eye closed, and then with your right eye open and your left eye closed. Repeat this a few times and record what you see.

5. You and your partner should now look at each other's eyes and record observations in the last row of the table.

Project-Based Inquiry Science

What Other Factor Affects How Bright an Object Appears?

10 min

Students observe their partners' eyes after five minutes in the dark, and then again, after exposure to bright light.

△ Guide

Students will need to work in relative darkness for five minutes. Assign a task they can perform in five minutes. This can be anything that does not require or encourage students to look at a bright light source, but keeps them using their eyes. For instance, you might have them write answers to the *Homework Options* from *Learning Set 4.1* if they haven't already. They should also make a table like the one in their text to record their observations. Before having them begin, quickly go over the procedure. Emphasize that at the end of five minutes, they will observe their partner's eyes. They will then look at a bright light with each eye covered for a minute and observe how this affects their vision, and how it affects the appearance of their pupils.

⬡ Get Going

Turn off the lights in the room and pull the blinds if possible. Note the time, have students make their tables, and give them an assignment for the remainder of the five minutes.

When five minutes have passed, have students observe their partner's eyes (with the lights still off). In the first row of their partner's table, they should record anything they notice.

When students have had time to record their observations, have them cover their left eye. Turn on the lights, and have students look at the lights with their uncovered right eye. Note the time, and after a minute, have students look at a wall, first with their left eye open and right eye closed, and then with their right eye open and left eye closed. They should repeat the process a few times, paying close attention to any differences between what they see through each eye. Have them record their observations in their table. Finally, have them observe their partner's eyes, and record observations in the last row of their partner's table.

NOTES

_____

_____

_____

_____

_____

_____

_____

Stop and Think

1. How did the appearance of your eyes after the activity compare with their appearance before the activity?

2. How did looking at a bright light with one eye change your vision in that eye? Did you and your partner experience the same change in vision?

3. How do you think the change in the appearance of your eyes affected your vision?

In the investigation, you discovered that another factor that affects the brightness of light you see is the size of your eyes' **pupils**. You may have noticed that when you look at a friend's eyes in bright sunlight, the pupils of his or her eyes are small. In bright light, your eyes protect themselves by reducing the size of the pupils, which reduces the amount of light that enters your eyes. In darkness, your pupils grow larger to allow more light into your eyes. This helps you to see in the dark.

> **pupil:** the circular opening in the center of the eye that controls the amount of light that enters the eye.

If you step outside on a clear night, at first you do not see many stars. Your pupils are still small from seeing bright indoor lights. After you have been outside for several minutes, your eyes are better adjusted to the darkness. Your pupils are much larger now. If you are far from city lights, now you can see thousands of stars. When your pupils are larger, they allow more light to enter your eyes. You can see a greater number of stars that are dim. These dim stars were there before your eyes adjusted to the dark, and they were just as bright. Your eyes could not detect the dim stars because too little light entered your eyes.

You may know that owls and other animals that see well in the dark benefit from having large eyes. The easiest way for humans to see better in the dark is to use binoculars. You may think binoculars only help you to see small details, but they also help you see objects that are too dim to see with the unaided eye. The lenses in binoculars are much larger than your pupils, so these "bigger eyes" collect more light than your eyes collect.

Suppose you look at one area of the sky, first with the binoculars and then without them. You can see many more stars with binoculars, more than a hundred thousand stars if you are far from city lights. This may make you wonder how many stars you could see if you were able to see every star in the universe.

Stop and Think

10 min

Students answer the Stop and Think *questions and have a class discussion.*

△ Guide

Have students answer the *Stop and Think* questions with their partners. Let them know they will share their answers with the class. As they work, monitor their progress. Then lead a class discussion of their answers.

1. Students should report that their pupils got larger in darkness and smaller in strong light.

2. Students should report that their eyes were more light-sensitive when their pupils were large.

3. Students should note that objects appeared brighter when their pupils were large and dimmer when their pupils were small. Vision for dim objects, like stars, would be better in darkness.

NOTE: There may be some variation in the way students' eyes respond to darkness.

Discuss how the size of an observer's pupils is another factor that affects how bright stars appear. Tell students that a person's pupils get smaller in bright light to protect the eyes from the light. In darkness, the pupils get larger to admit more light.

Point out that since pupils enlarge in the dark, stars appear brighter once a person's eyes adjust to the dark. The longer a person remains outside in the dark, the brighter the stars will appear. After a short time, he or she will begin to see dimmer stars that were not visible at first.

Then tell students that binoculars and telescopes make stars appear brighter in a way that is similar to pupils getting bigger. When pupils are big, they admit more light. Similarly, the lenses of binoculars and telescopes are much bigger than the human eye and collect more light. Many stars that are too dim to see with the naked eye are visible with telescopes and even binoculars.

NOTES

....

....

....

....

....

....

....

When you use binoculars, you notice that some stars appear a lot brighter than others. Astronomers use a number called **apparent magnitude** to compare the brightness of stars in the night sky. The smaller the number, the brighter the star appears. With binoculars, you can see stars with an apparent magnitude of about 9 or less. Using only your unaided eyes, in good conditions you can see stars with an apparent magnitude of about 6 or less. The brightest stars have negative apparent magnitudes. The brightest star in the night sky, Sirius, has an apparent magnitude of about −1.5. The Sun is much brighter, with an apparent magnitude of −27.

Astronomers use a number called **absolute magnitude** to describe how bright a star would be if it were viewed from a standard distance, which happens to be about 2 million astronomical units. For example, the Sun has an absolute magnitude of 4.8, while Sirius has an absolute magnitude of 1.4. So, Sirius would be much brighter than the Sun if the two stars were viewed from the same distance.

Compare Distances Using Parallax

You might wonder how scientists know how far away from Earth a star is. After all, a star could be bright because it is close to our solar system, or it could be bright because it gives off a lot of light. Scientists use a measurement called **parallax** to determine distances to stars. Parallax is the observable change in an object's apparent position when observed from two locations that are the same distance from the object. In the next investigation, you will use parallax to compare distances in your classroom or in a hallway near your classroom. This exploration will help you understand what parallax means and how it can be used to determine how far a star is from Earth.

Your teacher has set up observation areas at four stations. Two are set up for Investigation 1, and two are set up for Investigation 2. Your group will be visiting one of the stations and doing one of the investigations. In each investigation, you will make sketches of your observations of three different objects against a distant background. Everyone will draw two sketches of what they observe. To carry out the investigation correctly, you will need to read the entire procedure for your investigation before you begin. You will record your sketches on a *Parallax View* page.

apparent magnitude: the brightness of a star relative to other stars as seen from Earth.

absolute magnitude: the brightness a star would be relative to other stars if all were viewed from the same distance (about 2 million astronomical units).

parallax: the observable change in an object's apparent position relative to a distant background when observed from two locations that are the same distance from the object.

Materials

- ruler
- objects A, B, and C placed on desks
- masking tape for marking observation X's
- *Parallax View* pages

AST 172

Then introduce the concept of *apparent magnitude*. Tell students that apparent magnitude is a number that expresses how bright a star appears to be from Earth. Emphasize that lower numbers indicate greater brightness. So a star with an apparent magnitude of 1 is brighter than a star with an apparent magnitude of 10.

Introduce the concept of *absolute magnitude*. Tell students that absolute magnitude is a number that expresses how bright a star would appear from a certain distance. That is, if you could travel in space and get within a certain distance of a star, you would be able to see the star at its absolute magnitude. Sirius has an absolute magnitude of 1.4, while the Sun has an absolute magnitude of only 4.8. This means if you could view Sirius and the Sun from the same distance, Sirius would be much brighter, even though the Sun appears much brighter from Earth.

Compare Distances Using Parallax

Compare Distances Using Parallax

20 min

Students observe objects and measure the parallax in their observations.

parallax: the observable change in an object's apparent position relative to a distant background when observed from two locations that are the same distance from the object.

Materials
- ruler
- objects A, B, and C placed on desks
- masking tape for marking observation X's
- *Parallax View* pages

You might wonder how scientists know how far away from Earth a star is. After all, a star could be bright because it is close to our solar system, or it could be bright because it gives off a lot of light. Scientists use a measurement called **parallax** to determine distances to stars. Parallax is the observable change in an object's apparent position when observed from two locations that are the same distance from the object. In the next investigation, you will use parallax to compare distances in your classroom or in a hallway near your classroom. This exploration will help you understand what parallax means and how it can be used to determine how far a star is from Earth.

Your teacher has set up observation areas at four stations. Two are set up for Investigation 1, and two are set up for Investigation 2. Your group will be visiting one of the stations and doing one of the investigations. In each investigation, you will make sketches of your observations of three different objects against a distant background. Everyone will draw two sketches of what they observe. To carry out the investigation correctly, you will need to read the entire procedure for your investigation before you begin. You will record your sketches on a *Parallax View* page.

△ Guide

Tell students they will now explore how scientists determine the distances of stars from Earth. Scientists use a property of the perceived position of objects called *parallax* to determine how far away stars are. Parallax is the apparent change in an object's position relative to a distant background when observed from two locations that are the same distance from the object. Tell students they will now practice determining the distance of objects using parallax.

NOTES

....

....

....

....

....

Investigation 1: Procedure

Take turns following this procedure. Each person in your group should have a turn.

1. On the observation desk there will be one X marked by masking tape. Kneel on the floor and rest your chin on the X.

2. Close your left eye, or hold your left hand over your left eye. With your right eye, study objects A, B, and C on the tables in front of you.

3. Still looking with your right eye only, sketch the three objects in the *Sketch 1* box on your *Parallax View* page. Use most of the full width of the drawing area to make your sketch.

4. Still looking with your right eye only, and with your chin in the same position, study the far wall of the room. Add background details to your sketch to show which part of the background is behind each object.

5. Copy your sketch of the background from *Sketch 1* onto *Sketch 2* on your *Parallax View* page. Do not include objects A, B, or C. Draw the background to the same scale as in *Sketch 1*.

6. Now, put your chin back in exactly the same position as it was when you made your observations for *Sketch 1*. This time, open your left eye, and close your right eye. Sketch the three objects as seen by your left eye in the *Sketch 2* box on your *Parallax View* page. Make sure you show correctly which part of the background is behind each object.

Investigation 2: Procedure

Take turns following this procedure. Each person in your group should have a turn.

1. On the observation desk there will be two X's marked by masking tape. The centers of the X's are 50 cm apart. Kneel on the floor and rest your chin on the left X.

Parallax View

Name:_____ Date:_____
Group:_____
Distance between observation points:_____

Sketch 1

Sketch 2

Object	Description	Parallax—distance object shifted on background (in mm)	Actual distance from X to object (in mm)
A			
B			
C			
D			

Comparison between parallax and actual measurements:_____

AST 173

ASTRONOMY

⬡ Get Going

Distribute *Parallax View* pages and take students to the observation area where they can observe objects against a distant background. Explain the procedures for groups running *Investigations 1* and *2.* Show students the two sets of observing desks. One should have a single X marked with masking tape. The other should have two X's marked with masking tape, 50 cm apart. Point out that there are four objects at a certain distance from each observing desk. Groups will observe the four objects—groups running

Investigation 1 will observe the objects from the first desk, and groups running *Investigation 2* will observe them from the second desk.

Students running *Investigation 1* will rest their chin on the X and close their left eye. Looking through their right eye, they will sketch the four objects in the *Sketch 1* box of the *Parallax View* page, using the full width of the box. They will also draw the background, making clear the apparent position of the four objects against the background. They will copy the background into the *Sketch 2* box. Then they will observe the four objects through their left eye and sketch them on the background in *Sketch 2*.

Students running *Investigation 2* will rest their chin on the left X and observe the four objects through one eye. (They will make all of their observations through the same eye, so they should note which eye they initially keep open.) They will sketch the four objects in the *Sketch 1* box and then draw the background behind the objects. Then they will move their chin to the right X and sketch the four objects in the *Sketch 2* box, drawing the background behind the objects.

NOTES

....

....

....

....

....

....

....

....

....

2. You will make all of your observations with one eye closed and one eye open. Choose your left or your right eye, whichever you are more comfortable using. Close your other eye, or hold your hand over your other eye. Looking with one eye, study objects A, B, and C on the tables in front of you.

3. Still looking with the same eye, sketch the three objects in the *Sketch 1* box on your *Parallax View* page. Use most of the full width of the drawing area to make your sketch.

4. Still looking with one eye only and with your chin in the same position, study the far wall of the room. Add background details to your sketch to show which part of the background is behind each object.

5. Copy your sketch of the background from *Sketch 1* onto *Sketch 2* on your *Parallax View* page. Do not include objects A, B, or C. Draw the background to the same scale as in *Sketch 1*.

6. Move your chin to the X on the right side of the observation desk. Using the same eye that you chose in Step 2 (covering or closing the other eye), sketch the three objects in the *Sketch 2* box on your *Parallax View* page. Make sure to correctly show which part of the background is behind each object.

Analyze Your Data

Begin by looking at the differences in your two sketches. You should see that, although you were the same distance from the objects when you made both sketches, the objects are sketched in different places relative to the background. This is parallax. To use this method to compare distances to objects, scientists usually measure parallax on photographs. You will measure parallax on your sketch.

1. The first thing you need to record is the actual distance between your observation places. For those who did Investigation 2, the distance was 50 cm. For those who did Investigation 1, the distance was the distance between your two eyes. You may measure that distance, or you can use a distance of 5 cm, the average distance between people's eyes. Record the distance between your two observation points at the top of your *Parallax View* page.

When you have gone over the procedures, have groups get started, and help them with any difficulties that arise. Note that it may be difficult for students to keep one eye closed, especially when they try to draw their observations. You may wish to provide something they can use as an eye patch, or you may have another student cover the observing student's eye. Students may also find it difficult to draw their observations with their chins on the desk. It may be necessary for them to lift their head at intervals to check their drawings. If they lift their head at intervals, it is important for them to ensure that their drawings match what they see when their chins are on the desk and one eye is closed.

If necessary, you can have different groups perform this activity at different times. The setup does not need to be identical in every respect, but the distances between the observing stations, the objects, and the background should be the same.

Analyze Your Data

10 min

Students analyze their data.

---

behind each object.

Analyze Your Data

Begin by looking at the differences in your two sketches. You should see that, although you were the same distance from the objects when you made both sketches, the objects are sketched in different places relative to the background. This is parallax. To use this method to compare distances to objects, scientists usually measure parallax on photographs. You will measure parallax on your sketch.

1. The first thing you need to record is the actual distance between your observation places. For those who did Investigation 2, the distance was 50 cm. For those who did Investigation 1, the distance was the distance between your two eyes. You may measure that distance, or you can use a distance of 5 cm, the average distance between people's eyes. Record the distance between your two observation points at the top of your *Parallax View* page.

△ Guide

Have students analyze their data with their partners. Have them compare each of the sketches they made, noting how the position of the objects relative to the background is different in each sketch. Emphasize that this change in position, or parallax, allows scientists to compare the distances of objects in space.

As groups work, monitor their progress and check their work. Students will first need to record the distance between the two observation places on their *Parallax View* page—either 50 cm or 5 cm—depending on which experiment they did. They will need to measure the distance each object appeared to shift on their sketches (the parallax), and to record which of the objects was closest, which was farthest, and which was in the middle. This will allow them to compare the degree of parallax of the objects to the distance of the objects.

NOTES

....

....

....

....

....

2. Measure the parallax on your sketches. Using a ruler, measure the distance each object appeared to shift on your sketches. Measure in millimeters. Record the parallax in the middle column of the chart on your *Parallax View* page.

3. Measure the actual distances to objects A, B, and C in millimeters. Record your measurements in the last column of the chart on your *Parallax View* page.

4. Compare your parallax measurements to the actual distance to the objects. Record how the two measurements compare at the bottom of your *Parallax View* page.

Communicate

Share Your Results

Your teacher will make two tables, one table to collect all of the parallax measurements that the class made for Investigation 1 and one table for all of the parallax measurements for Investigation 2. When your group takes its turn sharing data, report which investigation your group carried out, then report the parallax measurements your group made for objects A, B, and C. Describe how you think parallax relates to the distance of an object.

After all of the data have been collected, examine the charts together. Discuss the results. Did any of the results surprise you? Discuss how accurately your parallax measurements could be used to compare actual distances to the objects. Then discuss how the procedure you followed might be used by astronomers to measure the distances to stars in the sky. What do you think are the difficulties in taking such measurements?

AST 175

ASTRONOMY

Communicate: Share Your Results

15 min

Students make a table and record groups' results.

△ Guide

Make a table on the board or on a transparency to record the class' results. Put the results of *Investigation 1* in one column and the results of *Investigation 2* in the other column. Ask groups what distances they each found, and to record their answers in the table.

Once the table is complete, lead a class discussion of the results. Ask the class if groups' results seem consistent. If not, what could explain the differences in the results? Ask them how confident they feel about having determined the correct distance. Was there anything they could have done differently to get more accurate results?

Stop and Think

10 min

Students have a class discussion of the Stop and Think *questions.*

Stop and Think

1. Which objects appear to have greater parallax when you shift observation points, objects closer to you or objects farther away? Why?

2. Which groups observed a greater parallax for each object, students performing Investigation 1 or students performing Investigation 2? Why?

3. Which groups had difficulty in measuring parallax for Object C, those who did Investigation 1 or those who did Investigation 2? Why?

Reflect

Scientists can only use parallax to find the distances to nearby stars. However, the parallax shift is very small, so it is difficult to measure.

1. What could you do to try to make the parallax easier to measure?

2. On Earth, what is the greatest distance apart that two observation points could be?

3. Think about Earth's orbit around the Sun. How do you think scientists might use two different observation points on Earth's orbit to calculate the distances to nearby stars? What positions in an orbit are farthest from each other? What is the advantage of using observation points that are this far apart?

Measuring Parallax of Stars

Exploring parallax of objects in your classroom is a bit easier than measuring parallax of stars. In the classroom, you only used parallax to compare distances. You could have checked your comparisons using a tape measure for the actual distances. Scientists, of course, cannot use a tape measure to find the actual distance to a star, but they can use parallax and geometry to calculate actual distances.

In your investigation, you learned that if you increase the distance between your observation points, the parallax you observe increases. To measure parallax to the stars, astronomers observe a star at one time of the year and then observe it again six months later. If the star is much closer than the other stars in the photograph, then the parallax shows up as a shift in the position of the star. In fact, the parallax is so small that it can only be measured using a telescope.

AST 176

△ Guide

Lead a class discussion of the *Stop and Think* questions. Look for evidence that students understand that the nearness of the object and the size of the shift in perspective contribute to the observed parallax. Students should discover that groups running *Investigation 2* observed greater parallax. They may recognize that groups that ran *Investigation 2* had more reliable results, because the parallax in their observations was greater in relation to any measurement errors.

1. Students should report that closer objects have greater parallax than objects farther away because the angle formed from the two eyes to the object is greater. If the angle is greater, the parallax is greater.

2. Students should observe that *Investigation 2* provided the greater parallax, because the angle formed by the two viewing points and the object was greater.

3. Students should realize that groups who did *Investigation 1* had greater difficulty in measuring parallax for Object C. This is because the eyes are only 5 cm apart and form a smaller angle than viewing points 50 cm apart.

△ Guide

Lead a class discussion of the *Reflect* questions. Students should recognize that the diameter of Earth is the greatest distance that can separate two observation points on Earth. However, they should also recognize that Earth's orbit provides the opportunity to make observations from two points separated by a much greater distance. Two positions on opposite sides of the Sun—that is, two positions six months apart—are as far apart as possible. As with their observations in *Investigations 1* and *2,* maximizing the parallax minimizes the effect of errors in measurement.

1. Students should realize that they can make the parallax easier to measure by increasing the distance between the viewing points.

2. Students should suggest that the greatest distance apart would be the diameter of the Earth, about 13,000 km.

3. Students might suggest that if the measurements were taken at one end of Earth's orbit and then again six months later at the other end of the orbit, the distance would be much larger—about 144 million km.

△ Guide

Discuss how astronomers measure the parallax of stars. Point out that determining the distance of stars by measuring their parallax is more challenging than determining the distance of objects in a room by measuring their parallax. Students probably had some sense of the size of the room to begin with, so they knew the objects were not at some distance that would be measured in astronomical units. They also could have checked the distances with a tape measure. But there is no obvious way to know what distances to the stars would be reasonable.

Tell students that another difficulty with determining the distances of stars using parallax is that the diameter of Earth is not great enough to get parallax measurements. If you measure the position of a star on one side of Earth and then on the opposite side of Earth, you will measure a parallax

Reflect

10 min

Students have a class discussion of the Reflect *questions.*

Measuring Parallax of Stars

5 min

Students discuss how scientists measure parallax.

4.2 **Explore**

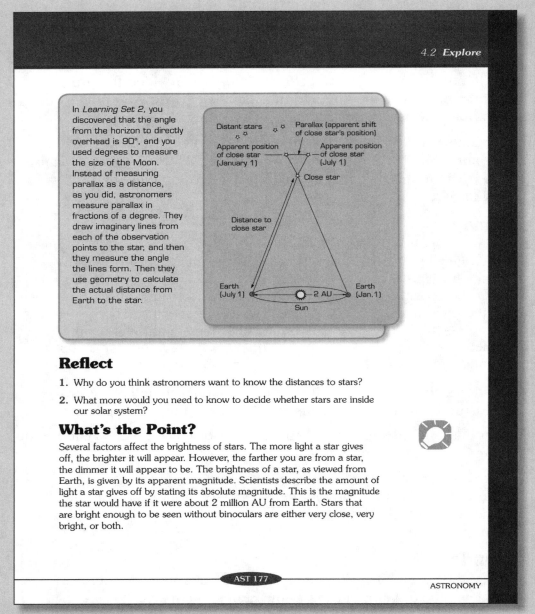

In *Learning Set 2*, you discovered that the angle from the horizon to directly overhead is 90°, and you used degrees to measure the size of the Moon. Instead of measuring parallax as a distance, as you did, astronomers measure parallax in fractions of a degree. They draw imaginary lines from each of the observation points to the star, and then they measure the angle the lines form. Then they use geometry to calculate the actual distance from Earth to the star.

Reflect

1. Why do you think astronomers want to know the distances to stars?

2. What more would you need to know to decide whether stars are inside our solar system?

What's the Point?

Several factors affect the brightness of stars. The more light a star gives off, the brighter it will appear. However, the farther you are from a star, the dimmer it will appear to be. The brightness of a star, as viewed from Earth, is given by its apparent magnitude. Scientists describe the amount of light a star gives off by stating its absolute magnitude. This is the magnitude the star would have if it were about 2 million AU from Earth. Stars that are bright enough to be seen without binoculars are either very close, very bright, or both.

AST 177

ASTRONOMY

of 0. In order to get useful measurements of parallax, scientists measure the position of a star at one time of the year, and then again six months later. This allows them to take measurements on opposite points of Earth's orbit, so that the distance between their observation points is the diameter of Earth's orbit. Point out the diagram showing this in student text.

Then point out that astronomers do not measure parallax using distances, as students did, but instead use angles. They draw an imaginary line to the star at each observation point, and then determine the angle at which the lines meet. This angle is shown in the diagram in the student text.

△ Guide

Lead a brief discussion of the *Reflect* questions. Listen for evidence that students understand that knowing the distances between space objects is vital to constructing a model of the universe. In order to determine whether something is part of our solar system, for instance, you would need to know how far away it is, and how far away other objects in the solar system are.

1. Students should know that the reason astronomers want to know the distances to stars is so they can construct a model of the universe.

2. Students should reply that they need to know the distance to the stars in order to know whether the stars are inside our solar system.

Reflect

5 min

Students engage in a discussion of the Reflect *questions.*

NOTES

Parallax is the apparent shift in an object's position when viewed from two observation points that are equal distances from the object. As the distance to an object increases, the parallax decreases. The parallax that you can observe can be increased by observing from two observation points with a greater separation.

Parallax is measurable if you make observations that are six months apart, when Earth is at opposite ends of its orbit. The distance between the observation points, 2 AU, is great enough to make it possible to use a telescope to observe parallax for the closest stars.

The Spitzer telescope is orbiting the Sun, away from Earth. Its images can be compared to Earth-based images, allowing scientists to compare images taken at the same time from two different points in space.

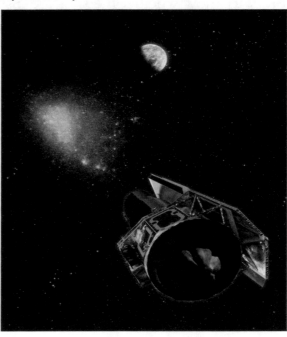

NOTES

....

....

....

Assessment Options

Targeted Concepts, Skills, and Nature of Science	How do I know if students got it?
Scientists often collaborate and share their findings. Sharing findings makes new information available and helps scientists refine their ideas and build on others' ideas. When another person's or group's idea is used, credit needs to be given.	**ASK:** When groups shared their findings, what measurements did they seem most unsure of? **LISTEN:** Students' answers will vary. Students often state that they are most unsure of the estimated distance by which the object appeared to shift position. **ASK:** Which possible sources of error came up most frequently when the class discussed the accuracy of the results? **LISTEN:** Estimated parallax distance, errors in calculating the scale, errors in observing positions of the objects relative to the background.
Scientists must keep clear, accurate and descriptive records of what they do so they can share their work with others; consider what they did, why they did it, and what they want to do next.	**ASK:** Why is it important to record your work when performing calculations and not just your answers on the *Parallax View* page? **LISTEN:** Students should answer that if you do not record your work, there is no way to check your calculations to determine whether an error was computational or due to inaccurate observations. **ASK:** Why is it useful to record the distances calculated by all of the groups in the class and not just your own? **LISTEN:** Students should answer that recording all groups' results provides a larger sample of trials. A larger sample of trials allows results to be averaged and decreases the effects of chance of random errors.

Targeted Concepts, Skills, and Nature of Science	How do I know if students got it?
Models are a representation of something in the world. Simulations use a model to imitate, or act out, real-life situations.	**ASK:** In the model that you created to simulate measuring the distance to stars using parallax, what did each of the following represent: the wall, the four objects, and students? **LISTEN:** Students represented an observer on Earth, the four objects represented nearby stars, and the wall represented the background of fixed stars.
Humans perceive the universe by the radiation it emits. Technological advances have greatly extended the scope of human perception and led to the observations upon which our current theories of the universe are based.	**ASK:** How does the number of stars visible through binoculars compare with the number of stars visible to the unaided eye? **LISTEN:** Students should answer that more stars are visible through binoculars than with the unaided eye. With the unaided eye, thousands of stars are visible; with binoculars, hundreds of thousands of stars are visible.

NOTES

....

....

....

Targeted Concepts, Skills, and Nature of Science	How do I know if students got it?
Some stars appear brighter than others. Stars may look bright because they give off a lot of light, or because they are relatively close to Earth. Apparent magnitude is a measure of a star's brightness relative to other stars as seen by an observer on Earth. Absolute magnitude is a measure of a star's brightness relative to other stars when all of the stars are viewed from the same distance.	**ASK:** What is the difference between apparent magnitude and absolute magnitude? **LISTEN:** Students should answer that apparent magnitude is a measure of a star's brightness relative to other stars as seen by an observer on Earth. Absolute magnitude is a measure of a star's brightness relative to other stars when all of the stars are viewed from the same distance. **ASK:** How does a star's distance from Earth affect its apparent magnitude? Its absolute magnitude? **LISTEN:** Students should describe that apparent magnitude decreases (meaning brightness increases) as distance from Earth decreases. Absolute magnitude remains constant because it is, by definition, measured at a standard distance from Earth.
Stars that are relatively close to our solar system appear to shift slightly in their position relative to distant stars when viewed from different positions, an effect known as parallax. The parallax of a star can be used to calculate its distance from Earth.	**ASK:** The star Castor is about five times farther from Earth than the star Procyon A. How would the parallax of these two stars compare? **LISTEN:** Students should answer that Procyon A would display a greater parallax than Castor.

Teacher Reflection Questions

- What classroom management issues did you face in carrying out this investigation? How could you improve these when doing this investigation with other classes?

- Which measurement or math skills did students have the most difficulty with? How might you help them to improve those skills?

- What kinds of questions were students asking during the *Communicate?* What can you do to get students actively thinking about what information they should be obtaining from these discussions?

NOTES

....

....

....

....

....

....

....

....

....

....

SECTION 4.3 INTRODUCTION

4.3 Read

The Milky Way

◀ *1 class period*

A class period is
considered to be one
40 to 50 minute class.

Overview

The concept of a galaxy as a system of stars is introduced and the Milky
Way is identified as the galaxy in which Earth and the Sun are located.
Students read how astronomers have constructed maps and other models
of the basic shape of the Milky Way galaxy by plotting the positions and
distances to stars. Students consider the need for a larger unit to measure
distances outside the solar system and the light-year is introduced and
described. Students read about the distinction between a representative and
a biased sample, and why astronomers need to work with a representative
sample of the more than 200 million stars that make up the Milky Way
galaxy when constructing maps and other models. Students then analyze
absolute magnitude data for the 25 brightest stars as seen from Earth and
the 25 closest stars to Earth, and reflect on whether these samples are biased
or representative of the stars that comprise the Milky Way galaxy. Students
then read a description of the structure of the Milky Way galaxy and Earth's
location within it. After reflecting on the organization of the stars that
comprise the Milky Way galaxy, students update the *Project Board* focusing
on the *What do we think we know?* and *What do we need to investigate?*
columns.

Targeted Concepts, Skills, and Nature of Science	Performance Expectations
Scientists often collaborate and share their findings. Sharing findings makes new information available and helps scientists refine their ideas and build on others' ideas. When another person's or group's idea is used, credit needs to be given.	Students share their individual answers to the *Reflect* questions with their group and the group's answers with the class. Students collaborate in a class discussion of information and ideas that should be added to the *Project Board*.

Targeted Concepts, Skills, and Nature of Science	Performance Expectations
Scientists must keep clear, accurate and descriptive records of what they do so they can share their work with others; consider what they did, why they did it, and what they want to do next.	Students make written notes while they are reading and keep a written record of their answers to the *Reflect* questions. Students analyze data samples and determine whether they have the characteristics of a representative or a biased data sample.
Other stars are like the Sun but are so far away that they look like points of light. Distances between stars are vast compared to distances within our solar system. Light from the Sun takes a few minutes to reach Earth, but light from the next nearest star takes a few years to arrive.	Students can compare and contrast distances within the solar system and distances between stars.
Astronomical Units and light-years are measures of distances between the Sun, Earth, and the stars.	Students define a light-year and distinguish between a light-year and an astronomical unit. Students convert between light-years and astronomical units.
A galaxy is a system of stars, cosmic dust and gas held together by gravitation. Galaxies typically contain billions of stars, may have different shapes, and may be thousands of light-years in diameter; the universe contains billions of such galaxies.	Students are able to describe a galaxy as a system of stars held together by gravitation. Students compare and contrast the characteristics of a galaxy and a solar system.
Our Sun is a medium-sized star within a spiral galaxy of stars known as the Milky Way.	Students are able to describe the approximate position of the Sun within the Milky Way galaxy.

Materials

1 per class	Class *Project Board*

Homework Options

Reflection

- **Science Content:** The star Alkaid, which is located at the end of the handle of the constellation known as the Big Dipper, is located 101 light-years from Earth. What was happening in the United States when the light from Alkaid that reaches Earth tonight first left the star? *(Students' answers will vary, but should refer to events that occurred 101 years ago.)*

- **Science Process:** The speed of light is about 300,000 km/s. It takes light from the Sun about 8 min 18 s to reach Earth. How could you calculate the distance to the Sun? *(Students should describe calculating the number of seconds in 8 min 18 s and multiply that number by 300,000.)*

Preparation for 4.4

- **Science Content:** What common objects have an appearance similar to that of the Milky Way galaxy? *(Student answers will vary, but may include objects such as a pinwheel, certain fan blades, certain flowers, the cross-section of certain snail shells, and so on.)*

- **Science Process:** How could you determine whether stars are equally distributed in the night sky? *(Students should answer that by observing equivalent areas of the sky and comparing the number of stars in those areas.)*

NOTES

....

....

....

....

NOTES

SECTION 4.3 IMPLEMENTATION

◀ *1 class period* *

4.3 Read

The Milky Way

One goal of astronomy is to make a map that shows the characteristics and locations in space of the stars in Earth's neighborhood, not just how they appear in the sky. To determine if a star could collide with another space object, you must understand how stars are organized.

In *Learning Set 3,* you read that the planets and other objects in our solar system formed from a large cloud of gas and dust and are organized into a system. Stars are also organized into systems. These systems are called galaxies. A **galaxy** is a system of stars, gas, and dust that is held together by the force of gravity. Earth and the Sun are part of the Milky Way galaxy. All of the stars you see in the sky are in the Milky Way galaxy. You already know that you can see thousands of stars in the sky with your unaided eye if you are far from city lights. When you use binoculars, as you know, that number jumps to hundreds of thousands of stars. But that is just a small fraction of the number of stars in the galaxy. The Milky Way galaxy contains hundreds of billions of stars!

galaxy: a system of stars, gas, and dust held together by gravity.

How Far Away Are the Stars in Our Galaxy?

To understand how our Sun and other stars are organized in the galaxy, astronomers have constructed maps and models of the Milky Way. To produce these maps, they needed to determine how far away the stars are. In the last section, you learned about the parallax method, which can be used to determine the distance to closer stars, including Alpha Centauri. To estimate the distance to other stars, astronomers assume that stars of the same type have the same brightness. Brighter stars of the same type are closer than dimmer stars of the same type. (You will learn more about types of stars in *Section 4.5.*)

In *Learning Set 3,* you read about the astronomical unit, or AU. The AU is equal to the average distance from Earth to the Sun. It is much easier to talk about distances in the solar system in AUs than in kilometers. However, the closest star system to Earth, Alpha Centauri, is about 280,000 AU from Earth. To make it easier to compare distances to stars, astronomers needed

AST 179

ASTRONOMY

4.3 Read

The Milky Way

5 min

Students are introduced to the Milky Way galaxy.

△ Guide

Begin by pointing out that students have developed an understanding of the structure of the solar system and the distances of objects within the solar system, and this will help them predict whether these objects might collide with each other. But they also need to learn about stars to determine if they are likely to collide with other space objects.

*A class period is considered to be one 40 to 50 minute class.

Tell students that stars are found in *galaxies,* which are systems of stars, gas, and dust that are held together by gravity. The Sun is a star in the Milky Way galaxy, and Earth, as a planet orbiting the Sun, is also in the Milky Way galaxy.

To construct models and maps of the Milky Way, scientists need to determine how far away the other stars in the Milky Way are. Tell students they will now learn about how scientists determine the distances of stars, and they will learn about the structure of the galaxy and of the observed universe outside the galaxy.

How Far Away Are the Stars in Our Galaxy?

5 min

The class discusses how scientists determine how far away stars are.

How Far Away Are the Stars in Our Galaxy?

To understand how our Sun and other stars are organized in the galaxy, astronomers have constructed maps and models of the Milky Way. To produce these maps, they needed to determine how far away the stars are. In the last section, you learned about the parallax method, which can be used to determine the distance to closer stars, including Alpha Centauri. To estimate the distance to other stars, astronomers assume that stars of the same type have the same brightness. Brighter stars of the same type are closer than dimmer stars of the same type. (You will learn more about types of stars in *Section 4.5.*)

In *Learning Set 3,* you read about the astronomical unit, or AU. The AU is equal to the average distance from Earth to the Sun. It is much easier to talk about distances in the solar system in AUs than in kilometers. However, the closest star system to Earth, Alpha Centauri, is about 280,000 AU from Earth. To make it easier to compare distances to stars, astronomers needed

△ Guide

Discuss how scientists estimate the distances of stars to construct maps and models of the universe. Scientists can use parallax to determine the distance of closer stars. Then, knowing that stars of the same type have the same brightness, they can use the apparent brightness of a star of a known type to estimate its distance.

NOTES

....

....

....

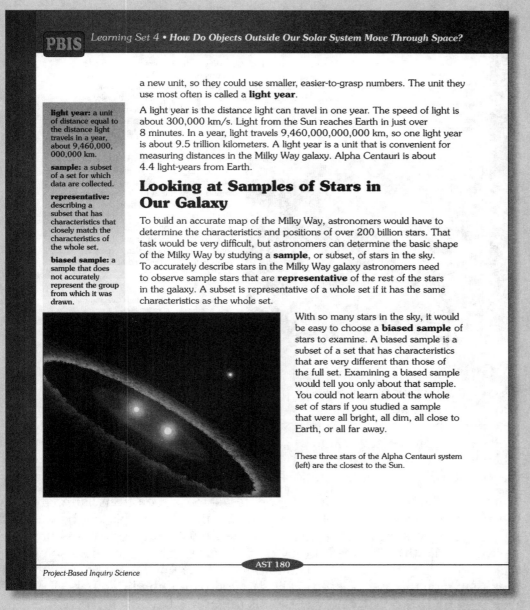

a new unit, so they could use smaller, easier-to-grasp numbers. The unit they use most often is called a **light year**.

A light year is the distance light can travel in one year. The speed of light is about 300,000 km/s. Light from the Sun reaches Earth in just over 8 minutes. In a year, light travels 9,460,000,000,000 km, so one light year is about 9.5 trillion kilometers. A light year is a unit that is convenient for measuring distances in the Milky Way galaxy. Alpha Centauri is about 4.4 light-years from Earth.

Looking at Samples of Stars in Our Galaxy

To build an accurate map of the Milky Way, astronomers would have to determine the characteristics and positions of over 200 billion stars. That task would be very difficult, but astronomers can determine the basic shape of the Milky Way by studying a **sample**, or subset, of stars in the sky. To accurately describe stars in the Milky Way galaxy astronomers need to observe sample stars that are **representative** of the rest of the stars in the galaxy. A subset is representative of a whole set if it has the same characteristics as the whole set.

light year: a unit of distance equal to the distance light travels in a year, about 9,460,000,000,000 km.

sample: a subset of a set for which data are collected.

representative: describing a subset that has characteristics that closely match the characteristics of the whole set.

biased sample: a sample that does not accurately represent the group from which it was drawn.

With so many stars in the sky, it would be easy to choose a **biased sample** of stars to examine. A biased sample is a subset of a set that has characteristics that are very different than those of the full set. Examining a biased sample would tell you only about that sample. You could not learn about the whole set of stars if you studied a sample that were all bright, all dim, all close to Earth, or all far away.

These three stars of the Alpha Centauri system (left) are the closest to the Sun.

Tell students that distances outside the solar system are so great that the astronomical unit is not convenient for discussing them. Scientists created the light-year, a much longer unit, to discuss these distances. Tell students that a light-year is the distance light travels in a year—about 9.5 trillion km. Alpha Centauri, the closest star system to Earth, is about 4.4 light-years from Earth (or 280,000 AU). Emphasize that 4.4 light-years is such a great distance that scientists cannot send probes to observe Alpha Centauri.

Looking at Samples of Stars in Our Galaxy

5 min

The class analyzes and discusses the samples of stars.

of a set for which data are collected.

representative: describing a subset that has characteristics that closely match the characteristics of the whole set.

biased sample: a sample that does not accurately represent the group from which it was drawn.

Looking at Samples of Stars in Our Galaxy

To build an accurate map of the Milky Way, astronomers would have to determine the characteristics and positions of over 200 billion stars. That task would be very difficult, but astronomers can determine the basic shape of the Milky Way by studying a **sample**, or subset, of stars in the sky. To accurately describe stars in the Milky Way galaxy astronomers need to observe sample stars that are **representative** of the rest of the stars in the galaxy. A subset is representative of a whole set if it has the same characteristics as the whole set.

With so many stars in the sky, it would be easy to choose a **biased sample** of stars to examine. A biased sample is a subset of a set that has characteristics that are very different than those of the full set. Examining a biased sample would tell you only about that sample. You could not learn about the whole set of stars if you studied a sample that were all bright, all dim, all close to Earth, or all far away.

These three stars of the Alpha Centauri system (left) are the closest to the Sun.

△ Guide

Discuss how astronomers use samples to determine the shape of the Milky Way. To directly study all of the stars in the Milky Way, they would have to determine the characteristics and positions of over 200 billion stars. Instead, they study representative samples of the stars in the galaxy. Emphasize that whenever you study a sample, it is possible to choose a *biased sample*. A biased sample is a sample that does not represent the whole group.

Point out the table showing the 25 brightest stars as seen from Earth, and the 25 closest stars to Earth. Tell students that the lists are biased, because they include stars only with certain characteristics (that is, brightness or nearness to Earth). This means they do not necessarily represent absolute magnitudes that are typical of stars throughout the universe. Ask students how they would expect these two lists to compare if the brightness of a star were determined only by how close it is to Earth. They should recognize that if distance from Earth were the only factor in a star's brightness, the list of the 25 brightest stars as seen from Earth, and the list of the 25 closest stars, would be identical. Then point out that most of the 25 brightest stars as seen from Earth have a very bright absolute magnitude or they are among the 25 closest stars to Earth. This suggests that proximity to Earth is one of the factors determining a star's apparent magnitude.

25 Brightest Stars as Seen from Earth		25 Closest Stars to Earth	
Star	**Absolute Magnitude**	**Star**	**Absolute Magnitude**
Deneb	−8.7	Sirius A	1.5
Rigel	−6.7	Procyon A	2.7
Canopus	−5.6	Alpha Centauri A	4.4
Antares	−5.4	Alpha Centauri B	5.7
Hadar	−5.4	Epsilon Eridani	6.2
Shaula	−5.1	61 Cygnus A	7.5
Betelgeuse	−5.0	61 Cygnus B	8.3
Acrux	−4.2	Lacaille 9352	9.8
Adhara	−4.1	GX Andromedae	10.3
Mimosa	−3.9	Lalande 21185	10.4
Spica	−3.6	Sigma 2398 A	11.2
Achernar	−2.8	Sirius B	11.3
Aldebaran	−0.6	Sigma 2398 B	12.0
Regulus	−0.5	Procyon B	13.0
Capella	−0.5	Ross 154	13.1
Arcturus	−0.3	Barnard's Star	13.2
Vega	0.6	Ross 128	13.5
Castor	0.6	Ross 248	14.8
Pollux	1.1	BL Ceti	15.4
Sirius A	1.4	Proxima Centauri	15.5
Fomalhaut	1.7	EZ Aquarii A	15.6
Altair	2.2	EZ Aquarii B	15.6
Procyon A	2.7	UV Ceti	15.9
Alpha Centauri A	4.4	EZ Aquarii C	16.3
Alpha Centauri B	5.7	Wolf 359	16.6

NOTE: Table does not include the Sun.

AST 181

ASTRONOMY

NOTES

....

Stop and Think

10 min

Students lead a discussion of the Stop and Think *questions.*

Stop and Think

The table on the previous page shows the absolute magnitude of each star, which is a measure of how much light each star gives off. The first column shows the 25 brightest stars you see in the night sky (based on apparent magnitude). The second column shows the 25 closest stars in the night sky. You can see that the characteristics of stars in the two lists are very different.

1. According to the sample of the 25 brightest stars as seen from Earth, are most stars very bright in absolute magnitude or very dim? How is this sample of the visible stars in the night sky biased?

2. According to the sample of the 25 stars closest to Earth, are most stars very bright in absolute magnitude or very dim? How is this sample of stars biased?

3. Four stars, Alpha Centauri A, Alpha Centauri B, Procyon A, and Sirius A are on both lists. Why do you think these stars are dimmer in absolute magnitude than most of the other stars on the 25 brightest stars list?

4. Which list do you think more accurately represents the absolute brightness of stars in the night sky? Support your answer using the data.

The Structure of the Milky Way

By choosing a representative sample of stars in the sky, astronomers have been able to make a map of the galaxy. The image on the facing page is a photograph of the Milky Way galaxy. The galaxy has a bright bulge in the center and several spiral arms. The Milky Way is about 100,000 light-years across and contains between 200 billion and 400 billion stars. The Sun is located in one spiral arm about 30,000 light-years from the center. The spiral arms all lie in a disk shape that is relatively thin, about 1,000 light-years deep. The bright center of the galaxy bulges out from the disk. There are many more stars close to the center of the galaxy than in the spiral arms.

On Earth, because we are inside the galaxy, we must infer the shape of the Milky Way by mapping the stars we see in three dimensions. Imagine looking from the location of the Sun in the first image. You see stars in every direction, but those stars are relatively close to us within the same

AST 182

Project-Based Inquiry Science

△ Guide

Lead a class discussion of the *Stop and Think* questions. Emphasize that both columns show the absolute magnitude of the stars—that is, how much light the stars give off— but the left column lists the 25 stars that appear brightest from Earth, and the right column lists the 25 stars that are closest to Earth. Listen for evidence that students understand selecting the most obvious (brightest) stars from the night sky gives you a biased sample, and a biased sample is not representative of the actual distribution of stars in the universe (or the actual structure of the universe). Also listen for evidence that students understand a star may appear bright because it is close to Earth or because it has great absolute magnitude. Also listen for evidence that students understand a biased sample is one that misrepresents the group in some way.

1. Students should see that most of the stars in the list of the 25 brightest stars are very bright. The sample is biased toward selecting stars by brightness only.

2. Students should see that most of the stars in the list of the 25 closest stars are very dim. The sample is biased toward selecting stars by distance only.

3. Students should reason that since those four stars are on both lists, they must be both bright and close to Earth. Overall, they must not be very bright stars.

4. Students may suggest that neither list represents the average of absolute brightness, because both lists are biased. Further criteria are needed to determine a list of stars representing a fair distribution of absolute magnitude.

△ Guide

Point out the pictures of the Milky Way in the student text. To an observer outside our galaxy, the Milky Way would appear as several spiral arms extending from a bright center, as shown in one of the images. The galaxy is about 100,000 light-years across. The Sun is about 30,000 light-years from the center, in one of the spiral arms. Emphasize that the Milky Way contains many stars, between 200 billion and 400 billion. From Earth, the bright center of the galaxy appears as a band of light that stretches across the sky.

The Structure of the Milky Way

5 min

Students discuss the structure of the Milky Way galaxy.

NOTES

....

....

....

....

....

....

spiral arm of the galaxy. Most of the stars are in the disk of the Milky Way galaxy, which appears as a faint band of light that stretches in a giant circle across the sky. You see a thicker, brighter band of stars when you look toward the center of the galaxy in the direction of the constellation Sagittarius. In the opposite direction, you see the band of stars continue, but it is much fainter because you are looking away from the galactic center. That is the view of the Milky Way galaxy that you have from Earth.

Until the invention of the telescope, observers could not tell that the band of light was made up of billions of stars. They could only tell it was a white band of light, which is what led to the name Milky Way.

Reflect

1. Compare the image of the galaxy to the solar system. How is the organization of the galaxy similar to that of the solar system, and how is it different? From the similarities, what can you infer about the center of the galaxy?

2. Using what you know about motions in the solar system, describe how you think the stars in the Milky Way move relative to each other.

What's the Point?

The Milky Way galaxy contains over 200 billion stars. Scientists have determined the basic shape of the galaxy by choosing a representative sample of the stars that are visible from Earth. The galaxy is disk-shaped with spiral arms in the disk and a central bulge. It is about 100,000 light-years in diameter, and the Sun is about 30,000 light-years from the center. A light year is a unit of distance equal to the distance that light can travel in one year.

The Milky Way galaxy, pictured above, resembles a giant pinwheel with swirling arms.

ASTRONOMY

△ Guide

Reflect

10 min

Students have a class discussion of the questions.

Lead a class discussion of the *Reflect* questions. (These questions can also be assigned for homework.) Ask students what similarities between the Milky Way and the solar system they see, and ask them what differences they see. They should recognize that both systems are organized around a center and have an overall disk shape. They may not be able to infer much about the center of the galaxy, but the question should engage them in using what they know to interpret the images of the galaxy. They may suspect that there is a massive body at the center of the galaxy, like the Sun at the center of the solar system, and that the gravity of this massive body keeps the rest of the galaxy from drifting away. They may also suggest that the Milky Way rotates.

1. Students should notice that the Milky Way galaxy resembles the nebular formation of the solar system. It appears to be rotating because of the spiral arms. It is a thin disk with a bulge at the center, much like the nebular formation of the solar system. Students may infer that there is a massive body at the center, much like our Sun, which holds the galaxy together through gravity.

2. Using the solar system as a model, students should answer that the stars in the Milky Way revolve around the galaxy center. They should also consider that the farther from the center of the galaxy, the longer it takes to complete one revolution around the center of the galaxy.

Assessment Options

Targeted Concepts, Skills, and Nature of Science	How do I know if students got it?
Scientists often collaborate and share their findings. Sharing findings makes new information available and helps scientists refine their ideas and build on others' ideas. When another person's or group's idea is used, credit needs to be given.	**ASK:** Why is it unlikely that a map of the Milky Way galaxy would be the work of a single astronomer? **LISTEN:** Students should answer that in order to build up a map of the Milky Way galaxy, information is needed about thousands upon thousands of stars. It is unlikely that a single astronomer could complete that many observations and perform all of the analysis and calculations necessary in their lifetime.

NOTES

....

....

....

....

Targeted Concepts, Skills, and Nature of Science	How do I know if students got it?
Scientists must keep clear, accurate and descriptive records of what they do so they can share their work with others; consider what they did, why they did it, and what they want to do next.	**ASK:** How is the *Project Board* helpful to your search for answers to the *Big Question?* **LISTEN:** Students should cite examples of how the *Project Board* serves as a vehicle for sharing ideas, keeping track of what they have learned, and seeing what they are doing in a larger context. **ASK:** Differentiate between a representative and a biased data sample. **LISTEN:** Students should describe that a representative sample has the same characteristics as the group from which it was drawn. A biased sample has characteristics that do not accurately represent the characteristics of the group from which it was drawn.
Other stars are like the Sun but are so far away that they look like points of light. Distances between stars are vast compared to distances within our solar system. Light from the Sun takes a few minutes to reach Earth, but light from the next nearest star takes a few years to arrive.	**ASK:** The planet Neptune is located 30 AU from the Sun. How does that compare with the distance to the nearest star? **LISTEN:** Students should identify that the nearest star, Alpha Centauri, is about 280,000 AU from Earth—nearly 10,000 times farther from Earth than Neptune. **ASK:** If the star Alpha Centauri exploded today, when would you see the explosion? Why? **LISTEN:** Students should answer that they would see the explosion in 4.4 years because that is how long it would take the light from the explosion to reach Earth.

Targeted Concepts, Skills, and Nature of Science	How do I know if students got it?
Astronomical units and light-years are measures of distances between the Sun, Earth, and the stars.	**ASK:** What is a light-year? **LISTEN:** Students should answer that it the distance light will travel in one year, about 9.5 trillion km.
A galaxy is a system of stars, cosmic dust and gas held together by gravitation. Galaxies typically contain billions of stars, may have different shapes, and may be thousands of light-years in diameter; the universe contains billions of such galaxies.	**ASK:** How is the Milky Way galaxy similar to our solar system? How is it different? **LISTEN:** Similarities include: • both are systems held together by gravity • both consist of objects orbiting a center • both contain objects that take longer to orbit as distance from the center increases Differences include: • our solar system consists of one star • the Milky Way consists of billions of stars • in our solar system, planets orbit a star, in the Milky Way stars orbit a central core • our solar system is about 1 light-year across, the Milky Way is about 100,000 light-years across
Our Sun is a medium-sized star within a spiral galaxy of stars known as the Milky Way.	**ASK:** Where is Earth located relative to the center of the Milky Way galaxy? **LISTEN:** Earth is located about one third of the way out from the center of the galaxy in one of its spiral arms.

Teacher Reflection Questions

- In this section, students were introduced to new information. What formative assessments did you use with the students to identify what they have learned?

- How does reading about the Milky Way galaxy set the stage for the focus of the next section of this *Learning Set?*

- In this section, students read about the Milky Way galaxy. What aspects of the reading were most interesting to students? Which ones were sources of some confusion?

NOTES

SECTION 4.4 INTRODUCTION

4.4 Explore

How Do Stars Move in the Milky Way Galaxy?

◀ *2 class periods*

A class period is considered to be one 40 to 50 minute class.

Overview

Students investigate the relationships among the different parts of the Milky Way galaxy. The section opens with a demonstration in which the teacher uses a model to simulate the motion of stars in the Milky Way galaxy. Pepper flakes sprinkled in a beaker of water represent stars in space. Light projected from beneath the beaker causes the flakes to cast shadows. The teacher stirs the water in the beaker and students observe patterns in the motion of the pepper flake shadows, and reflect on the motions they observe. Students then read how light can be analyzed using a spectroscope and the Doppler shift is introduced. Students experience the Doppler shift in a series of sound recordings made while a train is stationary, moving toward, and moving away from an observer. Students then read how the Doppler shift in a star's spectrum can be used to measure its motion toward or away from an observer and the motion of the stars in the Milky Way galaxy are described. Students compare and contrast the structures of the solar system and the Milky Way galaxy and update the *What are we learning?* and *What is our evidence?* columns of the *Project Board.*

Targeted Concepts, Skills, and Nature of Science	Performance Expectations
Scientists often collaborate and share their findings. Sharing findings makes new information available and helps scientists refine their ideas and build on others' ideas. When another person's or group's idea is used, credit needs to be given.	Students can compare and contrast the structures of the solar system and the Milky Way galaxy. Students engage in a class discussion in which they identify what they have learned and their supporting evidence.

Targeted Concepts, Skills, and Nature of Science	Performance Expectations
Scientists must keep clear, accurate and descriptive records of what they do so they can share their work with others; consider what they did, why they did it, and what they want to do next.	Students keep a written record of their responses to the *Stop and Think* and *Reflect* questions. Students keep a written record of their observations during the Doppler shift demonstration.
The Doppler shift is the shift in the wavelength of a spectrum line away from its normal wavelength caused by motion of the observer toward or away from the light source. If the light source is approaching the observer there is a blueshift toward shorter wavelengths of light. If the light source is moving away from the observer, there is a redshift towards longer wavelengths of light.	Students distinguish between the motion of stars showing a Doppler shift toward the red end of the spectrum and those showing a Doppler shift toward the blue end of the spectrum.
A galaxy is a system of stars, cosmic dust and gas held together by gravitation. Galaxies typically contain billions of stars, may have different shapes, and may be thousands of light-years in diameter; the universe contains billions of such galaxies.	Students describe a galaxy as a system of stars, cosmic dust and gas held together by gravitation. Students are able to describe the distribution of stars in the Milky Way galaxy.

Materials

1 per class	Beaker filled with water
	Ground pepper flakes
	Train-sound recording
	Class *Project Board*

NOTES

....

....

....

Activity Setup and Preparation

Before class, run the demonstration to make sure that the pepper flake shadows project clearly and determine the best technique for stirring so that a spiral pattern emerges.

Homework Options

Reflection

- **Science Content:** How is the structure of the Milky Way galaxy similar to the structure of the solar system in the early stages of its formation? *(Students should answer that both consist of a central ball containing a high concentration of matter surrounded by a thin spinning disk of matter.)*

Preparation for 4.5

- **Science Content:** What are some of the ways in which you think the light from different stars can be different? *(Student answers will vary, but may include characteristics such as brightness, color, and the spectrum it produces.)*

- **Science Process:** Suppose you were in a dark room with only one small opening to the outside through which light could enter the room. How do you think you might be able to determine whether light coming into the room was from the Sun, a bright incandescent light bulb, or a fluorescent light bulb? *(Student answers will vary. This question is meant to engage students in thinking about characteristics of light.)*

NOTES

....

....

....

....

....

....

NOTES

SECTION 4.4 IMPLEMENTATION

4.4 Explore

How Do Stars Move in the Milky Way Galaxy?

The stars are so far away that the fastest rocket ever built would take over 100,000 years to get to the nearest star beyond the Sun. Although scientists cannot send probes to study other stars, they can observe and measure the light that stars emit.

The Milky Way galaxy looks like a giant pinwheel, with a bright cluster at the center and several swirling arms. This pinwheel is not stationary. The stars within it are constantly in motion. In this section, you will investigate the relationships among the different parts of the Milky Way.

Demonstration

When you make chocolate milk, first you pour a large glass of milk, then you add the chocolate syrup. When you swirl around the milk with your spoon, you see a pattern of swirls on the surface of the milk. These swirls look a little like the spiral pattern in the Milky Way galaxy. You will now observe another demonstration that shows a pattern swirling about a center.

This photograph of the Milky Way was made by leaving the camera lens open for a long time. It shows some stars too dim to see with the unaided eye.

AST 184

Project-Based Inquiry Science

4.4 Explore

How Do Stars Move in the Milky Way Galaxy?

5 min

Demonstration

10 min

Students observe a demonstration using pepper flakes in a beaker of water of what motions might lead to a swirl pattern in a galaxy.

○ Engage

Begin by telling students that the stars within the Milky Way galaxy are constantly in motion. Tell them that in this section they will investigate how the stars within the Milky Way interact.

△ Guide

Next tell students you will demonstrate a swirling pattern similar to the swirling pattern of the Milky Way. They will see ground pepper flakes swirling in a beaker of water. They will need to pay attention to how the pepper flakes move and interact.

*A class period is considered to be one 40 to 50 minute class.

ASTRONOMY

Your teacher will create a model of the galaxy using a glass beaker half filled with water. To make the motion visible, ground pepper flakes are added. The beaker is placed on an overhead projector so you can see the light shining up through the beaker on a screen. The teacher will then use a spoon to rapidly swirl the pepper around the center. Watch the motion of the pepper-flake shadows on the screen after the teacher stops swirling the water. Look for evidence of collisions near the center and near the edges of the container.

Reflect

1. How were the ground pepper flakes distributed on the screen? How does this model look like the Milky Way galaxy as seen from above? How does it look different?

2. In what general direction did all of the flakes travel?

3. Describe the collisions near the center of the beaker. Describe the collisions nearer the edges of the beaker.

4. Were there more or fewer collisions in the outer parts of the beaker than near the middle? Why were there a larger or smaller number of collisions near the edges of the beaker?

spectrum (plural: spectra): the band of colors formed when white light is separated into its components.

How Do Astronomers Use Starlight to Study the Motion of Stars?

Like the solar system, the Milky Way galaxy is in motion. All of its stars, gas, and dust move in predictable paths. Astronomers can measure how a star moves by analyzing the star's light.

The light emitted by the Sun, and many other types of stars, appears as white light. However, when this light is passed through a prism, it separates into the colors of the rainbow. This is called the star's **spectrum**.

White light

An illustration of light passing through a prism.

AST 185

ASTRONOMY

If you have not already done so, set up the projector, focusing it so the contents of the beaker are clearly visible on the screen. Put a teaspoon of pepper flakes in a beaker or a plastic food container half full of water (1 or 2 cups) and vigorously stir. You will need to stir the water quickly enough to counteract the tendency of surface tension to hold the flakes in clumps near the surface. Put the beaker or container on the projector so students can observe as the pepper flakes swirl and then settle.

△ Guide

Lead a class discussion of the *Reflect* questions. Look for evidence students understand that a pattern similar to the pattern of the stars in the Milky Way resulted from nearly circular motion. This suggests the pattern of the stars in the Milky Way may result from nearly circular orbits around the center of the galaxy.

1. Students should report that they observed the ground pepper flakes were distributed in a swirling pattern in the water and that it looked exactly like the Milky Way galaxy as seen from above. It looked different because the specks were black like pepper, not white like starlight.

2. The students should state that the pepper flakes traveled in a clockwise direction, the same direction as the spoon.

3. Students should say that the collisions of pepper flakes near the center causes a thick clumping of flakes, much like the thick bulge of a galaxy. The collisions near the edge of the beaker were more diffused.

4. Students should report that there were many more collisions near the center of the beaker because the swirling motion was slower there. There were fewer collisions at the edge of the beaker because the motion was faster.

△ Guide

Tell students that stars and other objects in the Milky Way galaxy move in predictable paths. Astronomers can measure a star's motion by analyzing its light.

Discuss that light from a star is radiation that travels in waves. The color of light is determined by its wavelength, which, for visible light, can be measured in nanometers. Visible light can have wavelengths from 380 nanometers (dark violet) to 750 nanometers (red).

NOTES

....

....

Reflect

5 min

Students discuss and answer the Reflect *questions.*

How Do Astronomers Use Starlight to Study the Motion of Stars?

15 min

The class discusses how scientists determine the motion of stars.

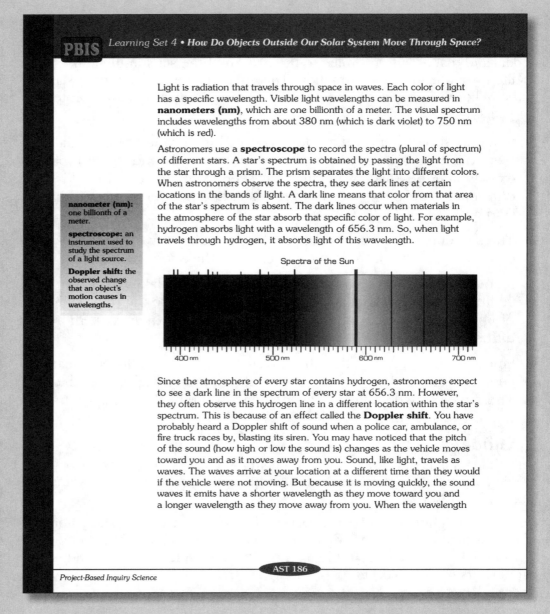

Light is radiation that travels through space in waves. Each color of light has a specific wavelength. Visible light wavelengths can be measured in **nanometers (nm)**, which are one billionth of a meter. The visual spectrum includes wavelengths from about 380 nm (which is dark violet) to 750 nm (which is red).

Astronomers use a **spectroscope** to record the spectra (plural of spectrum) of different stars. A star's spectrum is obtained by passing the light from the star through a prism. The prism separates the light into different colors. When astronomers observe the spectra, they see dark lines at certain locations in the bands of light. A dark line means that color from that area of the star's spectrum is absent. The dark lines occur when materials in the atmosphere of the star absorb that specific color of light. For example, hydrogen absorbs light with a wavelength of 656.3 nm. So, when light travels through hydrogen, it absorbs light of this wavelength.

nanometer (nm): one billionth of a meter.

spectroscope: an instrument used to study the spectrum of a light source.

Doppler shift: the observed change that an object's motion causes in wavelengths.

Spectra of the Sun

400 nm   500 nm   600 nm   700 nm

Since the atmosphere of every star contains hydrogen, astronomers expect to see a dark line in the spectrum of every star at 656.3 nm. However, they often observe this hydrogen line in a different location within the star's spectrum. This is because of an effect called the **Doppler shift**. You have probably heard a Doppler shift of sound when a police car, ambulance, or fire truck races by, blasting its siren. You may have noticed that the pitch of the sound (how high or low the sound is) changes as the vehicle moves toward you and as it moves away from you. Sound, like light, travels as waves. The waves arrive at your location at a different time than they would if the vehicle were not moving. But because it is moving quickly, the sound waves it emits have a shorter wavelength as they move toward you and a longer wavelength as they move away from you. When the wavelength

AST 186

Project-Based Inquiry Science

Tell students that one important concept in using light to determine a star's motion is the *spectrum* of a star. A star's spectrum contains the colors that make up the star's light. The Sun's light appears white, but it is composed of light of all the colors of the spectrum. When the Sun's light is passed through a prism, it separates into these colors.

Discuss how materials in the atmosphere of a star absorb light of certain colors. Hydrogen, in particular, absorbs light with a wavelength of 656.3 nanometers. This is important, because the atmosphere of every star contains hydrogen. When scientists record the spectrum of a star (using a spectroscope), a dark band usually appears where light with a wavelength of 656.3 nanometers should be.

Then tell students that scientists often discover stars that have light spectra with a dark band appearing in a surprising place. Even though the hydrogen in the star's atmosphere absorbs light with a wavelength of 656.3 nanometers, the dark band appears in a different place in the star's spectrum. Tell students that the explanation has to do with the star's motion.

Introduce the concept of a *Doppler shift*. A Doppler shift is an effect on the way we perceive the sound or light from a moving object. The student text uses the example of sound from a siren on a fire truck or other emergency vehicle. We perceive the sound from the siren differently as it approaches and as it moves away from us. As it approaches, it seems to have a louder pitch, because the crests of the sound waves reach us in more rapid succession. As the siren moves away, the sound appears to have a lower pitch, because the crests of the sound waves reach us in slower succession.

NOTES

Demonstration: Observe (Listen)

10 min

Students observe a demonstration of the Doppler shift in train whistles.

---

is shorter, the pitch is higher. When the wavelength is longer, the pitch is lower. The faster a vehicle is moving, the greater the change in the pitch of the siren.

The same thing happens with light waves. Because stars are moving at great speeds toward and away from Earth, the dark line for hydrogen shifts from one area of the spectrum to another. The following demonstration will help you understand how this works.

Demonstration

Observe (Listen)

Your teacher will play three sound recordings. The first recording will be a whistle on a train that is not moving. In the second recording, you will hear the sound of a train whistle coming toward you. In the third recording, you will hear the sound of a train whistle moving away from you. You will get to hear each recording twice. Just listen the first time. After the second time, record your observations in a table like the one below. Then work together with your group to answer the questions.

	Description of train whistle
Train not moving	
Train moving toward you	
Train moving away from you	

Stop and Think

1. How is the sound of a train whistle that is not moving different from the sound of a train whistle that is moving toward you?

2. How is the sound of a train whistle that is not moving different from the sound of a train whistle that is moving away from you?

3. How do you think you could you use sound to determine if a train that is far away is moving toward you or away from you?

AST 187

ASTRONOMY

△ Guide

Using three recordings of a train whistle, give a demonstration of the Doppler shift in sound. Play all three sounds in sequence—the whistle of a train not moving, the whistle of a train moving toward you, and the whistle of a train moving away—twice. The second time, have students record descriptions in a table like the one in their text.

△ Guide

When groups have had a chance to record their descriptions, have them work with their groups to answer the *Stop and Think* questions. As students work, monitor their progress and ask them what ideas they discussed.

1. Student descriptions should agree with the description of the Doppler shift — the effect that causes a sound emitted from an object moving toward you to be perceived as having a higher pitch than a sound emitted from a stationary object.

2. Students should know that a sound emitted from an object moving away is perceived as having a lower pitch than a sound emitted from a stationary object.

3. Students should recognize that they can conclude that the higher-pitched sound of a train whistle indicates that the train is approaching, while the lower-pitched sound of a train whistle indicates that the train is moving away. A stationary train could be identified by a whistle with a sound midway between a high pitch and a low pitch.

Stop and Think

5 min

Groups answer the Stop and Think *questions.*

NOTES

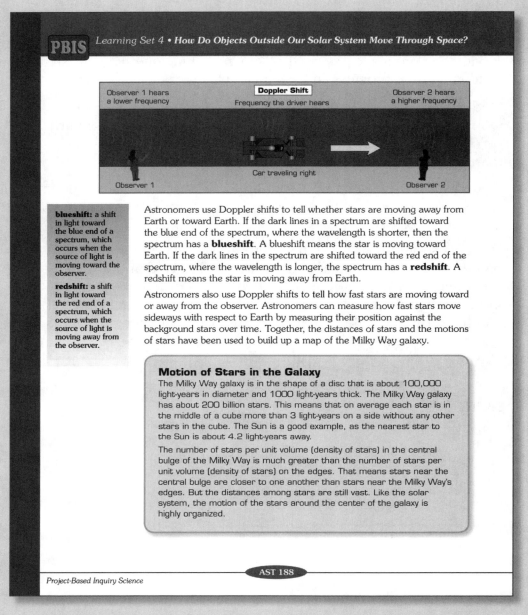

Doppler Shift
Frequency the driver hears

Observer 1 hears a lower frequency

Observer 2 hears a higher frequency

Car traveling right

Observer 1

Observer 2

blueshift: a shift in light toward the blue end of a spectrum, which occurs when the source of light is moving toward the observer.

redshift: a shift in light toward the red end of a spectrum, which occurs when the source of light is moving away from the observer.

Astronomers use Doppler shifts to tell whether stars are moving away from Earth or toward Earth. If the dark lines in a spectrum are shifted toward the blue end of the spectrum, where the wavelength is shorter, then the spectrum has a **blueshift**. A blueshift means the star is moving toward Earth. If the dark lines in the spectrum are shifted toward the red end of the spectrum, where the wavelength is longer, the spectrum has a **redshift**. A redshift means the star is moving away from Earth.

Astronomers also use Doppler shifts to tell how fast stars are moving toward or away from the observer. Astronomers can measure how fast stars move sideways with respect to Earth by measuring their position against the background stars over time. Together, the distances of stars and the motions of stars have been used to build up a map of the Milky Way galaxy.

Motion of Stars in the Galaxy

The Milky Way galaxy is in the shape of a disc that is about 100,000 light-years in diameter and 1000 light-years thick. The Milky Way galaxy has about 200 billion stars. This means that on average each star is in the middle of a cube more than 3 light-years on a side without any other stars in the cube. The Sun is a good example, as the nearest star to the Sun is about 4.2 light-years away.

The number of stars per unit volume (density of stars) in the central bulge of the Milky Way is much greater than the number of stars per unit volume (density of stars) on the edges. That means stars near the central bulge are closer to one another than stars near the Milky Way's edges. But the distances among stars are still vast. Like the solar system, the motion of the stars around the center of the galaxy is highly organized.

AST 188

Project-Based Inquiry Science

△ Guide

Tell students that something similar to what they observed with sound happens with light. As an object radiating light approaches, the crests of the light waves reach us in faster succession, so we perceive light with a shorter wavelength (closer to the blue end of the visible spectrum). As an object radiating light moves away, the crests of the light waves reach us in slower succession, so we perceive light with a longer wavelength (closer to the red end of the visible spectrum).

When the dark hydrogen band in a star's spectrum is shifted away from 656.3 nanometers, it is evidence of a Doppler shift. If the dark band is shifted toward the blue end of the spectrum, the spectrum has a blue shift, and scientists can conclude that the star is moving toward Earth. If the dark band is shifted toward the red end of the spectrum, the spectrum has a red shift, and astronomers can conclude that the star is moving away from Earth. Together with measurements of stars' changing positions laterally (sideways motion), measurements of red shift and blue shift allow scientists to construct maps of the Milky Way galaxy.

△ Guide

Discuss the facts about the structure of the galaxy in the text box. Tell students that on average, each star is alone in the middle of a cube more than 3 light-years in width. The nearest star to the Sun is 4.2 light-years away. The number of stars in a given volume near the center of the galaxy is much higher, but stars are still far apart from one another.

Motion of Stars in the Galaxy

10 min

The class discusses how scientists determine the motion of stars in the galaxy, and discuss the structure of the galaxy.

NOTES

....

....

....

....

....

....

....

....

....

....

Most stars move in the same direction around the center of the galaxy in a nearly circular orbit. These orbits take a very long time to complete. The Sun's orbit takes about 225 million years to complete. In fact, the Sun has orbited the galaxy only about 20 times during its lifetime. In comparison, Earth has orbited the Sun nearly 4.6 billion times.

Despite the length of time it takes to complete an orbit, the Sun still travels very quickly in its orbit. The Sun is about 30,000 light-years from the center of the Milky Way, and it travels about 100,000 light-years to complete one full orbit. Its average speed in its orbit is about 250 km/h. In *Learning Set 3*, you learned that Earth travels at a speed of about 30 km/h around the Sun. The entire solar system travels with the Sun as it orbits the galactic center, so Earth actually moves much faster around the center of the galaxy than it does around the Sun.

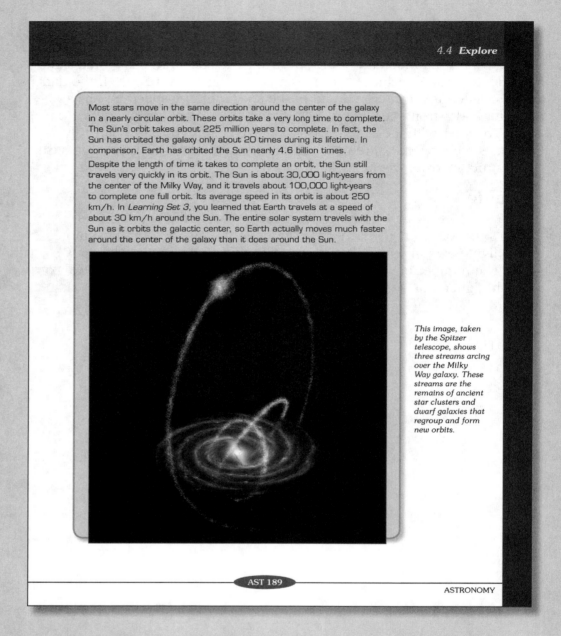

This image, taken by the Spitzer telescope, shows three streams arcing over the Milky Way galaxy. These streams are the remains of ancient star clusters and dwarf galaxies that regroup and form new orbits.

AST 189

ASTRONOMY

Tell students that the motions of stars in the galaxy are very regular, like the motions of planets in the solar system. Most stars move in the same direction around the center of the galaxy in nearly circular orbits. Because of the great distances, these orbits take a long time to complete. It takes about 225 million years for the Sun to complete an orbit even though the Sun travels in its orbit at a speed of 250 km/s.

Stop and Think

1. Suppose the Sun were closer to the center of the Milky Way galaxy. Do you think the Sun would be moving faster or more slowly than it does now in its orbit about the center of the galaxy? Why?

2. Earths orbits around the Sun while the Sun orbits around the center of our galaxy. A friend says this is like the Moon orbiting Earth as Earth orbits around the Sun. In what ways is that a good comparison? In what ways might the comparison be misleading?

3. Where in the Milky Way galaxy do you think collisions among stars are more likely—close to the center of the galaxy or near the edge? Why?

Reflect

In the last two sections, you learned about the structure and motions of the Milky Way galaxy.

1. How are the structures of our solar system and the Milky Way galaxy similar? How are they different?

2. How are the motions of our solar system and the Milky Way galaxy similar? How are the motions of these two systems different?

Update the *Project Board*

Add what you now know about stars and the milky way galaxy to the *What are we learning?* column of the *Project Board*. Be sure to support your ideas with evidence in the *What is our evidence?* column.

What's the Point?

Astronomers determine the motions of stars by observing their movement against a fixed background and by measuring the Doppler shift of the light they emit. The movement of most stars within the Milky Way galaxy is in the same direction, rotating about the center in nearly circular orbits.

AST 190

⚠ Guide

Once you have discussed how stars move in the galaxy, lead a class discussion of the *Stop and Think* questions, or have students work with their groups to answer them. It will be difficult for them to answer the questions with any confidence. Instead, look for signs that students are using everything they have learned about the galaxy and how stars move in the galaxy to support their ideas.

Stop and Think

10 min

Students discuss and answer the Stop and Think *questions with the class, or in their groups.*

1. Students should realize that if the Sun were closer to the center of the Milky Way galaxy, it would probably be moving more slowly. As in our solar system, the closer to the center (Sun), the slower the orbital speed.

2. Students may respond that this is a good comparison but that it might be misleading in terms of the distances and speeds involved. Galactic speeds and distances are much greater.

3. Students should know that the density of stars is greater near the center of the galaxy and so that is where most collisions will take place.

Reflect

10 min

Students have a class discussion of the Reflect *questions.*

> ### Reflect
>
> In the last two sections, you learned about the structure and motions of the Milky Way galaxy.
>
> 1. How are the structures of our solar system and the Milky Way galaxy similar? How are they different?
>
> 2. How are the motions of our solar system and the Milky Way galaxy similar? How are the motions of these two systems different?

△ Guide

Lead a class discussion of the *Reflect* questions, or have students answer them on their own.

1. Students should recognize that both our solar system and the Milky Way galaxy have large masses at the center and smaller masses roughly in a disk around the center. They should recognize differences between the two structures, such as that the Milky Way is organized in a spiral shape, while the solar system has no such pattern.

2. Students should recognize that most objects in both systems orbit the center in the same direction, but also that the stars orbiting the center of the galaxy have much faster orbits than the objects orbiting the Sun.

Update the Project Board

10 min

Students engage in a class discussion to update the Project Board.

> ### Update the *Project Board*
>
> Add what you now know about stars and the milky way galaxy to the *What are we learning?* column of the *Project Board*. Be sure to support your ideas with evidence in the *What is our evidence?* column.

△ Guide

Ask students what ideas from this discussion they can add to the *What are we learning?* column of the Project Board. Record their ideas on the class *Project Board* and have them record them in their own *Project Board* pages. Then ask them what evidence they have to support these ideas, and record their responses in the *What is our evidence?* column.

Assessment Options

Targeted Concepts, Skills, and Nature of Science	How do I know if students got it?
Scientists often collaborate and share their findings. Sharing findings makes new information available and helps scientists refine their ideas and build on others' ideas. When another person's or group's idea is used, credit needs to be given.	**ASK:** How likely do you think it is that a collision will occur between stars in the Milky Way galaxy? **LISTEN:** Students' answers will vary, but students should provide supporting evidence for their answers. For example: *I think it is unlikely, because the density of stars in the spiral arms of the galaxy is low. I think it is unlikely, because the stars in the Milky Way galaxy are orbiting the galactic core and their orbits do not seem to cross.*
Scientists must keep clear, accurate and descriptive records of what they do so they can share their work with others; consider what they did, why they did it, and what they want to do next.	**ASK:** In the demonstration, how did the sound of the whistle when the train was moving toward you compare with the sound it made when the train was standing still? **LISTEN:** Students should have observed that the train whistle made a higher pitched sound when it was moving toward the observer. **ASK:** Predict how the sound of the train whistle would change if the train were moving away from you faster than it was moving away in the sound recording. **LISTEN:** Students should predict that the sound would have an even lower pitch than that heard in the recording.

NOTES
....

ASTRONOMY

Targeted Concepts, Skills, and Nature of Science	How do I know if students got it?
The Doppler shift is the shift in the wavelength of a spectrum line away from its normal wavelength caused by motion of the observer toward or away from the light source. If the light source is approaching the observer there is a blue-shift towards shorter wavelengths of light. If the light source is moving away from the observer, there is a red-shift towards longer wavelengths of light.	**ASK:** The dark line in the spectrum of a star representing hydrogen is shifted toward the blue end of the spectrum. In what direction is the star moving? **LISTEN:** Students should identify that the star is moving toward Earth. **ASK:** An observer analyzes the spectrum of two stars. In both spectra, the dark hydrogen line is shifted toward the red end of the spectrum. However, the spectrum of one star is shifted farther toward the red than the other. What can you infer about the motion of the two stars? **LISTEN:** Students should answer that both are moving away from Earth, but the one whose hydrogen line is shifted farther toward the red end of the spectrum is moving away from Earth at a faster speed.
A galaxy is a system of stars, cosmic dust and gas held together by gravitation. Galaxies typically contain billions of stars, may have different shapes, and may be thousands of light-years in diameter; the universe contains billions of such galaxies.	**ASK:** What holds the billions of stars that make up a galaxy together? **LISTEN:** Students should identify mutual gravitational attraction. **ASK:** Where in a galaxy would gravitation be the strongest? Why? **LISTEN:** Students should identify near the galactic core because that is where the greatest amount of matter is concentrated.

NOTES

....

....

Teacher Reflection Questions

- Research into students' understanding of the concepts in this *Learning Set* indicates that often students have difficulty understanding that the galaxy is not crowded with stars and that stars are not evenly distributed throughout the galaxy. How well do you think your students understand these ideas? What did they say in discussions or in their written answers to the *Reflect* questions that makes you think they understand these ideas?

- What difficulties, if any, did students have when updating the *Project Board* with information about galaxies? If they did have any difficulties, what other guiding questions could you ask them to assist them in making a connection between the activities in this section and the *Big Question?*

- How were you able to connect the structure of the Milky Way to the structure of the solar system? How can you improve this connection in the future?

- Did the students understand the Doppler Shift and were you successful in transferring the concept from sound to light? How might you do this differently?

NOTES

NOTES

SECTION 4.5 INTRODUCTION

4.5 Read

What Does a Star's Light Reveal About a Star?

◀ *1 class period*

A class period is considered to be one 40 to 50 minute class.

Overview

In *Section 4.5*, the focus shifts from using the light from stars to determine their motion and distance from Earth to how the analysis of a star's light provides information about its composition, temperature and even its age. Students read about Annie Jump Cannon's painstaking work analyzing and categorizing stars into spectral classes and how the color of a star is related to its surface temperature. They then read how Hertzsprung and Russell studied Jump's data and developed their diagram showing the relationship between brightness and temperature of stars. Students then read a description of the characteristics of stars in the different regions of the Hertzsprung-Russell diagram. A *Be a Scientist* box describes information derived from observations of electromagnetic radiation other than visible light and Burnell and Hewish's discovery of pulsars. Students then read a description of the evolution of a star and the relationship between a star's mass and how it ends its life. The section concludes with students considering a set of questions about stellar evolution and the threat of collisions posed by stars and the events surrounding the final stages of their existence.

Targeted Concepts, Skills, and Nature of Science	Performance Expectations
Scientists often collaborate and share their findings. Sharing findings makes new information available and helps scientists refine their ideas and build on others' ideas. When another person's or group's idea is used, credit needs to be given.	Students recognize that it was access to Annie Jump Cannon's data that enabled Hertzsprung and Russell to recognize the relationship between brightness and temperature of stars.
Scientists must keep clear, accurate and descriptive records of what they do so they can share their work with others; consider what they did, why they did it, and what they want to do next.	Students should make detailed notes of important ideas as they read.

Targeted Concepts, Skills, and Nature of Science	Performance Expectations
Studying the work of different scientists provides understanding of scientific inquiry and reminds students that science is a human endeavor.	Students should recognize how Annie Jump Cannon's work categorizing stars by their spectra served as the basis for the development of the Hertzsprung-Russell diagram, which in turn served as the basis for work by many astronomers on the evolution of stars.
Stars form when gravity causes clouds of molecules to contract until nuclear fusion of light elements into heavier ones occurs. Fusion releases great amounts of energy over millions of years.	Students describe the stages in the life cycle of a typical star.
Stars differ from each other in size, temperature, and age.	Students identify the size and temperature of stars in different regions of the Hertzsprung-Russell diagram
The Hertzsprung-Russell diagram shows the relationship between the luminosity and temperature of stars. The majority of stars lie on a diagonal band that extends from hot stars of high luminosity in the upper left corner to cool stars of low luminosity in the lower right corner. This band is called the main sequence.	Students identify the regions representing main sequence, giant, supergiant and white dwarf stars on the Hertzsprung-Russell diagram. Students determine the temperature and luminosity of a star given its position on the Hertzsprung-Russell diagram.
Different wavelengths of the electromagnetic spectrum such as light and radio waves are used to gain information about distances and properties of components of the universe.	Students are able to describe analysis of stellar spectra yields data about the brightness, temperature and size of stars. Students can identify components of the universe whose existence is known because of observation and analysis of electromagnetic radiation other than visible light.

Materials

1 per class	Class *Project Board*

Homework Options

Reflection

- **Science Content:** What process is responsible for the energy emitted by a star? *(Students should identify nuclear fusion of lighter elements into heavier elements.)*

- **Science Content:** What characteristics of a star are plotted on the axes of the Hertzsprung-Russell diagram? *(Students should identify brightness on the vertical axis and surface temperature on the horizontal axis decreasing from left to right.)*

- **Science Content:** What do all of the stars on the main sequence have in common? *(Students should answer that they all get their energy from the fusion of hydrogen.)*

- **Science Content:** Which star color is associated with the highest surface temperatures? The lowest? *(Students should understand that blue stars have the highest surface temperatures; red stars have the lowest surface temperatures.)*

- **Science Content:** What remains of a star after a supernova takes place? *(Students should answer that the result is either a neutron star or a black hole.)*

- **Science Process:** What characteristics of a newly discovered star would you need to know to determine whether it is a main sequence star? *(Students should name its color and brightness.)*

- **Science Process:** How do astronomers determine the relative sizes of two stars that have the same color? *(Students should answer that stars of the same color emit the same amount of light per unit surface area. If one of the two stars has a lower absolute magnitude [is brighter at a standard distance from Earth] it is emitting more light energy and therefore must have a larger surface area.)*

NOTES

....

....

....

Preparation for 2.6

- **Science Content:** How would the brightness of stars in a galaxy outside the Milky Way galaxy compare with the brightness of stars within the Milky Way galaxy? *(Students should explain that the stars in the Milky Way galaxy would appear much brighter to an observer on Earth because they are much closer to Earth than the stars in a galaxy outside the Milky Way galaxy.)*

- **Science Process:** What are some of the challenges you think are faced by astronomers trying to observe stars in other galaxies? *(Student answers will vary, but may include: Other galaxies are so far from Earth that the light coming to us is very faint. The human eye may not be able to detect that faint light, so instruments that extend human perception are needed. There may be matter between Earth and a distant galaxy that blocks the faint light from distant galaxies.)*

NOTES

....

....

....

....

....

....

....

....

....

....

....

SECTION 4.5 IMPLEMENTATION

4.5 Read

What Does a Star's Light Reveal About a Star?

So far, you have read about how astronomers figure out the distance to a star and how they determine what the motion of a star is. You may wonder what the different types of stars are, how bright each type is, and if any of these objects could collide with other space objects.

Looking up at the sky from your home, you can tell that stars are points of light and that some are brighter than others. If you look up at the sky on a clear night, far from city lights, you may notice that stars have different colors. Astronomers can take images of stars from satellites above Earth's atmosphere, which gives the clearest possible view of the stars. In this type of image, shown here, it is easy to see that the universe is filled with a wide variety of stars of many different colors.

This image of the sky from space was taken by the Hubble Telescope.

One of the earliest astrophysicists, Annie Jump Cannon earned many honors for her groundbreaking work classifying stars. She credited her abilities to concentrate and record different stars partly on her lifelong hearing impairment.

Types of Stars

Annie Jump Cannon, a scientist at the Harvard College Observatory, began working on a catalog of stars in 1896. She had a strong background in math, physics, and astronomy. She worked at Harvard College for more than 40 years, classifying over 250,000 stars during her time there. She also developed the classification scheme for stars that astronomers still use. Cannon classified stars based on the surface

AST 191

ASTRONOMY

4.5 Read

What Does a Star's Light Reveal About a Star?

5 min

Students are introduced to the topic.

△ Guide

Begin by reminding students that stars appear to have different levels of brightness. Point out the picture of stars with varying brightness and color in the student text, and tell students that stars have different colors, as well, even though this can be hard to see with the unaided eye. Images taken from satellites, such as the one in the student text, can clearly show the variety of colors of stars.

*A class period is considered to be one 40 to 50 minute class.

○ Engage

Ask students what they think some of the other different characteristics of stars can be. They can have different colors. Can they also have different temperatures? Sizes?

Types of Stars

10 min

Students discuss how stars are classified.

META NOTES

You can also have students read this on their own in class or at home.

variety of stars of many different colors.

Types of Stars

Annie Jump Cannon, a scientist at the Harvard College Observatory, began working on a catalog of stars in 1896. She had a strong background in math, physics, and astronomy. She worked at Harvard College for more than 40 years, classifying over 250,000 stars during her time there. She also developed the classification scheme for stars that astronomers still use. Cannon classified stars based on the surface

One of the earliest astrophysicists, Annie Jump Cannon earned many honors for her groundbreaking work classifying stars. She credited her abilities to concentrate and record different stars partly on her lifelong hearing impairment.

△ Guide

Discuss the history of the classification system used for stars. The system was developed by Annie Jump Cannon at Harvard College Observatory. It is based on the surface temperature of each star. Surface temperature affects a star's spectrum; stars on the red end of the spectrum have relatively low surface temperatures (around 3000°C), while stars on the blue end of the spectrum have relatively high surface temperatures (30,000°C or higher). The Sun is a yellow star. A yellow star is hotter than a red star and cooler than a blue star. In her classification system, Cannon reordered the spectra in terms of increasing surface temperature.

NOTES

temperature of each star. Astronomers determine the temperature of a
star by looking at the star's spectrum. Cannon labeled the categories from
hottest to coldest using these letters: O, B, A, F, G, K, and M. The Sun, for
example, is a G-type star.

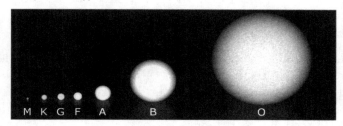

*Stars are classified
into one of several
lettered types and
given a number
based on their color
within that type.*

M K G F   A   B   O

**main sequence
star:** a typical
star, usually with a
diameter between
one-eighth and 10
times the Sun's
diameter.

giant star: a star
that is larger than a
main sequence star
of the same color.

Around 1910, two astronomers, Einar Hertzsprung and Henry Norris
Russell, independently studied Annie Jump Cannon's data. They both
discovered a relationship between the brightness of stars and the surface
temperature of stars. This relationship allowed astronomers to classify
stars further.

Hertzsprung and Russell made a diagram to illustrate this relationship. It
is known as the Hertzsprung-Russell diagram. On the Hertzsprung-Russell
diagram, shown on the next page, the brightness of the stars is shown on
the vertical axis, going from dimmer to brighter. The surface temperature is
along the horizontal axis, going from hotter to cooler.

When the stars are plotted on the Hertzsprung-Russell diagram, most
stars fall along a diagonal band. The stars in that band are known as main
sequence stars because they are in what is called the main sequence. It
is called the main sequence because most stars in it follow a relationship
among brightness, temperature, and size. Blue stars are very hot and bright.
The blue stars are also large. They may be more than 10 times the diameter
of the Sun and tens of thousands of time brighter. Red stars are cool and
dim. The red stars are also small. They are about an eighth the size of the
Sun and hundred times dimmer than the Sun.

Giant stars are stars that are larger than the stars on the main sequence.
These stars can have diameters 100 times greater than the Sun's diameter.
If the Sun were replaced by such a giant star, Earth would orbit the star just

AST 192

Project-Based Inquiry Science

Tell students that the size of a star also affects its appearance. The larger a
star is, the brighter it is. The surface temperature of a star can also affect its
brightness, but if two stars are the same color (that is, if they have the same
temperature), then they emit the same amount of light from each square
meter of the surface. If one is brighter (lower absolute magnitude) than the
other, it must also be larger.

Then discuss how the relationship between stars' brightness and their temperature allowed astronomers to further classify stars. One important category of stars they came up with is *main sequence stars*. In main sequence stars, the brightness of the star is directly related to its size. Larger main sequence stars are brighter and hotter and are on the blue end of the spectrum. Smaller main sequence stars are dimmer and cooler and are on the red end of the spectrum. Main sequence stars are distinguished from other types of stars by the observation that they produce energy by the fusion of hydrogen in their cores.

Giant stars are larger than stars on the main sequence, with diameters as great as 100 times the diameter of the Sun. Supergiant stars can be larger still. The largest known supergiant has a diameter 2000 times that of the Sun. White dwarfs are small, dim stars that radiate light due to heat generated by their great density.

NOTES

about at the star's surface. **Supergiant** stars are the largest and brightest stars. The largest star known today has a diameter more than 2000 times the diameter of the Sun. If the Sun were replaced by this star, the star would extend all the way out to the orbit of Saturn. Supergiants can be millions of times brighter than the Sun.

On the lower left side of the diagram, white dwarfs are some of the dimmest stars in the universe. **White dwarfs** have a similar mass to that of the Sun, but the mass is packed into an area about the size of Earth. White dwarfs are thousands of times dimmer than the Sun.

Most stars in the sky seem to come in systems of two or more stars called *binary stars*, so the Sun is unusual in that it is a single star. Many stars in the sky are also variable stars because they vary in brightness in a periodic cycle. The Sun's brightness is very steady. That is why conditions on Earth do not change wildly. Scientists think that planets suitable for life are more likely to be found orbiting single stars that are stable like the Sun.

supergiant star: a star that is hundreds or thousands of times larger than a main sequence star of the same color.

white dwarf: a star about the same size as Earth, with about the same mass as the Sun.

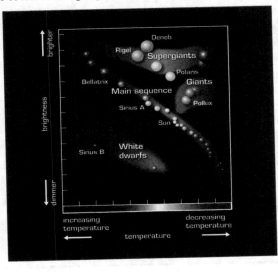

The Hertzsprung-Russell classification system of stars.

Introduce the concept of *binary stars* which are systems of two or more stars. Most stars belong to such systems. Solitary stars, like the Sun, are unusual. Also introduce *variable stars*. Variable stars are stars that vary in brightness in periodic cycles.

Be a Scientist: Radio Astronomy

5 min

Students read and discuss how astronomers use other types of radiation to explore the universe.

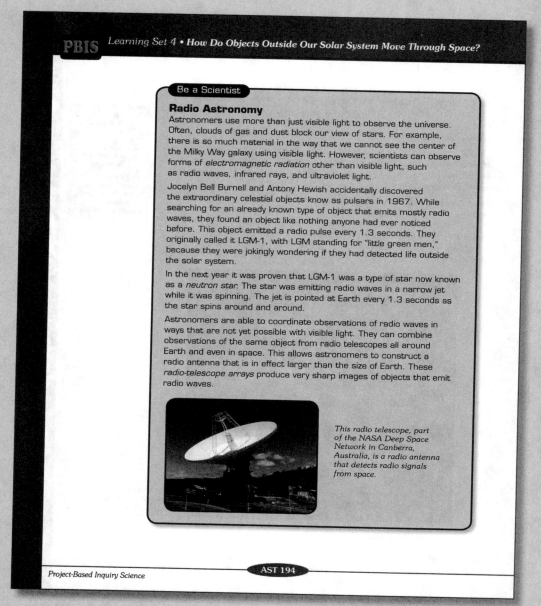

Be a Scientist

Radio Astronomy

Astronomers use more than just visible light to observe the universe. Often, clouds of gas and dust block our view of stars. For example, there is so much material in the way that we cannot see the center of the Milky Way galaxy using visible light. However, scientists can observe forms of *electromagnetic radiation* other than visible light, such as radio waves, infrared rays, and ultraviolet light.

Jocelyn Bell Burnell and Antony Hewish accidentally discovered the extraordinary celestial objects know as pulsars in 1967. While searching for an already known type of object that emits mostly radio waves, they found an object like nothing anyone had ever noticed before. This object emitted a radio pulse every 1.3 seconds. They originally called it LGM-1, with LGM standing for "little green men," because they were jokingly wondering if they had detected life outside the solar system.

In the next year it was proven that LGM-1 was a type of star now known as a *neutron star*. The star was emitting radio waves in a narrow jet while it was spinning. The jet is pointed at Earth every 1.3 seconds as the star spins around and around.

Astronomers are able to coordinate observations of radio waves in ways that are not yet possible with visible light. They can combine observations of the same object from radio telescopes all around Earth and even in space. This allows astronomers to construct a radio antenna that is in effect larger than the size of Earth. These *radio-telescope arrays* produce very sharp images of objects that emit radio waves.

This radio telescope, part of the NASA Deep Space Network in Canberra, Australia, is a radio antenna that detects radio signals from space.

Project-Based Inquiry Science

AST 194

△ Guide

Remind students that visible light is only a small part of the electromagnetic spectrum and tell them that astronomers collect other waves, such as radio waves to map a picture of the universe. These waves are emitted by distant stars and travel to Earth over vast periods of time. Tell them about neutron stars and that they spin rapidly on their axis, sometimes in milliseconds. Our Sun spins on its axis once in about 25 days.

4.5 **Read**

The Death of Stars

Earlier in this *Learning Set,* you discovered that stars travel in predictable paths around the center of the Milky Way galaxy, so they are not likely to collide with any of the planets or with objects within our solar system. However, a star does pose a danger when it uses up the hydrogen fuel in its core.

You read in *Section 4.2* about the fusion reactions that take place in the core of the Sun. The energy that is produced in fusion prevents a star's mass from simply collapsing in on itself. Like the Sun, main sequence stars use hydrogen fusion to produce helium. However, eventually the star runs out of hydrogen in its core. What happens next depends on how much mass the star has.

Because fusion is what keeps a star from collapsing in on itself, once fusion stops the core of a star starts to collapse. As the atoms are squeezed together, the core becomes hotter and hotter.

For stars much smaller than the Sun, the core will never get hot enough for fusion of elements other than hydrogen. The star collapses until it becomes a white dwarf, and then it eventually cools off. (You will learn, however, that sometimes a white dwarf can behave in a spectacular way.)

A white dwarf, pictured as a large white mass in this artist's illustration, is a dying star. The other, ringed star is extremely dense and is attracting matter from the white dwarf through its force of gravity.

Stars with about the same mass as the Sun generate more heat in their cores when the core collapses than do the smaller stars. The outer part of the star expands, and the star becomes a red giant. The core heats up enough so that fusion of helium occurs. However, eventually even the helium runs out, and the star loses its ability to produce energy from fusion. The core collapses into a white dwarf. The outer layers drift away, sometimes forming a glowing ring of gas around a star. This is what will happen to the Sun. It will expand until it becomes a red giant and then collapse, becoming a white dwarf—but not until about five billion years from now.

AST 195

ASTRONOMY

The Death of Stars

10 min

Students discuss how stars die.

△ Guide

Discuss what happens when a star uses up the hydrogen in its core. Depending on the mass of the star, it may become a white dwarf or a red giant, or it may explode in a *supernova,* leaving a neutron star or a black hole.

In main sequence stars, the energy produced by fusion in the core of a star keeps its great mass from collapsing in on itself. When the hydrogen runs out and the fusion stops, the core starts to compress and gets hotter and hotter. Small stars collapse until they become white dwarfs.

supernova: an explosion of a white dwarf or a star several times the mass of the Sun.

neutron star: a supernova remnant with more mass than the Sun packed into a sphere about 20 kilometers in diameter.

black hole: a body with mass so concentrated that light cannot escape its gravitational pull.

Stars that are much more massive than the Sun go through several cycles of collapsing. After each collapse, heavier and heavier elements are used as fuel for fusion, until iron is produced. Fusion that produces elements heavier than iron does not occur. Heavy elements that cannot undergo fusion build up in the core. The core collapses and a spectacular explosion called a **supernova** takes place.

The core of the star that remains after a supernova is so compact that it has more mass than the Sun in a sphere that is about 20 kilometers across. This is called a **neutron star**. A neutron star is so dense that a cube one millimeter on a side from the middle of the star would weigh about 1000 kilograms (a little more than a ton).

Neutron stars cannot exist beyond a certain size, about twice the mass of the Sun. If the core of the star that remains after a supernova has more mass than this, a **black hole** is formed. A black hole is an object so dense that light cannot escape from it. Black holes cannot be seen directly because no light ever leaves a black hole to reach our eyes. However, their existence can be inferred from their strong gravitational pull.

Anything that comes too close to a black hole will be caught by the pull of its gravity, with no chance of escape. You can think of the black hole as mass concentrated at a single point. The more mass there is in a black hole, the stronger its gravitational pull. The largest black holes have the mass of millions of stars and sit at the centers of galaxies. These black holes can pull objects in from much farther away than is possible for a black hole that has the mass of a single star.

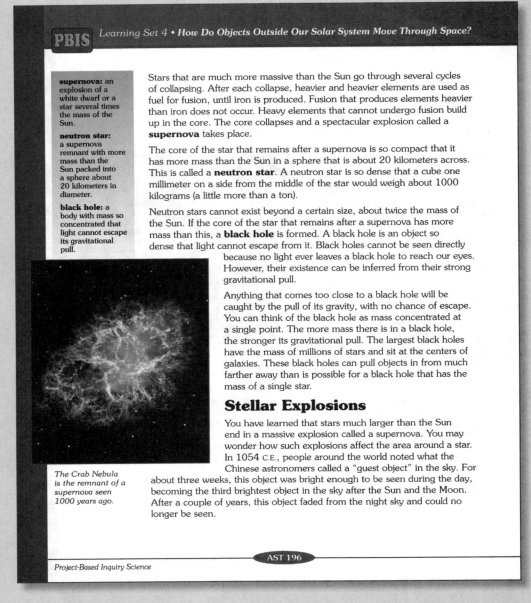

The Crab Nebula is the remnant of a supernova seen 1000 years ago.

Stellar Explosions

You have learned that stars much larger than the Sun end in a massive explosion called a supernova. You may wonder how such explosions affect the area around a star. In 1054 C.E., people around the world noted what the Chinese astronomers called a "guest object" in the sky. For about three weeks, this object was bright enough to be seen during the day, becoming the third brightest object in the sky after the Sun and the Moon. After a couple of years, this object faded from the night sky and could no longer be seen.

AST 196

Project-Based Inquiry Science

But in larger stars, elements other than hydrogen can undergo fusion. In a star with the mass of the Sun, more heat is generated in the core, and the outer part expands until the star becomes a red giant. The core becomes so hot that fusion of helium occurs. When the helium runs out, the core collapses into a white dwarf, and the outer layers drift away. The Sun will undergo this process starting in about 5 billion years.

In very massive stars (with mass more than eight times that of the Sun), fusion of heavier elements occurs as the core collapses. Eventually, the core has too much mass, and a spectacular explosion called a *supernova* takes place.

After a supernova, an extremely dense core called a neutron star remains. A neutron star contains the mass of the Sun in a sphere that is 20 km across. If the core that remains has a mass more than twice the mass of the Sun, a *black hole* forms. Black holes are so dense that light cannot escape the pull of their gravity. Because of this, they cannot be seen, and their presence must be inferred from their strong gravitational pull.

△ Guide

Discuss supernovas. The student text gives a historical example of a supernova that was observed by astronomers around the world about 1000 years ago. It was the third brightest object in the sky, after the Sun and the Moon.

Stellar Explosions

5 min

The class reads about and discusses supernovas.

NOTES

....

....

....

....

....

....

....

....

....

....

....

....

....

These ancient observers saw a supernova that took place over 7000 light-years from Earth. The supernova was the result of a star running out of fuel for fusion. The star exploded to form a neutron star. This star was too far away to have any effect on Earth besides briefly adding a new object to the night sky. At this location in the sky, astronomers now see the Crab Nebula, the remnant of the supernova explosion. A **nebula** is a cloud of gas and dust. Scientists can still see the Crab Nebula expanding nearly 1000 years after the ancient astronomers first reported the explosion.

nebula (plural: nebulae): a cloud of gas and dust in space.

A main sequence star has to have much more mass than the Sun for it to become a supernova. Recent studies suggest that such a supernova would have to be within 25 light-years of Earth for the radiation to have an impact on Earth's atmosphere. Fortunately, no stars within 25 light-years of Earth have enough mass to explode in this way. Unfortunately, there is another type of supernova that could be a threat to life on Earth.

The first supernova known to have been witnessed on Earth was seen in the year 185 C.E. It may have been the brightest object in the sky, aside from the Sun and the Moon. It had an absolute magnitude of −8 when it first occurred. However, this supernova was the result of an exploding white dwarf. This is a different kind of explosion from that of a main sequence star, and one that is much more dangerous.

Subrahmanyan Chandrasekhar was an Indian-born astronomer who became a U.S. citizen in 1953. In 1983, he won the Nobel prize for his work on the structure of stars. He is best known for his calculation that showed if a star forming a white dwarf has a mass greater than 1.4 times the mass of the Sun, it will explode as a supernova.

Astronomer Subrahmanyan Chandrasekhar won a Nobel prize for his investigations on the structure of stars.

As already mentioned, most stars in the universe are found in binary systems. If one of the two stars in a binary system becomes a white dwarf, it may begin to strip the other star of material. Once enough material falls onto the white dwarf so that its mass exceeds an account that Chandrasekhar calculated, a supernova occurs. In this explosion, the star is completely destroyed and matter and energy are ejected into space.

AST 197

ASTRONOMY

Tell students that a main sequence star has to have much more mass than the Sun for it to become a supernova. No star within 25 light-years of Earth has enough mass to become a supernova. However, in certain circumstances, a smaller star can lead to a supernova. If one star in a binary pair becomes a white dwarf, it can strip material from the other star. Over time, it can build up mass this way, until it becomes too massive and explodes in a supernova. This type of supernova is more powerful than the type caused by the collapsing core of a supergiant star, and if one occurred within 3000 light-years of Earth, it would probably affect life on Earth.

This type of supernova is much more powerful than the one caused by the collapsing core of a supergiant star. If such an explosion occurred within 3000 light-years of Earth, life on Earth would probably be affected.

Supernovas occur about once every 50 years in the Milky Way galaxy. Fortunately, it has probably been hundreds of millions of years since one happened close enough to Earth to be dangerous. In addition, the effects of supernovas are not all bad. Scientists think that a supernova can trigger the formation of new stars from the clouds of dust and gas in space. Most of the matter in stars is hydrogen and helium. Any other elements that are found in the universe were formed within stars and released by stars in events such as supernovas. This means that all of the material other than hydrogen and helium that is found on Earth—including most of what is found in you—was originally made inside a star.

Stop and Think

1. Describe the types of stars you can see in the night sky.

2. Describe the life cycle of the Sun, starting from the original nebula that formed it to its final stages as a red giant.

3. Give reasons why you think supernovas may or may not be more dangerous than collisions.

4. Astronomers theorize that the Milky Way has a supermassive black hole in its center. The Milky Way's black hole is estimated to contain over 4 million times the mass of the Sun. List reasons why or why not the center of the galaxy is a potential danger to Earth.

What's the Point?

Normal stars come in several types, ranging from red stars much smaller than the Sun to giant blue stars much larger than the Sun. Other types of stars include white dwarfs, giants, supergiants, and neutron stars. Most stars will eventually become white dwarfs once the process of fusion stops inside the star. Stars with enough mass can end in a violent explosion called a supernova, leading to the formation of a neutron star or a black hole. Supernovas may pose a threat to Earth, but only if they occur within 3000 light-years of Earth. Because the galaxy is 100,000 light-years across, most supernovas in the galaxy would be too far away to harm Earth.

AST 198

Project-Based Inquiry Science

Stop and Think

10 min

Students discuss and answer the Stop and Think *questions.*

Guide and Assess

Lead a class discussion of the *Stop and Think* questions. Listen for evidence that students understand how stars are classified, and the role of supernovas in the lives of stars. Also listen for evidence that they are synthesizing what they read here with everything else they have learned and can apply it to the *Big Question*. Can they compare the risk from supernovas to the risk from collisions?

1. Students should respond that they can see all types of stars in the night sky. The only limitations are the absolute magnitude of the star and its distance from the Earth.

2. Students should describe the Sun beginning as a bulge in the center of a spinning nebula of dust and gas. As gravity caused the collection and compression of the materials, the Sun took form as a massive sphere. When the internal temperatures became high enough, helium nuclei were fused from hydrogen nuclei, with the generation of much heat and light. A star is born. The Sun will continue this fusion reaction until the hydrogen fuel is nearly used up. With the loss of the constant supply of intense heat, the core of the Sun will collapse. This will generate more heat, initiating the fusion of helium, and the Sun will expand many hundreds of times to form a red giant.

3. Students may believe that a supernova is more dangerous than a collision because it can expand to cover far, far more volume than a single object in space. It is more like a net than a projectile. Other students may argue that a collision is more dangerous than a supernova because a collision, if it happens, is certain to cause destruction. The effect of a supernova is unknown.

4. Students may list the following reasons that the center of the galaxy is not a danger to Earth:

   - The center of the galaxy is too far away from Earth.

   - There is much more mass, in the form of stars, in the galaxy than in the alleged black hole at the center of the Milky Way.

   - Students who feel that the mass at the center of the galaxy is a danger may state that, sooner or later, Earth will be swept into it.

NOTES

....

....

....

....

Assessment Options

Targeted Concepts, Skills, and Nature of Science	How do I know if students got it?
Scientists often collaborate and share their findings. Sharing findings makes new information available and helps scientists refine their ideas and build on others' ideas. When another person's or group's idea is used, credit needs to be given.	**ASK:** How was the sharing of Annie Jump Cannon's data with the scientific community of benefit astronomy? **LISTEN:** Students should answer that sharing her findings made it possible for Hertzsprung and Russell to recognize that a relationship existed between the brightness and surface temperature (color) of stars. This, in turn, led to a clearer understanding of the life cycle of stars.
Scientists must keep clear, accurate and descriptive records of what they do so they can share their work with others; consider what they did, why they did it, and what they want to do next.	**ASK:** Why is it important to keep detailed notes as you read? **LISTEN:** Students' answers should indicate that if information is not recorded immediately, it can be forgotten or details may be recalled incorrectly.
Studying the work of different scientists provides understanding of scientific inquiry and reminds students that science is a human endeavor.	**ASK:** How did Hertzsprung and Russell build on the work of Annie Jump Cannon? **LISTEN:** Students should describe how they analyzed her data and recognized that a relationship existed between the brightness and surface temperature (color) of stars.
Stars form when gravity causes clouds of molecules to contract until nuclear fusion of light elements into heavier ones occurs. Fusion releases great amounts of energy over millions of years.	**ASK:** What prevents a star's mass from simply collapsing in on itself due to gravitational attraction? **LISTEN:** Students should answer that the energy produced by nuclear fusion pushing outwards counteracts the inward pull of gravity.

Targeted Concepts, Skills, and Nature of Science	How do I know if students got it?
Stars differ from each other in size, temperature, and age.	**ASK:** Describe the sizes and temperatures of main sequence, giant, supergiant, and white dwarf stars. **LISTEN:** Students' answers should be consistent with the position of these regions on the Hertzsprung-Russell diagram.
The Hertzsprung-Russell diagram shows the relationship between the luminosity and temperature of stars. The majority of stars lie on a diagonal band that extends from hot stars of high luminosity in the upper left corner to cool stars of low luminosity in the lower right corner. This band is called the main sequence.	**ASK:** In what region of the Hertzsprung-Russell diagram would you expect to find a star that is the same color as the Sun, but much brighter? Much dimmer? **LISTEN:** Students should identify that it would be brighter in the giant or supergiant region and dimmer in the white dwarf region. **ASK:** According to what you have read, as the Sun goes through the final stages of its life, in which regions of the Hertzsprung-Russell diagram will it be found? **LISTEN:** Students should describe how it first will move to the red giant region and then to the white dwarf region.

NOTES

....

....

....

Targeted Concepts, Skills, and Nature of Science	How do I know if students got it?
Different wavelengths of the electromagnetic spectrum such as light and radio waves are used to gain information about distances and properties of components of the universe.	**ASK:** How does the color of a star provide information about its temperature?
	LISTEN: Students should understand that the color of a star is due to the wavelengths of the light it emits. By observing matter that has been heated to different temperatures in a laboratory setting, scientists have been able to determine the wavelengths of light emitted at different temperatures. This information is then applied to determine the surface temperature of a star based on the wavelengths of light it emits.
	ASK: Give one example of an object that has been identified in the universe by observing electromagnetic radiation other than visible light.
	LISTEN: Students should identify neutron stars, or pulsars.

Teacher Reflection Questions

- What evidence do you have that students understand that the sharing of ideas and building on others' ideas are practices of scientists? How can you further their understanding of the importance of these practices?

- This section involved a lot of reading. How did you structure the reading segments to keep students engaged and maintain interest? What would you change next time?

- Do you feel that students can comprehend the vast distances and vast forces at play in the universe? How can you help them understand that the solar system is just a speck of dust in all of the universe?

- Do students understand the time-scales involved in events that occur in the universe and that hundreds of thousands of years pass between events? How can you help them to understand that it is highly unlikely that our civilization will suffer any external cataclysmic event?

NOTES

SECTION 4.6 INTRODUCTION

4.6 Explore

Can Galaxies Collide?

◀ *2 class periods*

A class period is
considered to be one
40 to 50 minute class.

Overview

Students expand the scope of their search for objects that could collide
with Earth beyond the Milky Way galaxy. Students read a description of
the Shapley-Curtis debate, involving the size and structure of the universe,
and Hubble's use of data from the Andromeda nebula to establish that the
Milky Way galaxy was just one small part of a larger universe. Students then
examine images of four distant galaxies and develop a system to classify
galaxies according to their structure. After sharing their ideas about how to
categorize galaxies with the class, students refine or revise their categories
based on feedback and new information shared by other groups. Students
then read about Hubble's system for classifying galaxies and evidence
of past collisions of galaxies. They consider the possible effects of one
galaxy colliding with another and update the *Project Board* with any new
recommendations and supporting evidence.

Targeted Concepts, Skills, and Nature of Science	Performance Expectations
Scientists often collaborate and share their findings. Sharing findings makes new information available and helps scientists refine their ideas and build on others' ideas. When another person's or group's idea is used, credit needs to be given.	Students collaborate in small groups to develop a system for classifying galaxies and share their results with the class.
	Students participate in a class discussion updating their *Project Board,* which is an organizing record of their ideas and what they are learning.
Scientists must keep clear, accurate and descriptive records of what they do so they can share their work with others; consider what they did, why they did it, and what they want to do next.	Students keep a written record of their answers to *Stop and Think* questions.
	Students keep a written record of their galaxy classification system and the reasons why their group chose to place each galaxy in a particular group.

Targeted Concepts, Skills, and Nature of Science	Performance Expectations
Studying the work of different scientists provides understanding of scientific inquiry and reminds students that science is a human endeavor.	Students describe how scientists like Edwin Hubble built on the work of other scientists, such as Henrietta Swan Leavitt.
The universe is vast and estimated to be over ten billion years old. The current theory is that the universe was created from an explosion called the Big Bang. A red-shift (the Doppler effect) in the light from very distant galaxies provides evidence for this theory.	Students describe the evidence supporting the idea that the universe is expanding and the Big Bang Theory of the origin of the universe.
Components of the universe include stars, galaxies, and nebulae.	Students identify major components of the universe such as stars, nebulae, and galaxies and distinguish between these components.
A galaxy is a system of stars, cosmic dust and gas held together by gravitation. Galaxies typically contain billions of stars, may have different shapes, and may be thousands of light-years in diameter; the universe contains billions of such galaxies.	Students cite evidence that the Milky Way galaxy is only a small part of a larger universe which contains billions of such galaxies.

Materials

1 per class	Class *Project Board*

NOTES

....

....

....

....

Homework Options

Reflection

- **Science Content:** How did your group's system for classifying galaxies compare with Hubble's system? *(Students' answers will vary, but should compare and contrast the system their group devised with Hubble's spiral, barred spiral, elliptical, and irregular categories.)*

- **Science Content:** How did Henrietta Swan Leavitt's study of stars help resolve the Shapley-Curtis debate? *(Students should recall that Leavitt's study of star brightness made it possible to calculate the distance to stars too far away for parallax to be used. This enabled Hubble to prove that the stars in the Andromeda Nebula were too far from Earth to be part of the Milky Way galaxy.)*

- **Science Content:** Describe the evidence supporting the Big Bang Theory. *(Students should describe how studies of the Doppler shifts of galaxies indicate that they are all rapidly moving apart from one another. If one could trace the galaxies back in time, there would be a point at which they were all very close to one another. Based upon the observed expansion rate, this occurred about 14 billion years ago. Thus, we have a model in which the universe started out with all of its matter in a small volume and then expanded outward in all directions, a motion very much like an explosion. For this reason, this model of the universe is called the Big Bang Theory.)*

- **Science Content:** Why does a collision between galaxies not necessarily result in many stars colliding with one another? *(Students should answer that the distance between the stars in a galaxy is so vast that galaxies are mostly empty space, which decreases the likelihood of collisions.)*

- **Science Content:** Even if stars do not collide, how would they be affected by passing close to one another? *(Students should cite that gravitational attraction between the stars could alter their paths and the paths of planets and smaller objects that orbit the stars.)*

Preparation for 4.7

- **Science Content:** In order to reach Earth's surface, light from a star must pass through Earth's atmosphere. How do you think this affects the star's light? *(Students should answer that Earth's atmosphere can block, bend and scatter the star's light.)*

- **Science Process:** Where could you place a telescope so that the effects of Earth's atmosphere on the light from stars would be minimized or even eliminated? *(Students may suggest placing it atop high mountains where the atmosphere is thinner, or placing it above Earth's atmosphere in space.)*

- **Science Process:** Suppose you were part of a group that had to decide which astronomy research projects were going to be funded over the next 5 years. What criteria would you use to decide which projects should be given funding? *(Students' answers will vary, but they should consider cost, complexity, and the likelihood of success as factors.)*

NOTES

SECTION 4.6 IMPLEMENTATION

◀ *2 class periods* *

4.6 Explore

Can Galaxies Collide?

In ancient times most people thought of the universe as the Sun, the Moon, and planets revolving around Earth. The stars were considered attached to a giant celestial sphere that defined the outer edge of the universe. It was not until the 17th century that astronomers began to recognize stars as other suns. The first parallax measurement, which showed that stars are very distant and not part of our solar system, was made in 1834.

At the beginning of the 20th century, scientists recognized that Earth and the Sun are part of the Milky Way galaxy, a vast collection of stars, gas, and dust. Many objects that looked like nebulae had been discovered with telescopes, and these were all thought to be part of the Milky Way galaxy.

By 1920, astronomers were sharply divided over whether these nebulae were within the Milky Way galaxy or whether they were separate galaxies. A famous debate between astronomers Harlow Shapley and Heber Curtis in 1920 captured the main ideas of the two points of view. Shapley argued that the Milky Way galaxy was the extent of the universe. Curtis argued that the Milky Way was just one small part of a much larger universe.

Astronomer Henrietta Swan Leavitt developed a way to estimate the distance to clusters of stars, like those on the left, by measuring their brightness.

AST 199

ASTRONOMY

4.6 Explore

Can Galaxies Collide?

10 min

Students discuss how astronomers study other galaxies.

△ Guide

Begin by letting students know they will explore the question, *Can Galaxies Collide?* First, they need to understand the relationship of other galaxies to the Milky Way. Tell them that astronomers did not always believe there were galaxies outside the Milky Way, and discuss the development of astronomers' current understanding. Ancient astronomers thought of the universe as composed of Earth, and around it, the Sun, the Moon, the planets, and a celestial sphere studded with stars. But even when

*A class period is considered to be one 40 to 50 minute class.

ASTRONOMY

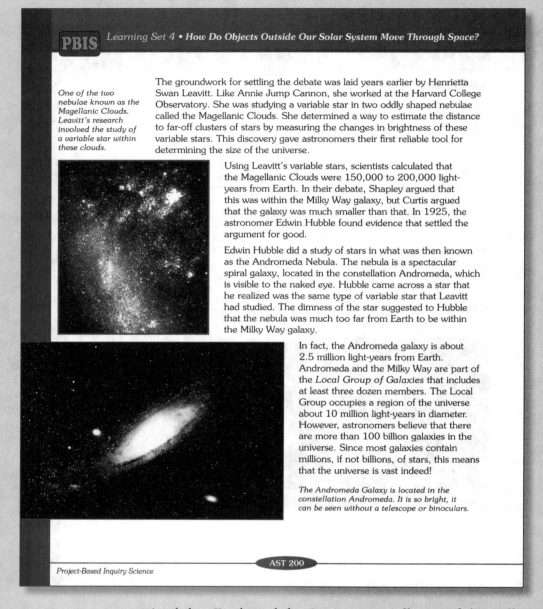

One of the two nebulae known as the Magellanic Clouds. Leavitt's research involved the study of a variable star within these clouds.

The groundwork for settling the debate was laid years earlier by Henrietta Swan Leavitt. Like Annie Jump Cannon, she worked at the Harvard College Observatory. She was studying a variable star in two oddly shaped nebulae called the Magellanic Clouds. She determined a way to estimate the distance to far-off clusters of stars by measuring the changes in brightness of these variable stars. This discovery gave astronomers their first reliable tool for determining the size of the universe.

Using Leavitt's variable stars, scientists calculated that the Magellanic Clouds were 150,000 to 200,000 light-years from Earth. In their debate, Shapley argued that this was within the Milky Way galaxy, but Curtis argued that the galaxy was much smaller than that. In 1925, the astronomer Edwin Hubble found evidence that settled the argument for good.

Edwin Hubble did a study of stars in what was then known as the Andromeda Nebula. The nebula is a spectacular spiral galaxy, located in the constellation Andromeda, which is visible to the naked eye. Hubble came across a star that he realized was the same type of variable star that Leavitt had studied. The dimness of the star suggested to Hubble that the nebula was much too far from Earth to be within the Milky Way galaxy.

In fact, the Andromeda galaxy is about 2.5 million light-years from Earth. Andromeda and the Milky Way are part of the *Local Group of Galaxies* that includes at least three dozen members. The Local Group occupies a region of the universe about 10 million light-years in diameter. However, astronomers believe that there are more than 100 billion galaxies in the universe. Since most galaxies contain millions, if not billions, of stars, this means that the universe is vast indeed!

The Andromeda Galaxy is located in the constellation Andromeda. It is so bright, it can be seen without a telescope or binoculars.

AST 200

astronomers recognized that Earth and the Sun are a small part of the Milky Way galaxy, they did not all believe that there might be more outside of the Milky Way.

Tell students that in the early twentieth century, the question of whether the entire universe was contained in the Milky Way galaxy, or whether some of the stars observed by astronomers were part of other galaxies, became the center of an important debate. The debate was settled only when an astronomer named Edwin Hubble was able to show that certain stars in the Andromeda Nebula were so distant that they could not be in the Milky Way, that the debate was settled. Students maybe interested to know, he used a method developed by Henrietta Swan Leavitt, to show that these stars were distant. Leavitt had found a way to estimate the distance of certain period stars. As a result of Hubble's and Leavitt's work, the Andromeda Nebula was recognized as a separate galaxy, now known as the Andromeda galaxy.

NOTES

Explore: Types of Galaxies

10 min

Students classify the galaxies using images.

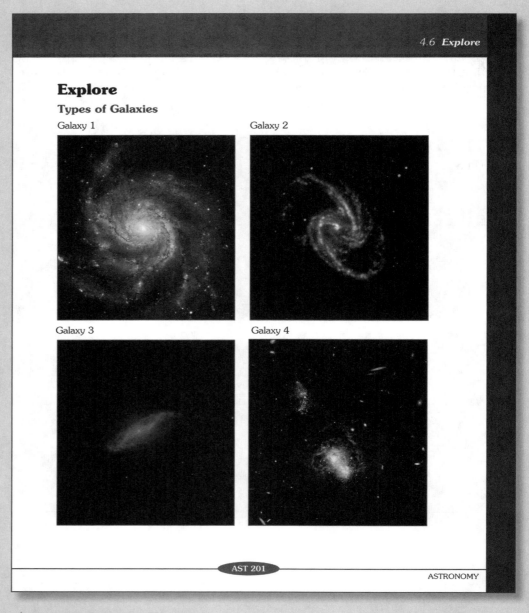

Explore

Types of Galaxies

Galaxy 1

Galaxy 2

Galaxy 3

Galaxy 4

AST 201

ASTRONOMY

△ Guide and Assess

Go over the procedure in the student text. Students in a group should examine all of the pictures, looking for similarities and differences. They should discuss their ideas with the group, and develop from three to six categories for the galaxies. They should classify the galaxies, ensuring that each galaxy is contained in one and only one category. Let students know they will share their classifications with the class.

Procedure

1. Look at the photographs of galaxies. Identify similarities and differences among the appearances of these galaxies.

2. Using the similarities and differences that you have identified, classify the galaxies using two or more categories.

3. Give a name to each category, and briefly describe the characteristics of galaxies within each category. Your categories should be defined so that each galaxy can be placed in one and only one category.

Communicate

Share Your Results

Choose one person from your group to share your classification of galaxies with the rest of the class. Listen to what the other groups have to say about their classifications. Be respectful of the other groups as they share their results. Ask questions if you do not understand how they came to their results. Note how the categories they chose differ from your categories.

After listening to all of the other groups, meet again with your group. Adjust your categories to get rid of any inconsistency or overlaps in your categories. Revise your categories to be what you think is the best way to classify galaxies.

Stop and Think

1. Describe any categories that were used by most of the groups in the class. Which galaxies were sorted into these categories, and what characteristics do they share?

2. Which galaxies caused groups to have the most varied opinions on how they should be classified? What were the characteristics of those galaxies?

3. Here is an image of an object that was named Arp 272. How would you categorize this object? Give reasons for your classification. If Arp 272 does not fit into your categories, how will you have to revise your categories?

Arp 272

Have students begin. As they work, ask them what ideas they have discussed. Students should describe the galaxies and isolate features that can be used to distinguish between them. They should begin to identify features that two or more galaxies share in common as the basis for categories.

Communicate: Share Your Results

15 min

Groups share their classifications and then revise them.

Communicate

Share Your Results

Choose one person from your group to share your classification of galaxies with the rest of the class. Listen to what the other groups have to say about their classifications. Be respectful of the other groups as they share their results. Ask questions if you do not understand how they came to their results. Note how the categories they chose differ from your categories.

After listening to all of the other groups, meet again with your group. Adjust your categories to get rid of any inconsistency or overlaps in your categories. Revise your categories to be what you think is the best way to classify galaxies.

△ Guide

Have groups share their classifications with the class. Emphasize that as each group shares their classification, students should make sure they understand the reasoning behind the classification, and ask questions to clarify if necessary.

Once students have heard all of the classifications again, have them meet with their groups to revise their classification.

Stop and Think

5 min

Groups answer the Stop and Think *questions.*

Stop and Think

1. Describe any categories that were used by most of the groups in the class. Which galaxies were sorted into these categories, and what characteristics do they share?

2. Which galaxies caused groups to have the most varied opinions on how they should be classified? What were the characteristics of those galaxies?

3. Here is an image of an object that was named Arp 272. How would you categorize this object? Give reasons for your classification. If Arp 272 does not fit into your categories, how will you have to revise your categories?

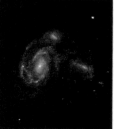

Arp 272

△ Guide

Have students work with their groups to answer the *Stop and Think* questions. As they discuss these questions, monitor their progress and ask them what ideas they have discussed. Students may decide that Arp 272 comprises two distinct spiral galaxies, that it is a single spiral galaxy with two centers, or that it cannot be put into any category with the galaxies they have observed. They should recognize that its inclusion in or exclusion from a category should be based on specific features it does or doesn't share with other galaxies.

1. Students will describe the categories used by most of the groups in the class and what the characteristics of each category are. They will also state which of the galaxies—1, 2, 3, 4—were placed in each category.

2. Student will probably report that Galaxy 3 and Galaxy 4 were the most difficult to categorize. Galaxy 3 had little to characterize it at all. Galaxy 4 seemed to have two centers.

3. Students would probably place Arp 272 in the same category as Galaxy 1 since the two galaxies are very similar. Arp 272 appears to be two spiral galaxies which are colliding. The galaxy on the right may be a barred spiral galaxy.

NOTES

....

....

....

....

....

....

....

....

....

....

Types of Galaxies

5 min

Students discuss the types of galaxies.

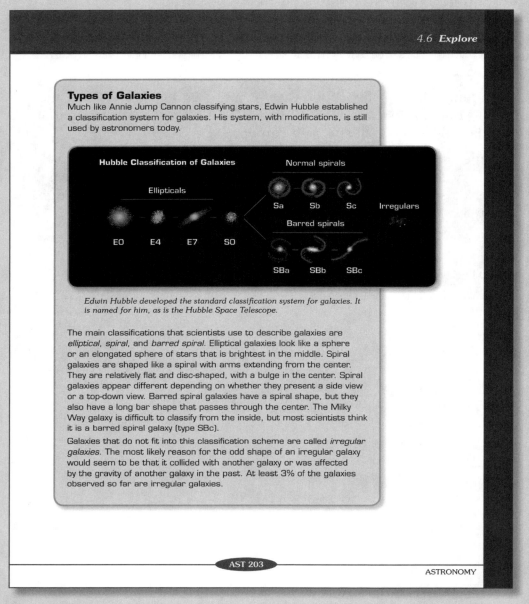

Types of Galaxies

Much like Annie Jump Cannon classifying stars, Edwin Hubble established a classification system for galaxies. His system, with modifications, is still used by astronomers today.

Hubble Classification of Galaxies

Ellipticals

Normal spirals

Sa   Sb   Sc

Barred spirals

E0   E4   E7   S0

SBa   SBb   SBc

Irregulars

Edwin Hubble developed the standard classification system for galaxies. It is named for him, as is the Hubble Space Telescope.

The main classifications that scientists use to describe galaxies are *elliptical*, *spiral*, and *barred spiral*. Elliptical galaxies look like a sphere or an elongated sphere of stars that is brightest in the middle. Spiral galaxies are shaped like a spiral with arms extending from the center. They are relatively flat and disc-shaped, with a bulge in the center. Spiral galaxies appear different depending on whether they present a side view or a top-down view. Barred spiral galaxies have a spiral shape, but they also have a long bar shape that passes through the center. The Milky Way galaxy is difficult to classify from the inside, but most scientists think it is a barred spiral galaxy (type SBc).

Galaxies that do not fit into this classification scheme are called *irregular galaxies*. The most likely reason for the odd shape of an irregular galaxy would seem to be that it collided with another galaxy or was affected by the gravity of another galaxy in the past. At least 3% of the galaxies observed so far are irregular galaxies.

AST 203

ASTRONOMY

△ Guide

Introduce Hubble's classification of galaxies. Tell students it was developed by the same Edwin Hubble who showed that the Andromeda galaxy was a separate galaxy and not a nebula within the Milky Way. Then discuss the categories in this classification. The major categories are: elliptical galaxies, spiral galaxies, and barred spiral galaxies. Galaxies that do not fit in any of these categories are called irregular galaxies, and they are believed to be the result of the collision of two galaxies.

Ask students how these categories correspond to the categories they developed. Students should be able to determine which of the galaxies they looked at are elliptical galaxies, which are spiral galaxies, and which are barred spiral galaxies. Ask them what category Arp 272 belongs in. They should recognize that this is a pair of spiral galaxies which are colliding.

NOTES

Colliding Galaxies

15 min

Students discuss how galaxies move, how this suggests the universe is expanding, and how galaxies can collide.

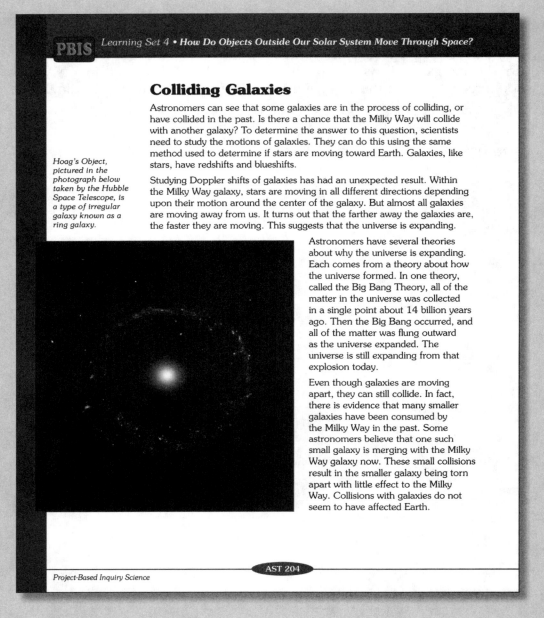

Colliding Galaxies

Astronomers can see that some galaxies are in the process of colliding, or have collided in the past. Is there a chance that the Milky Way will collide with another galaxy? To determine the answer to this question, scientists need to study the motions of galaxies. They can do this using the same method used to determine if stars are moving toward Earth. Galaxies, like stars, have redshifts and blueshifts.

Hoag's Object, pictured in the photograph below taken by the Hubble Space Telescope, is a type of irregular galaxy known as a ring galaxy.

Studying Doppler shifts of galaxies has had an unexpected result. Within the Milky Way galaxy, stars are moving in all different directions depending upon their motion around the center of the galaxy. But almost all galaxies are moving away from us. It turns out that the farther away the galaxies are, the faster they are moving. This suggests that the universe is expanding.

Astronomers have several theories about why the universe is expanding. Each comes from a theory about how the universe formed. In one theory, called the Big Bang Theory, all of the matter in the universe was collected in a single point about 14 billion years ago. Then the Big Bang occurred, and all of the matter was flung outward as the universe expanded. The universe is still expanding from that explosion today.

Even though galaxies are moving apart, they can still collide. In fact, there is evidence that many smaller galaxies have been consumed by the Milky Way in the past. Some astronomers believe that one such small galaxy is merging with the Milky Way galaxy now. These small collisions result in the smaller galaxy being torn apart with little effect to the Milky Way. Collisions with galaxies do not seem to have affected Earth.

AST 204

Project-Based Inquiry Science

△ Guide

Tell students that now that they know more about galaxies, they will again look at the questions, *Can Galaxies Collide?* and *Could the Milky Way collide with another galaxy?* Tell them astronomers study the motions of galaxies to answer these questions. Astronomers do this by examining the red shifts and blue shifts of the galaxies, just as they would with individual stars.

As one result of examining the red shifts and the blue shifts of galaxies, astronomers have found that almost all galaxies are moving away from us, and the farther away they are, the faster they are moving. This suggests that the universe is expanding. Tell them that in a universe that is expanding throughout, every galaxy will move away from every other galaxy. Explain that farther-away galaxies are moving faster than nearby galaxies is further evidence that the universe is expanding. In a universe that is expanding, the distance between galaxies that are farther away from one another will increase more quickly than the distance between galaxies that are close to one another.

You can see this in many ways. One way is to imagine galaxies situated along a line in space. If the distance along the line doubles, the distance between any two galaxies along the line doubles. If the original distance between two galaxies along the line is small (that is, if they are close together), the absolute increase in distance is small. If the original distance between two galaxies is great, the absolute increase in distance is great. The galaxy moving a great distance in a certain time moves more quickly than the galaxy moving a small distance in the same time.

There are several standard demonstrations you can use to show this, such as marking dots on a balloon, incrementally blowing it up, and then measuring the distances between dots with each increase, or putting marks on a rubber band and incrementally stretching it, again measuring the distances between marks with each increase.

This is consistent with one important theory for how the universe formed, the Big Bang Theory. According to this theory, all of the matter in the universe was condensed in a single point about 14 billion years ago. When the Big Bang occurred, the matter expanded outward in a great explosion. In this model, the present expansion of the universe is a continuation of the expansion of the Big Bang.

Emphasize that despite the evidence that most galaxies are moving away from one another, some galaxies can and do collide. Point out the picture of Hoag's Object, which may be the remains of two colliding galaxies. Collisions of galaxies may not involve many collisions of stars, because there is a great deal of space between stars in galaxies, but the gravity effects can alter the paths of the stars in the galaxies. A collision of galaxies can also heat gases in the galaxies, creating conditions that would be hostile to life on a planet like Earth.

Astronomers have found many examples of galaxies colliding. The collisions do not necessarily result in many stars colliding with one another. Remember, there is a lot of space between stars. But the collisions can alter the paths of stars in a gravitational tug of war.

The gas inside galaxies is heated as galaxies pass through each other. This can create intense conditions, with lots of radiation. It would be hard to imagine life existing on a planet circling a star in a region like this.

The Andromeda galaxy is one of the few galaxies moving toward Earth. Scientists believe there is a good chance Andromeda will collide with the Milky Way. Other galaxies are either too small or too far way to be a concern. This collision, out of all the intergalactic collisions, may be the one that affects life on Earth. Fortunately, this collision will not happen until more than 2 billion years from now.

Stop and Think

1. Describe how the known scale of the universe has changed from ancient times through now as more and more discoveries about objects in the night sky have been made.

2. List reasons why a collision with another galaxy is or is not a potential danger for Earth in the next 30 years.

Update the *Project Board*

In this section you have learned about the possibility of galaxies colliding with the Milky Way galaxy. Update the *Project Board* with your new knowledge to the *What are we learning?* and *What is our evidence?* columns.

What's the Point?

In the past 100 years, astronomers have discovered that the Milky Way galaxy is one galaxy among billions of galaxies. These galaxies can be classified into spiral, elliptical, barred elliptical, and irregular types. Many galaxies, including the Milky Way, show evidence of past collisions. Because of the vast distances between stars and the immense size of galaxies, the Milky Way can collide with another galaxy without affecting Earth.

AST 205

ASTRONOMY

Tell students that such a collision could be possible for the Milky Way. The Andromeda galaxy is moving toward Earth and may collide with it. However, this will not happen for more than 2 billion years.

△ Guide

Lead a class discussion of the *Stop and Think* questions, or assign them for homework. Students should recognize that the great distances between galaxies, and the evidence that most galaxies are moving away from the Milky Way, make it impossible that any galaxy will collide with the Milky Way in the next 30 years.

1. Students should describe the ancient view of the universe as comprising Earth, the Moon, and the Sun, with a celestial sphere carrying all of the stars. The planets were odd "wanderers" from the geocentric view. Today's view of the universe is one of unimaginable vastness. Billions of galaxies, each containing billions and billions of stars, almost all receding from each other at vast speeds. The edge of the universe has not yet been found.

2. Students will reason that it would be impossible for another galaxy to become a potential danger for Earth in the next 30 years. One of the nearest galaxies is the Andromeda galaxy and, while it is headed in our direction, it won't arrive for 2 billion years. The closest of galaxies is thousands of light-years away.

△ Guide

Ask students what they can now add to the *What are we learning?* column of the *Project Board*. Record their answers on the class *Project Board* and have them record their answers on their own *Project Board* pages. Then ask them what evidence they have, and record their answers on the *Project Board*.

Stop and Think

10 min

Lead a class discussion of the Stop and Think *questions, or assign them for homework.*

Update the Project Board

15 min

Lead a class discussion to update the Project Board.

NOTES

....

....

....

Assessment Options

Targeted Concepts, Skills, and Nature of Science	How do I know if students got it?
Scientists often collaborate and share their findings. Sharing findings makes new information available and helps scientists refine their ideas and build on others' ideas. When another person's or group's idea is used, credit needs to be given.	**ASK:** How did working on your system for classifying galaxies in a group affect the categories you created? **LISTEN:** Students should discuss how valid comments relating to observed characteristics of the galaxies and ideas shared by others in the group led them to revise their own ideas. **ASK:** When groups shared their classification systems and the class discussed them, what comments by other students did you find most helpful in revising your own system? **LISTEN:** Students should cite examples of valid comments relating to the criteria for grouping galaxies.
Scientists must keep clear, accurate and descriptive records of what they do so they can share their work with others; consider what they did, why they did it, and what they want to do next.	**ASK:** What record did you keep of your group's work in devising a classification system for galaxies? **LISTEN:** Students should describe notes and other evidence of the group process that lead to their classification system. **ASK:** In what ways is the *Project Board* helpful to our search for answers to the *Big Question?* **LISTEN:** Students should cite examples of how the *Project Board* serves as a vehicle for sharing ideas, keeping track of what they have learned, and seeing what they are doing in a larger context.

NOTES

....

Targeted Concepts, Skills, and Nature of Science	How do I know if students got it?
Studying the work of different scientists provides understanding of scientific inquiry and reminds students that science is a human endeavor.	**ASK:** Cite an example of one scientist studying another scientist's work that you read about in this section. **LISTEN:** Students should describe how Edwin Hubble built on the work of Henrietta Swan Leavitt to prove that galaxies existed outside the Milky Way galaxy.
The universe is vast and estimated to be over ten billion years old. The current theory is that the universe was created from an explosion called the Big Bang. A red-shift (the Doppler effect) in the light from very distant galaxies provides evidence for this theory.	**ASK:** How do scientists arrive at an age of 14 billion years for the universe? **LISTEN:** Students should answer that by working backward in time from the current rate and direction of motion of the galaxies to when they would all have been concentrated in a very small region of space, they figured out the age of the universe.
Components of the universe include stars, galaxies and nebulae.	**ASK:** Why were some galaxies considered nebulae by early observers? **LISTEN:** Students should answer that because the galaxies were so far away, telescopes could not resolve individual stars leading astronomers to classify some galaxies as nebulae.

NOTES

....

....

....

....

Targeted Concepts, Skills, and Nature of Science	How do I know if students got it?
A galaxy is a system of stars, cosmic dust and gas held together by gravitation. Galaxies typically contain billions of stars, may have different shapes, and may be thousands of light-years in diameter; the universe contains billions of such galaxies.	**ASK:** What evidence supports the idea that the Milky Way galaxy is only a small part of a much larger universe? **LISTEN:** Students should answer that Hubble used Leavitt's work on star brightness data to determine that the distance to in the Andromeda galaxy was too far from Earth (about 2.5 million light-years away) to be in the Milky Way galaxy. **ASK:** What is the current estimate for the number of galaxies in the universe? **LISTEN:** Students should identify that there are more than 100 billion galaxies in the universe.

Teacher Reflection Questions

- In what ways were students productively engaged during this section of the *Learning Set?* How could you tell?

- How did you implement the *Project Board* discussion to include students who feel inhibited about sharing their ideas?

- When managing discussions, it is important to foster thoughtful criticism of ideas while maintaining respectful interactions. Were there instances in your class discussions when students were not interacting respectfully? How could you help students develop better social-interaction skills?

- Do students understand that even if two galaxies collide, stars may not collide and most effects will occur because of gravity?

SECTION 4.7 INTRODUCTION

4.7 Read

How Is Technology Aiding New Discoveries in Astronomy?

◀ **2 class periods**

A class period is considered to be one 40 to 50 minute class.

Overview

Students examine case studies describing two space telescopes that are contributing to our knowledge and understanding of the universe: the Hubble Space Telescope and the Kepler Mission. Through readings and by viewing NASA video footage, students are made aware of the discoveries that are being made with these technologically advanced instruments.

Targeted Concepts, Skills, and Nature of Science	Performance Expectations
Scientists often collaborate and share their findings. Sharing findings makes new information available and helps scientists refine their ideas and build on others' ideas. When another person's or group's idea is used, credit needs to be given.	Students collaborate in small groups to design an ideal space mission and give a class presentation describing the mission goals and how they will be achieved.
Scientists must keep clear, accurate and descriptive records of what they do so they can share their work with others; consider what they did, why they did it, and what they want to do next.	Students keep a written record of their responses to the *Stop and Think* and *Reflect* questions. Students create posters detailing the goals of the ideal space mission planned by their group.
Humans perceive the universe by the radiation it emits. Technological advances have greatly extended the scope of human perception and led to the observations upon which our current theories of the universe are based.	Students can describe the advantages of space-based telescopes over Earth-based telescopes. Students are able to identify technological advances incorporated into the design of space-based telescopes.
Humankind's need to explore continues to lead to the development of knowledge and understanding of the nature of the Universe.	Students can describe new discoveries about the content and structure of the universe that have resulted from observations made using space-based telescopes.

Materials	
1 per group	Poster board Markers, or other supplies to make posters
1 per class	NASA videos Class *Project Board*

Homework Options

Reflection

- **Science Content:** Compare and contrast the missions of the Hubble and Kepler space telescopes. *(Students should understand that the Kepler telescope mission goal is to search for Earth-like planets orbiting other stars. The Hubble's primary mission is to survey the universe and record digital images of the universe that are free of the distortion of Earth's atmosphere.)*

- **Science Process:** How does measuring the brightness of stars every 30 minutes provide information about planets orbiting those stars? *(Students should answer that when a planet orbiting a star passes between the star and the telescope, some of the light from the star is blocked and it appears temporarily dimmer. The larger the planet, the more light it blocks, and the more it dims the star's light. The faster the planet moves, the shorter the time that it dims the star's light. Thus, by observing the rate and degree to which a star's light dims, astronomers can estimate the size and orbit of the planet.)*

Preparation for 4.BBQ

- **Science Content:** If you could observe a collision between any two objects in the universe, which two objects would you choose and why? *(Student answers will vary. This question is meant to create an anticipatory set for the proposal students will be asked to make in the* Back to the Big Question.*)*

- **Science Process:** Prioritize the objects outside the solar system that you learned about in this *Learning Set* according to the likelihood that they will be involved in a collision. *(Student answers will vary, but should include supporting evidence for their claimed order.)*

SECTION 4.7 IMPLEMENTATION

4.7 Read

How Is Technology Aiding New Discoveries in Astronomy?

Four hundred years ago, Galileo started looking at the sky with his new and improved telescope. He saw wonders he could not have imagined. He discovered that the markings on the Moon were impact craters. He was the first to see that another planet besides Earth has moons. He showed that Venus was orbiting the Sun and not Earth.

Galileo used a telescope that allowed him to see objects 20 times dimmer than the naked eye can see. Today, telescopes can detect objects that are billions of times dimmer than those Galileo was able to see. This has helped astronomers to learn much more about the characteristics of each planet and the Sun. Their knowledge of what is beyond the solar system also expands every day.

Currently, two important space telescopes are helping to build knowledge of the universe beyond our solar system. One is the Hubble Space Telescope, which was launched into space in 1990. The other is the Kepler Mission, which was launched in 2009. They are both telescopes, but their jobs are very different and the data they collect and send back to Earth are very different.

> **Case Study 1: The Hubble Space Telescope**
> The Hubble Space Telescope is actually six separate instruments that can view the universe in many different ways. It was placed in Earth orbit during a space shuttle mission in 1990. It was designed so that astronauts could repair the telescope in space if necessary. Five space shuttle missions between 1993 and 2009 have been launched to repair or increase the capabilities of the Hubble.
>
> The Hubble Space Telescope can do what no telescope on Earth can do—look at stars without having to look through Earth's atmosphere. In *Learning Set 3*, you learned that stars twinkle because the atmosphere distorts and scatters the light from stars. This limits the ability of

AST 206

Project-Based Inquiry Science

4.7 Read

How Is Technology Aiding New Discoveries in Astronomy?

5 min

Students are introduced to the activity.

△ Guide

Begin by briefly discussing the history and uses of telescopes. Galileo showed the great utility of telescopes for astronomy when he began studying objects in the solar system through his own telescope. He was able to see that the Moon was covered in craters, and he was able to prove that Venus was orbiting the Sun.

*A class period is considered to be one 40 to 50 minute class.

Tell students they will now find out how telescopes are used to make discoveries today. In particular, they will learn about two space telescopes, the Hubble Space Telescope and the Kepler Mission. Emphasize that they should pay attention to the specific uses of each telescope. The two telescopes share some things in common, but they are used for different purposes, and the data they send back to Earth are different.

Case Study 1: The Hubble Space Telescope

5 min

Students read about and discuss the Hubble Space Telescope.

Case Study 1: The Hubble Space Telescope

The Hubble Space Telescope is actually six separate instruments that can view the universe in many different ways. It was placed in Earth orbit during a space shuttle mission in 1990. It was designed so that astronauts could repair the telescope in space if necessary. Five space shuttle missions between 1993 and 2009 have been launched to repair or increase the capabilities of the Hubble.

The Hubble Space Telescope can do what no telescope on Earth can do—look at stars without having to look through Earth's atmosphere. In *Learning Set 3*, you learned that stars twinkle because the atmosphere distorts and scatters the light from stars. This limits the ability of

△ Guide

Describe the Hubble Space Telescope. Tell students it is a spacecraft orbiting Earth that contains six separate observational instruments. It was put in orbit by a space shuttle and has been repaired and upgraded by several space shuttle missions.

NOTES

....

....

....

....

....

....

telescopes on Earth to "see" objects that are very dim, or to view fine details on objects in space. In addition, the atmosphere blocks light at certain wavelengths from reaching the ground.

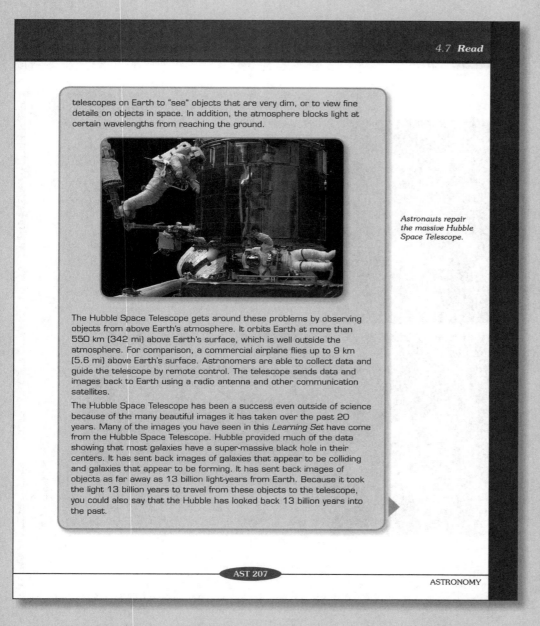

Astronauts repair the massive Hubble Space Telescope.

The Hubble Space Telescope gets around these problems by observing objects from above Earth's atmosphere. It orbits Earth at more than 550 km (342 mi) above Earth's surface, which is well outside the atmosphere. For comparison, a commercial airplane flies up to 9 km (5.6 mi) above Earth's surface. Astronomers are able to collect data and guide the telescope by remote control. The telescope sends data and images back to Earth using a radio antenna and other communication satellites.

The Hubble Space Telescope has been a success even outside of science because of the many beautiful images it has taken over the past 20 years. Many of the images you have seen in this *Learning Set* have come from the Hubble Space Telescope. Hubble provided much of the data showing that most galaxies have a super-massive black hole in their centers. It has sent back images of galaxies that appear to be colliding and galaxies that appear to be forming. It has sent back images of objects as far away as 13 billion light-years from Earth. Because it took the light 13 billion years to travel from these objects to the telescope, you could also say that the Hubble has looked back 13 billion years into the past.

Emphasize that the Hubble Space Telescope has a view of the stars undistorted by Earth's atmosphere, because it orbits outside the atmosphere. This is important, because the atmosphere distorts and scatters the light from stars and filters out light of certain wavelengths. The Hubble Space Telescope sends photographs taken from its orbit back to Earth, where scientists guide the telescope by remote control.

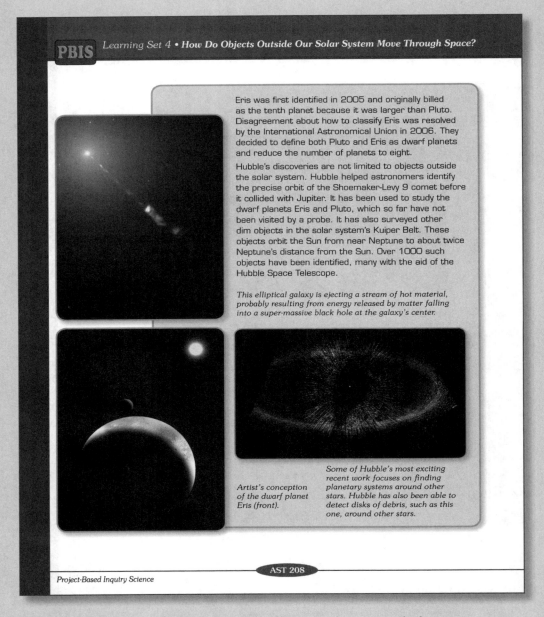

Eris was first identified in 2005 and originally billed as the tenth planet because it was larger than Pluto. Disagreement about how to classify Eris was resolved by the International Astronomical Union in 2006. They decided to define both Pluto and Eris as dwarf planets and reduce the number of planets to eight.

Hubble's discoveries are not limited to objects outside the solar system. Hubble helped astronomers identify the precise orbit of the Shoemaker-Levy 9 comet before it collided with Jupiter. It has been used to study the dwarf planets Eris and Pluto, which so far have not been visited by a probe. It has also surveyed other dim objects in the solar system's Kuiper Belt. These objects orbit the Sun from near Neptune to about twice Neptune's distance from the Sun. Over 1000 such objects have been identified, many with the aid of the Hubble Space Telescope.

This elliptical galaxy is ejecting a stream of hot material, probably resulting from energy released by matter falling into a super-massive black hole at the galaxy's center.

Artist's conception of the dwarf planet Eris (front).

Some of Hubble's most exciting recent work focuses on finding planetary systems around other stars. Hubble has also been able to detect disks of debris, such as this one, around other stars.

AST 208

Project-Based Inquiry Science

Tell students that the Hubble Space Telescope has provided important data to scientists. It provided most of the data showing galaxies that have black holes in their centers. It has sent back photographs of what appears to be galaxy creation, and of what appears to be galaxies colliding. And it has sent back photographs of objects 13 billion light-years away. It has also helped scientists observe objects within the solar system, including the Shoemaker-Levy 9 comet, which students read about earlier.

Observe

NASA Video: A Hubble Space Telescope Discovery

You will be watching a video about a recent Hubble Space Telescope discovery. The discovery took place when astronomers analyzed an image of the star Fomalhaut, which is 25 light-years from Earth. Fomalhaut, thanks to the Hubble Space Telescope, is one of the stars known to have a disk of debris around it. The video shows a Hubble image that marks the first time that astronomers have seen a certain type of object. Watch the video, taking notes as necessary. Be prepared to answer the questions below after the video is over.

Reflect

1. What was the discovery mentioned in the video? What is the significance of the discovery?

2. How do you think the Hubble Space Telescope helped make the discovery possible?

3. What further information do you think astronomers should try to find out about this new discovery?

Case Study 2: The Kepler Mission

The Kepler Mission is a telescope that will search for Earth-like planets that orbit other stars. It was launched in 2009 and will search nearby stars for planets until at least 2012. It will collect data on the planetary systems of other stars, and explore the structure and variety of the systems. The Kepler Mission will focus on the same 100,000 stars for its entire mission, measuring changes in their brightness every 30 minutes.

The Kepler Mission is named after Johannes Kepler, a German astronomer who worked in the early 17th century. He was the first to accurately describe the orbits of the planets around the Sun, summarizing his findings in what are now called Kepler's laws of planetary motion.

The method that the Kepler Mission will use is to look for planets that pass in front of stars. When a planet that is orbiting a star passes directly between the telescope and a star, a small portion of the light

AST 209

Observe: NASA Video: A Hubble Space Telescope Discovery

5 min

Students watch the NASA video on Fomalhaut.

△ Guide

Tell students they will now watch a video about a recent discovery made with the help of the Hubble Space Telescope. Emphasize that as they watch the video, students should think about how scientists made the discovery and how the Hubble Space Telescope helped.

Pause the video after 30 s, and ask students what the difference between direct and indirect observation is. How are scientists able to detect the presence of a planet indirectly? Start the video again.

Pause the video at 1:17. Ask students why it is significant when an object is near the same star in photos taken at different times. What can you conclude when an object is always near the same star? Also ask students if this is a direct or indirect observation and why. They should recognize that because the object itself is visible in the photographs, this is a direct observation.

Now show the rest of the video. When it is over, ask students what scientists knew before the discovery and what they learned from the discovery. Students should recognize that scientists knew there was a planet orbiting the star Fomalhaut before the discovery. But through the photographs, they were able to directly observe the planet. They were also able to learn that the planet was a young planet that was still forming.

Reflect

10 min

The students have a class discussion of the Reflect *questions.*

Reflect

1. What was the discovery mentioned in the video? What is the significance of the discovery?

2. How do you think the Hubble Space Telescope helped make the discovery possible?

3. What further information do you think astronomers should try to find out about this new discovery?

△ Guide

Lead a class discussion of the *Reflect* questions. Look for evidence that students understand that space telescopes like the Hubble Space Telescope make discoveries like this possible by providing photographs of objects that are too distant and dim to be seen through Earth's atmosphere.

1. Students should respond that a planet was discovered which revolved around a star, Fomalhaut. The significance was that this discovery was the first direct observation of a planet in another solar system. Previous planets' presence was inferred from data, not directly observed.

2. The Hubble Space Telescope was able to collect enough light from the planet to make it directly observable.

3. Students may wonder if there are other planets revolving around this star that are closer and might have life.

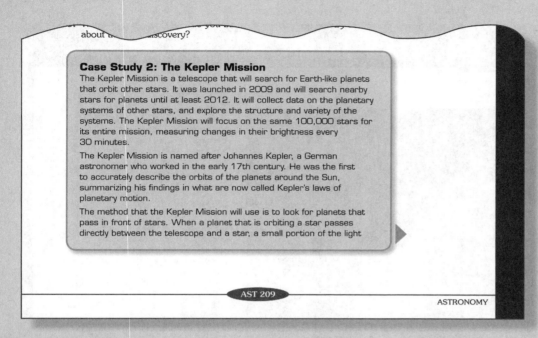

Case Study 2: The Kepler Mission

The Kepler Mission is a telescope that will search for Earth-like planets that orbit other stars. It was launched in 2009 and will search nearby stars for planets until at least 2012. It will collect data on the planetary systems of other stars, and explore the structure and variety of the systems. The Kepler Mission will focus on the same 100,000 stars for its entire mission, measuring changes in their brightness every 30 minutes.

The Kepler Mission is named after Johannes Kepler, a German astronomer who worked in the early 17th century. He was the first to accurately describe the orbits of the planets around the Sun, summarizing his findings in what are now called Kepler's laws of planetary motion.

The method that the Kepler Mission will use is to look for planets that pass in front of stars. When a planet that is orbiting a star passes directly between the telescope and a star, a small portion of the light

AST 209

ASTRONOMY

Case Study 2: The Kepler Mission

5 min

Students read about the Kepler Mission.

△ Guide

Describe the Kepler Mission telescope. Like the Hubble Space Telescope, Kepler Mission is a telescope in a spacecraft. It was launched in 2009 to search for Earth-like planets orbiting other stars.

NOTES

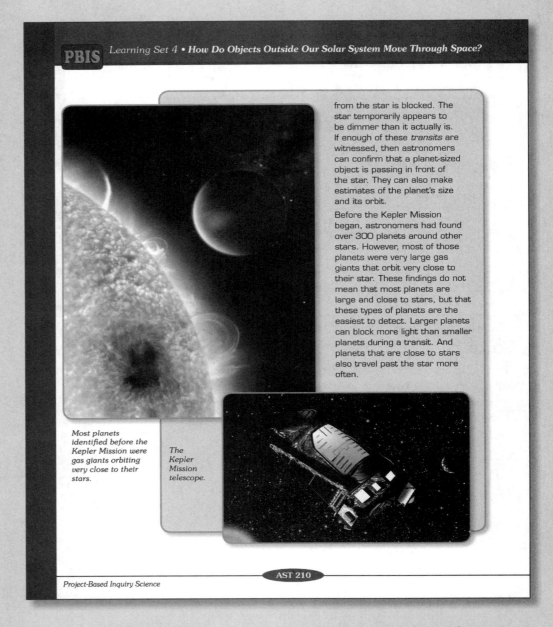

from the star is blocked. The star temporarily appears to be dimmer than it actually is. If enough of these *transits* are witnessed, then astronomers can confirm that a planet-sized object is passing in front of the star. They can also make estimates of the planet's size and its orbit.

Before the Kepler Mission began, astronomers had found over 300 planets around other stars. However, most of those planets were very large gas giants that orbit very close to their star. These findings do not mean that most planets are large and close to stars, but that these types of planets are the easiest to detect. Larger planets can block more light than smaller planets during a transit. And planets that are close to stars also travel past the star more often.

Most planets identified before the Kepler Mission were gas giants orbiting very close to their stars.

The Kepler Mission telescope.

AST 210

Project-Based Inquiry Science

Discuss how Kepler Mission looks for planets passing in front of stars. When a planet orbiting a star passes in front of the star, the star temporarily appears dimmer than it actually is. With repeated *transits* (as these events are called), scientists can verify that a planet-sized object is passing in front of the star. Observations of transits also allow scientists to estimate the planet's size and orbit.

The Kepler Mission is designed so that it will have the necessary accuracy to find planets about the size of Earth orbiting at distances that allow water to be in a liquid state. These planets are called Earth-like planets. To have this accuracy, Kepler has to be able to collect light from all the stars it is pointing at for a long time, and it has to have the ability to detect very slight changes in a star's light.

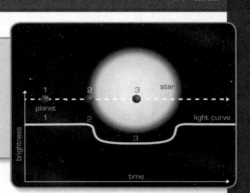

Observe

NASA Video: The Kepler Misson

You will watch a video that describes the Kepler Mission in more detail. Read the questions below before watching the video. Then, when you watch the video, take notes to prepare to answer the questions. Also, record questions about anything you find confusing or that you want to know more about.

By studying the variations in brightness of stars, or transits, astronomers can learn about the sizes and orbits of objects in space.

Reflect

1. What is an Earth-like planet? Do you think the Kepler mission will find more Earth-like planets or more Jupiter-sized planets?

2. What is the "Goldilocks Zone?" Why is this zone important to finding Earth-like planets?

3. What characteristics of a planet make it habitable? What would make it uninhabitable?

4. What advantages are there to focus on such a small area of space? What are the disadvantages?

5. A pixel is the smallest element of an image. A digital camera works by recording the amount of light that falls on an array of pixels. The pattern of brighter and darker pixels then becomes the image that you see on a display screen. Why is it important that the camera used in the Kepler Mission contains 95 million megapixels?

6. In your opinion, how likely is the mission to be successful?

AST 211

ASTRONOMY

Most of the extra-solar planets (planets outside our solar system) found before Kepler Mission are gas giants that orbit close to their star. This is because these types of planets are easier to detect. The Kepler Mission was designed to find planets the size of Earth that orbit their suns at distances that would allow liquid water to exist.

Observe: NASA Video: The Kepler Mission

15 min

Students watch the Kepler Mission video.

Observe

NASA Video: The Kepler Misson

You will watch a video that describes the Kepler Mission in more detail. Read the questions below before watching the video. Then, when you watch the video, take notes to prepare to answer the questions. Also, record questions about anything you find confusing or that you want to know more about.

By studying the variations in brightness of stars, or transits, astronomers can learn about the sizes and orbits of objects in space.

△ Guide and Evaluate

Tell students they will now watch a video showing the objectives of Kepler Mission and how Kepler Mission works. Go over the *Reflect* questions with the class before showing the video. Emphasize that students should think about these questions as they watch the video. Tell them to consider the differences between what Kepler Mission is looking for and what the Hubble Space Telescope is looking for.

Pause the video at 1:20 and ask students why scientists are interested in the habitable zone. Why is water in a liquid state important? Help them understand that life as we know it depends on water in a liquid state. Start the video again.

Pause the video at 1:58 and ask students what a transit is. They should understand that a transit is when a planet passes in front of a star and blocks some of the light from that star, so that the star appears temporarily dimmer from Earth. Start the video again.

Pause the video at 3:55 and ask students why scientists would want a camera with high resolution in Kepler. What does the number of pixels in the camera have to do with the resolution? Start the video again.

Pause the video at 4:40 and ask students whether Kepler will look at different regions of the sky or whether it will always be focused on one part of the sky. They should understand that it will always be focused on the same area of the sky. Emphasize that this portion of the sky is about the size of the portion that would be covered if you held your hand out at arm's length. Start the video again.

Pause the video at 5:30 and ask students roughly how many stars are in Kepler's field of view. Is the number in the hundreds, the thousands, or the millions? Emphasize that it is in the millions. Ask them how many of those stars are likely to have planets Kepler will be able to detect by their transits. This number is probably in the tens of thousands (between 1 and 10 percent of the 6.5 million stars in Kepler's field of view). Point out that the number of stars with interesting planets is expected to be lower still, perhaps a few thousand. Start the video again.

You may wish to replay segments of the video that were difficult for students before continuing.

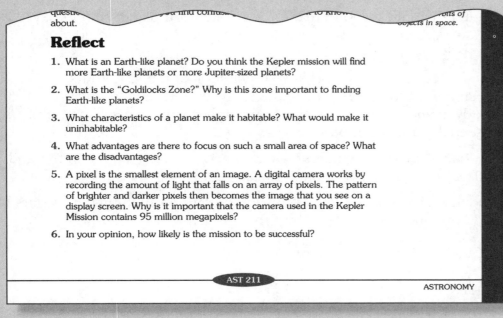

question... ...you find confus... ...t to know... ...its of
about. ...objects in space.

Reflect

1. What is an Earth-like planet? Do you think the Kepler mission will find more Earth-like planets or more Jupiter-sized planets?

2. What is the "Goldilocks Zone?" Why is this zone important to finding Earth-like planets?

3. What characteristics of a planet make it habitable? What would make it uninhabitable?

4. What advantages are there to focus on such a small area of space? What are the disadvantages?

5. A pixel is the smallest element of an image. A digital camera works by recording the amount of light that falls on an array of pixels. The pattern of brighter and darker pixels then becomes the image that you see on a display screen. Why is it important that the camera used in the Kepler Mission contains 95 million megapixels?

6. In your opinion, how likely is the mission to be successful?

AST 211

ASTRONOMY

Reflect

15 min

Students have a class discussion of the Reflect *questions.*

△ Guide and Evaluate

Lead a class discussion of the *Reflect* questions. Listen for evidence that students understand that scientists are using Kepler to look for planets that are as large as Earth, but smaller than Jupiter, and are far enough from their suns that any water on them will not vaporize, but near enough so that it will not freeze. To be habitable, a planet would need to have liquid water. For life as we know it to exist, students might also think about the importance of gravity and a planet's composition. If a planet were too small, it might not be able to sustain oceans or an atmosphere, making it unlikely for life to develop. If the planet were composed of gases, life as we know it might be unlikely to develop.

Students should understand that it is necessary for Kepler to stay focused on one region of the sky so it can detect patterns in repeated transits of individual stars. Emphasize that if Kepler observed only a single transit of an individual star, scientists would be unable to determine if the transit was the result of a planet orbiting that star or some other object coming between Kepler and the star.

1. Students should respond that an Earth-like planet will be approximately the size of Earth and about the same distance from a similar sun. It is more likely that the Kepler Mission will find more Jupiter-size planets than Earth-size planets because they are bigger.

2. Students should know that "the Goldilocks Zone" is that region in a solar system where water is not entirely frozen ("not too cold") and not entirely vapor ("not too hot"), but just right for life as we know it.

3. Students should respond that to be habitable, a planet should have an atmosphere and a temperature range that includes liquid water.

4. Students should respond that the Kepler Mission is investigating a small region of space because it will look at the same stars several times to see if evidence of a planet transiting its sun. The disadvantage of using this technique is that only a small portion of potential planets can be seen.

5. Students should reply that 95 mega pixels is a very large number and will permit a higher-resolution image.

6. Students' answers will vary, but should consider the number of stars surveyed and the time-length of the mission.

NOTES

....

....

....

....

....

....

....

....

....

....

....

....

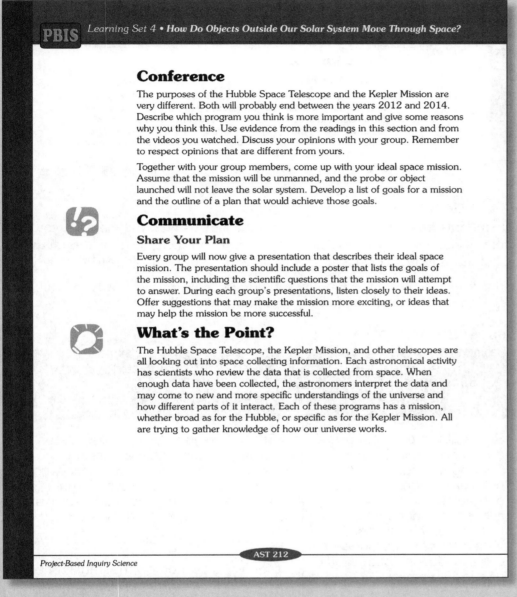

Conference

The purposes of the Hubble Space Telescope and the Kepler Mission are very different. Both will probably end between the years 2012 and 2014. Describe which program you think is more important and give some reasons why you think this. Use evidence from the readings in this section and from the videos you watched. Discuss your opinions with your group. Remember to respect opinions that are different from yours.

Together with your group members, come up with your ideal space mission. Assume that the mission will be unmanned, and the probe or object launched will not leave the solar system. Develop a list of goals for a mission and the outline of a plan that would achieve those goals.

Communicate

Share Your Plan

Every group will now give a presentation that describes their ideal space mission. The presentation should include a poster that lists the goals of the mission, including the scientific questions that the mission will attempt to answer. During each group's presentations, listen closely to their ideas. Offer suggestions that may make the mission more exciting, or ideas that may help the mission be more successful.

What's the Point?

The Hubble Space Telescope, the Kepler Mission, and other telescopes are all looking out into space collecting information. Each astronomical activity has scientists who review the data that is collected from space. When enough data have been collected, the astronomers interpret the data and may come to new and more specific understandings of the universe and how different parts of it interact. Each of these programs has a mission, whether broad as for the Hubble, or specific as for the Kepler Mission. All are trying to gather knowledge of how our universe works.

AST 212

Project-Based Inquiry Science

Conference

10 min

Groups develop plans for a space mission.

△ Guide

Have students work with their groups to decide whether they think the Hubble Space Telescope or the Kepler Mission is more important, and to develop descriptions of their reasons for this conclusion. Emphasize that students need to discuss differences of opinion respectfully.

Tell students that when they have finished with this, they should develop an ideal space mission. The mission should be unmanned, and the spacecraft should not leave the solar system. Have groups develop lists of goals for the mission and outlines of a plan to achieve those goals.

As groups work, monitor their progress and ask them what ideas they discussed. Ask them what reasons support their ideas.

Communicate: Share Your Plan

15 min

Groups present their plans.

Communicate

Share Your Plan

Every group will now give a presentation that describes their ideal space mission. The presentation should include a poster that lists the goals of the mission, including the scientific questions that the mission will attempt to answer. During each group's presentations, listen closely to their ideas. Offer suggestions that may make the mission more exciting, or ideas that may help the mission be more successful.

△ Guide

Let students know they will now share their plans with the class. Have them make posters listing the goals of the mission and the questions the mission will attempt to answer. Then have groups present their plans to the class.

As each group presents, students should ask questions to clarify anything they do not understand, and they should respectfully offer suggestions.

Assessment Options

Targeted Concepts, Skills, and Nature of Science	How do I know if students got it?
Scientists often collaborate and share their findings. Sharing findings makes new information available and helps scientists refine their ideas and build on others' ideas. When another person's or group's idea is used, credit needs to be given.	**ASK:** When your group collaborated to plan your ideal space mission, what goals did your group agree were most important to achieve? What challenges to achieving the mission's goals did your group anticipate? **LISTEN:** Students' answers will vary. This question is intended to focus students' attention on the importance of identifying criteria and constraints when planning a mission.
Scientists must keep clear, accurate and descriptive records of what they do so they can share their work with others; consider what they did, why they did it, and what they want to do next.	**ASK:** How did your group decide upon the order in which mission goals would be listed on the poster you created? **LISTEN:** Students' answers will vary. This question is intended to engage students in evaluating the way in which they organized information for their class presentation.

Targeted Concepts, Skills, and Nature of Science	How do I know if students got it?
Humans perceive the universe by the radiation it emits. Technological advances have greatly extended the scope of human perception and led to the observations upon which our current theories of the universe are based.	**ASK:** Summarize the advantages of space-based telescopes over Earth-based telescopes. **LISTEN:** Students' answers should include the resolution of space-based telescopes is not limited by the turbulence of Earth's atmosphere that causes stars to "twinkle" and space-based telescopes can observe infrared and ultraviolet radiation that are strongly absorbed by Earth's atmosphere. **ASK:** In addition to an optical telescope, what other technologically advanced instruments comprise the Hubble Space Telescope? **LISTEN:** Students should name specialized digital cameras such as the Wide Field and Planetary Camera and the Faint Object Camera; spectrographs, such as the High Resolution Spectrograph and the Faint Object Spectrograph; and a High Speed Photometer.
Humankind's need to explore continues to lead to the development of knowledge and understanding of the nature of the universe.	**ASK:** Describe several new discoveries about the universe that were made possible by information obtained with the Hubble Space Telescope and the Kepler Mission telescope? **LISTEN:** Students' answers will vary, but may include black holes at the centers of galaxies, galactic collisions, images of dwarf planets and Kuiper Belt objects.

NOTES

....

Teacher Reflection Questions

- What were the most difficult and most satisfying parts of using the PBIS approach toward inquiry? Why?

- How do you see your role with this Unit? How does that compare with how students may see your role?

- Did students understand the concept of image resolution and how the number of pixels affects resolution? How can you present this differently in the future?

- Which concepts did students have the most difficulty in comprehending? How might you better prepare them?

NOTES

_____

_____

_____

_____

_____

_____

_____

_____

_____

_____

_____

Back to the Big Question

How Can You Know if Objects in Space Will Collide?

◀ *1 class period*

A class period is considered to be one 40 to 50 minute class.

Overview

The section begins with students updating their *Big Question* page with information about objects outside the solar system and their possible role in collisions gained throughout the *Learning Set*. Students assume the role of science consultants to a movie producer and are charged with writing a report for the movie producer proposing a collision between space objects that could be used as the basis for a popular movie. Students work individually to propose one idea for a collision and to create an explanation that will convince the movie producer that the collision idea is realistic. Students then present their collision idea and supporting explanation to their group. After each group member's proposal has been considered, students collaborate to reach consensus on a collision to suggest for the movie and record the details of this collision on a poster. The group then collaborates to revise the explanation of the likelihood of a collision in space created at the end of *Learning Set 3* so that it will convince the movie producer that its collision idea is realistic. Students present their ideas and revised explanations to the class and reflect on how their explanation compares with those presented by other groups.

Targeted Concepts, Skills, and Nature of Science	Performance Expectations
Scientists often collaborate and share their findings. Sharing findings makes new information available and helps scientists refine their ideas and build on others' ideas. When another person's or group's idea is used, credit needs to be given.	Students share their individual ideas and supporting explanations for a realistic collision between space objects that could be used in a popular movie with their group.
	Students collaborate in groups to evaluate one another's ideas and supporting explanations for a collision that could realistically take place in space and reach consensus on a proposal.
	Groups share their proposed collision and supporting explanations for why it is realistic with the class.
	Students evaluate the proposals shared by other groups and offer constructive feedback.

Targeted Concepts, Skills, and Nature of Science	Performance Expectations
Scientists must keep clear, accurate and descriptive records of what they do so they can share their work with others; consider what they did, why they did it, and what they want to do next.	Students record their claim about whether the space objects in their proposal will collide along with any supporting evidence and science knowledge on a *Create Your Explanation* page. Students create a poster summarizing the details of each object involved in their proposed collision. Students write a report proposing a collision between space objects that could be used in a popular movie and an explanation that will convince the movie producer that the collision is realistic.

Materials	
2 per student	*Create Your Explanation* page
1 per group	Poster board Set of markers, or other poster-making supplies
1 per class	Class *Project Board*

Activity Setup and Preparation

Tell students beforehand that the *Create Your Explanation* page completed at the end of *Learning Set 3* will be needed for this activity.

Homework Options

Reflection

- **Science Content:** Summarize the relevant details of each of the objects involved in your group's proposed collision. *(Students' answers will vary, but should include each object's location, mass, path or orbit, speed and direction of motion, the effects of gravity and the effects of nearby objects.)*

- **Science Process:** What characteristics of a good explanation did you look for when you evaluated other groups' explanations,? *(Students should cite a claim, evidence and science knowledge that supported the claim, and a statement connecting the claim with the supporting evidence and science knowledge.)*

Learning Set 4

Back to the Big Question

How can you know if objects in space will collide?

You have considered objects within the solar system colliding with other space objects within the solar system. You now know enough about the rest of the Milky Way galaxy and other galaxies to consider the possibility of objects from outside of our solar system colliding with a solar-system object. Add what you know about these types of collisions to your *Big Question* page.

Revise Your Explanation

Now, you will revise your explanation of how you know if two space objects will collide. You have learned a lot since you last revised your explanation, so you will probably need to make several changes. Use a new *Create Your Explanation* page for your revised explanation. Remember that a good explanation has several parts to it.

Start by revising the claim your group agreed upon at the end of *Learning Set 3*. You will need to revise it to include what you now know about space objects outside of our solar system. Then, refine the evidence and science knowledge to support the new parts of your claim.

Develop an explanation statement that combines your claim, evidence, and science knowledge. This should state why you need all the different kinds of data you mention in your claim to predict if two space objects will collide.

Make sure the explanation is accurate and complete. Use what you now know about the motion of stars and other objects in the Milky Way galaxy to check the accuracy of your explanation statement. You may also consider what you learned about types of stars, how stars can change, and the different types of galaxies.

AST 213

ASTRONOMY

Learning Set 4

Back to the Big Question

10 min

Students update their Big Questions *pages.*

△ Guide

Tell students they have now learned enough about other bodies in space and the structures of the solar system and galaxies to consider the possibility of objects from outside the solar system colliding with a solar-system object or with each other. Have them record information about objects outside the solar system and how they might affect space collisions on their *Big Questions* pages.

*A class period is considered to be one 40 to 50 minute class.

Revise Your Explanation

15 min

Groups revise their explanations of the likelihood of a collision in space.

Revise Your Explanation

Now, you will revise your explanation of how you know if two space objects will collide. You have learned a lot since you last revised your explanation, so you will probably need to make several changes. Use a new *Create Your Explanation* page for your revised explanation. Remember that a good explanation has several parts to it.

Start by revising the claim your group agreed upon at the end of *Learning Set 3*. You will need to revise it to include what you now know about space objects outside of our solar system. Then, refine the evidence and science knowledge to support the new parts of your claim.

Develop an explanation statement that combines your claim, evidence, and science knowledge. This should state why you need all the different kinds of data you mention in your claim to predict if two space objects will collide.

Make sure the explanation is accurate and complete. Use what you now know about the motion of stars and other objects in the Milky Way galaxy to check the accuracy of your explanation statement. You may also consider what you learned about types of stars, how stars can change, and the different types of galaxies.

△ Guide

Distribute *Create Your Explanation* pages and tell students they will work with their groups to revise the explanation of the likelihood of a collision in space that they last revised and expanded at the end of *Learning Set 3*. Emphasize that they will use their revised explanations in their report to the movie producer. Also emphasize that the report to the movie producer should both convince the movie producer and answer the *Big Question* of the Unit, *How can you know if objects in space will collide?*

Draw students' attention to the specific parts of the explanation they will need to revise. They will need to begin by modifying the claim to reflect the specific characteristics of the objects involved in their proposed collision. Then they will need to gather new supporting evidence and science knowledge to support the modified claim. Finally, they will need to use reasons to connect the evidence and science knowledge to the claim. Students may already have identified some reasons why the evidence supports the claim when they chose their final proposal.

△ Guide and Assess

As groups revise their explanations, monitor their progress and ask them what ideas they have discussed. Emphasize that they should discuss how accurate they think their explanation is, and they should look for ways to make it more accurate.

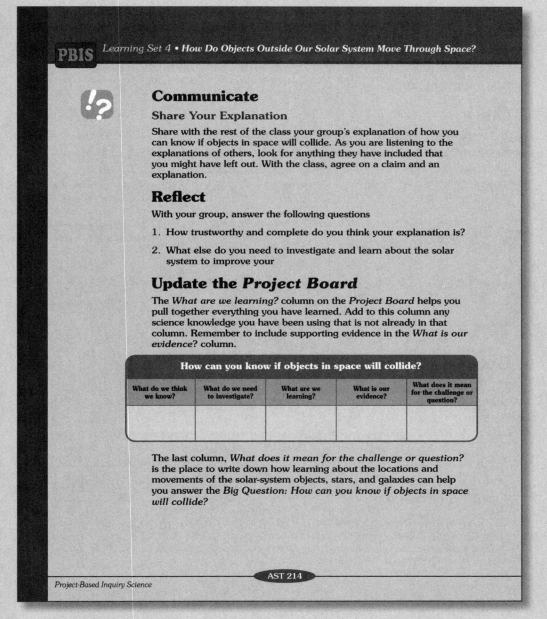

Communicate

Share Your Explanation

Share with the rest of the class your group's explanation of how you can know if objects in space will collide. As you are listening to the explanations of others, look for anything they have included that you might have left out. With the class, agree on a claim and an explanation.

Reflect

With your group, answer the following questions

1. How trustworthy and complete do you think your explanation is?

2. What else do you need to investigate and learn about the solar system to improve your

Update the *Project Board*

The *What are we learning?* column on the *Project Board* helps you pull together everything you have learned. Add to this column any science knowledge you have been using that is not already in that column. Remember to include supporting evidence in the *What is our evidence?* column.

How can you know if objects in space will collide?				
What do we think we know?	What do we need to investigate?	What are we learning?	What is our evidence?	What does it mean for the challenge or question?

The last column, *What does it mean for the challenge or question?* is the place to write down how learning about the locations and movements of the solar-system objects, stars, and galaxies can help you answer the *Big Question: How can you know if objects in space will collide?*

Communicate: Share Your Explanation

15 min

Students present their explanations to the class.

⬡ Get Going

Let students know they will present their explanations to the class. Have them make posters showing their claims, evidence, supporting science knowledge, and explanation statements.

Then have each group present their proposal and explanation to the class. Each group should begin by using their first poster to describe the details of their proposal. Then they should present their explanation using their second poster. They should tell the class their evidence and describe how it supports their claim.

△ Guide

Emphasize that as students listen to groups' explanations, they should think about how well the explanations connect the evidence and science knowledge to the claims. They should also evaluate how convincing the explanations are. Are they convinced? Would the movie producer be convinced?

Reflect

10 min

Students answer the Reflect questions.

Reflect

With your group, answer the following questions

1. How trustworthy and complete do you think your explanation is?

2. What else do you need to investigate and learn about the solar system to improve your

○ Get Going

When all groups have presented their explanations, have students work with their groups to answer the *Reflect* questions. Emphasize that they should use this as an opportunity to evaluate their explanations and the evidence that they have based on what they learned from other groups' explanations.

1. Student responses should indicate that they have done their best, given the time constraints. If they feel some pieces are missing, they should mention that.

2. Student answers will vary but should be reasonable.

NOTES

Update the *Project Board*

The *What are we learning?* column on the *Project Board* helps you pull together everything you have learned. Add to this column any science knowledge you have been using that is not already in that column. Remember to include supporting evidence in the *What is our evidence?* column.

How can you know if objects in space will collide?				
What do we think we know?	What do we need to investigate?	What are we learning?	What is our evidence?	What does it mean for the challenge or question?

The last column, *What does it mean for the challenge or question?* is the place to write down how learning about the locations and movements of the solar-system objects, stars, and galaxies can help you answer the *Big Question: How can you know if objects in space will collide?*

Update the Project Board

10 min

Students have a class discussion to update the Project Board.

△ Guide

When groups have had time to discuss the *Reflect* questions, ask them what science knowledge they can add to the *What are we learning?* column on the *Project Board*. Record their answers on the *Project Board* and have them record their answers on their own *Project Board* pages.

Then ask students how this new information can be applied to the *Big Question: How can you know if objects in space will collide?* Record their responses in the *What does it mean for the challenge or question?* column.

NOTES

_____

_____

_____

_____

_____

_____

Assessment Options

Targeted Concepts, Skills, and Nature of Science	How do I know if students got it?
Scientists often collaborate and share their findings. Sharing findings makes new information available and helps scientists refine their ideas and build on others' ideas. When another person's or group's idea is used, credit needs to be given.	**ASK:** What negotiations happened as your group was working toward consensus on the collision to propose to the movie producer? **LISTEN:** Students' answers will vary. This question is meant to engage students in an evaluation of their group process. **ASK:** Rank the explanations presented by other groups according to their persuasiveness. **LISTEN:** Students' answers will vary. This question is meant to engage students in an evaluation of the explanations presented by other groups in the class.

NOTES

....

....

....

....

....

....

Targeted Concepts, Skills, and Nature of Science	How do I know if students got it?
Scientists must keep clear, accurate and descriptive records of what they do so they can share their work with others; consider what they did, why they did it, and what they want to do next.	**ASK:** Anticipate the supporting evidence and science knowledge that would most likely persuade a movie producer that your proposed collision was realistic. **LISTEN:** Students' answers will vary, but should refer to evidence that the paths of the objects are likely to intersect and that the speed and mass of the objects involved would result in a spectacular collision. **ASK:** When you designed your poster, how did you decide on the order in which to present the characteristics of the objects involved in your proposed collision? **LISTEN:** Students' answers will vary, but may indicate that they chose an order that would indicate that the collision was realistic and would result in a high-interest collision as part of a movie. **ASK:** How was the *Create Your Explanation* page useful when writing your report for the movie producer? **LISTEN:** Students should describe how the *Create Your Explanation* page provided an outline of the major points to be made in the report.

Teacher Reflection Questions

- What difficulties did students have developing explanations? How did you address these? What ideas do you have for the future?

- Would modeling an explanation be beneficial for the students? What ideas do you have for modeling explanations?

- What difficulties, if any, did you have managing the class when they were updating the *Project Board?* What ideas do you have for managing *Project Board* updates?

NOTES

Answer the Big Question

How Can You Know if Objects in Space Will Collide?

◀ *1 class period*

A class period is considered to be one 40 to 50 minute class.

Overview

Students synthesize and apply the understandings gained in this Unit to answering the *Big Question*. Students are assigned to write a report for a movie producer consisting of three parts: a proposed collision between objects in space for a movie script, an explanation of why the collision is realistic for use in a popular movie, and a description of what the collision will look like on screen. The Unit concludes with students presenting their report to the class and the class discusses what they learned from the experience.

Materials	
1 per group	Poster board Markers or crayons for making poster
1 per class	Class *Project Board*

Homework Options

Reflection

- **Science Process:** How did you decide the priority you would give to the key elements of your pitch to the movie producer? What was difficult about making those decisions? *(This question is meant to get students to reflect on how they made choices in their final proposal, what was effective and what was not.)*

- **Science Process:** Describe how you used both the *Project Board* and the *Big Question* page in preparing the presentation about your collision to the class. *(Student should recognize that their descriptions utilized information from both sources and the importance of keeping records of what they have learned and supporting evidence.)*

NOTES

....

....

....

....

....

....

....

....

....

....

....

....

....

....

Answer the Big Question

How Can You Know if Objects in Space Will Collide?

Now you will have the opportunity to pull all of your learning together. In this Unit, you have learned about many different objects in space. You are now going to write a report for a movie producer describing the collision between two space objects, and explaining why the collision is realistic for use in a movie. The report will have three parts. *Part 1* will present the possible collision you suggest. *Part 2* will explain why this is a realistic suggestion. *Part 3* should convince the movie producer that this movie will be exciting and can be a hit. To do this, you will need to describe how the collision would look to a character in the movie or to a person in the audience.

Prepare to Write Your Report

Remember that the producer is counting on you, the science consultant, to come up with an idea for a possible collision that will make the movie realistic. The report has several parts.

Part 1: Propose a possible collision between space objects to be used in the movie. It should be realistic and affect Earth, the Sun, or the Moon.

Part 2: Construct a claim and explanation of why the collision you chose is realistic and would affect Earth, the Sun, and the Moon.

Part 3: Convince the producer that the collision you chose is scientifically accurate. To do this, develop an explanation statement that brings together your claim, evidence, and science knowledge. It should state why you need all the different kinds of data you mention in your claim to predict if two space objects will collide.

AST 215

ASTRONOMY

Answer the Big Question

How Can You Know if Objects in Space Will Collide?

5 min

Students are introduced to the activity.

△ Guide

Tell students they will now write a report to propose and convince a movie producer to use a certain collision that would be scientifically accurate and would be a popular movie. Tell them their reports will have three parts: the proposal, an explanation of why it is realistic, and a description of how it will look on screen, which should convince the producer that it will be exciting.

*A class period is considered to be one 40 to 50 minute class.

Prepare to Write Your Report

10 min

Students go through the process of preparing their report.

person in the audience.

Prepare to Write Your Report

Remember that the producer is counting on you, the science consultant, to come up with an idea for a possible collision that will make the movie realistic. The report has several parts.

Part 1: Propose a possible collision between space objects to be used in the movie. It should be realistic and affect Earth, the Sun, or the Moon.

Part 2: Construct a claim and explanation of why the collision you chose is realistic and would affect Earth, the Sun, and the Moon.

Part 3: Convince the producer that the collision you chose is scientifically accurate. To do this, develop an explanation statement that brings together your claim, evidence, and science knowledge. It should state why you need all the different kinds of data you mention in your claim to predict if two space objects will collide.

○ Engage

Describe to students the scenario for this report. A movie producer wants to make a movie featuring a collision in space and needs to know what kind of space collision would be possible and realistic. Students will be science consultants to the producer, and will develop proposals for what kind of space collision would be realistic, along with explanations for why they would be realistic. Students need to write a report proposing a collision that could be used, along with an explanation of why the proposed collision is realistic.

Ask students what kind of collision between space objects they think would be good in a movie. Tell them that thinking about this question is a good starting point for developing proposals.

Then tell them that they will first complete the proposal and then write an explanation supporting the proposal.

NOTES

....

....

....

....

PBIS

Choose a Collision

Each member in your group should propose one idea for a collision that could be used in a movie. Remember that you will need to convince a movie producer that your idea is realistic and dramatic. Make suggestions to improve everyone else's proposals and listen carefully to the ideas the rest of the group has about your proposal.

After everyone's proposal has been considered, the group will work together to reach agreement on which collision will be used for your report. Decide together which idea is most realistic and dramatic or develop a new idea based on group members' proposals. Record the details of this collision on a poster. Make sure to include relevant details for each object: location, mass, path or orbit, speed, direction of motion, the effects of gravity, and the effects of other nearby objects.

Revise Your Explanation

You must now develop a final claim and explanation that tells what data and methods scientist use to predict if two space objects will collide. You will need to use those types of data to support your collision choice. Begin by developing a claim that states what makes your collision realistic. You will use this explanation to answer the Big Question and help you answer your report.

Make a list of factors that should be considered, such as:

- the locations of the objects

- the mass of each object

- the paths or orbits of the objects

- the speed of each object and the direction of motion when the collision occurs

- the effects of gravity, perhaps from nearby massive objects

Communicate

Use the feedback from the class when developing your final explanation. Think about anything other class member thought you might have left out or could make clearer.

Choose a Collision

5 min

Students choose a collision to describe to the movie producer.

△ Guide

In groups, students will generate ideas for a realistic collision within the solar system which will affect the Earth, Moon, or the Sun. Students will discuss the various possibilities and then select one scenario. Have them develop the idea completely with full details on location, mass, path/orbit, speed, direction, gravity effects, and effect on nearby objects. Emphasize that they will report their scene to the class.

Revise Your Explanation

5 min

Students revise their explanation about how scientists know if two objects will collide.

> ### Revise Your Explanation
>
> You must now develop a final claim and explanation that tells what data and methods scientist use to predict if two space objects will collide. You will need to use those types of data to support your collision choice. Begin by developing a claim that states what makes your collision realistic. You will use this explanation to answer the Big Question and help you answer your report.
>
> Make a list of factors that should be considered, such as:
>
> - the locations of the objects
> - the mass of each object
> - the paths or orbits of the objects
> - the speed of each object and the direction of motion when the collision occurs
> - the effects of gravity, perhaps from nearby massive objects

△ Guide

Have students review their earlier claim and explanation so that they can make a final revision. They should choose an explanation that is supported by the data. Remind them that they will be reporting to the class.

Communicate

15 min

Students present their proposals and receive feedback from the class.

> ### Communicate
>
> Use the feedback from the class when developing your final explanation. Think about anything other class member thought you might have left out or could make clearer.

⬡ Get Going

Have students present their proposals and explanations to their assigned groups. As each student presents, the other members of the group should think about whether and how they could convince a movie producer that the idea is realistic. They should think about whether the described collision could occur and how it would occur, and they should consider the factors listed in their text. Emphasize that students should try to contribute to each other's proposals and explanations by suggesting evidence that might be used and other ways to improve the proposals.

When everyone in a group has presented, the groups should discuss which proposal should be used in the report. Emphasize that students need to respect each other's ideas.

When they reach agreement, the group should create a poster showing the details of the collision they agreed upon. The poster should show the location, mass, path or orbit, speed, and direction of each object involved, as well as the effects of gravity from each object and nearby objects.

☐ **Assess**

As groups work, monitor their progress. Pay attention to how students are contributing to the work of their group. Students should offer constructive comments about each other's proposals.

NOTES

_____

_____

_____

_____

_____

_____

_____

_____

_____

_____

_____

_____

Write Your Report

10 min

Students work with their groups to write their final reports.

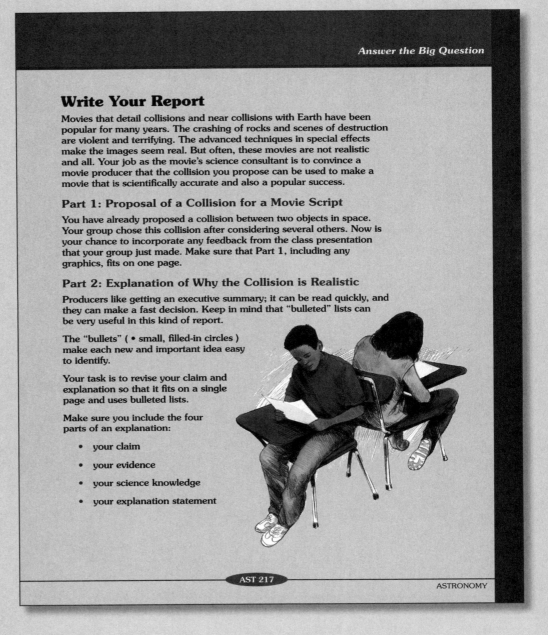

Write Your Report

Movies that detail collisions and near collisions with Earth have been popular for many years. The crashing of rocks and scenes of destruction are violent and terrifying. The advanced techniques in special effects make the images seem real. But often, these movies are not realistic and all. Your job as the movie's science consultant is to convince a movie producer that the collision you propose can be used to make a movie that is scientifically accurate and also a popular success.

Part 1: Proposal of a Collision for a Movie Script

You have already proposed a collision between two objects in space. Your group chose this collision after considering several others. Now is your chance to incorporate any feedback from the class presentation that your group just made. Make sure that Part 1, including any graphics, fits on one page.

Part 2: Explanation of Why the Collision is Realistic

Producers like getting an executive summary; it can be read quickly, and they can make a fast decision. Keep in mind that "bulleted" lists can be very useful in this kind of report.

The "bullets" (• small, filled-in circles) make each new and important idea easy to identify.

Your task is to revise your claim and explanation so that it fits on a single page and uses bulleted lists.

Make sure you include the four parts of an explanation:

- your claim
- your evidence
- your science knowledge
- your explanation statement

AST 217

ASTRONOMY

△ Guide

Discuss how students will construct each part. For Part 1, they should work with their groups to construct an improved proposal for a collision in space using the feedback they got from their class presentations. Their final proposal should fit on one page.

For Part 2, they should work with their groups to revise the explanations they created. The new, revised explanation should use a bulleted list, and it should fit on one page. Emphasize that the bulleted lists should make the explanations easier to read quickly. Remind students that each explanation needs to include a claim, evidence, science knowledge, and an explanation statement linking the evidence and science knowledge to the claim.

NOTES

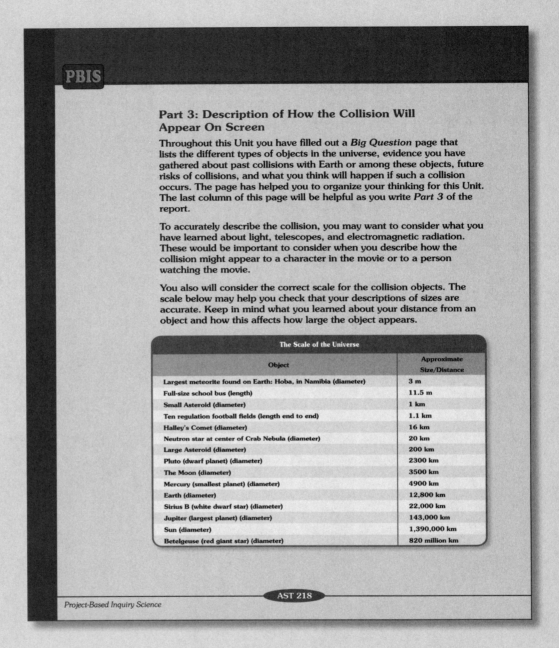

Part 3: Description of How the Collision Will Appear On Screen

Throughout this Unit you have filled out a *Big Question* page that lists the different types of objects in the universe, evidence you have gathered about past collisions with Earth or among these objects, future risks of collisions, and what you think will happen if such a collision occurs. The page has helped you to organize your thinking for this Unit. The last column of this page will be helpful as you write *Part 3* of the report.

To accurately describe the collision, you may want to consider what you have learned about light, telescopes, and electromagnetic radiation. These would be important to consider when you describe how the collision might appear to a character in the movie or to a person watching the movie.

You also will consider the correct scale for the collision objects. The scale below may help you check that your descriptions of sizes are accurate. Keep in mind what you learned about your distance from an object and how this affects how large the object appears.

The Scale of the Universe	
Object	**Approximate Size/Distance**
Largest meteorite found on Earth: Hoba, in Namibia (diameter)	3 m
Full-size school bus (length)	11.5 m
Small Asteroid (diameter)	1 km
Ten regulation football fields (length end to end)	1.1 km
Halley's Comet (diameter)	16 km
Neutron star at center of Crab Nebula (diameter)	20 km
Large Asteroid (diameter)	200 km
Pluto (dwarf planet) (diameter)	2300 km
The Moon (diameter)	3500 km
Mercury (smallest planet) (diameter)	4900 km
Earth (diameter)	12,800 km
Sirius B (white dwarf star) (diameter)	22,000 km
Jupiter (largest planet) (diameter)	143,000 km
Sun (diameter)	1,390,000 km
Betelgeuse (red giant star) (diameter)	820 million km

For Part 3, students should develop descriptions of how the collision they propose would appear to characters in a movie and how it would appear on a movie screen. To do this, they should think about everything they have learned about light, telescopes, and the appearance of objects moving through the universe. They should refer to their *Big Question* page to help them with this.

⬡ Get Going

Give students a time frame and have them get started. Let students know that when they have completed their reports, they will pitch them to you as if you were the movie producer. They should be prepared to quickly describe the report and to defend it.

△ Guide

As groups work on their reports, monitor their progress and help them with any difficulties they encounter.

NOTES

Communicate: Give Your Report

20 min

Groups "pitch" their reports to the movie producer.

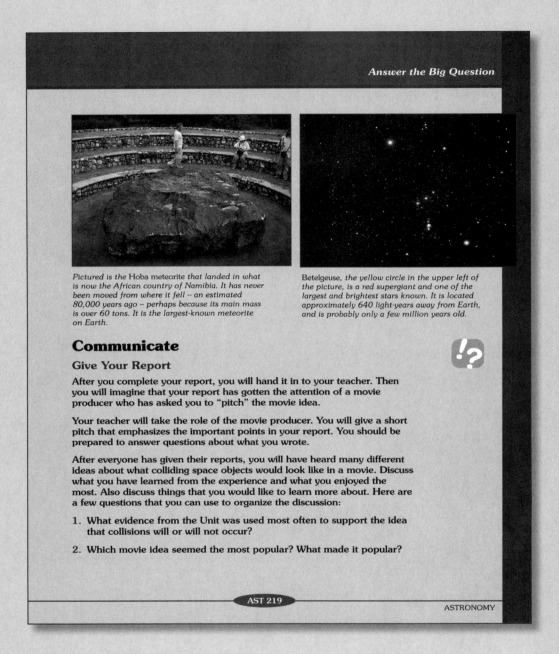

Pictured is the Hoba meteorite that landed in what is now the African country of Namibia. It has never been moved from where it fell -- an estimated 80,000 years ago -- perhaps because its main mass is over 60 tons. It is the largest-known meteorite on Earth.

Betelgeuse, the yellow circle in the upper left of the picture, is a red supergiant and one of the largest and brightest stars known. It is located approximately 640 light-years away from Earth, and is probably only a few million years old.

Communicate

Give Your Report

After you complete your report, you will hand it in to your teacher. Then you will imagine that your report has gotten the attention of a movie producer who has asked you to "pitch" the movie idea.

Your teacher will take the role of the movie producer. You will give a short pitch that emphasizes the important points in your report. You should be prepared to answer questions about what you wrote.

After everyone has given their reports, you will have heard many different ideas about what colliding space objects would look like in a movie. Discuss what you have learned from the experience and what you enjoyed the most. Also discuss things that you would like to learn more about. Here are a few questions that you can use to organize the discussion:

1. What evidence from the Unit was used most often to support the idea that collisions will or will not occur?

2. Which movie idea seemed the most popular? What made it popular?

AST 219

ASTRONOMY

△ Guide and Assess

Have groups pitch their reports to you. You may wish to have groups pitch their reports as they complete them, rather than having them hand them in and waiting for all groups to complete their reports.

As each group pitches their report, listen for evidence they have used feedback from the class to revise their proposal.

Also note whether groups used feedback they got from the class to revise their explanations. If the class suggested evidence or science knowledge that would be helpful, this should now be included. If the class thought the evidence and science knowledge available was insufficient to support the group's claim, then the claim should have been modified accordingly.

Assess how students used what they have learned about how we perceive objects in space—how we perceive light, how telescopes help perceive objects from space, and scale—to describe how the collision they propose would appear to a character in a movie and on screen. They should have considered the information from their *Big Question* pages and information from the *Project Board*.

NOTES

Project-Based Inquiry Science

AST 220

Teacher Reflection Questions

- What were the most difficult and most satisfying parts of using the PBIS approach toward inquiry? Why?

- How do you see your role with this Unit? How does that compare with how students may see your role?

Blackline Masters

Astronomy Blackline Masters

*Number indicates Learning Set.section.sequence within section

Impact Crater Experiment Planning Guide

Name:_____ Date:_____

Group:_____

Question

What question are you investigating and answering with this experiment?

Prediction

What you think the answer is and why do you think that?

Variable Identification

- What variable will you manipulate (change) in your experiment?

- What conditions and procedures will you keep the same (hold constant or control) in your experiment?

- What characteristics of each crater will you observe or measure?

- How many trials will you do for each value of your manipulated variable?

Procedure and Data

Write detailed instructions for how to conduct the experiment. Include the following:

- what object or objects you will drop or throw into the tub.

- how you will drop or throw the object

- how you will measure the resulting crater

- how many trials you will perform.

Name:_____ Date:_____

Group:_____

Data

Record the results for each trial in a table or chart to keep it organized.

Trends

Describe the general trends or patterns of your results.

Claims

What claims can you make based on the trends you identified?

Name:_____ Date:_____

Use this page to explain the lesson of your recent investigations.

Write a brief summary of the results from your investigation. You will use this summary to help you write your explanation.

Claim—a statement of what you understand or a conclusion that you have reached from an investigation or a set of investigations.

Evidence—data collected during investigations and trends in that data.

Science knowledge—knowledge about how things work. You may have learned this through reading, talking to an expert, discussion, or other experiences.

Write your explanation using your **Claim, Evidence** and **Science knowledge** from above.

Name: _____ **Date:** _____

Solar System Object	What characteristics does this object have?	How does this object move?
The Sun		
The Moon		
Inner Planets (Mercury, Venus, Earth, Mars)		
Outer planets (Jupiter, Saturn, Uranus, Neptune)		
Dwarf planets		
Asteroids, comets, meteoroids		
Other small solar-system bodies		

Name: _____ Date: _____

How Can You Know if Objects in Space Will Collide?

Type of Object	Evidence of Past Collisions	Chance of Future Collisions	What Would Happen?

Sundial Patterns

Name: _____ **Date:** _____

Mark the changing angle of the Sun and the height of the Sun above the horizon on the set of horizontal lines. Record the shadow directions and shadow lengths in the semicircle below. Two examples are shown.

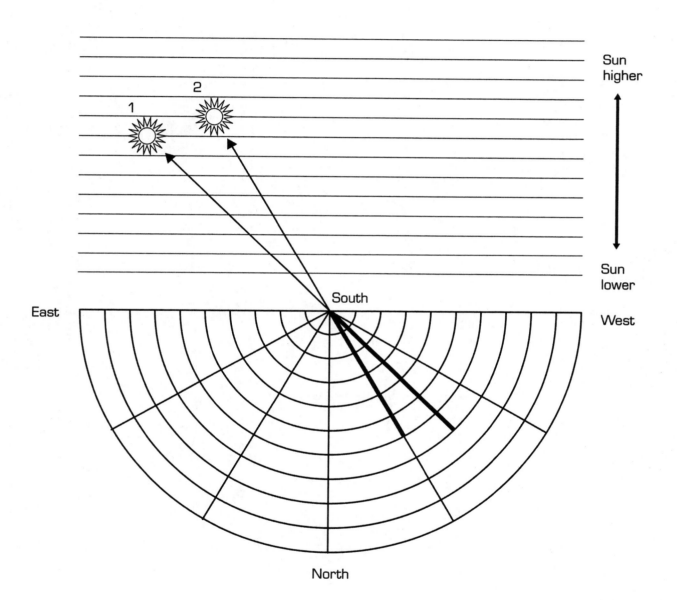

Phases of the Moon

Name: _____ Date: _____

Phase of the Moon	Sketch of model Moon's apparent shape	Diagram of positions of Sun, Moon, and Earth
New moon		**KEY** Sun = S, Moon = M, Earth = E
First quarter		
Full moon		
Last quarter		

Solar System Model

Name: _____ **Date:** _____

Scale 1 cm = _____ km

Solar-system object	Diameter (km)	Diameter of the model object (cm)	Model object that is the correct size	Average distance from the Sun (km)	Distance from the model Sun (cm)	Paces from the model Sun
Sun						
Mercury						
Venus						
Earth						
Mars						
Jupiter						
Saturn						
Uranus						
Neptune						

Planetary Orbit Observations

Name: _____ **Date:** _____

Month	Constellation behind Sun	Constellation appearing behind the planet			
		Mercury	Venus	Mars	Jupiter
January					
February					
March					
April					
May					
June					
July					
August					
September					
October					
November					
December					

Name:_____ **Date:**_____

Group:_____

Distance between observation points: _____

Sketch 1

Sketch 2

Object	Description	Parallax—distance object shifted on background (in mm)	Actual distance from X to object (in mm)
A			
B			
C			
D			

Comparison between parallax and actual measurements:_____

Project Board

What do we think we know?	**What do we need to investigate?**	**What are we learning?**	**What is our evidence?**	**What does it mean for the challenge or question?**

84 Business Park Drive, Armonk, NY 10504
Phone (914) 273-2233 Fax (914) 273-2227
www.its-about-time.com

Publishing Team

President
Tom Laster

Director of Product Development
Barbara Zahm, Ph.D

Creative Director
John Nordland

Managing Editor
Maureen Grassi

Production/Studio Manager
Robert Schwalb

Project Development Editor
Ruta Demery

Layout
Sean Campbell

Project Manager
Sarah V. Gruber

Illustrator
Dennis Falcon

Writers
Ed Denecke
Jake Gillis

Technical Art/Photo Research
Sean Campbell
Doreen Flaherty
Michael Hortens
Marie Killoran
Louise Landry
Cora Roman
MaryBeth Schulze

Editor, Student Edition
Nomi Schwartz

Editors, Teacher's Planning Guide
Kelly Crowley
Gary Hickernell
Nomi Schwartz

Pre-press
Rich Ciotti

Equipment Kit Developers
Dana Turner
Henry J. Garcia

NOTES

NOTES

NOTES

NOTES

NOTES

NOTES

NOTES

NOTES

NOTES

NOTES

NOTES

NOTES

NOTES

NOTES